BUSINESS STATISTICS
A TWO-SEMESTER Text for Business Management

Seventh Custom Edition for Ryerson University

Compiled by:

Darryl Smith and Clare Chua, Ph.D.
Ted Rogers School of Business
Ryerson University

With material from:

Business Statistics: A First Course, Fifth Edition
by David M. Levine, Timothy C. Krehbiel,
and Mark L. Berenson

Learning Solutions

New York   Boston   San Francisco
London   Toronto   Sydney   Tokyo   Singapore   Madrid
Mexico City   Munich   Paris   Cape Town   Hong Kong   Montreal

Cover Art: Front cover image courtesy of PhotoDisc/Getty Images, back cover photograph courtesy of Clare Chua.

Excerpts taken from:

Business Statistics: A First Course, Fifth Edition
by David M. Levine, Timothy C. Krehbiel, and Mark L. Berenson
Copyright © 2010, 2006, 2003, 2000, 1998 by Pearson Education, Inc.
Published by Prentice Hall
Upper Saddle River, New Jersey 07458

Pearson Learning Solutions, 501 Boylston Street, Suite 900, Boston, MA 02116
A Pearson Education Company
www.pearsoned.com

Printed in Canada

1 2 3 4 5 6 7 8 9 10 XXXX 15 14 13 12 11 10

000200010270595416

BK/CA

ISBN 10: 0-558-82907-4
ISBN 13: 978-0-558-82907-0

df	T Table Upper Tail Areas					
	0.25	0.1	0.05	0.025	0.01	0.005
1	1.000	3.078	6.314	12.706	31.821	63.657
2	0.816	1.886	2.920	4.303	6.965	9.925
3	0.765	1.638	2.353	3.182	4.541	5.841
4	0.741	1.533	2.132	2.776	3.747	4.604
5	0.727	1.476	2.015	2.571	3.365	4.032
6	0.718	1.440	1.943	2.447	3.143	3.707
7	0.711	1.415	1.895	2.365	2.998	3.499
8	0.706	1.397	1.860	2.306	2.896	3.355
9	0.703	1.383	1.833	2.262	2.821	3.250
10	0.700	1.372	1.812	2.228	2.764	3.169
11	0.697	1.363	1.796	2.201	2.718	3.106
12	0.695	1.356	1.782	2.179	2.681	3.055
13	0.694	1.350	1.771	2.160	2.650	3.012
14	0.692	1.345	1.761	2.145	2.624	2.977
15	0.691	1.341	1.753	2.131	2.602	2.947
16	0.690	1.337	1.746	2.120	2.583	2.921
17	0.689	1.333	1.740	2.110	2.567	2.898
18	0.688	1.330	1.734	2.101	2.552	2.878
19	0.688	1.328	1.729	2.093	2.539	2.861
20	0.687	1.325	1.725	2.086	2.528	2.845
21	0.686	1.323	1.721	2.080	2.518	2.831
22	0.686	1.321	1.717	2.074	2.508	2.819
23	0.685	1.319	1.714	2.069	2.500	2.807
24	0.685	1.318	1.711	2.064	2.492	2.797
25	0.684	1.316	1.708	2.060	2.485	2.787
26	0.684	1.315	1.706	2.056	2.479	2.779
27	0.684	1.314	1.703	2.052	2.473	2.771
28	0.683	1.313	1.701	2.048	2.467	2.763
29	0.683	1.311	1.699	2.045	2.462	2.756
30	0.683	1.310	1.697	2.042	2.457	2.750
40	0.681	1.303	1.684	2.021	2.423	2.704
50	0.679	1.299	1.676	2.009	2.403	2.678
60	0.679	1.296	1.671	2.000	2.390	2.660
70	0.678	1.294	1.667	1.994	2.381	2.648
80	0.678	1.292	1.664	1.990	2.374	2.639
90	0.677	1.291	1.662	1.987	2.368	2.632
100	0.677	1.290	1.660	1.984	2.364	2.626
110	0.677	1.289	1.659	1.982	2.361	2.621
120	0.677	1.289	1.658	1.980	2.358	2.617
∞	0.674	1.282	1.645	1.960	2.326	2.576

	0.995	0.99	0.975	0.95	0.9	0.1	0.05	0.025	0.01	0.005
					χ^2 Table		Upper Tail Areas			
1	0.00	0.00	0.00	0.00	0.02	2.71	3.84	5.02	6.63	7.88
2	0.01	0.02	0.05	0.10	0.21	4.61	5.99	7.38	9.21	10.60
3	0.07	0.11	0.22	0.35	0.58	6.25	7.81	9.35	11.34	12.84
4	0.21	0.30	0.48	0.71	1.06	7.78	9.49	11.14	13.28	14.86
5	0.41	0.55	0.83	1.15	1.61	9.24	11.07	12.83	15.09	16.75
6	0.68	0.87	1.24	1.64	2.20	10.64	12.59	14.45	16.81	18.55
7	0.99	1.24	1.69	2.17	2.83	12.02	14.07	16.01	18.48	20.28
8	1.34	1.65	2.18	2.73	3.49	13.36	15.51	17.53	20.09	21.95
9	1.73	2.09	2.70	3.33	4.17	14.68	16.92	19.02	21.67	23.59
10	2.16	2.56	3.25	3.94	4.87	15.99	18.31	20.48	23.21	25.19
11	2.60	3.05	3.82	4.57	5.58	17.28	19.68	21.92	24.72	26.76
12	3.07	3.57	4.40	5.23	6.30	18.55	21.03	23.34	26.22	28.30
13	3.57	4.11	5.01	5.89	7.04	19.81	22.36	24.74	27.69	29.82
14	4.07	4.66	5.63	6.57	7.79	21.06	23.68	26.12	29.14	31.32
15	4.60	5.23	6.26	7.26	8.55	22.31	25.00	27.49	30.58	32.80
16	5.14	5.81	6.91	7.96	9.31	23.54	26.30	28.85	32.00	34.27
17	5.70	6.41	7.56	8.67	10.09	24.77	27.59	30.19	33.41	35.72
18	6.26	7.01	8.23	9.39	10.86	25.99	28.87	31.53	34.81	37.16
19	6.84	7.63	8.91	10.12	11.65	27.20	30.14	32.85	36.19	38.58
20	7.43	8.26	9.59	10.85	12.44	28.41	31.41	34.17	37.57	40.00
21	8.03	8.90	10.28	11.59	13.24	29.62	32.67	35.48	38.93	41.40
22	8.64	9.54	10.98	12.34	14.04	30.81	33.92	36.78	40.29	42.80
23	9.26	10.20	11.69	13.09	14.85	32.01	35.17	38.08	41.64	44.18
24	9.89	10.86	12.40	13.85	15.66	33.20	36.42	39.36	42.98	45.56
25	10.52	11.52	13.12	14.61	16.47	34.38	37.65	40.65	44.31	46.93
26	11.16	12.20	13.84	15.38	17.29	35.56	38.89	41.92	45.64	48.29
27	11.81	12.88	14.57	16.15	18.11	36.74	40.11	43.19	46.96	49.64
28	12.46	13.56	15.31	16.93	18.94	37.92	41.34	44.46	48.28	50.99
29	13.12	14.26	16.05	17.71	19.77	39.09	42.56	45.72	49.59	52.34
30	13.79	14.95	16.79	18.49	20.60	40.26	43.77	46.98	50.89	53.67

F-Table Upper Tail Area of .05

Denominator df (rows) / **Numerator df** (columns)

Denom df	1	2	3	4	5	6	7	8	9	10	11	12	15	20	24	30	60	120	∞
1	161.4	199.5	215.7	224.6	230.2	234.0	236.8	238.9	240.5	241.9	243.0	243.9	245.9	248.0	249.1	250.1	252.2	253.3	254.3
2	18.5	19.0	19.2	19.2	19.3	19.3	19.4	19.4	19.4	19.4	19.4	19.4	19.4	19.4	19.5	19.5	19.5	19.5	19.5
3	10.1	9.6	9.3	9.1	9.0	8.9	8.9	8.8	8.8	8.8	8.8	8.7	8.7	8.7	8.6	8.6	8.6	8.5	8.5
4	7.71	6.94	6.59	6.39	6.26	6.16	6.09	6.04	6.00	5.96	5.94	5.91	5.86	5.80	5.77	5.75	5.69	5.66	5.63
5	6.61	5.79	5.41	5.19	5.05	4.95	4.88	4.82	4.77	4.74	4.70	4.68	4.62	4.56	4.53	4.50	4.43	4.40	4.37
6	5.99	5.14	4.76	4.53	4.39	4.28	4.21	4.15	4.10	4.06	4.03	4.00	3.94	3.87	3.84	3.81	3.74	3.70	3.67
7	5.59	4.74	4.35	4.12	3.97	3.87	3.79	3.73	3.68	3.64	3.60	3.57	3.51	3.44	3.41	3.38	3.30	3.27	3.23
8	5.32	4.46	4.07	3.84	3.69	3.58	3.50	3.44	3.39	3.35	3.31	3.28	3.22	3.15	3.12	3.08	3.01	2.97	2.93
9	5.12	4.26	3.86	3.63	3.48	3.37	3.29	3.23	3.18	3.14	3.10	3.07	3.01	2.94	2.90	2.86	2.79	2.75	2.71
10	4.96	4.10	3.71	3.48	3.33	3.22	3.14	3.07	3.02	2.98	2.94	2.91	2.85	2.77	2.74	2.70	2.62	2.58	2.54
11	4.84	3.98	3.59	3.36	3.20	3.09	3.01	2.95	2.90	2.85	2.82	2.79	2.72	2.65	2.61	2.57	2.49	2.45	2.40
12	4.75	3.89	3.49	3.26	3.11	3.00	2.91	2.85	2.80	2.75	2.72	2.69	2.62	2.54	2.51	2.47	2.38	2.34	2.30
13	4.67	3.81	3.41	3.18	3.03	2.92	2.83	2.77	2.71	2.67	2.63	2.60	2.53	2.46	2.42	2.38	2.30	2.25	2.21
14	4.60	3.74	3.34	3.11	2.96	2.85	2.76	2.70	2.65	2.60	2.57	2.53	2.46	2.39	2.35	2.31	2.22	2.18	2.13
15	4.54	3.68	3.29	3.06	2.90	2.79	2.71	2.64	2.59	2.54	2.51	2.48	2.40	2.33	2.29	2.25	2.16	2.11	2.07
16	4.49	3.63	3.24	3.01	2.85	2.74	2.66	2.59	2.54	2.49	2.46	2.42	2.35	2.28	2.24	2.19	2.11	2.06	2.01
17	4.45	3.59	3.20	2.96	2.81	2.70	2.61	2.55	2.49	2.45	2.41	2.38	2.31	2.23	2.19	2.15	2.06	2.01	1.96
18	4.41	3.55	3.16	2.93	2.77	2.66	2.58	2.51	2.46	2.41	2.37	2.34	2.27	2.19	2.15	2.11	2.02	1.97	1.92
19	4.38	3.52	3.13	2.90	2.74	2.63	2.54	2.48	2.42	2.38	2.34	2.31	2.23	2.16	2.11	2.07	1.98	1.93	1.88
20	4.35	3.49	3.10	2.87	2.71	2.60	2.51	2.45	2.39	2.35	2.31	2.28	2.20	2.12	2.08	2.04	1.95	1.90	1.84
21	4.32	3.47	3.07	2.84	2.68	2.57	2.49	2.42	2.37	2.32	2.28	2.25	2.18	2.10	2.05	2.01	1.92	1.87	1.81
22	4.30	3.44	3.05	2.82	2.66	2.55	2.46	2.40	2.34	2.30	2.26	2.23	2.15	2.07	2.03	1.98	1.89	1.84	1.78
23	4.28	3.42	3.03	2.80	2.64	2.53	2.44	2.37	2.32	2.27	2.24	2.20	2.13	2.05	2.01	1.96	1.86	1.81	1.76
24	4.26	3.40	3.01	2.78	2.62	2.51	2.42	2.36	2.30	2.25	2.22	2.18	2.11	2.03	1.98	1.94	1.84	1.79	1.73
25	4.24	3.39	2.99	2.76	2.60	2.49	2.40	2.34	2.28	2.24	2.20	2.16	2.09	2.01	1.96	1.92	1.82	1.77	1.71
26	4.23	3.37	2.98	2.74	2.59	2.47	2.39	2.32	2.27	2.22	2.18	2.15	2.07	1.99	1.95	1.90	1.80	1.75	1.69
30	4.17	3.32	2.92	2.69	2.53	2.42	2.33	2.27	2.21	2.16	2.13	2.09	2.01	1.93	1.89	1.84	1.74	1.68	1.62
40	4.08	3.23	2.84	2.61	2.45	2.34	2.25	2.18	2.12	2.08	2.04	2.00	1.92	1.84	1.79	1.74	1.64	1.58	1.51
60	4.00	3.15	2.76	2.53	2.37	2.25	2.17	2.10	2.04	1.99	1.95	1.92	1.84	1.75	1.70	1.65	1.53	1.47	1.39
120	3.92	3.07	2.68	2.45	2.29	2.18	2.09	2.02	1.96	1.91	1.87	1.83	1.75	1.66	1.61	1.55	1.43	1.35	1.25
∞	3.84	3.00	2.60	2.37	2.21	2.10	2.01	1.94	1.88	1.83	1.79	1.75	1.67	1.57	1.52	1.46	1.32	1.22	1.00

Brief Contents

Contents

*Content provided by Darryl Smith and Claire Chua, Ph.D. All other content taken from *Business Statistics: A First Course,* Fifth Edition, by David M. Levine, Timothy C. Krehbiel, and Mark L. Berenson.

*Content provided by Darryl Smith and Claire Chua, Ph.D. All other content taken from *Business Statistics: A First Course,* Fifth Edition, by David M. Levine, Timothy C. Krehbiel, and Mark L. Berenson.

6 The Normal Distribution   268

7 Sampling and Sampling Distributions   302

8 Statistical Applications in Quality Management   334

*Content provided by Darryl Smith and Claire Chua, Ph.D. All other content taken from *Business Statistics: A First Course,* Fifth
Edition, by David M. Levine, Timothy C. Krehbiel, and Mark L. Berenson.

*Content provided by Darryl Smith and Claire Chua, Ph.D. All other content taken from *Business Statistics: A First Course,* Fifth Edition, by David M. Levine, Timothy C. Krehbiel, and Mark L. Berenson.

*Content provided by Darryl Smith and Claire Chua, Ph.D. All other content taken from *Business Statistics: A First Course,* Fifth Edition, by David M. Levine, Timothy C. Krehbiel, and Mark L. Berenson.

14 Multiple Regression   638

*Content provided by Darryl Smith and Claire Chua, Ph.D. All other content taken from *Business Statistics: A First Course,* Fifth Edition, by David M. Levine, Timothy C. Krehbiel, and Mark L. Berenson.

Preface

Educational Philosophy

In our many years of teaching business statistics, we have continually searched for ways to improve the teaching of these courses. Our active participation in a series of Making Statistics More Effective in Schools and Business (MSMESB), Decision Sciences Institute (DSI), and American Statistical Association (ASA) conferences as well as the reality of serving a diverse group of students at large universities have shaped our vision for teaching these courses. Over the years, our vision has come to include these key principles:

1. **Show students the relevance of statistics.** Students need a frame of reference when learning statistics, especially when statistics is not their major. That frame of reference for business students should be the functional areas of business—that is, accounting, finance, information systems, management, and marketing. Each statistical topic needs to be presented in an applied context related to at least one of these functional areas. The focus in teaching each topic should be on its application in business, the interpretation of results, the presentation of assumptions, the evaluation of the assumptions, and the discussion of what should be done if the assumptions are violated.

2. **Familiarize students with software used in the business world.** Integrating business software into all aspects of an introductory statistics course allows the course to focus on interpretation of results instead of computations. Introductory business statistics courses should recognize that spreadsheet programs and statistical packages are commonly found on a business decision maker's desktop computer, therefore making the *interpretation* of results more important than the tedious hand calculations required to produce them.

3. **Provide guidance to students for using software.** Books should contain clear instructions to help students effectively use the programs that are integrated with the study of statistics, without having those instructions dominating the book or the courses in which they are used.

4. **Give students ample practice in understanding how to apply statistics to business.** Both classroom examples and homework exercises should involve actual or realistic data as much as possible. Students should work with data sets, both small and large, and be encouraged to look beyond the statistical analysis of data to the interpretation of results in a managerial context.

New to This Edition: Enhanced Statistics Coverage

This fifth edition of *Business Statistics: A First Course* enhances the statistical coverage of previous editions in a number of ways:

- *Think About This* essays in selected chapters provide greater insight to what has just been learned as well as raise important issues about the application of statistical knowledge.
- Revised simplified notation for test statistics in hypothesis testing.
- Many new applied examples and exercises with data from *The Wall Street Journal, USA Today*, and other sources have been added to the book.
- Student surveys are included as an integrating theme for exercises across many chapters.
- Even more illustrations of Microsoft Excel and Minitab results are included, all with cross-references to the appropriate software appendix sections.
- Each chapter ends with a Using Statistics Revisited section which reinforces the applications and lessons learned in the chapter.

New to This Edition: Expanded Hands-on Software Appendices

This fifth edition of *Business Statistics: A First Course* now contains separate and expanded appendices for using Microsoft Excel, Minitab, and PHStat2, the Excel add-in that is included on the Student CD-ROM:

- Totally rewritten Excel appendices contain instructions for using all versions of Excel, including Excel 2007. (Some sections contain two sets of instructions, one for using Excel 97 through Excel 2003, the other for using Excel 2007, when appropriate.)
- Minitab appendices feature the use of Minitab 15, the latest Minitab version, but are also fully compatible with Minitab 14.
- PHStat2 appendices at the end of each chapter identify the PHStat2 procedures that can be used for the chapter's statistical methods.
- New PHStat2 version (2.8) that is Excel 2007 compatible and contains new and enhanced procedures including the separate-variance *t* test, and one-way ANOVA.

Chapter-by-Chapter Changes in the Fifth Edition

Each chapter includes a new opening page that displays the chapter sections and subsections. The following changes have been made to this fifth edition:

Chapter 1 has completely new Sections 1.1, 1.2, 1.6, 1.7, and 1.8.

Chapter 2 has new examples throughout the chapter and uses a new mutual fund data set.

Chapter 3 has moved quartiles to the section with boxplots (name changed from box-and-whisker), and has new examples throughout the chapter using a new mutual fund data set.

Chapter 4 has a revised example throughout the chapter, and a *Think About This* essay about Bayes' theorem.

Chapter 5 has changed notation in the binomial and Poisson distributions with p changed to π, and successes changed to items of interest.

Chapter 6 has a revised normal distribution table with additional header lines and a *Think About This* essay about the normal distribution.

Chapter 7 has survey sampling and survey worthiness preceding sampling distributions and a *Think About This* essay on the pros and cons of web-based surveys.

Chapter 8 has control charts preceding total quality management and Six Sigma and has revised sections on total quality management and Six Sigma including a subsection on the role employees play in a Six Sigma organization (such as green belt or black belt).

Chapter 9 has a greatly reduced focus on the confidence interval estimate for the mean with sigma known, revised notation that uses a subscript for distributions that indicates the α level (such as $Z_{\alpha/2}$ or $t_{\alpha/2}$), a subsection on sigma known, and revised normal distribution and t distribution tables with additional header lines.

Chapter 10 has combined previous Sections 9.1 and 9.2 to reduce the emphasis on testing the population mean with sigma known, has moved the t test for the mean ahead of the one-tail test, changed notation to use a subscript for distributions to indicate the α level (such as $Z_{\alpha/2}$ or $t_{\alpha/2}$), revised notation that uses subscript *STAT* with the test statistic (such as Z_{STAT} and t_{STAT}), and revised normal distribution and t distribution tables with additional header lines.

Chapter 11 has revised notation that uses a subscript for distributions to indicate the α level (such as $Z_{\alpha/2}$, $t_{\alpha/2}$, or F_{α}), revised notation that uses subscript *STAT* with the test statistic (such as Z_{STAT}, t_{STAT}, and F_{STAT}), revised normal, t, and F distribution tables with additional header lines, revised F test for the difference between variances that consists of the larger variance divided by the smaller variance, and a *Think About This* essay that presents a business application of the differences between two means.

Chapter 12 has revised notation that uses a subscript for distributions to indicate the α level (such as χ_{α}^2), revised notation that uses subscript *STAT* with the test statistic (such as χ_{STAT}^2), and revised χ^2 distribution tables with additional header lines.

Chapter 13 has revised notation that uses the subscript *STAT* with the test statistic such as t_{STAT}, and a *Think About This* essay on using regression in the business world.

Chapter 14 has revised notation that uses the subscript *STAT* with the test statistic such as t_{STAT}.

Hallmark Features

We have continued many of the traditions of past editions and have highlighted some of those features below:

Using Statistics business scenarios—Each chapter begins with a Using Statistics example that shows how statistics is used in accounting, finance, information systems, management, or marketing. Each scenario is used throughout the chapter to provide an applied context for the concepts.

Emphasis on data analysis and interpretation of software results—We believe that the use of computer software is an integral part of learning statistics. Our focus emphasizes analyzing data by interpreting the results from Microsoft Excel or Minitab while reducing emphasis on doing computations. For example, in the coverage of tables and charts in Chapter 2, the focus is on the interpretation of various charts, not on their construction by hand. In our coverage of hypothesis testing in Chapters 10 through 12, extensive computer results have been included so that the *p*-value approach can be emphasized.

Pedagogical aides—An active writing style, boxed numbered equations, set-off examples to provide reinforcement for learning concepts, problems divided into "Learning the Basics" and "Applying the Concepts," key equations, and key terms are included.

Answers—Most answers to the even-numbered exercises are provided at the end of the book.

PHStat2—This add-in, included on the Student CD-ROM, extends the statistical capabilities of Microsoft Excel and executes the low-level menu selection and worksheet entry tasks associated with implementing statistical analysis in Excel. When combined with the Analysis ToolPak add-in, virtually all statistical methods taught in an introductory statistics course can be demonstrated using Microsoft Excel.

Web Cases—A chapter-ending Web Case is included for most of the chapters. By visiting Web sites related to the companies and researching the issues raised in the Using Statistics scenarios that start each chapter, students learn to identify misuses of statistical information. The Web Cases require students to sift through claims and assorted information in order to discover the data most relevant to the case. Students then determine whether the conclusions and claims are supported by the data. (Instructional tips for using the Web Cases and solutions to the Web Cases are included in the Instructor's Solutions Manual.)

Case studies and team projects—Detailed case studies are included in numerous chapters. A Managing the *Springville Herald* case is included at the end of most chapters as an integrating theme. A team project relating to mutual funds is included in many chapters as an integrating theme.

Visual Explorations—A Microsoft Excel add-in workbook allows students to interactively explore important statistical concepts in descriptive statistics, the normal distribution, sampling distributions, and regression analysis. For example, in descriptive statistics, students observe the effect of changes in the data on the mean, median, quartiles, and standard deviation. With the normal distribution, students see the effect of changes in the mean and standard deviation on the areas under the normal curve. In sampling distributions, students use simulation to explore the effect of sample size on a sampling distribution. In regression analysis, students have the opportunity of fitting a line and observing how changes in the slope and intercept affect the goodness of fit.

Supplement Package

The supplement package that accompanies this text includes the following:

Instructor's Solutions Manual—This manual includes solutions for end-of-section and end-of-chapter problems, answers to case questions, where applicable, and teaching tips for each chapter. Electronic solutions are provided in PDF and Word formats.

Student Solutions Manual—This manual provides detailed solutions to virtually all the even-numbered exercises and worked-out solutions to the self-test problems.

Test Item File—The Test Item File contains true/false, multiple-choice, fill-in, and problem-solving questions based on the definitions, concepts, and ideas developed in each chapter of the text.

TestGen software—A test bank has been designed for use with the TestGen test-generating software. This computerized package allows instructors to custom design, save, and generate classroom tests. The test program permits instructors to edit, add, or delete questions from the test bank; edit existing graphics and create new graphics; analyze test results; and organize a database of tests and student results. This software allows for flexibility and ease of use. It provides many options for organizing and displaying tests, along with a search-and-sort feature. The program can be found online at the Instructor's Resource Center.

Instructor's Resource Center—The Instructor's Resource Center contains the electronic files for the complete Instructor's Solutions Manual, the Test Item File, and Lecture PowerPoint presentations (**www.pearsonhighered.com**).

Course and Homework Management Tools

MyStatLab—Provides a rich and flexible set of course materials, featuring free-response exercises that are algorithmically generated for unlimited practice and mastery. Students can also use a variety of online tools to independently improve their understanding and performance in the course. Instructors can use MyStatLab's homework and test manager to select and assign their own online exercises and import TestGen tests for added flexibility.

Acknowledgments

We are extremely grateful to the Biometrika Trustees, American Cyanimid Company, the RAND Corporation, the American Society for Testing and Materials for their kind permission to publish various tables in Appendix E, and the American Statistical Association for its permission to publish diagrams from the *American Statistician*.

A Note of Thanks

We would like to thank Luis Borges, Medaille College; Dave Bregenzer, Utah State University; Faruk Guder, Loyola University; Kimberly Killmer Hollister, Montclair State University; John McKenzie, Babson College; Ram Misra, Montclair State University; Susan Pariseau, Merrimack College; Charlie Shi, Diablo Valley College; Erland Sorensen, Bentley College; and Yang Zhang, Depaul University for their comments, which have made this a better book.

We would especially like to thank Mark Pfaltzgraff, Susie Abraham, Kerri Tomasso, Valerie Patruno, Judy Leale, and Anne Fahlgren of the editorial, marketing, and production teams at Prentice Hall. We would like to thank our statistical reader and accuracy checker Annie Puciloski for her diligence in checking our work; Julie Kennedy for her copyediting; Dorothy Pychevicz for her proofreading; and Heidi Allgair of GGS Higher Education Resources, A Division of Premedia Global, Inc., for their work in the production of this text.

Finally, we would like to thank our parents, wives, and children for their patience, understanding, love, and assistance in making this book a reality. It is to them that we dedicate this book.

Concluding Remarks

We have gone to great lengths to make this text both pedagogically sound and error free. If you have any suggestions or require clarification about any of the material, or if you find any errors, please contact us at **davidlevine@davidlevinestatistics.com** or **Krehbitc@muohio.edu**. Include the phrase "BSAFC edition 5" in the subject line of your e-mail. For more information or questions about using PHStat2, review Appendix F and the PHStat2 readme file on the Student CD-ROM. For support issues, visit the PHStat2 Web site, **www.prenhall.com/phstat** and the Pearson Customer Technical Support website, **247.pearsoned.com**.

David M. Levine

Timothy C. Krehbiel

Mark L. Berenson

Business Statistics

1

Introduction and Data Collection

Learning Objectives

In this chapter, you learn:

- How statistics is used in business
- The sources of data used in business
- The types of data used in business
- The basics of Microsoft Excel
- The basics of Minitab

USING STATISTICS

@ Good Tunes

Good Tunes, a growing four-store home entertainment systems retailer, seeks to double their number of stores within the next three years. The managers have decided to approach local area banks for the funding needed to underwrite this expansion. They need to prepare an electronic slide show and a formal prospectus that will argue that Good Tunes is a thriving business and a good candidate for expansion.

You have been asked to assist in the process of preparing the slide show and prospectus. How would you do this job? Learning more about statistics would be a good start.

1.1 Why Learn Statistics

People use numbers every day to describe or analyze the world we live in. For example, consider these recent headlines:

- "Stocks May Fall, But Execs' Pay Doesn't" (G. Farrell and B. Hansen, **usatoday.com**, April 10, 2008)—In 2007, the median compensation for the CEOs of the 50 largest corporations in the S&P 500 was $15.7 million.
- "Americans Gulping More Bottled Water" (*USA Today*, February 28, 2007, p. 1D)—The annual per capita consumption of bottled water has increased from 18.8 gallons in 2001 to 28.3 gallons in 2006.
- "Paying More with Plastic" (*USA Today*, March 6, 2007, p. 1D)—Consumer payment with credit cards increased from 18% in 1995 to 25% in 2005, while payment in cash decreased to 14% from 21%.
- "The Real Most Valuable Players" (R. Adams, *The Wall Street Journal*, April 14, 2007, pp. P1, P4)—Economists have developed models to predict the real value of baseball player performance and have related it to player salary.

You will make better sense of the numbers in the stories behind these headlines if you understand statistics. **Statistics** is the branch of mathematics that transforms numbers into useful information for decision makers. Statistics provides a way of understanding and then reducing—but not eliminating—the variation that is part of any decision-making process, and also can tell you the known risks associated with making a decision.

Statistics does this by providing a set of methods for analyzing the numbers. These methods help you to find patterns in "the numbers" and enable you to determine whether differences in "the numbers" are just due to chance. As you learn these methods, you will also learn the appropriate conditions for using those methods. And because so many statistical methods must be computerized in order to be of practical benefit, as you learn statistics you also need to learn about the programs that help apply statistics in the business world.

1.2 Statistics in the Business World

In the business world, statistics has four important applications:

- To summarize business data
- To draw conclusions from that data
- To make reliable forecasts about business activities
- To improve business processes

The field of statistics consists of two branches, descriptive statistics and inferential statistics.

Descriptive statistics focuses on collecting, summarizing, presenting, and analyzing a set of data. You are probably familiar with presentations such as tables and charts, and statistics such as the mean and median from your previous school experience.

Inferential statistics uses data that have been collected from a small group to draw conclusions about a larger group. These methods are used to make decisions about which investment might lead to a higher return and what marketing strategy might lead to increased sales.

Looking at the first bulleted point above, descriptive statistics allows you to create different tables and charts to summarize your data. It also provides statistical measures such as the mean, median, and standard deviation to describe different characteristics of your data.

Drawing conclusions from your data is the heart of inferential statistics. Using these methods enables you to make decisions based on data rather than just on intuition.

Making reliable forecasts involves developing statistical models for prediction. These models enable you to develop more accurate predictions of future activities.

Improving business processes involves using managerial approaches that focus on quality improvement such as Six Sigma. These approaches are data-driven and use statistical methods as an integral part of the quality improvement approach.

To help you develop the skills for making better decisions, every chapter of *Business Statistics: A First Course* has a Using Statistics scenario. The scenarios describe realistic situations in which you will be asked to make decisions to transform data into statistical information. For example, in one chapter you will be asked to decide the location in a supermarket that best enhances sales of a cola drink; and in another chapter, you will be asked to forecast sales for a clothing store.

In the scenario on page 3, you must ask the following questions. What data should you include that will convince bankers to extend the credit that Good Tunes needs? How should you present that data?

However, presenting the bankers with the thousands of transactions would overwhelm them and not be very useful. You need to transform the transactions data into information by summarizing the details of each transaction in some useful way that would allow the bankers to (perhaps) uncover a favorable pattern about the sales over time.

One piece of information that the bankers would presumably want to see is the yearly dollar sales totals. Tallying and totaling sales is a common process of transforming data into information. When you tally sales—or any other relevant data about Good Tunes you choose to use—you follow normal business practice and tally by a business period such as by month, quarter, or year. When you do so, you end up with multiple values: sales for this year, sales for last year, sales for the year before that, and so on. How to determine the best way to refer to these multiple values requires learning the basic vocabulary of statistics.

1.3 Basic Vocabulary of Statistics

Variables are characteristics of items or individuals and are what you analyze when you use a statistical method. For the Good Tunes scenario, sales, expenses by year, and net profit by year are variables that the bankers would want to analyze.

> **VARIABLE**
>
> A **variable** is a characteristic of an item or individual.

When used in everyday speech, *variable* suggests that something changes or varies, and you would expect the sales, expenses, and net profit to have different values from year to year. These different values are the **data** associated with a variable, and more simply, the "data" to be analyzed.

Variables can differ for reasons other than time. For example, if you conducted an analysis of the composition of a large lecture class, you would probably want to include the variables class standing, gender, and major field of study. These variables would vary, too, because each student in the class is different. One student might be a sophomore, male, accounting major, while another may be a junior, female, finance major.

You also need to remember that values are meaningless unless their variables have **operational definitions**. These definitions are universally accepted meanings that are clear to all associated with an analysis. Even though the operational definition for sales per year might seem clear, miscommunication could occur if one person was referring to sales per year for the entire chain of stores and another to sales per year per store. Even individual values for variables sometimes need definition—for the class standing variable, for example, what *exactly* is meant by the words *sophomore* and *junior*? (Perhaps the most famous example of vague definitions was the definition of a valid vote in the state of Florida during the 2000 U.S. presidential election. Vagueness about the operational definitions there ultimately required a U.S. Supreme Court ruling.)

Four other basic vocabulary terms are population, sample, parameter, and statistic.

POPULATION
A **population** consists of all the items or individuals about which you want to draw a conclusion.

SAMPLE
A **sample** is the portion of a population selected for analysis.

PARAMETER
A **parameter** is a numerical measure that describes a characteristic of a population.

STATISTIC
A **statistic** is a numerical measure that describes a characteristic of a sample.

All the Good Tunes sales transactions for a specific year, all the customers who shopped at Good Tunes this weekend, all the full-time students enrolled in a college, and all the registered voters in Ohio are examples of populations. Examples of samples from these four populations would be 200 Good Tunes sales transactions randomly selected by an auditor for study, 30 Good Tunes customers asked to complete a customer satisfaction survey, 50 full-time students selected for a marketing study, and 500 registered voters in Ohio contacted via telephone for a political poll. In each sample, the transactions or people in the sample represent a portion of the items or individuals that make up the population.

The mean amount spent by all customers who shopped at Good Tunes this weekend is an example of a parameter because the amount spent in the entire population is needed. In contrast, the mean amount spent by the 30 customers completing the customer satisfaction survey is an example of a statistic because the amount spent by only the sample of 30 people is required.

1.4 How This Textbook Is Organized

If you are someone who likes to skim quickly through a book to learn a book's organization, you should know that we have organized the chapters of this book according to the four business tasks first listed in Section 1.2. We use those tasks—summarizing business data, drawing conclusions from that data, making reliable forecasts about business activities, and improving business processes—as a way of organizing our chapters.

Chapters 1 through 3 discuss methods of presenting and describing information. Chapters 4 through 11 discuss drawing conclusions about populations using sample information. Chapters 12 and 13 provide ways of making reliable forecasts and Chapter 14 introduces you to how you can apply statistical methods to improve business processes.

Don't worry if your instructor does not cover all of these chapters—introductory business statistics courses vary in their scope, length, and number of college credits. Traditionally, instructors start with descriptive statistics because some of these methods may already be familiar to you from everyday activities and that's the main reason we've put them in the first three chapters. Chapter 4 discusses probability concepts that are needed in Chapters 5 through 7. Chapters 8 through 11 cover inferential statistics. Chapter 8 introduces the confidence interval approach, while Chapter 9 develops the fundamental hypothesis testing concepts that are expanded on in Chapters 10 and 11. Understanding these concepts will allow you to fully answer questions such as "How can you make decisions about the many based on a few?"—a question business people uneducated in statistics often ask when they challenge the use of statistics. Chapters 12 and 13 cover regression models that are used to make reliable forecasts. Chapter 12 develops the simple regression model, while Chapter 13 expands the simple model to more complex situations. Chapter 14 provides some background into the total quality management and Six Sigma quality improvement approaches and introduces statistical methods used in quality improvement.

Remember that the goal of this book is *not* for you to become a statistician. The goal is to help you understand and apply appropriately the statistical methods commonly used in the area of business in which you are most interested—be it accounting, economics, finance, information systems, marketing, or management.

By the way, if you are the type of person who likes to read the last page of a book first, please don't. Introductory business statistics is somewhat cumulative and if you jump to the back of the book, you may find things a bit puzzling if you are only just beginning to learn statistics. So if you have happened to notice things such as strange-looking tables, don't fret—by the time you get to the point in this book where you need to use such tables, you will know how to use them effectively.

1.5 What is Data?

We can collect the data using a survey form as shown below:

---

1. Did you bring your textbook to class today?
   - ❑ Yes
   - ❑ No
2. How much time (in hours) do you usually spend studying per week? _____
3. How many courses did you enroll in this semester? _____
4. Your Class Year: _____ *(please check your answer below)*
   - ❑ Freshman
   - ❑ Sophomore
   - ❑ Junior
   - ❑ Senior
5. How did you come to school today?
   - ❑ Walk
   - ❑ Drive
   - ❑ Take the public transport
   - ❑ Car pool

We approached 12 students and asked them to fill in the survey form. The data collected is tabulated in Table 1.1 on page 8.

The data can be either qualitative (e.g. Yes, No, Drive, Walk, etc) or quantitative (e.g. 3.2 17.0, 3, 5, etc.).

1.6 Data Collection

The managers at Good Tunes believe that they will have a stronger argument for expansion if they can show the bankers that the customers of Good Tunes are highly satisfied with the service they received. How could the managers demonstrate that good service was the typical customer experience at Good Tunes?

In the Good Tunes scenario on page 3, the managers now face the twin challenges to first identify relevant variables for a customer satisfaction study and then devise a method for **data collection**, that is, collecting the values for those variables.

Many different types of circumstances, such as the following, require data collection:

- A marketing research analyst needs to assess the effectiveness of a new television advertisement.
- A pharmaceutical manufacturer needs to determine whether a new drug is more effective than those currently in use.
- An operations manager wants to improve a manufacturing or service process.
- An auditor wants to review the financial transactions of a company in order to determine whether the company is in compliance with generally accepted accounting principles.

TABLE 1.1

Student	Did you bring your textbook to class today?	How much time (in hours) do you usually spend studying per week?	How many courses did you enroll in this semester?	Class Year	How did you come to school today?
1	Yes	20.3	3	Freshman	Take public transport
2	Yes	12.5	5	Sophomore	Drive
3	No	10.3	6	Junior	Walk
4	Yes	2.5	4	Junior	Drive
5	No	0.5	5	Senior	Take public transport
6	Yes	7.2	2	Sophomore	Drive
7	Yes	5.5	5	Freshman	Take public transport
8	No	10.0	4	Freshman	Walk
9	No	4.8	4	Freshman	Walk
10	Yes	3.2	3	Freshman	Drive
11	Yes	17.0	5	Senior	Take public transport
12	Yes	4.3	6	Freshman	Take public transport

In each of these examples, and for the Good Tunes managers as well, collecting data from every item or individual in the population would be too difficult or too time-consuming. Because this is the typical case, data collection almost always involves collecting data from a sample. (Chapter 7 discusses methods of sample selection.)

Data sources are classified as being either **primary sources** or **secondary sources**. When the data collector is the one using the data for analysis, the source is primary. When the person performing the statistical analysis is not the data collector, the source is secondary. Organizations and individuals that collect and publish data typically use that data as a primary source and then let others use it as a secondary source. For example, the United States federal government collects and distributes data in this way for both public and private purposes. The Bureau of Labor Statistics collects data on employment and also distributes the monthly consumer price index. The Census Bureau oversees a variety of ongoing surveys regarding population, housing, and manufacturing and undertakes special studies on topics such as crime, travel, and health care.

Sources of data fall into one of four categories:

- Data distributed by an organization or an individual
- A designed experiment
- A survey
- An observational study

Market research firms and trade associations distribute data pertaining to specific industries or markets. Investment services such as Mergent (see **www.mergent.com**) provide financial data on a company-by-company basis. Syndicated services such as AC Nielsen provide clients with data that enables the comparison of client products with those of their competitors. Daily newspapers are filled with numerical information regarding stock prices, weather conditions, and sports statistics.

Outcomes of a designed experiment are another data source. These outcomes are the result of an experiment, such as a test of several laundry detergents to compare how well each detergent removes a certain type of stain. Developing proper experimental designs is a subject mostly beyond the scope of this book because such designs often involve sophisticated statistical procedures. However, some of the fundamental experimental design concepts are discussed in Chapter 10.

Conducting a survey is a third type of data source. People being surveyed are asked questions about their beliefs, attitudes, behaviors, and other characteristics. For example, people could be asked their opinion about which laundry detergent best removes a certain type of stain. (This could lead to a result different from a designed experiment seeking the same answer.)

Conducting an observational study is the fourth important data source. A researcher collects data by directly observing a behavior, usually in a natural or neutral setting. Observational studies are a common tool for data collection in business. For example, market researchers use focus groups to elicit unstructured responses to open-ended questions posed by a moderator to a target audience. Observational study techniques are also used to enhance teamwork or improve the quality of products and services.

Identifying the most appropriate source is a critical task because if biases, ambiguities, or other types of errors flaw the data being collected, even the most sophisticated statistical methods will not produce useful information. For the Good Tunes example, variables relevant to the customer experience could take the form of survey questions related to various aspects of the customer experience, examples of which are shown in Figure 1.1. The survey might also ask questions that seek to classify customers into groups for later analysis.

FIGURE 1.1

Questions about the Good Tunes customer experience

> 1. How many days did it take from the time you ordered your merchandise to the time you received it? _____
>
> 2. Did you buy any merchandise that was featured in the Good Tunes Sunday newspaper sales flyer for the week of your purchase? Yes _____ No_____
>
> 3. Was this your first purchase at Good Tunes? Yes _____ No_____
>
> 4. Are you likely to buy additional merchandise from Good Tunes in the next 12 months? Yes _____ No_____
>
> 5. How much money (in U.S. dollars) do you expect to spend on stereo and consumer electronics equipment in the next 12 months? _____
>
> 6. How do you rate the overall service provided by Good Tunes with respect to your recent purchase?
>
> Excellent ☐   Very good ☐   Fair ☐   Poor ☐
>
> 7. How do you rate the selection of products offered by Good Tunes with respect to other retailers of home entertainment systems?
>
> Excellent ☐   Very good ☐   Fair ☐   Poor ☐
>
> 8. How do you rate the quality of the items you recently purchased from Good Tunes?
>
> Excellent ☐   Very good ☐   Fair ☐   Poor ☐

One good way for Good Tunes to avoid data-collection flaws would be to distribute the questionnaire to a random sample of customers (Chapter 7 explains how to collect a random sample). A poor way would be to rely on a business-rating Web site that allows online visitors to rate a merchant. Such Web sites cannot provide assurance that those who do the ratings are representative of the population of customers, or that they even *are* customers.

1.7 Types of Data

Statisticians classify data as either being categorical (qualitative) or numerical (quantitative) and further classify numerical data as having either discrete or continuous values. Figure 1.2 shows the relationships and provides examples of each type of data.

FIGURE 1.2
Types of data

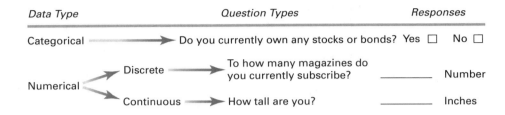

Categorical data (also known as **qualitative data**) have values that can only be placed into categories, such as yes and no. "Do you currently own stocks and bonds?" and Questions 2 through 4 in Figure 1.1 are examples of categorical variables, all of which have yes or no as their values. Categorical data can also have more than two possible responses. For example, you could ask customers to indicate the day of the week on which they made their purchases. In Figure 1.1, there are four possible responses to Questions 6 through 8.

Numerical data (also known as **quantitative data**) have values that represent quantities. For example, Questions 1 and 5 in Figure 1.1 are numerical data. Numerical data are further subdivided as discrete or continuous data.

Discrete data have numerical values that arise from a counting process. "The number of magazines subscribed to" is an example of a discrete numerical data because the response is one of a finite number of integers. You subscribe to zero, one, two, and so on magazines. The number of items that a customer purchases is also a discrete numerical data because you are counting the number of items purchased.

Continuous data produce numerical responses that arise from a measuring process. The time you wait for teller service at a bank is an example of a continuous numerical data because the response takes on any value within a *continuum*, or interval, depending on the precision of the measuring instrument. For example, your waiting time could be 1 minute, 1.1 minutes, 1.11 minutes, or 1.113 minutes, depending on the precision of the measuring device you use.

Theoretically, with sufficient precision of measurement, no two continuous values are identical. As a practical matter, however, most measuring devices are not precise enough to detect small differences, and tied values for a continuous data (i.e., two or more items or individuals with the same value) are sometimes present in experimental or survey data.

1.8 Measurement Scales

Data can be classified according to the type of measurement scale that is involved. The measurement scale is the set of all the possible values that could result when the data is collected. The type of measurement scale often dictates what calculations can be performed and what type of graphical display will be appropriate.

Qualitative (Categorical) Data

a) Nominal: Data indicates a category. The categories have no particular *order* or *ranking*. (Note: Alphabetic order is not a consideration.) The categories may be numeric or non-numeric. In either case, the data is *qualitative*.

Examples:

i. Marital Status: Single, married, divorced or widowed. On a survey the results of this question could be recorded as: 1 = single, 2 = married, etc. Even though the data is recorded as numbers, it is still *qualitative.*

ii. Colour of cars: Blue, red, silver, etc.

iii. Check-out lane used in grocery store: 1, 2, 3, etc. Note: The checkout lanes could have been labelled A, B, C or if the store had various colour schemes, the lanes could have been indicated by their colour.

The only type of **calculations** that can be performed is the number of responses in each category can be *counted.* Bar, pie and Pareto charts may be useful for displaying the results of this type of data collection.

b) Ordinal: Data is similar to nominal in that categories are involved, however, there is a natural *order* to the categories. We can say that one category is higher or better than another. Again the categories can be numeric or non-numeric and are considered as being *qualitative.* Bar and pie charts are appropriate graphs for displaying results.

Examples:

i. Professorial rank: Lecturer, assistant professor, associate professor, and professor.

ii. Rating of a product: Very poor, poor, average, good, and excellent.

iii. Order of finish in a sporting event: 1st, 2nd, 3rd, etc.

iv. Letter grades: A+, A, A−, B+, etc.

Once again, the only type of calculation that can be performed with the data is, the number of values in each category can be counted.

Quantitative (Numerical) Data

c) Interval: The distinguishing feature of interval data, as compared to nominal and ordinal, is the data has *units of measurement.* The data must be numeric and is *quantitative.* As a result, the interval between data values has a meaning. The other characteristic of significance in interval data is that the value "0" (zero) is only an *arbitrary reference point.* In other words, a value of zero does not mean there is no amount of the characteristic being measured.

Examples:

i. Temperature: 0° C does not mean there is no heat.

ii. Calendar scale: The date "0" is just a reference point.

In all cases, with an interval scale, we can subtract data values and get meaningful results.

Example 1: The difference between 10° C and 11° C is the same as the difference between 20° C and 21° C. If one had a container of water at 10° C and a similar sized container at 20° C, then the exact same amount of heat must be added to both containers to increase the temperature to 11° C and 21° C, respectively.

Example 2: The difference between the dates Jan. 1 and Jan. 8 is 7 days, and this is the exact same amount of time as the difference between Feb. 11 and Feb. 18. **Note:** Interval data is *not* of great importance to us in business, because, other than when measuring temperature, we rarely come across this type of data.

d) Ratio: This type of data has the characteristics of interval data, but, in addition, the "0" value does mean the absence of the characteristic being measured, i.e. 0 = 'nothing' and the *ratio* of data values is meaningful. Ratio data is the most common type of numeric data that we will encounter.

Ratio data may be continuous or discrete.

Examples of *discrete* ratio data:

> The number of students in this class.
> The number of classes you will attend.

Examples of continuous data include data dealing with: time, distance, area, volume, weight, and money.

The name ratio is appropriate because meaningful results occur when two data values are divided. For example:

$$\frac{10\ km}{5\ km} = 2$$ In other words, 10 km. is twice the distance as 5 km.

Now consider the following:

$$\frac{10\ C}{5\ C} = 2$$ In other words, 10° C is twice as hot as 5° C ???

(Temperature is measured on an interval scale, thus the result of a division is not meaningful.)

Also, the same is true for discrete data. If you attend 12 classes and your friend attends 6 classes, we can say you attended twice as many classes as your friend.

All types of calculations can be performed with ratio data. Histograms, polygons, ogives, stem-and-leaf displays, and box-whisker plots are all useful graphs of ratio data.

CLASSIFICATION OF DATA				
Types of Data	Qualitative (Categorical)		Quantitative (Numerical)	
Measurement Scale	Nominal	Ordinal	Interval	Ratio
Numerical Value			Continuous/ Discrete	Continuous/ Discrete

1.9 Downgrade of Measurement Scale

From the statistical point of view, a nominal scale is the lowest measurement level. On the other hand, a ratio scale is the highest level of measurement. It is possible to downgrade a higher scale level to the next level of measurement scale. For example, age variable can be measured as a ratio scale and can be converted to an ordinal scale as shown in Example 1 and Example 2.

Example 1

Variable: Age	Measurement scale
1. What is your age?_____ years.	Ratio scale
2. What is your age? [ ] 15 and under 20 [ ] 20 and under 25 [ ] 25 and under 30	Ordinal scale

Example 2

Variable: Salary	Measurement scale
1. What is your salary? $ _____	Ratio scale
2. What is your salary? [ ] 0 and under 10000 [ ] 10000 and under 20000 [ ] 20000 and under 30000	Ordinal scale

If possible, it is better to collect data in the highest scale (i.e. ratio scale). Sometimes, these questions (Variables: Age and Salary) are too personal to respondents. Therefore they may not respond to these questions. For this reason, we will downgrade the data.

Problems for Section 1.7–9

LEARNING THE BASICS

1.1 Three different beverages are sold at a fast-food restaurant—soft drinks, tea, and coffee. Explain why the type of beverage sold is an example of a categorical variable.

1.2 Soft drinks are sold in three sizes at a fast-food restaurant—small, medium, and large. Explain why the size of the soft drink is an example of a categorical variable.

1.3 Suppose that you measure the time it takes to download an MP3 file from the Internet. Explain why the download time is a continuous numerical variable.

APPLYING THE CONCEPTS

✓ SELF Test **1.4** For each of the following variables, determine whether the variable is categorical or numerical. If the variable is numerical, determine whether the variable is discrete or continuous.
a. Number of telephones in a household
b. Length of the longest long-distance call made in a month
c. Whether someone in the household owns a cell phone
d. Whether there is a high-speed Internet connection in the household

1.5 The following information is collected from students upon exiting the campus bookstore during the first week of classes:
a. Amount of time spent shopping in the bookstore
b. Number of textbooks purchased
c. Academic major
d. Gender
Classify each of these variables as categorical or numerical. If the variable is numerical, determine whether the variable is discrete or continuous.

1.6 For each of the following variables, determine whether the variable is categorical or numerical. If the variable is numerical, determine whether the variable is discrete or continuous.
a. Name of Internet provider
b. Amount of time spent surfing the Internet in a week
c. Number of e-mails received in a week
d. Number of online purchases made in a month

1.7 For each of the following variables, determine whether the variable is categorical or numerical. If the variable is numerical, determine whether the variable is discrete or continuous.

a. Amount of money spent on clothing in the past month
b. Favorite department store
c. Most likely time period during which shopping for clothing takes place (weekday, weeknight, or weekend)
d. Number of pairs of shoes owned

1.8 Suppose the following information is collected from Robert Keeler on his application for a home mortgage loan at the Metro County Savings and Loan Association:
a. Monthly payments: $1,427
b. Number of jobs in past 10 years: 1
c. Annual family income: $86,000
d. Marital status: Married
Classify each of the responses by type of data

1.9 The director of market research at a large department store chain wanted to conduct a survey throughout a metropolitan area to determine the amount of time working women spend shopping for clothing in a typical month.
a. Describe both the population and the sample of interest, and indicate the type of data the director might want to collect.
b. Develop a first draft of the questionnaire needed in (a) by writing a series of three categorical questions and three numerical questions that you feel are appropriate for this survey.

1.10 Consider the following questions being asked on a survey. The possible responses for each person are given. What is the measurement scale of the response data?
1. What was the rating of the restaurant that you last had dinner out with your partner?
   Answer: a) ★
               b) ★★
               c) ★★★
               d) ★★★★
               e) ★★★★★
2. What is the rating of your favourite television show?
   Answer: a) TV-G
               b) TV-PG
               c) TV-14
               d) TV-MA
3. On your income tax form: What is your marital status?
   Answer: a) Married
               b) Common Law
               c) Widowed
               d) Divorced
               e) Separated
               f) Single

4. What is your level of education?

    Answer: **a)** Elementary School

    b) High School

    c) College

    d) University-Undergrad

    e) University-Post Grad

5. What stock-exchange are the majority of your stock investments listed on?

    Answer: **a)** TSX

    b) NYSE

    c) AMEX

    d) NASDAQ

    e) VSE

6. What type of accommodation do you usually choose for your overnight stay when on a car trip?

    Answer: **a)** Hotel

    b) Motel

    c) Bed & Breakfast

    d) Country Inn

    e) Cabin/Cottage

7. What was the rating of the last motel that you stayed in?

    Answer: **a)** ★

    b) ★★

    c) ★★★

    d) ★★★★

    e) ★★★★★

8. What is your postal code? Answer: _____

9. What was the rating of the last movie that you saw in a theatre:

    Answer: **a)** G

    b) PG

    c) PG-13

    d) R

    e) NC-17

    f) X

10. What is your favourite meat?

    Answer: **a)** Beef

    b) Pork

    c) Chicken

    d) Veal

    e) Lamb

1.11 Refer to the chart below, from the Autumn 1999 issue of Canadian Social Trends, that shows data regarding seniors with driver's licenses who have a health condition. Many seniors were surveyed and much data was obtained from each respondent. The responses to 4 questions were used to obtain the data to allow the researchers to construct the chart shown. What measurement scale is used for each variable? Are the numerical values discrete or continuous?

Question	Measurement Scale	Discrete/Continuous

EXERCISES

1.12 The following chart was produced by asking two questions in a survey. Assume that this survey was given to the registered nurses employed in Nursing. The responses to two questions were used to obtain the data to allow the researchers to construct the bar chart shown below.

FIGURE 1.3

Proportion of registered nurses employed in Nursing by age and year

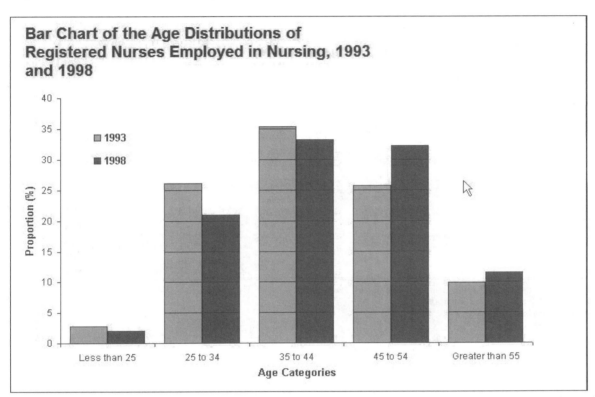

Source: Registered Nurses Database (RNDB), 1998. (The bar chart appeared on the National Resources Canada's website: http://atlas.nrcan.gc.ca/site/english/maps/health/resources/nursing/nursing_figure7.gif/image_view)

I. What are the two questions?
  Question 1: _____
  Question 2: _____
II. What is the highest measurement scale that applies to the set of response data from the first question?
  a) Nominal
  b) Ordinal
  c) Interval
  d) Ratio – Discrete
  e) Ratio – Continuous
III. What is the highest measurement scale that applies to the set of response data from the second question?
  a) Nominal
  b) Ordinal
  c) Interval
  d) Ratio – Discrete
  e) Ratio – Continuous

1.13 Refer to the table published in the Canadian Social Trends (CST), that shows data regarding adults aged between 22 and 29 years old with a sense of community and who have a higher odds of voting.

Ten questions were asked to obtain data in order to formulate the following table. One of the questions was "What is your gender?" and another was "Did you volunteer in the past year?"

Your task is to identify the remaining 8 questions. For each questions, identify the type of measurement scale applies to the set of response data. Use the following measurement scales below:
  (a) Nominal
  (b) Ordinal
  (c) Interval - Continuous
  (d) Ratio – Discrete
  (e) Ratio – Continuous

Use the table below to record your answers.

CST — 22- to 29-year-olds with a very strong sense of community have higher odds of voting than those with a weaker sense of belonging

	Odds ratio		Odds ratio
Age[1]	1.03	**Region**	
Youth involvement[2]	1.03	*Quebec*	*1.00*
Number of groups of which a member	1.11[3]	Atlantic	0.38*
		Ontario	0.30*
Sex		Prairies	0.32*
Female	*1.00*	British Columbia	0.36*
Male	1.08	**Educational level**	
Place of birth		*University degree*	*1.00*
Foreign-born	*1.00*	Less than high school	0.25*
Canadian-born	4.27*	High school graduate	0.48*
Religious observance		Some post-secondary	0.74
Rarely/never	*1.00*	Diploma or certificate	0.68*
Weekly	0.86	**Main activity**	
Sometimes	1.40*	*Other[4]*	*1.00*
Volunteer in past year		Labour force	1.10
No	*1.00*	Student	0.81
Yes	1.42*	**Household income**	
Sense of belonging to community		*$60,000 or more*	*1.00*
Very weak	*1.00*	Less than $20,000	0.51*
Very strong	1.74*	$20,000 to $29,999	0.74
Somewhat strong	1.30	$30,000 to $39,999	0.75
Somewhat weak	1.26	$40,000 to $49,999	1.00
		$50,000 to $59,999	0.66*

Note: This table presents the odds that a respondent voted in the last election prior to the survey, relative to the odds of a benchmark group when all other variables in the analysis are held constant. Benchmark group is shown in italics.
*   Statistically significant difference from benchmark group ($p < 0.05$).
1.   For each additional year, the odds of voting increase by 3%.
2.   For each additional activity during youth, the odds of voting increase by 3%.
3.   For each additional group, the odds of voting increase by 11%, which is statistically significant ($p < 0.05$).
4.   "Other" includes activities such as homemaking, retirement, volunteer work or illness.
Source: Statistics Canada, General Social Survey, 2003.

Source Canadian Social Trends, Issue: Winter 2005, page 5. website: http://dsp-psd.tpsgc.gc.ca/Collection-R/Statcan/ 11-008-XIE/0030511-008-XIE.pdf

Question	What is the measurement scale? (a) Nominal (b) Ordinal (c) Interval Continuous (d) Ratio – Discrete (e) Ratio - Continuous
1	
2	
3	
4	
5	
6	
7	
8	

1.14   Refer to the chart below that shows data regarding the majority of young adults who are engaged in at least one non-voting political activity. The following chart was produced by asking a question in a survey. What type of measurement scale applies to the set of response data?

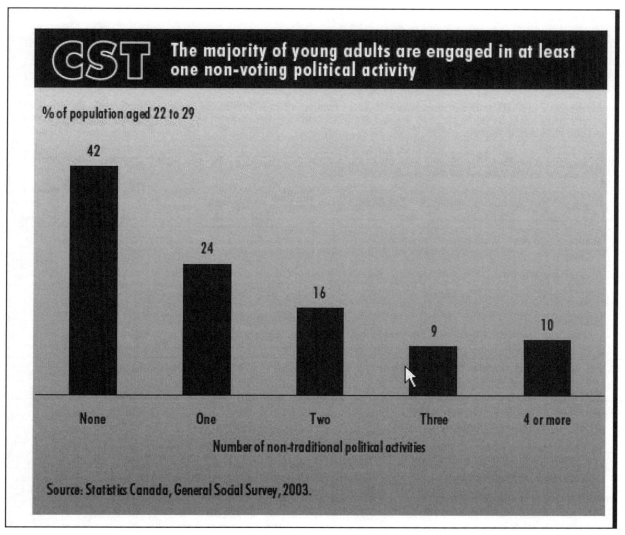

Source Canadian Social Trends, Issue: Winter 2005, page 3. website: http://dsp-psd.tpsgc.gc.ca/Collection-R/ Statcan/11-008-XIE/0030511-008-XIE.pdf

a) Nominal
b) Ordinal
c) Interval - Continuous
d) Ratio – Discrete
e) Ratio - Continuous

Government Travel Survey of Visitors to Canada

26

☐ REG   ☐ PERS
☐ CHARTER   ☐ SELF

Confidential when completed
Version française disponible

Dear visitor :

We are currently conducting a travel survey between Canada and overseas countries and we would be interested in knowing about the trip you have taken to Canada. Information from this voluntary survey will be used by members of the Canadian travel industry and government tourism organizations to better understand and serve you, the travelling public.

We would appreciate it if you could spare 10 to 15 minutes of your time to complete this questionnaire. If you require assistance, do not hesitate to ask our Statistics Canada representative. Upon completion, please return the questionnaire to her/him.

This survey is conducted under the authority of the *Statistics Act* (R.S.C. 1985, c. S19) and individual information from your questionnaire will be kept strictly confidential.

Thank you for your co-operation on this important survey and have a nice flight.

---

1. Where do you live? *Usual place of residence*

Country

01 ○ United Kingdom   03 ○ Germany   ▶   Other, specify _____

02 ○ France   04 ○ Japan

If Canada or United States, please return the questionnaire to our representative.

City/Town _____   *State/Province/Territory* _____

1a. Are you travelling as a member of i) a crew or ii) a military or diplomatic corps or one of their dependents?

1 ○ Yes ▶ If *«yes»*, please return the questionnaire to our representative.

2 ○ No

2a. Where and when did you <u>enter</u> Canada?

Name of Canadian border crossing or airport _____

Day Month Year
| | | : | | | |

2b. Where will you <u>leave</u> Canada?

01 ○ Halifax International Airport

02 ○ Montreal - Dorval / Mirabel Airport

03 ○ Pearson International Airport, Toronto (T1, T2, T3)

04 ○ Calgary International Airport

05 ○ Vancouver International Airport

When will you <u>leave</u> Canada?

Day Month Year   Nights
| | | : | | | | | | |

2c. When <u>entering</u> Canada, did you travel...

1 ○ From U.S.A. only   2 ○ Directly from another country   3 ○ From another country via the U.S.A.

▼

Please return the questionnaire to our representative.

2d. When <u>leaving</u> Canada, will you travel...

4 ○ To U.S.A. only   5 ○ Directly to another country   6 ○ To another country via the U.S.A.

8-2200-400.1: 2001-07-16   STC/ECT-250-02797

☐ COMP   ☐ PART   ☐ OOS

Statistics Canada   Statistique Canada

Canadä

3. In the next questions we will be referring to a <u>travelling party</u>. In your travelling party include only those for whom you feel comfortable reporting <u>spending</u> and <u>activities</u>. A travelling party usually refers to friends and/or family members travelling together.

How many people including yourself were in the <u>travelling party</u>?

4. How many people in the <u>travelling party</u> were in each of the following groups?

Age groups ▶	Under 2 years	2 to 11	12 to 14	15 to 19	20 to 24	25 to 34	35 to 44	45 to 54	55 to 64	65 to 74	75 and over
	01	02	03	04	05	06	07	08	09	10	11
Female ▶											
	12	13	14	15	16	17	18	19	20	21	22
Male ▶											

5. What was the <u>travelling party's main</u> reason for taking this trip to Canada?
Check one only.
(e.g. If a person on a business trip took his/her family along to visit relatives, check reason for trip as "business".)

Business

01 ◯ Meetings   02 ◯ Convention, conference, trade show, seminar   03 ◯ Other work

Pleasure

04 ◯ Holiday, vacation   05 ◯ Visit friends or relatives   06 ◯ Visit second home, cottage, condo   07 ◯ Attend events, attractions

Other

08 ◯ Personal (medical, wedding, etc.)   09 ◯ In transit to / from other countries *and* passing through Canada Customs   ◯ In transit to / from other countries *without* passing through Canada Customs   ▶ If «*In transit to / from other countries without* passing through Canada Customs », please return the questionnaire to our representative.

10 ◯ Educational study   11 ◯ Shopping   12 ◯ Other – Specify

6. On this trip in Canada did anyone in the <u>travelling party</u>...
Check all that apply.

21 ◯ Visit friends or relatives
22 ◯ Attend a festival or fair
23 ◯ Attend a cultural performance (*a play, a concert, etc.*)
24 ◯ Visit a museum or art gallery
25 ◯ Visit a historic site
26 ◯ Visit a zoo, aquarium or botanical garden
27 ◯ Attend a sports event
28 ◯ Go shopping
29 ◯ Go sightseeing
30 ◯ Go to a bar or night club
31 ◯ Go to a casino

32 ◯ Visit a theme or amusement park
33 ◯ Visit a national or provincial nature park
34 ◯ Participate in sports or outdoor activities *Specify* ▼

35 ◯ Boating - motor boat, sail boat, kayak, canoe or other
36 ◯ Golfing
37 ◯ Downhill skiing or snow boarding
38 ◯ Hunting
39 ◯ Fishing
◯ Other sports or outdoor activities *Specify* ▼

7. How would you rate the following aspects of your trip in Canada?

	Good	Average	Poor	Not applicable
Transportation services	01 ◯	06 ◯	11 ◯	◯
Accommodation services	02 ◯	07 ◯	12 ◯	◯
Hospitality of local people	03 ◯	08 ◯	13 ◯	◯
Value for your money	04 ◯	09 ◯	14 ◯	◯
Variety of things to see and do	05 ◯	10 ◯	15 ◯	◯

8. While in Canada, what place(s) did the <u>travelling party</u> visit?
Please name all places visited even if you did not stay overnight. (Exclude stop-overs at airports.)

Please print.

Where did the travelling party stay?
Check all that apply.

Name of city(ies) / town(s) visited	Name of province(s) / territory(ies) visited	Number of nights spent at each place	Hotel	Motel	Home of friends or relatives	Camping or trailer park	Cottage or cabin	Other
_____			1○	2○	3○	4○	5○	6○
_____			1○	2○	3○	4○	5○	6○
_____			1○	2○	3○	4○	5○	6○
_____			1○	2○	3○	4○	5○	6○
_____			1○	2○	3○	4○	5○	6○
_____			1○	2○	3○	4○	5○	6○
_____			1○	2○	3○	4○	5○	6○
_____			1○	2○	3○	4○	5○	6○
_____			1○	2○	3○	4○	5○	6○
_____			1○	2○	3○	4○	5○	6○
_____			1○	2○	3○	4○	5○	6○
_____			1○	2○	3○	4○	5○	6○

9. Does anyone in the <u>travelling party</u> own any of the accommodations used on this trip?   1○ Yes ▶ Go to Question 11   2○ No ▶ Go to Question 11

For administrative use only

10. When <u>entering</u> Canada, did you travel ...
1○ From U.S.A. only   2○ Directly from another country   3○ From another country via the U.S.A.

When <u>leaving</u> Canada, will you travel ...
4○ To U.S.A. only   5○ Directly to another country   6○ To another country via the U.S.A.

11. For this trip, what means of transportation did you use

a) . . . to <u>enter</u> Canada?
Check one only.

Commercial: 01○ Plane   02○ Train   03○ Boat   04○ Bus
Other: 05○ Private automobile   06○ Rented automobile   07○ Private plane   08○ Private boat   09○ Other

b) . . . to <u>leave</u> Canada?
Check one only.

10⊘ Plane   11○ Train   12○ Boat   13○ Bus   14○ Private automobile   15○ Rented automobile   16○ Private plane   17○ Private boat   18○ Other

c) . . . <u>while</u> in Canada?
Check all that apply.

19○ Plane   20○ Train   21○ Boat   22○ Bus   23○ Private automobile   24○ Rented automobile   25○ Private plane   26○ Private boat   27○ Other (metro, subway, taxi)

12. Please report the routes, carriers and fares (including taxes) to enter and leave Canada.
Please print.
▼

a) From which country did the <u>travelling party</u> come immediately before entering Canada (excluding stop-overs at airports)?

Name of airline or other carrier

b) To which country the <u>travelling party</u> is going immediately upon leaving Canada (excluding stop-overs at airports)?
○ France
○ United Kingdom
○ Germany
○ Japan
○ Other, specify

Name of airline or other carrier

c) Fares

Round trip fare *(including package tours)* for <u>entire travelling party</u>

Currency *(if other than CAN $)*
○ French franc
○ British pound
○ EMU Euro
○ German mark
○ Japanese yen
○ Other, specify

OR

Entry fare for the <u>travelling party</u>

Currency *(if other than CAN $)*
○ French franc
○ British pound
○ EMU Euro
○ German mark
○ Japanese yen
○ Other, specify

Return fare for the <u>travelling party</u>

Currency *(if other than CAN $)*
○ French franc
○ British pound
○ EMU Euro
○ German mark
○ Japanese yen
○ Other, specify

13. What class of fares were used?
Check all that apply.

1 ○ First class   3 ○ Economy class   5 ○ Frequent flyer plan
2 ○ Business class   4 ○ Charter class

---

14. Were these fares part of a package?

○ No   1 ○ Yes ▶

Which of the following item(s) was (were) also included? *Check all that apply.*

2 ○ Accommodation / meals   4 ○ Rented car
3 ○ Accommodation only   5 ○ Other

---

15. For this trip, what was the <u>total spending in Canada</u> for all persons in the <u>travelling party</u>?

Include cash/credit transactions for food, accommodation, entertainment, merchandise, gifts, auto operation, local transportation, etc. even if paid for by someone else or a business. Include all taxes and tips. Exclude fares and/or packages reported in Question 12. Estimates appreciated.

Amount
| | | | | | .00

Number of persons included in spending ▶ | |

Currency *(if other than CAN $)*
○ French franc
○ British pound
○ EMU Euro
○ German mark
○ Japanese yen
○ Other, specify | |

---

16. Please distribute <u>total spending</u> (as reported in Question 15) in each of the following categories. Estimates appreciated.

If estimates can not be provided, report approximate percentages (%) of total spending.

The sums in Questions 15 and 16 should agree.

	Amount	or	%
Accommodation						.00	or				
Transportation in Canada *(include gasoline expenditures, rented car, intercity plane, bus and train fares, boat tours, local bus, taxi)*						.00	or				
Food and beverage						.00	or				
Recreation and entertainment						.00	or				
Other *(souvenirs, shopping, photos, etc.)* Specify major items. ▼						.00	or				

---

17. What percentage of total expenditures *(including fares)* was paid ...

personally? *(including family/friends)* | | | %
by business? | | | %
by government? | | | %

---

18. <u>After</u> your first arrival to Canada, did you at any time during this trip leave Canada for the U.S.A. and then return?

If yes, please report the place(s) and date(s) of exit and the place(s) of re-entry.

Please print.

1 ○ Yes ▶ How many times? | | 2 ○ No

Place of exit from Canada (border crossing / airport)	Date of exit Day Month Year	Place of re-entry to Canada (border crossing / airport)	Number of nights in U.S.A.

---

19. If you visited the U.S.A. <u>before</u> entering Canada, how long did you stay in the U.S.A.?

1 ○ Under 24 hours   2 ○ 1 – 2 nights   3 ○ 3 or more nights   4 ○ Not applicable

---

COMMENTS

We welcome comments on any aspect of your trip including those which would help us to better understand your responses.

_____

_____

_____

_____

THANK YOU VERY MUCH FOR YOUR CO-OPERATION

8-2200-400.1

1.10 Microsoft Excel and Minitab

In a previous generation, the use of statistical methods in business was limited, often to those few who were fortunate to have access to specialized statistical calculators or large mainframe computers. Today, statistical functionality is so commonplace that many simple statistical tasks, once done exclusively with pencil and paper or simple hand calculators, are now done electronically with the assistance of computers.

Minitab and Microsoft Excel are desktop programs that business people use for statistics. Minitab is an example of a **statistical package**, a program engineered from the ground up to perform statistical analysis as accurately as possible. Microsoft Excel is a general purpose data analysis component of Microsoft Office that is based on electronic spreadsheets that are used in accounting and financial applications. As a general purpose tool, Excel can perform many functions, but none as well as other programs that are more singularly focused (see References 1, 2, 3, and 6). When it comes to teaching introductory business statistics, both programs have their proponents, with those favoring Minitab noting that Minitab as a complete statistical program while those favoring Excel noting that Excel is a program found on many business desktops (and in many business school courses).

Although you are probably more familiar with Microsoft Excel than with Minitab, both programs share many similarities. This is no coincidence as Minitab was inspired by Omnitab, a mainframe computer program from the 1960s that can be considered an ancestor to all electronic spreadsheet programs. Both Minitab and Excel use **worksheets** (their name for spreadsheets) to store the data you have collected for analysis. Worksheets are tabular arrangements of data, in which the intersections of rows and columns form **cells**, boxes into which you make entries. In both Minitab and Excel, the data for each variable are placed in individual columns. (The instructions in this book assume this standard practice.) Both Excel and Minitab allow you to save worksheets, programming information, and results in one file, called **workbooks** in Excel and **projects** in Minitab. Minitab also allows you to save individual worksheets in separate Minitab worksheet (.mtw) files. (The Student CD-ROM packaged with this book contains the data for problems and chapter examples as both Excel workbook files and Minitab worksheet files.)

1.11 Learning To Use Statistical Programs

Because using computer programs to assist in statistical decision making is a common occurrence in the business world, you will probably want to learn to use Minitab, Microsoft Excel, or some other program to help you perform statistical analysis. To learn to use these programs properly, you need to be able to:

- Understand underlying statistical concepts
- Understand how to organize and present information
- Understand how to operate your program's user interface
- Know how to review results for errors
- Make and secure clearly named backups of your work

Understanding the underlying statistical concepts and knowing how to organize and present results are two things that can be overlooked in the rush to "use" a statistical program. If you do not take the time to do these things, you can produce misleading results or, worse, appear as someone ignorant in the necessary foundations of statistics.

Sometimes people wrongly focus on trying to extensively memorize a program's commands or menu choices. You will not need to do that in order to be able to do the other three bulleted abilities. Instead, train yourself to use reference materials to find the instructions that you need when you need them. For example, the Microsoft Excel, PHStat2 (the Excel add-in that simplifies your use of Excel), and Minitab appendices that appear at the end of each chapter will enable you to recreate the in-chapter examples and solve the in-chapter problems. You can also consult Appendix C if you are concerned about your basic computing skills or want to know more about the conventions used in this book to describe computer operations.

Don't worry too much about the program you use. Any choice will help you see how statistical programs are a necessary part of a business decision maker's daily routine.

USING STATISTICS @ Good Tunes Revisited

In the Using Statistics scenario, you were asked to assist in preparing a slide show and prospectus for the Good Tunes company. The managers had decided to approach banks for funding the expansion of their company, but were not sure what type of data to present and how to present it. A first step was to summarize the details of thousands of transactions into useful information in the form of yearly dollar sales totals. Second, since Good Tunes prides itself in providing its customers with high-quality service, you decided to gather data that would support this aspect of the company.

Of the four sources of data discussed in this chapter (data distributed by an organization or an individual, a designed experiment, a survey, and an observational study), you decided to survey customers on various aspects of their experience with Good Tunes. The survey constructed also contains questions that seek to classify customers into groups for later analyses. Because Good Tunes has so many customers, gathering information from the entire population of customers was deemed impractical. Instead, a random sample of customers will be selected to take the survey.

A survey containing eight questions was constructed (see Figure 1.1 on page 9). The first and fifth questions of the survey will produce numerical data. The responses to the first question (number of days) are discrete, and the responses to the fifth question (amount of money spent) are continuous. Questions 2–4 and 6–8 will produce categorical data. Next, you will need to select the proper types of analyses for the different types of data collected. Chapter 2 presents graphical displays (for example, tables and charts), and Chapter 3 presents descriptive numerical measures (for example, mean, median, and mode).

SUMMARY

In this chapter, you have been introduced to the role of statistics in turning data into information. You learned that businesses use statistics to summarize and draw conclusions from data, to make reliable forecasts, and to improve business processes. In addition, you studied data collection, the various types of data used in business, and the importance of using computer programs such as Microsoft Excel and Minitab. In the next two chapters, tables and charts and a variety of descriptive numerical measures that are useful for data analysis are developed.

KEY TERMS

categorical data   10
cell   22
continuous data   10
data   5
data collection   7
descriptive statistics   4
discrete data   10
inferential statistics   4

numerical data   10
operational definition   5
parameter   6
population   6
primary source   8
projects   22
qualitative data   10
quantitative data   10

sample   6
secondary source   8
statistic   6
statistical package   22
statistics   4
variable   5
workbooks   22
worksheets   22

CHAPTER REVIEW PROBLEMS

CHECKING YOUR UNDERSTANDING

1.15 What is the difference between a sample and a population?

1.16 What is the difference between a statistic and a parameter?

1.17 What is the difference between descriptive statistics and inferential statistics?

1.18 What is the difference between a categorical variable and a numerical variable?

1.19 What is the difference between a discrete variable and a continuous variable?

1.20 What is an operational definition and why is it so important?

APPLYING THE CONCEPTS

1.21 Go to the official Microsoft Excel Web site, **www.microsoft.com/office/excel**, or the official Minitab Web site, **www.minitab.com**. Explain how you think Microsoft Excel or Minitab could be useful in the field of statistics.

1.22 The Gallup organization releases the results of recent polls at its Web site, **www.gallup.com**. Go to this site and read an article of interest.
a. Describe the population of interest.
b. Describe the sample that was collected.
c. Describe a parameter of interest.
d. Describe the statistic used to describe the parameter in (c).

1.23 According to its home page, "Swivel is a place where curious people explore data—all kinds of data." Go to **www. swivel.com** and explore a data set of interest to you.
a. Which of the four sources of data best describes the source of the data set you selected?
b. Describe a variable in the data set you selected.
c. Is the variable categorical or numerical?
d. If the variable in (c) is numerical, is it discrete or continuous?

1.24 At the U.S. Census Bureau site, **www.census.gov**, click **Survey of Business Owners** in the "Business & Industry" section and read about The Survey of Business Owners. Click on **Sample SBO-1 Form** to view a survey form.
a. Give an example of a categorical variable found in this survey.
b. Give an example of a numerical variable found in this survey.
c. Is the variable you selected in (b) discrete or continuous?

1.25 Gallup's 2008 annual Environment Poll indicates that 28% of respondents have made major changes in their shopping and living habits over the last five years to help protect the environment, 55% of respondents have made minor changes, and 17% have made no changes (J. Jones, "In the U.S., 28% Report Major Changes to Live 'Green'," **www.gallup.com**, April 18, 2008). The results are based on telephone interviews with 1,102 people living in the United States, aged 18 and older, conducted March 6–9, 2008.
a. Describe the population of interest.
b. Describe the sample that was collected.
c. Describe a parameter of interest.
d. Describe the statistic used to describe the parameter in (c).

1.26 Three professors at Northern Kentucky University compared two different approaches to teaching courses in the school of business (M. W. Ford, D. W. Kent, and S. Devoto, "Learning from the Pros: Influence of Web-Based Expert Commentary on Vicarious Learning about Financial Markets," *Decision Sciences Journal of Innovative Education*, January 2007, 5(1), 43–63). At the time of the study, there were 2,100 students in the business school and 96 students were involved in the study. Demographic data collected on these 96 students included class (freshman, sophomore, junior, senior), age, gender, and major.
a. Describe the population of interest.
b. Describe the sample that was collected.
c. For each of the four demographic variables mentioned above, indicate if they are categorical or numerical.

1.27 A manufacturer of cat food was planning to survey households in the United States to determine purchasing habits of cat owners. Among the questions to be included are those that relate to
1. where cat food is primarily purchased.
2. whether dry or moist cat food is purchased.
3. the number of cats living in the household.
4. whether the cat is pedigreed.
a. Describe the population.
b. For each of the four items listed, indicate whether the variable is categorical or numerical. If it is numerical, is it discrete or continuous?
c. Develop five categorical questions for the survey.
d. Develop five numerical questions for the survey.

STUDENT SURVEY DATABASE

1.28 A sample of 50 undergraduate students answered the following survey.
1. What is your gender? Female _____ Male _____
2. What is your age (*as of last birthday*)? _____
3. What is your height (*in inches*)? _____

4. What is your current registered class designation?
   Freshman _____ Sophomore _____
   Junior _____ Senior _____
5. What is your major area of study?
   Accounting _____ Economics/Finance _____
   Information Systems _____
   International Business _____ Management _____
   Marketing/Retailing _____ Other _____
   Undecided _____
6. At the present time, do you plan to attend graduate school? Yes _____ No _____ Not sure _____
7. What is your current cumulative grade point average? _____
8. What would you expect your starting annual salary (*in $000*) to be if you were to seek employment immediately after obtaining your bachelor's degree? _____
9. What do you anticipate your salary to be (*in $000*) after five years of full-time work experience? _____
10. What is your current employment status?
    Full-time _____ Part-time _____ Unemployed _____
11. How many clubs, groups, organizations, or teams are you currently affiliated with on campus?
12. How satisfied are you with the student advisement services on campus? _____

Extremely	1	2	3	4	5	6	7	Extremely
unsatisfied			Neutral					satisfied

13. About how much money did you spend this semester for textbooks and supplies? _____
    a. Which variables in the survey are categorical?
    b. Which variables in the survey are numerical?
    c. Which variables are discrete numerical variables?
   The results of the survey are in the file **Undergradsurvey**.

1.29 A sample of 40 MBA students answered the following survey:
1. What is your gender? Female _____ Male _____
2. What is your age (*as of last birthday*)? _____
3. What is your height (*in inches*)? _____

4. What is your current major area of study?
   Accounting _____ Economics/Finance _____
   Information Systems _____
   International Business _____ Management _____
   Marketing/Retailing _____ Other _____
   Undecided _____
5. What is your graduate cumulative grade point average? _____
6. What was your undergraduate major?
   Biological Sciences _____ Business
   Administration _____ Computers or Math _____
   Education _____ Engineering _____
   Humanities _____ Performing Arts _____
   Physical Sciences _____ Social Sciences _____
   Other _____
7. What was your undergraduate cumulative grade point average? _____
8. What was your GMAT score? _____
9. What is your current employment status? _____
   Full-time _____ Part-time _____
   Unemployed _____
10. How many different full-time jobs have you held in the past 10 years? _____
11. What do you expect your annual salary (*in $000*) to be immediately after completion of the MBA program? _____
12. What do you anticipate your salary to be (*in $000*) after five years of full-time work experience following the completion of the MBA program? _____
13. How satisfied are you with the student advisement services on campus?

Extremely	1	2	3	4	5	6	7	Extremely
unsatisfied			Neutral					satisfied

14. About how much money did you spend this semester for textbooks and supplies? _____
    a. Which variables in the survey are categorical?
    b. Which variables in the survey are numerical?
    c. Which variables are discrete numerical variables?
   The results of the survey are in the file **Gradsurvey**.

END-OF-CHAPTER CASES

At the end of most chapters, you will find a continuing case study that allows you to apply statistics to problems faced by the management of the *Springville Herald*, a daily newspaper. Complementing this case are a series of Web Cases that extend many of the Using Statistics scenarios that begin each chapter.

LEARNING WITH THE WEB CASES

People use statistical techniques to help communicate and present important information to others both inside and outside their businesses. Every day, as in these examples, people misuse these techniques:

- A sales manager working with an "easy-to-use" charting program chooses an inappropriate chart that obscures data relationships.

- The editor of an annual report presents a chart of revenues with an abridged *Y*-axis that creates the false impression of greatly rising revenues.
- An analyst generates meaningless statistics about a set of categorical data, using analyses designed for numerical data.

Identifying and preventing misuses of statistics, whether intentional or not, is an important responsibility for all managers. The Web Cases help you develop the skills necessary for this important task.

Web Cases send you to Web sites that are related to the Using Statistics scenarios that begin each chapter. You review internal documents as well as publicly stated claims, seeking to identify and correct the misuses of statistics. Unlike a traditional case study, but much like real-world situations, not all of the information you encounter will be relevant to your task, and you may occasionally discover conflicting information that you need to resolve before continuing with the case.

To assist your learning, the Web Case for each chapter begins with the learning objective and a summary of the problem or issue at hand. Each case directs you to one or more Web pages where you can discover information to answer case questions that help guide your exploration. If you prefer, you can view these pages by opening corresponding HTML files that can be found in the **Web Case** folder on the Student CD-ROM. You can find an index of all files/pages by opening the `SpringvilleCC.htm` file in the **Web Case** folder or by visiting the Springville Chamber of Commerce page, at **www.prenhall.com/Springville/SpringvilleCC.htm**.

WEB CASE EXAMPLE

To illustrate how to learn from a Web Case, open a Web browser and link to **www.prenhall.com/Springville/Good_Tunes.htm**, or open the `Good_Tunes.htm` file in the Student CD-ROM **Web Case** folder. This Web page represents the home page of Good Tunes, the online retailer mentioned in the Using Statistics scenario in this chapter. Recall that the privately held Good Tunes is seeking financing to expand its business by opening retail locations. Because it is in management's interest to show that Good Tunes is a thriving business, it is not too surprising to discover the "our best sales year ever" claim in the "Good Times at Good Tunes" entry at the top of their home page.

The claim also serves as a hyperlink, so click on **our best sales year ever** to display the page that supports the claim. How would you support such a claim? with a table of numbers? a chart? remarks attributed to a knowledgeable source? Good Tunes has used a chart to present "two years ago" and "latest twelve months" sales data by category. Are there any problems with the choices made on this Web page? *Absolutely!*

First, note that there are no scales for the symbols used, so it is impossible to know what the actual sales volumes are. In fact, as you will learn in Section 2.6, charts that incorporate symbols in this way are considered examples of *chartjunk* and would never be used by people seeking to properly use graphs.

This important point aside, another question that arises is whether the sales data represent the number of units sold or something else. The use of the symbols creates the impression that unit sales data are being presented. If the data are unit sales, does such data best support the claim being made, or would something else, such as dollar volumes, be a better indicator of sales at Good Tunes?

Then there are those curious chart labels. "Latest twelve months" is ambiguous; it could include months from the current year as well as months from one year ago and therefore may not be an equivalent time period to "two years ago." But the business was established in 1997, and the claim being made is "best sales year ever," so why hasn't management included sales figures for *every* year?

Is Good Tunes management hiding something, or are they just unaware of the proper use of statistics? Either way, they have failed to properly communicate a vital aspect of their story.

In subsequent Web Cases, you will be asked to provide this type of analysis, using the open-ended questions of the case as your guide. Not all the cases are as straightforward as this sample, and some cases include perfectly appropriate applications of statistics.

REFERENCES

1. McCullough, B. D., and D. Heiser, "On the Accuracy of Statistical Procedures in Microsoft Excel 2007," *Computational Statistics and Data Analysis*, 52 (2008), 4568–4606.
2. McCullough, B. D., and B. Wilson, "On the Accuracy of Statistical Procedures in Microsoft Excel 97," *Computational Statistics and Data Analysis*, 31 (1999), 27–37.
3. McCullough, B. D., and B. Wilson, "On the Accuracy of Statistical Procedures in Microsoft Excel 2003," *Computational Statistics and Data Analysis*, 49 (2005), 1244–52.
4. *Microsoft Excel 2007* (Redmond, WA: Microsoft Corporation, 2007).
5. *Minitab Release 15* (State College, PA: Minitab, Inc., 2006).
6. Nash, J. C., "Spreadsheets in Statistical Practice—Another Look," *The American Statistician*, 60 (2006), 287–89.

APPENDIX A1a

A1.1 INTRODUCTION TO MICROSOFT EXCEL

Microsoft Excel Overview

Microsoft Excel is the electronic worksheet program of Microsoft Office. Although not a specialized statistical program, Excel contains basic statistical functions and includes Data Analysis Tool Pak procedures that you can use to perform selected advanced statistical methods. You can also install the Prentice Hall PHStat2 add-in (included with the CD-ROM packaged with this text) to extend and enhance the Data Analysis Tool Pak that Microsoft Excel contains. (You do not need to use PHStat2 in order to use Microsoft Excel with this text, although using PHStat2 will simplify using Excel for statistical analysis.)

In Microsoft Excel, you create or open and save files that are called **workbooks**. Workbooks are collections of worksheets and related items such as charts that contain the original data as well as the calculations and results associated with one or more analyses. Because of its widespread distribution, Microsoft Excel is a convenient program to use, but some statisticians express concern about its lack of fully reliable and accurate results for some statistical procedures. Although Microsoft has improved many statistical functions starting with Excel 2003, you should be cautious about using Microsoft Excel to perform analyses on data other than the data used in this text. (If you plan to install PHStat2, make sure to first read Appendix F and any PHStat2 read-me file that may appear on the included CD-ROM.)

Using Microsoft Excel Worksheets

In Microsoft Excel, you enter data into worksheets that are organized as lettered columns and numbered rows. Typically, you enter the data for each variable in a separate column, using the row 1 cell for a variable label and each subsequent row for a single observation. You should follow the good practice of entering only one set of data per worksheet.

To refer to a specific entry, or cell, you use a *Sheetname!ColumnRow* notation. For example, Data!A2 refers to the cell in column A and row 2 in the Data worksheet. To refer to a specific group or **range** of cells, you use a *Sheetname!Upperleftcell:Lowerrightcell* notation. For example, Data!A2:B11 refers to the 20 cells that are in rows 2 though 11 in columns A and B of the Data worksheet.

Each Microsoft Excel worksheet has its own name. Automatically, Microsoft Excel names worksheets in the form of **Sheet1**, **Sheet2**, and so on. You should rename your worksheets, giving them more self-descriptive names, by double-clicking the sheet tabs that appear at the bottom of each sheet, typing a new name, and pressing the Enter key.

Using Formulas in Excel Worksheets

Formulas are worksheet cell entries that perform a calculation or some other task. You enter formulas by typing the equal sign symbol (=) followed by some combination of mathematical or other data-processing operations.

For simple formulas, you use the symbols +, −, *, /, and ^ for the operations addition, subtraction, multiplication, division, and exponentiation (a number raised to a power), respectively. For example, the formula =Data!B2 + Data!B3 + Data!B4 + Data!B5 adds the contents of the cells B2, B3, B4, and B5 of the Data worksheet and displays the sum as the value in the cell containing the formula. You can also use Microsoft Excel *functions* in formulas to simplify formulas. For example, the formula =SUM(Data!B2:B5) that uses the Excel SUM() function is a shorter equivalent to the formula of the previous sentence. You can also use cell or cell range references that do not contain the *Sheetname!* part, such as B2 or B2:B5. Such references *always* refer to the worksheet in which the formula has been entered.

Formulas allow you to create generalized solutions and give Excel its distinctive ability to automatically recalculate results when you change the values of the supporting data. Typically, when you use a worksheet, you see only the results of any formulas entered, not the formulas themselves. However, for your reference, many illustrations of Microsoft Excel worksheets in this text also show the underlying formulas adjacent to the results they produce. When using Excel, you can select **Tools → Options** and in the **View** tab of the **Options** dialog box that appears, select the **Formulas** check box, and click the **OK** button to see onscreen the formulas themselves and not their results. To restore the original view, uncheck the **Formulas** check box.

Using the Microsoft Excel Chart Wizard

You use the Microsoft Excel Chart Wizard to generate a wide variety of charts. The Chart Wizard is one of several Microsoft Office **wizards**, sets of linked dialog boxes that guide you, step-by-step, through the task of creating something. To use the Chart Wizard, you first select **Insert → Chart**. Then you make selections and enter information about the properties of the chart as you step through the dialog boxes by clicking a Next button. Clicking the **Finish** button in the last dialog box ends the wizard and creates the chart. At any point, you can cancel the operation of the wizard by clicking a **Cancel** button or move to a previous dialog box by clicking **Back**.

The Chart Wizards of the various versions of Microsoft Excel differ slightly. For Microsoft Excel 2003, the four-step wizard (see Figure A1.1 below) requires you to do the following:

Step 1: Choose the chart type.

Step 2: Enter the workbook locations of the source data for the values to be plotted and the source data for chart labeling information (if any).

Step 3: Specify the formatting and labeling options for the chart. (See further comments at right.)

Step 4: Choose the workbook location of the chart. You will always create a better-scaled chart if you choose the "as new sheet" instead of the "as object in (a worksheet)" option.

You can change these settings after the chart has been produced by right-clicking on the chart and making the appropriate selection from the shortcut menu that appears. For example, to reconsider the settings associated with the Step 3 dialog box, you would select **Chart Options** from the shortcut menu.

The automatic settings in the Step 3 dialog box create imperfectly designed charts. When you are using the Chart Wizard to generate charts for problems and examples from this text, in the dialog box you should select the tabs listed below (see Figure A1.2) and apply the following instructions (if a tab does not appear in the Step 3 dialog box for a particular chart type, ignore the instruction for the tab):

- Select the **Titles** tab and enter a title and axis labels, if appropriate.
- Select the **Axes** tab and then select both the **(X) axis** and **(Y) axis** check boxes. Also select the **Automatic** option button under the (X) axis check box.
- Select the **Gridlines** tab and deselect (uncheck) all the choices under the (X) axis heading and under the (Y) axis heading.
- Select the **Legend** tab and deselect (uncheck) the **Show legend** check box.
- Select the **Data Labels** tab and in the Data labels group, select the **None** option button.

FIGURE A1.1 Microsoft Excel Chart Wizard Dialog Boxes

FIGURE A1.2 Chart Wizard Step 3 Dialog Box Tabs

Opening and Saving Workbooks

You open workbooks to use data and results that have been created by you or others at an earlier time. To open a Microsoft Excel workbook, first select **File ➜ Open**. In the Open dialog box that appears (see Figure A1.3), you select the file to be opened and then click the **OK** button. If you cannot find your file, you may need to do one or more of the following:

- Use the scroll bars or the slider, if present, to scroll through the entire list of files.
- Select the correct folder from the **Look in** drop-down list at the top of the dialog box.
- Change the **Files of type** value from the drop-down list at the bottom of the dialog box. You should select **Text Files** from the list to see any text files; to list every file in the folder, select **All Files**.

FIGURE A1.3 Microsoft Excel Open Dialog Box

To save a workbook, select **File ➜ Save As** to display the Save As dialog box, which is similar to the Open dialog box. Enter (or edit) the name of the file in the **File name** box and click the **OK** button. If applicable, you can also do the following:

- Change to another folder by selecting that folder from the **Save in** drop-down list.
- Change the **Save as type** value to something other than the default choice, **Microsoft Excel Workbook**. "**Text (Tab delimited)**" or "**CSV (Comma delimited)**" are two file types sometimes used to share Excel data with other programs.

After saving your work, you should consider saving your file a second time, using a different name, in order to create a backup copy of your work. Files opened from non-writable disks, such as the CD-ROM packaged with this text, cannot be saved to their original folders.

Printing Workbooks

To quickly print Excel worksheets you can select **File ➜ Print** and then click the **OK** button in the Print dialog box. However, except for the simplest worksheets, you will probably want to preview the printed output and make any necessary adjustments before actually printing. To do this, select the worksheet to be printed and then select **File ➜ Print Preview**. If the preview contains formatting errors, click the **Close** button, make the changes necessary, and reselect **File ➜ Print Preview**. When you are satisfied with the results, click the **Print** button in the Print Preview window and then click the **OK** button in the Print dialog box.

The Print dialog box contains settings to select the printer to be used, what parts of the workbook to print (the active worksheet is the default), and the number of copies to produce (1 is the default). If you need to change these settings, change them before clicking the **OK** button.

After printing, you should verify the contents of your printout. Most printing failures will trigger the display of an error message that you can use to figure out the source of the failure. You can customize your printouts by selecting **File ➜ Page Setup** (or clicking the Setup button in the Print Preview window) and making the appropriate entries in the Page Setup dialog box (not shown) before printing your worksheets.

APPENDIX A1b

SPSS—Version 15 Lesson 1

Introduction

OVERVIEW

We will use SPSS 15.0 Student Version for this course. When you open SPSS either by clicking the short-cut icon, or by selecting **programs/SPSS/spsswin** from the explorer window, or by **start/SPSS**, a "What would you like to do?" menu appears. It allows you to select one of the following:

Run the tutorial
Type in data
Run an existing query
Create new query using Database Wizard
Open an existing data source

As you gain experience with SPSS, you will probably skip this screen by clicking on Cancel or you will select "Don't show this dialog in the future."

The **Tutorial** feature provides a useful introduction to various aspects of SPSS. To view a tutorial, key in the following instructions:

From the opening menu select **Run the tutorial/OK**

> or if you have passed this window

Help/Tutorial

You will now be shown an **Introduction** tutorial on SPSS version 15. Click on the word *Introduction* and get the expanded list of topics and then click *Sample Files*. Use the next button (right arrow) until you have viewed information on the following topics:

Sample Files
Starting SPSS
Opening a Data File
Running an Analysis*
Viewing Results*
Creating Charts*
Using the Help System
Help Contents Tab
Help Index Tab
Dialog Box Help
Statistics Coach (skip)
Case Studies (skip)
Reading Data
Basic Structure of an SPSS Data File
Reading an SPSS Data File
Reading Data from Spreadsheets

Close the tutorial at this point.

***Do not study** these topics in this tutorial. It is useful to quickly look at the demonstration in order to get an idea of what types of things we will be using SPSS for. You can always go through this tutorial at another time, although you may find it more useful choosing a tutorial on the specific topic that you are interested in learning about.

At the end of the *Introduction* tutorial return to SPSS Data Editor window by clicking the **Untitled1[DataSet0] – SPSS Data Editor** button at the very bottom of the screen.

Now click on **Help/Topics/**if necessary click **Contents** tab / under **Help Topics/Base System/**select **Data Editor.** Read the information regarding the data editor.

Now choose **Entering Data** from the 'Related Topics' list. Read the general information.

Now choose from the 'Related Topics' list: **To Enter Numeric Data** and **To Enter Non-numeric Data.**

You may have to come back to this screen at other times during the course to receive guidance on how to enter various data.

The **Help** feature is also useful for finding information on specific topics. This feature works similarly to the help feature in MS Word or Excel.

Summary

SPSS uses a routine of 4 basic steps.

1. Input data into the data editor
2. Select a procedure from the menus
3. Select variables for analysis
4. Examine and modify the results

SPSS utilizes two important file types, data files and output files.

Data file: Data is input into an Untitled Data Editor worksheet until it is renamed and saved by the researcher. Data files are identified by the extension **.sav** on the filename chosen by the researcher.

Output file: The SPSS output appears in a <u>viewer window</u> titled **Output1** which may be renamed and saved by the researcher. Output files are identified by the extension **.spo** (**SP**SS **O**utput). It is possible to edit the viewer window. The output may be rearranged, other output may be inserted, output may be deleted, and tables may be edited using the SPSS word processing capability.

You will switch between windows by using similar methods to other computer packages, i.e. click on the appropriate buttons on the Start button bar at the very bottom of the screen.

Entering, Saving and Printing Data

The following data was obtained by surveying 25 customers who used a bank machine that has just recently been installed in a downtown restaurant.

The survey took note of the customer's gender, how long the customer waited in line (rounded to the nearest minute), the type of transaction the customer performed and the amount involved in the transaction. (A simplified scenario is presented where each customer only performed one transaction.) The results are shown in the table below.

Customer	Gender	Waiting Time (minutes)	Type of Transaction	Amount ($)
1	Male	5	Withdrawal	100
2	Female	6	Bill Payment	83.56
3	Female	12	Withdrawal	60
4	Male	15	Withdrawal	40
5	Male	18	Deposit	512.81
6	Male	4	Bill Payment	56.82
7	Female	5	Withdrawal	200
8	Male	4	Deposit	2,315.23

Customer	Gender	Waiting Time (minutes)	Type of Transaction	Amount ($)
9	Male	14	Withdrawal	120
10	Female	21	Withdrawal	100
11	Female	0	Bill Payment	112.15
12	Male	7	Deposit	648.65
13	Male	8	Withdrawal	80
14	Male	9	Deposit	847.97
15	Female	16	Withdrawal	120
16	Male	6	Withdrawal	100
17	Female	6	Bill Payment	72.49
18	Male	12	Bill Payment	87.63
19	Female	11	Withdrawal	100
20	Male	2	Withdrawal	200
21	Male	1	Deposit	638.92
22	Female	3	Withdrawal	40
23	Female	9	Withdrawal	100
24	Male	14	Bill Payment	38.47
25	Male	3	Withdrawal	100

Example 1a:

Open SPSS and select **Type in data/OK** from the opening menu. Now click on the variable view tab. A variable definition summary screen now appears. In the first column key in the 4 variable names gender, waittime, transtyp, amount. Now skip to the decimals column and adjust the first three variables to have '0' decimals. The fourth variable will have the default of '2' decimals.

In the Label column key in the following labels:

Gender
Waiting Time (minutes)
Type of Transaction
Amount of the Transaction

Now you will perform two <u>labeling</u> procedures. Click on the Values button for the 'gender' variable. Use the value '0' to represent females and the value '1' to represent males. To do this type '0' in the **Value** Box and then type 'Female' in the **Value Label** box and then click the **Add** button. Repeat in similar fashion for the 'Male' label. When finished with the label values, click the **OK** button.

Now click on the Values button for the 'transtyp' variable. Use the following values:

1 = Withdrawal
2 = Deposit
3 = Bill Payment

Move the cursor to the **Align** column and click on the ▼ to activate the pop-up menu and select **Center** for the first three variables.

Move the cursor to the **Type** column for the 'amount' variable. Click on the numeric button. Choose **Dollar/$#,###.##/OK**

Now click on the Data view tab and enter the data as follows:

1	5	1	100
0	6	3	83.56
0	12	1	60
.	.	.	.
.	.	.	.
.	.	.	.

The input data will now appear exactly as shown below.

To <u>save</u> this data, select from the main toolbar:

File / Save as (select the appropriate drive and folder) key in the filename **Lesson1 – Ex. 1a** (in the File name box) and verify that the 'Save as type' box contains SPSS (*.sav). Click **Save**

To **print** this file, select from the main toolbar:

File / Print / All / OK

You should obtain the printout as shown on the following page. Note that the 'case number' column is included.

	gender	waitingtime	transtype	amount
1	Male	5	Withdrawal	100
2	Female	6	Bill Payment	83.56
3	Female	12	Withdrawal	60
4	Male	15	Withdrawal	40
5	Male	18	Deposit	512.81
6	Male	4	Bill Payment	56.82
7	Female	5	Withdrawal	200
8	Male	4	Deposit	2,315.23

	gender	waitingtime	transtype	amount
9	Male	14	Withdrawal	120
10	Female	21	Withdrawal	100
11	Female	0	Bill Payment	112.15
12	Male	7	Deposit	648.65
13	Male	8	Withdrawal	80
14	Male	9	Deposit	847.97
15	Female	16	Withdrawal	120
16	Male	6	Withdrawal	100
17	Female	6	Bill Payment	72.49
18	Male	12	Bill Payment	87.63
19	Female	11	Withdrawal	100
20	Male	2	Withdrawal	200
21	Male	1	Deposit	638.92
22	Female	3	Withdrawal	40
23	Female	9	Withdrawal	100
24	Male	14	Bill Payment	38.47
25	Male	3	Withdrawal	100

If you want someone else to be able to understand your input data, then you should print a copy showing the labels associated with the variable values. From the main toolbar select **View / Value Labels**

In order to read the labels better, you may want to widen the transtyp column by clicking on the **Variable View** tab and placing the cursor in the third variable cell in the **Columns** column and increasing the value from 8 to 11.

The data will now appear as follows:

Note that if you print the data now, it will appear as it does on the screen.

Sorting Data

At this stage you should read the following SPSS help feature. Make summary notes as you go along.

Help / Topics / Index Key in 'sort' then click the **Display** button.

Read the help information.

Example 1b:

Suppose we want to sort the cases in ascending order based on the waiting time and if waiting times are equal then in descending order of the amount of the transaction.

Make sure you are in Data View. Select from the main toolbar

Data/Sort Cases then highlight **Waiting Time (Minutes) [waittime]** ▶ **Ascending** then highlight **Amount of Transaction [amount]** ▶ **Descending / OK**

You should now have the data as shown below.

	gender	waittime	transtyp	amount	var
1	Female	0	Bill Payment	$112.15	
2	Male	1	Deposit	$638.92	
3	Male	2	Withdrawal	$200.00	
4	Male	3	Withdrawal	$100.00	
5	Female	3	Withdrawal	$40.00	
6	Male	4	Deposit	$2315.23	
7	Male	4	Bill Payment	$56.82	
8	Female	5	Withdrawal	$200.00	
9	Male	5	Withdrawal	$100.00	
10	Male	6	Withdrawal	$100.00	
11	Female	6	Bill Payment	$83.56	
12	Female	6	Bill Payment	$72.49	
13	Male	7	Deposit	$648.65	
14	Male	8	Withdrawal	$80.00	
15	Male	9	Deposit	$847.97	
16	Female	9	Withdrawal	$100.00	
17	Female	11	Withdrawal	$100.00	
18	Male	12	Bill Payment	$87.63	
19	Female	12	Withdrawal	$60.00	
20	Male	14	Withdrawal	$120.00	
21	Male	14	Bill Payment	$38.47	
22	Male	15	Withdrawal	$40.00	
23	Female	16	Withdrawal	$120.00	
24	Male	18	Deposit	$512.81	
25	Female	21	Withdrawal	$100.00	

To save and print this sorted version of the file:

From the main menu toolbar choose **File/Save as** Select the appropriate drive Key-in the file-name **Lesson 1 – Ex. 1b** and check that the Save as type box contains SPSS(*sav) **Save**

If you want to print this data select **File / Print / All / OK**

Then to leave SPSS select **File / Exit**

APPENDIX E1

Introduction to Microsoft Excel

E1.1 Opening and Saving Workbooks

As discussed in Section 1.7, Microsoft Excel uses worksheets that are stored in workbooks. You open and save workbooks by selecting the storage folder to use and then specifying the file name of the workbook. You begin the process by selecting **File** from the Excel menu bar in Excel 97–2003 or by clicking the **Office Button** in Excel 2007. You then select either **Open** or **Save As**. These selections display nearly identical Open and Save As dialog boxes that vary only slightly owing to the different Excel versions (Figure E1.1 shows the Excel 2007 Save As dialog box).

Inside these dialog boxes, you select the storage folder using the drop-down list at the top of these dialog boxes. You enter, or select from the list box, a file name for the workbook in the **File name** box. You click **Open** or **Save** to complete the task. Sometimes when saving files, you will want to change the file type before you click **Save**. If you use Excel 2007 and want to save your workbook in the format used by earlier Excel versions, select **Excel 97–2003 Workbook (*.xls)** from the **Save as type** drop-down list before you click **Save** (shown in Figure E1.1). If you use any version of Excel and want to save data in a form that can be opened by programs that cannot open Excel workbooks, you might select either **Text (Tab delimited) (*.txt)** or **CSV (Comma delimited) (*.csv)** as the save type.

When you go to open a file and cannot find its name in the list box, verify that the current **Look in** folder is the correct one. If that fails to help, change the file type to **All Files** (*.*) to see all files in the current folder. (This technique will help you discover inadvertent misspellings or missing file extensions that otherwise prevents the file from being displayed.)

Although all versions of Microsoft Excel include a **Save** command, you should avoid this choice until you gain experience. Using Save makes it too easy for you to inadvertently overwrite your work, and in Excel 2007, it saves your workbook in the new **.xlsx** workbook format that cannot be used by earlier Excel versions. If you open a workbook from a nonmodifiable source, such as the Student CD-ROM, Excel will mark the workbook "read-only," so you must use Save As to save any changes you make to the workbook. (Excel will prevent you from using Save in such situations.)

E1.2 Creating New Workbooks

You create a new workbook through a straightforward process that varies depending on the version of Excel you are using. In Excel 97 or 2000, you select **File ➔ New**. In Excel 2002 (also known as Excel XP) or 2003, you select **File ➔ New** and then click **Blank workbook** in the New Workbook task pane. In Excel 2007, you click **Office Button ➔ New** and in the New Workbook dialog box, you first click **Blank workbook** and then **Create**.

New workbooks are created with a fixed number of worksheets. You can delete extra worksheets or insert more sheets by right-clicking a sheet tab and clicking either **Delete** or **Insert**.

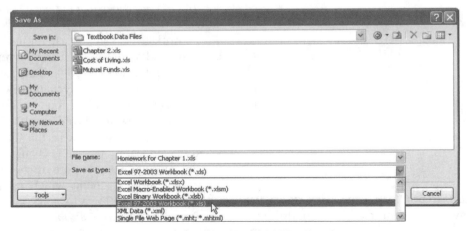

FIGURE E1.1   Save As dialog box (Excel 2007 version)

E1.3 Printing Worksheets

When you want to print the contents of a workbook, you should print one sheet at a time to get the best results. You print sheets by first previewing their printed form onscreen and then making any adjustments to the worksheet and/or to the print setup settings.

To print a specific worksheet, you first click on the sheet tab of that worksheet to make the worksheet the currently active one. Then you display the Print Preview window. If you use a version of Excel other than 2007, select **File → Print Preview**. If you use Excel 2007, click **Office Button**, move the mouse pointer over **Print** (do not click) and select **Print Preview** from the Preview and Print gallery.

The Print Preview windows for all Excel versions are similar to one another. Figure E1.2 shows a partial window for Excel 2003 (top) and Excel 2007 (bottom). If the preview contains errors or displays the worksheet in an undesirable manner, click **Close** (or **Close Print Preview** in Excel 2007), make the changes necessary, and reselect the preview command. You can customize your printout by clicking **Setup** (or **Page Setup**) and making the appropriate entries in the Page Setup dialog box, which is similar for all Excel versions. For example, to print your worksheet with grid lines and numbered row and lettered column headings (similar to the appearance of the worksheet onscreen), you click the **Sheet** tab in the Page Setup dialog box and then click **Gridlines** and **Row and column headings** and click **OK** (see Figure E1.3). (You can find more information about using Page Setup in Section F4 of Appendix F.)

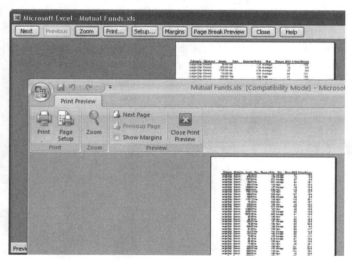

FIGURE E1.2   Partial Print Preview windows (Excel 2003 and 2007 versions)

When you are ready to print, you can click **Print** in the Print Preview window, but to gain maximum control over your printout, click **Close** (or **Close Print Preview**) and then select **File → Print** (Excel 97–2003) or **Office Button → Print** (Excel 2007). In the Print dialog box that appears, you

FIGURE E1.3   Sheet tab of the Page Setup dialog box (Excel 2003 version)

can select the printer to use, make sure you are printing only the currently active worksheet, or print multiple copies at once.

E1.4 Worksheet Entries and References

As first discussed in Section 1.7, worksheets are tabular arrangements of data in which standard practice dictates that you enter the data for each variable in individual columns. You use the cursor keys or your pointing device to move a **cell pointer** through a worksheet and to select a cell for entry. As you type an entry, it appears in the formula bar, and you place that entry into the cell by either pressing the **Tab** or **Enter** keys or clicking the checkmark button in the formula bar.

As you enter the data for a variable in a column, follow the standard practice of using the row 1 cell to store a name or label for the variable. Should you be entering two or more sets of data, consider placing each set of data in a separate worksheet.

In worksheets that you use for intermediate calculations or final results, you might enter **formulas**, instructions to perform a calculation or some other task, in addition to the numeric and text entries you otherwise make into cells. Proper formulas use values found in one or more other cells to produce a new displayed result. The displayed results automatically change; that is, the formula is recalculated, when the values in other cells change. (Such **recalculation** was the original novel feature of spreadsheet programs and led to such programs being widely used in accounting.)

To refer to a cell in a formula, you use a **cell address** in the form *SheetName!ColumnRow*. For example, **Data!A2** refers to the cell in the Data worksheet that is in column A and row 2. You can also use just the *ColumnRow* portion of a full address, for example, **A2**, if you are referring to a cell on the same worksheet as the one into which you are entering a formula. If the sheet name contains spaces or special characters, for example, **City Data** or **Figure-1.2**, you must enclose the sheet name in a pair of single quotes, as in **'City Data'!A2** or **'Figure-1.2'!A2**.

When you want to refer to a group of cells, for example, to the cells of a column that store the data for a particular variable, you use a **cell range**. A cell range names the upper leftmost cell and the lower rightmost cell of the group using the form *SheetName!UpperLeftCell:LowerRightCell*. For example, the cell range **Data!B1:B51** identifies the cells in the UndergradSurvey.xls workbook that store the data for the gender variable (with cell B1 storing the variable label "Gender" as explained earlier). Cell ranges can extend over multiple columns; the cell range **Data!B1:E51** in the same workbook would refer to the data for the gender, age, height, and class variables.

As with a single cell reference, you can skip the *SheetName!* part of the reference if you are referring to a cell range on the current worksheet, and you must use a pair of single quotes if a sheet name contains spaces or special characters. However, in many cases in the Excel instructions in this book, including the sheet name will be necessary in a cell reference in order to get the proper results. Because sheet names are used so frequently, you should change the names that Excel assigns to worksheets (names in the form **Sheet1**, **Sheet2**, and so on) to more meaningful words or phrases. To do so, double-click a sheet tab, type the new name, and press **Enter**.

(Although not a form used in this book, cell references can include a workbook name in the form **'[*Workbook Name*]*SheetName*'!*ColumnRow*** or **'[*WorkbookName*] *SheetName*'!*UpperLeftCell:LowerRightCell***. You may discover such references if you inadvertently copy certain types of worksheets or chart sheets from one workbook to another.)

E1.5 Entering Formulas Into Worksheets

You enter formulas by typing the equal sign symbol (=) and then a combination of mathematical or other data-processing operations. For simple formulas, you use the symbols +, -, *, /, and ∧ for the operations addition, subtraction, multiplication, division, and exponentiation (a number raised to a power), respectively. For example, the formula **=Data!B2 + Data!B3 + Data!B4** adds the contents of the cells B2, B3, and B4 of the Data worksheet and displays the sum as the value in the cell containing the formula. You can also use **worksheet functions** in formulas to simplify formulas.

To use a worksheet function in a formula, either type the function as shown in the instructions in this book or use the Excel Function Wizard feature to insert the function. To use this feature, select **Insert → Function** (Excel 97–2003) or **Formulas → Function Wizard** (Excel 2007) and then make entries and selections in one or more dialog boxes.

E1.6 Verifying Formulas and Worksheets

If you use formulas in your worksheets, you should review and verify formulas before you use their results. To view the formulas in a worksheet, press **Ctrl + `** (grave accent key). To restore the original view, the results of the formulas, press **Ctrl + `** a second time.

As you create and use more complicated worksheets, you may want to visually examine the relationships among a formula and the cells it uses (called the precedents) and the cells that use the results of the formula (the dependents). To display arrows that visually show these relationships, use the formula auditing feature of Excel. Select **Tools → Auditing** (Excel 97 or 2000), or **Tools → Formula Auditing** (Excel 2002 or 2003), or **Formulas** (Excel 2007). Then select one of the choices from the auditing submenu (Excel 97–2003) or from the **Formula Auditing** group (Excel 2007). When you are finished, selecting **Remove All Arrows** restores your display by removing all auditing arrows.

E1.7 Enhancing Workbook Presentation

By formatting the display of individual cells and by rearranging the contents of your workbook, you can enhance the presentation of your workbook.

You can find the most common cell-formatting operations on the Formatting toolbar (Excel 97–2003) or in the Home tab (Excel 2007). Most worksheets shown as illustrations in this book use the **Boldface**, **Fill Color**, **Merge-and-Center**, and **Borders** features to highlight particular cells or cell ranges. Experiment with these features to develop your own style that maximizes the effectiveness of your presentations.

You may also want to rearrange the content of your workbooks. Use the copy-and-paste combination keystroke shortcuts, **Crtl+C** and **Ctrl+V**, to copy content from one cell to another on the same worksheet. Copying cells that contain formulas is not necessarily as straightforward as you might expect. If your formula uses references in the format discussed in Section E1.4, Excel will change to reflect the difference, or offset, between the original (source) cell and the cell into which you are pasting the formula (the target cell). For example, when you copy the formula =A2 + B2 in cell C2 down to cell C3, an offset of one row, Excel pastes the formula =A3 + B3 in C3 to reflect that one-row offset. Cell ranges also get changed, so if you copy the formula =SUM(A1:A4) from cell A5 to cell B5, the formula is changed to =SUM(B1:B4).

You can stop Excel from making such changes by inserting a U.S. dollar symbol ($) before either the column letter or row number (or both) of a cell reference to form an **absolute reference**, for example, $A$2. Do not confuse the use of the U.S. dollar symbol with the format operation that displays numbers as U.S. currency values. To format cell values for U.S. currency display, you use the **Currency ($)** format button, available on the Formatting toolbar (Excel

97–2003) and in the Number group of **Home** tab (Excel 2007).

Finally, you can also copy entire worksheets for convenience or clarity. To copy a worksheet to a new workbook, you first select the worksheet by clicking its sheet tab. Then you right-click the tab and select **Move or Copy** from the shortcut menu that appears. In the **To book** drop-down list of the Move or Copy dialog box (see Figure E1.4), first select **(new book)** or the name of the preexisting target workbook, and then click **Create a copy** and then click **OK**.

FIGURE E1.4 Move or Copy dialog box (Excel 2007 version)

E1.8 Using Add-Ins

Add-ins can simplify the task of creating something to add to a workbook. Add-ins are programming components not included in the main Excel program and may need to be **installed**, or added, to your computer system separately. Add-ins are not always available for you to use because they can be disabled by other users or system security settings. However, the little extra effort you need to ensure that the right add-ins are installed and enabled is well worth the features that add-ins bring to Excel.

As you use Microsoft Excel with this book, you will use the Excel **Analysis ToolPak** add-in for some statistical tasks. The Analysis ToolPak add-in (which the book simply calls the "ToolPak" from this point forward) adds statistical procedures to Excel, but creates worksheets that do not contain formulas. Should you later change your data, you must repeat the ToolPak procedure to get updated results. Some Excel versions come with the ToolPak preinstalled; others require that you separately install this component from your Microsoft Office or Excel program setup disk. (See Appendix F for additional information about installing the ToolPak.)

As you use Microsoft Excel, you may choose to use **PHStat2**, the Prentice Hall statistics add-in that is included

on the Student CD-ROM. If you plan to use PHStat2, you first need to run its setup program, using the instructions found in Appendix F and in the Student CD-ROM PHStat2 readme file. PHStat2 adds a PHStat menu of procedures to the Excel menu bar in Excel 97–2003 and the Add-ins tab in Excel 2007. Unlike the ToolPak, PHStat2 usually creates worksheets that contain formulas and that will produce new results as the underlying data changes. Sometimes, though, PHStat2 asks the ToolPak to create sheets on its behalf, and the resulting sheets are similar to the no-formulas sheets that the ToolPak creates. In many such cases, PHStat2 enhances the sheets it asks the ToolPak to create, correcting errors the ToolPak makes or adding new formula-based calculations. (If you plan to use PHStat2, be sure to read Appendix P1, which immediately follows this appendix.)

In all Excel versions other than Excel 97, all add-ins that you open will be screened by Microsoft Office security components. If you use Excel 2000, 2002, or 2003, you can review and change the security settings by selecting **Tools →** **Macro → Security** to display a Security dialog box (similar to the one shown in Figure E1.5 for Excel 2003). To use an add-in such as PHStat2 that is "not signed," you would click **Medium** and then click **OK**.

FIGURE E1.5 Security dialog box (Excel 2003 version)

If you use Excel 2007, click the **Office Button**, and then click **Excel Options** in the Office menu. In the Excel Options dialog box (see Figure E1.6) click **Trust Center** in the left pane to display information about security issues. Then click **Trust Center Settings** (obscured in Figure E1.6) to display the Trust Center dialog box. To use an add-in such as PHStat2 that is not signed, click **Add-Ins** in the left pane, and then clear all checkboxes in the right pane (see Figure E1.6). Then click **Macro Settings** in the left pane and click **Disable all macros with notification** in the right pane (see Figure E1.6). On some systems, you may also have to click **Trusted Locations** in the left pane and add the file location of the add-in.

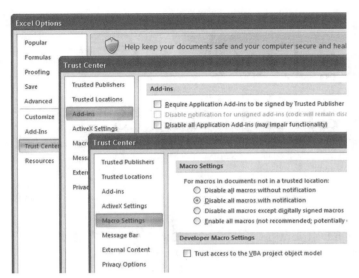

FIGURE E1.6   Excel Options and Trust Center panes (Excel 2007)

FIGURE E1.7   Macro warning dialog boxes (Excel 2003 and 2007)

With the Security screen set to an appropriate level, you will see a macro virus warning dialog box when you open an add-in such as PHStat2. Figure E1.7 shows the Excel 2003 and Excel 2007 warning boxes. You click the **Enable Macros** button to allow virus-free add-ins, such as PHStat2, to be opened and used.

2

Presenting Data in Tables and Charts

Learning Objectives

In this chapter, you learn:

- To develop tables and charts for categorical data
- To develop tables and charts for numerical data
- The principles of properly presenting graphs

@ Choice Is Yours, Part I

Choice Is Yours is a service that helps customers make wise investment choices. You've been hired to assist investors interested in mutual funds, a market basket of securities. According to **investopedia.com**, "A mutual fund is nothing more than a collection of stocks and/or bonds. You can think of a mutual fund as a company that brings together a group of people and invests their money in stocks, bonds, and other securities. Each investor owns shares, which represent a portion of the holdings of the fund." (You can learn more at **investopedia.com/university/mutualfunds**.)

The Choice Is Yours company previously selected a sample of 868 mutual funds that it believes might be of interest to its customers. You have been asked to present data about these funds in a way that will help customers make good investment choices. What facts about each mutual fund would you collect to help customers compare and contrast the many funds?

A good starting point would be to collect data that would help customers classify mutual funds into various categories. You could research such things as the amount of risk involved in a fund's investment strategy and whether the fund focuses on growth securities, those companies that are expected to grow quickly in the next year, or on value securities, those companies whose stock prices are currently considered undervalued. You might also investigate whether a mutual fund specializes in a certain size company and whether the fund charges management fees that would reduce the percentage return earned by an investor.

Of course, you would want to know how well the fund performed in the past. You would also want to supply the customer with several measures of each fund's past performance. Even though past performance is no assurance of future performance, past data could give customers insight into how well each mutual fund has been managed.

As you further think about your task, you realize that all these data for all 868 mutual funds would be a lot for anyone to review. How could you "get your hands around" such data and explore it in a comprehensible manner?

To get your hands around the data described in this chapter's Using Statistics scenario, you need to use methods of descriptive statistics, defined in Chapter 1 as the branch of statistics that collects, summarizes, presents and analyzes data. In this scenario, you need to use descriptive techniques for both categorical variables (to help investors classify the mutual funds) and numerical variables (to help show the return each fund has achieved). Reading this chapter will help you prepare tables and charts that are appropriate for both types of variables. You'll also learn techniques to help answer questions that require two variables, such as "Do growth-oriented mutual funds have lower returns than value mutual funds?" and "Do growth funds tend to be riskier investments than value funds?"

Many examples in this chapter use a sample of 868 mutual funds, the data for which you can find in the Data worksheet of the `Mutual Funds.xls` workbook or in the Minitab worksheet `Mutual Funds.mtw` on the Student CD-ROM.

2.1 Tables and Charts for Categorical Data

When you have categorical data, you tally responses into categories and then present the frequency or percentage in each category in tables and charts.

The Summary Table

A **summary table** indicates the frequency, amount, or percentage of items in a set of categories so that you can see differences between categories. A summary table lists the categories in one column and the frequency, amount, or percentage in a different column or columns. Table 2.1 illustrates a summary table based on a recent survey (see the `Banking` file) that asked people where they prefer to do their banking (K. Chu, "Online Banks Launch Checking Accounts," *USA Today*, January 18, 2007, p. 1B). In Table 2.1, the most common choices are in person at branch and on the Internet, followed by drive-through service at branch and ATM. Very few respondents mentioned automated or live telephone.

TABLE 2.1
Banking Preference

Banking Preference	Percentage (%)
ATM	16
Automated or live telephone	2
Drive-through service at branch	17
In person at branch	41
Internet	24

EXAMPLE 2.1

Summary Table of Levels of Risk of Mutual Funds

The 868 mutual funds that are part of the Using Statistics scenario are classified according to their risk level, categorized as low, average, and high. Construct a summary table of the mutual funds, categorized by risk.

SOLUTION From Table 2.2, you can see that fewer than 25% of the funds are low-risk funds. There are more high-risk funds (355, or 40.90%) than low-risk (202, or 23.27%) or average-risk funds (311, or 35.83%). More than 75% of the funds are average risk or high risk.

TABLE 2.2

Frequency and Percentage Summary Table Pertaining to Risk Level for 868 Mutual Funds

Fund Risk Level	Number of Funds	Percentage of Funds (%)
Low	202	23.27
Average	311	35.83
High	355	40.90
Total	868	100.00

The Bar Chart

In a **bar chart**, a bar shows each category. The length of the bar represents the amount, frequency, or percentage of values falling into a category. Figure 2.1 displays the bar chart for where people prefer to do their banking presented in Table 2.1.

Bar charts allow you to compare percentages in different categories. In Figure 2.1, respondents are most likely to bank in person at a branch and on the Internet, followed by drive-through service at a branch and ATM. Very few respondents mentioned automated or live telephone.

FIGURE 2.1

Microsoft Excel bar chart for where people prefer to do their banking.

See Sections E2.4 or P2.3 to create this. (Minitab users, see Section M2.2 to create an equivalent chart.)

EXAMPLE 2.2

Bar Chart of Levels of Risk of Mutual Funds

Construct a bar chart for the levels of risk of mutual funds (based on the information in Table 2.2) and interpret the results.

SOLUTION From Figure 2.2, you can see that approximately 200 of the funds are low risk, whereas more than 650 of the 868 funds are either average risk or high risk. There are more high-risk funds than average-risk or low-risk funds.

FIGURE 2.2

Microsoft Excel bar chart of the levels of risk of mutual funds

See Sections E2.4 or P2.3 to create this. (Minitab users, see Section M2.2 to create an equivalent chart.)

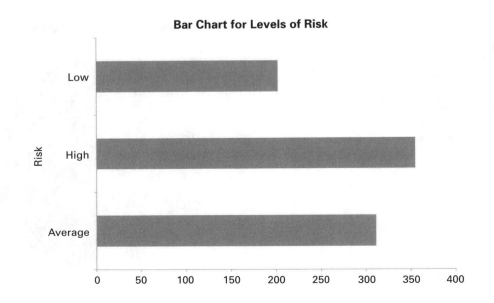

The Pie Chart

The **pie chart** is a circle broken up into slices that represent categories. The size of each slice of the pie varies according to the percentage in each category. In Table 2.1 on page 44, for example, 41% of the respondents stated that they prefer to bank in person at the branch. Thus, in constructing the pie chart, the 360 degrees that makes up a circle is multiplied by 0.41, resulting in a slice of the pie that takes up 147.6 degrees of the 360 degrees of the circle. From Figure 2.3, you can see that the pie chart lets you visualize the portion of the entire pie that is in each category. In this figure, bank in person at the branch takes 41% of the pie and automated or live telephone takes only 2%.

FIGURE 2.3

Microsoft Excel pie chart for where people prefer to do their banking

See Sections E2.4 or P2.3 to create this. (Minitab users, see Section M2.3 to create an equivalent chart.)

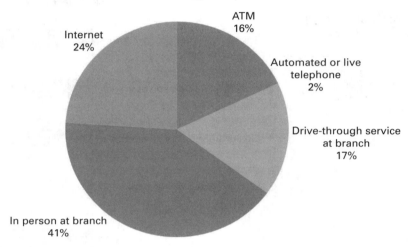

Pie Chart for Banking Preferences

Which chart should you use—a bar chart or a pie chart? The selection of a particular chart often depends on your intention. If a comparison of categories is most important, you should use a bar chart. If observing the portion of the whole that is in a particular category is most important, you should use a pie chart.

EXAMPLE 2.3

Pie Chart of Levels of Risk of Mutual Funds

Construct a pie chart for the levels of risk of mutual funds (see Table 2.2) and interpret the results.

SOLUTION From Figure 2.4, you can see that 41% of the funds are high risk, 36% are average risk, and only 23% are low risk.

FIGURE 2.4

Microsoft Excel pie chart of the levels of risk of mutual funds

See Sections E2.4 or P2.3 to create this. (Minitab users, see Section M2.3 to create an equivalent chart.)

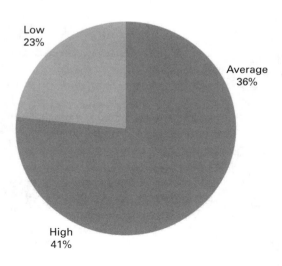

Pie Chart for Levels of Risk

The Pareto Chart

In a **Pareto chart**, the responses in the categories are plotted as vertical bars in descending order, according to their frequencies, and are combined with a cumulative percentage line on the same chart. The Pareto chart can identify situations in which the Pareto principle occurs.

PARETO PRINCIPLE

The **Pareto principle** exists when the majority of items in a set of data occur in a small number of categories and the few remaining items are spread out over a large number of categories. These two groups are often referred to as the "vital few" and the "trivial many."

The Pareto chart has the ability to separate the "vital few" from the "trivial many," enabling you to focus on the important categories. In situations in which the data involved consist of defective or nonconforming items, the Pareto chart is a powerful tool for prioritizing improvement efforts.

Table 2.3 presents data for a large injection-molding company that manufactures plastic components used in computer keyboards, washing machines, automobiles, and television sets (see the Keyboard defects file). The data presented in Table 2.3 consist of all computer keyboards with defects produced during a three-month period.

TABLE 2.3

Summary Table of Causes of Defects in Computer Keyboards in a Three-Month Period

Cause	Frequency	Percentage
Black spot	413	6.53
Damage	1,039	16.43
Jetting	258	4.08
Pin mark	834	13.19
Scratches	442	6.99
Shot mold	275	4.35
Silver streak	413	6.53
Sink mark	371	5.87
Spray mark	292	4.62
Warpage	1,987	31.42
Total	6,324	100.01*

*Result differs slightly from 100.00 due to rounding.
Source: *Extracted from U. H. Acharya and C. Mahesh, "Winning Back the Customer's Confidence: A Case Study on the Application of Design of Experiments to an Injection-Molding Process,"* Quality Engineering, 11, 1999, pp. 357–363.

Table 2.4 presents a summary table for the computer keyboard data in which the categories are ordered based on the frequency of defects present (rather than arranged alphabetically). The percentages and cumulative percentages for the ordered categories are also included as part of the table.

In Table 2.4, the first category listed is warpage (with 31.42% of the defects), followed by damage (with 16.43%), followed by pin mark (with 13.19%). The two most frequently occurring categories, warpage and damage, account for 47.85% of the defects; the three most frequently occurring categories—warpage, damage, and pin mark—account for 61.04% of the defects, and so on.

Figure 2.5 is a Pareto chart based on the results displayed in Table 2.4.

TABLE 2.4

Ordered Summary Table of Causes of Defects in Computer Keyboards in a Three-Month Period

Cause	Frequency	Percentage	Cumulative Percentage
Warpage	1,987	31.42	31.42
Damage	1,039	16.43	47.85
Pin mark	834	13.19	61.04
Scratches	442	6.99	68.03
Black spot	413	6.53	74.56
Silver streak	413	6.53	81.09
Sink mark	371	5.87	86.96
Spray mark	292	4.62	91.58
Shot mold	275	4.35	95.93
Jetting	258	4.08	100.01*
Total	6,324	100.01*	

Result differs slightly from 100.00 due to rounding.

FIGURE 2.5

Microsoft Excel Pareto chart for the keyboard defects data

See Sections E2.5 or P2.4 to create this. (Minitab users, see Section M2.4 to create an equivalent chart.)

A Pareto chart presents the bars vertically, along with a cumulative percentage line. The cumulative line is plotted at the midpoint of each category, at a height equal to the cumulative percentage. If you follow the line, you see that these first three categories account for about 60% of the defects. Because the categories in the Pareto chart are ordered by the frequency of occurrences, decision makers can see where to concentrate efforts to improve the process. Attempts to reduce defects due to warpage, damage, and pin marks should produce the greatest payoff. Then, efforts can be made to reduce scratches, black spots, and silver streaks.

In order for a Pareto chart to include all categories, even those with few defects, in some situations you need to include a category labeled *Other* or *Miscellaneous*. In these situations, the bar representing these categories should be placed to the right of the other bars.

EXAMPLE 2.4

Pareto Chart of Banking Preference

Construct a Pareto chart of banking preference (see Table 2.1).

SOLUTION In Figure 2.6, in person at branch and on the Internet account for 65% of the banking preferences; 98% of the respondents would prefer in person at branch, on the Internet, drive-through at branch, and ATM.

FIGURE 2.6

Microsoft Excel Pareto chart for banking preference

See Sections E2.5 or P2.4 to create this. (Minitab users, see Section M2.4 to create an equivalent chart.)

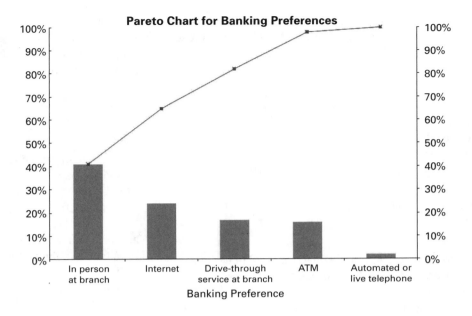

Problems for Section 2.1

LEARNING THE BASICS

2.1 A categorical variable has three categories with the following frequencies of occurrence:

Category	Frequency
A	13
B	28
C	9

a. Compute the percentage of values in each category.
b. Construct a bar chart.
c. Construct a pie chart.
d. Construct a Pareto chart.

2.2 A categorical variable has four categories with the following percentages of occurrence:

Category	Percentage	Category	Percentage
A	12	C	35
B	29	D	24

a. Construct a bar chart.
b. Construct a pie chart.
c. Construct a Pareto chart.

APPLYING THE CONCEPTS

2.3 A survey of 705 workers asked how much they used the Internet at work. The results (*USA Today, Snapshots*, March 21, 2006, p. 1B) were as follows:

Use of the Internet at Work	%
Too much	5
More than I should	4
Within limits	60
Very little	5
Do not use	26

a. Construct a bar chart, a pie chart, and a Pareto chart.
b. Which graphical method do you think is best to portray these data?
c. Based on this survey, what conclusions can you reach about the use of the Internet at work?

SELF Test **2.4** A survey of 1,264 women asked who was their most trusted shopping advisers. The results (*USA Today, Snapshots*, October 19, 2006, p. 1B) were as follows:

Shopping Advisers	%
Advertising	7
Friends/family	45
Manufacturer Web sites	5
News media	11
Online user reviews	13
Retail Web sites	4
Salespeople	1
Other	14

a. Construct a bar chart, a pie chart, and a Pareto chart.
b. Which graphical method do you think is best to portray these data?
c. What conclusions can you reach concerning women's most trusted shopping advisers?

2.5 What changes in their compensation package do workers in the United States want most? A survey by HudsonIndex.com indicated the following:

Perks	%
More money	42
Better health care	20
Better retirement	12
Work/family balance	10
Other	16

Source: *Adapted from Anne R. Carey and Chad Palmer, "What Workers Want,"* **www.usatoday.com**, *April 9, 2007.*

a. Construct a bar chart, a pie chart, and a Pareto chart.
b. Which graphical method do you think is best to portray these data?
c. What conclusions can you reach concerning which perks workers want most?

2.6 The following table represents the North American power generation in 2007:

Source	%
Coal	47
Hydropower	13
Natural gas	19
Nuclear	19
Wind	1
Other	1

Source: *Data extracted from J. Schmit, "Taking on the solar Challenge,"* USA Today, *January 21, 2008, pp. 1B, 2B.*

a. Construct a Pareto chart.
b. What percentage of power is derived from coal, nuclear, or natural gas?
c. Construct a pie chart.
d. For these data, do you prefer the Pareto chart or the pie chart? Why?

2.7 An article (K. Delaney, "How Search Engine Rules Cause Sites to Go Missing," *The Wall Street Journal*, March 13, 2007, pp. B1, B4) discussed the amount of Internet search results that Web surfers typically scan before selecting one. The following table represents the results for a sample of 2,369 people:

Amount of Internet Search Results Scanned	Percentage (%)
A few search results	23
First page of search results	39
First two pages	19
First three pages	9
More than first three pages	10

a. Construct a bar chart and a pie chart.
b. Which graphical method do you think is best to portray these data?
c. What conclusions can you reach concerning how people scan Internet search results?

2.8 U.S. companies spent more than $250 billion in advertising in 2005 (K. Delaney, "In Latest Deal, Google Steps Further into World of Old Media," *The Wall Street Journal*, January 18, 2006, pp. A1, A6). The spending was as follows:

Media	Amount ($billions)	Percentage (%)
Cinema	0.4	0.16
Direct mail	44.5	17.35
Internet	10.0	3.90
Magazines	23.9	9.32
Newspapers	50.2	19.57
Outdoor	5.7	2.22
Radio	20.6	8.03
TV	55.4	21.60
Other	45.8	17.86

a. Construct a bar chart and a pie chart.
b. Which graphical method do you think is best to portray these data?
c. What conclusions can you reach concerning how U.S. companies spend their advertising dollars?

2.2 Organizing Numerical Data

When the number of data values is large, you can organize numerical data into an ordered array or a stem-and-leaf display to help understand the information you have. Suppose you decide to undertake a study that compares the cost of a restaurant meal in an urban area to the cost of a similar meal in the suburbs outside the city. The data file Restaurants contains the data for 50 urban restaurants and 50 suburban restaurants, as shown in Table 2.5. The data are not arranged in order from lowest to highest. This arrangement makes it difficult to arrive at conclusions concerning the price of meals in the two geographical areas.

TABLE 2.5

Cost per Person at 50 Urban Restaurants and 50 Suburban Restaurants

Urban

65	48	32	27	47	45	36	55	48	33
45	46	39	44	45	63	54	20	55	73
51	34	28	65	44	43	50	29	33	41
41	52	48	48	38	52	33	40	36	51
39	38	22	35	35	16	74	57	52	68

Suburban

47	43	44	41	44	48	50	48	38	36
28	25	44	55	20	36	30	44	24	32
29	42	53	27	68	34	30	24	61	34
47	29	26	42	54	51	34	39	39	40
42	40	61	27	37	37	40	39	43	36

The Ordered Array

An **ordered array** is a sequence of data, in rank order, from the smallest value to the largest value. Table 2.6 contains ordered arrays for the cost of meals at urban restaurants and suburban restaurants. From Table 2.6 you can see that the cost of a meal at the urban restaurants is between $16 and $74 and the cost of a meal at the suburban restaurants is between $20 and $68.

TABLE 2.6

Ordered Arrays of Cost per Person at 50 Urban Restaurants and 50 Suburban Restaurants

Urban

16	20	22	27	28	29	32	33	33	33
34	35	35	36	36	38	38	39	39	40
41	41	43	44	44	45	45	45	46	47
48	48	48	48	50	51	51	52	52	52
54	55	55	57	63	65	65	68	73	74

Suburban

20	24	24	25	26	27	27	28	29	29
30	30	32	34	34	34	36	36	36	37
37	38	39	39	39	40	40	40	41	42
42	42	43	43	44	44	44	44	47	47
48	48	50	51	53	54	55	61	61	68

Stem-and-Leaf Display

EXAMPLE 2.5   The following data appeared in the Education Quarterly Review—Vol. 5, No. 2—1998.

Table 2.7 shows the percentage of the population in various age groups that have postsecondary education

TABLE 2.7

	Age Group	
Country	26 to 35	46 to 55
United States	45.1	41.6
Canada	41.2	34.9
New Zealand	31.5	26.6
Australia	29.0	28.4
Sweden	28.6	32.4
Belgium	35.0	20.2
United Kingdom	25.3	23.0
Switzerland	23.2	23.3
Ireland	22.4	14.9
Netherlands	23.5	22.5
Poland	16.8	17.9

Suppose we would like to compare the data for each age group.

One graphical tool that can be used to organize the data is a **STEM-and-LEAF** display. This diagram should be considered when the number of data values is not more than 50.

The recommended Stem-and-Leaf display for the 26 to 35 age group data is as follows:

**% of Population with Postsecondary Education
for people aged 26 to 35 years**

Stem (tens)	Leaf
1	6
2	2 3 3
2	5 8 9
3	1
3	5
4	1
4	5

Rules and Conventions

There is more than one set of rules and conventions regarding the drawing of a stem-and-leaf display. The purpose of a stem-and-leaf display is to organize a small amount of data in an easy-to-understand diagram. We will use the following set of rules and conventions.

Stems:
1. Should be from 6 to 13 stems.
2. Should be consecutive numbers or repeated numbers. The numbers may each be repeated twice or 5 times.
3. Units must be indicated if stem not to be taken at face value
4. There must be at least one leaf associated with the first and last stem

Leaves:
1. The leaf for each data value is the next *single* digit after the stem

   Note: When the stems are repeated twice, the leaves 0–4 go with the first stem and the leaves 5–9 go with the second. (This order is reversed when the stems are negative values.) (refer to Table 2.8)
   When the stems are repeated 5 times, the leaves 0–1 go with the first stem, 2–3 with the second, etc. (This order is reversed when the stems are negative values.) (refer to Table 2.8)

2. There is no rounding off.
3. They are written in ascending order.

4. They must be evenly spaced.

5. No commas or dashes between the numbers are allowed.

How to construct Stem-and-Leaf display with negative and positive numbers?

If the data contain both positive and negative numbers, use $+0$ and -0 as stem values as shown in Example 2.6.

EXAMPLE 2.6

The following data represents share change in percent.

n.a.
(19.4)
(81.1)
n.a.
9.2
(17.6)
(36.9)
(32.8)
(2.3)
(33.1)
n.a.
(5.9)
(0.5)
(15.7)
(0.7)
(24.3)
(56.3)
(18.5)
4.9
n.a.

Share Change in percent

Stem (ten)	Leaf
-8	1
-7	
-6	
-5	6
-4	
-3	6 3 2
-2	4
-1	9 8 7 5
-0	5 2 0
0	4 9

For negative numbers: The leaves were arranged in descending order.

For positive numbers: The leaves were arranged in ascending order.

TABLE 2.8

Repeat stem twice	Leaves Values	Repeat Stem five times	Leaves Values
First Stem	5 to 9	First Stem	8 and 9
Second Stem	0 to 4	Second Stem	6 and 7
		Third Stem	4 and 5
		Fourth Stem	2 and 3
		Fifth Stem	0 and 1

Note: For the positive values, the leaves are arrange in ascending order (i.e. 0, 1, 2, 3, 4, 5, 6, 7, 8, 9)

For the negative values: The leaves are arrange in descending order (i.e. 9, 8, 7, 6, 5, 4, 3, 2, 1, 0)

Compare two stem-and-leaf displays

In order to compare the two sets of data, we will set up the stem-and-leaf display for the second age group. (Note: When comparing data, you should try to use a similar set-up for each stem-and-leaf display.)

% of Population with Postsecondary Education
for people aged 46 to 55 years

Stem (tens)	Leaf
1	4
1	7
2	0 2 3 3
2	6 8
3	2 4
3	
4	1

Conclusion: Both age groups have the most data in the 20–30 percent range. The percentages are generally lower for the higher age group.

EXAMPLE 2.7

The following data represents the selling price ($ 000's) of 2 bedroom homes in Cartersville for the month of December:

96   93   88   107   125   127   112   127   117
95   113   96   135   132   111   148   156   139

The following stem-and-leaf display would be appropriate:

Prices of 2-bedroom Homes
($ 000's)

Stem (tens)	Leaf
8	8
9	3 5 6 6
10	7
11	1 2 3 7
12	5 7 7
13	2 5 9
14	8
15	6

EXAMPLE 2.8

The following data represents the management expense ratio (MER) in percent for a group of Canadian balanced mutual funds:

2.13   2.25   2.25   2.26   2.26   2.41   2.36   2.50   2.08
2.53   2.48   2.04   2.18

The following stem-and-leaf display would be appropriate:

MER (%)

Stem	Leaf
2.0	4 8
2.1	3 8
2.2	5 5 6 6
2.3	6
2.4	1 8
2.5	0 3

EXAMPLE 2.9a

Suppose a survey of employees for a certain department of a certain company reveal that they paid the following amounts of income taxes last year:

$20,130 $20,161 $20,207 $20,175 $20,213 $20,147
$20,189 $20,215 $20,264 $20,219 $20,252 $20,173
$20,209 $20,155 $20,128

The following stem-and-leaf display would be appropriate.

Annual Taxes ($)

(00's)	
201	2 3
201	4 5
201	6 7 7
201	8
202	0 0 1 1 1
202	
202	5
202	6

EXAMPLE 2.9b

Suppose the tax data is:

$20,130 $20,161 $20,207 $20,175 $20,213 $20,147
$20,189 $20,215 $20,264 $20,219 $20,252 $20,173
$20,209 $20,155 $20,128   **$20,312**   **$20,364**

The following stem-and-leaf display would be appropriate.

Annual Taxes ($)

(00's)	
201	2 3 4
201	5 6 7 7 8
202	0 0 1 1 1
202	5 6
203	1
203	6

EXAMPLE 2.9c   Suppose the tax data is:

$20,130 $20,161 $20,207 $20,175 $20,213 $20,147
$20,189 $20,215 $20,264 $20,219 $20,252 $20,173
$20,209 $20,155 $20,128 $20,312 $20,364   **$20,438**
$20,567 $20,619

The following stem-and-leaf display would be appropriate.

Annual Taxes ($)

(00's)	
201	2 3 4 5 6 7 7 8
202	0 0 1 1 1 5 6
203	1 6
204	3
205	6
206	1

EXAMPLE 2.10   The following data shows the precipitation (in cm.) for 30 Canadian cities for a certain year.

64.6   53.2   7.1   99.2   12.1   15.3   44.4   41.4   57.6
148.6   23.5   11.7   33.3   39.1   30.8   28.6   43.6   79.7
43.5   41.8   83.8   31.0   29.7   52.8   33.9   115.2   30.3
7.5   36.5   41.9

The following stem-and-leaf display would be appropriate:

Precipitation (cm) for Canadian cities

(00's)	
0	0 0 1 1 1
0	2 2 2 3 3 3 3 3 3 3
0	4 4 4 4 4 4 5 5 5
0	6 7
0	8 9
1	1
1	
1	4

Problems for Section 2.2

LEARNING THE BASICS

2.9 The following data represent the daily average hotel cost and rental car cost for 20 U.S. cities during a week in October 2003. `HOTEL-CAR`

City	Hotel	Cars
San Francisco	205	47
Los Angeles	179	41
Seattle	185	49
Phoenix	210	38
Denver	128	32
Dallas	145	48
Houston	177	49
Minneapolis	117	41
Chicago	221	56
St. Louis	159	41
New Orleans	205	50
Detroit	128	32
Cleveland	165	34
Atlanta	180	46
Orlando	198	41
Miami	158	40
Pittsburgh	132	39
Boston	283	67
New York	269	69
Washington D.C.	204	40

Source: Extracted from The Wall Street Journal, *October 10, 2003, W4.*

a. Place the data for hotel cost and rental car cost into two ordered arrays.
b. Construct stem-and-leaf displays for hotel cost and rental car cost.
c. Does the ordered array or the stem-and-leaf display provide more information? Discuss.
d. Around what value, if any, are the hotel cost and rental car cost concentrated? Explain.

2.10 Refer to Table 2.9 that shows data regarding the first 20 companies taken from The FP500 Canada's 500 Largest Corporations table that appeared in the June 2003 issue of National Post Business.

Construct stem-and-leaf displays for the following data:
a. Profit rank
b. Asset rank
c. Revenues for 2002
d. Assets for 2002

e. Number of Employees
f. Share Price Change—1 year percent
g. Profits as a percent of Assets
h. Profits as a percent of Equity

STEM-AND-LEAF DISPLAY EXERCISES

2.11 Refer to Table 2.10 that shows data regarding the first 21 companies taken from the Financial Post Magazine website (http://www.financialpost.com/magazine/fp500/list.html).

For the 21 companies listed in Table 2.10, construct stem-and-leaf displays for the following data:
a. Revenue amount 2007
b. Profit amount 2007
c. Revenue Change
d. Profit Change
e. Profit Rank

2.12 Refer to Table 2.11: 'Telecommunications Industry Annual ranking of America's largest corporations by Revenues, Profits' data that appeared in the April 30, 2007 issue of Fortune 500 magazine available online.

Using the data listed in Table 2.11, construct stem-and-leaf displays for the following data:
a. Revenues ($ million).
b. Profits ($ million).
c. Profits % change from 2005
d. Revenues % change from 2005
e. 1000 revenues rank

2.13 Refer to Table 2.12 that shows the stock summary data for companies with name starting with letter A traded on the Nasdaq on 8 May, 2008. The data was taken from the Financial Post Magazine's website - http://www.financialpost.com/markets/market-data/market-nasdaq.html?tmp=nasdaq

Using the data listed in Table 2.12, construct stem-and-leaf displays for the following data:
a. Volume
b. High/Ask Price
c. Low/Bid Price
d. Close/Previous Price
e. Net Change
f. 52 week High Price
g. 52 week Low Price

TABLE 2.9

FP500 CANADA'S 500 LARGEST CORPORATIONS

	RANK BY REVENUE		Industry	REVENUES			ASSETS		
2002	**2001**			2002 $'000s	% Change	% Sales Outside Canada	2002 $'000s	% Change	Rank
1	1	General Motors of Canada Ltd., Oshawa, ON	Vehicle	37,000,000	n.a.	n.a.	n.a.	n.a.	n.a.
2	4	George Weston Ltd., Toronto	Conglom	27,446,000	11.3	n.a.	16,630,000	2.2	34
3	7	Bombardier Inc., Montreal (Ja03)	High-tech	23,664,900	9.4	n.a.	29,009,400	4.5	20
4	8	Ford Motor Co. of Canada, Ltd., Oakville, ON	Vehicle	23,328,700	8.1	n.a.	11,398,000	8.0	48
5	3	Royal Bank of Canada, Montreal (Oc02)	Bank	23,234,000	(9.0)	n.a.	376,956,000	4.9	1
6	18	Sun Life Financial Services of Canada, Toronto	Life	23,101,000	38.4	72	123,438,000	53.7	6
7	5	Onex Corp., Toronto	Conglom	22,653,000	(4.8)	85	19,890,000	(4.7)	27
8	17	Magna International Inc.*, Aurora, ON	Vehicle	20,364,470	19.3	70	16,004,076	27.1	35
9	6	BCE Inc., Montreal	Telecom	19,768,000	(8.9)	n.a.	39,563,000	(27.2)	14
10	13	Alcan Inc.*, Montreal	Mining	19,687,800	0.7	94	27,674,964	(0.4)	21
11	12	DaimlerChrysler Canada Inc., Windsor, ON	Vehicle	19,353,000	(5.2)	n.a.	n.a.	n.a.	n.a.
12	14	Power Corp. of Canada, Montreal	Conglom	19,017,000	3.6	30	70,136,000	2.0	11
13	10	The Bank of Nova Scotia, Toronto (Oc02)	Bank	18,310,000	(13.0)	n.a.	296,380,000	4.2	2
14	9	Canadian Imperial Bank of Commerce, Toronto (Oc02)	Bank	17,055,000	(20.3)	n.a.	273,293,000	(4.9)	4
15	16	Imperial Oil Ltd., Toronto	Energy	16,890,000	(1.5)	13	11,868,000	10.3	44
16	11	The Toronto-Dominion Bank, Toronto (Oc02)	Bank	16,680,000	(20.3)	n.a.	278,040,000	(3.4)	3
17	2	Nortel Networks Corp.*, Brampton, ON	High-tech	16,538,380	(39.1)	n.a.	23,382,804	(27.5)	24
18	19	Manulife Financial Corp., Toronto	Life	16,532,000	1.9	80	81,195,000	3.3	9
19	15	Bank of Montreal, Montreal (Oc02)	Bank	13,059,000	(24.2)	n.a.	252,864,000	5.6	5
20	20	Hydro-Québec, Montreal	Utility	13,002,000	3.4	28	59,078,000	(1.3)	12

PROFITS				PROFITS AS % OF...			GROWTH			EMPLOYEES & OWNERSHIP					
2002 $'000s	% Change	Rank	EPS $0.00	Revenue	Assets	Equity	5-Year % Profit Growth	Share Price Change 1 Year %	5 Year %	Employees	Symbol	Exchange	Major Shareholder(s)	% Foreign	RANK 2002
n.a.	n.a.	n.a.	n.a.	n.a.	n.a.	n.a.	n.a.	n.a.	n.a.	24,500	(Pr)		General Motors, US	100	1
690,000	18.6	24	5.05	2.5	4.2	17.2	182.8	(19.4)	106.9	139,000	WN	T	W. Galen Weston 62%		2
(615,200)	(257.4)	569	(0.47)	(2.6)	(2.2)	(18.0)	(246.4)	(81.1)	(68.8)	75,000	BBD.B	T	Bombardier family 63%		3
n.a.	n.a.	n.a.	n.a.	n.a.	n.a.	n.a.	n.a.	n.a.	n.a.	15,074	(Pr)		Ford Motor Co., US	100	4
2,762,000	14.6	3	3.96	11.9	0.8	15.0	64.5	9.2	36.7	59,549	RY	T,NY	Widely held	20	5
997,000	13.2	15	1.84	4.3	1.0	8.8	95.1	(17.6)	n.a.	11,800	SLF	T,NY	Widely held		6
(145,000)	(118.2)	546	(0.90)	(0.6)	(0.7)	(8.9)	(366.4)	(36.9)	55.0	98,000	OCX	T	Gerald Schwartz 67% voting		7
869,780	(3.1)	19	9.15	4.3	6.1	11.1	44.1	(32.8)	(26.8)	73,000	MG.A	T,NY	Stronach Trust 58%		8
2,475,000	373.2	4	2.74	12.5	5.3	16.6	259.4	(2.3)	(53.7)	66,266	BCE	T,NY	Widely held	14	9
587,180	7,486.3	31	1.81	3.0	2.1	4.3	(9.4)	(33.1)	(8.5)	50,000	AL	T,NY	Widely held		10
n.a.	n.a.	n.a.	n.a.	n.a.	n.a.	n.a.	n.a.	n.a.	n.a.	n.a.	(Pr)		DaimlerChrysler Corp., US	100	11
645,000	4.4	27	2.81	3.4	0.9	12.8	94.9	(5.9)	31.1	28,000	POW	T	Paul Desmarais Sr. 65%		12
1,797,000	(17.2)	7	3.36	9.8	0.6	12.2	18.7	(0.5)	39.6	49,000	BNS	T,NY	Widely held		13
653,000	(61.3)	26	1.37	3.8	0.2	5.4	(57.9)	(15.7)	(3.3)	42,552	CM	T, NY	Widely held		14
1,210,000	(2.7)	14	3.19	7.2	10.7	25.1	42.9	(0.7)	73.4	6,460	IMO	T,AM	Exxon Mobil Corp., US	70	15
(76,000)	(105.5)	533	(0.25)	(0.5)	n.a.	(0.6)	(107.0)	(24.3)	5.9	42,817	TD	T	Widely held		16
(5,549,950)	86.9	574	(1.43)	(33.6)	(19.9)	(106.6)	n.a.	(56.3)	(86.4)	52,600	NT	T,NY	Widely Held		17
1,370,000	17.4	12	2.90	8.3	1.7	16.1	(65.8)	(18.5)	n.a.	32,400	MFC	T,NY	Widely held		18
1,417,000	(3.7)	11	2.73	10.9	0.6	12.6	8.6	4.9	4.4	33,000	BMO	T,NY	Widely held		19
1,526,000	37.7	9	n.a.	11.7	2.6	10.5	94.1	n.a.	n.a.	20,972	(Cr)		Quebec government		20

TABLE 2.10   FP 500 Ranking of Canada's Companies

FINANCIAL POST
BUSINESS   **FP500**

Home FP500 Rankings Crown Corps Profit Leaders Largest Subsidiaries Buy the database

Last year's FP500 rankings   Canada's Top Companies 2008   Search

First · Previous 1 - 50 ▾ Next · Last

Ranking			Revenue		Profit		
2007	2006	Company	Amt. 2007 (x1000)	Change	Amt. 2007 (x1000)	Change	Rank
1	1	Royal Bank of Canada, Toronto (Oc07)	$41,307,000	14.6%	$5,492,000	16.2%	2
2	2	Manulife Financial Corp., Toronto	$35,533,000	3.9%	$4,229,000	6.5%	6
▲ 3	4	George Weston Ltd., Toronto	$32,815,000	2.0%	$563,000	365.3%	61
▼ 4	3	General Motors of Canada Ltd., Oshawa, Ont.	$31,675,000	-5.0%	-	-	-
5	5	Power Corp. of Canada, Montreal	$29,408,000	-3.0%	$1,363,000	5.0%	28
6	6	Magna International Inc.*, Aurora, Ont.	$27,995,958	2.1%	$712,062	18.9%	52
7	7	Alcan Inc.*, Montreal (De06)	$26,808,894	8.9%	$2,029,860	1199.4%	22
▲ 8	10	The Bank of Nova Scotia, Halifax (Oc07)	$26,427,000	17.5%	$4,045,000	13.0%	8
▲ 9	11	The Toronto-Dominion Bank, Toronto (Oc07)	$25,209,000	13.0%	$3,997,000	-13.2%	9
▼ 10	8	Imperial Oil Ltd., Calgary	$25,069,000	2.3%	$3,188,000	4.7%	12
▲ 11	15	Onex Corp., Toronto	$23,433,000	25.8%	$228,000	-77.2%	119
▲ 12	13	Canadian Imperial Bank of Commerce, Toronto (Oc07)	$23,289,000	15.5%	$3,296,000	24.6%	10
▲ 13	16	EnCana Corp.*, Calgary	$23,033,004	23.9%	$4,251,966	-33.7%	5
14	14	Petro-Canada, Calgary	$21,710,000	14.8%	$2,733,000	57.1%	15
▼ 15	9	Sun Life Financial Inc., Toronto	$21,188,000	-12.8%	$2,290,000	6.8%	17
▼ 16	12	Chrysler Canada Inc., Windsor, Ont. (De06)	$20,534,000	-1.4%	-	-	-
17	17	Bank of Montreal, Montreal (Oc07)	$20,344,000	12.1%	$2,131,000	-20.0%	20
▲ 18	19	Bombardier Inc.*, Montreal (Ja08)	$18,538,854	10.1%	$335,703	10.3%	98
▼ 19	18	BCE Inc., Montreal	$17,866,000	0.9%	$4,057,000	102.1%	7
▲ 20	21	Suncor Energy Inc., Calgary	$17,212,000	20.0%	$2,832,000	-4.7%	14
▲ 21	27	Husky Energy Inc., Calgary	$15,518,000	22.5%	$3,214,000	17.9%	11

Source: http://www.financialpost.com/magazine/fp500/list.html

TABLE 2.11   FORTUNE 500: Telecommunications Industry Annual ranking of America's largest corporations by Revenues, Profits

Rank	Company	1,000 revenues rank	REVENUES		PROFITS	
			$ millions	% change from 2005	$ millions	% change from 2005
1	Verizon Communications	13	93,221	24	2,197	−16
2	AT&T	27	63,055	44	2,356	54
3	Sprint Nextel	53	43,531	26	1,329	−26
4	Comcast	84	25,700	15	1,533	173
5	DIRECTV Group	160	14,756	12	1,420	323
6	Qwest Communications	178	13,923	0	593	N.A.
7	Echostar Communications	252	9,818	17	608	−60
8	Alltel	256	9,723	2	1,129	−15
9	Liberty Global	340	6,813	29	706	N.A.
10	Virgin Media	347	6,637	83	−984	−228
11	Cablevision Systems	380	6,007	15	−126	−234
12	Charter Communications	409	5,613	7	−1,670	N.A.

From the April 30th, 2007 issue
Source: http://money.cnn.com/magazines/fortune/fortune500/

TABLE 2.12

Stock summary data for companies with name starting with letter A traded on the Nasdaq.

Company	Security	Ticker	Volume	High/Ask	Low/Bid	Close/Previous	Net Change	High	Low
A-Power Energy Generation	com	APWR	223,539	10.88	10.09	10.75	+0.73	31.80	3.00
AAON Inc	com	AAON	41,035	21.05	20.62	21.00	+0.50	23.00	12.79
ABIOMED Inc	com	ABMD	93,186	6.98	6.58	6.98	+0.33	20.06	4.67
AC Moore Arts & Crafts	com	ACMR	15,187	3.39	3.26	3.36	−0.01	8.78	0.71
ACADIA Phrmctcls Inc	com	ACAD	84,387	1.94	1.75	1.81	+0.07	8.84	0.73
ACI Worldwide Inc	com	ACIW	194,814	14.33	13.96	14.13	+0.09	22.49	8.86
ADA-ES Inc	com	ADES	900	3.95	3.80	3.86	+0.01	11.98	2.41
ADAM Inc	com	ADAM	3,198	3.33	3.14	3.31	+0.08	7.80	1.96
ADC Telecommuns Inc	com	ADCT	997,080	7.54	7.09	7.43	−0.11	17.45	2.48
ADTRAN Inc	com	ADTN	264,258	20.37	19.56	19.94	+0.19	26.50	12.14
AEP Industries Inc	com	AEPI	15,482	24.63	21.68	23.00	+1.54	28.58	10.43
AEterna Zentaris Inc	com	AEZS	40,060	1.33	1.24	1.32	+0.06	1.48	0.261
AFC Enterprises Inc	com	AFCE	45,533	6.06	5.33	5.62	−0.17	10.14	2.85
AMAG Pharmaceuticals Inc	com	AMAG	155,664	54.65	52.73	54.54	+1.86	55.00	18.33
AMCORE Financial Inc	com	AMFI	12,981	1.40	1.30	1.38	+0.12	14.50	0.59
AMERCO	com	UHAL	14,552	33.45	31.64	33.20	+1.30	59.85	22.01
AMERISAFE Inc	com	AMSF	83,309	17.81	16.85	17.78	+1.00	21.96	12.51
AMICAS Inc	com	AMCS	2,099	2.59	2.44	2.48	+0.01	2.96	1.27
ANADIGICS Inc	com	ANAD	176,563	3.04	2.86	3.04	+0.13	13.94	1.13
ANSYS Inc	com	ANSS	296,247	27.11	26.20	26.65	−0.06	49.81	18.00

Source: http://www.financialpost.com/markets/market-data/commodity-cash_prices.html?tmp=cash_prices

2.3 Tables and Charts for Numerical Data

When you have a data set that contains a large number of values, reaching conclusions from an ordered array or stem-and-leaf is often difficult. You need to use tables and charts in such circumstances. There are many different tables and charts to visually present numerical data. These include the frequency and percentage distributions, histogram, polygon, and cumulative percentage polygon (ogive).

The Frequency Distribution

The frequency distribution helps you draw conclusions from a large set of data.

A **frequency distribution** is a summary table in which the data are arranged into numerically ordered class groupings.

The following scenario is just one of many reasons why one would want to make a frequency distribution.

In most production or manufacturing situations quality is related to variability. Specifically,

the lower the variability - the higher the quality.

Ideally, the goal is to have a production process with NO variability. Unfortunately, most production processes use machines, and people who are not perfect, and thus there usually is some level of variability in the items being produced.

In Chapter 8 we will learn about some Statistical Process Control Charts, which are used to control variable measures. These charts would not be necessary if there was no variability in the variable being controlled.

To use the control charts correctly, it is necessary that the variable being controlled fit a Normal Distribution (Bell-Curve). Simply put, most of the measurements should be near the target value, with fewer and fewer measurements occurring the farther we go from the target value.

EXAMPLE 2.11   The high-voltage output of a certain power supply that is to be used in copying machines must be 300 ± 50 volts, i.e. from 250 to 350 volts. In setting up a quality control chart, data from a sample of 125 power supplies is to be used. The results are given as follows:

333	297	285	300	279	311	298	300	305	262
289	315	305	302	273	282	313	330	300	271
303	330	290	291	300	290	340	293	309	287
292	312	295	296	302	308	268	296	294	306
295	320	322	328	326	316	290	291	320	315
301	292	291	299	298	308	295	296	325	333
309	304	306	292	327	295	302	302	276	331
293	306	286	310	277	309	307	304	323	288
285	292	342	311	316	297	304	316	305	320
303	296	332	336	313	282	294	341	334	317
296	312	307	328	326	301	309	313	275	328
326	303	308	310	285	317	318	319	314	325
284	289	312	319	298					

The first question that needs to be answered is:

Does the data appear to fit a bell-curve?

In order to get a picture of the *shape* of the distribution of data, we need to *group* the data into a **Frequency distribution.**

General Guidelines for Making a Frequency Distribution:

(**Note:** The guidelines below will be very useful for a person just learning to make a frequency distribution or for getting a general impression about the distribution of the data. When one has experience and is intimately familiar with the data being organized then several of these general guidelines may not be the most appropriate.)

A possible frequency distribution for the voltage data is:

Power Supply Voltage (Volts)	# of power supplies
260 and under 270	2
270 " " 280	6
280 " " 290	11
290 " " 300	29
300 " " 310	31
310 " " 320	21
320 " " 330	14
330 " " 340	8
340 " " 350	3

The data is grouped into **classes** or intervals.

Number of classes: It is recommended not to have to few or too many classes. For the problems you will solve in this course you should use from 5 to 10 classes.

Notation for indicating classes: There are several possible notations that are used to designate the classes. In this text we will use the **'and under'** notation, e.g. 260 and under 270. The numerical values used in designating the classes when using the 'and under' notation are called **boundaries.**

The student will also likely come across classes that have been set up using the 'to' notation, e.g. 260 to 269.

Class width (CW):   A class that has an **upper** and **lower** boundary has a finite class width. Unless one has a special reason for doing otherwise. The class width is determined by the formula

$$CW = \frac{(\text{Upper boundary} - \text{Lower boundary})}{5}$$

it is best if the class width is an 'easy' number to work with. Recommended class widths are shown in the table below:

For narrower classes					For wider classes		
← Divide by 10					Multiple by 10 →		
	0.01	0.1		1		10	100
	0.02	0.2		2		20	200
etc	0.025	0.25(if the data has		2.5 (if the data has		25	250 etc
		at least 2 decimals)		at least one decimal)			
	0.05	0.5		5		50	500

Note: *In this course, when you are asked to make a frequency distribution, all classes must have the **same class width.***

Boundaries: There are several guidelines that should be used to determine the actual numerical values of the boundaries.

They should *look like* the data, i.e. have the same number of decimal places as the data.

Each boundary should be a **multiple** of the chosen class width.

There must be **no gaps** between the classes, i.e. the upper boundary of one class will also be the lower boundary of the next class.

The lowest data value should belong to the first class and the highest data value should belong to the last class.

Example: If CW = 20 is chosen and the data ranges from L = 112 to H = 196 then use the following set of classes:

Note: L = Lowest
H = Highest

$$
\begin{array}{llll}
100 & \text{and under} & 120 \\
120 & `` & `` & 140 \\
140 & `` & `` & 160 \\
160 & `` & `` & 180 \\
180 & `` & `` & 200 \\
\end{array}
$$

Frequency: Given the symbol f = number of data values which belong to the class

Determine class width

$$\text{Estimated Class Width} = \frac{\text{Highest value} - \text{Lowest value}}{\text{Minimum number of classes recommended}}$$

$$\text{Estimated Class Width} = \frac{\text{Highest value} - \text{Lowest value}}{5}$$

You should choose a recommended class width (i.e. from a list of "easy" numbers) closest to the estimated class width. For example, if the estimated class width is 15.3, you may choose either 10 or 20. Whichever class width you choose to construct the frequency distribution, you must always check that the number of classes is between 5 and 10 classes.

Referring back to our voltage data, you will see that the frequency distribution shown above follows all the recommended guidelines.

You should also note that there may be more than one frequency distribution that follows the guidelines above for any set of data. The following frequency distribution of the voltage data would also be acceptable.

Power Supply Voltage (Volts)	# of power supplies
260 and under 280	8
280 " " 300	40
300 " " 320	52
320 " " 340	22
340 " " 360	3

By observing the frequencies in either distribution, we can see that most of the data is close to the target value of 300, and there are fewer and fewer data values as we move further away from the target on the high and low sides.

Frequency distributions are often used to summarize data and give a general idea of where the data values are located. They also give an indication as to the 'shape' of a set of data.

EXAMPLE 2.12 Suppose that for a particular process we are filling cereal boxes. The boxes are labelled as having 450 gm. We have set the filling machine to make sure that most boxes weigh more than 450 grams. There are two machines used to fill these cereal boxes. The results of random samples of 25 boxes from each machine are shown below. The numbers indicate the weight, in grams, of each box.

Machine A: 450.8   454.3   456.4   458.1   456.5   457.6   454.7   458.6   451.2   450.6
              455.9   454.2   458.4   458.0   452.6   456.8   449.2   450.3   451.5   452.7
              457.3   452.8   449.7   454.1   455.9

Machine B: 455.4   450.2   456.2   458.8   456.5   454.1   455.0   456.9   457.8   455.5
              456.3   455.1   456.8   453.3   456.5   454.1   453.8   457.2   455.1   449.4
              455.6   455.7   457.2   454.3   454.9

Make a frequency distribution of each set of results.

Weight of a box (grams)	Machine A # boxes	Machine B # boxes
449.0 and under 450.0	2	1
450.0 " " 451.0	3	1
451.0 " " 452.0	2	0
452.0 " " 453.0	3	0
453.0 " " 454.0	0	2
454.0 " " 455.0	4	4
455.0 " " 456.0	2	7
456.0 " " 457.0	3	6
457.0 " " 458.0	2	3
458.0 " " 49.0	4	1

The frequency distribution shows that machine B appears to be doing a better job of producing a more consistent product.

EXAMPLE 2.13   Consider the following set of measurements:

3.56	3.46	3.48	3.50	3.42	3.43	3.52
3.49	3.44	3.50	3.48	3.56	3.50	3.52
3.47	3.48	3.46	3.50	3.56	3.38	3.41
3.37	3.47	3.49	3.45	3.44	3.50	3.49
3.46	3.46	3.55	3.52	3.44	3.50	3.45
3.44	3.48	3.46	3.52	3.46	3.48	3.48
3.32	3.40	3.52	3.34	3.46	3.43	**3.30**
3.46	3.59	3.63	3.59	3.47	3.38	3.52
3.45	3.48	3.31	3.46	3.40	3.54	3.46
3.51	3.48	3.50	**3.68**	3.60	3.46	3.52
3.48	3.50	3.56	3.50	3.52	3.46	3.48
3.46	3.52	3.56	3.52	3.48	3.46	3.45
3.46	3.54	3.54	3.48	3.49	3.41	3.41
3.45	3.34	3.44	3.47	3.47	3.41	3.48

Notation: L = Lowest and H = Highest

L = 3.30   H = 3.68

An appropriate frequency distribution would be as follows:

Classes	f
3.30 and under 3.35	4
3.35 " " 3.40	3
3.40 " " 3.45	15
3.45 " " 3.50	42
3.50 " " 3.55	23
3.55 " " 3.60	8
3.60 " " 3.65	2
3.65 " " 3.70	1

EXAMPLE 2.14   Refer to the Table 2.13 (on page 66) from the July 2000 Report on Business.

a) Make a frequency distribution of the previous inventory turnover data.

Previous Inventory Turnover	# of Companies	
0.0 and under 5.0	3	
5.0 " " 10.0	7	Since the
10.0 " " 15.0	3	
15.0 " " 20.0	1	L = 3.5
20.0 " " 25.0	1	H = 23.1

TABLE 2.13

RETAILERS												
	REVENUE		PROFIT		RETURN ON CAPITAL		INVENTORY TURNOVER		DAYS RECEIVABLE		OPERATING REVENUE PER STORE	
COMPANY AND YEAR END	$000	% CH'GE	$000	% CH'GE	1-YR %	5-YR %	CURRENT	PREVIOUS	CURRENT	PREVIOUS	$000	
DEPARTMENT STORES												
Hudson's Bay Co.(Ja00)	7,295,751	3	96,035	132	8.04	4.94	4.5	4.6	30	35	14,592	
Sears Canada(Ja00)	6,131,200	12	199,600	36	20.64	14.05	7.9	8.0	30	43	55,738	
Zellers Inc.(Ja00)	4,598,000	2	na	na	na	na	na	na	na	na	14,018	
Costco Canada(Au99)	3,087,962	7	na	na	na	na	na	na	na	na	102,932	
Jean Coutu Group (PJC)(My99)	2,289,370	18	74,307	18	19.25	18.78	7.5	7.2	21	23	4,156	
North West Co. Fund(Ja00)	626,469	0	27,957	73	11.72	9.64	5.5	5.1	28	32	3,539	
Industry Average		4		41	11.65	9.41	10.3	10.3	24	29	25,234	
CLOTHING STORES												
Dylex Ltd.(Ja00)	1,081,767	0	-36,387	-283	-17.14	11.01	6.6	6.9	3	3	1,685	
Reitmans (Canada)(Ja00)	526,811	19	51,707	273	38.88	12.92	15.7	14.2	2	2	812	
Suzy Shier(Ja00)	357,733	7	6,070	-55	9.09	14.06	7.9	6.9	5	5	754	
Mark's Work Wearhouse(Ja00)	321,187	11	6,387	11	18.53	21.94	4.0	4.1	16	17	1,815	
Boutiques San Francisco(Ja00)	226,769	12	5,555	-15	15.24	16.47	7.3	7.2	3	4	1,271	
Château Stores of Canada(Ja00)	168,666	5	5,269	-10	17.71	16.02	na	23.1	na	2	na	
Industry Average		6		-19	16.48	15.31	6.8	11.7	7	5	1,437	
SPECIALITY STORES												
Canadian Tire Corp.(Ja00)	4,728,259	9	145,929	-13	12.72	13.68	10.7	10.6	63	64	10,996	
Future Shop(Ap99)[a]	1,960,274	11	-82,245	-2,176	-118.93	6.63	9.5	7.1	4	3	22,531	
Katz Group(Ja00)	1,700,000	113	na	na	na	na	na	na	na	na	3,400	
Rona Inc.(De99)	988,385	21	14,706	9	17.18	18.98	14.0	15.3	20	15	2076	
Hartco Enterprises(Ja00)	850,279	5	-4,774	-156	-1.64	11.90	7.7	13.4	10	12	15,184	
Reno-Depot Inc.(De99)	588,000	na	na	na	na	na	na	na	na	na	na	
Chapters Inc.(Ap99)	577,880	24	10,301	20	15.16	na	3.1	3.5	4	4	1,829	
Grand & Toy Ltd.(De99)	568,195	19	na	na	na	na	na	na	na	na	na	
Industry Average		72		-463.2	-15.10	14.98	10.0	8.2	23	18	9,386	

b) Make a frequency distribution for the return on capital 1-yr % data.

Return on Capital – 1yr %	# of Companies
−125.00 and under −100.00	1
−100.00 " " −75.00	0
−75.00 " " −50.00	0
−50.00 " " −25.00	0
−25.00 " " 0.00	2
0.00 " " 25.00	11
25.00 " " 50.00	1

Since the

$L = -118.93$

$H = 38.88$

Problems for Section 2.3

FREQUENCY DISTRIBUTIONS

2.14 Refer to Table 2.14, which shows data regarding the first 32 companies taken from The Top 1000 Ranking by Profits table that appeared in the July 2003 issue of the Report on Business.

Construct frequency distributions for the following data:
a. Revenue rank
b. Market Capitalization

c. P/E Ratio
d. Per Share Data—Price/Sales
e. Debt/Equity Ratio
f. Revenue % change
g. Earnings per Share—Latest Year (Exclude values reported in $US)
h. Number of Employees

TABLE 2.14

▶Ranking by profits

PROFIT RANK 2002	2001	COMPANY AND YEAR END	PROFIT $000	% CH'GE	REVENUE $000	RANK	%CH'GE	MARKET CAP $ MIL	DIV YIELD %	P/E RATIO	PER SHARE DATA PRICE/SALES	CASH FLOW
1	1	Royal Bank of Canada(Oc02) ON	2,762,000	15	23,234,000	3	-9	36,197	2.79	13.74	1.58	6.59
2	30	BCE Inc.(De02) QC	2,475,000	382	19,809,000	8	2	26.102	4.21	10.40	1.22	6.04
3	2	Bank of Nova Scotia(Oc02) ON	1,797,000	-17	18.310,000	12	-13	23,129	3.16	13.66	1.26	8.44
4	4	Bell Canada(De02) QC	1,504,000	-5	15,685,000	20	7	nm	nm	nm	nm	13.43
5	5	Bank of Montreal(Oc02) ON	1,417,000	-4	13,059,000	21	-24	18,764	3.15	13.96	1.43	4.45
6	10	Manulife Financial(De02) ON	1,378,000	19	16,532,000	18	2	15,923	1.74	11.86	1.03	4.84
7	7	EnCana Corp.(De02) AB	1,224,000	-5	11,031,000	25	112	23.361	.82	16.71	1.85	9.04
8	8	Imperial Oil(De02) ON	1,210,000	-2	15,821,000	19	-2	16,996	1.87	14.06	1.09	4.64
9	14	Sun Life Financial Services(De02) ON	998,000	13	23,101,000	4	37	16,517	2.10	14.52	.63	9.38
10	15	Power Financial(De02) QC	988,000	12	18,700,000	11	3	12,591	2.87	13.35	.68	5.16
11	12	Petro-Canada(De02) AB	974,000	15	9,917,000	28	14	12,892	.82	13.18	1.30	8.66
12	9	Thomson Corp.(De02) ON	(US)615,000	-21	(US)7.768,000	23	7	27,348	2.64	28.77	2.21	(US)4.32
13	29	Great-West Lifeco(De02) MB	962,000	76	16,632,000	16	4	13,648	2.54	14.72	.84	3.79
14	13	Magna International(De02) ON	(US)554,000	-4	(US)13,044,000	7	17	8,417	2.43	9.62	.38	20.25
15	21	TransCanada PipeLines(De02) AB	805,000	17	5,300,000	48	-1	10,990	4.36	14.69	2.10	3.82
16	20	Husky Energy(De02) AB	804,000	23	6,385,000	40	-3	6.882	2.19	8.76	1.08	(US)5.02
17	39	Suncor Energy(De02) AB	761,000	96	4,913,000	52	17	11,090	.69	15.06	2.26	3.21
18	27	Loblaw Companies(De02) ON	728,000	29	23,099,000	5	7	14,905	.89	20.46	.65	4.05
19	24	George Weston Ltd.(De02) ON	690,000	19	27,464,000	1	11	11,938	1.06	17.87	.43	12.25
20	3	Cdn. Imp. Bank of Commerce(Oc02) ON	653,000	-61	17,055,000	13	-20	13.914	4.13	28.29	.82	4.78
21	23	Power Corp.(De02) QC	645,000	4	19,011.000	10	3	7,997	2.21	12.81	.53	8.61
22	31	Enbridge Inc.(De02) AB	610,100	26	4.830.600	54	13	7,233	3.57	11.84	1.50	4.57
23	344	Alcan Inc.(De02) QC	(US)374,000	nm	(US)12,553,000	9	-1	14,894	2.03	25.65	.76	(US)6.39
24	19	Cdn. Natural Resources(De02) AB	574,800	-12	4,114,900	59	15	6,261	1.07	10.49	1.47	17.71
25	18	Canadian National Railway Co.(De02) QC	571,000	-21	6.173,000	41	8	12,891	1.32	22.74	2.10	8.14
26	11	Shell Canada(De02) AB	561,000	-44	7,314,000	35	-5	13,575	1.63	24.24	1.88	4.45
27	17	Talisman Energy(De02) AB	524,000	-29	5,379,000	47	5	7,450	1.06	15.24	1.42	19.74
28	45	Investors Group(De02) MB	511,759	87	1,940,036	102	10	7,058	3.21	14.35	3.63	3.02
29	41	Canada Life Financial(De02) ON	499,000	46	8,598,000	32	7	6,463	1.49	13.21	.77	4.68
30	36	Canadian Pacific Railway Ltd.(De02) AB	496,000	33	3,692,600	62	-1	4,937	1.64	9.95	1.35	5.98
31	44	Great-West Life Assurance(De02) MB	475,000	68	10,766,000	26	7	nm	nm	nm	nm	1.180.76
32	34	Nexen Inc.(De02) AB	452,000	0	3,102,000	77	1	4,212	.88	10.25	1.35	9.75

DEBT/ EQUITY	EARNINGS PER SHARE LATEST YEAR	PREVIOUS YEAR	2 YEARS AGO	RETURN ON COMMON EQUITY ONE-YEAR %	RANK	FIVE-YEAR %	RANK	NUMBER OF EMPLOYEES	INDUSTRY	MAJOR SHAREHOLDER	PROFIT
0.4	3.96	3.55	3.53	15.96	159	17.16	99	59,770	banks	Widely held	1
1.2	2.74	0.56	7.43	17.99	127	26.69	23	66,266	tele	Widely held	2
0.4	3.36	4.12	3.67	12.85	230	15.64	118	44,633	banks	Widely held	3
1.6	3.90	4.18	4.09	19.00	111	21.38	55	54,258	tele	BCE Inc. 100%	4
0.3	2.73	2.72	3.30	13.37	218	14.92	138	33,912	banks	Widely held	5
0.2	2.90	2.40	2.22	16.17	154	14.74	143	13,000	insur	Widely held	6
0.6	2.92	5.02	4.09	13.94	194	19.13	67	3,646	oilprd	Widely held	7
0.3	3.19	3.15	3.40	25.35	62	22.24	50	6.460	integ	Exxon Mobil Corp. (U.S.) 69.6%	8
0.2	1.84	2.08	1.49	8.82	355	na	nr	14,905	insur	Widely held	9
0.3	2.72	2.44	2.18	17.33	136	18.89	72	18.300	fin	Power Corp. of Canada 67 4%	10
0.5	3.71	3.19	3.28	18.29	123	13.00	180	4.470	integ	Government of Canada 18.74%	11
0.5	(US)0.93	(US)1.19	(US)1.96	7.32	397	15.34	131	44.000	serv	Woodbridge Company Ltd.69%	12
0.2	2.53	1.39	1.72	22.86	74	17.53	96	14.000	insur	Power Financial Corp.64.99%	13
0.1	(US)5.83	(US)6.55	(US)7.04	11.85	262	12.45	195	70,800	auto	Stronach Trust 66.3%	14
1.6	1.56	1.30	1.50	13.37	219	8.63	309	2.767	pipeline	Widely held	15
0.5	1.88	1.49	1.39	16.73	146	nm	nr	2,753	integ	Li Ka-sning 71.5%	16
0.8	1.64	0.79	0.79	28.25	51	17.72	93	3,422	integ	Widely held	17
1.0	2.64	2.04	1.71	18.93	113	15.58	122	122,000	food	George Weston Ltd. 61%	18
1.4	5.05	4.42	3.66	18.27	124	21.10	57	142,850	food	W. Galen Weston 62.13%	19
0.3	1.37	4.19	4.97	5.22	461	12.58	189	42,552	banks	Widely held	20
0.4	2.81	2.74	2.93	13.66	205	15.74	117	19,000	mgt	Paul Desmarais and associates 65%	21
1.8	3.60	2.91	2.54	20.08	101	16.94	103	4,000	pipeline	Widely held	22
0.4	(US)1.15	(US)-0.02	(US)2.45	4.32	486	5.76	373	48,100	mining	Widely held	23
0.8	4.46	5.30	6.70	13.51	211	16.29	107	1,573	oilprd	Widely held	24
0.8	2.87	3.72	3.91	8.93	352	10.29	250	23,190	trans	Widely held	25
0.3	2.03	3.67	3.04	11.45	271	17.54	95	3,825	integ	Shell Investments (1996) Ltd. 78%	26
0.7	3.73	5.25	6.41	12.88	229	11.17	226	1,565	oilprd	Widely held	27
0.5	1.86	1.05	1.35	20.01	103	22.45	48	3,285	fin	Power Financial Corp. 56.2%	28
0.1	3.05	2.13	2.22	13.80	200	nm	nr	6,768	insur	Widely held	29
1.0	3.13	2.35	3.36	15.60	165	11.38	217	16,116	trans	Widely held	30
0.2	na	na	na	14.39	185	12.63	187	7,000	insur	Great-West Lifeco Inc. 100%	31
0.8	3.34	3.40	4.52	29.17	45	26.11	26	2,767	oilprd	Ontario Teachers' Pension Plan 20%	32

Reprinted by permission from "Report on Business," *The Globe and Mail*, 2004.

2.15 The data displayed below represent the cost of electricity during July 2004 for a random sample of 50 one-bedroom apartments in a large city. UTILITY

Raw Data on Utility Charges ($)

96	171	202	178	147	102	153	197	127	82
157	185	90	116	172	111	148	213	130	165
141	149	206	175	123	128	144	168	109	167
95	163	150	154	130	143	187	166	139	149
108	119	183	151	114	135	191	137	129	158

Form a frequency distribution where the class width is $25.

2.16 A manufacturing company produces steel housings for electrical equipment. The main component part of the housing is a steel trough that is made out of a 14-gauge steel coil. It is produced using a 250-ton progressive punch press with a wipe-down operation putting two 90-degree forms in the flat steel to make the trough. The distance from one side of the form to the other is critical because of weatherproofing in outdoor applications. The company requires that the width of the trough be between 8.31 inches and 8.61 inches. The following are the widths of the troughs in inches for a sample of $n = 49$.

8.312	8.343	8.317	8.383	8.348	8.410	8.351	8.373
8.481	8.422	8.476	8.382	8.484	8.403	8.414	8.419
8.385	8.465	8.498	8.447	8.436	8.413	8.489	8.414
8.481	8.415	8.479	8.429	8.458	8.462	8.460	8.444
8.429	8.460	8.412	8.420	8.410	8.405	8.323	8.420
8.396	8.447	8.405	8.439	8.411	8.427	8.420	8.498
8.409

Make a frequency distribution of this data.

2.17 The manufacturing company in problem 2.13 also produces electric insulators. If the insulators break when in use, a short circuit is likely to occur. To test the strength of the insulators, destructive testing in high-powered labs is carried out to determine how much *force* is required to break the insulators. Force is measured by observing how many pounds must be applied to the insulator before it breaks. The strength of 30 insulators tested are as follows. FORCE

1,870	1,728	1,656	1,610	1,634	1,784	1,522	1,696
1,592	1,662	1,866	1,764	1,734	1,662	1,734	1,774
1,550	1,756	1,762	1,866	1,820	1,744	1,788	1,688
1,810	1,752	1,680	1,810	1,652	1,736		

Construct a frequency distribution of this data.

FREQUENCY DISTRIBUTION EXERCISES

2.18 Refer to Table 2.15 that shows data regarding the first 21 companies taken from the Financial Post Magazine website *(http://www.financialpost.com/magazine/fp500/list.html)*.

For the 21 companies listed in Table 2.15, construct frequency distributions for the following data:
a. Revenue amount 2007
b. Profit amount 2007
c. Revenue Change
d. Profit Change

2.19 Refer to Table 2.16: 'Telecommunications Industry Annual ranking of America's largest corporations by Revenues, Profits' data that appeared in the April 30, 2007 issue of Fortune 500 magazine available online.

Using the data listed in Table 2.16, construct frequency distributions for the following data:
a. Revenues ($ million).
b. Profits ($ million).
c. Profits % change from 2005
d. Revenues % change from 2005
e. 1000 revenues rank

2.20 Refer to Table 2.17 that shows the stock summary data for companies with name starting with letter A traded on the Nasdaq on 8 May, 2008. The data was taken from the Financial Post Magazine's website—*http://www.financial post.com/markets/market-data/market-nasdaq.html?tmp= nasdaq*

Using the data listed in Table 2.17, construct frequency distributions for the following data:
a. Volume
b. High/Ask Price
c. Low/Bid Price
d. Close/Previous Price
e. Net Change
f. 52 week High Price
g. 52 week Low Price

TABLE 2.15

FP 500 Ranking of Canada's Companies

FINANCIAL POST
BUSINESS   FP500

Home FP500 Rankings Crown Corps Profit Leaders Largest Subsidiaries Buy the database

Last year's FP500 rankings

Canada's Top Companies 2008

Search

First · Previous | 1 - 50 ▾ | Next · Last

		Ranking		Revenue		Profit		
2007	**2006**	**Company**		**Amt. 2007 (x1000)**	**Change**	**Amt. 2007 (x1000)**	**Change**	**Rank**
1	1	Royal Bank of Canada, Toronto (Oc07)	⮞	$41,307,000	14.6%	$5,492,000	16.2%	2
2	2	Manulife Financial Corp., Toronto	⮞	$35,533,000	3.9%	$4,229,000	6.5%	6
▲ 3	4	George Weston Ltd., Toronto	⮞	$32,815,000	2.0%	$563,000	365.3%	61
▼ 4	3	General Motors of Canada Ltd., Oshawa, Ont.	⮞	$31,675,000	-5.0%	-	-	-
5	5	Power Corp. of Canada, Montreal	⮞	$29,408,000	-3.0%	$1,963,000	5.0%	28
6	6	Magna International Inc.*, Aurora, Ont.	⮞	$27,995,958	2.1%	$712,062	18.9%	52
7	7	Alcan Inc.*, Montreal (De06)	⮞	$26,808,894	8.9%	$2,029,860	1199.4%	22
▲ 8	10	The Bank of Nova Scotia, Halifax (Oc07)	⮞	$26,427,000	17.5%	$4,045,000	13.0%	8
▲ 9	11	The Toronto-Dominion Bank, Toronto (Oc07)	⮞	$25,209,000	13.0%	$3,997,000	-13.2%	9
▼ 10	8	Imperial Oil Ltd., Calgary	⮞	$25,069,000	2.3%	$3,188,000	4.7%	12
▲ 11	15	Onex Corp., Toronto	⮞	$23,433,000	25.8%	$228,000	-77.2%	119
▲ 12	13	Canadian Imperial Bank of Commerce, Toronto (Oc07)	⮞	$23,289,000	15.5%	$3,296,000	24.6%	10
▲ 13	16	EnCana Corp.*, Calgary	⮞	$23,033,004	23.9%	$4,251,966	-33.7%	5
14	14	Petro-Canada, Calgary	⮞	$21,710,000	14.8%	$2,733,000	57.1%	15
▼ 15	9	Sun Life Financial Inc., Toronto	⮞	$21,188,000	-12.8%	$2,290,000	6.8%	17
▼ 16	12	Chrysler Canada Inc., Windsor, Ont. (De06)	⮞	$20,534,000	-1.4%	-	-	-
17	17	Bank of Montreal, Montreal (Oc07)	⮞	$20,344,000	12.1%	$2,131,000	-20.0%	20
▲ 18	19	Bombardier Inc.*, Montreal (Ja08)	⮞	$18,538,854	10.1%	$335,703	10.3%	98
▼ 19	18	BCE Inc., Montreal	⮞	$17,866,000	0.9%	$4,057,000	102.1%	7
▲ 20	21	Suncor Energy Inc., Calgary	⮞	$17,212,000	20.0%	$2,832,000	-4.7%	14
▲ 21	27	Husky Energy Inc., Calgary	⮞	$15,518,000	22.5%	$3,214,000	17.9%	11

Source: http://www.financialpost.com/magazine/fp500/list.html

TABLE 2.16   FORTUNE 500: Telecommunications Industry Annual ranking of America's largest corporations by Revenues, Profits

			REVENUES		PROFITS	
Rank	Company	1,000 revenues rank	$ millions	% change from 2005	$ millions	% change from 2005
1	Verizon Communications	13	93,221	24	2,197	−16
2	AT&T	27	63,055	44	2,356	54
3	Sprint Nextel	53	43,531	26	1,329	−26
4	Comcast	84	25,700	15	1,533	173
5	DIRECTV Group	160	14,756	12	1,420	323
6	Qwest Communications	178	13,923	0	593	N.A.
7	Echostar Communications	252	9,818	17	608	−60
8	Alltel	256	9,723	2	1,129	−15
9	Liberty Global	340	6,813	29	706	N.A.
10	Virgin Media	347	6,637	83	−984	−228
11	Cablevision Systems	380	6,007	15	−126	−234
12	Charter Communications	409	5,613	7	−1,670	N.A.

From the April 30th, 2007 issue
Source: http://money.cnn.com/magazines/fortune/fortune500/

TABLE 2.17

Stock summary data for companies with name starting with letter A traded on the Nasdaq.

Stock Description			Daily Trading					52 Week	
Company	Security	Ticker	Volume	High/Ask	Low/Bid	Close/Previous	Net Change	High	Low
A-Power Energy Generation	com	APWR	223,539	10.88	10.09	10.75	+0.73	31.80	3.00
AAON Inc	com	AAON	41,035	21.05	20.62	21.00	+0.50	23.00	12.79
ABIOMED Inc	com	ABMD	93,186	6.98	6.58	6.98	+0.33	20.06	4.67
AC Moore Arts & Crafts	com	ACMR	15,187	3.39	3.26	3.36	−0.01	8.78	0.71
ACADIA Phrmctcls Inc	com	ACAD	84,387	1.94	1.75	1.81	+0.07	8.84	0.73
ACI Worldwide Inc	com	ACIW	194,814	14.33	13.96	14.13	+0.09	22.49	8.86
ADA-ES Inc	com	ADES	900	3.95	3.80	3.86	+0.01	11.98	2.41
ADAM Inc	com	ADAM	3,198	3.33	3.14	3.31	+0.08	7.80	1.96
ADC Telecommuns Inc	com	ADCT	997,080	7.54	7.09	7.43	−0.11	17.45	2.48
ADTRAN Inc	com	ADTN	264,258	20.37	19.56	19.94	+0.19	26.50	12.14
AEP Industries Inc	com	AEPI	15,482	24.63	21.68	23.00	+1.54	28.58	10.43
AEterna Zentaris Inc	com	AEZS	40,060	1.33	1.24	1.32	+0.06	1.48	0.261
AFC Enterprises Inc	com	AFCE	45,533	6.06	5.33	5.62	−0.17	10.14	2.85
AMAG Pharmaceuticals Inc	com	AMAG	155,664	54.65	52.73	54.54	+1.86	55.00	18.33
AMCORE Financial Inc	com	AMFI	12,981	1.40	1.30	1.38	+0.12	14.50	0.59
AMERCO	com	UHAL	14,552	33.45	31.64	33.20	+1.30	59.85	22.01
AMERISAFE Inc	com	AMSF	83,309	17.81	16.85	17.78	+1.00	21.96	12.51
AMICAS Inc	com	AMCS	2,099	2.59	2.44	2.48	+0.01	2.96	1.27
ANADIGICS Inc	com	ANAD	176,563	3.04	2.86	3.04	+0.13	13.94	1.13
ANSYS Inc	com	ANSS	296,247	27.11	26.20	26.65	−0.06	49.81	18.00

Source: http://www.financialpost.com/markets/market-data/commodity-cash_prices.html?tmp=cash_prices

The Relative Frequency Distribution and the Percentage Distribution

Because you usually want to know the proportion or the percentage of the total that is in each group, the relative frequency distribution or the percentage distribution is preferred to the frequency distribution.

The **proportion** in each group is equal to the number of frequencies in each class divided by the total number of values. The **relative frequency** is another word for the proportion. You then compute the percentage in each group by multiplying the proportion by 100%.

COMPUTING THE PROPORTION OR RELATIVE FREQUENCY

The proportion or relative frequency is the number of frequencies in each class divided by the total number of values.

$$\text{Proportion} = \text{Relative Frequency} = \frac{\text{frequency in each class}}{\text{total number of values}} \qquad \textbf{(2.2)}$$

Thus, if there are 80 values and the frequency in a certain class is 20, the proportion of values in that class is

$$\frac{20}{80} = 0.25$$

and the percentage is

$$0.25 \times 100\% = 25\%$$

When you are comparing two or more groups that have different sample sizes, you must use either a relative frequency distribution or a percentage distribution. You form the **relative frequency distribution** by first determining the frequency (the number of values) in each class and then dividing by the total number of values. See Equation (2.2). For example, there are 50 urban restaurants and the cost per meal at 3 of these restaurants is between $25 and $30. Therefore, the proportion (or relative frequency) of meals that cost between $25 and $30 at urban restaurants is

$$\frac{3}{50} = 0.06$$

You form the **percentage distribution** by multiplying each proportion (or relative frequency) by 100%. Thus, the proportion of meals at urban restaurants that cost between $50 and $55 is 7 divided by 50, or 0.14, and the percentage is 14%. Table 2.18 presents the relative frequency distribution and percentage distribution of the cost of meals at urban and suburban restaurants.

TABLE 2.18

Relative Frequency Distributions and Percentage Distributions of the Cost of Meals at Urban and Suburban Restaurants

	Urban		Suburban	
Cost per Meal ($)	**Relative Frequency**	**Percentage**	**Relative Frequency**	**Percentage**
15 and under 20	0.02	2.0	0.00	0.0
20 and under 25	0.04	4.0	0.06	6.0
25 and under 30	0.06	6.0	0.14	14.0
30 and under 35	0.10	10.0	0.12	12.0
35 and under 40	0.16	16.0	0.18	18.0
40 and under 45	0.12	12.0	0.26	26.0
45 and under 50	0.18	18.0	0.08	8.0
50 and under 55	0.14	14.0	0.08	8.0
55 and under 60	0.06	6.0	0.02	2.0
60 and under 65	0.02	2.0	0.04	4.0
65 and under 70	0.06	6.0	0.02	2.0
70 and under 75	0.04	4.0	0.00	0.0
Total	1.00	100.0	1.00	100.0

From Table 2.18, you conclude that meals cost more at urban restaurants than at suburban restaurants. Also 18% of the meals cost between $45 and $50 at urban restaurants as compared to 8% of the meals at suburban restaurants; and only 6% of the meals cost between $25 and $30 at urban restaurants as compared to 14% of the meals at suburban restaurants.

EXAMPLE 2.15

Relative Frequency Distributions and Percentage Distributions of the 2006 Return for Growth and Value Mutual Funds

In the Using Statistics scenario, you are interested in comparing the 2006 return for growth and value mutual funds. Construct relative frequency distributions and percentage distributions for the growth funds and the value funds.

SOLUTION You conclude (see Table 2.19) that the 2006 return for the growth funds is much lower than for the value funds. For example, 5.82% of growth funds have negative returns, while none of the value funds have negative returns. Of the growth funds, 16.16% have returns between 0 and 5 as compared to only 0.25% of the value funds. Also, more of the value funds have higher returns. For example, 51.49% of the value funds have a return between 15 and 20, whereas only 8.41% of the growth funds have a return between 15 and 20.

TABLE 2.19

Relative Frequency Distributions and Percentage Distributions of the 2006 Return for Growth and Value Mutual Funds

2006 Return	Growth		Value	
	Proportion	Percentage	Proportion	Percentage
−10 and under −5	0.0129	1.29	0.0000	0.00
−5 and under 0	0.0453	4.53	0.0000	0.00
0 and under 5	0.1616	16.16	0.0025	0.25
5 and under 10	0.4073	40.73	0.0347	3.47
10 and under 15	0.2608	26.08	0.2525	25.25
15 and under 20	0.0841	8.41	0.5149	51.49
20 and under 25	0.0259	2.59	0.1757	17.57
25 and under 30	0.0022	0.22	0.0173	1.73
30 and under 35	0.0000	0.00	0.0000	0.00
35 and under 40	0.0000	0.00	0.0025	0.25
Total*	1.0001	100.01	1.0001	100.01

*Error due to rounding

Relative Frequency or Percentage Distributions

Consider the following frequency distributions of manufacturing personnel salaries at ABC Inc. and XYZ Inc.

TABLE 2.20

Salary ($000's)	ABC Inc. # Employees	XYZ Inc. # Employees
20 and under 25	24	10
25 " " 30	41	23
30 " " 35	44	31
35 " " 40	29	14
40 " " 45	15	8
45 " " 50	7	2

Notice that there is a large difference in the number of manufacturing employees in the two companies, therefore it is difficult to *compare* the salary distributions by looking at the frequencies.

If we were to set up a **relative frequency** or **percentage** distribution for the two sets of salaries, it would be much easier to make comparisons.

TABLE 2.21

Salary ($000')	ABC Inc.			XYZ Inc.		
	f	rf	%	f	rf	%
20 and under 25	24	0.150	15.0	10	0.114	11.4
25 " " 30	41	0.256	25.6	23	0.261	26.1
30 " " 35	44	0.275	27.5	31	0.352	35.2
35 " " 40	29	0.181	18.1	14	0.159	15.9
40 " " 45	15	0.094	9.4	8	0.091	9.1
45 " " 50	7	0.044	4.4	2	0.023	2.3
Total	160	1.000	100.0	88	1.000	100.0

Relative Frequency: $rf = f/n$ where: f = frequency
n = sample size

Note: We will use a maximum of 3 decimals for rf and thus 1 decimal for %.

FIGURE 2.7
Percentage Histograms

The Cumulative Distribution

The **cumulative percentage distribution** provides a way of presenting information about the percentage of items that are less than a certain value. For example, you might want to know what percentage of the urban restaurant meals cost less than $20, less than $30, less than $50, and so on. The percentage distribution is used to form the cumulative percentage distribution. Table 2.22 illustrates how to develop the cumulative percentage distribution for the cost of meals at urban restaurants. This table shows that 0.00% of the meals cost less than $15, 2% cost less than $20, 6% cost less than $25 (because 4% of the meals cost between $20 and $25), and so on, until all 100% of the meals cost less than $75.

FIGURE 2.8
Percentage Polygons

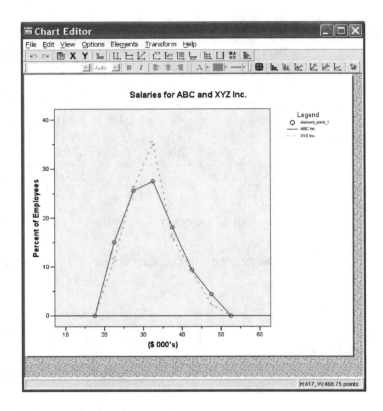

TABLE 2.22

Developing the Cumulative Percentage Distribution for the Cost of Meals at Urban Restaurants

Cost per Meal ($)	Percentage	Percentage of Meals Less Than Lower Boundary of Class Interval
15 and under 20	2	0
20 and under 25	4	2
25 and under 30	6	6 = 2 + 4
30 and under 35	10	12 = 2 + 4 + 6
35 and under 40	16	22 = 2 + 4 + 6 + 10
40 and under 45	12	38 = 2 + 4 + 6 + 10 + 16
45 and under 50	18	50 = 2 + 4 + 6 + 10 + 16 + 12
50 and under 55	14	68 = 2 + 4 + 6 + 10 + 16 + 12 + 18
55 and under 60	6	82 = 2 + 4 + 6 + 10 + 16 + 12 + 18 + 14
60 and under 65	2	88 = 2 + 4 + 6 + 10 + 16 + 12 + 18 + 14 + 6
65 and under 70	6	90 = 2 + 4 + 6 + 10 + 16 + 12 + 18 + 14 + 6 + 2
70 and under 75	4	96 = 2 + 4 + 6 + 10 + 16 + 12 + 18 + 14 + 6 + 2 + 6
75 and under 80	0	100 = 2 + 4 + 6 + 10 + 16 + 12 + 18 + 14 + 6 + 2 + 6 + 4

Table 2.23 summarizes the cumulative percentages of the cost of urban and suburban restaurant meals. The cumulative distribution clearly shows that the cost of meals is lower in suburban restaurants than in urban restaurants. Table 2.26 shows that 20% of the meals at suburban restaurants cost less than $30 as compared to only 12% of the meals at urban restaurants; 32% of the meals at suburban restaurants cost less than $35 as compared to only 22% of the meals at urban restaurants; and 76% of the meals at suburban restaurants cost less than $45 as compared to only 50% of the meals at urban restaurants.

TABLE 2.23
Cumulative Percentage Distributions of the Cost of Urban and Suburban Restaurant Meals

Cost ($)	Urban Percentage of Restaurants with Meals Less Than Indicated Value	Suburban Percentage of Restaurants with Meals Less Than Indicated Value
15	0	0
20	2	0
25	6	6
30	12	20
35	22	32
40	38	50
45	50	76
50	68	84
55	82	92
60	88	94
65	90	98
70	96	100
75	100	100

EXAMPLE 2.16

Cumulative Percentage Distributions of the 2006 Return for Growth and Value Mutual Funds

In the Using Statistics scenario, you are interested in comparing the 2006 return of growth and value mutual funds. Construct cumulative percentage distributions for the growth funds and the value funds.

SOLUTION The cumulative distribution in Table 2.24 indicates that more of the growth funds have lower returns than the value funds. The table shows that 5.82% of the growth funds have negative returns as compared to none of the value funds; 21.98% of the growth funds have returns below 5 as compared to 0.25% of the value funds; and 62.71% of the growth funds have returns below 10 as compared to 3.72% of the value funds.

TABLE 2.24

Cumulative Percentage Distributions of the 2006 Return for Growth and Value Funds

2006 Return	Growth Fund Percentage Less Than Indicated Value	Value Fund Percentage Less Than Indicated Value
−10	0.00	0.00
−5	1.29	0.00
0	5.82	0.00
5	21.98	0.25
10	62.71	3.72
15	88.79	28.97
20	97.20	80.46
25	99.79	98.03
30	100.00	99.76
35	100.00	99.76
40	100.01*	100.01*

Error due to rounding.

Graphing Frequency Distributions

Histogram: A histogram is a graph of 'touching rectangles'. The horizontal axis represents the class boundaries. No other values are shown on this axis. The vertical axis shows the class frequencies.
(The above rules only apply to histograms where the classes are all of equal width. We are not concerned in this course with how to draw other types of histograms.)

FIGURE 2.9

Frequency HISTOGRAM
– Power Supply Voltages
(using SPSS version 13)

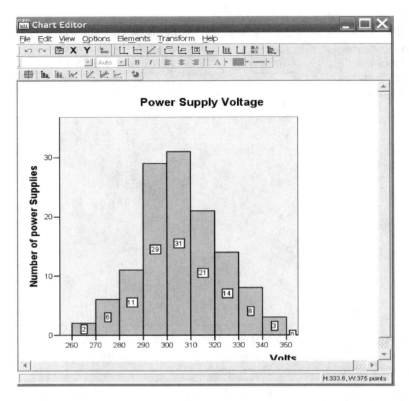

Polygon: A polygon is a graph in the shape of a many-sided closed figure. (Some texts show a smooth curve, but this is technically not a polygon.) The horizontal axis shows the class **midpoints**. No other values are shown on this axis. The vertical axis shows the class frequencies. In order to *close* the polygon, an extra class midpoint on the left and right side is used.

The class midpoints may be calculated as follows:

$$m = \frac{lower\ boundary\ +\ upper\ boundary}{2}$$

(The above rules only apply to polygons where the classes are all of equal width. We are not concerned with how to draw other types of polygons.)

FIGURE 2.10

Frequency POLYGON –
Power Supply Voltages
(using SPSS version 13)

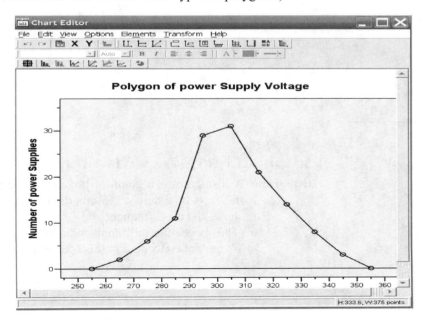

Note: Both graphs, the histogram and the polygon, show that the data has roughly a bell-curve shape.

The Polygon

Constructing multiple histograms on the same graph when comparing two or more sets of data is confusing. Superimposing the vertical bars of one histogram on another histogram makes interpretation difficult. When there are two or more groups, you should use a percentage polygon.

> **PERCENTAGE POLYGON**
>
> A **percentage polygon** is formed by having the midpoint of each class represent the data in that class and then connecting the sequence of midpoints at their respective class percentages.

Figure 2.11 displays percentage polygons for the cost of meals at urban and suburban restaurants. The polygon for the cost of meals at suburban restaurants is concentrated to the left of (corresponding to lower cost) the polygon for the cost of meals at urban restaurants. The highest percentage of meals at the suburban restaurants are for a class midpoint of $42.50, whereas the highest percentage of meals at the urban restaurants are for a class midpoint of $47.50.

FIGURE 2.11

Microsoft Excel percentage polygons of the cost of restaurant meals for urban and suburban restaurants

See Section P2.7 to create this.

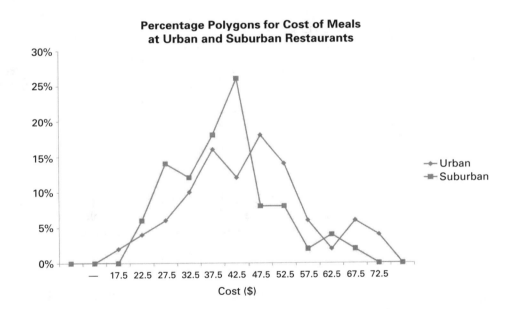

The polygons in Figure 2.11 have points whose values on the X axis represent the midpoint of the class interval. For example, look at the points plotted at $X = 42.5$ ($42.50). The point for the cost of meals at suburban restaurants (the higher one) represents the fact that 26% of the meals at these restaurants cost between $40 and $45. The point for the cost of meals at urban restaurants (the lower one) represents the fact that 12% of meals at these restaurants cost between $40 and $45.

When you construct polygons or histograms, the vertical (Y) axis should show the true zero, or "origin," so as not to distort the character of the data. The horizontal (X) axis does not need to show the zero point for the variable of interest, although the range of the variable should include the major portion of the axis.

EXAMPLE 2.17

Percentage Polygons of the 2006 Return for Growth and Value Mutual Funds

In the Using Statistics scenario, you are interested in comparing the 2006 return of growth and value mutual funds. Construct percentage polygons for the 2006 return for growth funds and value funds.

SOLUTION Figure 2.12 shows that the distribution of the 2006 return of growth funds is lower than the value funds, which has more high returns. The highest percentage of 2006 returns for the growth funds is at 7.5, whereas the highest percentage of 2006 returns for the value funds is at 17.5.

FIGURE 2.12

Microsoft Excel percentage polygons of the 2006 return

See Section P2.7 to create this.

PIE CHART

Occasionally a pie chart is necessary to graph a frequency distribution. The situations that would make it difficult, if not impossible, to draw either a histogram or polygon would include the existence of: 1) open-ended classes or 2) classes of unequal width.

Consider the following example:

The grades of students in a QMS102 class have been summarized in the following table.

TABLE 2.25

Grades	# students	%
Less than 50	5	10
50 and under 60	12	24
60 " " 70	17	34
70 " " 80	10	20
80 " " 100	6	12

The following pie chart was produced using SPSS.

FIGURE 2.13

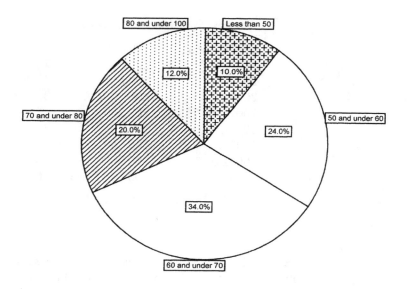

Pie Chart of Grades

Cumulative Distributions and OGIVES

EXAMPLE 2.18   A soft-drink bottling machine is periodically tested to determine if it is functioning within certain limits. The frequency distribution below is a summary of the measurements for 255 bottles, where the data shows how much soft-drink was in each bottle.

TABLE 2.26

Amount in a 2 litre bottle(ml)	# of bottles
1999.00 and under 1999.50	5
1999.50 " " 2000.00	10
2000.00 " " 2000.50	20
2000.50 " " 2001.00	35
2001.00 " " 2001.50	55
2001.50 " " 2002.00	50
2002.00 " " 2002.50	40
2002.50 " " 2003.00	30
2003.00 " " 2003.50	10
Total	255

Suppose this frequency distribution is the only data we have available and we would like to know the answers to the following questions.

a. What percent of the bottles had less than 2000.00 ml?
b. What percent of the bottles had less than 2002.70 ml?
c. What percent of the bottles had more than 2001.25 ml?
d. Thirty percent of the bottles have at most _____ ml.
e. 25% of the bottles have at least _____ ml.

To answer these questions, we must plot an **OGIVE**. But first we will have to determine the *cumulative relative 'less-than' frequency* (crf) for each class as follows:

$$crf = rf \text{ of the class} + rf \text{ of all previous classes}$$

TABLE 2.27

Amount in a 2 litre bottle(ml)	f	rf	crf	c%
1999.00 and under 1999.50	5	0.020	0.020	2.0
1999.50 " " 2000.00	10	0.039	0.059	5.9
2000.00 " " 2000.50	20	0.078	0.137	13.7
2000.50 " " 2001.00	35	0.137	0.274	27.4
2001.00 " " 2001.50	55	0.216	0.490	49.0
2001.50 " " 2002.00	50	0.196	0.686	68.6
2002.00 " " 2002.50	40	0.157	0.843	84.3
2002.50 " " 2003.00	30	0.118	0.961	96.1
2003.00 " " 2003.50	10	0.039	1.000	100.0
Total	255	1.000		

The crf values in the above table are called 'less-than' because they show the fraction of the data that is less than the upper boundary of the class. For example, the crf of the '2001.00 and under 2001.50' class shows that 0.490 (or 49%) of the bottles had less than 2001.50 ml.

Now to plot the OGIVE we use:

Horizontal axis: Standard graph axis
Vertical axis: crf or c%

Plot the crf for each class at the *upper* boundary.

Join the points with straight lines. (Start the graph at the 1st boundary)

For our example, we get the OGIVE shown below:

FIGURE 2.14

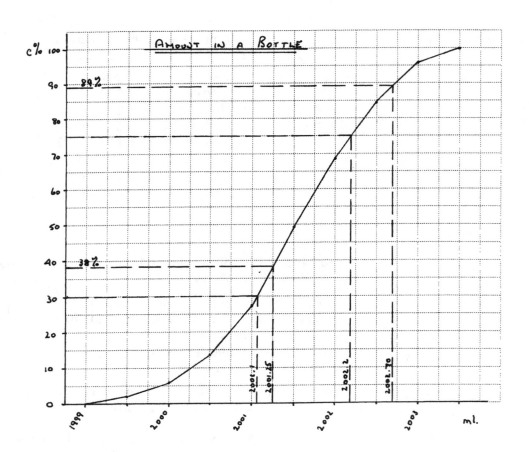

The answers to the questions posed at the beginning of this discussion are:

a. 5.9% (from c%)
b. 89%
c. 62%
d. 2001.1 ml
e. 2002.2 ml

The rules given on the previous page for constructing an Ogive apply to *any* cumulative relative frequency distribution, i.e. even those where there are classes of *unequal width* or *open-ended* classes.

EXAMPLE 2.19   A survey of employees in a large company revealed the following results regarding the amount of time employees had been in their current job position. The results were summarized as follows:

TABLE 2.28

Time in Current Position (years)	Percent
less than 1	15.0
1 and under 3	27.4
3 " " 6	22.2
6 " " 10	13.9
10 " " 20	15.5
20 and over	6.0
Total	100

Based on these results:

a. Approximately what percent of quality professionals had been in the current position for 5 years or more?
b. Seventy percent of quality professionals had been in their current position for less than _____ years.

The calculations necessary to construct a Percentage Ogive from the above data are shown below.

TABLE 2.29

Time in current position (years)	Percent	Cumulative Percent
less than 1	15.0	15.0
1 and under 3	27.4	42.4
3 " " 6	22.2	64.6
6 " " 10	13.9	78.5
10 " " 20	15.5	94.0
20 and over	6.0	100.0
Total	100	

The Ogive is plotted on the following page.

FIGURE 2.15

The answers to the questions are:

a. 43%
b. 7.5 years

The Cumulative Percentage Polygon (Ogive)

The **cumulative percentage polygon**, or **ogive**, displays the variable of interest along the X axis and the cumulative percentages along the Y axis.

Figure 2.16 illustrates the Microsoft Excel cumulative percentage polygons of the cost of meals at urban and suburban restaurants. Most of the curve of the cost of meals at the urban restaurants is located to the right of the curve for the suburban restaurants. This indicates that the urban restaurants have fewer meals that cost below a particular value. For example, 38% of the meals at urban restaurants cost less than $40 as compared to 50% of the meals at suburban restaurants.

FIGURE 2.16

Microsoft Excel cumulative percentage polygons of the cost of restaurant meals at urban and suburban restaurants

See Section P2.7 to create this.

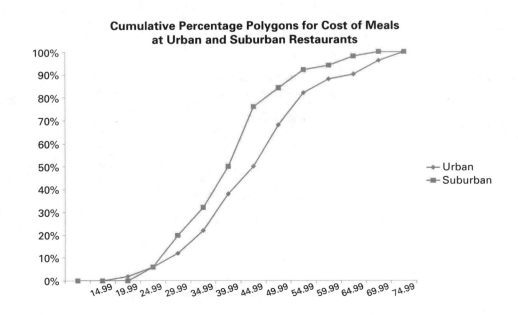

EXAMPLE 2.20

Cumulative Percentage Polygons of the 2006 Return for Growth and Value Mutual Funds

In the Using Statistics scenario, you are interested in comparing the 2006 return of growth and value mutual funds. Construct cumulative percentage polygons of the 2006 return for the growth funds and the value funds.

SOLUTION Figure 2.17 illustrates the Microsoft Excel cumulative percentage polygons of the 2006 return for growth and value funds. The curve for the 2006 return of value funds is located to the right of the curve for the growth funds. This indicates that the value funds have fewer 2006 returns below a particular value. For example, 88.79% of the growth funds have 2006 returns less than 15 as compared to 28.97% of the value funds. You can conclude that, in general, the value funds outperformed the growth funds in 2006.

FIGURE 2.17

Microsoft Excel cumulative percentage polygons of the 2006 return of growth funds and value funds

See Section P2.7 to create this.

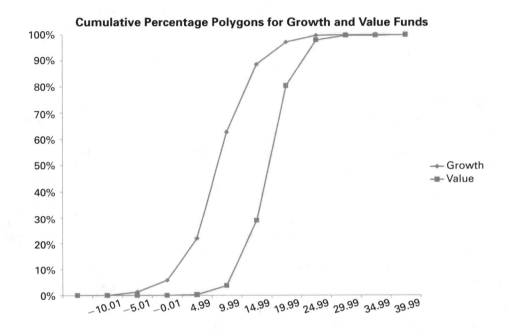

Cumulative Percentage Polygons for Growth and Value Funds

Problems for Section 2.3

OGIVES

2.21 The National Association of Real Estate Agents has collected the following data on a sample of 170 salespersons. The classes represent their total annual commission.

Total Annual Commission	# people	rf	crf
$ 0 and under $ 5,000	5		
5,000 " " 10,000	9		
10,000 " " 15,000	11		
15,000 " " 20,000	48		
20,000 " " 30,000	62		
30,000 " " 40,000	19		
40,000 " " 50,000	9		
50,000 and over	7		
Total	170		

Construct an ogive that will help you answer the following questions:

a. Approximately what percentage of the salespeople earn more than $27,000?

b. Approximately how much is earned by the 'middle' salesperson?

c. Approximately how much would a salesperson have to earn to be in the top 25% ?

2.22 A Pharmaceutical company sells 78 different products. The distribution of the annual sales amounts last year for these products is shown below:

Annual Sales ($ 000)	Number of Products
0 and under 10	17
10 " " 50	20
50 " " 100	24
100 " " 150	13
150 " " 250	4
Total	78

Construct an ogive and use it to determine:

a. How many products had annual sales of less than $80,000 last year?

b. What percentage of the products had sales of $120,000 or more last year?

2.23 The distribution of a company's stock according to the number of shares held is shown below:

Number of Shares Held	% of Shareholders
0 and under 50	25
50 " " 100	19
100 " " 500	41
500 " " 1000	12
1000 " " 2000	3
Total	100

Construct an ogive and use it to determine:

a. What percentage of shareholders held 200 or more shares?

b. The 20 percent of shareholders with the most shares each held how many shares or more?

LEARNING THE BASICS

2.24 The values for a set of data vary from 11.6 to 97.8.

a. If these values are grouped into nine classes, indicate the class boundaries.

b. What class-interval width did you choose?

c. What are the nine class midpoints?

2.25 The GMAT scores from a sample of 50 applicants to an MBA program indicate that none of the applicants scored below 450. A frequency distribution was formed by choosing class intervals 450 to 499, 500 to 549, and so on, with the last class having an interval from 700 to 749. Two applicants scored in the interval 450 to 499, and 16 applicants scored in the interval 500 to 549.

a. What percentage of applicants scored below 500?

b. What percentage of applicants scored between 500 and 549?

c. What percentage of applicants scored below 550?

d. What percentage of applicants scored below 750?

APPLYING THE CONCEPTS

2.26 The following data (contained in the file Utility) represent the cost of electricity during July 2008 for a random sample of 50 one-bedroom apartments in a large city:

Raw Data on Utility Charges ($)									
96	171	202	178	147	102	153	197	127	82
157	185	90	116	172	111	148	213	130	165
141	149	206	175	123	128	144	168	109	167
95	163	150	154	130	143	187	166	139	149
108	119	183	151	114	135	191	137	129	158

a. Form a frequency distribution and a percentage distribution that have class intervals with the upper class boundaries $99, $119, and so on.

b. Construct a histogram and a percentage polygon.

c. Form a cumulative percentage distribution and plot a cumulative percentage polygon.

d. Around what amount does the monthly electricity cost seem to be concentrated?

2.27 As player salaries have increased, the cost of attending baseball games has increased dramatically. The data in the file BBCost represent the cost of four tickets, two beers, four soft drinks, four hot dogs, two game programs, two baseball caps, and the parking fee for one car for each of the 30 major league teams 2007. The following is a histogram created for these data.

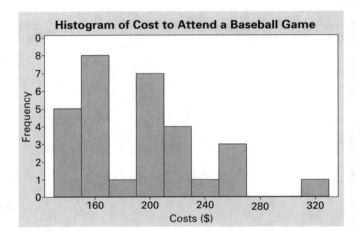

What conclusions can you reach concerning the cost of attending a baseball game at different ballparks?

2.28 The data in the file PropertyTaxes contains the property taxes per capita for the fifty states and the District of Columbia. The following is a histogram and cumulative percentage polygon created for these data.

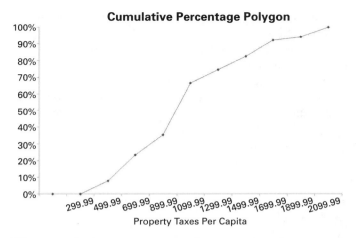

Cumulative Percentage Polygon

(y-axis: 0% to 100% in 10% increments; x-axis: Property Taxes Per Capita: 299.99, 499.99, 699.99, 899.99, 1099.99, 1299.99, 1499.99, 1699.99, 1899.99, 2099.99)

What conclusions can you reach concerning the property taxes per capita?

2.29 One operation of a mill is to cut pieces of steel into parts that will later be used as the frame for front seats in an automobile. The steel is cut with a diamond saw and requires the resulting parts to be within ±0.005 inch of the length specified by the automobile company. The data in the file **Steel** comes from a sample of 100 steel parts. The measurement reported is the difference in inches between the actual length of the steel part, as measured by a laser measurement device, and the specified length of the steel part. For example, the first value, −0.002, represents a steel part that is 0.002 inch shorter than the specified length.

a. Construct a percentage histogram.
b. Is the steel mill doing a good job in meeting the requirements set by the automobile company? Explain.

✓SELF Test **2.30** A manufacturing company produces steel housings for electrical equipment. The main component part of the housing is a steel trough that is made out of a 14-gauge steel coil. It is produced using a 250-ton progressive punch press with a wipe-down operation that puts two 90-degree forms in the flat steel to make the trough. The distance from one side of the form to the other is critical because of weatherproofing in outdoor applications. The company requires that the width of the trough be between 8.31 inches and 8.61 inches. The following (contained in the file **Trough**) are the widths of the troughs, in inches, for a sample of 49 troughs.

8.312	8.343	8.317	8.383	8.348	8.410	8.351	8.373
8.481	8.422	8.476	8.382	8.484	8.403	8.414	8.419
8.385	8.465	8.498	8.447	8.436	8.413	8.489	8.414
8.481	8.415	8.479	8.429	8.458	8.462	8.460	8.444
8.429	8.460	8.412	8.420	8.410	8.405	8.323	8.420
8.396	8.447	8.405	8.439	8.411	8.427	8.420	8.498
8.409							

a. Construct a frequency distribution and a percentage distribution.
b. Construct a percentage histogram and a percentage polygon.

c. Plot a cumulative percentage polygon.
d. What can you conclude about the number of troughs that will meet the company's requirements of troughs being between 8.31 and 8.61 inches wide?

2.31 The manufacturing company in Problem 2.30 also produces electric insulators. If the insulators break when in use, a short circuit is likely to occur. To test the strength of the insulators, destructive testing in high-powered labs is carried out to determine how much *force* is required to break the insulators. Force is measured by observing how many pounds must be applied to the insulator before it breaks. The strengths of 30 insulators (contained in the file **Force**) are as follows:

1,870	1,728	1,656	1,610	1,634	1,784	1,522	1,696
1,592	1,662	1,866	1,764	1,734	1,662	1,734	1,774
1,550	1,756	1,762	1,866	1,820	1,744	1,788	1,688
1,810	1,752	1,680	1,810	1,652	1,736		

a. Construct a frequency distribution and a percentage distribution.
b. Construct a percentage histogram and a percentage polygon.
c. Plot a cumulative percentage polygon.
d. What can you conclude about the strength of the insulators if the company requires a force measurement of at least 1,500 pounds before breaking?

2.32 The ordered arrays in the accompanying table (and contained in the file **Bulbs**) show the life (in hours) of a sample of forty 100-watt lightbulbs produced by Manufacturer A and a sample of forty 100-watt lightbulbs produced by Manufacturer B.

Manufacturer A					Manufacturer B				
684	697	720	773	821	819	836	888	897	903
831	835	848	852	852	907	912	918	942	943
859	860	868	870	876	952	959	962	986	992
893	899	905	909	911	994	1,004	1,005	1,007	1,015
922	924	926	926	938	1,016	1,018	1,020	1,022	1,034
939	943	946	954	971	1,038	1,072	1,077	1,077	1,082
972	977	984	1,005	1,014	1,096	1,100	1,113	1,113	1,116
1,016	1,041	1,052	1,080	1,093	1,153	1,154	1,174	1,188	1,230

a. Form a frequency distribution and a percentage distribution for each manufacturer, using the following class-interval widths for each distribution:
  1. Manufacturer A: 650 but less than 750, 750 but less than 850, and so on.
  2. Manufacturer B: 750 but less than 850, 850 but less than 950, and so on.
b. Construct percentage histograms on separate graphs and plot the percentage polygons on one graph.
c. Form cumulative percentage distributions and plot cumulative percentage polygons on one graph.
d. Which manufacturer has bulbs with a longer life— Manufacturer A or Manufacturer B? Explain.

2.33 The following data (contained in the file `Drink`) represent the amount of soft drink in a sample of fifty 2-liter bottles:

2.109 2.086 2.066 2.075 2.065 2.057 2.052 2.044 2.036 2.038
2.031 2.029 2.025 2.029 2.023 2.020 2.015 2.014 2.013 2.014
2.012 2.012 2.012 2.010 2.005 2.003 1.999 1.996 1.997 1.992
1.994 1.986 1.984 1.981 1.973 1.975 1.971 1.969 1.966 1.967
1.963 1.957 1.951 1.951 1.947 1.941 1.941 1.938 1.908 1.894

a. Construct a frequency distribution and a percentage distribution.
b. Construct a histogram and a percentage polygon.
c. Form a cumulative percentage distribution and plot a cumulative percentage polygon.
d. On the basis of the results of (a) through (c), does the amount of soft drink filled in the bottles concentrate around specific values?

Review Problems for Sections 2.2 and 2.3

2.34 The ordered arrays in the accompanying table deal with the life (in hours) of a sample of forty 100-watt lightbulbs produced by manufacturer A and a sample of forty 100-watt lightbulbs produced by manufacturer B. BULBS

Manufacturer A					Manufacturer B				
684	697	720	773	821	819	836	888	897	903
831	835	848	852	852	907	912	918	942	943
859	860	868	870	876	952	959	962	986	992
893	899	905	909	911	994	1,004	1,005	1,007	1,015
922	924	926	926	938	1,016	1,018	1,020	1,022	1,034
939	943	946	954	971	1,038	1,072	1,077	1,077	1,082
972	977	984	1,005	1,014	1,096	1,100	1,113	1,113	1,116
1,016	1,041	1,052	1,080	1,093	1,153	1,154	1,174	1,188	1,230

a. Form a frequency distribution and percentage distributions for each manufacturer using a class width of 100 hours.
b. Plot the percentage histograms on separate graphs and plot the percentage polygons on one graph.
c. Form the cumulative percentage distributions and plot the ogives on one graph.
d. From the Ogives, for each manufacturer, what percentage of the bulbs lasts longer than 950 hours?

2.35 The following data represent the amount of soft drink in a sample of 50 2-liter bottles. DRINK

2.109 2.086 2.066 2.075 2.065 2.057 2.052 2.044
2.036 2.038 2.031 2.029 2.025 2.029 2.023 2.020
2.015 2.014 2.013 2.014 2.012 2.012 2.012 2.010
2.005 2.003 1.999 1.996 1.997 1.992 1.994 1.986
1.984 1.981 1.973 1.975 1.971 1.969 1.966 1.967
1.963 1.957 1.951 1.951 1.947 1.941 1.941 1.938
1.908 1.894

a. Construct the frequency distribution and the percentage distribution.
b. Plot a histogram and a percentage polygon.

c. Form the cumulative percentage distribution and plot the cumulative percentage polygon.
d. From the Ogive, what percent of the bottles have from 1.97 to 2.03 liters?

2.36 Refer to the mutual fund data in Table 2.33 that appeared in the Canadian Mutual Funds table of the June 3, 2004 issue of The Globe and Mail. Construct stem-and-leaf displays for the following data:
a. Equitable Life Valuation data
b. Equitable Life Change data
c. Equitable Life Percent Change data
d. MD Management Change data
e. MD Management Percent Change data

2.37 Refer to the mutual fund data in Table 2.33 that appeared in the Canadian Mutual Funds table of the June 3, 2004 issue of The Globe and Mail. Construct frequency distributions for the following data:
a. Manulife Mix Funds Valuation data
b. Manulife Mix Funds Change data
c. Manulife Mix Funds Percent Change data
d. CI-Clarica Mutual Funds Valuation data
e. Transamerica Growsafe 75/100 Valuation data
f. Transamerica Growsafe 75/100 Percent Change data

2.38 Refer to the mutual fund data on the pages 94–97. Set up the classes that would be appropriate to group the following data: (Do *not* determine the frequency.)
a. Percent return for the year ending May 2008 for funds with an Mstar rating of 2.
b. Percent return for the year ending May 2007 for funds with an Mstar rating of 3.
c. Percent return for the year ending May 2005 for all funds.
d. Expense ratio for funds with an Mstar rating of 4.
e. Expense ratio for funds with an Mstar rating of 2.
f. Total assets in millions of dollars for funds with an Mstar rating of 1.
g. Total assets in millions of dollars for funds with an Mstar rating of 5.

TABLE 2.30

fund	valuation	chg	% chg
EQUITABLE LIFE			
AIM Cdn Premier 06/01	10.01	+.01	+.07
Accum Income 06/01	23.26	-.03	-.15
American Gwth 06/01	10.48	+.04	+.37
Asian-Pacific 06/01	6.38	+.01	+.17
Asset Allocat 06/01	16.72	-.01	-.06
Bissett Div Inc 06/01	10.19	-.01	-.10
Cdn Bond 06/01	15.55	-.02	-.15
Cdn Stock 06/01	20.17	-.01	-.05
CommonStock 06/01	29.96	-.02	-.05
European Equity 06/01	7.23	-.02	-.22
International 06/01	11.49	+.02	+.17
MB Cdn Eq Value 06/01	18.21	-.04	-.24
Mack US Em Grth 06/01	10.15	+.09	+.84
Templeton Grwth 06/01	9.39	+.02	+.17
Tmplton Glo Bnd 06/01	12.32	+.04	+.36
Trimark Europls 06/01	10.51	+.02	+.15
Trimark Glo Bal 06/01	10.48	+.02	+.17
US Equity 06/01	6.30	+.02	+.32

fund	valuation	chg	% chg
MD MANAGEMENT			
MD Balanced	18.08	-.06	-.33
MD Bnd & Mtg	10.39	-.01	-.10
MD Bond	7.10	-.03	-.42
MD Dividend	16.66	-.03	-.18
MD Equity	19.03	-.03	-.16
MD Glo Bond	11.27	-.03	-.27
MD Glo Equ RSP	7.07	unch	unch
MD Growth	10.37	unch	unch
MD Growth RSP	9.82	unch	unch
MD Int'l Growth	6.64	unch	unch
MD Int'l Value	10.13	unch	unch
MD Intl Gr RSP	6.46	unch	unch
MD Select	15.39	-.04	-.26
MD US LgCpGrRSP	6.07	unch	unch
MD US LrCap Val	8.42	unch	unch
MD US LrCpVlRSP	8.25	unch	unch
MD US Lrg Cp Gr	4.79	unch	unch
MD US Sml Cp Gr	3.68	-.01	-.27
MDPIM Cdn Equ-A	11.01	-.04	-.36
MDPIM US Equ-A	7.39	-.02	-.27

fund	valuation	chg	% chg
MANULIFE MIX FUNDS			
AIM Am MidCp Gw	12.26	-.04	-.33
AIM Cd First Cl	12.25	-.05	-.41
Cd Lg Cap Gw Cl	12.85	-.07	-.54
Cd Lg Cap ValCl	12.12	-.02	-.16
Cd Lg Cp CoreCl	12.05	-.02	-.17
Cdn Equ Val Cl	12.65	-.02	-.16
E&P Gw Opp Cl	14.38	-.04	-.28
E&P US MidCapCl	11.81	-.05	-.42
FI Can DiscEqCl	13.07	-.08	-.61
FI Gwth Amer Cl	11.09	-.03	-.27
FI Intl Port Cl	11.60	-.02	-.17
Global Equ Cl	10.86	-.01	-.09
Global Sect Cl	11.31	-.06	-.53
Global SectCl-H	11.31	-.05	-.44
Global Val Cl	12.48	-.01	-.08
Int'l Growth Cl	11.29	-.01	-.09
Int'l Value Cl	12.27	+.01	+.08
Japanese Class	12.63	-.12	-.94
SM Tot Cd Eq Cl	13.26	+.02	+.15
SM Total Glo Cl	12.00	-.04	-.33
SM Total USEqCl	11.33	-.03	-.26
SMTotal Gl Cl-H	12.00	-.04	-.33
Sht Term Yld Cl	10.21	unch	unch
Str Bond Class	10.30	-.03	-.29
Tri Sel Cdn Cl	12.13	-.03	-.25
Trimark Glo Cl	11.41	+.04	+.35
US Lg Cap Gw Cl	10.40	-.01	-.10
US Lg Cp CoreCl	10.77	-.01	-.09
US Lg Cp Val Cl	10.92	-.02	-.18
US MidCp Val Cl	11.51	-.03	-.26

fund	valuation	chg	% chg
CI - CLARICA MUTUAL FUNDS			
Alpine CdnRes	10.35	-.08	-.77
Alpine CdnRes A	10.46	-.07	-.66
Alpine GrthEq	13.09	-.04	-.30
Alpine GrthEq A	13.28	-.05	-.38
Cdn Blu Chip Z	11.35	-.04	-.35
Cdn BlueChip	16.34	-.06	-.37
Cdn BlueChip A	16.51	-.07	-.42
Cdn Div Cl Z	10.86	-.04	-.37
Cdn Divers	14.71	-.05	-.34
Cdn Divers A	14.96	-.05	-.33
Cdn Equity	12.80	-.02	-.16
Cdn Equity A	12.82	-.02	-.16
Cdn Lrg Cap Val	10.55	+.01	+.09
Cdn Small/Mid A	21.02	-.04	-.19
Cdn Sml/Mid Cap	18.40	-.03	-.16
Clarica Balance	11.64	-.02	-.17
Glo Lrg Cap Val	10.52	+.04	+.38
Global Bond	9.91	-.04	-.40
Global Bond A	9.91	-.03	-.30
Prem Bond	11.34	-.04	-.35
Prem Bond A	11.49	-.04	-.35
Prem Int'l	12.43	-.03	-.24
Prem Int'l A	12.78	-.03	-.23
Prem Mtg	10.34	-.02	-.19
Prem Mtg A	10.46	-.02	-.19
Sig Corp Bond	9.83	-.02	-.20
Sum Cdn Equ	15.37	-.05	-.32
Sum Cdn Equ A	15.50	-.05	-.32
Sum Div Gwth	15.18	-.02	-.13
Sum Div Gwth A	14.91	-.02	-.13
Sum For Equ	14.46	-.03	-.21
Sum For Equ A	14.96	-.03	-.20
Sum Gwth&Inc	14.09	-.03	-.21
Sum Gwth&Inc A	14.50	-.03	-.21
US Small Cap	8.44	-.02	-.24
US Small Cap A	8.54	-.01	-.12

fund	valuation	chg	% chg
TRANSAMERICA GROWSAFE3 75/100			
AGF Int Val7510 06/01	4.51	+.00	+.02
AIC AmFoc 7510 06/01	5.07	-.01	-.19
AIC DivCan 7510 06/01	5.38	-.00	-.01
Agg AA GIF 7510	3.63	-.00	-.03
Bal AA GIF 7510	4.47	-.01	-.12
CI Gl Boom 7510 06/01	4.82	-.00	-.10
CI Global 7510 06/01	5.46	-.00	-.01
CanAsian 7510	4.21	-.01	-.14
CanEuro 7510	3.14	+.02	+.75
CanUS 21st 7510	2.86	-.01	-.24
CanUS L Cap7510	4.16	+.02	+.38
Cdn Bal 7510	4.77	-.02	-.46
Cdn Bond 7510	5.91	-.02	-.34
Cdn Equity 7510	3.40	-.03	-.79
Cdn Lg Cap 7510	4.17	-.01	-.35
Cdn MMF 7510	5.29	+.00	+.00
CdnEqVal 7510 06/01	5.62	+.00	+.04
CdnFixPay 7510 06/01	5.67	-.01	-.18
Con AA GIF 7510	4.88	-.01	-.20
Fid Can AA 7510 06/01	5.66	+.03	+.46
Fid IntPort7510 06/01	4.78	-.06	-1.19
Fid TrueNrt7510 06/01	5.75	+.01	+.19
Grow AA GIF7510	4.11	-.00	-.06
MacIvyGwinc7510 06/01	5.68	+.01	+.17
TD Div Inc 7510 06/01	6.12	-.00	-.03
TOP AggrGw 7510 06/01	3.66	+.01	+.24
TOP Bal 7510 06/01	4.50	+.01	+.19
TOP CdnMgr 7510 06/01	5.75	+.00	+.02
TOP Cons 7510 06/01	5.00	+.01	+.14
TOP GloMgr 7510 06/01	4.89	+.01	+.13
TOP GloSect7510 06/01	4.90	+.01	+.29
TOP Growth 7510 06/01	4.24	+.01	+.20
TOP USMgrs 7510 06/01	4.80	+.02	+.39
US EqVal 7510 06/01	5.74	+.03	+.47
US Equity 7510	3.68	-.00	-.01

Fund Name	Mstar Rating	Fund Type	Fund Sub-Type	Fund Categy	% Ret YrEnd May08	Quart YrEnd May08	% Ret YrEnd May07	Quart YrEnd May07	% Ret YrEnd May06	Quart YrEnd May06	% Ret YrEnd May05	Quart YrEnd May05	% Ret YrEnd May04	Quart YrEnd May04	Exp Ratio	Total Asset $Mill
RBC O'Shaughnessy US Value	5	Equity	US Eq	USEq	-16.5	3	21.4	2	4.9	1	13.4	1	21.5	1	1.57	1271.9
Dynamic Power American Growth Class	5	Equity	US Eq	USEq	-9.9	1	17.3	2	0.6	1	13.4	1	27.7	1	2.59	93.9
IG AGF US Growth Class B	5	Equity	US Eq	USEq	-4.2	1	18.8	1	-1	2	-5.2	4			3.29	
Dynamic Power American Growth	5	Equity	US Eq	USEq	8.8	1	17.5	2	-0.5	1	12	1	28.6	1	2.55	221.1
Dynamic American Value	5	Equity	US Eq	USEq	-2	2	16.9	1	16.7	1	1.6	1	26.4	1	2.55	198
SEI US Large Cap Synthetic Class P	5	Equity	US Eq	USEq	-9.2	1	19.1	1	5.1	1	6.3	1	17.9	2	1.5	0
TD US Index Currency Neutral - e	5	Equity	US Eq	USEq	-8.1	1	20.6	1	6.6	1	7.8	1	19.2	1	0.48	119.1
IG AGF US Growth B	5	Equity	US Eq	USEq	-4.3	1	19.2	1	-0.9	1	-5.2	4			3.14	
TD US Index Currency Neutral - I	5	Equity	US Eq	USEq	-8.4	2	20.2	1	6.2	1	7.3	1	19	1	0.85	119.1
McLean Budden American Equity	5	Equity	US Eq	USEq	-10.7	1	19.2	1	-3.9	2	-1.4	2	19.2	1	1.25	729.3
IG AGF US Growth A	5	Equity	US Eq	USEq	-4.2	1	19.4	1	-0.8	1	-5.1	4			2.99	104.9
CI American Value Corporate Class	5	Equity	US Eq	USEq	-5.9	2	19.1	1	-5.9	3	7.4	1	17.9	2	2.31	349.2
Altamira Precision US Curr Neutral Idx	5	Equity	US Eq	USEq	-8.5	2	20.5	1	6.5	3	7.2	1	18.8	1	0.53	122.6
RBC US Index Currency Neutral	5	Equity	US Eq	USEq	-8.4	2	20	1	6.6	1	7.1	1	18.7	2	0.7	313.1
Emissary US Small/Mid Cap	4	Equity	US Eq	USEq	-11.5	2	18.5	2	-4.4	2	-4	3	21	1	2.93	6.2
IA Clarington Navellier US All Cap A	4	Equity	US Eq	USEq	-9.3	1	10.8	4	10.5	1	-1.4	2	23.7	2	2.88	37
BMO US Equity	4	Equity	US Eq	USEq	-12.5	2	18.7	1	-2.5	1	7	1	16.8	2	2.44	505.3
BMO US Equity Index	4	Equity	US Eq	USEq	-11.1	1	18.8	1	2.3	1	4.3	1	16.8	2	1.22	130
RBC US Equity	4	Equity	US Eq	USEq	-6.5	1	15.9	3	-1.9	2	-1.1	2	15.6	3	2.02	2887
RBC US Equity Advisor	4	Equity	US Eq	USEq	-6.5	1	15.8	3	-2.1	2	-1	2			2.2	
GGOF American Equity Ltd Mutual	4	Equity	US Eq	USEq	-19.6	4	20.2	1	-5.3	3	-0.3	2	20.4	1	2.75	28.2
GGOF American Equity Ltd Classic	4	Equity	US Eq	USEq	-19.2	4	20.8	1	-4.8	3	0.3	1	21.1	1	2.21	15.6
Marquis US Equity Pool	4	Equity	US Eq	USEq	-5.1	1	11.3	4	2.4	1					2.9	5.4
Mac Universal US Gr Lead (Unhed) CI	4	Equity	US Eq	USEq	1	1	9.8	4	-3.8	2	-8.5	4			2.69	16.7
imaxx US Equity Growth	4	Equity	US Eq	USEq	-7.8	1	8.8	4	2.1	1	-1.3	1			2.84	4
CI American Equity	4	Equity	US Eq	USEq	-19.6	4	21.8	1	-3	2	0.1	1	19.7	1	2.31	322.5
CI American Equity Corporate Class	4	Equity	US Eq	USEq	-19.4	4	21.9	1	-3.1	2	-0.6	2	23.1	1	2.31	8.2
Investors US Large Cap Growth A	4	Equity	US Eq	USEq	-4.5	1	14.5	3	-6.7	4	-5.6	2	23.4	1	2.71	211.6
Franklin Flex Cap Growth Corp Class	4	Equity	US Eq	USEq	-6.8	1	12.4	4	-8.6	4	-3.4	3			2.65	16
CI American Managers Corporate Class	4	Equity	US Eq	USEq	-14.3	3	15.7	3	-0.5	1	4.7	1	26.6	1	2.31	317.4
CI American Value	4	Equity	US Eq	USEq	-6.1	1	19.9	1	-5.3	3	8.7	1	20.7	1	2.31	267.1
Marquis US Equity Pool Series V	4	Equity	US Eq	USEq	-2.5	1	14.2	3	5	2	-1.1	2	19.3	3	0.32	27.6
MD American Value	4	Equity	US Eq	USEq	-10.6	2	13.3	3	-1.8	2	-1.7	2	19.3	1	1.72	112.4
IG AGF US Growth C	4	Equity	US Eq	USEq	-4.3	1	19.2	1	-0.9	2	-5.3	4	11.1	4	3.17	
Investors US Large Cap Growth B	4	Equity	US Eq	USEq	-4.6	1	14.3	3	-6.8	4	-5.8	4			2.86	
Investors US Large Cap Growth Class B	4	Equity	US Eq	USEq	-5.2	1	14.2	3	-6.7	4	-6.1	4			3.01	
North Growth US Equity	4	Equity	US Eq	USEq	-14.8	3	15.9	3	-7.8	4	11.3	1	25.4	1	1.2	240.6
Investors US Large Cap Value C	4	Equity	US Eq	USEq	-15.6	3	17.6	2	-3.4	2	0	2	9.4	4	2.87	
Middlefield US Growth Class	4	Equity	US Eq	USEq	-3.6	1	10.7	4	-0.1	4	3.1	2	16.8	2	2.43	1.6
Investors US Opportunities C	4	Equity	US Eq	USEq	-17.4	3	22.7	1	-8.5	4	-0.7	2	16.1	2	2.88	
Fidelity American Disciplined Eq Sr T8	4	Equity	US Eq	USEq	-8.3	1	19.7	1	2.2	1	5.3	1	13.7	3	2.65	8.4
Fidelity American Disciplined Eq Sr S8	4	Equity	US Eq	USEq	-8.1	1	19.9	1	2.2	1	5.5	1	13.7	3	2.45	1.9
Fidelity American Disciplined Eq Sr B	4	Equity	US Eq	USEq	-8.3	1	19.9	1	2.4	1	5.5	1	13.5	3	2.45	69.7
Fidelity American Disciplined Eq Sr A	4	Equity	US Eq	USEq	-11.2	2	19.6	1	2	1	5.4	2	13.5	3	2.65	77.6
Standard Life US Equity Legend Series	4	Equity	US Eq	USEq	-7.6	1	17.7	2	-7.2	4	-0.7	1	18.4	2	1.15	4.1
Synergy American	4	Equity	US Eq	USEq	-7.5	1	15.7	3	0.7	1	9.7	1	12.6	3	2.31	300.9
Synergy American Corporate Class	4	Equity	US Eq	USEq	-8.2	1	15.1	3	0.4	1	10	1	11.8	3	2.31	14.1
Fidelity American Disciplined Eq Cl B	4	Equity	US Eq	USEq	-8.2	1	19.7	1	1.9	1	5	1	13.4	3	2.65	16.5
Fidelity American Disciplined Eq Cl A	4	Equity	US Eq	USEq	-8.4	1	19.4	1	1.7	1	4.9	1	13.4	3	2.85	13.1

Fund	Rating				V1	R1	V2	R2	V3	R3	V4	R4	V5	R5	MER	Assets
IG AGF US Growth Class A	4	Equity	US Eq	USEq	-4.1	1	19	1	-0.9	1	-5.1	4	11	4	3.14	12
TD Dow Jones Industrial Avg Index - I	4	Equity	US Eq	USEq	-12.7	2	19.8	1	-5.3	3	-4.7	4	15.4	3	0.85	43.8
AGF American Growth Class D	4	Equity	US Eq	USEq	-3.4	1	20	1	0.3	1	-4.3	3	12.3	3	2.45	
IG Mackenzie Universal US Gr Leaders CLB	3	Equity	US Eq	USEq	0.3	4	9	4	-3.8	2	-8.8	4			3.16	27.1
IG Goldman Sachs US Equity C	3	Equity	US Eq	USEq	-19.6	4	10.2	4	-2.1	1	-3.2	3	20	1	3.17	43.8
Leith Wheeler US Equity Series B	3	Equity	US Eq	USEq	-21.5	2	17.2	1	-0.3	3	-3.4	3	19.3	1	1.34	16.2
TD Dow Jones Industrial Avg Index - e	3	Equity	US Eq	USEq	-12.3	4	20.3	3	-4.9	2	-4.2	3	15.9	2	0.31	
Emissary US Value	3	Equity	US Eq	USEq	-18.6	3	13	2	-3.4	2	-2.3	2	17.2	2	2.92	137.5
Investors US Opportunities Class B	3	Equity	US Eq	USEq	-17.2	2	22.2	1	-8.4	1	-1.2	2			2.97	31.7
Férique American	3	Equity	US Eq	USEq	-16.7	3	18.9	3	-4.9	3	-1.6	3	17	2	0.96	741.5
DFA US Value	3	Equity	US Eq	USEq	-22.4	4	16.8	2	3.5	1	5.2	1	13.6	3	1.61	15.1
TD US Blue Chip Equity - A	3	Equity	US Eq	USEq	-10.8	2	15.9	3	-7.4	4	-5	4	15.7	3	2.44	65.1
Professionals Qc American Index	3	Equity	US Eq	USEq	-14.3	2	17.4	2	-5.9	2	-1.6	2	22.8	1	0.88	741.5
PH&N US Growth A	3	Equity	US Eq	USEq	-11.1	2	13.2	2	-2.2	3	-3.8	3	13.6	3	1.22	0.4
TD US Blue Chip Equity - I	3	Equity	US Eq	USEq	-10.9	2	15.9	3	-7.4	4	-5.1	4			2.44	5.8
Standard Life US Equity E	3	Equity	US Eq	USEq	-11.7	3	16.8	2	-7.9	4	-1.2	4	12.7	3	1.91	13.1
Counsel Select America	3	Equity	US Eq	USEq	-14.3	3	11.1	4	-5.8	3	-0.3	2	16.7	2	2.83	28.4
TD US Equity Advantage Portfolio-A	3	Equity	US Eq	USEq	-14	3	16.3	3	-5.1	4	-2.1	3			2.57	289.6
Standard Life US Equity A	3	Equity	US Eq	USEq	-12.3	2	16.1	2	-8.4	4	-1.8	3	16.2	2	2.43	32.7
CIBC US Index RRSP	3	Equity	US Eq	USEq	-14.4	2	17.9	2	-5.8	3	-1.8	3	16.3	2	0.97	485.4
SEI US Large Co Equity Class P	3	Equity	US Eq	USEq	-15	3	15	3	-4.4	3	-0.7	2	17.9	2	2.43	13.9
CIBC US Equity Index	3	Equity	US Eq	USEq	-13.7	3	17.3	2	-4.1	2	-1.1	2	15.8	4	0.98	112.9
Investors US Opportunities Class A	3	Equity	US Eq	USEq	-17.1	3	22.3	3	-8.3	4	0.6	2			2.82	
Mac Universal US Blue Chip Cl	3	Equity	US Eq	USEq	-7.7	1	12.3	4	0.8	1	-0.7	4	6.5	1	2.43	211.4
Investors US Opportunities B	3	Equity	US Eq	USEq	-17.4	3	22.7	3	-8.5	4	-0.5	2	19.9	1	2.85	3.5
Investors US Opportunities A	3	Equity	US Eq	USEq	-17.3	3	22.9	3	-8.3	4	-1.7	2			2.7	2.4
Fidelity American Value Sr A	3	Equity	US Eq	USEq	-20.1	4	14.9	4	-4.5	3	-1.7	2	19.9	4	2.54	
Fidelity American Value Sr B	3	Equity	US Eq	USEq	-19.9	4	15.1	4	-4.4	2	-0.4	2	8.9	2	2.34	150.8
Investors US Large Cap Value Class B	3	Equity	US Eq	USEq	-15.4	3	17.1	3	-3.2	2	-0.3	1	17.7	2	2.84	13.1
Investors US Large Cap Value Class A	3	Equity	US Eq	USEq	-15.2	3	17.3	2	-3	2	-4.6	1	16.3	2	2.69	22.1
TD US Equity Advantage Portfolio-I	3	Equity	US Eq	USEq	-13.9	3	16.4	2	-5.1	3	-1.9	4	45		2.44	45
Scotia US Value	3	Equity	US Eq	USEq	-9.8	2	9.5	4	-4.4	3	-1.1	3	16.8	2	2.46	359.7
Scotia US Index	3	Equity	US Eq	USEq	-14.4	3	17.5	2	-5.5	3	0.1	3	16.8	3	0.94	
TD US Index - e	3	Equity	US Eq	USEq	-13.7	2	18.4	2	-5.2	2	-1.5	2	15.7	2	0.33	141.1
Investors US Large Cap Value B	3	Equity	US Eq	USEq	-15.5	4	17.6	2	-3.4	2	-2.4	2	88.5		2.84	88.5
Fidelity Growth America Sr B	3	Equity	US Eq	USEq	-21.2	4	12.7	4	-2.3	4	0.2	2	11.7	4	2.43	2213.4
Scotia CanAm Index	3	Equity	US Eq	USEq	-14.8	3	17.4	2	-5.3	3	-4.7	3	5.4	4	1.02	5.1
Investors US Large Cap Value A	3	Equity	US Eq	USEq	-15.4	3	17.8	3	-3.2	3	-5.9	2	16.6	2	2.69	14.1
National Bank American Index Plus	3	Equity	US Eq	USEq	-15.1	3	15.8	2	-7.9	2	-1.3	1	17.2	2	1.89	359.7
Investors US Large Cap Growth Class A	3	Equity	US Eq	USEq	-5.1	1	14.3	1	-6.5	4	-1.6	4	14.7	3	2.86	19
TD US Index - I	3	Equity	US Eq	USEq	-13.9	3	18.2	3	-5.3	2	1.4	4	20.4	1	0.53	681.8
Renaissance US Index	3	Equity	US Eq	USEq	-13.6	3	16.7	2	-6	3	-5.1	2	20.6	1	1.82	76.1
TD US Large-Cap Value - A	3	Equity	US Eq	USEq	-17.6	3	18.9	1	-5.4	3	1.3	2	8	4	2.44	681.8
Renaissance US Equity Value	3	Equity	US Eq	USEq	-20	4	17.5	2	-4.4	2	-2.3	2	16.1	2	2.62	17.3
TD US Large-Cap Value - I	3	Equity	US Eq	USEq	-17.7	3	19	1	-5.4	2	-8.5	4			2.44	16.1
Capital Intl-US Equity Cl I	3	Equity	US Eq	USEq	-17.4	3	11.8	4	-2	2	-1.6	2	15.7	3	0.08	53.7
Mac Universal US Growth Leaders	3	Equity	US Eq	USEq	0	4	10.4	4	-3.5	2	-1.4	1	21.6	1	2.73	510.8
RBC US Index	3	Equity	US Eq	USEq	-14.2	4	18	2	-5.6	3	-1.5	3			0.85	18.9
TD US Quantitative Equity - I	3	Equity	US Eq	USEq	-17.7	3	15.2	3	-5.4	2	-5	4	15.4	3	1.53	9
Manulife US Core	3	Equity	US Eq	USEq	-20.8	4	13.4	3	-2.5	4	-4.5	2	15	2	2.45	0.7
National Bank American Index	3	Equity	US Eq	USEq	-13	2	19.3	3	-5.3	3	-3.8	4	11.9	3	1.24	0.4
Maritime Life Elite American Eq Pooled	3	Equity	US Eq	USEq	-14.1	3	12.8	3	-3.9	3		2			0.44	
Maritime Life Elite US Special Eq Pooled	3	Equity	US Eq	USEq	-10.6	2	14.4	2	-5.8	2		3			0.49	

Fund																
HSBC US Equity	3	Equity	US Eq	USEq	-14.9	3	16	3	-5.6	3	-3.3	3	10.4	4	2.33	24.3
IA Clarington American	3	Equity	US Eq	USEq	-12.7	2	17.9	2	-4.3	2	-3.9	3	10.5	4	2.4	29.8
Beutel Goodman American Equity	3	Equity	US Eq	USEq	-11	4	19.6	1	-6.1	1	3.6	1	23.3	1	1.42	1
imaxx TOP US Managers GIP 75/75	3	Equity	US Eq	USEq	-21.6	1	14.4	3	-0.1	3	-2.7	2			3.24	15.3
Quadrus Mac Univ US Growth Leaders	3	Equity	US Eq	USEq	0.1	1	10.4	4	-3.4	2	-8.6	4	7.9	1	2.69	33.6
Mawer US Equity	3	Equity	US Eq	USEq	-6.1	2	12.4	4	-6.9	4	-2.9	3	20.2	3	1.28	8.2
MLI US Large Cap Growth Class GIFe2	3	Equity	US Eq	USEq	-9.3	3	13.4	3	-8.2	4					3.36	31.5
MLI US Large Cap Growth Class GIFe	3	Equity	US Eq	USEq	-9.8	3	12.9	3	-8.7	4	-3.9	3			3.9	2
MLI American Equity Index GIFe2	3	Equity	US Eq	USEq	-15.9	2	16.5	2	-7.4	3	-4.7	4			2.76	620.7
AGF American Growth Class	3	Equity	US Eq	USEq	-3.9	4	19.4	4	-0.3	1	-3.1	1	13.7	3	2.95	2.6
imaxx TOP US Managers GIP 75/100	3	Equity	US Eq	USEq	-21.8	3	14.1	3	-0.3	3	12.3	1	11.8	3	3.49	52.5
Acker Finley Select US Value 50	3	Equity	US Eq	USEq	-27.9	2	18.4	2	15.6	1	-8.6	4			1.94	151.7
IG Mackenzie Universal US Gr Leaders CLA	3	Equity	US Eq	USEq	0.5	1	9.2	4	-3.7	2	-6.1	4			3.02	6.9
MLI Renaissance US Basic Value GIFe2	2	Equity	US Eq	USEq	-20.8	3	16.5	2	-5.4	2	-2.9	3	7.4	1	3.52	
IG Fidelity US Equity Class B	2	Equity	US Eq	USEq	-22	4	11.4	4	-2.6	2	-3	3			3.21	241.4
IG Goldman Sachs US Equity A	2	Equity	US Eq	USEq	-19.4	4	10.4	4	-2	4	-3.2	3			2.99	
IG Goldman Sachs US Equity B	2	Equity	US Eq	USEq	-19.5	4	10.2	4	-2.1	4	-2.8	2	14.7	3	3.14	15.4
IG Fidelity US Equity Class A	2	Equity	US Eq	USEq	-21.9	4	11.5	3	-2.4	4	-0.4	3	15.4	3	3.06	10
IG Goldman Sachs US Equity Class A	2	Equity	US Eq	USEq	-20	4	10.2	2	-2.1	4	-0.5	2			3.12	
IG Goldman Sachs US Equity Class B	2	Equity	US Eq	USEq	-20.1	4	10	4	-2.3	4	-2.7	2			3.27	
IG FI US Equity C	2	Equity	US Eq	USEq	-21.9	4	11.5	3	-2.7	3	-2.7	3			3.17	
IG FI US Equity B	2	Equity	US Eq	USEq	-21.8	4	11.5	3	-2.7	3	-2.5	3			3.14	89
IG FI US Equity A	2	Equity	US Eq	USEq	-21.7	4	11.7	2	-2.5	3			15.4	3	2.99	54.2
IA Clarington US Dividend T	2	Equity	US Eq	USEq	-20.7	4	19.3	4	-6.5	3	-5.7	3			2.66	7.1
Renaissance US Equity Growth	2	Equity	US Eq	USEq	-18.1	3	14.1	4	-8.5	4	-6.7	4	16.2	2	2.62	4.1
AIM Trimark Core American Equity Cl	2	Equity	US Eq	USEq	-13.9	3	12.1	4	-9.6	4	-6.7	4	11.7	4	2.68	0.7
Putnam US Voyager D	2	Equity	US Eq	USEq	-12.2	2	11.1	4	-8.3	4	-6.5	4	12.8	4	1.93	10.9
MLI Renaissance US Basic Value GIFe	2	Equity	US Eq	USEq	-21.2	4	15.9	2	-5.9	2	-1.5	3	18.3	1	4.05	9.5
Putnam US Value D	2	Equity	US Eq	USEq	-27.4	4	17	2	-5.1	2	-4.4	2	15.2	3	1.93	5.8
Franklin Templeton US Rising Div A	2	Equity	US Eq	USEq	-17.3	4	10.9	4	-7.8	4	-2.4	3	11.9	3	2.59	4.5
MLI Fidelity Growth America GIF encore 2	2	Equity	US Eq	USEq	-22.1	4	11.6	4	-3.3	4	-5.8	2	16	3	3.4	
Investors US Large Cap Growth C	2	Equity	US Eq	USEq	-4.7	1	14.3	4	-6.9	4	-1.6	4	6.2	2	2.88	0.5
Fidelity Growth America Sr T8	2	Equity	US Eq	USEq	-21.5	4	12.4	3	-2.5	3	-1.5	2	16.7	2	2.63	8.2
Saxon US Equity Investor Series	2	Equity	US Eq	USEq	-19.5	4	13.6	3	-5.7	4	-1.7	3	16.7	2	1.86	0.3
Fidelity Growth America Sr S8	2	Equity	US Eq	USEq	-21.2	4	13	3	-2.3	3	-2.9	2	16.8	2	2.43	47.7
Fidelity Growth America Sr A	2	Equity	US Eq	USEq	-21.5	4	12.4	4	-2.5	3	-1.8	2	10.3	4	2.63	45.8
Scotia US Growth	2	Equity	US Eq	USEq	-11.1	2	13.1	4	-8	4	-1.9	3	16.2	3	2.53	1.2
Fidelity Growth America Cl B	2	Equity	US Eq	USEq	-21.3	4	12.5	4	-2.7	3	-3.4	3	16.2	2	2.58	1.5
Fidelity Growth America Cl A	2	Equity	US Eq	USEq	-21.5	4	12.3	3	-2.8	3	-3.5	3	6.3	4	2.78	8.5
Fidelity American Opportunities Sr B	2	Equity	US Eq	USEq	-12.8	2	11.2	3	-1.1	4	-3.8	3	6.3	4	2.45	9.4
Fidelity American Opportunities Sr A	2	Equity	US Eq	USEq	-13	2	11	3	-1.3	4	-3.9	4	5.8	4	2.65	0.5
Fidelity American Opportunities Cl B	2	Equity	US Eq	USEq	-13.1	2	11	3	-1.4	4	-8.1	4	5.8	4	2.64	0.8
Fidelity American Opportunities Cl A	2	Equity	US Eq	USEq		2	10.8	3	-1.6	4	-2.9	4	11.3	4	2.84	52.2
Ethical American Multi-Strategy	2	Equity	US Eq	USEq	-15.7	1	10.6	4	1.1	4	-8.8	2	15.2	2	2.31	9.8
MLI Fidelity Growth America GIF encore	2	Equity	US Eq	USEq	-22.5	2	11	4	-3.8	4	-6.3	2	16.1	2	3.93	12
Emissary US Growth	2	Equity	US Eq	USEq	-13.3	2	9.3	4	-7.4	4	-2.1	4	11.8	4	2.93	6.1
Trimark US Companies Class	2	Equity	US Eq	USEq	-11.7	2	12.7	4	-10.5	4	-4.2	2	13	3	2.86	475
Desjardins American Equity Value	2	Equity	US Eq	USEq	-21	4	18	2	-6.4	3	-2.1	3	10.1	3	2.49	3.3
MLI American Equity Index GIFe	2	Equity	US Eq	USEq	-16.4	3	14.8	3	-7.6	3	-7.1	3	15.7	3	3.34	16.4
CIBC North American Demographics	2	Equity	US Eq	USEq	-16.8	3	15	3	-8.7	3	-3.7	4			2.74	322.5
PH&N US Equity A	2	Equity	US Eq	USEq	-13.7	4	12.9	3	-5.9	4	-0.2	3	18.8	2	1.16	73.7
PH&N US Dividend Income A	2	Equity	US Eq	USEq	-19.1	3	11.2	4	-6.5	3			20.5	2	1.15	33.3
AGF US Value Class	2	Equity	US Eq	USEq	-34.2	4	19.6	2	2.8	1		1			2.85	

Fund					%Ret	Q	%Ret	Q	%Ret	Q	%Ret	Q	Exp.	Total Asset ($Mill)
MDPIM US Equity Pool	2	Equity	US Eq	USEq	-18.1	3	17.2	2	-3	2	9.2	4	1.35	666.1
MD American Growth	2	Equity	US Eq	USEq	-9.9	2	13.7	3	-6.1	3	11.4	4	1.44	304.2
Capital Intl-US Equity Cl H	2	Equity	US Eq	USEq	-18	3	11.1	4	-2.8	2	18.9	1	0.77	17.3
Capital Intl-US Equity Cl D	2	Equity	US Eq	USEq	-18.6	3	10.3	4	-3.4	2	18.4	2	1.47	17.3
Capital Intl-US Equity Cl A	2	Equity	US Eq	USEq	-19	4	9.8	4	-3.9	2			1.97	17.3
Manulife US Large Cap Value Class	2	Equity	US Eq	USEq	-20.1	4	17.1	2	-2.6	3	13.2	3	2.8	4.4
AIM American Growth	2	Equity	US Eq	USEq	-16.1	3	11.3	4	-6	4	13.6	3	2.93	18
BMO US Growth	2	Equity	US Eq	USEq	-12.6	2	14.7	3	0.3	1	14.4	3	2.48	71.3
Trimark US Companies	2	Equity	US Eq	USEq	-11.4	2	12.9	3	-5.7	4	11.4	4	2.61	76.3
Altamira US Larger Company	2	Equity	US Eq	USEq	-11.9	2	12.9	3	-7.3	4	10.6	4	2.67	34.4
imaxx US Equity Value	1	Equity	US Eq	USEq	-27	4	13.6	3	-6.9	4	16.1	2	2.74	6
Brandes US Equity	1	Equity	US Eq	USEq	-34.6	4	22.3	1	-6.3	3	24.6	1	2.6	69.9
AIC Value Corporate Class	1	Equity	US Eq	USEq	-34.6	4	23.5	1	-2.2	3	14.6	3	2.47	8
CI Value Trust Corporate CI Shares Cl Z	1	Equity	US Eq	USEq	-34	4	16.7	2	-1.4	4			2.31	77.7
AIC Value	1	Equity	US Eq	USEq	-35.2	4	23.1	1	-7.1	2	15.2	3	2.52	131.6
AIC American Focused Corporate Class	1	Equity	US Eq	USEq	-39.4	4	6.2	4	8.7	1	9.1	4	2.35	37.3
CI Value Trust Corporate Class	1	Equity	US Eq	USEq	-34.1	4	16.4	2	-10.2	2	15.2	3	2.57	856.4
AIC American Focused	1	Equity	US Eq	USEq	-39.5	4	6.1	4	8.3	1	8.6	4	2.44	308.4
Meritas US Equity	1	Equity	US Eq	USEq	-17.2	3	13	3	-8.3	4	11.4	4	2.87	11.8
Northwest US Equity	1	Equity	US Eq	USEq	-27.7	4	14.7	4	-5.9	3	14.3	3	2.86	16.5
Mac Focus America Class	1	Equity	US Eq	USEq	-11	2	8.1	2	-10.7	4	13.5	3	2.43	4.5
Desjardins CI Value Trust Sector	1	Equity	US Eq	USEq	-34.2	4	16.3	4	-10.1	4			2.75	297.4
Putnam US Value A	1	Equity	US Eq	USEq	-27.9	3	16.3	2	-5.7	3	14.4	3	2.62	19.5
First Trust DOW 10 Strategy Trust 2003	1	Equity	US Eq	USEq	-23.7	4	23.9	1	-10.7	4	11.6	4	2.74	3.1
Putnam US Voyager A	1	Equity	US Eq	USEq	-12.9	2	10.4	4	-9	4	12.1	3	2.64	1.4

Expense Ratio: The manager's annual fee for managing and administering the fund, expressed as a percentage of total fund value. Some funds charge additional administrative fees not included in this figure. For full information on management and administrative costs, consult the fund prospectus.

Total Asset ($Mill): the current assets plus non-current assets.

Fund Table: Canadian Balanced and US Equity funds as of May 30, 2008.

Annual Returns: An annual return is the fund or portfolio return, for any 12-month period, including reinvested dividends.

Quartile Rankings: The quartile (1 to 4) in which this fund's "% YrEnd MmmYY" is positioned, relative to all others in its peer group. For example, if a mutual fund has a "Quart YrEnd Nov02" value of "1", that means this fund's rate of return for the 12 months ending November 30, 2002 is in the top 25% of all other mutual funds in its fund category. If it was "4" then this indicates the rate of return is amongst the bottom 25% of all its peers (e.g. Canadian Equity mutual funds or Canadian Bond segregated funds). Quartiles are useful since they indicate how the subject fund performs relative to its peers in its category. Many managers set the first (1) or second (2) quartile as their on-going goal as it indicates that the fund is outperforming the median fund within this category of funds.

2.4 Cross Tabulations

The study of patterns that may exist between two or more categorical variables is common in business. Often, by cross-tabulating the data, these patterns can be explained.

The Contingency Table

A **contingency table** presents the results of two categorical variables as **cross tabulations**. The joint responses are classified so that the categories of one variable are located in the rows and the categories of the other variable are located in the columns. The values located at the intersections of the rows and columns are called **cells**. Depending on the type of contingency table constructed, the cells for each row-column combination contain the frequency, the percentage of the overall total, the percentage of the row total, or the percentage of the column total.

Suppose that in the Using Statistics scenario, you want to examine whether there is any pattern or relationship between the level of risk and the objective of the mutual fund (growth versus value). Table 2.31 summarizes this information for all 868 mutual funds.

TABLE 2.31

Contingency Table Displaying Fund Objective and Fund Risk

See Sections E2.11, P2.8, or M2.7 to create this.

| OBJECTIVE | RISK LEVEL | | | |
	High	Average	Low	Total
Growth	302	140	22	464
Value	53	171	180	404
Total	355	311	202	868

You construct this contingency table by tallying the joint responses for each of the 868 mutual funds with respect to objective and risk into one of the six possible cells in the table. The first fund listed in the Mutual Funds file is classified as a growth fund with a low risk. Thus, you tally this joint response into the cell that is the intersection of the first row and third column. The remaining 867 joint responses are recorded in a similar manner. Each cell contains the frequency for the row-column combination.

In order to further explore any possible pattern or relationship between objective and fund risk, you can construct contingency tables based on percentages. You first convert these results into percentages based on the following three totals:

1. The overall total (i.e., the 868 mutual funds)
2. The row totals (i.e., 464 growth funds and 404 value funds)
3. The column totals (i.e., 355 high, 311 average, and 202 low)

Tables 2.32, 2.33, and 2.34 summarize these percentages.

TABLE 2.32

Contingency Table Displaying Fund Objective and Fund Risk, Based on Percentage of Overall Total

| OBJECTIVE | RISK LEVEL | | | |
	High	Average	Low	Total
Growth	34.79	16.13	2.53	53.46
Value	6.11	19.70	20.74	46.54
Total	40.90	35.83	23.27	100.00

TABLE 2.33

Contingency Table Displaying Fund Objective and Fund Risk, Based on Percentage of Row Total

| OBJECTIVE | RISK LEVEL | | | |
	High	Average	Low	Total
Growth	65.09	30.17	4.74	100.00
Value	13.12	42.33	44.55	100.00
Total	40.90	35.83	23.27	100.00

TABLE 2.34

Contingency Table Displaying Fund Objective and Fund Risk, Based on Percentage of Column Total

	RISK LEVEL			
OBJECTIVE	**High**	**Average**	**Low**	**Total**
Growth	85.07	45.02	10.89	53.46
Value	14.93	54.98	89.11	46.54
Total	100.00	100.00	100.00	100.00

Table 2.32 shows that 40.9% of the mutual funds sampled are high risk, 53.46% are growth funds, and 34.79% are high-risk funds that are growth funds. Table 2.33 shows that 65.09% of the growth funds are high risk and 4.74% are low risk. Table 2.34 shows that 85.07% of the high-risk funds and only 10.89% of the low-risk funds are growth funds. The tables reveal that growth funds are more likely to be high risk, whereas value funds are more likely to be low risk.

Problems for Section 2.4

LEARNING THE BASICS

2.39 The following data represent the responses to two questions asked in a survey of 40 college students majoring in business—What is your gender? (male = M; female = F) and What is your major? (accounting = A; computer information systems = C; marketing = M):

Gender:	M	M	M	F	M	F	F	M	F	M	F	M	M	M	M	F	F	M	F	F
Major:	A	C	C	M	A	C	A	A	C	C	A	A	A	M	C	M	A	A	A	C
Gender:	M	M	M	M	F	M	F	F	M	M	F	M	M	M	M	F	M	F	M	M
Major:	C	C	A	A	M	M	C	A	A	A	C	C	A	A	A	A	C	C	A	C

a. Tally the data into a contingency table where the two rows represent the gender categories and the three columns represent the academic-major categories.
b. Construct contingency tables based on percentages of all 40 student responses, based on row percentages and based on column percentages.

APPLYING THE CONCEPTS

2.40 Each day at a large hospital, several hundred laboratory tests are performed. The rate at which these tests are done improperly (and therefore need to be redone) seems steady, at about 4%. In an effort to get to the root cause of these non-conformances (i.e., tests that need to be redone), the director of the lab decided to keep records over a period of one week. The laboratory tests were subdivided by the shift of workers who performed the lab tests. The results are as follows:

LAB TESTS	SHIFT		
PERFORMED	**Day**	**Evening**	**Total**
Nonconforming	16	24	40
Conforming	654	306	960
Total	670	330	1,000

a. Construct contingency tables based on total percentages, row percentages, and column percentages.
b. Which type of percentage—row, column, or total—do you think is most informative for these data? Explain.
c. What conclusions concerning the pattern of nonconforming laboratory tests can the laboratory director reach?

2.41 A sample of 500 shoppers was selected in a large metropolitan area to determine various information concerning consumer behavior. Among the questions asked was "Do you enjoy shopping for clothing?" The results are summarized in the following table:

ENJOY SHOPPING	GENDER		
FOR CLOTHING	**Male**	**Female**	**Total**
Yes	136	224	360
No	104	36	140
Total	240	260	500

a. Construct contingency tables based on total percentages, row percentages, and column percentages.
b. What conclusions do you draw from these analyses?

2.42 As more Americans use cell phones, they question where it is okay to talk on cell phones. The following is a table of results, in percentages, for 2000 and 2006 (extracted from W. Koch, "Businesses Put a Lid on Chatterboxes," *USA Today*, February 7, 2006, p. 3A):

OK TO TALK ON A CELL	YEAR	
PHONE IN A RESTAURANT	**2000**	**2006**
Yes	31	21
No	69	79
Total	100	100

Discuss the changes in attitude concerning the use of cell phones in restaurants between 2000 and 2006.

2.43 An experiment was conducted by James Choi, David Laibson, and Brigitte Madrian to study the choices made in fund selection. When presented with four S&P 500 index funds that were identical except for their fees, under-graduate and MBA students chose the funds as follows (in percentages). Note that because the funds are identical, the best choice is the fund with the lowest fee.

	STUDENT GROUP	
FUND	**Undergraduate**	**MBA**
Lowest fee	19	19
Second-lowest fee	37	40
Third-lowest fee	17	23
Highest fee	27	18

Source: *Data extracted from J. Choi, D. Laibson, and B. Madrian, "Why Does the Law of One Practice Fail? An Experiment on Mutual Funds,"* **www.som.yale.edu/faculty/jjc83/fees.pdf.**

What do these results tell you about the differences between undergraduate and MBA students in their ability to choose S&P 500 index funds?

2.44 Where people turn to for news is different for various age groups. A study indicated where different age groups primarily get their news.

	AGE GROUP		
MEDIA	**Under 36**	**36–50**	**50+**
Local TV	107	119	133
National TV	73	102	127
Radio	75	97	109
Local newspaper	52	79	107
Internet	95	83	76

What differences are there in the age groups?

2.5 Scatter Plots and Time-Series Plots

When analyzing a single numerical variable such as the cost of a restaurant meal or the 2006 return, the appropriate charts to use include histograms, polygons, and cumulative percentage polygons, developed in Section 2.3. This section discusses scatter plots and time-series plots, which are used when you have two numerical variables.

The Scatter Plot

You use a **scatter plot** to examine possible relationships between two numerical variables. For each observation, you plot one variable on the horizontal X axis and the other variable on the vertical Y axis. For example, a marketing analyst could study the effectiveness of advertising by comparing weekly sales volumes and weekly advertising expenditures. Or a human resources director interested in the salary structure of the company could compare the employees' years of experience with their current salaries.

To demonstrate a scatter plot, you can examine the relationship between the cost of different items in various cities (extracted from K. Spors, "Keeping Up with . . . Yourself," *The Wall Street Journal*, April 11, 2005, p. R4). Table 2.35 provides the cost of a fast-food hamburger meal and the cost of two movie tickets in 10 cities around the world. The Cost of Living file contains the complete data set.

TABLE 2.35

Cost of a Fast-Food Hamburger Meal and Cost of Two Movie Tickets in 10 Cities

City	Hamburger	Movie Tickets
Tokyo	5.99	32.66
London	7.62	28.41
New York	5.75	20.00
Sydney	4.45	20.71
Chicago	4.99	18.00
San Francisco	5.29	19.50
Boston	4.39	18.00
Atlanta	3.70	16.00
Toronto	4.62	18.05
Rio de Janeiro	2.99	9.90

For each city, you plot the cost of a fast-food hamburger meal on the X axis, and the cost of two movie tickets on the Y axis. Figure 2.18 presents a Microsoft Excel scatter plot for these two variables.

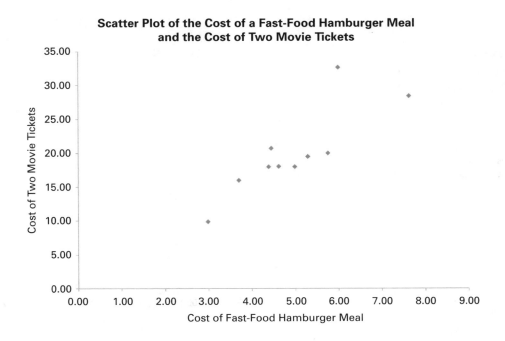

Although there is some variation, there appears to be a clearly increasing (positive) relationship between the cost of a fast-food hamburger meal and the cost of two movie tickets. In other words, cities in which the cost of a fast-food hamburger meal is low seem to also have a low cost of two movie tickets. Other pairs of variables may have a decreasing (negative) relationship in which one variable decreases as the other increases. The scatter plot will be studied again in Chapter 3, when the coefficient of correlation and the covariance are presented, and in Chapter 13, when regression analysis is developed.

The Time-Series Plot

A **time-series plot** is used to study patterns in the values of a numerical variable over time. Each value is plotted as a point in two dimensions with the time period on the horizontal X axis and the variable of interest on the Y axis.

To demonstrate a time-series plot, you can examine the yearly movie attendance, in billions, from 1999 to 2006 (extracted from C. Passy, "Good Night and Good Luck," *Palm Beach Post*, February 5, 2006, p. 1J and S. Bowles, "Box Office Breaks Its Downward Cycle," *USA Today*, March 7, 2007, p. 1D). Table 2.36 presents the data for the yearly movie attendance (see

TABLE 2.36

Movie Attendance, in Billions, from 1999 to 2006

Year	Attendance
1999	1.47
2000	1.42
2001	1.49
2002	1.63
2003	1.57
2004	1.53
2005	1.41
2006	1.45

the file **Movies**). Figure 2.19 is a time-series plot of the movie attendance (in billions) from 1999 to 2006. You can see that although movie attendance increased from 1999 to 2002, it declined from 2003 to 2005, before increasing slightly in 2006. Attendance in 2005 and 2006 was below attendance in 1999.

FIGURE 2.19

Microsoft Excel time-series plot of movie attendance from 1999 to 2006

See Section E2.13 to create this. (Minitab users, see Section M2.8 to create an equivalent chart.)

Problems for Section 2.5

LEARNING THE BASICS

2.45 The following is a set of data from a sample of $n = 11$ items:

X	7	5	8	3	6	10	12	4	9	15	18
Y	21	15	24	9	18	30	36	12	27	45	54

a. Construct a scatter plot.
b. Is there a relationship between X and Y? Explain.

2.46 The following is a series of annual sales (in millions of dollars) over an 11-year period (1996 to 2006):

Year	1996	1997	1998	1999	2000	2001	2002	2003	2004	2005	2006
Sales	13.0	17.0	19.0	20.0	20.5	20.5	20.5	20.0	19.0	17.0	13.0

a. Construct a time-series plot.
b. Does there appear to be any change in real annual sales over time? Explain.

APPLYING THE CONCEPTS

✓**SELF** **2.47** There are several methods for calculating
Test fuel economy. The following table (contained in the file **Mileage**) indicates the mileage as calculated by owners and by current government standards for nine car models:

Car	Owner	Government
2005 Ford F-150	14.3	16.8
2005 Chevrolet Silverado	15.0	17.8
2002 Honda Accord LX	27.8	26.2
2002 Honda Civic	27.9	34.2
2004 Honda Civic Hybrid	48.8	47.6
2002 Ford Explorer	16.8	18.3
2005 Toyota Camry	23.7	28.5
2003 Toyota Corolla	32.8	33.1
2005 Toyota Prius	37.3	56.0

Source: *Data extracted from J. Healey, "Fuel Economy Calculations to be Altered," USA Today, January 11, 2006, p. 1B.*

a. Construct a scatter plot with owner mileage on the X axis and current government standards mileage on the Y axis.
b. Does there appear to be a relationship between owner and current government standards mileage? If so, is the relationship positive or negative?

2.48 The file **Chicken** contains data on the calories and total fat (in grams per serving) for a sample of 20 chicken sandwiches from fast-food chains:

Source: *Data extracted from "Fast food: Adding Health to the Menu," Consumer Reports, September 2004, pp. 28–31.*

a. Construct a scatter plot with calories on the X axis and total fat on the Y axis.

b. What conclusions can you reach about the relationship between the calories and total fat in chicken sandwiches?

2.49 College basketball is big business, with coaches' salaries, revenues, and expenses in millions of dollars. The file Colleges-Basketball contains the coaches' salary and revenue for college basketball at selected schools in a recent year (extracted from R. Adams, "Pay for Playoffs," *The Wall Street Journal*, March 11–12, 2006, pp. P1, P8).

a. Do you think schools with higher revenues also have higher coaches' salaries?

b. Construct a scatter plot with revenue on the X axis and coaches' salaries on the Y axis.

c. Does the scatter plot confirm or contradict your answer to (a)?

2.50 College football players trying out for the NFL are given the Wonderlic standardized intelligence test. The file Wonderlic contains the average Wonderlic scores of football players trying out for the NFL and the graduation rate for football players at selected schools (extracted from S. Walker, "The NFL's Smartest Team," *The Wall Street Journal*, September 30, 2005, pp. W1, W10).

a. Construct a scatter plot with average Wonderlic score on the X axis and graduation rate on the Y axis.

b. What conclusions can you reach about the relationship between the average Wonderlic score and graduation rate?

2.51 The U.S. Bureau of Labor Statistics compiles data on a wide variety of workforce issues. The following table (contained in the file Unemployment) gives the monthly seasonally adjusted civilian unemployment rate for the United States from 2000 to 2007:

Month	2000	2001	2002	2003	2004	2005	2006	2007
January	4.0	4.2	5.7	5.8	5.7	5.2	4.7	4.6
February	4.1	4.2	5.7	5.9	5.6	5.4	4.8	4.5
March	4.0	4.3	5.7	5.9	5.7	5.1	4.7	4.4
April	3.8	4.4	5.9	6.0	5.5	5.1	4.7	4.5
May	4.0	4.3	5.8	6.1	5.6	5.1	4.6	4.5
June	4.0	4.5	5.8	6.3	5.6	5.0	4.6	4.6
July	4.0	4.6	5.8	6.2	5.5	5.0	4.8	4.7
August	4.1	4.9	5.7	6.1	5.4	4.9	4.7	4.7
September	3.9	5.0	5.7	6.1	5.4	5.1	4.6	4.7
October	3.9	5.3	5.7	6.0	5.4	4.9	4.4	4.8
November	3.9	5.5	5.9	5.9	5.4	5.0	4.5	4.7
December	3.9	5.7	6.0	5.7	5.4	4.9	4.5	5.0

Source: *"U.S. Bureau of Labour Statistics"* **www.bls.gov,** *April 22, 2008.*

a. Construct a time-series plot of the U.S. unemployment rate.

b. Does there appear to be any pattern?

2.52 In 2008, Wal-Mart Stores, Inc., operated more than 7,200 Wal-Marts, Supercenters, Sam's Clubs, and Neighborhood Markets, and reported revenues exceeding $373 bil-

lion. Sales for Wal-Mart are highly seasonal, and therefore you need to consider quarterly revenue. The fiscal year for the company ends on January 31. Thus, the fourth quarter of 2008 includes November and December of 2007 and January of 2008. The following table lists the quarterly revenues, in billions of dollars, from 2001 to 2008 (see the file Wal-Mart).

Quarter	2001	2002	2003	2004	2005	2006	2007	2008
1 (Feb–Apr)	43.0	48.6	55.0	56.7	64.8	71.6	79.6	85.4
2 (May–July)	46.1	53.3	59.7	62.6	69.7	76.8	84.5	91.2
3 (Aug–Oct)	45.7	51.8	58.8	62.4	68.5	75.4	83.5	90.9
4 (Nov–Jan)	56.6	64.2	71.1	74.5	82.2	88.6	98.1	106.3

Source: *Data extracted from Wal-Mart Stores. Inc.,* **investor.walmartstores.com,** *April 22, 2008.*

a. Construct a time-series plot of Wal-Mart's quarterly revenues.

b. What conclusions can you reach about the seasonal pattern and long-term growth in Wal-Mart's revenues?

2.53 The following table contained in the file Tvchannels (extracted from "At Home With More TV Channels," *USA Today*, April 10, 2007, p. A1) shows the average number of TV channels that the U.S. home received from 1985 to 2005:

Year	Number of TV Channels Received
1985	18.8
1990	33.2
1995	41.1
2000	61.4
2005	96.4

a. Construct a time-series plot for the average number of TV channels that the U.S. home received from 1985 to 2005.

b. What pattern, if any, is present in the data?

c. If you had to make a prediction of the average number of TV channels that the U.S. home will receive in 2010, what would you predict?

2.54 The following data, contained in the file Hotels, provide the average hotel room rate from 1996 to 2006 (data extracted from *USA Today* Snapshots, February 13, 2008, p. 1A) :

Year	Rates ($)	Year	Rates ($)
1996	70.63	2002	83.54
1997	75.31	2003	82.52
1998	78.62	2004	86.23
1999	81.33	2005	90.88
2000	85.89	2006	97.78
2001	88.27		

a. Construct a time-series plot.

b. What pattern, if any, is present in the data?

c. If you had to make a prediction of the average room rate in 2007, what would you predict?

2.6 Misusing Graphs and Ethical Issues

Good graphical displays clearly and unambiguously reveal what the data convey. Unfortunately, many graphs presented in the media (broadcast, print, and online) are incorrect, misleading, or so unnecessarily complicated that they should never be used. To illustrate the misuse of graphs, the chart presented in Figure 2.20 is similar to one that was printed in *Time* magazine as part of an article on increasing exports of wine from Australia to the United States.

In Figure 2.20, the wineglass icon representing the 6.77 million gallons for 1997 does not appear to be almost twice the size of the wineglass icon representing the 3.67 million gallons for 1995, nor does the wineglass icon representing the 2.25 million gallons for 1992 appear to be twice the size of the wineglass icon representing the 1.04 million gallons for 1989. Part of the reason for this is that the three-dimensional wineglass icon is used to represent the two dimensions of exports and time. Although the wineglass presentation may catch the eye, the data should instead be presented in a summary table or a time-series plot.

FIGURE 2.20

"Improper" display of Australian wine exports to the United States, in millions of gallons

Source: *Based on S. Watterson, "Liquid Gold—Australians Are Changing the World of Wine. Even the French Seem Grateful," Time, November 22, 1999, p. 68.*

We're drinking more . . .
Australian wine exports to the U.S. in millions of gallons

| 1.04 | 2.25 | 3.67 | 6.77 |
| 1989 | 1992 | 1995 | 1997 |

In addition to the type of distortion created by the wineglass icons in the *Time* magazine graph displayed in Figure 2.20, improper use of the vertical and horizontal axes leads to distortions. Figure 2.21 presents another graph used in the same *Time* magazine article.

FIGURE 2.21

"Improper" display of amount of land planted with grapes for the wine industry

Source: *Based on S. Watterson, "Liquid Gold—Australians Are Changing the World of Wine. Even the French Seem Grateful," Time, November 22, 1999, pp. 68–69.*

...they're growing more...
Amount of land planted with grapes for the wine industry

1997–1998
243,644
acres

1979–1980
172,075
acres

1949–1950
135,326
acres

1969–1970
150,300
acres

1989–1990
146,204
acres

1959–1960
130,201
acres

There are several problems in this graph. First, there is no zero point on the vertical axis. Second, the acreage of 135,326 for 1949–1950 is plotted above the acreage of 150,300 for 1969–1970. Third, it is not obvious that the difference between 1979–1980 and 1997–1998 (71,569 acres) is approximately 3.5 times the difference between 1979–1980 and 1969–1970 (21,775 acres). Fourth, there are no scale values on the horizontal axis. Years are plotted next to the acreage totals, not on the horizontal axis. Fifth, the values for the time dimension are not properly spaced along the horizontal axis. The value for 1979–1980 is much closer to 1989–1990 than it is to 1969–1970.

Other types of eye-catching displays that you typically see in magazines and newspapers often include information that is not necessary and just adds excessive clutter. Figure 2.14 represents one such display. The graph in Figure 2.22 shows those products with the largest market share for soft drinks. The graph suffers from too much clutter, although it is designed to show the differences in market share among the soft drinks. The display of the fizz for each soft drink takes up too much of the graph relative to the data. The same information could have been conveyed with a bar chart or pie chart.

FIGURE 2.22

"Improper" plot of market share of soft drinks

Source: *Based on Anne B. Carey and Sam Ward, "Coke Still Has Most Fizz," USA Today, May 10, 2000, p. 1B.*

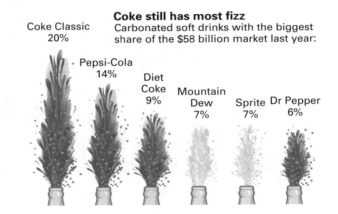

Some guidelines for developing good graphs are as follows:

- The graph should not distort the data.
- The graph should not contain **chartjunk**, unnecessary adornments that convey no useful information.
- Any two-dimensional graph should contain a scale for each axis.
- The scale on the vertical axis should begin at zero.
- All axes should be properly labeled.
- The graph should contain a title.
- The simplest possible graph should be used for a given set of data.

Often these guidelines are unknowingly violated by individuals unaware of how to construct appropriate graphs.

Another issue is the temptation to create pretty charts if you use programs such as Microsoft Excel. Excel allows you to easily create fancy charts that may appear pretty, but are unwise choices. Taking a simple pie chart and making it prettier by adding exploded 3D slices is unwise as this can complicate a viewer's interpretation of the data. Uncommon chart choices such as doughnut, radar, surface, bubble, cone, and pyramid charts may look visually striking, but obscure the data in most cases.

To most effectively present information, make sure that the tables and charts you create are simple and clear.

Ethical Concerns

Inappropriate graphs raise ethical concerns. Such graphs can obscure unfavorable information or create false impressions of data, even if the inappropriate chart was developed naively. Consider the following sets of sales trend charts as shown in Figure 2.23. A casual viewer of these charts might think model B had the best sales trend and that models A and D had similar trends. A more careful examination of these line graphs shows that model B has the weakest sales trend and that model C and D actually have the *same* sales trend. A casual viewer gets misled because of the inconsistent scaling of the *Y* axis.

FIGURE 2.23
Four sales trend charts

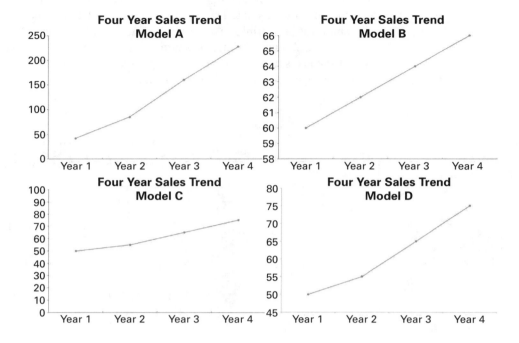

Problems for Section 2.6

APPLYING THE CONCEPTS

2.55 (Student Project) Bring to class a chart from a Web site, newspaper, or magazine that you believe to be a poorly drawn representation of a numerical variable. Be prepared to submit the chart to the instructor with comments as to why you believe it is inappropriate. Do you believe that the intent of the chart is to purposely mislead the reader? Also, be prepared to present and comment on this in class.

2.56 (Student Project) Bring to class a chart from a Web site, newspaper, or magazine that you believe to be a poorly drawn representation of a categorical variable. Be prepared to submit the chart to the instructor with comments as to why you consider it inappropriate. Do you believe that the intent of the chart is to purposely mislead the reader? Also, be prepared to present and comment on this in class.

2.57 (Student Project) According to its home page, Swivel is "a place where curious people explore data—all kinds of data." Go to **www.swivel.com** and explore the various graphical displays.

a. Select a graphical display that you think does a good job revealing what the data convey. Discuss why you think it is a good graphical display.

b. Select a graphical display that you think needs a lot of improvement. Discuss why you think that it is a poorly constructed graphical display.

2.58 The following visual display contains an overembellished chart similar to one that appeared in *USA Today*, dealing with the average consumer's Valentine's Day spending ("USA Today Snapshots: The Price of Romance," *USA Today*, February 14, 2007, p. 1B).

a. Describe at least one good feature of this visual display.
b. Describe at least one bad feature of this visual display.
c. Redraw the graph, using the guidelines given on page 99.

2.59 The following visual display contains an overembellished chart similar to one that appeared in *USA Today*, dealing with the estimated number of hours the typical American will spend using various media ("USA Today Snapshots: Minding Their Media," *USA Today*, March 2, 2007, p. 1B).

Media Usage
Estimated number of hours the typical American will spend using various media this year.

Listening to music — 175
Reading newspapers — 175
Using Internet — 195
Listening to Radio — 974
Watching TV — 1555

a. Describe at least one good feature of this visual display.
b. Describe at least one bad feature of this visual display.
c. Redraw the graph, using the guidelines given on page 99.

2.60 The following visual display contains an overembellished chart similar to one that appeared in *USA Today*, dealing with which card is safer to use ("USA Today Snapshots: Credit Card vs. Debit Card," *USA Today*, March 14, 2007, p. 1B).

Credit Card vs. Debit Card:
Which one is safer to use?

Don't Mind 49%
Credit Card 32%

a. Describe at least one good feature of this visual display.
b. Describe at least one bad feature of this visual display.
c. Redraw the graph, using the guidelines given on page 99.

2.61 An article in *The New York Times* (D. Rosato, "Worried About the Numbers? How About the Charts?" *The New York Times*, September 15, 2002, p. B7) reported on research done on annual reports of corporations by Professor Deanna Oxender Burgess of Florida Gulf Coast University. Professor Burgess found that even slight distortions in a chart changed readers' perception of the information. The article displayed sales information from the annual report of Zale Corporation and showed how results were exaggerated.

Using Internet or library sources, study the most recent annual report of a selected corporation. Find at least one chart in the report that you think needs improvement and develop an improved version of the chart. Explain why you believe the improved chart is better than the one included in the annual report.

2.62 Figures 2.1, 2.3, and 2.6 consist of a bar chart, a pie chart, and a Pareto chart for where people prefer to do their banking.
a. Use the chart features of Microsoft Excel to construct an exploded pie chart, a doughnut chart, a cone chart, and a pyramid chart for where people prefer to do their banking.
b. Which graphs do you prefer—the bar chart, pie chart, and Pareto chart or the exploded pie chart, doughnut chart, cone chart, and pyramid chart? Explain.

2.63 Figures 2.2 and 2.4 consist of a bar chart and a pie chart for the risk level for the mutual fund data.
a. Use the chart features of Microsoft Excel to develop an exploded pie chart, a doughnut chart, a cone chart, and a pyramid chart for the risk level of the mutual funds.
b. Do you prefer the bar chart and pie chart, or the exploded pie chart, doughnut chart, cone chart, and pyramid chart? Explain.

USING STATISTICS @ Choice Is Yours, Part I Revisited

In the Using Statistics scenario, you were hired by the Choice Is Yours Investment company to assist investors interested in mutual funds, a market basket of securities. A sample of 868 mutual funds was selected and information on the funds and past performance history recorded. For each of the 868 funds, data were collected on nine variables. With so much information, summarizing all these numbers required the use of properly selected graphical displays.

From bar charts and pie charts, you were able to illustrate that about 41% of the funds were classified as high risk, about 36% average risk, and only about 23% low risk. Cross tabulations of the funds by risk level and whether the funds main objective was growth or value, revealed that growth funds are more likely to be high risk, whereas value funds are more likely to be low risk. After constructing histograms on the 2006 return, you were able to conclude that both types of funds had returns that were approximately bell-shaped. The growth funds had more low returns as compared to the value funds, which had more high returns. The return for growth funds was concentrated between 0 and 15, whereas the return for vale funds is concentrated between 10 and 25. With these insights, you can inform your clients on how the different funds performed. Of course, past performance history does not guarantee future performance.

Graphical methods such as these are an important first step in summarizing and interpreting data. Although the proper display of data (as discussed in section 2.6) helps to avoid ambiguity, graphical methods always contain a certain degree of subjectivity. Next, you will need to select the proper types of numerical measures to further describe the mutual funds' past performance. Chapter 3 presents descriptive numerical measures (for example, mean, median, and mode).

SUMMARY

As you can see in Table 2.37, this chapter discusses data presentation. You have used various tables and charts to draw conclusions about where people prefer to bank, about the cost of restaurant meals in an urban area and its suburbs, and about the set of mutual funds in the Using Statistics scenario. Now that you have studied tables and charts, in Chapter 3 you will learn about a variety of numerical descriptive measures useful for data analysis and interpretation.

TABLE 2.37

Roadmap for Selecting Tables and Charts

	Type of Data	
Type of Analysis	**Numerical**	**Categorical**
Tabulating, organizing, and graphically presenting the values of a variable	Ordered array, stem-and-leaf display, frequency distribution, relative frequency distribution, percentage distribution, cumulative percentage distribution, histogram, polygon, cumulative percentage polygon **(Sections 2.2 and 2.3)**	Summary table, bar chart, pie chart, Pareto chart **(Section 2.1)**
Graphically presenting the relationship between two variables	Scatter plot, time-series plot **(Section 2.5)**	Contingency table **(Section 2.4)**

KEY EQUATIONS

WIDTH OF INTERVAL

$$\text{Width of interval} = \frac{\text{Range}}{\text{number of classes}} \qquad (2.1)$$

PROPORTION

$$\text{Proportion} = \text{Relative Frequency} = \frac{\text{frequency in each class}}{\text{total number of values}} \qquad (2.2)$$

KEY TERMS

bar chart   45
cells   92
chartjunk   99
class grouping   62
class midpoint   76
classes   62
contingency table   92
cross tabulations   92
cumulative percentage distribution   73

cumulative percentage polygon (ogive)   82
frequency distribution   61
histogram   79
ogive (cumulative percentage polygon)   82
ordered array   51
Pareto chart   47
Pareto principle   47
percentage distribution   71
percentage polygon   77

pie chart   46
proportion   71
relative frequency   71
relative frequency distribution   71
scatter plot   94
stem-and-leaf display   52
summary table   44
time-series plot   95

CHAPTER REVIEW PROBLEMS

CHECKING YOUR UNDERSTANDING

2.64 How do histograms and polygons differ in terms of construction and use?

2.65 Why would you construct a summary table?

2.66 What are the advantages and/or disadvantages of using a bar chart, a pie chart, or a Pareto chart?

2.67 Compare and contrast the bar chart for categorical data with the histogram for numerical data.

2.68 What is the difference between a time-series plot and a scatter plot?

2.69 Why is it said that the main feature of the Pareto chart is its ability to separate the "vital few" from the "trivial many"? Discuss.

2.70 What are the three different ways to break down the percentages in a contingency table?

APPLYING THE CONCEPTS

2.71 The following data represent the breakdown of the price of a new college textbook:

Revenue Categories	Percentage	
Publisher	64.8	
Manufacturing costs		32.3
Marketing and promotion		15.4
Administrative costs and taxes		10.0
After-tax profit		7.1
Bookstore	22.4	
Employee salaries and benefits		11.3
Operations		6.6
Pretax profit		4.5
Author	11.6	
Freight	1.2	

Source: *Data extracted from T. Lewin, "When Books Break the Bank," The New York Times, September 16, 2003, pp. B1, B4.*

a. Using the four categories publisher, bookstore, author, and freight, construct a bar chart, a pie chart, and a Pareto chart.

b. Using the four subcategories of publisher and three subcategories of bookstore along with the author and freight categories, construct a Pareto chart.

c. Based on the results of (a) and (b), what conclusions can you reach concerning who gets the revenue from the sales of new college textbooks? Do any of these results surprise you? Explain.

2.72 The following data represent the payment method used by young adults between 18 and 24 years of age:

Payment Method	Percentage
Cash	37
Check	2
Credit card	16
Debit card	44
Other	1

a. Construct a bar chart, a pie chart, and a Pareto chart.

b. What conclusions can you reach about the payment method used by young adults between 18 and 24 years of age?

2.73 People conduct hundreds of millions of search queries every day. In response, businesses are estimated to spend almost $20 billion annually on online ad spending (K. J. Delaney, "The New Benefits of Web-Search Queries," *The Wall Street Journal*, February 6, 2007, p. B3). The following represents the categories of online ad spending and the results of a Yahoo! keyword tool for searches related to sneakers.

Estimated 2007 U.S. Online Ad Spending

Type	Spending ($billions)
Classified	3.32
Display ads	3.90
Paid search	8.29
Rich media/video	2.15
Other	1.85
Total	19.51

Results of a Yahoo! Keyword Tool for Searches Related to "Sneakers"

Search result	Number of Occurrences
Jordan sneaker	13,240
Nike sneaker	8,139
Puma sneaker	6,768
Sneaker	58,995
Sneaker pimps*	15,357

Sneaker pimps is a British electropop band.

a. For type of online ad spending, construct a bar chart, a pie chart, and a Pareto chart.

b. Which graphical method do you think is best to portray these data?

c. For the results of "sneakers" searches, construct a bar chart, a pie chart, and a Pareto chart.

d. Which graphical method do you think is best to portray these data?

e. What conclusions can you reach concerning online ad spending and the results of "sneakers" searches?

2.74 The owner of a restaurant serving Continental-style entrées is interested in studying patterns of patron demand for the Friday-to-Sunday weekend time period. Records are maintained that indicate the type of entrée ordered. The data are as follows:

Type of Entrée	Number Served
Beef	187
Chicken	103
Duck	25
Fish	122
Pasta	63
Shellfish	74
Veal	26

a. Construct a percentage summary table for the types of entrées ordered.

b. Construct a bar chart, a pie chart, and a Pareto chart for the types of entrées ordered.

c. Do you prefer a Pareto chart or a pie chart for these data? Why?

d. What conclusions can the restaurant owner reach concerning demand for different types of entrées?

2.75 Suppose that the owner of the restaurant in Problem 2.63 is also interested in studying the demand for dessert during the same time period. She decided that two other variables, along with whether a dessert was ordered, are to be studied: the gender of the individual and whether a beef entrée is ordered. The results are as follows:

DESSERT ORDERED	GENDER		
	Male	Female	Total
Yes	96	40	136
No	224	240	464
Total	320	280	600

DESSERT ORDERED	BEEF ENTRÉE		
	Yes	No	Total
Yes	71	65	136
No	116	348	464
Total	187	413	600

a. For each of the two contingency tables, construct a contingency table of row percentages, column percentages, and total percentages.

b. Which type of percentage (row, column, or total) do you think is most informative for each gender? for beef entrée? Explain.

c. What conclusions concerning the pattern of dessert ordering can the owner of the restaurant reach?

2.76 The following data (extracted from R. Wolf, "Paper-Trail Voting Gets Organized Opposition," *USA Today*, April 24, 2007, p. 2A) represent the method for recording votes in the November 2006 election, broken down by percentage of counties in the United States using each method and the number of counties using each method in 2000 and 2006.

Method	Percentage of Counties Using Method in 2006
Electronic	36.6
Hand-counted paper ballots	1.8
Lever	2.0
Mixed	3.0
Optically scanned paper ballots	56.2
Punch card	0.4

Method	Number of Counties	
	2000	2006
Electronic	309	1,142
Hand-counted paper ballots	370	57
Lever	434	62
Mixed	149	92
Optically scanned paper ballots	1,279	1,752
Punch card	572	13

a. Construct a pie chart and a Pareto chart for the percentage of counties using the various methods.

b. What conclusions can you reach concerning the type of voting method used in November 2006?

c. What differences are there in the methods used in 2000 and 2006?

2.77 In summer 2000, a growing number of warranty claims on Firestone tires sold on Ford SUVs prompted Firestone and Ford to issue a major recall. An analysis of warranty-claims data helped identify which models to recall. A breakdown of 2,504 warranty claims based on tire size is given in the following table:

Tire Size	Warranty Claims
23575R15	2,030
311050R15	137
30950R15	82
23570R16	81
331250R15	58
25570R16	54
Others	62

Source: *Data extracted from Robert L. Simison, "Ford Steps Up Recall Without Firestone," The Wall Street Journal, August 14, 2000, p. A3.*

The 2,030 warranty claims for the 23575R15 tires can be categorized into ATX models and Wilderness models. The type of incident leading to a warranty claim, by model type, is summarized in the following table:

Incident	ATX Model Warranty Claims	Wilderness Warranty Claims
Tread separation	1,365	59
Blowout	77	41
Other/unknown	0,422	66
Total	1,864	166

Source: *Data extracted from Robert L. Simison, "Ford Steps Up Recall Without Firestone," The Wall Street Journal, August 14, 2000, p. A3.*

a. Construct a Pareto chart for the number of warranty claims by tire size. What tire size accounts for most of the claims?

b. Construct a pie chart to display the percentage of the total number of warranty claims for the 23575R15 tires that come from the ATX model and Wilderness model. Interpret the chart.

c. Construct a Pareto chart for the type of incident causing the warranty claim for the ATX model. Does a certain type of incident account for most of the claims?

d. Construct a Pareto chart for the type of incident causing the warranty claim for the Wilderness model. Does a certain type of incident account for most of the claims?

2.78 One of the major measures of the quality of service provided by any organization is the speed with which the organization responds to customer complaints. A large family-held department store selling furniture and flooring, including carpet, had undergone a major expansion in the past several years. In particular, the flooring department had expanded from 2 installation crews to an installation supervisor, a measurer, and 15 installation crews. During a recent year, the company got 50 complaints concerning carpet installation. The following data (contained in the file **Furniture**) represent the number of days between the receipt of the complaint and the resolution of the complaint:

```
54   5  35 137  31  27 152   2 123  81  74  27
11  19 126 110 110  29  61  35  94  31  26   5
12   4 165  32  29  28  29  26  25   1  14  13
13  10   5  27   4  52  30  22  36  26  20  23
33  68
```

a. Construct a frequency distribution and a percentage distribution.

b. Construct a histogram and a percentage polygon.

c. Form a cumulative percentage distribution and plot a cumulative percentage polygon (ogive).

d. On the basis of the results of (a) through (c), if you had to tell the president of the company how long a customer should expect to wait to have a complaint resolved, what would you say? Explain.

2.79 Data concerning 71 of the best-selling domestic beers in the United States are located in the file **Domesticbeer**. The values for three variables are included: percentage alcohol, number of calories per 12 ounces, and number of carbohydrates (in grams) per 12 ounces.

Source: *Data extracted from* **www.Beer100.com**, *May 1, 2008.*

a. Construct a percentage histogram for each of the three variables.

b. Construct three scatter plots: percentage alcohol versus calories, percentage alcohol versus carbohydrates, and calories versus carbohydrates.

c. Discuss the information you learned from studying the graphs in (a) and (b).

2.80 The data in the file **Spending** are the federal *per capita* spending, in thousands of dollars, for each state in 2004.

a. Develop an ordered array.

b. Plot a percentage histogram.

c. What conclusions can you reach about the differences in federal per-capita spending between the states?

2.81 The data in the file **SavingsRate** are the yields for a money market account, a one-year certificate of deposit (CD), and a five-year CD for 38 banks in south Florida, as of March 28, 2008 (extracted from **www.Bankrate.com**, March 28, 2008).

a. Construct a percentage histogram for each of the three variables.

b. Construct three scatter plots: money market account versus one-year CD, money market account versus five-year CD, and one-year CD versus five-year CD.

c. Discuss the information you learned from studying the graphs in (a) and (b).

2.82 The data in the file `CEO` represent the total compensation (in $millions) of CEOs of the large public companies in 2007 (extracted from "The Boss's Pay" *The Wall Street Journal*, April 14, 2008, pp. R5–R7).

a. Construct a frequency distribution and a percentage distribution.

b. Construct a histogram and a percentage polygon.

c. Construct a cumulative percentage distribution and plot a cumulative percentage polygon (ogive).

d. Based on (a) through (c), what conclusions can you reach concerning CEO compensation in 2007?

e. Are there any companies whose CEO has a total compensation below $500,000? If so, go to the company's Web site and see if you can find out a reason why the CEO has a total compensation below $500,000.

2.83 Studies conducted by a manufacturer of "Boston" and "Vermont" asphalt shingles have shown product weight to be a major factor in customers' perception of quality. Moreover, the weight represents the amount of raw materials being used and is therefore very important to the company from a cost standpoint. The last stage of the assembly line packages the shingles before the packages are placed on wooden pallets. When a pallet is full (a pallet for most brands holds 16 squares of shingles), it is weighed, and the measurement is recorded. The company expects pallets of its "Boston" brand-name shingles to weigh at least 3,050 pounds but less than 3,260 pounds. For the company's "Vermont" brand-name shingles, pallets should weigh at least 3,600 pounds but less than 3,800. The file `Pallet` contains the weights (in pounds) from a sample of 368 pallets of "Boston" shingles and 330 pallets of "Vermont" shingles.

a. For the "Boston" shingles, construct a frequency distribution and a percentage distribution having eight class intervals, using 3,015, 3,050, 3,085, 3,120, 3,155, 3,190, 3,225, 3,260, and 3,295 as the class boundaries.

b. For the "Vermont" shingles, construct a frequency distribution and a percentage distribution having seven class intervals, using 3,550, 3,600, 3,650, 3,700, 3,750, 3,800, 3,850, and 3,900 as the class boundaries.

c. Construct percentage histograms for the "Boston" shingles and for the "Vermont" shingles.

d. Comment on the distribution of pallet weights for the "Boston" and "Vermont" shingles. Be sure to identify the percentage of pallets that are underweight and overweight.

2.84 The data in the file `States` represent the results of the American Community Survey, a sampling of households taken in all states during the 2000 U.S. Census. For each of the variables average travel-to-work time in minutes, percentage of homes with eight or more rooms, median household income, and percentage of mortgage-paying homeowners whose housing costs exceed 30% of income:

a. Construct a frequency distribution and a percentage distribution.

b. Construct a histogram and a percentage polygon.

c. Construct a cumulative percentage distribution and plot a cumulative percentage polygon.

d. What conclusions about these four variables can you make based on the results of (a) through (c)?

2.85 The data in the file `Protein` indicate calorie and cholesterol information concerning popular protein foods (fresh red meats, poultry, and fish).
Source: *U.S. Department of Agriculture.*

a. Construct a percentage histogram for the amount of calories.

b. Construct a percentage histogram for the amount of cholesterol.

c. What conclusions can you reach from your analyses in (a) and (b)?

2.86 In Figure 2.18, a scatter plot of the relationship between the cost of a fast-food hamburger meal and the cost of movie tickets in 10 different cities was constructed. The file `Cost of Living` also includes the overall cost index, the monthly rent for a two-bedroom apartment, the cost of a cup of coffee with service, the cost of dry-cleaning a men's blazer, and the cost of toothpaste.

a. Construct six separate scatter plots. For each, use the overall cost index as the *Y* axis. Use the monthly rent for a two-bedroom apartment, the costs of a cup of coffee with service, a fast-food hamburger meal, dry-cleaning a men's blazer, toothpaste, and movie tickets as the *X* axis.

b. What conclusions can you reach about the relationship of the overall cost index to these six variables?

2.87 In Problem 2.48, using the data in the file `Chicken`, you constructed a scatter plot of calories with the total fat content of chicken sandwiches.

a. Construct a scatter plot of calories on the *Y* axis and carbohydrates on the *X* axis.

b. Construct a scatter plot of calories on the *Y* axis and sodium on the *X* axis.

c. Which variable (total fat, carbohydrates, or sodium) seems to be most closely related to calories? Explain.

2.88 The file `Gas Prices` contains the monthly average price of gasoline in the United States from January 2003, to April 2008. Prices are in dollars per gallon.
Source: *"U.S. Department of Energy,"* **www.eia.doe.gov**, *May 2, 2008.*

a. Construct a time-series plot.

b. What pattern, if any, is present in the data?

2.89 The data contained in the file `Drink` represent the amount of soft drink filled in a sample of 50 consecutive 2-liter bottles. The results are listed horizontally in the order of being filled:

2.109   2.086 2.066 2.075 2.065 2.057 2.052 2.044 2.036 2.038

2.031   2.029 2.025 2.029 2.023 2.020 2.015 2.014 2.013 2.014

2.012   2.012 2.012 2.010 2.005 2.003 1.999 1.996 1.997 1.992

1.994   1.986 1.984 1.981 1.973 1.975 1.971 1.969 1.966 1.967

1.963   1.957 1.951 1.951 1.947 1.941 1.941 1.938 1.908 1.894

a. Construct a time-series plot for the amount of soft drink on the Y axis and the bottle number (going consecutively from 1 to 50) on the X axis.

b. What pattern, if any, is present in these data?

c. If you had to make a prediction of the amount of soft drink filled in the next bottle, what would you predict?

d. Based on the results of (a) through (c), explain why it is important to construct a time-series plot and not just a histogram, as was done in Problem 2.30.

2.90 The S&P 500 Index tracks the overall movement of the stock market by considering the stock prices of 500 large corporations. The data file `Stocks2008` contains weekly data for this index as well as the daily closing stock price for three companies from January 2, 2008 to May 1, 2008. The variables included are:

WEEK—Week ending on date given

S&P—Weekly closing value for the S&P 500 Index

GE—Weekly closing stock price for General Electric

IBM—Weekly closing stock price for IBM

APPL—Weekly closing stock price for Apple

Source: *Data extracted from* **finance.yahoo.com,** *May 2, 2008.*

a. Construct a time-series plot for the weekly closing values of the S&P 500 Index, General Electric, IBM, and Apple.

b. Explain any patterns present in the plots.

c. Write a short summary of your findings.

2.91 (Class Project) Let each student in the class respond to the question "Which carbonated soft drink do you most prefer?" so that the teacher can tally the results into a summary table.

a. Convert the data to percentages and construct a Pareto chart.

b. Analyze the findings.

2.92 (Class Project) Let each student in the class be cross-classified on the basis of gender (male, female) and current employment status (yes, no) so that the teacher can tally the results.

a. Construct a table with either row or column percentages, depending on which you think is more informative.

b. What would you conclude from this study?

c. What other variables would you want to know regarding employment in order to enhance your findings?

REPORT WRITING EXERCISES

2.93 Referring to the results from Problem 2.83 concerning the weight of "Boston" and "Vermont" shingles, write a report that evaluates whether the weight of the pallets of the two types of shingles are what the company expects. Be sure to incorporate tables and charts into the report.

2.94 Referring to the results from Problem 2.77 concerning the warranty claims on Firestone tires, write a report that evaluates warranty claims on Firestone tires sold on Ford SUVs. Be sure to incorporate tables and charts into the report.

TEAM PROJECT

The data file `Mutual Funds` contains information regarding nine variables from a sample of 868 mutual funds. The variables are:

Category—Type of stocks comprising the mutual fund (small cap, mid cap, large cap)

Objective—Objective of stocks comprising the mutual fund (growth or value)

Assets—In millions of dollars

Fees—Sales charges (no or yes)

Expense ratio—Ratio of expenses to net assets in percentage

Return 2006—Twelve-month return in 2006

Three-year return—Annualized return, 2004–2006

Five-year return—Annualized return, 2002–2006

Risk—Risk-of-loss factor of the mutual fund (low, average, or high)

2.95 For the expense ratio:

a. Construct a percentage histogram.

b. Plot percentage polygons of the expense ratio for mutual funds that have fees and mutual funds that do not have fees on the same graph.

c. What conclusions about the expense ratio can you reach based on the results of (a) and (b)?

2.96 For the three-year annualized return from 2004 to 2006:

a. Construct a percentage histogram.

b. Plot percentage polygons of the three-year annualized return from 2004 to 2006 for growth mutual funds and value mutual funds on the same graph.

c. What conclusions about the three-year annualized return from 2004 to 2006 can you reach based on the results of (a) and (b)?

2.97 For the five-year annualized return from 2002 to 2006:

a. Construct a percentage histogram.

b. Plot percentage polygons of the five-year annualized return from 2002 to 2006 for growth mutual funds and value mutual funds on the same graph.

c. What conclusions about the five-year annualized return from 2002 to 2006 can you reach based on the results of (a) and (b)?

STUDENT SURVEY DATABASE

2.98 Problem 1.28 describes a survey of 50 undergraduate students (see the file `Undergradsurvey`). For these data, construct all the appropriate tables and charts and write a report summarizing your conclusions.

2.99 Problem 1.28 describes a survey of 50 undergraduate students (see the file `Undergradsurvey`).

a. Select a sample of 50 undergraduate students at your school and conduct a similar survey for those students.

b. For the data collected in (a), construct all the appropriate tables and charts and write a report summarizing your conclusions.

c. Compare the results of (b) to those of Problem 2.98.

2.100 Problem 1.29 describes a survey of 40 MBA students (see the file `Gradsurvey`). For these data, construct all appropriate tables and charts and write a report summarizing your conclusions.

2.101 Problem 1.29 describes a survey of 40 MBA students (see the file `Gradsurvey`).

a. Select a sample of 40 MBA students in your MBA program and conduct a similar survey for those students.

b. For the data collected in (a), construct all the appropriate tables and charts and write a report summarizing your conclusions.

c. Compare the results of (b) to those of Problem 2.100.

MANAGING THE *SPRINGVILLE HERALD*

Advertising fees are an important source of revenue for any newspaper. In an attempt to boost these revenues and to minimize costly errors, the management of the *Herald* has established a task force charged with improving customer service in the advertising department. Open a Web browser and link to **www.prenhall.com/HeraldCase/Ad_Errors.htm** (or open the `Ad_Errors.htm` file in the Student CD-ROM's Herald Case folder) to review the task force's data collection. Identify the data that are important in describing the customer service problems. For each set of data you identify, construct the graphical presentation you think is most appropriate for the data and explain your choice. Also, suggest what other information concerning the different types of errors would be useful to examine. Offer possible courses of action for either the task force or management to take that would support the goal of improving customer service.

WEB CASE

In the Using Statistics scenario, you were asked to gather information to help make wise investment choices. Sources for such information include brokerage firms and investment counselors. Apply your knowledge about the proper use of tables and charts in this Web Case about the claims of foresight and excellence by a Springville financial services firm.

Visit the EndRun Financial Services Web site at **www.prenhall.com/Springville/EndRun.htm** (or open the `EndRun.htm` file in the Student CD-ROM's Web Case folder). Review the company's investment claims and supporting data and then answer the following.

1. How does the presentation of the general information about EndRun on its home page affect your perception of the business?

2. Is EndRun's claim about having more winners than losers a fair and accurate reflection of the quality of its investment service? If you do not think that the claim is a fair and accurate one, provide an alternate presentation that you think is fair and accurate.

3. EndRun's "Big Eight" mutual funds are part of the sample found in the `Mutual Funds` worksheet. Is there any other relevant data from that file that could have been included in the Big Eight table? How would that new data alter your perception of EndRun's claims?

4. EndRun is proud that all Big Eight funds have gained in value over the past five years. Do you agree that EndRun should be proud of its selections? Why or why not?

REFERENCES

1. Huff, D., *How to Lie with Statistics* (New York: Norton, 1954).
2. *Microsoft Excel 2007* (Redmond, WA: Microsoft Corporation, 2007).
3. *Minitab for Windows Version 15* (State College, PA: Minitab, Inc., 2006).
4. Tufte, E. R., *Beautiful Evidence* (Cheshire, CT: Graphics Press, 2006).
5. Tufte, E. R., *Envisioning Information* (Cheshire, CT: Graphics Press, 1990).
6. Tufte, E. R., *The Visual Display of Quantitative Information*, 2nd ed. (Cheshire, CT: Graphics Press, 2002).
7. Tufte, E. R., *Visual Explanations* (Cheshire, CT: Graphics Press, 1997).
8. Wainer, H., *Visual Revelations: Graphical Tales of Fate and Deception from Napoleon Bonaparte to Ross Perot* (New York: Copernicus/Springer-Verlag, 1997).

APPENDIX A2a

CALCULATOR LESSON 1A

CASIO FX-9750G OR CFX-9850GB CALCULATOR

Introduction

To install the batteries and make the initial adjustments follow the instructions on the PINK pages inside the front cover of the owner's manual.

The GFX-9850GB has three keyboards:

i. The Primary keyboard
    –indicated on the keys

ii. The **Shift** keyboard
    –indicated in *yellow* above the keys

iii. The **ALPHA** keyboard
    –indicated in *red* above the keys

Common Operations

Clear screen	**AC/ON**
Insert	**SHIFT INS**
Delete	**DEL**
Move cursor	**Use cursor arrows**
Erase the last entry	**Use cursor arrow and typeover**
Power (exponent)	^

The function keys F1, F2 . . . F6 directly under the display are used to select functions shown at the bottom of the display at various times.

Calculations

RUN Mode:

Highlight the RUN icon and press **EXE**

or press **1 EXE** when the main menu screen is visible.

Note: If you change your mind about which *mode* you want to select, just press the menu key and this will always return you to the main menu screen.

EXAMPLE 2.21

To calculate the average of 38, 20, 18 and 23:

Enter the following into the calculator:
(38+20+18+23)÷4 EXE   You should get the result 24.75   Try it.

Correcting errors

Inserting: Suppose we should have entered 148 instead of 18 in the example above. Use the replay arrows, i.e. ◄ or ►, to position the cursor at the end or beginning of the previously entered calculation. Move the cursor until it is located under the 8 in 18. The 8 will flash on and off. Press **SHIFT INS**. A square blank cursor will now be flashing on and off. Press **4** followed by **EXE.**

We now have the following calculation:
(38+20+148+23)÷4 EXE   You should get the result 57.25   Try it.

Note: You may insert several digits consecutively without pressing **SHIFT INS** each time. The cursor will be insert mode any time that it appears as a square blank cursor.

Deleting

If, in fact, the original value of 18 is correct, we can delete the 4 as follows. Use the replay cursor followed by any cursor key to position the cursor under the 4. The 4 will flash on and off. Press the **DEL** key followed by **EXE**. We will now get the answer 24.75 of the original calculation.

Using the ANSWER of the Previous Calculation

Suppose we want to add 10 to the previously calculated average. Press + (the word Ans will appear on the display) and **10 EXE**. The result 34.75 will appear.

Now suppose we want to calculate 30/34.75 . Press **30 ÷ SHIFT Ans EXE** and the result 0.8633093525 appears.

Note: The calculator displayed 10 decimals for the answer above, however, it keeps 15 digits internally in case this number is to be used in further calculations. In this way round off errors are not likely to have occurred in the digits shown on the display.

Note: Suppose the calculator has shut off due to being inactive for several minutes, use the **AC/ON** key to turn the calculator back on. Choose the RUN icon and press **EXE** . The screen will be blank. Now press the ▲ cursor key followed by **EXE** and the screen will return to the last calculation that was done when the calculator was last on.

Working with DATA LISTS

LIST Mode:

Press the **MENU** key.

Highlight the LIST icon and press **EXE**

You will now have 6 blank lists set up on the screen. You can only see the Lists 1 to 4 at first, but if you move the ► cursor key you will be able to scroll over to the other 2 lists.

You can enter the data from the first example in List 1 as follows:

38 EXE
20 EXE
18 EXE
23 EXE

Note: If you make a mistake, use the following options on the bottom of the display: (If you are in **STAT mode**, use the F6 key (▷) to bring up these options.)

DEL	DEL-A	INS
F3	F4	F5

Now, if you press **F3** you can *delete* a highlighted data value. If you press **F5** you can create a space to *insert* a data value into the list. All other values will shift downward. To *change* a data value just highlight and typeover the old value and then key **EXE**.

Sorting a List

When on the list screen press the **F1** key (if you want to sort a list in ascending order). The calculator will ask you how many lists you want to sort. Answer this and press **EXE** . The calculator will now ask which list(s). Answer this and press **EXE** .

The calculator will immediately sort the list(s) specified.

Deleting a List

To delete a list, place the cursor on any entry in the list and press the **F4** key. The calculator will give you one last chance to change your mind. Delete the highlighted list by answering YES (**F1**).

Error Messages

When you make a syntax error, i.e. you key something that the calculator cannot understand, it tries to point out where the error has occurred. Key in the following:

2 ÷ × 5 – 3 ENTER

The calculator will respond **Syn ERROR** at the bottom of the screen.

Press the left or right cursor arrow and the calculator will return to the calculation and the cursor will be flashing on the entry that is causing the problem.

The SET-UP menu

The SET UP menu allows you to modify the default settings for the calculator. For example, you may want your answer to a series of calculations to have only 2 decimal places (possibly because the numbers represent dollars and cents). In order to FIX the number of decimal places to any calculation result you would get on the main calculation (RUN) screen and press:

SHIFT SETUP then scroll to **DISPLAY** and choose F1 (Fix) then choose the appropriate number of decimal places, in this case **F3** (for 2 decimals). Now press the **EXIT** key to return to the previous screen.

Now key in the following calculation: **2 ÷ 3 EXE** The calculator shows **.67**

To return to the normal 10 digits with floating point, you will have to reenter the **NORM1** setting from the SETUP menu.

APPENDIX A2b

CALCULATOR LESSON 1B

CASIO FX-9750GII CALCULATOR

Introduction
Common Operations

Clear screen	**AC$^{/ON}$**
Insert	**SHIFT INS**
Delete	**DEL**
Move cursor	**Use cursor arrows**
Erase the last entry	**Use cursor arrow and typeover**
Power ON	**AC$^{/ON}$**
Power OFF	**Shift AC$^{/ON}$**

The function keys F1, F2 … F6 directly under the display are used to select functions shown at the bottom of the display at various times.

Calculations

RUN-MAT Mode: Highlight the RUN icon and press **EXE**

or   press **1 EXE** when the main menu screen is visible.

Note: If you change your mind about which *mode* you want to select, just press the **MENU** key and this will always return you to the main menu screen.

EXAMPLE 2.22

To calculate the average of 54, 36, 27 and 15:

Select **"RUN-MAT"** mode and enter the following into the calculator:
(54+36+27+15)÷4 EXE   You should get the result 33   Try it.

Correcting errors

Inserting: Suppose we should have entered 157 instead of 15 in the example above. Use the replay arrows, i.e. ◄ or ► , to position the cursor at the end or beginning of the previously entered calculation. Move the cursor until it is located under the 5 in 15. The 5 will flash on and off. Press **SHIFT INS**. A square blank cursor will now be flashing on and off. Press **4** followed by **EXE.**

We now have the following calculation:
(54+36+27+157)÷4 EXE   You should get the result 68.5   Try it.

Note: You may insert several digits consecutively without pressing **SHIFT INS** each time. The cursor will be insert mode any time that it appears as a square blank cursor.

Deleting

If, in fact, the original value of 15 is correct, we can delete the 7 as follows. Use the replay cursor followed by any cursor key to position the cursor under the 7. The 7 will flash on and off. Press the **DEL** key followed by **EXE**. We will now get the answer 33 of the original calculation.

Using the ANSWER of the Previous Calculation

Suppose we want to add 20 to the previously calculated average. Press **+** (the word Ans will appear on the display) and **20 and del 4 and type 5**. The result 30.4 will appear.

Now suppose we want to calculate 30/30.4. Press **30 ÷ SHIFT Ans EXE** and the result 0. 9868421053 appears.

Note: The calculator displayed 10 decimals for the answer above, however, it keeps 15 digits internally in case this number is to be used in further calculations. In this way round off errors are not likely to have occurred in the digits shown on the display.

Note: Suppose the calculator has shut off due to being inactive for several minutes, use the **AC/ON** key to turn the calculator back on. Choose the RUN icon and press **EXE** . The screen will be blank. Now press the ▲ cursor key followed by **EXE** and the screen will return to the last calculation that was done when the calculator was last on.

SORT YOUR DATA

STAT MODE   Press the **MENU** key.
                     Highlight the STAT icon and press **EXE**

You will now have 26 blank lists set up on the screen. You can only see the Lists 1 to 4 at first, but if you move the ► cursor key you will be able to scroll over to the other lists.

You can enter the data from the first example in List 1 as follows:
Note: Key in the number and then press **EXE**.

54 EXE
27 EXE
36 EXE
15 EXE

Note: If you make a mistake, use the following options on the bottom of the display. If you have other options, use the F6 key (▷) to bring up these options.

OPTIONS	TOOL	EDIT	DEL	DEL-A	INS	▶

FUNCTIONS	F1	F2	F3	F4	F5	F6

(1) Option **EDIT(F2)**

If you wish to **change** a data value, place the cursor on the data value you want to change and press **F2 (EDIT)**. Suppose you want to change 15 to 26. Place the cursor on 15, press **DEL** key to delete 15 and then enter **26 EXE**.

(2) Option **DEL<F3>**

If you wish to **delete** a data value, place the cursor on the value you want to delete and press **F3 (DEL)**.

(3) Option **DEL-A(F4)**

If you wish to **delete** the whole list of data, place the cursor on any entry in the list and press **F4 (DEL-A)**. The calculator will give you one last chance to change your mind. Delete the highlighted list by answering YES **(F1)**. If you do not wish to proceed with the delete procedure, you press <NO> **F2**.

(4) Option **INS(F5)**

If you wish to **insert** one data value into the list, place the cursor on the value and press **F5 (INS)** to **insert** a data value above the highlighted data value.

(5) Option **TOOL(F1)**

To **sort** the data that was entered in List 1, you press **F1 (TOOL)**.

The calculator will show the following options on the bottom of the display.

OPTIONS	SRT-A	SRT-D	TOP	BTM

FUNCTIONS	F1	F2	F3	F4

The option **SRT-A** will sort a list in **A**scending order

The option **SRT-D** will sort a list in **D**scending order

The option **TOP** will bring the cursor to the top of the list.

The option **BTM** will bring the cursor to the bottom of the list.

Sorting a List

Press the **F1 (SRT-A)** key if you want to sort a list in ascending order. The calculator will ask you how many lists you want to sort. Answer this (by entering **1** if you have **one** list to sort) and press **EXE**. The calculator will now ask which list(s). Answer this (by entering **1** if the data is in List **1**) and press **EXE**.

The calculator will immediately sort the list(s) specified.

APPENDIX A2c

A2.1 MICROSOFT EXCEL

You can use Microsoft Excel to create many of these tables and charts discussed in this chapter. If you have not already read Appendix A1a, "Introduction to Microsoft Excel," on page 27, you should do so now.

Summary Tables

Use the PivotTable Wizard to generate a summary table. If you are not familiar with PivotTables, first read the "Using the PivotTable Wizard" (see Appendix F). To generate a summary table, open the **MUTUALFUNDS2004.xls** workbook to the **Data** worksheet. Select **Data ➔ PivotTable and PivotChart Report** (**Data ➔ PivotTable Report** in Microsoft Excel 97) and make these entries in the PivotTable Wizard dialog boxes:

Step 1: Select the **Microsoft Excel list or database** option and the **PivotTable** option (if it appears) and click **Next**.

Step 2: Enter **J1:J122** as the **Range** and click **Next**.

Step 3: Select the **New worksheet** option and click the **Layout** button.

In the Layout dialog box, first drag a copy of the **Risk** label to the **ROW** area. Then drag a second copy of the **Risk** label to the **DATA** area, which changes the label to **Count of Risk**. Click **OK** to return to the main Step 3 dialog box and click the **Options** button to continue.

In the PivotTable Options dialog box, enter a self-descriptive name for the table in the **Name** edit box and **0** in the **For empty cells, show** edit box. Click **OK** to return to the main Step 3 dialog box.

Click **Finish** in the main Step 3 dialog box to produce the PivotTable.

Rename the new worksheet with a self-descriptive name. (You can close any floating toolbars or windows that appear over the PivotTable to better view your table.)

To add a percentage column, enter **Percentage** in cell **C4** of the new worksheet and enter the formula **=B5/B$8** in cell **C5**. Copy this formula down through cell **C7**. Format the cell range **C5:C7** for percentage display. Adjust the number of decimals displayed and adjust the column C width if you would like to produce a table similar to Figure A2.1.

OR See section G.1 (**One-Way Tables & Charts**) if you want PHStat2 to produce a summary table for you.

Count of Risk		
Risk ▼	Total	Percentage
average	46	38%
high	17	14%
low	58	48%
Grand Total	121	

FIGURE A2.1 Completed Summary Table

Bar or Pie Chart

Use the Microsoft Excel Chart Wizard to generate a bar or pie chart. If you are not familiar with this wizard, first read "Using the Chart Wizard" (see page 27). First create a PivotTable summary table. With the table onscreen, click a cell outside the table, select **Insert ➔ Chart**, and make these entries in the Chart Wizard dialog boxes:

Step 1: Click either **Bar** (for a bar chart) or **Pie** from the **Standard Types Chart type** box and leave the first **Chart sub-type** selected. Click **Next**.

Step 2: With the blinking cursor in the **Data range** box, click the PivotTable to have Excel fill in the address of the PivotTable for you. Click **Next**.

Step 3: Select the formatting and labeling chart options for the chart. (See "Using the Microsoft Excel Chart Wizard" on page 27 for suggestions.) Click **Next**.

Step 4: Select **As new sheet** and click **Finish**.

If field buttons appear on the chart, right-click any field button and select **Hide PivotChart Field Buttons** from the shortcut menu.

OR See section G.1 (**One-Way Tables & Charts**) if you want PHStat2 to produce a bar or pie chart for you.

Pareto Diagram

See section G.1 (**One-Way Tables & Charts**) if you want PHStat2 to produce a Pareto diagram as a Microsoft Excel chart. (There are no Microsoft Excel commands that directly produce a Pareto diagram.)

Ordered Array

Organize your worksheet so that each variable appears in its own column, enter a variable column heading in row 1, and enter the values for the variable starting in row 2. (This is the format of the Excel files included on the CD-ROM packaged with this text.) Select **Data ➔ Sort**. In the Sort dialog box, select the variable to be sorted from the **Sort by** drop-down list. Select either the first **Ascending** or **Descending** option button and leave the **Header row** option button selected and click **OK**.

Stem-and-Leaf Display

See section G.2 (**Stem-and-Leaf Display**) if you want PHStat2 to produce a stem-and-leaf display as a Microsoft Excel chart. (There are no Microsoft Excel commands that directly produce stem-and leaf displays.)

Frequency Distributions and Histograms

Use the Data Analysis ToolPak to create frequency distributions and histograms. Open to the worksheet containing the data you want to summarize. Select **Tools ➔ Data Analysis**. From the list that appears in the Data Analysis dialog box, select **Histogram** and click **OK**. In the Histogram dialog box (see Figure A2.2), enter the cell range of the data in the **Input Range**. Then select **Labels** if you are using data that are arranged like the data in the Excel files on the CD-ROM packaged with this text. Finish by selecting **Chart Output** and clicking **OK**. (See section G.3 (**Histograms & Polygons**) for an explanation of the **Bin Range**.)

FIGURE A2.2 Data Analysis Histogram Dialog Box

The frequency distribution and histogram will appear together on a separate worksheet.

OR See section G.3 (**Histogram & Polygons**) if you want PHStat2 to produce a frequency distribution and a histogram for you.

Percentage and Cumulative Percentage Polygons

See section G.3 (**Histogram & Polygons**) if you want PHStat2 to produce percentage and cumulative percentage polygons as Microsoft Excel charts. (There are no Microsoft Excel commands that directly produce percentage and cumulative percentage polygons.)

Cross-Classification Table and Side-by-Side Chart

Use the PivotTable and Chart Wizards to create a two-way cross-classification table and a side-by-side chart. To create a cross-classification table, open the MUTUALFUNDS2004.xls workbook to the **Data** worksheet. Select **Data → PivotTable and PivotChart Report** (**Data → PivotTable Report** in Microsoft Excel 97) and make these entries in the PivotTable Wizard dialog boxes:

Step 1: Select the **Microsoft Excel list or database** option and the **PivotTable** option (if it appears) and click **Next**.

Step 2: Enter **C1:J122** as the **Range** and click **Next**.

Step 3: Select the **New worksheet** option and click the **Layout** button.
  In the Layout dialog box, first drag a copy of the **Objective** label to the **ROW** area. Then drag a second copy of the **Objective** label to the **DATA** area, which changes the label to **Count of Objective**. Drag a copy of the **Risk** label to the **COLUMN**

area. Click **OK** to return to the main Step 3 dialog box and click the **Options** button to continue.
  In the PivotTable Options dialog box, enter a self-descriptive name for the table in the **Name** edit box and **0** in the **For empty cells, show** edit box. Click **OK** to return to the main Step 3 dialog box.
  Click **Finish** in the main Step 3 dialog box to produce the PivotTable.

To create a side-by-side chart, click a cell outside the two-way table, select **Insert → Chart**, and make these entries in the Chart Wizard dialog boxes:

Step 1: Click **Bar** from the **Standard Types Chart type** box and leave the first **Chart sub-type** selected. Click **Next**.

Step 2: With the blinking cursor in the **Data range** box, click the PivotTable to have Excel fill in the address of the PivotTable for you. Click **Next**.

Step 3: Select the formatting and labeling chart options for the chart. (See "Using the Microsoft Excel Chart Wizard" on page 27 for suggestions.) Click **Next**.

Step 4: Select **As new sheet** and click **Finish**.
  If field buttons appear on the chart, right-click any button and select **Hide PivotChart Field Buttons** from the shortcut menu.

OR See section G.4 (**Two-Way Tables & Charts**) if you want PHStat2 to produce a two-way summary table and a side-by-side chart for you.

Scatter Diagram

Use the Chart Wizard to generate a scatter diagram. To create a scatter diagram, open the MUTUALFUNDS2004.xls workbook to the **Data** worksheet. Select **Insert → Chart**, and make these entries in the Chart Wizard dialog boxes:

Step 1: Click **XY (Scatter)** from the **Standard Types Chart type** box and leave the first **Chart sub-type** selected. Click **Next**.

Step 2: Enter **F1:G122** in the **Data range** box, select the **Columns** option, and click **Next**.

Step 3: Select the formatting and labeling chart options for the chart. (See "Using the Microsoft Excel Chart Wizard" on page 27 for suggestions.) Click **Next**.

Step 4: Select **As new sheet** and click **Finish**.

Be aware that the Chart Wizard always assumes that the first column of the data range (column F in this example) contains the X variable data. If you have a sheet in which the Y variable data appears first, you will need to first rearrange your columns (or copy them out of order to a new sheet) before using the Chart Wizard.

Using Microsoft Excel for Tables and Charts

E2.1 Introduction

This appendix describes how to use Microsoft Excel to create tables and charts. Because Excel 2007 changes many table and chart features, some appendix sections contain paired sets of instructions, such as Sections E2.2A and E2.2B, one for use with Excel 97–2003, the other for use with Excel 2007. Use only the set of instructions that applies to the Excel version that you have.

Before continuing, you should review the material in Appendix E1 on page 37 and Appendix C if you have not done so already.

Occasionally PHStat2 will be the only reasonable way to accomplish a task using Microsoft Excel. In such cases, an Excel appendix section will refer you to the appropriate PHStat2 appendix section.

E2.2 Creating Summary Tables

To create a summary table from unsummarized data, you create a PivotTable. To create a summary table from data already summarized in table form, enter the contents of the table into a blank worksheet, using row 1 cells for column headings.

You create a PivotTable by dragging the variable names of the unsummarized data into a form or template. Because the process differs between Excel 97–2003 and Excel 2007, use the instructions of either Sections E2.2A or E2.2B to complete this task.

E2.2A Creating PivotTables (Excel 97–2003)

To create a PivotTable in Excel 97–2003, open to the worksheet that contains your unsummarized data and select **Data → PivotTable Report** (Excel 97) or **Data → PivotTable and PivotChart Report** (Excel 2000–2003). When you make these selections you start the PivotTable Wizard, a sequence of three dialog boxes (four in Excel 97) that step you through the process of creating a PivotTable. Figure E2.1 shows the dialog boxes for Excel 2003. (Other versions have similar dialog boxes; Excel 97 uses four dialog boxes, breaking the third box into two.)

You step through these dialog boxes by clicking **Next** to advance to the next dialog box or **Back** to move back to a previous one. At any point, you can click **Cancel** to stop creating a PivotTable or click **Finish** to end the wiz-

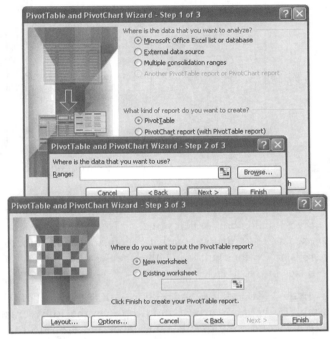

FIGURE E2.1 PivotTable Wizard steps (Excel 2003)

ard and create a PivotTable. To create a summary table, make the following entries in the Wizard Step dialog boxes:

Wizard Step 1 Click **Microsoft Excel list or database** as the source data and **PivotTable** as the report type. (You do not select a report type in Microsoft Excel 97; PivotTable is assumed.)

Wizard Step 2 Enter the cell range of the data to be summarized in the PivotTable. This cell range must contain variable labels (column headings) in the first row of the range because the wizard, in Step 3, will use the cells in the first row as the names for your variables.

Wizard Step 3 First, click the **New worksheet** option as the location for your PivotTable. Then click **Layout** to display the Layout dialog box (see Figure E2.2). Design your table using the instructions in the next paragraph and then click **OK** to return to the Step 3 box. Then, click **Options** to display the PivotTable Options dialog box (see Figure E2.2). Enter 0 as the **For empty cells, show** value and click **OK** to return to the Wizard Step 3 dialog box. Then, click **Finish** to create the PivotTable.

FIGURE E2.2 PivotTable Layout and Options dialog boxes (Excel 2000–2003)

(If you use Excel 97, the Layout dialog box appears as the Step 3 dialog box. When you click **Next** in this box, you then see a Step 4 dialog box that contains location options. There is no Options button in either the Step 3 or Step 4 dialog boxes in Excel 97.)

In the Layout dialog box of Step 3, drag the label of the variable to be summarized and drop it in the ROW area. Drag a second copy of this same label and drop it in the DATA area. This second label changes to **Count of variable name** to indicate that a count, or tally, of the occurrences of each category will be shown in the DATA area.

After Excel creates the PivotTable, close any floating PivotTable toolbar windows. Enter a title in cell A1 of the new worksheet that contains your PivotTable. Also, rename the new worksheet, using a descriptive name. In cell C4, enter **Percentage** and in cell C5, enter the formula in the form =**B5/B$***n*, in which ***n*** is the row that contains the Grand Total. (If you do not understand the significance of the $ symbol, you can review Section E1.7.) For example, if the Grand Total row is row 8, enter =**B5/B$8**. Copy this formula down through all the category rows and format the cell range that contains these formulas for percentage display. Further adjust the table display as is necessary, using Section E1.7 as your guide. (You may also need to adjust the width of columns by dragging the column rules at the top of the worksheet.)

E2.2B Creating Pivottables (Excel 2007)

To create a PivotTable in Excel 2007, open to the worksheet that contains your unsummarized data and select **Insert → PivotTable**. In the Create PivotTable dialog box (see Figure E2.3), leave the **Select a table or range** option selected and change, if necessary, the **Table/Range** cell range. (In Figure E2.3, the cell range is for the mutual funds data found in the

FIGURE E2.3 Create PivotTable dialog box and PivotTable Field List task pane (Excel 2007)

Data worksheet of **Mutual Funds.xls**.) Select the **New Worksheet** option and click **OK**.

In the PivotTable Field List task pane, drag the label of the variable to be summarized and drop it in the **Row Labels** box. Drag a second copy of this same label and drop it in the Σ **Values** box. This second label changes to **Count of variable name** to indicate that a count, or tally, of the occurrences of each category will be shown in the DATA area.

Right-click the PivotTable and click **Table Options** in the shortcut menu that appears. In the PivotTable Options dialog box (a reorganized version of the older one shown in Figure E2.2), click the **Layout & Format** tab, check **For empty cells show**, enter **0** as its value, and then click **OK**. Close the PivotTable Field List task pane. Enter a title in cell A1 of the new worksheet that contains your PivotTable. Also, rename the new worksheet, using a descriptive name.

In cell C4, enter **Percentage** and in cell C5, enter the formula in the form $=B5/B\$n$, in which n is the row that contains the Grand Total. (If you do not understand the significance of the $ symbol, you can review Section E1.7.) For example, if the Grand Total row is row 8, enter $=B5/B\$8$. Copy this formula down through all the category rows and format the cell range that contains these formulas for percentage display. Further adjust the table display as is necessary, using Section E1.7 as your guide. (You may also need to adjust the width of columns by dragging the column rules at the top of the worksheet.)

E2.3 Creating Charts: Overview

Although Microsoft Excel contains many features that create tables and charts, you can easily get improper results or otherwise get frustrated if you do not properly organize your worksheet data first. In Excel, charts are linked to sets of worksheet data, and the arrangement of that data influences the chart Excel creates. For example, when creating a scatter plot, Excel will always consider the first column of data as the X variable data. If you wanted to create the scatter plot of the cost of a fast-food hamburger meal and the cost of two movie tickets (Figure 2.18 on page 95), you would want to place the meal costs in a column to the left of the column containing the ticket costs.

The best way to avoid arrangement errors is to place your data on a separate worksheet using consecutive columns starting with column A. (Data worksheets in the Student CD-ROM Excel workbook files have this arrangement.) If you are using Microsoft Excel 2007, you should also select your data by dragging the mouse over your data, as explained in Appendix C, to prevent Excel 2007 from making a "bad" guess as to the table or chart you seek.

With these simple steps you will eliminate the most common errors that occur when using Excel charting features. However, creating a chart using Excel charting features does not necessarily end your task. Many charts will need minor reformatting to pass the strictest presentation standards. Illustrations in this book reflect such formatting and appendix sections throughout the book include reformatting instructions when appropriate.

Some charts, especially those created in Excel 97–2003, contain colored backgrounds (typically gray) that can interfere with clear printing or displaying of the chart. To remove the background in an Excel 97–2003 chart, right-click the background and click **Format Plot Area** in the shortcut menu. In the dialog box that appears, click the **None** option of the **Area** group and click **OK**. (This was done for all the charts shown in this book.) To remove a background in Excel 2007, right-click the chart background and select **Layout → Plot Area** and select **None** in the Plot Area gallery.

Occasionally, you may open to a chart sheet and see only part of a (too-large) chart or see a (too-small) chart surrounded by a too-large frame mat. To display an optimally sized chart in Excel 97–2003, open to the chart sheet and press **Esc**. Select **View → Zoom** and then, in the Zoom dialog box, select the **Fit selection** option and click **OK**. To display an optimally sized chart in Excel 2007, use the Zoom slider on the lower right of the Excel window frame or click the chart and then select **Format** and use the items in the Size group. Finally, if the symbols, captions, and/or legends and titles prove too big or too small for you, you can usually change these elements by right-clicking over them and clicking the shortcut menu choice that contains the word **Format**.

If you use PHStat2, the charts created by PHStat2 will generally include these minor reformatting and enhancements discussed above.

E2.3A Creating Charts (Excel 97–2003)

To create a chart in Excel 97–2003, open to the worksheet containing your unsummarized data and select **Insert → Chart** to begin the Chart Wizard, a sequence of four dialog boxes that step you through the process of creating a chart. (Figure E2.4 shows these dialog boxes for Excel 2003. Excel 97, 2000, and 2002 have similar sets of dialog boxes.) To create a chart, make the following entries in the Wizard Step dialog boxes:

Wizard Step 1 Choose the chart type from either the **Standard Types** or **Custom Types** tab. Most of the charts you create in this text are chart types found in the Standard Types tab.

Wizard Step 2 Enter the cell range of the data to be charted in the **Data Range** tab. For some types of charts, you also enter the cell range or ranges that contain chart labeling information in the **Series** tab. Cell ranges in the Series tab must always be entered with their worksheet names as a formula, in the form $=SheetName!CellRange$.

Wizard Step 3 Enter titles and select formatting options for your chart in the various tabs of this dialog box. Unless told otherwise in later instructions, make the following entries and selections:

FIGURE E2.4 Chart Wizard dialog boxes (Excel 2003)

In the **Titles** tab, enter a title and enter axis labels if appropriate. In the **Axes** tab, click both the (X) axis and (Y) axis check boxes and click **Automatic** under the (X) axis check box. In the **Gridlines** tab, clear all the check boxes. In the **Legend** tab, clear the **Show legend** check box. In the **Data Labels** tab, click the **None** option under the **Data labels** heading. In the **Data Table** tab, clear the **Show data table** check box. (Not all tabs are displayed for all chart types. If a tab is not displayed, skip the instructions for the tab.)

Wizard Step 4 Click the **As new sheet** option to place the chart on its own chart sheet. Then click **Finish** to create the chart.

*Because the Wizard Step 4 dialog box instructions never vary, they are not explicitly listed in later instructions. You should always click **As new sheet** and **Finish** in this dialog box when you create a chart.*

If you discover a mistake in your chart after your chart is created, right-click the chart and select **Chart Type, Source Data, Chart Options**, or **Location** to return to versions of the Wizard Step 1, Step 2, Step 3, or Step 4 dialog boxes, respectively.

E2.3B Creating Charts (Excel 2007)

To create a chart in Excel 2007, open to the worksheet that contains your unsummarized data. Select the cell range of the data to be charted. If your cell range contains two nonadjacent areas, hold down the **Ctrl** key as you drag and select each area. Select **Insert** and in the **Charts** group, click the chart type. From the drop-down gallery that appears, click the chart sub-type you want. To help distinguish sub-types, move the mouse pointer over a sub-type and wait for a description to be displayed. In Figure E2.5, the description for the bar chart "clustered bar" sub-type is displayed.

Customize your chart by clicking the chart and selecting the **Layout** tab of the Chart Tools ribbon group (or PivotChart Tools, if the chart is based on a PivotTable). Review the settings for the members of the **Labels** and **Axes** groups in this tab. Unless told otherwise in later instructions, make the following entries and selections (for a given chart type, some of these items may be disabled and not available):

Click **Chart Title** and choose either **Centered Overlay Title** or **Above Chart**. Click **Axes Titles → Primary Horizontal Axis Title → Title Below Axis**. Click **Axes Titles → Primary Vertical Axis Title → Rotated Title**. (For charts with secondary axes, select **Title Below Axis** as the **Secondary Horizontal Axis Title** and **None** as the **Secondary Vertical Axis Title**.) Click **Data Labels → None** and click **Data Table → None**.

Click **Axes → Primary Horizontal Title → Show Left to Right Axis**. Click **Axes → Primary Vertical Title → Show Default Axis**. Some charts have secondary axes; for

FIGURE E2.5 Selecting a chart sub-type (Excel 2007)

such charts, select **None** as the **Secondary Horizontal Axis Title** and **Show Default Axis** as the **Secondary Vertical Axis Title**. Click **Gridlines**. Select **None** for both the **Primary Horizontal Gridlines** and **Primary Vertical Gridlines**. Also select **None** for secondary gridlines, if the chart contains those as well.

Excel 2007 creates charts on worksheets. To move a chart to its own chart sheet (recommended), right-click the chart frame and click **Move Chart** in the shortcut menu that appears. In the Move Chart dialog box that appears, select the **New sheet** option and click **OK**.

E2.4 Creating Bar and Pie Charts: Overview

You create bar and pie charts from summary tables such as PivotTables using Excel charting features. You cannot create bar and pie charts directly from unsummarized data using Excel unless you use PHStat2.

E2.4A Creating Bar and Pie Charts (Excel 97–2003)

Open to the worksheet that contains your summary table. If your summary table is a PivotTable, click a cell that is outside your PivotTable. Select **Insert ➔ Chart** to begin the Chart Wizard and make the following entries in the Wizard Step dialog boxes:

Wizard Step 1 Click the **Standard Types** tab. For a bar chart, click **Bar** as the **Chart type** and then click the first **Chart**

sub-type choice, labeled **Clustered Bar** when selected. For a pie chart, click **Pie** as the **Chart type** and then click the first **Chart sub-type** choice, labeled **Pie** when selected.

Wizard Step 2 Click the **Data Range** tab and enter the cell range of the category labels and the frequency counts as the **Data range**. If you used the instructions in Section E2.2 to create your summary table, this range will always start with cell A4 and end with a cell in column B. (You do not include the column C cells that contain the percentages.) Click the **Columns** option if it is visible. In some Excel versions the model chart shown in the dialog box contains additional boxed labels that you can ignore for now.

Wizard Step 3 Click the **Titles** tab. Enter a title as the **Chart title** and, if you are creating a bar chart, enter appropriate values for the **Category (X) axis** and **Value (Y) axis** titles. For a bar chart, click, in turn, the **Axes**, **Gridlines**, **Legend**, **Data Labels**, and **Data Table** tabs and adjust the settings, as discussed in Section E2.3A. For a pie chart, click the **Legend** tab and clear **Show legend** and then click the **Data Labels** tab. If you are using Excel 97 or Excel 2000, click the **Show label and percent** option; otherwise, click **Category name** and **Percentage**.

If the chart created contains the additional boxed labels, such as "Drop Page Fields Here," that you ignored in the Step 2 dialog box, right-click the category drop-down list on the chart sheet and click **Hide PivotChart Field Buttons**. This eliminates the clutter and makes your chart look more like the ones throughout Chapter 2.

E2.4B Creating Bar and Pie Charts (Excel 2007)

Open to the worksheet that contains your summary table. Click a cell inside your table and then select **Insert**. For a bar chart, click **Column** in the Charts group, and then click **Clustered Column** in the chart gallery. For a pie chart, click **Pie** in the Charts group, and then click **Pie** in the chart gallery. Adjust chart settings as discussed in Section E2.3B.

E2.5 Creating Pareto Charts: Overview

You create a Pareto chart from a modified summary table by using Excel charting features. You modify your summary table by adding a column for cumulative percentage. If you have used the Section E2.2 instructions to create a PivotTable, enter the heading **Cumulative Pctage** in cell D4 and enter the formula **=C5** in cell D5. In cell D6, enter the formula **=C6+D5** and copy this formula down through all the category rows of the summary table. Format the column D cell range that contains formulas for percentage display. Adjust the number of decimals displayed and the width of column D as necessary.

If you use Excel 2007, click cell B5 (the first frequency) and select **Home → Sort & Filter** (in the Editing group) → **Sort Largest to Smallest**. If you use Excel 97–2003, right-click cell A4 and click **Field Settings** in the shortcut menu (**Field**, if using Microsoft Excel 97). In the PivotTable Field dialog box that appears (see Figure E2.6), click **Advanced**. In the PivotTable Field Advanced Options dialog box that appears (also see Figure E2.4), select the **Descending** option and **Count of** *variable* from the **Using field** drop-down list. Click **OK** to return to the PivotTable Field dialog box and then click **OK** in that dialog box to return to the worksheet. (These last steps reorder the category rows in the table in descending order.)

With these changes, you can proceed to creating the actual Pareto chart using the instructions appropriate for the Excel version you use.

E2.5A Creating a Pareto Chart (Excel 97–2003)

With your workbook opened to the worksheet that contains the modified summary table, click a cell that is outside the summary table. Select **Insert → Chart** to begin the Chart Wizard and make the following entries in the Wizard Step dialog boxes:

Wizard Step 1 Click the **Custom Types** tab. Click **Built-in** and then click **Line - Column on 2 Axes** as the **Chart type**.

Wizard Step 2 Click the **Data Range** tab. Enter the cell range of the percentage and cumulative percentage frequencies, without their column headings, in the **Data range** edit box. This range will always start with cell C4 and end with a cell in column D. Click the **Columns** option in the **Series in** group and then click the **Series** tab. Enter as a **formula**

FIGURE E2.6 PivotTable Field and PivotTable Field Advanced Options dialog boxes (Excel 97–2003)

the column A cell range that contains the category labels as the **Category (X) axis labels**. Leave the **Second category (X) axis labels** box blank, if it appears.

Wizard Step 3 Click the **Titles** tab. Enter a title as the **Chart title**, the name of the variable in the **Category (X) axis** edit box, and **Percentage** in the **Value (Y) axis** edit box. Leave the other two boxes blank. Click, in turn, the **Gridlines**, **Legend**, **Data Labels**, and **Data Table** tabs and use the settings discussed in Section E2.3A.

The Pareto chart that the wizard creates contains a secondary (right) *Y*-axis scale that improperly extends past 100%. To correct this error, right-click that axis (you will see the popup message **Secondary Value Axis** when your mouse is properly positioned) and click **Format Axis** in the shortcut menu. In the **Scale** tab of the Format Axis dialog box, change the **Maximum** value to **1** and click **OK**. Right-click the primary (left) axis and repeat these instructions if the left axis needs rescaling too (you will see the popup message **Value Axis** when your mouse is properly positioned).

E2.5B Creating a Pareto Chart (Excel 2007)

Select the cell range of the data to be charted. (This range will begin with cell C4, if you used the Section E2.2B instructions to create a PivotTable.) Select **Insert → Column** (in the Charts group) and select the first sub-type, identified as **Clustered Column** when you move the mouse pointer over that sub-type and pause. Select **Format** and select the cumulative percentage series from the drop-down list in the Current Selection group. Then select **Format Selection** (from the same group) and in the Format Data Series dialog box select the **Secondary Axis** in the **Series**

Options panel and click **Close**. With the cumulative percentage series still selected in the Current Selection group, select **Design → Change Chart Type**, and in the **Change Chart Type** gallery, select the line chart identified as **Line with Markers** and click **OK**.

If your chart contains extraneous plots—for example, a plot of percentage frequencies—delete such plots one series at a time by doing the following: Select **Format** and then select an extraneous series from the drop-down list in the Current Selection group. Select **Design → Select Data**. In the Select Data Source dialog box (see Figure E2.7), select the extraneous **Legend Entries** series (**Percentage** in Figure E2.7) and click **Remove** and then **OK**.

FIGURE E2.7 The Select Data Source dialog box (Excel 2007)

Relocate your chart to a chart sheet and customize your chart, using the instructions in Section E.2.3B. If the secondary (right) *Y*-axis scale improperly extends past 100%, right-click the axis and click **Format Axis** in the shortcut menu. In the **Scale** tab of the Format Axis dialog box, change the value in the **Maximum** edit box to **1** and click **Close**. Right-click the primary (left) axis and repeat these instructions if the left axis needs rescaling too.

E2.6 Creating Ordered Arrays

To create an ordered array, first organize your worksheet so that each variable appears in its own column, enter a column heading in row 1, and enter the values for the variable starting in row 2. Select the data to be sorted. If you use Excel 97–2003, select **Data → Sort**. In the Sort dialog box, select the variable to be sorted from the Sort by drop-down list. Click the **Ascending** option button, click **Header row**, and click **OK**. If you use Excel 2007, select **Home → Sort & Filter** (in the Editing group) → **Sort Smallest to Largest**.

E2.7 Creating Stem-and-Leaf Displays

No Microsoft Excel features directly create stem-and-leaf displays.

E2.8 Creating Bins for Frequency Distributions

To create frequency distributions using Excel features, you must first translate your class groupings into what Excel calls **bins**.

Bins are numbers in an ordered list that define ranges for each row of a frequency distribution or each bar of a histogram. Unlike class groupings, which have well-defined lower and upper boundary values, the boundary values of each bin are implied. For a particular bin number, the range defined is all values that are less than or equal to the bin number and that are greater than the previous bin number, which must be a lower value.

In Chapter 2, Tables 2.20–2.21 use class groupings in the form *valueA but less than valueB*. You can translate class groupings in this form into nearly equivalent bins by creating a list of bin numbers that are slightly less than each *valueB* that appears in the class groupings. For example, the class groupings could be translated into nearly equivalent bins by using this list of bin numbers: 14.99 ("slightly less" than 15.0), 19.99, 24.99, 29.99, 34.99, 39.99, 44.99, 49.99, 54.99, 59.99, 64.99, 69.99, and 74.99).

If you have class groupings in the form "all values from *valueA* to *valueB*," such as the set 0.0 through 4.9, 5.0 through 9.9, 10.0 through 14.9, and 15.0 through 19.9, you can approximate each class grouping by choosing a bin number slightly more than each *valueB*, as in this list of bin numbers: 4.99 (slightly more than 4.9), 9.99, 14.99, and 19.99.

Because the first bin number always represents a range with no explicit lower boundary (other than negative infinity), a first bin can never have a midpoint. (You may have noticed in this chapter that in the charts in which midpoints are used as labels, the first bin is labeled with – and not with a midpoint.) To enter a list of bin numbers, use a blank column in the worksheet that contains your unsummarized data, entering the column heading "Bins" in the row 1 cell.

Unlike the frequency distributions shown in Chapter 2, you typically include frequency, percentage frequency, and cumulative percentage frequencies as columns of one table and not as separate tables. Also, unlike what is done in Chapter 2, in Excel, you create frequency distributions for individual categories, one at a time (e.g., growth funds or value funds) and not frequency distributions that contain two categories (e.g., growth and value funds). To create multiple category tables, you must combine columns from the individual tables using copy-and-paste operations.

FIGURE E2.8 The Data Analysis Histogram dialog box

E2.9 Creating Frequency Distributions and Histograms

To create frequency distributions and histograms from unsummarized data, use the ToolPak **Histogram** procedure. This procedure requires that you first translate your class groupings into bins, as explained in the previous section.

Open to the worksheet that contains the unsummarized data and verify that bin values have been placed in their own column. Begin the ToolPak add-in and select **Histogram** from the **Analysis Tools** list and then click **OK**. In the Histogram dialog box (see Figure E2.8), enter the cell range of the data to be summarized as the **Input Range**. Enter the cell range of the list of bin numbers (including the column heading "Bins") as the **Bin Range**. (If you leave Bin Range blank, the procedure creates a set of bins for you, but such bins are often not as well chosen as the ones you can specify yourself.) Click **Labels** to indicate that the first cells of the Input Range and Bin Range contain a label. Click **New Worksheet Ply** and **Cumulative Percentage**, and then click **Chart Output** (if you want to create a histogram). Click **OK** to create the frequency distribution (and histogram) on a new worksheet.

The frequency distribution that the ToolPak creates improperly contains an open-ended bin labeled **More**. To eliminate the More class, first manually add the frequency count of the More row to the count of the preceding bin and set the cumulative percentage of the preceding bin to 100%. Then, select the entire row containing the More row. Next, select **Edit → Delete** in Excel 97–2003 or right-click the selected row in Excel 2007. In the Delete dialog box, click **Shift cells up** and then click **OK**.

As you correct your frequency distribution, your histogram also changes, and the bar representing the incorrect More group disappears. However, the histogram will still contain these errors: There are gaps between the bars, the bins are labeled with their maximum bin values and not with

their midpoint values, and the secondary Y axis scale exceeds 100%.

To eliminate the gaps between bars, right-click inside one of the histogram bars. (You will see a popup message that begins with **Series 'Frequency'** when your mouse is properly positioned.) Click **Format Data Series** in the shortcut menu to display the Format Data Series dialog box. If you use Excel 97–2003, click the **Options** tab, change the value of **Gap width** to **0**, and click **OK**. If you use Excel 2007, move the **Gap Width** slider to **No Gap** in the **Series Options** panel of this dialog box.

To change the bin labels, enter the list of midpoint values in column D of the worksheet. Cell D2 should contain the heading **Midpoints** and cell D3 should contain ——— (which you should enter as '– to avoid an error). Right-click the tinted background of the chart. (You will see the ToolTip **Plot Area** when your mouse is properly positioned.) Click **Source Data** (Excel 97–2003) or **Select Data** (Excel 2007) in the shortcut menu. If you use Excel 97–2003, select the **Series** tab in the Source Data dialog box and enter the cell range of the midpoints as a formula, in the form =*SheetName*!*CellRange*, in the **Category (X) axis labels** box. Then delete the entry for the **Second category(X) axis labels** and click **OK**. If you use Excel 2007, click the **Edit** button under the **Horizontal (Categories) Axis Labels** heading in the Select Data Source dialog box. In the Axis Labels dialog box, enter the cell range of the midpoints as a formula, in the form =*SheetName*!*CellRange*, and click **OK**. (This range should start with the first midpoint value and not with the midpoint column heading.) Click **OK** a second time (in the original dialog box) to complete the task.

To rescale the secondary Y axis, right-click on the secondary (right) Y axis. (You will see a popup message that includes the words **Secondary** and **Axis** when your mouse is properly positioned.) Click **Format Axis** in the shortcut menu. If you use Excel 97–2003, change the **Maximum** in the **Scale** tab of the Format Axis dialog box to **1** and click **OK**. If you use Excel 2007, select the **Fixed** option for **Maximum** and enter **1** as the maximum value in the **Axis Options** panel of the Format Axis dialog box, and then click **OK**.

If you want to add a percentage frequency column to the frequency distribution, select column C and then select **Insert → Columns**. In the new column C, enter the heading **Percentage** in cell C2. Enter the formula **=B3/SUM(B:B)** in cell C3 and copy the formula down the column through the rest of the frequency distribution. Format column C for percentage display to complete the column.

E2.10 Creating Percentage and Cumulative Percentage Polygons

No Microsoft Excel features directly create percentage or cumulative percentage polygons.

E2.11 Creating Contingency Tables: Overview

You create a contingency table from unsummarized data by creating a PivotTable using instructions adapted from Section E2.2. To create a contingency table from data already summarized in table form, enter the contents of the table into a blank worksheet, using the column A and row 1 cells for row and column headings.

E2.11A Creating Contingency Tables (Excel 97–2003)

Adapt the instructions of Section E2.2A, "Creating PivotTables (Excel 97–2003)." When you get to the Step 3 instructions, modify them as follows. In the Layout dialog box in Step 3, first drag the label of the first variable to be summarized and drop it in the ROW area. Drag a second copy of this same label and drop it in the DATA area. (The label changes to **Count of variable name**.) Then drag the label of the second variable and drop it in the COLUMN area. In the PivotTable Options dialog box, also in Step 3, verify that both **Grand total for columns** and **Grand totals for rows** are checked (they should be) and that you have entered **0** as the **For empty cells, show** value. (Excel 97 does not contain this options dialog box.)

E2.11B Creating Contingency Tables (Excel 2007)

Adapt the instructions of Section E2.2B, "Creating PivotTables (Excel 2007)." When you get to the instructions for using the PivotTable Field List task pane, modify them as follows. In the PivotTable Field List task pane, drag the label of the variable to be summarized and drop it in the **Row Labels** box. Drag a second copy of this same label and drop it in the Σ **Values** box. (This second label changes to **Count of variable name**.) Then drag the label of the second variable and drop it in the **Column Labels** area. When you later right-click the PivotTable, click **PivotTable Options** in the shortcut menu. In the **Total & Filters** tab of the PivotTable Options dialog box, verify that both **Show grand totals for columns** and **Show grand totals for rows** are checked. Also, as stated in Section E2.2B, click the **Layout & Format** tab, check **For empty cells show**, and enter **0** as its value, and then click **OK**.

E2.12 Creating Scatter Plots: Overview

You use Excel charting features to create scatter plots. To create a scatter plot, the columns to be plotted must be arranged X variable column first, then Y variable column, reading left-to-right. (If your data are arranged Y then X, first cut and paste the Y variable column so it appears to the right of the X variable column before continuing.)

E2.12A Creating Scatter Plots (Excel 97–2003)

Open to the worksheet containing the properly arranged columns. Select **Insert ➔ Chart** (to begin the Chart Wizard) and make the following entries in the Wizard Step dialog boxes:

Wizard Step 1 Click **XY (Scatter)** from the Standard Types Chart type box and click the first Chart sub-type.

Wizard Step 2 Enter the cell range of the two variables in the **Data range** box and select the **Columns** option. If the two variables are in nonadjacent columns, first type or point to the cell range of the first variable, then type a comma, then type or point to the cell range of the second variable, and then press **Enter**. Do not make any entries in the **Series** tab of this dialog box.

Wizard Step 3 Click the **Titles** tab. Enter a title as the **Chart title** and enter appropriate values for the **Value (X) axis** and **Value (Y) axis** titles. Click, in turn, the **Axes**, **Gridlines**, **Legend**, and **Data Labels** tabs and use the formatting settings given in Section E2.3A.

E2.12B Creating Scatter Plots (Excel 2007)

Open to the worksheet containing the properly arranged columns. Select Insert fi Scatter and click the Scatter with only Markers gallery choice. Finish by relocating your chart to a chart sheet and customizing your chart using the instructions in Section E.2.3B.

E2.13 Creating Time-Series Plots

You create time-series plots by using Excel charting features with a time-series worksheet in which the time periods have been entered into columns. If your data are arranged with the numerical variable before the time variable, first cut and paste the numerical variable column so it appears to the right of the time variable column before continuing.

E2.13A Creating a Time-Series Plot (Excel 97–2003)

Open to the worksheet containing the properly arranged columns. Select **Insert ➔ Chart** to begin the Chart Wizard and make the following entries in the Wizard Step dialog boxes:

Wizard Step 1 Click **Line** from the Standard Types Chart type box and select the first Chart sub-type in the second row, identified as **Line with markers displayed at each data value**.

Wizard Step 2 Enter the cell range of the two variables in the **Data range** box and select the **Columns** option. If the variables are in nonadjacent columns, first type or point to the cell range of the first variable, then type a comma, then type or point to the cell range of the second variable, and then press **Enter**. Do not make any entries in the **Series** tab of this dialog box.

Wizard Step 3 Click the **Titles** tab. Enter a title as the **Chart title** and enter appropriate values for the **Value (X)** axis and **Value (Y) axis** titles. Click, in turn, the **Axes**, **Gridlines**, **Legend**, **Data Labels**, and **Data Table** tabs and use the formatting settings that are given in Section E2.3A.

E2.13B Creating a Time-Series Plot (Excel 2007)

Open to the worksheet containing the properly arranged columns. In the Select Data Source dialog box, select **Insert → XY (Scatter) → Scatter with Straight Lines and Markers**. Finish by relocating your chart to a chart sheet and customizing your chart using the instructions in Section E.2.3B.

TABLE R.1

2001 Census of Population (46 Large Urban Centres, Census Tracts (neighbourhoods))

2001 Population by Age and Sex—Toronto (932 areas)		
Characteristic:	**0001.00**	**0002.00**
Population, 1996 (100% data)	695	563
Population, 2001 (100% data)	626	658
Male, total population	345	320
0–4 years, Male population	15	10
5–9 years, Male population	25	20
10–14 years, Male population	20	40
15–19 years, Male population	20	30
20–24 years, Male population	30	10
25–29 years, Male population	40	10
30–34 years, Male population	40	15
35–39 years, Male population	40	15
40–44 years, Male population	30	25
45–49 years, Male population	35	35
50–54 years, Male population	15	50
55–59 years, Male population	15	30
60–64 years, Male population	10	10
65–69 years, Male population	5	5
70–74 years, Male population	10	10
75–79 years, Male population	0	10
80–84 years, Male population	0	0
85+ years, Male population	0	0

TABLE R.2

Profile of Income of Individuals, Families and Households, Social and Economic Characteristics of Individuals, Families and Households, Housing Costs, and Religion, for Census Metropolitan Areas and Census Agglomerations, 2001 Census

Toronto	
Title	**Count**
Census family income in 2000 of all families—20% Sample Data	1,280,960
Under $10,000	64,190
$ 10,000–$19,999	66,645
$ 20,000–$29,999	112,350
$ 30,000–$39,999	120,075
$ 40,000–$49,999	119,000
$ 50,000–$59,999	113,210
$ 60,000–$69,999	111,850
$ 70,000–$79,999	100,170
$ 80,000–$89,999	86,690
$ 90,000–$99,999	73,065
$100,000 and over	313,720
Average family income $	81,245
Median family income $	63,700

TABLE R.3

Profile of Income of Individuals, Families and Households, Social and Economic Characteristics of Individuals, Families and Households, Housing Costs, and Religion, for Census Metropolitan Areas and Census Agglomerations, 2001 Census

Title	Count
Total income in 2000 of population 15 years and over—20% Sample Data	3,728,980
Without income	214,230
With income	3,514,750
Under $1,000	168,025
$ 1,000–$ 2,999	159,175
$ 3,000–$ 4,999	132,710
$ 5,000–$ 6,999	136,835
$ 7,000–$ 9,999	188,715
$10,000–$11,999	142,605
$12,000–$14,999	223,650
$15,000–$19,999	288,290
$20,000–$24,999	262,395
$25,000–$29,999	247,090
$30,000–$34,999	267,745
$35,000–$39,999	217,710
$40,000–$44,999	198,250
$45,000–$49,999	141,795
$50,000–$59,999	228,750
$60,000 and over	511,015

Toronto

Title	Count
Total number of children at home—20% Sample Data	1,641,660
Under 6 years of age	351,595
6–14 years	560,230
15–17 years	178,705
18–24 years	326,785
25 years and over	224,345
Total number of private households by household size—100% Data	1,634,755
1 person	360,870
2 persons	448,290
3 persons	288,305
4-5 persons	451,485
6 or more persons	85,805

	1999					
Data including employer-sponsored registered pension plans	**Age of the individual/family unit member with the highest pre-tax income**					
	Total	**Under 35**	**35–44**	**45–54**	**55–64**	**65 and older**
			%			
All family units' net worth groups	**100.0**	**100.0**	**100.0**	**100.0**	**100.0**	**100.0**
Negative	5.9	15.2	4.8	x	x	x
Less than $5,000	9.3	17.0	7.7	5.6	7.1	6.3
$5,000 to $14,999	8.0	15.3	7.3	4.5	x	5.1
$15,000 to $29,999	5.7	9.2	6.6	3.7	x	3.4
$30,000 to $49,999	6.4	9.2	7.5	4.8	x	4.5
$50,000 to $74,999	7.3	9.1	9.1	5.7	x	6.0
$75,000 to $99,999	5.6	5.7	7.2	5.3	x	4.3
$100,000 to $149,999	8.9	6.5	12.8	9.0	6.2	8.6
$150,000 to $249,999	13.4	5.9	16.4	15.8	13.0	17.7
$250,000 to $499,999	16.1	4.6	13.8	24.3	20.5	23.9
$500,000 to $999,999	9.3	x	5.0	13.4	21.3	13.7
$1,000,000 and over	4.0	x	1.8	5.0	10.5	6.0

x Data unavailable, not applicable or confidential.
1. Family units: economic families (a group of two or more persons who live in the same dwelling and are related to each other by blood, marriage, common law or adoption) and unattached individuals (a person living either alone or with others to whom he or she is unrelated).
Source: *Statistics Canada, Survey of Financial Security.*

TABLE R.6

Profile of Labour Force Activity, Class of Worker, Occupation, Industry, Place of Work, Mode of Transportation, Language of Work and Unpaid Work, for Census Metropolitan Areas and Census Agglomerations, 2001 Census

Title	Count
Total population 15 years and over by hours spent doing unpaid housework—20% Sample Data	3,728,980
No hours of unpaid housework	439,155
Less than 5 hours of unpaid housework	977,565
5 to 14 hours of unpaid housework	1,205,890
15 to 29 hours of unpaid housework	662,550
30 to 59 hours of unpaid housework	315,790
60 hours or more of unpaid housework	128,030

3

Numerical Descriptive Measures

Learning Objectives

In this chapter, you learn:

- To describe the properties of central tendency, variation, and shape in numerical data
- To compute descriptive summary measures for a population
- To construct and interpret a boxplot
- To describe the covariance and the coefficient of correlation

@ Choice Is Yours, Part II

The tables and charts you prepared for the sample of 868 mutual funds has proved useful to the customers of the Choice Is Yours service. However, customers have become frustrated trying to evaluate mutual fund performance. Although they know how the 2006 returns are distributed, they have no idea what a typical 2006 rate of return would be for a particular category of mutual funds, such as low-risk funds, nor do they know how that typical value compares to the typical values of other categories. They also have no idea of the extent of the variability in the 2006 rate of return. Are all the values relatively similar, or do they include very small and very large values? Are there a lot of small values and a few large ones, or vice versa, or are there a similar number of small and large values?

How could you help the customers get answers to these questions so that they could better evaluate the mutual funds?

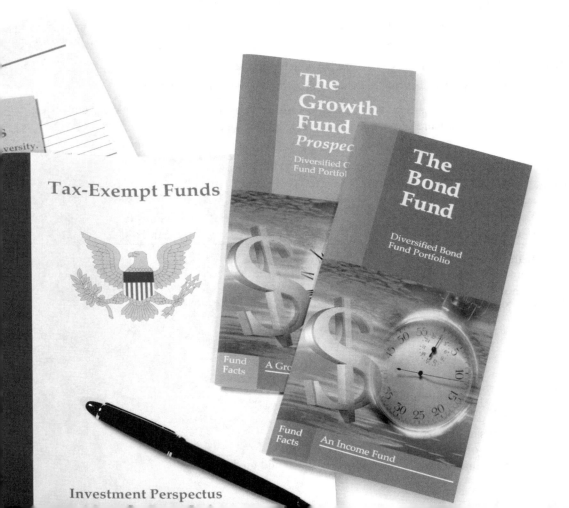

The customers in the Using Statistics scenario are asking questions about numerical variables. When summarizing and describing numerical variables, you need to do more than just prepare the tables and charts discussed in Chapter 2. You need to consider the central tendency, variation, and shape of each numerical variable.

CENTRAL TENDENCY

The **central tendency** is the extent to which all the data values group around a typical or central value.

VARIATION

The **variation** is the amount of dispersion, or scattering, of values away from a central value.

SHAPE

The **shape** is the pattern of the distribution of values from the lowest value to the highest value.

This chapter discusses ways you can measure the central tendency, variation, and shape of a variable. You will also learn about the covariance and the coefficient of correlation, which help measure the strength of the association between two numerical variables. Using these measures would give the customers of the Choice Is Yours service the answers they seek.

3.1 Descriptive Statistics I: Measures of Central Tendency

Descriptive statistics are numbers calculated to describe various aspects of a data set. The two most important types of descriptive statistics are:

Measures of Central Tendency: A single value to represent the data set.

Measures of Variability: A single value to describe how spread out the data is.

In this section you will learn how to calculate various measures of central tendency and also how to calculate a measure of position, which is a related topic.

Mean

I: Arithmetic Mean (Average):

Symbol:	Population Parameter	Sample Statistic
Mean (Average)	μ	$\bar{x}$
Standard Deviation	σ	s
Variance	σ^2	s^2
Size (Number of items or elements)	N	n

Symbol: Sample Mean: $\bar{x}$ Population Mean: μ

Formula: $\bar{x} = \dfrac{\sum x}{n}$ $\mu = \dfrac{\sum x}{N}$

where: x = data
n = sample size
N = population size
$\sum$ = summation   therefore $\sum x$ = add up the data

EXAMPLE 3.1

A fast food franchise has many outlets across the country. One small restaurant in the city where you live has seven full-time employees who earn $38, 20, 20, 18, 18, 18 and 23 thousand annually. Calculate the average salary of these employees.

SOLUTION:

$$\bar{x} = \frac{\sum x}{n} = \frac{38 + 20 + 20 + 18 + 18 + 18 + 23}{7} = \$22.1 \text{ thou. per employee}$$

Note: Regarding the form of the answer, use one more figure than the data if the data has 1 or 2 figures. Otherwise, the answer should look like the data.

Example: If data is: 1.3   2.4   3.6   then $\bar{x} = 2.53$

If the data has 3 or more figures, the answer should look like the data.
e.g. If data is: 234, 315 and 484   then $\bar{x} = 344$

II. Weighted Mean

EXAMPLE 3.2

The salaries of all the employees in the outlets in the city where you live can be summarized in the following table:

Job Classification	Number of Employees	Annual Salary ($000's)
Senior Management	3	52
Middle Management	10	38
Cooking Staff	45	20
Serving Staff	74	18
Maintenance Staff	7	23

Calculate the average salary of these employees.

SOLUTION: In this example the salary figures again need to be averaged. However, we realize that it would be incorrect to add the figures and divide by 5 since this would only be correct if there were an equal number of employees in each category. To take into account the differing number of employees in each category, we must use the **Weighted** method to calculate the mean salary. Many textbooks call the result of this calculation, the **Weighted Mean**.
    The formula for the weighted mean is as follows:

$$\bar{x} = \frac{\sum wx}{\sum w}$$

where x = data
        w = weights   i.e. numbers to indicate the relative importance of each data value in the overall result.
    In this example:
        x = the salaries
        w = the number of employees.

$$\bar{x} = \frac{\sum wx}{\sum w} = \frac{(3 \times 52) + (10 \times 38) + (45 \times 20) + (74 \times 18) + (7 \times 23)}{3 + 10 + 45 + 74 + 7}$$

$$= \frac{2929}{139} = \$21.1 \text{ thou. per employee}$$

Note: This formula also is 'logical' in that the denominator is 139, which is the total number of employees.

Sometimes the *relative frequency* or *percentages* are used as weights.

EXAMPLE 3.3

A cruise ship does several week-long cruises during a year. The ship is not always fully occupied. There are three types of cabins on this particular ship: interior (no port hole), deluxe exterior (porthole), and luxury exterior (private balcony). The price for each type of cabin and estimated percent of passengers in each type of cabin for the next cruise is shown below.

Cabin Style	Price each Person ($)	Percent of Passengers
Interior	1900	40
Deluxe exterior	2400	45
Luxury exterior	3200	15

Calculate the average revenue per person earned by the cruise company.

SOLUTION: In this example:

$$x = \text{the price for each person}$$
$$w = \text{the percentages.}$$

$$\bar{x} = \frac{\sum wx}{\sum w} = \frac{(40 \times 1900) + (45 \times 2400) + (15 \times 3200)}{40 + 45 + 15}$$

$$= \frac{23200}{100} = \$2,320 \text{ per person.}$$

There are two other common scenarios where the weighted mean is necessary.

a) Data to be averaged are themselves *averages*.
b) Data to be averaged are *percentages*.

EXAMPLE 3.4

Illustration of (A)

A car manufacturing company has assembly lines in four plants. Some data regarding the car production on these assembly lines for the past week are shown below.

Production Line	Number of Cars Produced	Average time per car (minutes)
Toronto	134	257
Montreal	105	248
Calgary	97	272
Vancouver	82	286

Calculate the overall average production time for all these cars.

SOLUTION: In this example:

$$x = \text{the average times}$$
$$w = \text{the number of cars.}$$

$$\bar{x} = \frac{\sum wx}{\sum w} = \frac{(134 \times 257) + (105 \times 248) + (97 \times 272) + (82 \times 286)}{134 + 105 + 97 + 82}$$

$$= \frac{110314}{418} = 264 \text{ min. per car}$$

EXAMPLE 3.5

Illustration of (B)

The following data refers to three divisions of a medium sized business.

Division	Profit Margin (%)	Sales ($ millions)
A	5	10
B	6	5
C	7	35

Calculate the overall average profit margin for the three divisions.

SOLUTION: In this example:

$$x = \text{the profit margin}$$

$$w = \text{the sales.}$$

$$\bar{x} = \frac{\sum wx}{\sum w} = \frac{(10 \times 5) + (5 \times 6) + (35 \times 7)}{10 + 5 + 35}$$

$$= \frac{325}{50} = 6.5\% \text{ (per division)}$$

One final scenario involving the calculating of a mean is also common.

III: Another Type of Mean

EXAMPLE 3.6

In a particular province there are three provincial parks. The Ministry of Natural Resources is interested in the concentration of moose in these parks. The results of a survey yielded the following data.

Provincial Park	Number of Moose	Area of park (km^2)
Moose Forest	134	2575
Moose Swamp	105	2037
Moosonee	97	2892

Calculate the overall average number of moose per square kilometer.

SOLUTION:

$$\bar{x} = \frac{\sum moose}{\sum area} = \frac{134 + 105 + 97}{2575 + 2037 + 2892}$$

$$= \frac{336}{7504} = 0.0448 \text{ moose per km}^2.$$

Note: When no other rule applies to the result of a particular calculation, we will use a general rule of **3 significant digits** (or more if the zeros are to the left of the decimal point).

The arithmetic mean is by far the most important measure of central tendency.

IV: Grouped data - Mean:
Suppose the only data available to us is in the form of a frequency or relative frequency (or percentage) distribution. Then in order to estimate the mean of the data we need to use the **class midpoints** to represent all the values in each class. We then use the weighted method to calculate the mean where the frequencies or relative frequencies will be the appropriate weights.

EXAMPLE 3.7 On a particular Saturday the amount paid for parking in a small downtown parking lot has been summarized in the following table:

Cost of Parking ($)	Number of cars (f)	%	Midpoint (m)
2.00 and under 4.00	20	18.3	3.00
4.00 '' '' 6.00	37	33.9	5.00
6.00 '' '' 10.00	29	26.6	8.00
10.00 '' '' 15.00	15	13.8	12.50
15.00 '' '' 20.00	8	7.3	17.50
Total	109	99.9	

Estimate the mean amount paid for parking.

SOLUTION: a) Using the frequencies as weights: (Note the symbols in the formula)

$$\bar{x} = \frac{\sum fm}{\sum f} = \frac{(20 \times 3.00) + (37 \times 5.00) + (29 \times 8.00) + (15 \times 12.50) + (8 \times 17.50)}{20 + 37 + 29 + 15 + 8}$$

$$= \frac{804.50}{109} = \$7.38 \text{ per customer.}$$

b) Using the percentages as weights:

$$\bar{x} = \frac{\sum \%m}{\sum \%}$$

$$= \frac{(18.3 \times 3.00) + (33.9 \times 5.00) + (26.6 \times 8.00) + (13.8 \times 12.50) + (7.3 \times 17.50)}{18.3 + 33.9 + 26.6 + 13.8 + 7.3}$$

$$= \frac{737.45}{99.9} = \$7.38 \text{ per customer.}$$

CALCULATOR LESSON 2

CASIO FX-9750GII CALCULATOR

Lesson 2—Calculations using STAT mode

STAT Mode: Press the **MENU** key.
Highlight the STAT icon and press **EXE**

You will now have 26 blank lists set up on the screen. You can only see List 1 to List 4 at first, but if you move the ▶ cursor key you will be able to scroll over to the other lists.

You can enter the data from the first example in the introductory handout in List 1 as follows:

38 EXE
20 EXE
20 EXE
20 EXE
18 EXE
18 EXE
23 EXE

EXAMPLE 1 (revisited)   To calculate the average of the salary data, use the **F6** key (▷) if necessary to get the following menu choices at the bottom of the display:

GRPH	CALC	TEST	INTR	DIST	▷
F1	F2	F3	F4	F5	F6

Now press **F2** (CALC) and you will get the following on-screen menu items:

1 VAR	2 VAR	REG			SET
F1	F2	F3			F6

Now press **F6** (SET) and you will get the following display:

1 Var	XList	:	List1
1 Var	Freq	:	1
2 Var	Xlist	:	List1
2 Var	YList	:	List2
2 Var	Freq	:	1

List 1	List 2	List 3	List 4	List 5	List 6

The first row will be highlighted. To select the desired list for your **1Var XList**, press **F1** (List). The calculator will now ask which list(s). Answer this (by entering **1** if the data is in List **1**) and press **EXE**.

You also want to have the 1Var Freq as **F1 (1)**.

Now press **EXIT** to return to the display of the data.

Now press **F1 (1 VAR)** and a full range of 1-variable statistics will appear. The result $\bar{x} = 22.4285714$ will be at the top of the list.

Now press **EXIT** to return to the data list display.

Weighted Data

Recall from the Measures of Central Tendency lecture notes that in example 2 we needed to calculate the mean salary for the following group of people:

TABLE 3.1

Job Classification	Number of Employees	Annual Salary ($000's)
Senior Management	3	52
Middle Management	10	38
Cooking Staff	45	20
Serving Staff	74	18
Maintenance Staff	7	23

Enter the values for the annual salary in List 1 and the corresponding values for the number of employees in List 2. The following keystrokes will calculate the **weighted** statistics:

Now enter the salaries **52 EXE   38 EXE   20 EXE   18 EXE   23 EXE** under List 1.

Position the cursor at the top of List 2. Now enter the weights (frequencies) **3 EXE   10 EXE   45 EXE   74 EXE   7 EXE**

Now press **F2** (CALC) **F6** (SET)

Highlight 1 Var XList: and press **F1** (List) and enter **1** for List 1 and press **EXE**. Then highlight 1 Var Freq: and choose List (**F2**) and enter **2** for List 2 and press **EXE**. Now press **EXIT**.

Press **F1** (1 VAR) and a full range of 1-variable weighted statistics will appear. The result $\bar{x} = 21.0719424$ will be at the top of the list. That is, the average salary is \$21.1 thou as we saw in the notes on measures of central tendency.

The Median

The **median** is the middle value in an ordered array of data that has been ranked from smallest to largest. Half the values are smaller than or equal to the median, and half the values are larger than or equal to the median. The median is not affected by extreme values, so you can use the median when extreme values are present.

MEDIAN:

Symbol: Sample or population $- \tilde{x}$

The technical definition of the median is that it is the value such that at most 50% of the data values are less than the median and at most 50% of the data values are more than the median. In other words, the median occupies the *middle position* of the data after it is sorted into an **order array**, either ascending or descending.

Let i = the position of the median

To calculate i we use: $i = \dfrac{n + 1}{2}$

Once 'i' is calculated there are two possibilities regarding how to determine the median of a data set.

EXAMPLE 3.9

There is an EVEN number of data values

The following data represents the ages, in years, of 20 employees working at a retail outlet.

63, 52, 38, 20, 21, 18, 29, 28, 45, 40, 24, 25, 22, 20, 29, 20, 18, 20, 18, 22

The corresponding **data array** in ascending order is:

18, 18, 18, 20, 20, 20, 20, 21, 22, 22, 24, 25, 28, 29, 29, 38, 40, 45, 52, 63

The **position** of the median is: $i = \dfrac{n + 1}{2} = \dfrac{20 + 1}{2} = 10.5\text{th position}$

Therefore, the median is: $\tilde{x} = \dfrac{10\text{th value} + 11\text{th value}}{2} = \dfrac{22 + 24}{2} = 23 \text{ years}$

Note: The mean is $\bar{x} = 28.6$ years. The mean is higher than the median because most of the data is in the 18 to 29 range, with a few larger values which will have the effect of increasing the mean.

EXAMPLE 3.10

There is an ODD number of data values

The following data represents the ages, in years, of 17 employees working at a retail outlet.

$$63, 52, 38, 20, 21, 18, 29, 28, 45, 40, 24, 25, 22, 20, 29, 20, 18$$

The corresponding **data array** in ascending order is:

$$18, 18, 20, 20, 20, 21, 22, 24, 25, 28, 29, 29, 38, 40, 45, 52, 63$$

The **position** of the median is: $i = \dfrac{n+1}{2} = \dfrac{17+1}{2} = 9\text{th position}$

Therefore, the median is: $\widetilde{x} = 9\text{th value} = 25 \text{ years}$

Which is a Better Measure of Central Tendency? Mean or Median

The following examples show situations that illustrate when the median might be the preferred number to represent a data set, i.e. when the median is preferred over the mean.

EXAMPLE 3.11

The following data represents the prices of houses sold last week in a particular neighbourhood. The data has been put into an array.

$$\$200,000 \quad 205,000 \quad 210,000 \quad 220,000 \quad 225,000$$

a) If you read that the mean house price in this neighbourhood was

$$\bar{x} = \$212,000$$

then you would get a certain impression as to the size and type of the *typical* house in the neighbourhood.

b) If you read that the median house price is this neighbourhood was

$$\text{median} = \widetilde{x} = \$210,000$$

then you would get the same impression as to the size and type of the *typical* house in the neighbourhood.

Conclusion: If the mean and median are **close,** then the **mean** will give the correct impression and is the preferred measure.

EXAMPLE 3.12

The following data represents the prices of houses sold last week in a particular neighbourhood. The data has been put into an array.

$$\$200,000 \quad 205,000 \quad 210,000 \quad 220,000 \quad 425,000$$

a) If you read that the mean house price in this neighbourhood was

$$\bar{x} = \$252,000$$

then you would get a certain impression as to the size and type of the typical house in the neighbourhood.

b) If you read that the median house price is this neighbourhood was

$$\widetilde{x} = \$210,000$$

then you would get a different impression as to the size and type of the typical house in the neighbourhood.

Conclusion: If the mean and median are **not close,** then the **median** will give the correct impression. The reason why the mean and the median were not close, was the fact that the data set had **unbalanced extreme values.**

10% RULE:

To help you determine if the mean and median are really different use the following rule:

Calculate the 'difference' between the mean and median.

Calculate '10% of the smaller' of the mean or median.

If   Difference $<$ 10% of smaller   conclude $\bar{x} = \tilde{x}$
in which case the <u>mean</u> is the preferred measure.

If   Difference $>$ 10% of smaller   conclude $\bar{x} \neq \tilde{x}$
in which case the <u>median</u> is the preferred measure.

Apply the 10% rule and we have:

Example 3.11: Difference $= 2,000 <$ 10% of smaller $= 21,000$

Example 3.12: Difference $= 42,000 >$ 10% of smaller $= 21,000$

The Mode

The **mode** is the value in a set of data that appears most frequently. Like the median and unlike the mean, extreme values do not affect the mode. Often, there is no mode or there are several modes in a set of data. For example, consider the time-to-get-ready data shown as follows:

29   31   35   39   39   40   43   44   44   52

There are two modes, 39 minutes and 44 minutes, because each of these values occurs twice.

EXAMPLE 3.13

Determining the Mode

A systems manager in charge of a company's network keeps track of the number of server failures that occur in a day. Determine the mode for the following data, which represents the number of server failures in a day for the past two weeks:

1   3   0   3   26   2   7   4   0   2   3   3   6   3

SOLUTION The ordered array for these data is

0   0   1   2   2   3   3   3   3   3   4   6   7   26

Because 3 appears five times, more times than any other value, the mode is 3. Thus, the systems manager can say that the most common occurrence is having three server failures in a day. For this data set, the median is also equal to 3, and the mean is equal to 4.5. The value 26 is an extreme value. For these data, the median and the mode better measure central tendency than the mean.

A set of data has no mode if none of the values is "most typical." Example 3.14 presents a data set with no mode.

EXAMPLE 3.14

Data with no Mode

The bounced check fees ($) for a sample of 10 banks is

$$26 \quad 28 \quad 20 \quad 21 \quad 22 \quad 25 \quad 18 \quad 23 \quad 15 \quad 30$$

Compute the mode.

SOLUTION These data have no mode. None of the values is most typical because each value appears once.

Measures of Position

So far we have seen several measures of the 'centre' of a data set. Sometimes we are interested in the relative 'position' of a data value in a data set. There are several ways to determine position in a data set. One way involves the calculation of a percentile.

PERCENTILES:

Symbol: $P_k = k^{th}$ percentile

The kth percentile in a data set is the value such that at most k% of the data is lower than the value and at most $(100 - k)$% of the data is higher than the value.

There are three steps involved in calculating percentile value.

 i. Arrange the data into an *ascending* data array.

 ii. Calculate the rank of the kth percentile using

$$r = Rank\ of\ P_k = Half\ Round\left[n\frac{k}{100} + \frac{1}{2} \right]$$

NOTATION:

n = number of observations in the data set
k = % of observations less than or equal to P_k.
"Half Round" means round to the nearest half.
  Example: Half Round (2.3) = 2.5,
       Half Round (3.8) = 4, Half Round (7.7) = 7.5
       Round .25 and .75 DOWN if k < 50 OR
       Round .25 and .75 UP if k > 50

 iii. Compute P_k

$$P_k = x_r\ (if\ the\ rank\ is\ an\ integer)\ or\ = \frac{x_{r-1/2} + x_{r-1/2}}{2}\ (if\ rank\ is\ a\ fractional\ half)$$

At this point it would beneficial to demonstrate the calculation of various percentiles by referring examples 3.15, 3.16, 3.17, and 3.18.

EXAMPLE 3.15

Consider the following data: 4, 6, 8, 10, 16

a) Determine Q1
   Step 1: Arrange the data into an *ascending* data array.
       4, 6, 8, 10, 16
   Step 2: Calculate the r (rank)
       Note Q1 is equivalent to 25th percentile, i.e. P_{25}.

$$r = \textit{Half Round}\left[5\left(\frac{25}{100}\right) + \frac{1}{2}\right] = \text{Half Round } (1.75) \sim 1.5$$

Since the decimal ends with 0.75 and k is less than 50, you ROUND Down to 1.5.

Step 3: Compute P_k.

Data	4	6	8	10	16
Rank	1	2	3	4	5

Note: Rank = 1.5 is between rank 1 and rank 2 and so you take the average of the corresponding values of rank 1 and rank 2 which are 4 and 6 as shown below.

$$P_{25} = Q_1 = \frac{(\textit{1st value } + \textit{2nd value})}{2} = \frac{4 + 6}{2} = 5$$

b) Determine Median.
   Step 1: Arrange the data into an *ascending* data array.
        4, 6, 8, 10, 16
   Step 2: Calculate the r (rank)
        Note Median is equivalent to Q2 which is equivalent to P_{50}.

$$r = \textit{Half Round}\left[5\left(\frac{50}{100}\right) + \frac{1}{2}\right] = \text{Half Round } (3) = 3$$

Step 3: Compute P_k.

Data	4	6	8	10	16
Rank	1	2	3	4	5

$$P_{50} = Q_2 = 3^{\text{rd}} \text{ value} = 8$$

c) Determine Q_3
   Step 1: Arrange the data into an *ascending* data array.
        4, 6, 8, 10, 16
   Step 2: Calculate the r (rank)
        Note Q3 is equivalent to 75th percentile, i.e. P_{75}.

$$r = \textit{Half Round}\left[5\left(\frac{75}{100}\right) + \frac{1}{2}\right] = \text{Half round } (4.25) \sim 4.5$$

Since the decimal ends with 0.75 and k is greater than 50, you ROUND UP to 4.5.

Step 3: Compute P_k.

Data	4	6	8	10	16
Rank	1	2	3	4	5

Note: Rank = 4.5 is between rank 4 and rank 5 and so you take the average of the corresponding values of rank 4 and rank 5 which are 10 and 16 as shown below.

$$P_{75} = Q_3 \frac{(\textit{4th value } + \textit{5th value})}{2} = \frac{10 + 16}{2} = 13$$

You can use the CASIO calculator to obtain Q_1, Median and Q_3 by following these calculator steps:

1. From the Main Menu, select the STAT mode.
2. Enter data (4, 6, 8, 10, 16) in List 1.
3. Select CALC (F2)

4. Select SET (F6)
5. Set the following,
   1 Var XList : List 1
   1 Var Freq : 1
   After you have finished with setting, press **EXIT**
6. Select "**1 Var**" (**F1**) for the results

RESULTS (with casio FX-9750GII)
Scroll down until you get to
Q1   :5
Med   :8
Q3   :13

EXAMPLE 3.16   Consider the following data: 3, 5, 9, 13, 17, 21

a) Determine Q1
   Step 1: Arrange the data into an *ascending* data array.
           3, 5, 9, 13, 17, 21
   Step 2: Calculate the r (rank)
           Note Q1 is equivalent to 25th percentile, i.e. P_{25}.

   $$r = Half\,Round\left[6\left(\frac{25}{100}\right) + \frac{1}{2}\right] = \text{Half Round } (2) = 2$$

   Step 3: Compute P_k.

Data	3	5	9	13	17	21
Rank	1	2	3	4	5	6

   $$P_{25} = Q_1 = 2^{nd} \text{ value} = 5$$

b) Determine Median.
   Step 1: Arrange the data into an *ascending* data array.
           3, 5, 9, 13, 17, 21
   Step 2: Calculate the r (rank)
           Note: Median is equivalent to Q2 which is equivalent to P_{50}.

   $$r = Half\,Round\left[6\left(\frac{50}{100}\right) + \frac{1}{2}\right] = \text{Half Round } (3.5) = 3.5$$

   Step 3: Compute P_k.

Data	3	5	9	13	17	21
Rank	1	2	3	4	5	6

   Note: Rank = 3.5 is between rank 3 and rank 4 and so you take the average of the corresponding values of rank 3 and rank 4 which are 9 and 13 as shown below.

   $$P_{50} = Q_2 = \frac{(3rd\ value\ +\ 4th\ value)}{2} = \frac{9 + 13}{2} = 11$$

c) Determine Q3
   Step 1: Arrange the data into an *ascending* data array.
           3, 5, 9, 13, 17, 21

Step 2: Calculate the r (rank)

Note Q3 is equivalent to 75th percentile, i.e. P$_{75}$.

$$r = Half\,Round\left[6\left(\frac{75}{100}\right) + \frac{1}{2}\right] = Half\,Round\,(5) = 5$$

Step 3: Compute P$_k$.

Data	3	5	9	13	17	21
Rank	1	2	3	4	5	6

$$P_{75} = Q_3 = 5^{th}\,value = 17$$

You can use the CASIO calculator to obtain Q_1, Median and Q_3 by following these calculator steps:

1. From the Main Menu, select the STAT mode.
2. Enter data (3, 5, 9, 13, 17, 21) in List 1.
3. Select CALC (F2)
4. Select SET (F6)
5. Set the following,
   1 Var XList : List 1
   1 Var Freq : 1
After you have finished with setting, press **EXIT**
6. Select **"1 Var" (F1)** for the results

RESULTS (with casio FX-9750GII)
Scroll down until you get to
Q1   :5
Med   :11
Q3   :17

EXAMPLE 3.17 Consider the following data: 6, 8, 9, 16, 19, 23

a) Determine P$_{20}$

Step 1: Arrange the data into an *ascending* data array.
   6, 8, 9, 16, 19, 23

Step 2: Calculate the r (rank)

$$r = Half\,Round\left[6\left(\frac{20}{100}\right) + \frac{1}{2}\right] = Half\,Round\,(1.7) \sim 1.5$$

Step 3: Compute P$_k$.

Data	6	8	9	16	19	23
Rank	1	2	3	4	5	6

Note: Rank = 1.5 is between rank 1 and rank 2 and so you take the average of the corresponding values of rank 1 and rank 2 which are 4 and 6 as shown below.

$$P_{20} = \frac{(1st\,value\,+\,2nd\,value)}{2} = \frac{6 + 8}{2} = 7$$

b) Determine P$_{30}$

Step 1: Arrange the data into an *ascending* data array.
   6, 8, 9, 16, 19, 23

Step 2: Calculate the r (rank)

$$r = Half\,Round\left[6\left(\frac{30}{100}\right) + \frac{1}{2}\right] = Half\,Round\,(2.3) \sim 2.5$$

Step 3: Compute P_k.

Data	6	8	9	16	19	23
Rank	1	2	3	4	5	6

Note: Rank = 2.5 is between rank 2 and rank 3 and so you take the average of the corresponding values of rank 2 and rank 3 which are 8 and 9 as shown below.

$$P_{30} = \frac{(2nd\,value\,+\,3rd\,value)}{2} = \frac{8+9}{2} = 8.5$$

EXAMPLE 3.18   The following data represents the ages, in years, of 20 employees working at a retail outlet. The data has already been arranged in an ascending data array.

18, 18, 18, 20, 20, 20, 20, 21, 22, 22, 24, 25, 28, 29, 29, 38, 40, 45, 52, 63

a) Determine the 80th percentile.

Step 1: Arrange the data into an *ascending* data array.

18, 18, 18, 20, 20, 20, 20, 21, 22, 22, 24, 25, 28, 29, 29, 38, 40, 45, 52, 63

Step 2: Calculate the r (rank)

$$r = Half\,Round\left[20\left(\frac{80}{100}\right) + \frac{1}{2}\right] = Half\,Round\,(16.5) = 16.5$$

Step 3: Compute P_k.

Data	18	18	18	20	20	20	20	21	22	22	24	25	28	29	29	38	40	45	52	63
Rank	1	2	3	4	5	6	7	8	9	10	11	12	13	14	15	16	17	18	19	20

Note: Rank = 16.5 is between rank 16 and rank 17 and so you take the average of the corresponding values of rank 16 and rank 17 which are 38 and 40 as shown below.

$$P_{80} = \frac{(16th\,value\,+\,17th\,value)}{2} = \frac{38+40}{2} = 39\ years$$

b) Determine the 34th percentile.

Step 1: Arrange the data into an *ascending* data array.

18, 18, 18, 20, 20, 20, 20, 21, 22, 22, 24, 25, 28, 29, 29, 38, 40, 45, 52, 63

Step 2: Calculate the r (rank)

$$r = Half\,Round\left[20\left(\frac{34}{100}\right) + \frac{1}{2}\right] = Half\,Round\,(7.3) = 7.5$$

Step 3: Compute P_k.

Data	18	18	18	20	20	20	20	21	22	22	24	25	28	29	29	38	40	45	52	63
Rank	1	2	3	4	5	6	7	8	9	10	11	12	13	14	15	16	17	18	19	20

Note: Rank = 7.5 is between rank 7 and rank 8 and so you take the average of the corresponding values of rank 7 and rank 8 which are 20 and 21 as shown below.

$$P_{34} = \frac{(7th\,value\,+\,8th\,value)}{2} = \frac{20+21}{2} = 20.5\ years$$

c) Determine the 61st percentile.

Step 1: Arrange the data into an *ascending* data array.

18, 18, 18, 20, 20, 20, 20, 21, 22, 22, 24, 25, 28, 29, 29, 38, 40, 45, 52, 63

Step 2: Calculate the r (rank)

$$r = Half\ Round\left[20\left(\frac{61}{100}\right) + \frac{1}{2}\right] = Half\ Round\ (12.7) = 12.5$$

Step 3: Compute P_k.

Data	18	18	18	20	20	20	20	21	22	22	24	25	28	29	29	38	40	45	52	63
Rank	1	2	3	4	5	6	7	8	9	10	11	12	13	14	15	16	17	18	19	20

Note: Rank = 12.5 is between rank 12 and rank 13 and so you take the average of the corresponding values of rank 12 and rank 13 which are 20 and 21 as shown below.

$$P_{34} = \frac{(12th\ value\ +\ 13th\ value)}{2} + \frac{25 + 28}{2} = 26.5\ years$$

QUARTILES:

Some of the percentiles have special names. These are

$$P_{25} = Q_1 = 1^{st}\ quartile$$

$$P_{50} = Q_2 = 2^{nd}\ quartile = the\ median$$

$$P_{75} = Q_3 = 3^{rd}\ quartile$$

We will use the calculator to give us the values of the quartiles. From the calculator we get: $Q_1 = 20$ years   and $Q_3 = 33.5$ years

Problems for Section 3.1

3.1 A company has invited its entire human resources staff from each office across the country to attend a conference at the head office in Toronto. The following information is available:

Office	Return Airfare	# of Offices	# of HR Staff per Office
Calgary	$400	2	4
Halifax	350	1	2
Montreal	330	2	3
Ottawa	300	2	3
Vancouver	500	3	5

a. What is the median return airfare per office?
b. What is the mean return airfare per person?

3.2 The following sample data was obtained at 8:00 pm at a popular downtown restaurant. There were 15 tables occupied at that time.

Number of guests at the table	Food Bill for the table ($)	Liquor Bill for the table ($)
2	48.75	15.75
2	36.75	26.00
4	90.55	22.90
4	87.45	42.45
2	41.25	14.00
4	83.30	29.75
6	109.40	44.05
4	88.25	21.55
4	93.45	22.00
2	36.50	16.45
2	42.60	18.00
4	105.80	37.57
4	84.65	18.95
5	110.35	43.95
4	83.55	22.50

a. What is the 40th percentile table liquor bill?
b. What was the average food bill for the 15 tables?
c. How much did the average person spend on food?
d. In order to be in the top 32% of the amount spent on food, a table would have to spend at least what amount?

3.3 A referendum was held on a particular issue affecting the GTA Megacity. The following table shows the results.

Municipality	Number of votes	% in Favour
City of Toronto	482,000	45
East York	152,000	63
North York	365,000	27
Etobicoke	298,000	48
Scarborough	456,000	33

a. What was the overall percent in favour of the issue?

3.4 A specialty bookstore concentrates mainly on selling used books and magazines. Paperbacks sell for $1.00 each, hardcover books are $5.00 each and magazines sell for $0.50 each. Of the 50 books sold on Tuesday, 40 were paperback and the remainder were hardcover. They also sold 15 magazines. What was the mean price per item sold?

3.5 Rye Pizza sells soft drinks in three sizes: small, medium and large. The small size costs $0.75, the medium is $0.90 and the large is $1.15 . On a typical weekday 25% of the soft drinks sold are small, 45% are medium and 30% are large. What is the typical daily mean price per soft drink sold?

3.6 A particular oak dining table requires time in three manufacturing stages: 2 hours of cutting, 4 hours of assembly, and 6 hours of finishing. The wood-cutters are paid $10 per hour, the assemblers get $15 per hour and the finishers get $20 per hour. What is the average hourly labour cost to manufacture one table?

3.7 The personnel director at recovery Hospital wanted a study made of overtime hours and associated costs of the nurses. Ten (10) nurses were randomly selected and the following data was obtained for August.

Nurse	O/T Hours	Pay ($/hr)	Nurse	O/T Hours	Pay ($/hr)
1	13	35	6	15	25
2	13	35	7	5	30
3	12	20	8	12	35
4	15	25	9	6	30
5	7	30	10	7	25

a. What was the average number of hours of overtime worked per nurse?
b. What was the average hourly overtime pay rate per nurse?
c. What was the average pay per hour of overtime?

3.8 The following table shows some data regarding the top 4 chains of toy stores. For the chains and stores in this table:

Chain	# of Stores	Average Sales/ Store ($ 000)
Toys 'R' Us	144	7,236
Child World	79	3,582
Kay bee	361	507
Lionel	56	3,232

a. What is the average sales of a toy store?
b. What is the mean sales of the 4 toy store chains?
c. Data regarding several retail chains is shown in the table below. What is the overall % gain in sales for the chains shown?

Company/ Chain	Sales (000,000)	% Gain (Loss)	Number of Stores	% Gain (Loss)
Radio Shack	$1,515	28	4,398	7
Mervyn's	1,336	26	92	15
Toys 'R' Us	1,042	33	144	20
Marshall's	830	35	137	27
Saks Fifth Avenue	710	2	34	6
Lerners	682	(4)	790	3
Nordstrum	613	17	36	6

3.9 The table below shows data dealing with product liability.

	Status of Injured Persons/Parties				
Liability Category Claim	Injured Party	# of persons receiving Payment	% of persons receiving Payment	% of total Payment	Average payment per person
Bodily Injury	Employee	875	10.6	42.0	$97,884
	Purchaser	5,562	67.5	28.7	10,544
	User	1,441	17.5	22.5	31,836
	Other	364	4.4	6.8	38,016
Property Damage	Employee	12	0.2	0.0	$ 325
	Purchaser	3,928	78.7	64.3	4,372
	User	359	7.2	22.8	22,468
	Employee	695	3.9	12.9	6,176

a. What was the average payment to a person who suffered bodily injury?
b. What was the average payment to a purchaser involved in all type of claims?

3.10 An extensive study was conducted to determine whether there are differences in the characteristics of holiday travellers that are less than 50 years old as compared to those that are more than 50 years old. One of the items of interest was the amount spent for a one-day trip. The results are shown below:

Cost of One-day Trip	Under 50 years old (n = 480)	Over 50 years old (n = 325)
$ 0 and under 50	2%	1%
50 " " 100	7	5
100 " " 200	12	9
200 " " 300	20	13
300 " " 400	29	20
400 " " 500	18	17
500 " " 750	6	14
750 " " 1000	3	10
1000 " " 2000	2	7
2000 " " 3000	1	4

a. For which group of travellers, if any, would the median be a better measure of central tendency than the mean?

b. For the under 50 group, 360 of those surveyed would have spent less than $___.

3.11 Based on the data in the following table:

a. What is the overall average tobacco sales revenue per person?

b. What is the mean amount of federal tax per state?

c. Would the mean or median better represent the state tobacco taxes?

d. Which state(s) had the 60th percentile federal tobacco taxes?

	Under-Age Smoking			
	Number of smokers under 18 years old	State tobacco taxes ($ millions)	Federal tobacco taxes ($ millions)	Sales revenue ($ millions)
California	300,000	20.6	11.8	125.0
New York	190,000	14.6	7.4	78.2
Texas	200,000	16.6	8.0	76.0
Illinois	130,000	7.8	5.2	49.2
Florida	125,000	8.4	5.0	49.2
Pennsylvania	130,000	8.0	5.2	47.8
Ohio	125,000	4.6	5.0	43.6
Michigan	110,000	5.6	4.4	41.0
New Jersey	85,000	6.6	3.4	33.2
Alabama	50,000	2.8	3.4	31.4

3.12 The following is a portion of a table that appeared in the Dec. 1, 2002 issue of the Toronto Star.

Cancer surgery wait Times

In 2002, the average wait time for cancer surgery at the Princess Margaret Hospital and University Health Network was 54 days. This is an increase from 43 days in 2000.

Average wait time from the decision to operate to the date of surgery:

Hospital	Days	Cases
Princess Margaret Hospital	35	144
Toronto General Hospital	33	537
Toronto Western Hospital	5	10

What is the overall average wait time per patient for the three hospitals shown?

3.13 Based on the following table that appeared in Globe and Mail, Classroom Edition, of March 1994:

a. Was the overall mean price per room higher for 3 star hotels than 2 star hotels?

b. What is the median number of rooms for all the hotels in the table?

c. It would be reported that 40% of the hotels had a selling price higher than $___ ?

Eastern Canada

Hotel	Level of quality	Location	Number of rooms	Selling price $million	Buyer origin
Hotel Strata, Mississauga	2-star	Toronto	129	$2.7	Domestic
Royal Connaught	3-star	Hamilton	206	$4.5	Domestic
Chestnut Park	3-star	Toronto	520	$28.4	Hong Kong
Carlton Place	2-star	Toronto	528	$8.5	Indonesia/Singapore
Howard Johnson, Scarborough	2-star	Toronto	192	$5.6	China
Howard Johnson	2-star	Ottawa	108	$3.7	Domestic
Best Western, Rose City Inn	1-star	Windsor	147	$2.5	Domestic
Sutton Place	4-star	Toronto	280*	$29.2	Hong Kong
Hotel Aurora	2-star	Aurora	98	$3.5	Domestic
Rock Haven Motor Inn	1-star	Peterborough	86	$1.0	Iranian
Skyline Triumph	2-star	Toronto	380	$9.5	Domestic

Western Canada

Hotel	Level of quality	Location	Number of rooms	Selling price $million	Buyer origin
Delta River Inn	4-star	Vancouver	416	$30.0	Domestic/Hong Kong
Skyline Hotel	3-star	Calgary	385	$26.0	Domestic
Cherrywood Inn	2-star	Edmonton	136	$2.9	Domestic
Coast Lakeside Inn	3-star	Penticton	200	$13.5	Domestic
Best Western, Port O'Call	3-star	Calgary	201	$8.5	East African

*Plus 161 apartment units.

Source: Colliers Macaulay Nicolis

3.14 The following data came from the Sales & Marketing Management, Survey of Buying Power, 1998. For the states shown in the table below:

a. What is the projected overall average retail sales per household in 2002?

b. What is the projected overall % increase in the number of households from 1998 to 2003?

Survey of Buying Power (Regional and State Summaries for 5-year Projections)

REGION STATE	1/1/98 TOTAL POP. (000s)	1/1/2003 TOTAL POP. (000s)	% CHANGE 1998–2003	1/1/2003 TOTAL HSHLDS. (000s)	% CHANGE 1998–2003	2002 TOTAL RETAIL SALES ($000)	% CHANGE 1997–2002
NEW ENGLAND							
Connecticut	3,271.1	3,275.2	.1	1,246.1	1.4	39,848,761	15.0
Maine	1,243.7	1,260.1	1.3	496.2	3.5	13,998,071	12.2
Massachusetts	6,133.5	6,241.1	1.8	2,384.6	3.3	66,722,629	12.6
New Hampshire	1,179.1	1,242.3	5.4	472.5	7.0	17,284,399	18.6
Rhode Island	987.0	978.5	−.9	372.5	.1	8,590,400	9.4
Vermont	590.4	601.6	1.9	235.4	4.3	6,407,914	11.4

3.15 A survey of 300 prize winners of a certain contest revealed the following results:

a. What was their mean prize value?

b. How many won prizes of less than $500?

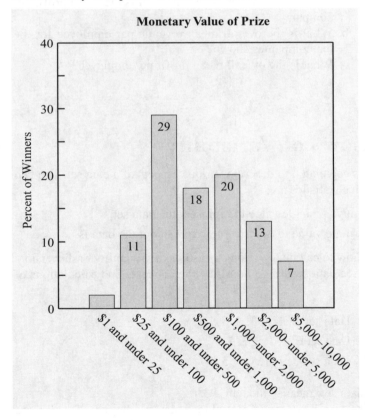

3.16 Based on the following table, what is the mean size of institutions that make extensive use of TQM (Total Quality Management)?

Breakdown by Size of Institution

Student Population	Number of Institutions Responding	Percent of Institutions Responding	Number of Institutions Extensively using TQM	Percent of Institutions Extensively using TQM
0 and under 2,000	19	8	3	7
2,000 " " 5,000	58	24	7	17
5,000 " " 10,000	65	27	13	31
10,000 " " 15,000	41	17	6	14
15,000 " " 25,000	35	14	9	22
25,000 " " 35,000	15	6	3	7
35,000 " " 50,000	10	4	1	2

3.17 The following table appeared in the June 19, 2003 issue of the Toronto Star.

Auto productivity

Top 10 assembly plants in North America by labour-hours per vehicle.

Nissan, Smyrna, Tenn. Midsize car	15.74
GM, Oshawa #1 Midsize car	16.44
GM, Oshawa #2 Midsize car	17.08
Ford, Chicago Midsize car	17.71
Ford, Atlanta Midsize car	17.78
Nissan, Smyrna Small pickup	18.23
Nissan, Smyrna Small SUV	18.35
GM, Lansing, Mich Compact car	18.59
GM, Lansing Midsize car	18.64
Toyota Georgetown #1 Midsize car	20.06

SOURCE: Harbour and Associates

Last month there were 2400 cars produced at Oshawa #1, 3000 cars produced at Oshawa #2, 1800 midsize cars produced at Lansing and 1500 compact cars produced at Lansing. What was the overall average labour hours per car for these four GM plants?

3.18 The following is a portion of a chart that appeared in the May 25, 2003 issue of the Toronto Star.

By the numbers

Housing outlook... Ontario home starts will jump 3 per cent this year to 86,000, but fall back to 80,000 in 2004.

Home sales... Existing-home sales in Canada's 25 major markets declined less than 1 per cent in April, but the average price rose.

Seasonally adjusted

	Apr. 2003	Mar. 2003	% change
Dollar volume (billions)			
	$4.6	$4.8	-3.6%
Sales	21,905	22,085	-0.8%
Average price			
	$217,073	$203,589	6.6%
New listings			
	35,247	34,611	1.8%

What was the overall average price of houses sold in Canada's 25 major markets for the 2 months March and April 2003?

3.19 The table below appeared in the Financial Post of December 2, 1998.

World oil giants

		Profit US$billion	Rev. per employee US$	Employees
1	Exxon Corp./Mobil Corp. (U.S.)	11.8	96,170	122,700
2	Royal Dutch/Shell Group (Britain/Netherlands)	7.8	74,286	105,000
3	British Petroleum/Amoco (Britain)	4.0	70,859	56,450
4	Total SA/Petrofina SA (France)	2.9	67.391	69,066
5	Texaco Inc. (U.S.)	2.7	92,109	29,313
6	Elf Aquitaine (France)	0.96	11,469	83,700
7	ENI (Italy)	3.0	37,417	80,178
8	Chevron Corp. (U.S.)	3.3	84,615	39,362
9	PDVSA (Venezuela)	4.8	84,818	56,592
10	SK (South Korea)	0.125	4,086	30,595

SOURCE: COMPANY REPORTS

a. For the 10 companies shown, what is the mean profit per company?
b. What is the overall mean revenue per employee for the ten companies shown?
c. What is the overall mean profit per employee?

3.2   Descriptive Statistics II: Measures of Variability

Descriptive statistics are numbers calculated to describe various aspects of a data set. The two most important types of descriptive statistics are:

Measures of Central Tendency: A single value to represent the data set.

Measures of Variability: A single value to describe how spread out the data is.

In this section we will learn how to calculate various measures of variability or dispersion. We will use the following three data sets to demonstrate the concepts and calculations of variability measures:

> Data set A: 1, 2, 3, 4, 5
> Data set B: 1, 1, 3, 3, 5, 5
> Data set C: 1, 1, 1, 5, 5, 5

It should be noted for each data set: mean = median = 3

In other words, the most important measures of central tendency are the same for all three data sets, but the data sets themselves are different, therefore there must be some other aspect of them that is different. It is the fact that they have different amounts of **variability**.

Range (R)

Symbol: R for sample or population range

Formula: $R = High - Low$

EXAMPLE 3.19

Data set A: $R = 5 - 1 = 4$

Data set B: $R = 5 - 1 = 4$

Data set C: $R = 5 - 1 = 4$

These results would seem to indicate that the three data sets had the same amount of variability. This would appear not to be true, since our intuition would seem to indicate that the three data sets would have different amounts of variability.

From this example we can see why the range has limited use. It only considers the high and low values of a data set and ignores the values in between. These in-between values should have some input in determining the variability of a data set.

It should be noted, however, that the range can be useful to measure variability in some cases. For many years the range has been the preferred way to measure variability when setting up quality control charts which are used to monitor the mean and the variability of repeated processes.

In this course, you will only calculate the range if you are told to do so.

EXAMPLE 3.20

Computing the Range in the 2003 Return of Small Cap High-Risk Mutual Funds

The 121 mutual funds that are part of the "Using Statistics" scenario (see page 129) are classified according to the risk level of the mutual funds (low, average, and high) and type (small cap, mid cap, and large cap). Compute the range of the 2003 return for the small cap mutual funds with high risk. **MUTUALFUNDS2004**

SOLUTION: Ranked from the smallest to the largest, the 2003 return for the nine small cap mutual funds with high risk is:

37.3   39.2   44.2   44.5   53.8   56.6   59.3   62.4   66.5

Therefore, using Equation (3.7), the range = $66.5 - 37.3 = 29.2$.

The largest difference between any two returns for the small cap mutual funds with high risk is 29.2.

The range measures the *total spread* in the set of data. Although the range is a simple measure of total variation in the data, it does not take into account *how* the data are distributed between the smallest and largest values. In other words, the range does not indicate if the values are evenly distributed throughout the data set, clustered near the middle, or clustered near one or both extremes. Thus, using the range as a measure of variation when at least one value is an extreme value is misleading.

Interquartile Range (IQR)

Symbol: IQR for sample or population

Formula: $IQR = Q_3 - Q_1$

EXAMPLE 3.21

Data set A: $IQR = 4.5 - 1.5 = 3$

Data set B: $IQR = 5 - 1 = 4$

Data set C: $IQR = 5 - 1 = 4$

These results would seem to indicate that data set A has less variability than data sets B and C. This is an improvement over the previous results based on the range (as we shall see shortly). However, data sets B and C do not have the same amount of variability.

The interquartile range is often preferred over the range as a measure of variability since the range can easily be influenced by one extreme value.

Consider the following example:

EXAMPLE 3.22

Data set D: 1, 3, 3, 4, 4, 4, 5, 5, 5, 5, 6, 6, 6, 7, 7, 7, 8, 8, 9, 10

Data set E: 1, 3, 3, 4, 4, 4, 5, 5, 5, 5, 6, 6, 6, 7, 7, 7, 8, 8, 9, 20

Suppose we use the *range* to measure the variability of these two data sets:

Data set D: $R = 10 - 1 = 9$ Data set E: $R = 20 - 1 = 19$

Intuitively, we would not expect that data set E would have twice as much variability as data set E, i.e. the range does not seem to be a good measure of variability in this case.
Now, suppose we use the *interquartile range* to measure the variability:

Data set D: $IQR = 7 - 4 = 3$ Data set E: $IQR = 7 - 4 = 3$

Intuitively, we would not say that both data sets have exactly the same variability. However, this appears to be closer to the truth that the conclusion that the range results lead us to. The IQR is not affected by one or two extreme values as the range is.

EXAMPLE 3.23

Computing the Interquartile Range for the 2003 Return of Small Cap High-Risk Mutual Funds

The 121 mutual funds that are part of the "Using Statistics" scenario (see page 129) are classified according to the risk level of the mutual funds (low, average, and high) and type (small cap, mid cap, and large cap). Compute the interquartile range of the 2003 return for the small cap mutual funds with high risk. **MUTUALFUNDS2004**

SOLUTION: Ranked from smallest to largest, the 2003 return for the nine small cap mutual funds with high risk is:

37.3   39.2   44.2   44.5   53.8   56.6   59.3   62.4   66.5

Using Equation (3.8) and the earlier results, $Q_1 = 41.7$ and $Q_3 = 60.85$.

Interquartile range $= 60.85 - 41.7 = 19.15$

Therefore, the interquartile range in the 2003 return is 19.15.

Because the interquartile range does not consider any value smaller than Q_1 or larger than Q_3, it cannot be affected by extreme values. Summary measures such as the median, Q_1, Q_3, and the interquartile range, which cannot be influenced by extreme values, are called **resistant measures**.

Variance

Symbol: Sample variance s^2 Population variance σ^2

Formula: Sample $s^2 = \dfrac{\sum(x - \bar{x})^2}{n - 1}$ Population $\sigma^2 = \dfrac{\sum(x - \mu)^2}{N}$

Note: For the first time, we will get a different result for a descriptive measure if a data is a sample instead of a population. Previously, only the symbol was different (if anything was different).
We now have a measure of variability that takes into account <u>all</u> the values in a data set.

EXAMPLE 3.24   **Data set A:**

x	$x - \bar{x}$ or $x - \mu$	$(x - \bar{x})^2$ or $(x - \mu)^2$
1	−2	4
2	−1	1
3	0	0
4	1	1
5	2	4
		10

Sample: $s^2 = \dfrac{10}{5-1} = 2.5$ Population: $\sigma^2 = \dfrac{10}{5} = 2$

Data set B:

x	$x - \bar{x}$ or $x - \mu$	$(x - \bar{x})^2$ or $(x - \mu)^2$
1	−2	4
1	−2	4
3	0	0
3	0	0
5	2	4
5	2	4
		16

Sample: $s^2 = \dfrac{16}{6-1} = 3.2$ Population: $\sigma^2 = \dfrac{16}{6} = 2.67$

Data set C:

x	$x - \bar{x}$ or $x - \mu$	$(x - \bar{x})^2$ or $(x - \mu)^2$
1	−2	4
1	−2	4
1	−2	4
5	2	4
5	2	4
5	2	4
		24

Sample: $s^2 = \dfrac{24}{6-1} = 4.8$ Population: $\sigma^2 = \dfrac{24}{6} = 4$

Conclusion: Based on these results, data set A has the least amount of variability, while data set C has the most. These results are reasonable when we understand that variability in statistics has nothing to do with 'how many different values are there' but instead has to do with 'does the data seem to be close to the mean or does the data tend to be further from the mean'.

Variance is a good measure of variability in that it takes into account all values. However, variance has major practical disadvantage: the units don't make sense. The units of variance = (data units)^2. For example, if the data in data set A is $, then the variance is 2.5$^2 ??? The unit square (^{2}) does not make sense. If the data is people, the variance is 2.5 people^2 ??? Again, 'people^2' does not make sense. Because of this problem, variance cannot have a *practical* interpretation. In statistics, variance is used almost exclusively in the theoretical development of formulas.

Standard Deviation

Symbol: Sample standard deviation s Population standard deviation σ

Formula: Sample $s = \sqrt{s^2} = \sqrt{\dfrac{\Sigma(x - \bar{x})^2}{n - 1}}$ Population $\sigma = \sqrt{\sigma^2}$

EXAMPLE 3.25

Data set A: $s = \sqrt{2.5} = 1.58$

Data set B: $s = \sqrt{3.2} = 1.79$

Data set B: $s = \sqrt{4.8} = 2.19$

We can see that the conclusions regarding which data set is the most variable and which is the least variable is the same as when we compared variances.

The main advantage of standard deviation, for practical purposes, is that the units are the *same* as the data.

Rounding rule for standard deviation   Regarding the form of the answer when calculating standard deviation (when rounding is obviously necessary): use three (3) figures or a number that looks like the data, whichever has the most figures. This rule also applies to the use of standard deviation in further calculations, although it is sometimes easier to use results stored in memory of your calculator or computer.

Ex. 1: If data is: 10,   11,   13,   15   then $s = 2.22$

Ex. 2: If data is: 2,315   4,156   7,542   9,587   then $s = 3,275$

Ex. 3: If data is: 2,315   2,320   2,325   2,330   then $s = 6.45$

Ex. 4: If data is: 23.46   56.82   83.47   92.61   then $s = 31.05$

EXAMPLE 3.26

Computing the Variance and Standard Deviation of the 2003 Return of Small Cap High-Risk Mutual Funds

The 121 mutual funds that are part of the "Using Statistics" scenario (see page 129) are classified according to the risk level of the mutual funds (low, average, and high) and type (small cap, mid cap, and large cap). Compute the variance and standard deviation of the 2003 return for the small cap mutual funds with high risk. MUTUALFUNDS2004

SOLUTION: Table 3.2 illustrates the computation of the variance and standard deviation for the return in 2003 for the small cap mutual funds with high risk. Using Equation (3.9)

$$S^2 = \frac{\displaystyle\sum_{i=1}^{n}(X_i - \bar{X})^2}{n - 1}$$

$$= \frac{(44.5 - 51.53)^2 + (39.2 - 51.53)^2 + \cdots + (66.5 - 51.53)^2}{9 - 1}$$

$$= \frac{891.16}{8}$$

$$= 111.395$$

Using Equation (3.10), the sample standard deviation S is

$$S = \sqrt{S^2} = \sqrt{\frac{\sum_{i=1}^{n} (X_i - \overline{X})^2}{n-1}} = \sqrt{111.395} = 10.6\%$$

TABLE 3.2

Computing the Variance of the 2003 Return for the Small Cap Mutual Funds with High Risk

$\overline{X} = 51.5333$

Return 2003	Step 1: $(X_i - \overline{X})$	Step 2: $(X_i - \overline{X})^2$
44.5	−7.0333	49.4678
39.2	−12.3333	152.1111
62.4	10.8667	118.0844
59.3	7.7667	60.3211
56.6	5.0667	25.6711
53.8	2.2667	5.1378
37.3	−14.2333	202.5878
44.2	−7.3333	53.7778
66.5	14.9667	224.0011
	Step 3: Sum:	Step 4: Divide by $(n-1)$:
	891.16	111.395

The following summarizes the characteristics of the range, interquartile range, variance, and standard deviation.

- The more spread out, or dispersed, the data are, the larger the range, interquartile range, variance, and standard deviation.
- The more concentrated, or homogeneous the data are, the smaller the range, interquartile range, variance, and standard deviation.
- If the values are all the same (so that there is no variation in the data), the range, interquartile range, variance, and standard deviation will all equal zero.
- None of the measures of variation (the range, interquartile range, standard deviation, and variance) can *ever* be negative.

Coefficient of Variation

All of the above measures of variability are **absolute** measures. It is often better (i.e. you get more meaningful results) to compare factors using **relative** measures. The coefficient of variation is a relative measure of variability.

Symbol: CV (coefficient of variation)

Formula: Sample $CV = \dfrac{s}{\overline{x}} \times 100$ Population $CV = \dfrac{\sigma}{\mu} \times 100$

EXAMPLE 3.27

The following information for 4 stocks is to be analyzed.

TABLE 3.3

Stock	Price	Dividend
ABC Company	$25	$0.70
DEF Company	47	1.50
HIJ Company	78	2.00
XYZ Company	92	3.00

Compare the variability of the prices and dividends.

SOLUTION: Since the sizes of the numbers in the two data sets are quite a bit different, it will be best to use a relative measure to compare the variability.

$$\text{Price:} \quad CV = \frac{s}{\bar{x}} \times 100 = \frac{30.23}{60.50} \times 100 = 50\%$$

$$\text{Dividend:} \quad CV = \frac{s}{\bar{x}} \times 100 = \frac{0.963}{1.80} \times 100 = 54\%$$

Using the *10% rule* to compare CV's: Diff = 4 < 10% of the smaller = 5

Conclusion: The dividends and the prices have approximately the same amount of variability.

Note: If we had just looked at the standard deviation, we would have concluded (rather obviously because of the size of the numbers) that the prices were more variable.

Note: Since the data is a sample, we use $CV = \frac{s}{\bar{x}} \times 100$ to calculate CV.

Rounding rule for CV One decimal if < 10%. No decimals if > 10%.

EXAMPLE 3.28

The following table shows data for the houses that are being built on a short street in a new subdivision.

TABLE 3.4

House number	Size Square ft.	Price ($000's)
1002	2400	269
1004	2650	289
1006	2200	225
1008	2150	219
1010	2500	249

Compare the variabilty of the sizes and the prices.

SOLUTION: Since the *units* of the data are *different,* the only way to compare the variability of these two sets of data is to use the coefficient of variation.

$$\text{Size:} \quad CV = \frac{s}{\bar{x}} \times 100 = \frac{208}{2380} \times 100 = 8.7\%$$

$$\text{Price:} \quad CV = \frac{s}{\bar{x}} \times 100 = \frac{29.4}{250} \times 100 = 12\%$$

Using the 10% rule to compare CV's: Diff = 3.3 > 10% of the smaller = 0.87

Conclusion: The prices are relatively more variable than the sizes.

EXAMPLE 3.29

Comparing Two Coefficients of Variation When Two Variables Have Different Units of Measurement

The operations manager of a package delivery service is deciding on whether to purchase a new fleet of trucks. When packages are stored in the trucks in preparation for delivery, you need to consider two major constraints—the weight (in pounds) and the volume (in cubic feet) for each item.

The operations manager samples 200 packages, and finds that the mean weight is 26.0 pounds, with a standard deviation of 3.9 pounds, and the mean volume is 8.8 cubic feet, with a standard deviation of 2.2 cubic feet. How can the operations manager compare the variation of the weight and the volume?

SOLUTION: Because the measurement units differ for the weight and volume constraints, the operations manager should compare the relative variability in the two types of measurements.

For weight, the coefficient of variation is

$$CV_W = \left(\frac{3.9}{26.0}\right) 100\% = 15\%$$

For volume, the coefficient of variation is

$$CV_V = \left(\frac{2.2}{8.8}\right) 100\% = 25\%$$

Since the difference $> 10\%$ of the smaller, thus, relative to the mean, the package volume is much more variable than the package weight.

EXAMPLE 3.30

Comparing Two Coefficients of Variation When Two Variables Have Different Units of Measurement

The operations manager of a package delivery service is deciding whether to purchase a new fleet of trucks. When packages are stored in the trucks in preparation for delivery, you need to consider two major constraints—the weight (in pounds) and the volume (in cubic feet) for each item.

The operations manager samples 200 packages and finds that the mean weight is 26.0 pounds, with a standard deviation of 3.9 pounds, and the mean volume is 8.8 cubic feet, with a standard deviation of 2.2 cubic feet. How can the operations manager compare the variation of the weight and the volume?

SOLUTION Because the measurement units differ for the weight and volume constraints, the operations manager should compare the relative variability in the two types of measurements.

For weight, the coefficient of variation is

$$CV_W = \left(\frac{3.9}{26.0}\right) 100\% = 15\%$$

For volume, the coefficient of variation is

$$CV_V = \left(\frac{2.2}{8.8}\right) 100\% = 25\%$$

Since the difference $>10\%$ smaller, thus, relative to the mean, the package volume is much more variable than the package weight.

Problems for Section 3.2

3.20 Last year's travel expenditures ($) by the 12 members of a university's business council were as follows:

    0   0 173   378   441 733 759
  857 958 985 1434 2063

a. Calculate the mean travel expenditure per member.
b. Determine the median travel expenditure per member.
c. Determine the 80th percentile of this data.
d. Determine the range and the interquartile range of the data.
e. Calculate the coefficient of variation of the data.

3.21 The number of defective items in 12 recent production lots of 1000 items each from Plant A were as follows:

   3   1 0 0 2 21 4 1 1 0 2 5

a. Calculate the mean number of defective per lot.
b. The mean number of defectives per lot in a group of 16 lots from Plant B was 3.5. What was the total number of defective items in these 16 lots?
c. What is the median number of defective items per lot?
d. Why does the median differ substantially from the mean of this data?
e. The median number of defectives per lot for 20 lots from Plant C was 4. What was the total number of defectives in these 20 lots?
f. What is the standard deviation of the number of defectives per lot for Plant A?

3.22 The change in enrollment between this year and last year in seven programs at a particular university are:

   –614 –103 41 258 313 387 490

a. Calculate the mean enrollment change per program. Does the fact that the mean is positive imply that the combined total enrollment in the seven programs has increased? Explain.
b. Determine the median enrollment change per program.
c. Calculate the standard deviation of enrollment change. Does the fact that the standard deviation is positive relate to the fact that the mean was positive? Explain.

3.23 Refer to problem 3.2 in Descriptive Statistics Exercises—Set 1:
What is the standard deviation of the liquor bill for a table?

3.24 Refer to problem 3.8 in Descriptive Statistics Exercises—Set 1:
What is the standard deviation of the sales of a toy store?

3.25 Refer to problem 3.10 in Descriptive Statistics Exercises—Set 1:
What is the standard deviation of the cost of a one-day trip for people under 50 years old?

3.26 Refer to problem 3.15 in Descriptive Statistics Exercises—Set 1:
What is the standard deviation of the monetary value of the prizes?

3.27 Refer to problem 3.17 in Descriptive Statistics Exercises—Set 1:
What is the standard deviation of the labour hours per car for the four GM plants?

3.28 Refer to problem 3.19 in Descriptive Statistics Exercises—Set 1:
What is the standard deviation of the company profits?

3.29 A suburban farm grows strawberries in a large field where prospective customers go to pick-their-own. A survey of 200 customers showed that 30% picked one basket, 50% picked two baskets and the remainder picked three baskets. What is the mean number of baskets of strawberries per customer? What is the standard deviation?

3.30 The means and standard deviations of revenue per farm ($000) and volume harvested per farm (Thou. kg.) for two farm products in Western Canada are as follows:

| Grain | Revenue per Farm | | Volume per Farm | |
	Mean	Std. Dev.	Mean	Std. Dev.
Wheat	12.56	4.03	76.7	22.9
Barley	14.49	5.89	106.3	35.4

Is revenue or volume relatively more variable for wheat? Is the same true for barley?

3.31 The table below appeared in the May 1995 issue of the Report on Business.

Can Brooks Catch Up

Coutu's current stores outperform its newly acquired Brooks outlets

Coutu stores averaged sales of $6 million in 94

Number of franchises 227
Selling space per store .... 7,700 sq.ft.
System-wide retail sales 1994 .... $1.34 billion

...and the U.S. Maxi outlets averaged $4 million

Number of stores 21
Selling space per store .... 12,000 sq.ft.
1994 sales .... $85 million

...while Brooks lagged far behind at $1.9 million

Number of stores 221
Selling space per store .... 6,000 sq.ft.
1994 sales .... $425.8 million

a. What is the overall average selling space per store for all 469 stores?

b. What is the overall average sales per store for all 469 stores?

3.32 The percentage distribution of hourly earnings for the 2100 plant employees of the ABC Corp. is shown below:

Hourly Earnings ($)	Percent of Employees
14.00 and under 16.00	12
16.00 " " 18.00	24
18.00 " " 20.00	44
20.00 " " 25.00	15
25.00 " " 30.00	5

Calculate the mean and standard deviation of hourly earnings of the employees at ABC Corp.

3.33 Refer to the table 'Who works the hardest' and determine if the five countries indicated were more variable in terms of average hours worked or gross domestic product in 2000?

Who works the hardest
Average annual hours worked per person.

Buying power
Gross domestic product, in 1995 U.S. dollars adjusted for purchasing power parity.

SOURCE: Organization for Economic Co-operation and Development

Z Scores

An **extreme value** or **outlier** is a value located far away from the mean. *Z* scores are useful in identifying outliers. The larger the *Z* score, the greater the distance from the value to the mean. The **Z score** is the difference between the value and the mean, divided by the standard deviation.

Z SCORES	
$$Z = \frac{X - \overline{X}}{S}$$	**(3.7)**

For the time-to-get-ready data, the mean is 39.6 minutes, and the standard deviation is 6.77 minutes. The time to get ready on the first day is 39.0 minutes. You compute the *Z* score for Day 1 by using Equation (3.7):

$$Z = \frac{X - \overline{X}}{S}$$

$$= \frac{39.0 - 39.6}{6.77}$$

$$= -0.09$$

Table 3.5 shows the *Z* scores for all 10 days. The largest *Z* score is 1.83 for Day 4, on which the time to get ready was 52 minutes. The lowest *Z* score was -1.57 for Day 2, on which the time to get ready was 29 minutes. As a general rule, a *Z* score is considered an outlier if it is less than -3.0 or greater than $+3.0$. None of the times met that criterion to be considered outliers.

TABLE 3.5

Z Scores for the 10 Getting-Ready Times

	Time (X)	Z Score
	39	−0.09
	29	−1.57
	43	0.50
	52	1.83
	39	−0.09
	44	0.65
	40	0.06
	31	−1.27
	44	0.65
	35	−0.68
Mean	39.6	
Standard deviation	6.77	

EXAMPLE 3.31

Computing the Z Scores of the Number of Calories in Iced Coffee Drinks

The data in the file CoffeeDrink represent the calories of 16-ounce iced coffee drinks at Dunkin' Donuts and Starbucks. Compute the Z scores of the calories of 16-ounce iced coffee drinks.

SOLUTION Table 3.6 illustrates the Z scores of the calories of 16-ounce iced coffee drinks. The largest Z score is 1.33, for an iced coffee drink with 530 calories. The lowest Z score is −1.24, for an iced coffee drink with 240 calories. There are no apparent outliers in these data because none of the Z scores are less than −3.0 or greater than +3.0.

TABLE 3.6

Z Scores of the Number of Calories in Iced Coffee Drinks

	Calories	Z Scores
	240	−1.24
	260	−1.06
	350	−0.27
	350	−0.27
	420	0.35
	510	1.15
	530	1.33
Mean	380	
Standard Deviation	113.1371	

3.3 Descriptive Statistics III

Shape

Shape is the pattern of the distribution of data values throughout the entire range of all the values. A distribution is either symmetrical or skewed. In a **symmetrical** distribution, the values below the mean are distributed exactly as the values above the mean. In this case, the low and high values balance each other out. In a **skewed** distribution, the values are not symmetrical around the mean. This skewness results in an imbalance of low values or high values.

Shape influences the relationship of the mean to the median in the following ways:

- Mean < median: negative, or left-skewed
- Mean = median: symmetric, or zero skewness
- Mean > median: positive, or right-skewed

Figure 3.1 depicts three data sets, each with a different shape.

FIGURE 3.1

A comparison of three data sets differing in shape

| Panel A | Panel B | Panel C |
| Negative, or left-skewed | Symmetrical | Positive, or right-skewed |

The data in Panel A are negative, or **left-skewed**. In this panel, most of the values are in the upper portion of the distribution. A long tail and distortion to the left is caused by some extremely small values. These extremely small values pull the mean downward so that the mean is less than the median.

The data in Panel B are symmetrical. Each half of the curve is a mirror image of the other half of the curve. The low and high values on the scale balance, and the mean equals the median.

The data in Panel C are positive, or **right-skewed**. In this panel, most of the values are in the lower portion of the distribution. A long tail on the right is caused by some extremely large values. These extremely large values pull the mean upward so that the mean is greater than the median.

3.4 Numerical Descriptive Measures for a Population

Sections 3.1 and 3.2 present various statistics that described the properties of central tendency and variation for a sample. If your data set represents numerical measurements for an entire population, you need to calculate and interpret parameters, summary measures for a population. In this section, you will learn about three population parameters: the population mean, population variance, and population standard deviation.

To help illustrate these parameters, first review Table 3.7, which contains the one-year return for the five largest bond funds (in terms of total assets) as of May 5, 2008. (The data are contained in the file Largest bonds .)

TABLE 3.7

One-Year Return for the Population Consisting of the Five Largest Bond Funds

Bond Fund	One-Year Return
Pimco: Total Rtn; Inst	11.0
Vanguard Tot Bd; Inv	6.7
American Funds Bond; A	0.8
Dodge & Cox Income	4.4
Vanguard GNMA; Inv	7.3

Source: *Data extracted from* The Wall Street Journal, *May 5, 2008, p. R2.*

The Population Mean

The **population mean** is represented by the symbol μ, the Greek lowercase letter mu. Equation (3.8) defines the population mean.

POPULATION MEAN

The population mean is the sum of the values in the population divided by the population size N.

$$\mu = \frac{\sum_{i=1}^{N} X_i}{N} \qquad (3.8)$$

where

$$\mu = \text{population mean}$$

$$X_i = i\text{th value of the variable } X$$

$$\sum_{i=1}^{N} X_i = \text{summation of all } X_i \text{ values in the population}$$

To compute the mean one-year return for the population of bond funds given in Table 3.7, use Equation (3.8):

$$\mu = \frac{\sum_{i=1}^{N} X_i}{N} = \frac{11.0 + 6.7 + 0.8 + 4.4 + 7.3}{5} = \frac{30.2}{5} = 6.04$$

Thus, the mean percentage return for these bond funds is 6.04.

The Population Variance and Standard Deviation

The **population variance** and the **population standard deviation** measure variation in a population. Like the related sample statistics, the population standard deviation is the square root of the population variance. The symbol σ^2, the Greek lowercase letter sigma squared, represents the population variance, and the symbol σ, the Greek lowercase letter sigma, represents the population standard deviation. Equations (3.9) and (3.10) define these parameters. The denominators for the right-side terms in these equations use N and not the $(n - 1)$ term that is used in the equations for the sample variance and standard deviation.

POPULATION VARIANCE

The population variance is the sum of the squared differences around the population mean divided by the population size N.

$$\sigma^2 = \frac{\sum_{i=1}^{N} (X_i - \mu)^2}{N} \qquad (3.9)$$

where

$$\mu = \text{population mean}$$

$$X_i = i\text{th value of the variable } X$$

$$\sum_{i=1}^{N} (X_i - \mu)^2 = \text{summation of all the squared differences between the } X_i \text{ values and } \mu$$

POPULATION STANDARD DEVIATION

$$\sigma = \sqrt{\frac{\sum_{i=1}^{N}(X_i - \mu)^2}{N}} \qquad\qquad \textbf{(3.10)}$$

To compute the population variance for the data of Table 3.7, you use Equation (3.9):

$$
\begin{aligned}
\sigma^2 &= \frac{\sum_{i=1}^{N}(X_i - \mu)^2}{N} \\
&= \frac{(11.0 - 6.04)^2 + (6.7 - 6.04)^2 + (0.8 - 6.04)^2 + (4.4 - 6.04)^2 + (7.3 - 6.04)^2}{5} \\
&= \frac{24.6016 + 0.4356 + 27.4576 + 2.6896 + 1.5876}{5} \\
&= \frac{56.772}{5} = 11.3544
\end{aligned}
$$

Thus, the variance of the one-year returns is 11.3544 squared percentage return. The squared units make the variance hard to interpret. You should use the standard deviation that is expressed in the original units of the data (percentage return). From Equation (3.10),

$$\sigma = \sqrt{\sigma^2} = \sqrt{\frac{\sum_{i=1}^{N}(X_i - \mu)^2}{N}} = \sqrt{11.3544} = 3.3696$$

Therefore, the typical percentage return differs from the mean of 6.04 by approximately 3.3696. This large amount of variation suggests that these large bond funds produce results that differ greatly.

The Empirical Rule

In most data sets, a large portion of the values tend to cluster somewhere near the median. In right-skewed data sets, this clustering occurs to the left of the mean—that is, at a value less than the mean. In left-skewed data sets, the values tend to cluster to the right of the mean—that is, greater than the mean. In symmetrical data sets, where the median and mean are the same, the values often tend to cluster around the median and mean, producing a bell-shaped distribution. You can use the **empirical rule** to examine the variability in such distributions:

- Approximately 68% of the values are within a distance of ± 1 standard deviation from the mean.
- Approximately 95% of the values are within a distance of ± 2 standard deviations from the mean.
- Approximately 99.7% of the values are within a distance of ± 3 standard deviations from the mean.

The empirical rule helps you measure how the values distribute above and below the mean and can help you identify outliers. The empirical rule implies that for bell-shaped distributions, only about 1 out of 20 values will be beyond two standard deviations from the mean in either direction. As a general rule, you can consider values not found in the interval $\mu \pm 2\sigma$ as potential outliers. The rule also implies that only about 3 in 1,000 will be beyond three standard deviations from the mean. Therefore, values not found in the interval $\mu \pm 3\sigma$ are almost always considered outliers.

EXAMPLE 3.32

Using the Empirical Rule

A population of 12-ounce cans of cola is known to have a mean fill-weight of 12.06 ounces and a standard deviation of 0.02. The population is known to be bell-shaped. Describe the distribution of fill-weights. Is it very likely that a can will contain less than 12 ounces of cola?

SOLUTION

$$\mu \pm \sigma = 12.06 \pm 0.02 = (12.04, 12.08)$$

$$\mu \pm 2\sigma = 12.06 \pm 2(0.02) = (12.02, 12.10)$$

$$\mu \pm 3\sigma = 12.06 \pm 3(0.02) = (12.00, 12.12)$$

Using the empirical rule, approximately 68% of the cans will contain between 12.04 and 12.08 ounces, approximately 95% will contain between 12.02 and 12.10 ounces, and approximately 99.7% will contain between 12.00 and 12.12 ounces. Therefore, it is highly unlikely that a can will contain less than 12 ounces.

For heavily skewed data sets, or those not appearing bell-shaped for any other reason, the Chebyshev rule discussed next should be applied instead of the empirical rule.

The Chebyshev Rule

The **Chebyshev rule** (reference 1) states that for any data set, regardless of shape, the percentage of values that are found within distances of k standard deviations from the mean must be at least

$$(1 - 1/k^2) \times 100\%$$

You can use this rule for any value of k greater than 1. Consider $k = 2$. The Chebyshev rule states that at least $[1 - (1/2)^2] \times 100\% = 75\%$ of the values must be found within ± 2 standard deviations of the mean.

The Chebyshev rule is very general and applies to any type of distribution. The rule indicates *at least* what percentage of the values fall within a given distance from the mean. However, if the data set is approximately bell-shaped, the empirical rule will more accurately reflect the greater concentration of data close to the mean. Table 3.8 compares the Chebyshev and empirical rules.

TABLE 3.8

How Data Vary Around the Mean

	% of Values Found in Intervals Around the Mean	
Interval	**Chebyshev (any distribution)**	**Empirical Rule (bell-shaped distribution)**
$(\mu - \sigma, \mu + \sigma)$	At least 0%	Approximately 68%
$(\mu - 2\sigma, \mu + 2\sigma)$	At least 75%	Approximately 95%
$(\mu - 3\sigma, \mu + 3\sigma)$	At least 88.89%	Approximately 99.7%

EXAMPLE 3.33

Using the Chebyshev Rule

As in Example 3.29, a population of 12-ounce cans of cola is known to have a mean fill-weight of 12.06 ounces and a standard deviation of 0.02. However, the shape of the population is unknown, and you cannot assume that it is bell-shaped. Describe the distribution of fill-weights. Is it very likely that a can will contain less than 12 ounces of cola?

SOLUTION

$$\mu \pm \sigma = 12.06 \pm 0.02 = (12.04, 12.08)$$

$$\mu \pm 2\sigma = 12.06 \pm 2(0.02) = (12.02, 12.10)$$

$$\mu \pm 3\sigma = 12.06 \pm 3(0.02) = (12.00, 12.12)$$

Because the distribution may be skewed, you cannot use the empirical rule. Using the Chebyshev rule, you cannot say anything about the percentage of cans containing between 12.04 and 12.08 ounces. You can state that at least 75% of the cans will contain between 12.02 and 12.10 ounces and at least 88.89% will contain between 12.00 and 12.12 ounces. Therefore, between 0 and 11.11% of the cans will contain less than 12 ounces.

You can use these two rules for understanding how data are distributed around the mean when you have sample data. In each case, you use the value you calculated for $\overline{X}$ in place of μ and the value you calculated for S in place of σ. The results you compute using the sample statistics are *approximations* because you used sample statistics $(\overline{X}, S)$ and not population parameters (μ, σ).

Problems for Section 3.4

LEARNING THE BASICS

3.34 The following is a set of data for a population with $N = 10$:

$$7 \quad 5 \quad 11 \quad 8 \quad 3 \quad 6 \quad 2 \quad 1 \quad 9 \quad 8$$

a. Compute the population mean.
b. Compute the population standard deviation.

3.35 The following is a set of data for a population with $N = 10$:

$$7 \quad 5 \quad 6 \quad 6 \quad 6 \quad 4 \quad 8 \quad 6 \quad 9 \quad 3$$

a. Compute the population mean.
b. Compute the population standard deviation.

APPLYING THE CONCEPTS

3.36 The data in the file `Tax` represent the quarterly sales tax receipts (in thousands of dollars) submitted to the comptroller of the Village of Fair Lake for the period ending March 2008 by all 50 business establishments in that locale:

10.3	11.1	9.6	9.0	14.5
13.0	6.7	11.0	8.4	10.3
13.0	11.2	7.3	5.3	12.5
8.0	11.8	8.7	10.6	9.5
11.1	10.2	11.1	9.9	9.8
11.6	15.1	12.5	6.5	7.5
10.0	12.9	9.2	10.0	12.8
12.5	9.3	10.4	12.7	10.5
9.3	11.5	10.7	11.6	7.8
10.5	7.6	10.1	8.9	8.6

a. Compute the mean, variance, and standard deviation for this population.
b. What percentage of these businesses have quarterly sales tax receipts within ± 1, ± 2, or ± 3 standard deviations of the mean?
c. Compare and contrast your findings with what would be expected on the basis of the empirical rule. Are you surprised at the results in (b)?

3.37 Consider a population of 1,024 mutual funds that primarily invest in large companies. You have determined that μ, the mean one-year total percentage return achieved by all the funds, is 8.20 and that σ, the standard deviation, is 2.75. According to the empirical rule, what percentage of these funds is expected to be
a. within ± 1 standard deviation of the mean?
b. within ± 2 standard deviations of the mean?

c. According to the Chebyshev rule, what percentage of these funds are expected to be within ± 1, ± 2, or ± 3 standard deviations of the mean?
d. According to the Chebyshev rule, at least 93.75% of these funds are expected to have one-year total returns between what two amounts?

3.38 The file `Collegetuition` contains the tuition and fees for public four-year colleges in each of the 50 states for the 2006–2007 school year. The amounts do not include room and board. The file also contains the percentage increase in tuition and fees from 2005–2006 to 2006–2007 (extracted from Sandra Block, "Rising Costs Make Climb to Higher Education Steeper," **usatoday.com**, January 12, 2007).
a. Compute the population mean and population standard deviation for tuition and fees.
b. Interpret the parameters in (a).
c. Compute the population mean and population standard deviation for the percentage increase from 2005–2006 to 2006–2007.
d. Interpret the parameters in (c).

3.39 The data in the file `Energy` contains the per-capita energy consumption, in kilowatt hours, for each of the 50 states and the District of Columbia during a recent year.
a. Compute the mean, variance, and standard deviation for the population.
b. What proportion of these states has average per-capita energy consumption within ± 1 standard deviation of the mean, within ± 2 standard deviations of the mean, and within ± 3 standard deviations of the mean?
c. Compare and contrast your findings versus what would be expected based on the empirical rule. Are you surprised at the results in (b)?
d. Repeat (a) through (c) with the District of Columbia removed. How have the results changed?

3.40 Thirty companies comprise the DJIA. Just how big are these companies? One common method to measure the size of a company is to use its market capitalization, which is computed by taking the number of stock shares multiplied by the price of a share of stock. On May 5, 2008, the market capitalization of these companies ranged from General Motors's $12.7 billion to Exxon-Mobil's $477.2 billion. The entire population of market capitalization values is recorded in the file `Dowmarketcap`.
Source: *Data extracted from* **money.cnn.com**, *May 5, 2008.*

a. Calculate the mean and standard deviation of the market capitalization for this population of 30 companies.
b. Interpret the parameters calculated in (a).

3.5 Box-Whisker Plot

Sections 3.1 through 3.3 discuss measures of central tendency, variation, and shape. Another way of describing numerical data is through an exploratory data analysis that includes the quartiles, the five-number summary, and the boxplot.

The box-whisker plot is a graphical display that is used to get a general picture of a set of data. The main conceptual difference from the box-whisker plot and previous graphical displays that we have discussed is that the box-whisker plot shows some the values of descriptive statistics.

EXAMPLE 3.34

The following data shows the number of days absent from work for 50 employees in a large company. The data has been arranged into an ascending data array.

1	2	4	4	5	5	5	10	10	11
12	13	13	14	19	20	22	23	25	26
26	26	27	27	27	28	29	29	29	30
31	31	32	33	35	35	36	52	54	61
68	74	81	84	95	123	126	137	152	173

The following statistics have been calculated using the CASIO CFX-9850GB calculator.

Mean: 40.7   Min: 1
Median: 27.5   Max: 173
Q1:   13
Q3:   52
IQR: 39

The first step in drawing the box whisker plot is to lay out an appropriate horizontal scale.

The box is then formed with the first and third quartiles determining the location of the sides. The **mean** may be indicated with a '+' sign. The *median* is indicated by a line across the box. The **inner left and right fences** are then calculated, but are not plotted on the diagram.

$$\text{LIF} = Q_1 - (1.5 \times \text{IQR}) \qquad \text{RIF} = Q_3 + (1.5 \times \text{IQR})$$

The whiskers may now be drawn using the following procedure:

i. Imagine plotting all the data between the edge of the box and the inner fences (including data that falls on the fence) as points.
ii. Two(2) rules now apply for the whisker. Each whisker is as long as possible, but
   a) They can't go past the inner fence.
   b) They must end at a data point.

Now we can calculate the location of the **left and right outer fences** as follows:

$$\text{LOF} = \text{LIF} - (1.5 \times \text{IQR}) \qquad \text{ROF} = \text{RIF} + (1.5 \times \text{IQR})$$

All data values that fall between the fences are called **outliers** and are plotted individually using a special symbol. SPSS uses a 'o' symbol to indicate outliers. Outliers are values that are *somewhat unusual* in that they lie away from the majority of the data.

All data values that lie beyond the outer fences are called **extremes** and are also plotted using a special symbol. SPSS uses an '*' symbol to indicate extremes. Extremes are *unusual* values that are often of extreme interest to the statistical analyst.

Example

$$LIF = Q_1 - (1.5 \times IQR) = 13 - (1.5 \times 39) = -45.5$$
$$LOF = LIF - (1.5 \times IQR) = -45.5 - (1.5 \times 39) = -104$$
$$RIF = Q_3 + (1.5 \times IQR) = 52 + (1.5 \times 39) = 110.5$$
$$ROF = RIF + (1.5 \times IQR) = 110.5 + (1.5 \times 39) = 169$$

The complete box-whisker plot is shown below.

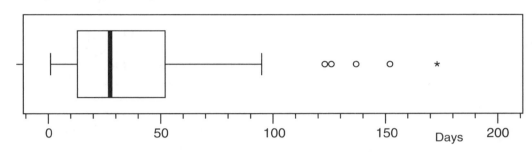

CALCULATOR LESSON 3

CASIO FX-9750GII CALCULATOR

Lesson 3—Graph a Box-Whisker Plot

EXAMPLE 3.35

The following data shows the response times, in days, for 50 customer complaints for a large car dealership. The data has been arranged into an ascending data array.

1	2	4	4	5	5	5	10	10	11
12	13	13	14	19	20	22	23	25	26
26	26	27	27	27	28	29	29	29	30
31	31	32	33	35	35	36	52	54	61
68	74	81	84	95	123	126	137	152	173

Follow these steps to draw the box-whisker plot.

Step 1: From the **Main Menu** select **STAT mode**

Step 2: Enter data into **List 1**

Step 3: Press **F1 (GRPH)**

Step 4: Select F6(SET), then enter the following items:

StatGraph1
Graph Type   : ▶ (press **F6**) and select **BOX (F2)**
XList   : List (F1) and type **1** (if you input your data in List 1)
Frequency   : 1 (F1)
Outlier   : ON (F1)

Now press **EXE**, and then select **GPH1 (F1)**

The calculator will now show the box-whisker plot.
To obtain a full range of 1-variable statistics, press **F1 (1 VAR)** at the bottom left hand corner of the screen. The result is

$$\bar{x} = 40.7$$
$$\Sigma x = 2035$$
$$\Sigma x^2 = 164603$$
$$\sigma x = 40.4421809$$
$$sx = 40.8527719$$
$$n = 50$$
$$minx = 1$$
$$Q1 = 13$$
$$Med = 27.5$$
$$Q3 = 52$$
$$maxX = 173$$
$$Mod = 5$$
$$Mod = 26$$
$$Mod = 27$$
$$Mod = 29$$
$$Mod{:}n = 4$$
$$Mod{:}F = 3$$

To go back to view the plot, press **F6(DRAW)**.

Problems for Section 3.5

3.41 The following data was obtained by taking a sample of stocks listed in the Financial Times. All of these stocks have had recent trends of price increases.

Stock	Closing Price	Volume ($00's)	Yield %	P/E Ratio
Abitibi-Price	20.25	31435	0.7	67.5
Agnico Eagle	19.38	7529	na	55.4
Air Canada	7.75	13010	na	na
Alberta Energy	20.75	9934	1.9	15.6
Arbor Me	18.50	770	0.3	21.8
Atlantis	1.90	3896	na	14.6
Brascan Cl	19.38	2616	5.4	57.5
Brunswick	11.12	749	3.1	na
Canadex j	33.30	62	na	20.6
Donohue Sv	16.75	1938	1.6	23.8
Electrohom	10.38	920	1.0	7.7
Finning	21.62	1658	1.5	19.3
Gennum	18.50	4	0.4	14.6
Hemlo gold	15.38	3091	1.3	24.4
Ipsco	26.25	1873	1.8	17.5
Jordan Petrol	10.62	356	na	31.3
Kerr Addison	24.50	292	2.5	37.1
Lynx Energy	11.00	10	na	13.6
MDS Helth	14.38	60	1.0	13.2
Noranda	27.50	26426	3.6	32.5
Okanaga	3.30	46	0.6	33.0
Pagurian nv	4.50	3898	6.7	13.6

Stock	Closing Price	Volume ($00's)	Yield %	P/E Ratio
Rio Algom	25.75	24697	2.3	21.6
Shaw Ind	13.75	557	1.0	16.0
Tombill A	5.50	2	3.3	7.6
Versa Services	10.12	699	2.2	21.5
Wetsmin	5.62	388	3.5	na
XL Foods	0.78	1315	na	7.8

a. Draw the box-whisker plot for the VOLUME data.
b. Draw the box-whisker plot for the YIELD data.

3.42 Refer to problem 3.20 in Descriptive Statistics Exercises—Set 2:

Draw the box-whisker plot for the travel expense data?

3.43 Refer to problem 3.21 in Descriptive Statistics Exercises—Set 2:

Draw the box-whisker plot for the number of defectives data?

3.44 Refer to problem 3.22 in Descriptive Statistics Exercises—Set 2:

Draw the box-whisker plot for the university enrollment data?

Exploratory Data Analysis

A **five-number summary** that consists of

$$X_{\text{smallest}} \quad Q_1 \quad \text{Median} \quad Q_3 \quad X_{\text{largest}}$$

provides a way to determine the shape of a distribution. Table 3.9 explains how the relationships among the "five numbers" allows you to recognize the shape of a data set.

For the sample of 10 getting-ready times, the smallest value is 29 minutes and the largest value is 52 minutes. Calculations done on pages 167–168 show that the and $Q_3 = 44$. Therefore, the five-number summary is

$$29 \quad 35 \quad 39.5 \quad 44 \quad 52$$

The distance from X_{smallest} to the median ($39.5 - 29 = 10.5$) is slightly less than the distance from the median to X_{largest} ($52 - 39.5 = 12.5$). The distance from X_{smallest} to Q_1 ($35 - 29 = 6$) is slightly less than the distance from Q_3 to X_{largest} ($52 - 44 = 8$). Therefore, the getting-ready times are slightly right-skewed.

TABLE 3.9   Relationships Among the Five-Number Summary and the Type of Distribution

Comparison	Type of Distribution		
	Left-Skewed	Symmetric	Right-Skewed
The distance from X_{smallest} to the median versus the distance from the median to X_{largest}.	The distance from X_{smallest} to the median is greater than the distance from the median to X_{largest}.	Both distances are the same.	The distance from X_{smallest} to the median is less than the distance from the median to X_{largest}.
The distance from X_{smallest} to Q_1 versus the distance from Q_3 to X_{largest}.	The distance from X_{smallest} to Q_1 is greater than the distance from Q_3 to X_{largest}.	Both distances are the same.	The distance from X_{smallest} to Q_1 is less than the distance from Q_3 to X_{largest}.
The distance from Q_1 to the median versus the distance from the median to Q_3.	The distance from Q_1 to the median is greater than the distance from the median to Q_3.	Both distances are the same.	The distance from Q_1 to the median is less than the distance from the median to Q_3.

EXAMPLE 3.36

Computing the Five-Number Summary of the Number of Calories in Iced Coffee Drinks

The data in the file **CoffeeDrink** represent the calories of 16-ounce iced coffee drinks at Dunkin' Donuts and Starbucks. Compute the five-number summary of the number of calories of 16-ounce iced coffee drinks.

SOLUTION From previous computations for the calories of 16-ounce iced coffee drinks (see page 158), the median $= 350$, $Q_1 = 260$, and $Q_3 = 510$. In addition, the smallest value in the data set is 240, and the largest value is 530. Therefore, the five-number summary is

$$240 \quad 260 \quad 350 \quad 510 \quad 530$$

The three comparisons listed in Table 3.9 are used to evaluate skewness. The distance from X_{smallest} to the median ($350 - 240 = 110$) is less than the distance ($530 - 350 = 180$) from the median to X_{largest}. The distance from X_{smallest} to Q_1 ($260 - 240 = 20$) is the same as the distance from Q_3 to X_{largest} ($530 - 510 = 20$). The distance from Q_1 to the median ($350 - 260 = 90$) is less than the distance from the median to Q_3 ($510 - 350 = 160$). Two comparisons indicate a right-skewed distribution whereas the other indicates a symmetric distribution. Therefore, you can conclude that the number of calories in iced coffee drinks is right-skewed.

EXAMPLE 3.37

The Boxplots of the 2006 Returns of Growth and Value Mutual Funds

The 868 mutual funds (Mutual Funds) that are part of the Using Statistics scenario are classified according to whether the mutual funds are growth or value funds. Construct the boxplot of the 2006 returns for growth and value mutual funds.

SOLUTION Figure 3.3 shows the 2006 return for the growth and value mutual funds and Figure 3.4 illustrates Minitab boxplots. The median return, the quartiles, and the minimum and maximum return are much higher for the value funds than for the growth funds. Both the growth and value funds appear to be fairly symmetrical between the quartiles, but the value funds seem to have more extremely high returns.

FIGURE 3.3

PHStat2 boxplots of the 2006 return for growth and value mutual funds

See Appendix E3.3 to create this.

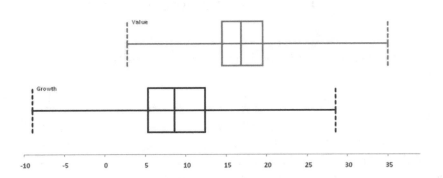

Boxplots for the Growth and Value Funds
2006 Return

FIGURE 3.4

Minitab boxplots of the 2006 return for growth and value mutual funds

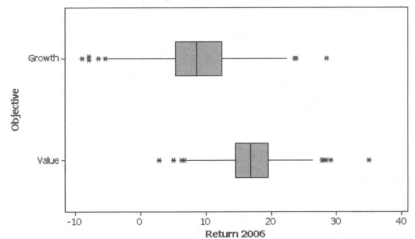

Boxplot of Return 2006

Notice that in Figure 3.4, several * appear in the boxplots. This indicates outliers that are more than 1.5 times the interquartile range beyond the quartiles.

Figure 3.5 demonstrates the relationship between the boxplot and the polygon for four different types of distributions. (*Note:* The area under each polygon is split into quartiles corresponding to the five-number summary for the boxplot.)

Panels A and D of Figure 3.5 are symmetrical. In these distributions, the mean and median are equal. In addition, the length of the left tail is equal to the length of the right tail, and the median line divides the box in half.

Panel B of Figure 3.5 is left-skewed. The few small values distort the mean toward the left tail. For this left-skewed distribution, there is a heavy clustering of values at the high end of the

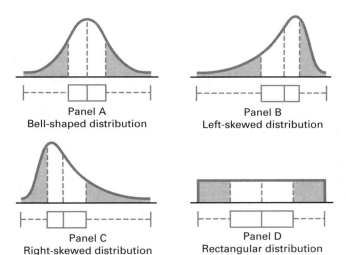

FIGURE 3.5
Boxplots and corresponding polygons for four distributions

Panel A
Bell-shaped distribution

Panel B
Left-skewed distribution

Panel C
Right-skewed distribution

Panel D
Rectangular distribution

scale (i.e., the right side); 75% of all values are found between the left edge of the box (Q_1) and the end of the right tail ($X_{largest}$). There is a long left tail that contains the smallest 25% of the values, demonstrating the lack of symmetry in this data set.

Panel C of Figure 3.5 is right-skewed. The concentration of values is on the low end of the scale (i.e., the left side of the boxplot). Here, 75% of all values are found between the beginning of the left tail and the right edge of the box (Q_3). There is a long right tail that contains the largest 25% of the values, demonstrating the lack of symmetry in this data set.

Problems for Section 3.5

LEARNING THE BASICS

3.45 The following is a set of data from a sample of $n = 6$:

7   4   9   7   3   12

a. Compute the first quartile (Q_1), the third quartile (Q_3), and the interquartile range.
b. List the five-number summary.
c. Construct a boxplot and describe the shape.
d. Compare your answer in (c) with that from Problem 3.2(d). Discuss.

3.46 The following is a set of data from a sample of $n = 7$:

12   7   4   9   0   7   3

a. Compute the first quartile (Q_1), the third quartile (Q_3), and the interquartile range.
b. List the five-number summary.
c. Construct a boxplot and describe the shape.
d. Compare your answer in (c) with that from Problem 3.3(d). Discuss.

3.47 The following is a set of data from a sample of $n = 5$:

7   −5   −8   7   9

a. Compute the first quartile (Q_1), the third quartile (Q_3), and the interquartile range.
b. List the five-number summary.
c. Construct a boxplot and describe the shape.
d. Compare your answer in (c) with that from Problem 3.4(d). Discuss.

APPLYING THE CONCEPTS

3.48 The data file **Chicken** contains the total fat, in grams per serving, for a sample of 20 chicken sandwiches from fast-food chains. The data are as follows:

7   8   4   5   16   20   20   24   19   30
23   30   25   19   29   29   30   30   40   56

Source: *Data extracted from "Fast Food: Adding Health to the Menu,"* Consumer Reports, *September 2004, pp. 28–31.*

a. Compute the first quartile (Q_1), the third quartile (Q_3), and the interquartile range.
b. List the five-number summary.
c. Construct a boxplot and describe the shape.

3.49 The data in the file **Dark chocolate** represent the cost ($) per ounce for a sample of 14 dark chocolate bars.

0.68   0.72   0.92   1.14   1.42   0.94   0.77   0.57   1.51
0.57   0.55   0.86   1.41   0.90

Source: *Data extracted from "Dark Chocolate Which Bars are Best?"* Consumer Reports, *September 2007, pp. 1–8.*

a. Compute the first quartile (Q_1), the third quartile (Q_3), and the interquartile range.
b. List the five-number summary.
c. Construct a boxplot and describe the shape.

3.50 The data file **Themeparks** contains data on the starting admission price (in $) for one-day tickets to 10 theme parks in the United States:

58   63   41   42   29   50   62   43   40   40

Source: *Data extracted from C. Jackson and E. Gamerman, "Rethinking the Thrill Factor," The Wall Street Journal, April 15–16, 2006, pp. P1, P4.*

a. Compute the first quartile (Q_1), the third quartile (Q_3), and the interquartile range.
b. List the five-number summary.
c. Construct a boxplot and describe the shape.

✓ **SELF** **Test** **3.51** The data in the file **SUV** represent the overall miles per gallon (MPG) of 2008 SUVs priced under $30,000.

23, 20, 21, 22, 18, 18, 17, 17, 19, 19, 19,
17, 21, 18, 18, 18, 17, 17, 16, 20, 16, 22

Source: *Data extracted from "Vehicle Ratings," Consumer Reports, April 2008, p. 40.*

a. Compute the first quartile (Q_1), the third quartile (Q_3), and the interquartile range.
b. List the five-number summary.
c. Construct a boxplot and describe the shape.

3.52 The data in the file **Savings Rate** are the yields for a money market account, a one-year certificate of deposit (CD), and a five-year CD for 38 banks in South Florida as of March 28, 2008 (data extracted from **Bankrate.com**, March 28, 2008).
a. List the five-number summary for the yield of the money market account, one-year CD, and a five-year CD.
b. Construct boxplots for the yield of the money market account, one-year CD, and a five-year CD.

c. What similarities and differences are there in the distributions for the yield of the money market account, one-year CD, and a five-year CD?

3.53 A bank branch located in a commercial district of a city has developed an improved process for serving customers during the noon-to-1:00 p.m. lunch period. The waiting time, in minutes (defined as the time the customer enters the line to when he or she reaches the teller window), of a sample of 15 customers during this hour is recorded over a period of one week. The results are contained in the data file **Bank1** and are listed below:

4.21   5.55   3.02   5.13   4.77   2.34   3.54   3.20

4.50   6.10   0.38   5.12   6.46   6.19   3.79

Another branch, located in a residential area, is also concerned with the noon-to-1 p.m. lunch hour. The waiting time, in minutes (defined as the time the customer enters the line to when he or she reaches the teller window), of a sample of 15 customers during this hour is recorded over a period of one week. The results are contained in the data file **Bank2** and are listed below:

9.66   5.90   8.02   5.79   8.73   3.82   8.01   8.35

10.49   6.68   5.64   4.08   6.17   9.91   5.47

a. List the five-number summaries of the waiting times at the two bank branches.
b. Construct boxplots and describe the shape of the distribution for the two bank branches.
c. What similarities and differences are there in the distributions of the waiting time at the two bank branches?

3.6 The Covariance and the Coefficient of Correlation

In Section 2.5, you used scatter plots to visually examine the relationship between two numerical variables. This section presents two measures of the relationship between two numerical variables: the covariance and the coefficient of correlation.

The Covariance

The **covariance** measures the strength of the linear relationship between two numerical variables (X and Y). Equation (3.14) defines the **sample covariance**, and Example 3.38 illustrates its use.

THE SAMPLE COVARIANCE

$$\text{cov}(X, Y) = \frac{\displaystyle\sum_{i=1}^{n}(X_i - \bar{X})(Y_i - \bar{Y})}{n - 1} \tag{3.14}$$

EXAMPLE 3.38

Computing the Sample Covariance

In Figure 2.21, you examined the relationship between the cost of a fast-food hamburger meal and the cost of two movie tickets in 10 cities around the world (extracted from K. Spors, "Keeping Up with . . . Yourself," *The Wall Street Journal*, April 11, 2005, p. R4). The data file `Cost of living` contains the complete data set. Compute the sample covariance.

SOLUTION Table 3.10 provides the cost of a fast-food hamburger meal and the cost of two movie tickets in 10 cities around the world.

TABLE 3.10

Cost of a Fast-Food Hamburger Meal and Cost of Two Movie Tickets in 10 Cities

City	Hamburger	Movie Tickets
Tokyo	5.99	32.66
London	7.62	28.41
New York	5.75	20.00
Sydney	4.45	20.71
Chicago	4.99	18.00
San Francisco	5.29	19.50
Boston	4.39	18.00
Atlanta	3.70	16.00
Toronto	4.62	18.05
Rio de Janeiro	2.99	9.90

Figure 3.6 contains a Microsoft Excel worksheet that calculates the covariance for these data. The Calculations area of Figure 3.6 breaks down Equation (3.14) into a set of smaller calculations. From cell C20, or by using Equation (3.14) directly, you find that the covariance is 6.8378:

$$\text{cov}(X, Y) = \frac{61.5399}{10 - 1}$$
$$= 6.8378$$

FIGURE 3.6

Microsoft Excel worksheet for the covariance between the cost of a fast-food hamburger meal and the cost of two movie tickets in 10 cities

See Appendix E3.4 to create this.

	A	B	C	
1	Covariance Analysis			
2				
3	Hamburger Meal	Movie Ticket	(X-XBar)(Y-YBar)	
4	5.99	32.66	12.6749	=(A4 - $C$16) * (B4 - $C$17)
5	7.62	28.41	21.8860	=(A5 - $C$16) * (B5 - $C$17)
6	5.75	20.00	-0.0948	=(A6 - $C$16) * (B6 - $C$17)
7	4.45	20.71	-0.3105	=(A7 - $C$16) * (B7 - $C$17)
8	4.99	18.00	-0.0234	=(A8 - $C$16) * (B8 - $C$17)
9	5.29	19.50	-0.1938	=(A9 - $C$16) * (B9 - $C$17)
10	4.39	18.00	1.2504	=(A10 - $C$16) * (B10 - $C$17)
11	3.70	16.00	5.2733	=(A11 - $C$16) * (B11 - $C$17)
12	4.62	18.05	0.7442	=(A12 - $C$16) * (B12 - $C$17)
13	2.99	9.90	20.3335	=(A13 - $C$16) * (B13 - $C$17)
14		:		
15		Calculations		
16		XBar	4.9790	=AVERAGE(A4:A13)
17		YBar	20.1230	=AVERAGE(B4:B13)
18		n-1	9	=COUNT(A4:A13) - 1
19		Sum	61.5399	=SUM(C4:C13)
20		Covariance	6.8378	=C19 / C18

The covariance has a major flaw as a measure of the linear relationship between two numerical variables. Because the covariance can have any value, you are unable to determine the relative strength of the relationship. In other words, you cannot tell whether the value 6.8378 is an indication of a strong relationship or a weak relationship. To better determine the relative strength of the relationship, you need to compute the coefficient of correlation.

The Coefficient of Correlation

The **coefficient of correlation** measures the relative strength of a linear relationship between two numerical variables. The values of the coefficient of correlation range from -1 for a perfect negative correlation to $+1$ for a perfect positive correlation. Perfect means that if the points were plotted in a scatter plot, all the points could be connected with a straight line. When dealing with population data for two numerical variables, the Greek letter ρ is used as the symbol for the coefficient of correlation. Figure 3.7 illustrates three different types of association between two variables.

FIGURE 3.7

Types of association between variables

Panel A
Perfect negative
correlation ($\rho = -1$)

Panel B
No correlation
($\rho = 0$)

Panel C
Perfect positive
correlation ($\rho = +1$)

In Panel A of Figure 3.7, there is a perfect negative linear relationship between X and Y. Thus, the coefficient of correlation, ρ, equals -1, and when X increases, Y decreases in a perfectly predictable manner. Panel B shows a situation in which there is no relationship between X and Y. In this case, the coefficient of correlation, ρ, equals 0, and as X increases, there is no tendency for Y to increase or decrease. Panel C illustrates a perfect positive relationship where ρ equals $+1$. In this case, Y increases in a perfectly predictable manner when X increases.

Correlation alone cannot prove that there is a causation effect—that is, that the change in the value of one variable caused the change in the other variable. A strong correlation can be produced simply by chance, by the effect of a third variable not considered in the calculation of the correlation, or by a cause-and-effect relationship. You would need to perform additional analysis to determine which of these three situations actually produced the correlation. Therefore, you can say that causation implies correlation, but correlation alone does not imply causation.

Equation (3.15) defines the **sample coefficient of correlation**, r.

THE SAMPLE COEFFICIENT OF CORRELATION

$$r = \frac{\text{cov}(X, Y)}{S_X S_Y}$$

(3.15)

where

$$\text{cov}(X, Y) = \frac{\sum_{i=1}^{n}(X_i - \overline{X})(Y_i - \overline{Y})}{n - 1}$$

$$S_X = \sqrt{\frac{\sum_{i=1}^{n}(X_i - \overline{X})^2}{n - 1}}$$

$$S_Y = \sqrt{\frac{\sum_{i=1}^{n}(Y_i - \overline{Y})^2}{n - 1}}$$

When you have sample data, you calculate the sample coefficient of correlation, r. When using sample data, you are unlikely to have a sample coefficient of exactly $+1, 0,$ or -1. Figure 3.8 presents scatter plots along with their respective sample coefficients of correlation, r, for six data sets, each of which contains 100 values of X and Y.

FIGURE 3.8

Six Minitab scatter plots and their sample coefficients of correlation, r

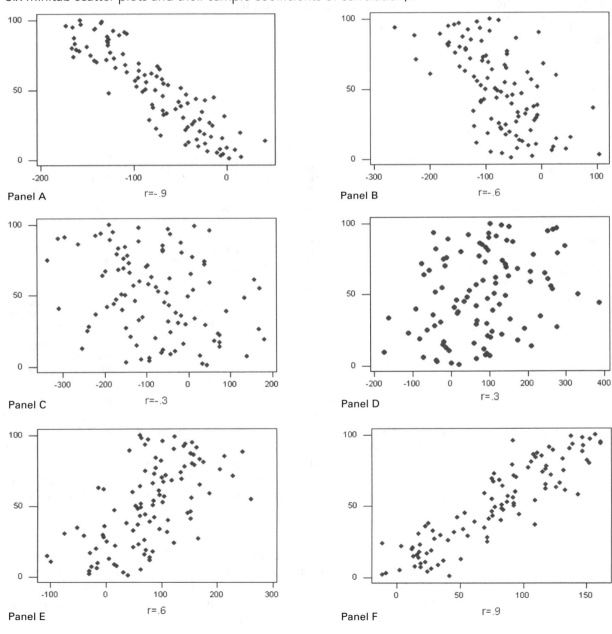

Panel A $r=-.9$

Panel B $r=-.6$

Panel C $r=-.3$

Panel D $r=.3$

Panel E $r=.6$

Panel F $r=.9$

In Panel A, the coefficient of correlation, r, is -0.9. You can see that for small values of X, there is a very strong tendency for Y to be large. Likewise, the large values of X tend to be paired with small values of Y. The data do not all fall on a straight line, so the association between X and Y cannot be described as perfect. The data in Panel B have a coefficient of correlation equal to -0.6, and the small values of X tend to be paired with large values of Y. The linear relationship between X and Y in Panel B is not as strong as that in Panel A. Thus, the coefficient of correlation in Panel B is not as negative as that in Panel A. In Panel C, the linear relationship between X and Y is very weak, $r = -0.3$, and there is only a slight tendency for the small values of X to be paired with the large values of Y. Panels D through F depict data sets that have positive coefficients of correlation because small values of X tend to be paired with small values of Y, and the large values of X tend to be associated with large values of Y.

EXAMPLE 3.39

Computing the Sample Coefficient of Correlation

Consider the cost of a fast-food hamburger meal and the cost of two movie tickets in 10 cities around the world (see Table 3.10). From Figure 3.7 and Equation (3.15) on page 174, compute the sample coefficient of correlation.

SOLUTION

$$r = \frac{\text{cov}(X, Y)}{S_X S_Y}$$

$$= \frac{6.8378}{(1.2925)(6.337)}$$

$$= 0.8348$$

FIGURE 3.9

Microsoft Excel worksheet for the sample coefficient of correlation, r, between the cost of a fast-food hamburger meal and two movie tickets

See Appendix E3.5 to create this. (Use Section M3.3 to create the Minitab equivalent.)

	A	B	C	D	E	
1	Hamburger Meal	Movie Ticket	(X-XBar)^2	(Y-YBar)^2	(X-XBar)(Y-YBar)	
2	5.99	32.66	1.0221	157.1764	12.6749	
3	7.62	28.41	6.9749	68.6744	21.8860	
4	5.75	20.00	0.5944	0.0151	-0.0948	
5	4.45	20.71	0.2798	0.3446	-0.3105	
6	4.99	18.00	0.0001	4.5071	-0.0234	
7	5.29	19.50	0.0967	0.3881	-0.1938	
8	4.39	18.00	0.3469	4.5071	1.2504	
9	3.70	16.00	1.6358	16.9991	5.2733	
10	4.62	18.05	0.1289	4.2973	0.7442	
11	2.99	9.90	3.9561	104.5097	20.3335	
12		Sums:	15.03589	361.41901	61.5399	
13						
14				Calculations		
15			XBar		4.979	=AVERAGE(A2:A11)
16			YBar		20.123	=AVERAGE(B2:B11)
17			n-1		9	=COUNT(A2:A11)-1
18			Covariance		6.83777	=E12 / E17
19			S$_X$		1.2925	=SQRT(C12 / E17)
20			S$_Y$		6.3370	=SQRT(D12 / E17)
21			r		0.8348	=CORREL(A2:A11, B2:B11)

The cost of a fast-food hamburger meal and the cost of two movie tickets are positively correlated. Those cities with the lowest cost of a fast-food hamburger meal tend to be associated with the lowest cost of two movie tickets. Those cities with the highest cost of a fast-food hamburger meal tend to be associated with the highest cost of two movie tickets. This relationship is strong, as indicated by a coefficient of correlation, $r = 0.8348$.

You cannot assume that having a low cost of a fast-food hamburger meal caused the low cost of two movie tickets. You can only say that this is what tended to happen in the sample.

In summary, the coefficient of correlation indicates the linear relationship, or association, between two numerical variables. When the coefficient of correlation gets closer to $+1$ or -1, the linear relationship between the two variables is stronger. When the coefficient of correlation is near 0, little or no linear relationship exists. The sign of the coefficient of correlation indicates whether the data are positively correlated (i.e., the larger values of X are typically paired with the larger values of Y) or negatively correlated (i.e., the larger values of X are typically paired with the smaller values of Y). The existence of a strong correlation does not imply a causation effect. It only indicates the tendencies present in the data.

Problems for Section 3.6

LEARNING THE BASICS

3.54 The following is a set of data from a sample of $n = 11$ items:

| X | 7 | 5 | 8 | 3 | 6 | 10 | 12 | 4 | 9 | 15 | 18 |
| Y | 21 | 15 | 24 | 9 | 18 | 30 | 36 | 12 | 27 | 45 | 54 |

a. Compute the covariance.
b. Compute the coefficient of correlation.
c. How strong is the relationship between X and Y? Explain.

APPLYING THE CONCEPTS

3.55 An article (P. Lim, "An Around-the-World Ticket for Your Portfolio," *The New York Times*, June 3, 2007, p. B5) that discussed investment in foreign stocks (over the last five years) stated that the coefficient of correlation between the return on investment of U.S. stocks (as expressed by the S & P 500) and the German stock market was 0.89, U.S. stocks (as expressed by the S & P 500) and Brazilian stock market was 0.68, and U.S. stocks (as expressed by the S & P 500) and the Japanese stock market was 0.29. What conclusions can you make about the strength of the relationship between the return on investment of U.S. stocks and each of these three other types of investments?

3.56 According to the Mortgage Bankers Association, home mortgage applications were rising as lower loan rates fostered home purchases and refinancings ("Mortgage Applications Creep Up as Rates Fall," **www.usatoday.com**, April 25, 2007).
a. Is the article implying that the number of home mortgages and loan rates are positively correlated, negatively correlated, or independent?
b. If you believe that the article is implying that the number of home mortgages and loan rates are correlated, do you believe that there is a cause-and-effect relationship? Discuss.

3.57 The data in the file **CoffeeDrink** represent the calories and fat, in grams, of 16-ounce iced coffee drinks at Dunkin' Donuts and Starbucks:
a. Compute the the covariance.
b. Compute the coefficient of correlation.
c. Which do you think is more valuable in expressing the relationship between calories and fat—the covariance or the coefficient of correlation? Explain.
d. What conclusions can you reach about the relationship between calories and fat?

Product	Calories	Fat
Dunkin' Donuts Iced Mocha Swirl latte (whole milk)	240	8.0
Starbucks Coffee Frappuccino blended coffee	260	3.5
Dunkin' Donuts Coffee Coolatta (cream)	350	22.0
Starbucks Iced Coffee Mocha Expresso (whole milk and whipped cream)	350	20.0
Starbucks Mocha Frappuccino blended coffee (whipped cream)	420	16.0
Starbucks Chocolate Brownie Frappuccino blended coffee (whipped cream)	510	22.0
Starbucks Chocolate Frappuccino Blended Crème (whipped cream)	530	19.0

Source: *Data extracted from "Coffee as Candy at Dunkin' Donuts and Starbucks,"* Consumer Reports, *June 2004, p. 9.*

3.58 There are several methods for calculating fuel economy. The following table (contained in the file **Mileage**) indicates the mileage, as calculated by owners and by current government standards:

Car	Owner	Government
2005 Ford F-150	14.3	16.8
2005 Chevrolet Silverado	15.0	17.8
2002 Honda Accord LX	27.8	26.2
2002 Honda Civic	27.9	34.2
2004 Honda Civic Hybrid	48.8	47.6
2002 Ford Explorer	16.8	18.3
2005 Toyota Camry	23.7	28.5
2003 Toyota Corolla	32.8	33.1
2005 Toyota Prius	37.3	56.0

Source: *Data extracted from J. Healey, "Fuel Economy Calculations to Be Altered,"* USA Today, *January 11, 2006, p. 1B.*

a. Compute the covariance.
b. Compute the coefficient of correlation.
c. Which do you think is more valuable in expressing the relationship between owner and current government standards mileage—the covariance or the coefficient of correlation? Explain.
d. What conclusions can you reach about the relationship between owner and current government standards mileage?

3.59 College basketball is big business, with coaches' salaries, revenues, and expenses in millions of dollars. The data file `Colleges-basketball` contains the coaches' salaries and revenue for college basketball at selected schools in a recent year (data extracted from R. Adams, "Pay for Playoffs," *The Wall Street Journal*, March 11–12, 2006, pp. P1, P8).
a. Compute the covariance.
b. Compute the coefficient of correlation.
c. What conclusions can you reach about the relationship between a coach's salary and revenue?

3.60 College football players trying out for the NFL are given the Wonderlic standardized intelligence test. The data in the file `Wonderlic` contains the average Wonderlic score of football players trying out for the NFL and the graduation rate for football players at selected schools (data extracted from S. Walker, "The NFL's Smartest Team," *The Wall Street Journal*, September 30, 2005, pp. W1, W10).
a. Compute the covariance.
b. Compute the coefficient of correlation.
c. What conclusions can you reach about the relationship between the average Wonderlic score and graduation rate?

3.7 Presenting Descriptive Statistics: Pitfalls and Ethical Issues

This chapter describes how a set of numerical data can be characterized by the statistics that measure the properties of central tendency, variation, and shape. In business, descriptive statistics such as the ones you have learned about are frequently included in summary reports that are prepared periodically.

The volume of information available on the Internet, in newspapers, and in magazines has produced much skepticism about the objectivity of data. When you are reading information that contains descriptive statistics, you should keep in mind the quip often attributed to the famous nineteenth-century British statesman Benjamin Disraeli: "There are three kinds of lies: lies, damned lies, and statistics."

For example, in examining statistics that are provided, you need to compare the mean and the median. Are they similar or are they very different? Or, is only the mean provided? The answers to these questions will enable you to know whether the data are skewed or symmetrical and whether the median might be a better measure of central tendency than the mean. In addition, you should look to see whether the standard deviation has been included in the statistics provided. Without the standard deviation, it is difficult to determine the amount of variation that exists in the data.

Ethical considerations arise when you are deciding what results to include in a report. You should document both good and bad results. In addition, when making oral presentations and presenting written reports, you need to give results in a fair, objective, and neutral manner. Unethical behavior occurs when you selectively fail to report pertinent findings that are detrimental to the support of a particular position.

USING STATISTICS

@ Choice Is Yours, Part II Revisited

In the Using Statistics scenario, you were hired by the Choice Is Yours investment company to assist investors interested in mutual funds. A sample of 868 mutual funds including 464 with a growth objective (i.e., funds holding stock in companies that are expected to grow quickly in the next year) and 404 with a value objective (i.e., funds holding stock in companies whose stock prices are currently considered undervalued). By comparing these two categories, you were able to provide your investors with valuable insights.

The 2006 returns for both the growth funds and the value funds were approximately symmetrical as indicated by the boxplots (see Figure 3.3 or Figure 3.4), The descriptive statistics (see Figure 3.2) allowed you to compare the central tendency and variability of returns between the growth and value funds. The mean indicated that the growth funds returned an average of 8.71 and the median indicated that half of the funds had returns of 8.60 or more. The value funds' central tendencies were much larger than the growth funds—they had an average of

16.88 and half the funds had returns of 16.85 or more. Moreover, the value funds showed less variability in their returns than the growth funds—they had a range of 32.20 as compared to 37.50; an interquartile range of 5.00 as compared to 7.08; and a standard deviation of 3.96 as compared to 5.42. Thus, not only did a typical value fund have a higher return in 2006 than a typical growth fund, the sample of 404 value funds had returns that were much more closely clustered near the center. An interesting insight is that while 75% of the value funds had returns of 14.50 or higher ($Q_1 = 14.50$), only 25% of the growth funds had returns of 12.40 or higher ($Q_3 = 12.40$). Although past performance is no assurance of future performance, in 2006, the value funds greatly outperformed the growth funds.

SUMMARY

In this and the previous chapter, you studied descriptive statistics—how data are presented in tables and charts, and then summarized, described, analyzed, and interpreted. In Chapter 2, you were able to present useful information through the use of pie charts, histograms, and other graphical methods. In Chapter 3, you learned how numerical descriptive measures such as the mean, median, quartiles, range and standard deviation are used to describe the char-

acteristics of central tendency, variability and shape. You also learned how the coefficient of correlation is used to describe the relationship between two numerical variables. Table 3.11 provides a list of the numerical descriptive measures covered in this chapter.

In the next chapter, the basic principles of probability are presented in order to bridge the gap between the subject of descriptive statistics and the subject of inferential statistics.

TABLE 3.11

Summary of Numerical Descriptive Measures

Type of Analysis	Numerical Data
Describing central tendency, variation, and shape of a numerical variable	Mean, median, mode, quartiles, range, interquartile range, variance, standard deviation, coefficient of variation, Z scores, boxplot **(Sections 3.1, 3.2, 3.3, 3.4, 3.5)**
Describing the relationship between two numerical variables	Covariance, coefficient of correlation **(Section 3.6)**

KEY EQUATIONS

Sample Mean

$$\overline{X} = \frac{\sum_{i=1}^{n} X_i}{n} \tag{3.1}$$

Median

$$\text{Median} = \frac{n+1}{2} \text{ ranked value} \tag{3.2}$$

Range

$$\text{Range} = X_{\text{largest}} - X_{\text{smallest}} \tag{3.3}$$

Sample Variance

$$S^2 = \frac{\sum_{i=1}^{n} (X_i - \overline{X})^2}{n-1} \tag{3.4}$$

Sample Standard Deviation

$$S = \sqrt{S^2} = \sqrt{\frac{\sum_{i=1}^{n} (X_i - \overline{X})^2}{n-1}} \tag{3.5}$$

Coefficient of Variation

$$CV = \left(\frac{S}{\overline{X}}\right)100\% \tag{3.6}$$

Z Scores

$$Z = \frac{X - \overline{X}}{S} \tag{3.7}$$

Population Mean

$$\mu = \frac{\displaystyle\sum_{i=1}^{N} X_i}{N} \tag{3.8}$$

Population Variance

$$\sigma^2 = \frac{\displaystyle\sum_{i=1}^{N}(X_i - \mu)^2}{N} \tag{3.9}$$

Population Standard Deviation

$$\sigma = \sqrt{\frac{\displaystyle\sum_{i=1}^{N}(X_i - \mu)^2}{N}} \tag{3.10}$$

Interquartile Range

$$\text{Interquartile range} = Q_3 - Q_1 \tag{3.13}$$

Sample Covariance

$$\text{cov}(X, Y) = \frac{\displaystyle\sum_{i=1}^{n}(X_i - \overline{X})(Y_i - \overline{Y})}{n - 1} \tag{3.14}$$

Sample Coefficient of Correlation

$$r = \frac{\text{cov}(X, Y)}{S_X S_Y} \tag{3.15}$$

KEY TERMS

EXTRA PROBLEMS FOR CHAPTER 3

3.61 The following table appeared in the May 28th, 1998 issue of the Toronto Star.

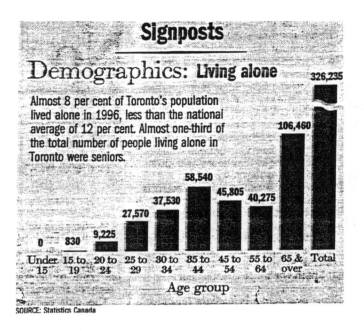

In 1996, excluding seniors (aged 65 and over), what was the average age of people who lived alone in Toronto?

3.62 The following ad appeared in the Feb. 7th, 1997 issue of the Real Estate News. It shows the rental costs for various condos in Harbour Square.

HARBOUR SQUARE RENTALS

250 Queens Quay W.#806 2br $1,200 mo.
270 Queens Quay W.#1301 1br $1,295 mo.
270 Queens Quay W.#602 1br $1,295 mo.
270 Queens Quay W.#2302 1br Furnished
$1,595 mo.
77 Harbour Sq.   #2611 1br $1,500 mo.
401 Queens Quay W.#204 1br $1,950 mo.
105 Victoria   #305 1br $1,150 mo.
                  #306 2br $1,450 mo.
                  #807 1br $1,200 mo.
                  #1007 1br $1,200 mo.

Carrie Bynford 203-6636.
Harry Stinson R.E. Ltd.

What is the mean monthly rent for an unfurnished one bedroom condo?

3.63 Ryerson Memorial Hospital wants to compare its annual patient turnover rate per bed with other similar hospitals. The turnover rates for a sample of 80 beds at Ryerson were summarized and organized in the following frequency distribution. (An annual turnover of 21 per bed indicates that, during the year, 21 patients occupied the same hospital bed.)

Annual turnover rate patients per bed	Number of beds
10 and under 15	4
15 " " 20	9
20 " " 25	13
25 " " 30	25
30 " " 35	15
35 " " 40	7
40 " " 50	5
50 " " 60	2

a. What is the mean turnover rate?
b. What is the median turnover rate?
c. What is the standard deviation of the turnover rate?

3.64 The following table shows room rates for a resort hotel in Nova Scotia for the time period Jan.1 to Dec. 31, 2003.

2003 Room Rates	1/1– 7/3	8/3– 30/3	31/3– 31/5	1/6– 30/6	1/7– 1/9	2/9– 8/10	9/10– 1/12	2/12– 20/12	21/12– 31/12
A Oceanfront									
1 double bed	75	125	85	100	150	95	85	75	125
B Oceanfront									
2 double beds	85	135	95	110	160	105	95	85	135
C Oceanfront Effic.									
2 double beds	105	155	115	130	180	125	115	105	155
D 2 room suite									
3 double beds	120	175	130	150	200	140	130	120	175
E Oceanfront Suite									
3 double beds	140	200	150	175	225	165	150	140	200
Extra Person	5	8	5	5	10	7	5	5	10

a. For the 9 time periods, what was the mean extra person rate?
b. This hotel has 20% type A rooms, 15% type B, 30% type C, 25% type D and the remainder are type E. If the hotel was fully booked (with no extra people in any room) on Oct. 1st, then what was the mean revenue per room? What was the standard deviation?
c. On April 20th the only rooms occupied were 25 type A, 13 type B and 5 type E. What was the average revenue per bed on that day? If every bed was occupied by 2 people, what was the mean and standard deviation of the number of people per rented room on that day?

3.65 The following data refers to the OAC average grades of students being accepted into first year of several Ontario universities.

Grade Distribution of New 1ˢᵗ Year Students

University	60–70	70–75	75–80	80–85	85–90	≥ 90
Brock	5.8	22.1	26.7	26.0	13.1	6.3
Guelph	0	0.2	27.6	37.9	21.4	12.9
McMaster	0.1	10.5	24.2	32.4	19.7	13.1
Queen's	0	0.2	3.2	21.9	36.8	37.9
Ryerson	0.5	23.0	31.0	29.3	12.4	3.8
Toronto	0	1.2	8.9	26.0	36.6	27.3

a. Based on the above data, is the average entering grade higher for Brock or Ryerson, or is the average about the same? How do the standard deviations compare?
b. What about Ryerson compared to Queen's?

3.66 The table below appeared in the April 9th, 1998 edition of The Globe and Mail.

Municipal salary comparisons

	Mayor's salary	Councillor's salary
Barrie	$45,000	$11,705
Brantford	$54,758	$11,000
Burlington	$56,000	$27,000
Cambridge	$47,000	$14,500
Gloucester	$69,020	$21,585
Kingston	$52,000	$13,000
Kitchener	$54,440	$22,640
Markham	$60,669	$34,287
Nepean	$72,603	$24,146
Oakville	$45,000	$17,000
Oshawa	$49,610	$18,540
Richmond Hill	$53,074	$29,185
St. Catharines	$51,759	$10,664
Thunder Bay	$57,342	$26,343
Toronto	$101,084	$63,915
Vaughan	$62,792	$38,126
Windsor	$88,236	$26,645
AVERAGE	$60,023	$24,134

Source: KPMG

a. Which are more variable, the Mayor's salaries or the Councillor's salaries for the 17 cities shown?
b. Draw a box whisker diagram for the Mayor's salaries.
c. Is the mean or median a better indication of the typical councillor's salary?

3.67 The following table and graphical display appeared in the March 21st, 1998 issue of The Globe and Mail.

Major English-language specialty channels

Year ended Aug. 31, 1997	Total subscribers	Cable revenue per subscriber per month	Advertising revenue per subscriber per month	Profit margin before interest and taxes
TSN	6,401,276	$1.25	$0.66	36.0%
MuchMusic	6,048,240	0.11	0.26	27.5
YTV	7,150,000	0.29	0.32	21.0
Weather	8,167,204	0.22	0.04	19.2
Vision*	6,115,792	0.07	0.02	4.2
Newsworld	7,316,000	0.46	0.14	0.4
WTN	4,676,286	0.32	0.07	14.0
Discovery	4,584,298	0.39	0.15	1.9
Showcase	3,644,440	0.34	0.15	15.7
Life	3,793,871	0.31	0.16	11.5
CMT	6,290,810	0.05	0.08	14.0
Bravo!	3,947,159	0.26	0.05	12.5

* Almost half of Vision's total revenue of $12.5-million a year comes from other revenue such as donations.

Note: Does not include latest tier of channels as pay period started Jan. 18, 1998

Source: Canadian Radio-television and Telecommunications Commission

The growth of specialty TV channels

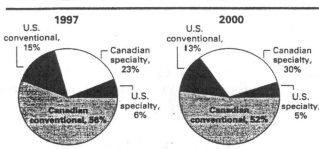

Source: Nielsen People Meter data plus Initiative Media estimates

a. Which factor is more uniform over the 12 stations: (i) Cable revenue per subscriber or (ii) Advertising revenue per subscriber?
b. Draw the box-whisker plot for the "Advertising revenue per subscriber" data.
c. If the total advertising revenue per channel is $20 per conventional Canadian channel, $15 million per specialty Canadian channel, $12 million per conventional U.S. channel and $10 million per U.S. specialty channel, will the overall average advertising revenue per channel in the year 2000 be higher or lower than the average was in 1989?

3.68 The following table shows the number of unemployed persons by province for the months of October 1995 and October 1996. Were the numbers of unemployed persons across the provinces relatively more variable in 1995 or 1996?

	Unemployment	(x 1,000)
	October 1995	October 1996
Newfoundland	150	118
P. E. I.	25	31
New Brunswick	75	69
Nova Scotia	79	63
Quebec	250	278
Ontario	300	280
Manitoba	85	85
Saskatchewan	95	87
Alberta	63	43
British Columbia	105	81

3.69 A survey of 137 randomly selected students was conducted and their annual incomes are summarized in the table below.

Annual Income ($000's)	# of Students
0.0 and under 2.5	36
2.5 and under 5.0	43
5.0 and under 7.5	18
7.5 and under 10.0	19
10.0 and under 15.0	16
15.0 and under 20.0	5

What is the mean income of the 137 students? What is the standard deviation?

3.70 The following table appeared in the April 1995 Report on Business Magazine.

Most Respected: the Top Five

Canada's best corporations excel in profitability, innovation and global reach

Rank	Company	Revenues	Net income
		($ millions)	
1	Royal Bank of Canada (Oc94) financial services	13,434	1,169
2	BCE (De94) telecommunications	21,670	1,178
3	Bombardier (Ja94) aviation, mass transit eqpt.	4,769	176
4	Bank of Montreal (Oc94) financial services	9,108	825
5	Northern Telecom (De94) telecommunications eqpt.	8,874	408

Are the five most respected companies more similar in terms of Revenues or Net Incomes?

3.71 A wholesale appliance distributing firm is studying its accounts receivables for two successive months. Two samples of 50 accounts were selected and the amount of receivables for each has been summarized in the table below.

Accounts Receivables ($)	# of accounts in March	# of accounts in April
0 and under 2,000	6	10
2,000 and under 5,000	13	14
5,000 and under 10,000	17	13
10,000 and under 15,000	10	10
15,000 and under 25,000	0	3
25,000 and under 50,000	4	0
Total	50	50

In which month were the accounts receivable amounts more variable?

3.72 The following display appeared in the March 23rd, 1995 edition of the USA Today. For all the films made from 1989 to 1994, what was the overall average production cost per movie?

Big picture for film industry

The movie business is thriving despite competition from broadcast and cable TV, home video and other forms of entertainment:

Theater admissions are growing

in millions

1989	1.26
1990	1.19
1991	1.14
1992	1.17
1993	1.24
1994	1.29

Major studios are making more films . . .

Films made		Films to be made in 1995[1]	
1989	157	Buena Vista	25
1990	158	Warner Bros.	35
1991	150	Sony	30
1992	141	Paramount	25
1993	156	Universal	20
1994	168	Fox	25
		New Line	25

. . . and, on average, each one is more expensive

Total cost, in millions

| $32.7 | $38.8 | $38.1 | $42.4 | $44 | $50.4 |
| 1989 | 1990 | 1991 | 1992 | 1993 | 1994 |

Average production cost, in millions

| $23.5 | $26.8 | $26.1 | $28.9 | $29.9 | $34.3 |

Average advertising and print costs, in millions

| $9.2 | $12.0 | $12.0 | $13.5 | $14.1 | $16.1 |

1 Estimates
Sources: Motion Picture Association of America, Merrill Lynch

3.73 The following table appeared in March 26th, 1998 edition of The Globe and Mail.

Average work days lost per year

	Total	For illness	Personal or family
All employees	7.4	6.2	1.2
Men	6.3	5.3	0.9
Men with preschoolers	5.9	4.2	1.8
Women	9.1	7.6	1.5
Women with preschoolers	11.7	7.5	4.2
Company size			
Under 20 employees	6.2	4.9	1.3
Over 500 employees	9.0	7.8	1.2
Union status			
Union member	10.7	9.4	1.3
Non-union member	5.6	4.5	1.1
Job status			
Permanent	7.6	6.4	1.2
Non-permanent	5.4	4.2	1.2

Source: Statistics Canada

The following data is applicable to a new division being set up by the Statistics Consulting Company.

	% Employees	Average Daily Salary
Men	8	$400
Men with preschoolers	62	250
Women	20	320
Women with preschoolers	10	200

a. What is the average number of days lost per employee due to illness during the first year of operation of the new division? What is the standard deviation?

b. What is the difference in the average daily salary between the men and the women of this new division?

c. What is the standard deviation of the daily salary for the men?

3.74 The following chart appeared in the Royal Bank Business Report of January 1995.

a. What is the average Employment Size of a Canadian business? (Assume that the data covers all Canadian Businesses.)

b. What is the standard deviation of Employment Size?

3.75 The following table appeared in the December 8th, 1995 issue of the Toronto Star.

a. Did the median profit increase or decrease in 1994 compared to 1993?

b. For the sample of 6 banks shown above, were bank profits relatively more variable in 1994 or 1995?

c. In 1993 there were 215 branches of the Royal Bank, 427 branches of CIBC, 385 branches of the Bank of Montreal, 453 branches of the Bank of Nova Scotia, 288 branches of the Toronto Dominion Bank and 154 branches of the National Bank. What was the overall average profit and per branch in 1993? What was the standard deviation?

CHAPTER REVIEW PROBLEMS

CHECKING YOUR UNDERSTANDING

3.76 What are the properties of a set of numerical data?

3.77 What is meant by the property of central tendency?

3.78 What are the differences among the mean, median, and mode, and what are the advantages and disadvantages of each?

3.79 How do you interpret the first quartile, median, and third quartile?

3.80 What is meant by the property of variation?

3.81 What does the Z score measure?

3.82 What are the differences among the various measures of variation, such as the range, interquartile range, variance, standard deviation, and coefficient of variation, and what are the advantages and disadvantages of each?

3.83 How does the empirical rule help explain the ways in which the values in a set of numerical data cluster and distribute?

3.84 How do the empirical rule and the Chebyshev rule differ?

3.85 What is meant by the property of shape?

3.86 How do the covariance and the coefficient of correlation differ?

APPLYING THE CONCEPTS

3.87 The American Society for Quality (ASQ) conducted a salary survey of all its members. ASQ members work in all areas of manufacturing and service-related institutions, with a common theme of an interest in quality. For the U.S. survey, e-mails were sent to 70,645 members, and 10,848 valid responses were received. The two most common job titles were manager and quality engineer. Another title is Master Black Belt, who is a person who takes a leadership role as the keeper of the Six Sigma process. Descriptive statistics concerning salaries for these three titles are given below (data extracted from H. Lindborg, "Navigate Your Career Path with QP's Annual Salary Survey," *Quality Progress*, December 2007, pp. 21–50). Compare the salaries of managers, quality engineers, and Master Black Belts.

Title	Sample Size	Minimum	Maximum	Standard Deviation	Mean	Median
Manager	1,848	25,000	184,000	23,179	82,976	80,000
Quality Engineer	1,190	18,000	163,000	17,871	71,093	70,000
Master Black Belt	131	48,000	183,500	21,946	108,879	110,000

3.88 In New York State, savings banks are permitted to sell a form of life insurance called savings bank life insurance (SBLI). The approval process consists of underwriting, which includes a review of the application, a medical information bureau check, possible requests for additional medical information and medical exams, and a policy compilation stage during which the policy pages are generated and sent to the bank for delivery. The ability to deliver approved policies to customers in a timely manner is critical to the profitability of this service to the bank. During a period of one month, a random sample of 27 approved policies was selected, and the following total processing times in days were recorded; the data are contained in the file **Insurance**:

73 19 16 64 28 28 31 90 60 56 31 56 22 18
45 48 17 17 17 91 92 63 50 51 69 16 17

a. Compute the mean, median, first quartile, and third quartile.
b. Compute the range, interquartile range, variance, standard deviation, and coefficient of variation.
c. Construct a boxplot. Are the data skewed? If so, how?
d. What would you tell a customer who enters the bank to purchase this type of insurance policy and asks how long the approval process takes?

3.89 One of the major measures of the quality of service provided by any organization is the speed with which it responds to customer complaints. A large family-held department store selling furniture and flooring, including carpet, had undergone a major expansion in the past several years. In particular, the flooring department had expanded from 2 installation crews to an installation supervisor, a measurer, and 15 installation crews. A sample of 50 complaints concerning carpet installation was selected during a recent year. The data in the file **Furniture** represent the number of days between the receipt of a complaint and the resolution of the complaint:

54   5   35 137 31 27 152   2 123 81 74 27 11
19 126 110 110 29 61   35 94   31 26   5 12   4
165   32   29   28 29 26   25   1   14 13 13 10   5
27   4   52   30 22 36   26 20   23 33 68

a. Compute the mean, median, first quartile, and third quartile.
b. Compute the range, interquartile range, variance, standard deviation, and coefficient of variation.
c. Construct a boxplot. Are the data skewed? If so, how?
d. On the basis of the results of (a) through (c), if you had to tell the president of the company how long a customer should expect to wait to have a complaint resolved, what would you say? Explain.

3.90 A manufacturing company produces steel housings for electrical equipment. The main component part of the housing is a steel trough that is made out of a 14-gauge steel coil. It is produced using a 250-ton progressive punch press with a wipe-down operation, putting two 90-degree forms in the flat steel to make the trough. The distance from one side of the form to the other is critical because of weatherproofing in outdoor applications. The company requires that the width of the trough be between 8.31 inches and 8.61 inches. The file **Trough** contains the widths of the troughs, in inches, for a sample of $n = 49$:

8.312 8.343 8.317 8.383 8.348 8.410 8.351 8.373 8.481 8.422

8.476 8.382 8.484 8.403 8.414 8.419 8.385 8.465 8.498 8.447

8.436 8.413 8.489 8.414 8.481 8.415 8.479 8.429 8.458 8.462

8.460 8.444 8.429 8.460 8.412 8.420 8.410 8.405 8.323 8.420

8.396 8.447 8.405 8.439 8.411 8.427 8.420 8.498 8.409

a. Calculate the mean, median, range, and standard deviation for the width. Interpret these measures of central tendency and variability.
b. List the five-number summary.
c. Construct a boxplot and describe its shape.
d. What can you conclude about the number of troughs that will meet the company's requirement of troughs being between 8.31 and 8.61 inches wide?

3.91 The manufacturing company in Problem 3.90 also produces electric insulators. If the insulators break when in use, a short circuit is likely to occur. To test the strength of the insulators, destructive testing is carried out to determine how much force is required to break the insulators. Force is measured by observing how many pounds must be applied to the insulator before it breaks. The data from 30 insulators from this experiment are contained in the file **Force**:

1,870 1,728 1,656 1,610 1,634 1,784 1,522 1,696 1,592 1,662

1,866 1,764 1,734 1,662 1,734 1,774 1,550 1,756 1,762 1,866

1,820 1,744 1,788 1,688 1,810 1,752 1,680 1,810 1,652 1,736

a. Calculate the mean, median, range, and standard deviation for the force needed to break the insulator.
b. Interpret the measures of central tendency and variability in (a).
c. Construct a boxplot and describe its shape.
d. What can you conclude about the strength of the insulators if the company requires a force measurement of at least 1,500 pounds before breakage?

3.92 The data contained in the file **Tuition2006** consist of the in-state tuition and fees and the out-of-state tuition and fees for four-year colleges with the highest percentage of students graduating within six years.
Source: *U.S. Department of Education, 2006.*

For each variable:
a. Compute the mean, median, first quartile, and third quartile.
b. Compute the range, interquartile range, variance, standard deviation, and coefficient of variation.
c. Construct a boxplot. Are the data skewed? If so, how?
d. Compute the coefficient of correlation between the in-state tuition and fees and the out-of-state tuition and fees.
e. What conclusions can you reach concerning the in-state tuition and fees and the out-of-state tuition and fees?

3.93 A quality characteristic of interest for a tea-bag-filling process is the weight of the tea in the individual bags. If the bags are underfilled, two problems arise. First, customers may not be able to brew the tea to be as strong as they wish. Second, the company may be in violation of the truth-in-labeling laws. For this product, the label weight on the package indicates that, on average, there are 5.5 grams of tea in a bag. If the mean amount of tea in a bag exceeds the label weight, the company is giving away product. Getting an exact amount of tea in a bag is problematic because of variation in the temperature and humidity inside the factory, differences in the density of the tea, and the extremely fast filling operation of the machine (approximately 170 bags per minute). The data in the file **Teabags** shown below provide the weight, in grams, of a sample of 50 tea bags produced in one hour by a single machine:

5.65 5.44 5.42 5.40 5.53 5.34 5.54 5.45 5.52 5.41

5.57 5.40 5.53 5.54 5.55 5.62 5.56 5.46 5.44 5.51

5.47 5.40 5.47 5.61 5.53 5.32 5.67 5.29 5.49 5.55

5.77 5.57 5.42 5.58 5.58 5.50 5.32 5.50 5.53 5.58

5.61 5.45 5.44 5.25 5.56 5.63 5.50 5.57 5.67 5.36

a. Compute the mean, median, first quartile, and third quartile.
b. Compute the range, interquartile range, variance, standard deviation, and coefficient of variation.
c. Interpret the measures of central tendency and variation within the context of this problem. Why should the company producing the tea bags be concerned about the central tendency and variation?
d. Construct a boxplot. Are the data skewed? If so, how?
e. Is the company meeting the requirement set forth on the label that, on average, there are 5.5 grams of tea in a bag? If you were in charge of this process, what changes, if any, would you try to make concerning the distribution of weights in the individual bags?

3.94 The manufacturer of Boston and Vermont asphalt shingles provides its customers with a 20-year warranty on most of its products. To determine whether a shingle will last as long as the warranty period, accelerated-life testing is conducted at the manufacturing plant. Accelerated-life testing exposes the shingle to the stresses it would be subject to in a lifetime of normal use via an experiment in a laboratory setting that takes only a few minutes to conduct. In this test, a shingle is repeatedly scraped with a brush for a short period of time, and the shingle granules removed by the brushing are weighed (in grams). Shingles that experience low amounts of granule loss are expected to last longer in normal use than shingles that experience high amounts of granule loss. In this situation, a shingle should experience no more than 0.8 gram of granule loss if it is expected to last the length of the warranty period. The data file **Granule** contains a sample of 170 measurements made on the company's Boston shingles and 140 measurements made on Vermont shingles.

a. List the five-number summary for the Boston shingles and for the Vermont shingles.

b. Construct side-by-side boxplots for the two brands of shingles and describe the shapes of the distributions.

c. Comment on the shingles' ability to achieve a granule loss of 0.8 gram or less.

3.95 A study conducted by Zagat Survey concluded that many first-rate restaurants are located in hotels across the United States. Travelers can find quality food, service, and décor without leaving their hotels. The top-rated hotel restaurant is The French Room, located in The Adolphus Hotel in Dallas, Texas. The estimated price for dinner, including one drink and tip, at The French Room is $80. The highest price reported is $179 at Alain Ducasse, located in the Jumeirah Essex House in New York City (extracted from Gary Stoller, "Top Restaurants Check into Luxury Hotels," *USA Today*, April 11, 2006, p. 5B). The file **Bestrest** contains the top 100 hotel restaurants in the United States and the variables state, city, restaurant, hotel, cost (estimated price of dinner including one drink and tip), and rating (1 to 100, with 1 the top-rated restaurant).

a. Construct the five-number summary of dinner price.

b. Construct a boxplot of dinner price and interpret the distribution of dinner prices.

c. Calculate and interpret the correlation coefficient of the rating and dinner price.

3.96 The data in the file **Chicken** contains the characteristics for a sample of 20 chicken sandwiches from fast-food chains.

a. Compute the correlation coefficient between calories and carbohydrates.

b. Compute the correlation coefficient between calories and sodium.

c. Compute the correlation coefficient between calories and total fat.

d. Which variable (total fat, carbohydrates, or sodium) seems to be most closely related to calories? Explain.

3.97 In Example 3.37, the correlation coefficient between the cost of a fast-food hamburger meal and the cost of movie tickets in 10 different cities was computed. The data file **Cost of living** also includes the overall cost index, the monthly rent for a two-bedroom apartment, and the costs of a cup of coffee with service, dry cleaning for a men's blazer, and toothpaste.

a. Compute the correlation coefficient between the overall cost index and the monthly rent for a two-bedroom apartment, the cost of a cup of coffee with service, the cost of a fast-food hamburger meal, the cost of dry-cleaning a men's blazer, the cost of toothpaste, and the cost of movie tickets. (There will be six separate correlation coefficients.)

b. What conclusions can you reach about the relationship of the overall cost index to each of these six variables?

3.98 The data in the file **Spending** is the per-capita spending, in thousands of dollars, for each state in 2004.

a. Compute the mean, median, first quartile, and third quartile.

b. Compute the range, interquartile range, variance, standard deviation, and coefficient of variation.

c. Construct a boxplot. Are the data skewed? If so, how?

d. What conclusions can you reach concerning per-capita spending, in thousands of dollars, for each state in 2004?

3.99 The data in the file **CEO** represent the total compensation (in $millions) of CEOs of large public companies (data extracted from "The Boss's Pay," *The Wall Street Journal*, April 14, 2008, pp. R5–R7).

a. Compute the mean, median, first quartile, and third quartile.

b. Compute the range, interquartile range, variance, standard deviation, and coefficient of variation.

c. Construct a boxplot. Are the data skewed? If so, how?

d. What conclusions can you draw concerning the total compensation (in $millions) of CEOs?

3.100 You are planning to study for your statistics examination with a group of classmates, one of whom you particularly want to impress. This individual has volunteered to use Microsoft Excel or Minitab to get the needed summary information, tables, and charts for a data set containing several numerical and categorical variables assigned by the instructor for study purposes. This person comes over to you with the printout and exclaims, "I've got it all—the means, the medians, the standard deviations, the boxplots, the pie charts—for all our variables. The problem is, some of the output looks weird—like the boxplots for gender and for major and the pie charts for grade point index and for height. Also, I can't understand why Professor Krehbiel said we can't get the descriptive stats for some of the variables—I got them for everything! See, the mean for height is 68.23, the mean for grade point index is 2.76, the mean for gender is 1.50, the mean for major is 4.33." What is your reply?

REPORT WRITING EXERCISES

3.101 Data concerning 71 of the best-selling domestic beers in the United States are located in the file **Domesticbeer**. The values for three variables are included:

percentage alcohol, number of calories per 12 ounces, and number of carbohydrates (in grams) per 12 ounces.

Source: *Data extracted from www.Beer100.com, May 6, 2008.*

Your task is to write a report based on a complete descriptive evaluation of each of the numerical variables—percentage alcohol, number of calories per 12 ounces, and number of carbohydrates (in grams) per 12 ounces. Appended to your report should be all appropriate tables, charts, and numerical descriptive measures.

TEAM PROJECTS

The data file [Mutual Funds] contains information regarding nine variables from a sample of 868 mutual funds:

  Category—Type of stocks comprising the mutual fund (small cap, mid cap, large cap)

  Objective—Objective of stocks comprising the mutual fund (growth or value)

  Assets—In millions of dollars

  Fees—Sales charges (no or yes)

  Expense ratio—Ratio of expenses to net assets in percentage

  Return 2006—Twelve-month return in 2006

  Three-year return—Annualized return, 2004–2006

  Five-year return—Annualized return, 2002–2006

  Risk—Risk-of-loss factor of the mutual fund (low, average, high)

3.102 For expense ratio in percentage, three-year return, and five-year return,

a. Compute the mean, median, first quartile, and third quartile.

b. Compute the range, interquartile range, variance, standard deviation, and coefficient of variation.

c. Construct a boxplot. Are the data skewed? If so, how?

d. What conclusions can you reach concerning these variables?

3.103 You wish to compare mutual funds that have fees to those that do not have fees. For each of these two groups, for the variables expense ratio in percentage, Return 2006, three-year return, and five-year return,

a. Compute the mean, median, first quartile, and third quartile.

b. Compute the range, interquartile range, variance, standard deviation, and coefficient of variation.

c. Construct a boxplot. Are the data skewed? If so, how?

d. What conclusions can you reach about differences between mutual funds that have fees and those that do not have fees?

3.104 You wish to compare mutual funds that have a growth objective to those that have a value objective. For each of these two groups, for the variables expense ratio in percentage, three-year return, and five-year return,

a. Compute the mean, median, first quartile, and third quartile.

b. Compute the range, interquartile range, variance, standard deviation, and coefficient of variation.

c. Construct a boxplot. Are the data skewed? If so, how?

d. What conclusions can you reach about differences between mutual funds that have a growth objective and those that have a value objective?

3.105 You wish to compare small cap, mid cap, and large cap mutual funds. For each of these three groups, for the variables expense ratio in percentage, Return 2006, three-year return, and five-year return,

a. Compute the mean, median, first quartile, and third quartile.

b. Compute the range, interquartile range, variance, standard deviation, and coefficient of variation.

c. Construct a boxplot. Are the data skewed? If so, how?

d. What conclusions can you reach about differences between small cap, mid cap, and large cap mutual funds?

STUDENT SURVEY DATA BASE

3.106 Problem 1.28 describes a survey of 50 undergraduate students (see the file [Undergradsurvey]). For these data, for each numerical variable,

a. Compute the mean, median, first quartile, and third quartile.

b. Compute the range, interquartile range, variance, standard deviation, and coefficient of variation.

c. Construct a boxplot. Are the data skewed? If so, how?

d. Write a report summarizing your conclusions.

3.107 Problem 1.28 describes a survey of 50 undergraduate students (see the file [Undergradsurvey]).

a. Select a sample of 50 undergraduate students at your school and conduct a similar survey for those students.

b. For the data collected in (a), repeat (a) through (d) of Problem 3.106.

c. Compare the results of (b) to those of Problem 3.106.

3.108 Problem 1.29 describes a survey of 40 MBA students (see the file [Gradsurvey]). For these data, for each numerical variable,

a. Compute the mean, median, first quartile, and third quartile.

b. Compute the range, interquartile range, variance, standard deviation, and coefficient of variation.

c. Construct a boxplot. Are the data skewed? If so, how?

d. Write a report summarizing your conclusions.

3.109 Problem 1.25 describes a survey of 40 MBA students (see the file [Gradsurvey]).

a. Select a sample of 40 graduate students from your MBA program and conduct a similar survey for those students.

b. For the data collected in (a), repeat (a) through (d) of Problem 3.108.

c. Compare the results of (b) to those of Problem 3.108.

MANAGING THE *SPRINGVILLE HERALD*

For what variable in the Chapter 2 "Managing the *Springville Herald*" case are numerical descriptive measures needed? For the variable you identify:

1. Compute the appropriate numerical descriptive measures, and construct a boxplot.

2. Identify another graphical display that might be useful and construct it. What conclusions can you reach from that plot that cannot be made from the boxplot?

3. Summarize your findings in a report that can be included with the task force's study.

WEB CASE

Apply your knowledge about the proper use of numerical descriptive measures in this continuing Web Case.

Visit EndRun Financial Services, at **www.prenhall.com/Springville/EndRun.htm** (or open the `EndRun.htm` file in the Student CD-ROM Web Case folder) a second time and reexamine their supporting data and then answer the following:

1. Can descriptive measures be computed for any variables? How would such summary statistics support EndRun's claims? How would those summary statistics affect your perception of EndRun's record?

2. Evaluate the methods EndRun used to summarize the results of its customer survey (see **www.prenhall.com/Springville/ER_Survey.htm** or the `ER_Survey.htm` file on the Student CD-ROM Web Case folder). Is there anything you would do differently to summarize these results?

3. Note that the last question of the survey has fewer responses than the other questions. What factors may have limited the number of responses to that question?

REFERENCES

1. Kendall, M. G., A. Stuart, and J. K. Ord, *Kendall's Advanced Theory of Statistics, Volume 1: Distribution Theory*, 6th ed. (New York: Oxford University Press, 1994).

2. *Microsoft Excel 2007* (Redmond, WA: Microsoft Corporation, 2007).

3. *Minitab for Windows Version 15* (State College, PA: Minitab, Inc., 2006).

4. Tukey, J., *Exploratory Data Analysis* (Reading, MA: Addison-Wesley, 1977).

5. Velleman, P. F., and D. C. Hoaglin, *Applications, Basics, and Computing of Exploratory Data Analysis* (Boston: Duxbury Press, 1981).

Profile of School Attendance, Education, Field of Study, Highest Level of Schooling and Earnings, for Census Metropolitan Areas[1] and Census Agglomerations, 2001 Census

Toronto	
Title	**Count**
Total population 15 years and over with employment income, by sex and work activity—20% Sample Data	2,659,225
Average employment income $	38,598
Standard error of average employment income $	95
Worked full year, full time	1,508,125
Average employment income $	51,112
Standard error of average employment income $	145
Worked part year or part time	1,083,230
Average employment income $	22,655
Standard error of average employment income $	106

Number of Children at Home (8) and Family Structure (7) for Census Families in Private Households, for Canada, Provinces, Territories and Federal Electoral Districts (1996 Representation Order), 2001 Census—20% Sample Data

	Canada				
Title	**Family Structure (7)**				
	Total— Family structure	**Total couple families**	**Married couples**	**Common-law couples**	**Total lone- parent families**
Total families without children at home	3,059,225	3,059,225	2,431,725	627,505	0
Total families with children at home	5,311,795	4,000,605	3,469,700	530,905	1,311,185
1 child at home	2,285,110	1,483,435	1,229,055	254,375	801,675
2 children at home	2,087,355	1,716,265	1,518,475	197,790	371,085
3 or more children at home	939,325	800,905	722,170	78,730	138,425
Total children at home	9,582,615	7,579,255	6,666,195	913,060	2,003,360
Average number of children at home per family	1.1	1.1	1.1	0.8	1.5

Number of Children at Home (8) and Family Structure (7) for Census Families in Private Profile of Marital Status, Common-law Status, Families, Dwellings and Households, for Census Metropolitan Areas and Census Agglomerations, 2001 Census

Toronto	
Title	**Count**
Total number of children at home—20% Sample Data	1,641,660
Average number of children at home per census family	1.3
Number of family persons	3,993,575
Average number of persons per census family	3.1
Total number of occupied private dwellings—20% Sample Data	1,634,755
Average number of rooms per dwelling	6.1
Average number of bedrooms per dwelling	2.6

	1999				
	Net worth quintile[2]				
	Lowest quintile ($10,000 or less)	Second quintile ($10,000 to $65,700)	Middle quintile ($65,700 to $166,500)	Fourth quintile ($166,500 to $372,600)	Highest quintile ($372,600 and more)
	%				
All family units' income groups[3]	**100.0**	**100.0**	**100.0**	**100.0**	**100.0**
Less than $10,000	29.0	6.9	3.1	x	x
$10,000 to $19,999	37.3	22.0	15.0	9.7	4.9
$20,000 to $29,999	18.9	25.9	17.2	18.2	9.2
$30,000 to $39,999	8.3	19.4	19.6	15.8	15.3
$40,000 to $49,999	3.8	13.0	17.0	15.0	13.2
$50,000 to $74,999	x	11.6	21.5	25.7	26.6
$75,000 and more	x	x	6.6	13.3	29.6

x Data unavailable, not applicable or confidential.

1. Family units: economic families (a group of two or more persons who live in the same dwelling and are related to each other by blood, marriage, common law or adoption) and unattached individuals (a person living either alone or with others to whom he or she is unrelated).
2. All family units, whether individuals or families, are ranked from lowest to highest by the value of their net worth. The ranked family units are then divided into five groups, each containing an equal number of family units. Net worth was calculated with employer-sponsored registered pension plans included as an asset.
3. Total family income after tax.

Source: Statistics Canada, Survey of Financial Security.

	All family units (1999)		Family units with private pension assets (1999)	
			Average amount	Median[1] amount
	%	%	$	$
All ages[4]	**100.0**	**100.0**	**118,100**	**50,000**
Under 35	25.5	4.8	26,600	10,000
35–44	24.7	14.2	63,600	36,700
45–54	19.6	26.8	141,800	89,100
55–64	11.9	27.7	247,400	160,300
65 and older	18.3	26.6	185,300	115,700
All education levels[5]	**100.0**	**100.0**	**118,100**	**50,000**
Less than high school	26.9	16.6	94,400	47,000
Graduated high school	23.4	20.3	105,200	42,400
Non-university certificate[6]	28.3	24.0	92,500	40,500
University certificate or bachelor's degree	14.5	22.3	153,700	73,000
Degree or certificate above bachelor's[7]	6.8	16.8	228,100	125,000

1. The value at which half of all family units have lower net worth and half have higher net worth.
4. Age of the individual/family member with the highest pre-tax income.
5. Education level of the individual/family member with the highest pre-tax income.
6. Includes certificates or diplomas from trade or vocational schools, community colleges, CEGEPs, technical institutes and hospital schools of nursing.
7. Includes certificate above bachelor's degree, master's degree, doctorate, degrees in law, medicine, dentistry, veterinary medicine and optometry.
Source: Statistics Canada, Survey of Financial Security.
Last modified: November 30, 2001.

APPENDIX A3a

A3.1   MICROSOFT EXCEL

For Descriptive Statistics

Use the Data Analysis ToolPak. Open to the worksheet containing the data you want to summarize. Select **Tools →
Data Analysis**. From the list that appears in the Data Analysis dialog box, select **Descriptive Statistics** and click
OK. In the Descriptive Statistics dialog box (see Figure A3.1), enter the cell range of the data in the **Input Range** box. Choose the **Columns** option and **Labels in First Row** if you are using data that are arranged like the data in the Excel files on the CD-ROM packaged with this text. Finish by selecting **New Worksheet Ply**, **Summary statistics**, **Kth Largest**, and **Kth Smallest**, and clicking **OK**. Results appear on a separate worksheet.

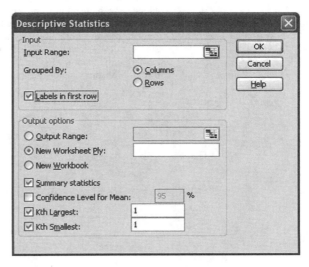

FIGURE A3.1 Data Analysis Descriptive
Statistics Dialog Box

OR you can use any of these sample statistics worksheet functions in your own formulas including AVERAGE (for mean), MEDIAN, MODE, QUARTILE, STDEV, VAR, MIN, MAX, SUM, COUNT, LARGE, or SMALL.

To enter one of these functions into a worksheet, select an empty cell and then select **Insert → Function.** In the Function dialog box, select **Statistical** from the drop-down list and then scroll to and select the function you want to use. Click **OK**. In the Function Arguments dialog box, enter the cell range of the data to be summarized and click **OK**. (For LARGE and SMALL, enter **1** as the **K** value;

and for QUARTILE, enter either **1** or **3** as the **Quart** value, for either first or third quartile.) In versions of Microsoft Excel earlier than Excel 2003, you may encounter errors in results when using the QUARTILE function.

For Box-and-Whisker Plot

See section G.5 (**Box-and-Whisker Plot**) if you want PHStat2 to produce a box-and-whisker plot as a Microsoft Excel chart. (There are no Microsoft Excel commands that directly produce box-and-whisker plots.)

APPENDIX A3b

SPSS—Version 15 Lesson 2

Lesson 3—Descriptive Statistics

INDEPENDENT READING

At this stage you should read the following help features. Cancel the SPSS opening window. Now look at the following tutorial.

Help / Tutorial / Table of contents (if necessary) / **Working With Output / Next** (as often as necessary)

The tutorial will take you through

Using the Viewer

Stop when this part is finished.

Example 1: The following data shows the response times, in days, for 50 customer complaints for a large car dealership. The data has been arranged into an ascending data array.

1	2	4	4	5	5	5	10	10	11
12	13	13	14	19	20	22	23	25	26
26	26	27	27	27	28	29	29	29	30
31	31	32	33	35	35	36	52	54	61
68	74	81	84	95	123	126	137	152	173

Create a SPSS data file where the above raw data is entered and save it as **Lesson 3 - Ex.1.sav.**

Define the variable and fix data at zero decimal places. Give the variable a label **Response Time - Days**

Explore Procedure

Now return to the SPSS Data Editor window. Make the following menu selections:

Analyze / Descriptive Statistics / Explore... Response Time - Days (Highlight) ▶ (for Dependent List) **Statistics** (for Display)/ **Statistics** / check **Percentiles / Continue / OK**

At this point you will get a set of exploratory information about the data in the SPSS Viewer window. The first table will be a *Case Processing Summary*. This table allows you to check to see how much data was used to produce the results that follow it. This table is only of interest to the researcher and would never be included in any report.

The next table is called *Descriptives* (shown below) and includes the several statistics, including measures of the center and measures of variability.

Descriptives

			Statistic	Std. Error
Response Time (days)	Mean		40.70	5.777
	95% Confidence	Lower Bound	29.09	
	Interval for Mean	Upper Bound	52.31	
	5% Trimmed Mean		36.37	
	Median		27.50	
	Variance		1668.949	
	Std. Deviation		40.853	
	Minimum		1	
	Maximum		173	
	Range		172	
	Interquartile Range		40	
	Skewness		1.731	.337
	Kurtosis		2.444	.662

You can customize this table to suit your needs. One would be by deleting any items that you are not interested in. First activate the table by double-clicking on it so that a fuzzy border appears around the table. (Close the Pivot Trays window.) Then just **Highlight** and **Delete** any items you don't want. You can easily produce the edited table shown below.

Descriptives

		Statistic
Response Time (days)	Mean	40.70
	Median	27.50
	Variance	1668.949
	Std. Deviation	40.853
	Minimum	1
	Maximum	173
	Range	172
	Interquartile Range	39.50
	Skewness	1.731

The next table (shown below) is a table of <u>Percentiles</u> that was asked for by checking off the percentiles box.

Percentiles

		Percentiles				
		5	10	25	50	75
Weighted Average (Definition1)	Response Time (days)	3.10	5.00	13.00	27.50	52.50
Turkey's Hinges	Response Time (days)			13.00	27.50	52.00

Percentiles

	Percentiles	
	90	95
Weighted Average (Definition 1)	120.20	143.75

Note: **Tukey's Hinges** are the quartiles calculated with a different formula than the weighted average (definition 1) formula.

Descriptives Procedure

For another method that can be used to calculate descriptive statistics (without the graphing options), then you would choose the following from the SPSS Data Editor window:

Analyze / Descriptive Statistics / Descriptives... Response Time - Days (Highlight) ▶ (for Variables) **Options** / check **Mean Std. Deviation Range / Continue / OK**

The output for this procedure is shown below:

Descriptive Statics

	N	Range	Mean	Std. Deviation
Response Time (days)	50	172	40.70	40.853
Valid N (listwise)	50			

Note: This procedure is useful when you know what you want and you don't want a table with a lot of extra items.

Frequencies Procedure

You may also calculate descriptive statistics by using the following procedure:

Analyze / Descriptive Statistics / Frequencies... Response Time - Days (Highlight) ▶ (for Variables) **Statistics** check **Mean Median Std. deviation Range / Quartiles / Cut points for** key 5 in the equal groups box / **Percentiles** key 33 in the percentiles box / **Add** key 67 in the percentiles box) **Add / Continue** (Now verify that the Display frequency tables option is not selected.) **OK**

The Frequencies: Statistics window is shown below.

The 'Frequencies' output is shown below.

Statistics

Response Time (days)

N	Valid	50
	Missing	0
Mean		40.70
Median		27.50
Std. Deviation		40.853
Range		172
Percentiles	20	11.20
	25	13.00
	33	21.66
	40	26.00
	50	27.50
	60	30.60
	67	33.34
	75	52.50
	80	66.60

You may now want to save the results as they appear in the SPSS Viewer window.

File / Save as / Lesson 3 – Ex.1.spo / File / Close / File / Exit

Subgroups of one variable

Recall the file **Lesson – Ex. 1a.sav**

Suppose we want to calculate the mean and standard deviation of the waiting times for the females and males separately.

Choose **Data / Split file...** and fill in the following window as shown on the next page:

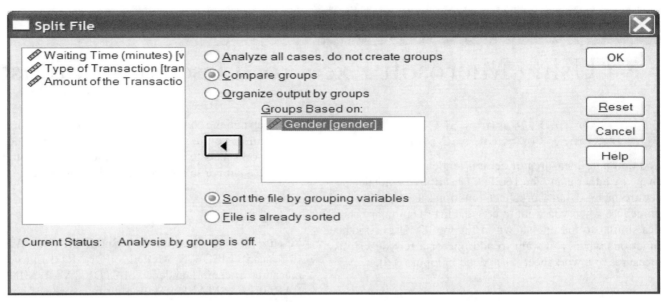

Important note: The **Split file** procedure will cause you input data file to be sorted by the 'Groups Based on:' variable. Usually you want your original data file <u>not</u> to be sorted, therefore **DO NOT SAVE** the sorted data file when you close the file. if you do want the sorted file then save it under a different name.

Now choose **Analyze / Descriptive Statistics / Frequencies...** Waiting time (minutes) (Highlight) ▶ (for Variables) **Statistics** check **Mean Std. deviation / Continue / OK**

The results are shown below:

Statistics

Waiting Time (minutes)

Female	N	Valid	10
		Missing	0
	Mean		8.90
	Std. Deviation		6.297
Male	N	Valid	15
		Missing	0
	Mean		8.13
	Std. Deviation		5.303

Note: You may also use the **Descriptives** or **Explore** procedures to get similar results in different layouts. You can also include the 'Gender' variable in the **Factor List:** box of the **Explore** procedure.

APPENDIX E3

Using Microsoft Excel for Descriptive Statistics

E3.1 Computing Measures of Central Tendency, Variation, and Shape

You compute measures of central tendency, variation, and shape by either using the ToolPak Descriptive Statistics procedure or by using worksheet functions. Use the ToolPak procedure when you want to create a list of summary statistics similar to the one shown in Figure 3.2. Use worksheet functions when you want to add one or a few descriptive measures to a worksheet (as is done in Figure 3.6).

Using ToolPak Descriptive Statistics

Open to the worksheet containing your data to be summarized. Select **Tools → Data Analysis** (Excel 97–2003) or **Data → Data Analysis** (Excel 2007). In the Data Analysis dialog box, select **Descriptive Statistics** from the **Analysis Tools** list and then click **OK**. In the Descriptive Statistics dialog box (shown in Figure E3.1), enter the cell range of the data as the **Input Range**. Click the **Columns** option and **Labels in first row**. Finish by clicking **New Worksheet Ply**, **Summary statistics**, **Kth Largest**, and **Kth Smallest**, and then **OK**.

FIGURE E3.1 ToolPak Descriptive Statistics dialog box

To compute descriptive statistics for a variable by subgroups, as was done in Figure 3.2 for the growth and value subgroups, first sort your data by the categorical variable to which the subgroups belong. Next, repeat the instructions given at the left for each subgroup using the cell range of the

subgroup and the New Worksheet Ply option each time. Then copy and paste the results found in the second and subsequent worksheets to this first sheet to create a multiple column table similar to the one shown in Figure 3.2.

Using Worksheet Functions

You use the worksheet functions SUM, COUNT, AVERAGE (for mean), MEDIAN, MODE, or QUARTILE, to compute measures of central tendency or STDEV, VAR, MIN, MAX, LARGE, or SMALL to compute measures of shape and variation. For all but QUARTILE, enter a formula in the form *=WorksheetFunction(cell range of data to be summarized)*. For QUARTILE enter the formula in the form *=WorksheetFunction(cell range of data to be summarized, quartile number)*. Use 1 as the *quartile number* to compute the first quartile, 2 to compute the second quartile (the median), or 3 to compute the third quartile. In Excel versions earlier than Excel 2003, you may encounter some minor errors in results when using the QUARTILE function.

E3.2 Computing Measures for a Population

To compute the population variance and standard deviation, use the worksheet functions VARP and STDEVP. To use either function, enter a formula into a blank cell in the form *=WorksheetFunction(cell range of data to be summarized)*.

E3.3 Creating Boxplots

You create boxplots by entering a five-number summary into the tinted cell range B2:B6 of the **Plot** worksheet of the **Boxplot.xls** workbook. The workbook uses the contents of this range to create a boxplot on the Plot worksheet.

E3.4 Computing the Covariance

You compute the covariance by making entries in the **Covariance** worksheet of the **Covariance.xls** workbook, shown in Figure 3.6. If you want to use this worksheet with other pairs of variables, follow the instructions in the worksheet for modifying the table area. The worksheet gains its flexibility by the cell C18 formula that uses the COUNT function to determine the sample size n. This allows the worksheet to always use the proper value of $n - 1$ for the covariance calculation when you change the size of the table area.

E3.5 Computing the Coefficient of Correlation

You compute the correlation coefficient by making entries in the **Correlation** worksheet of the `Correlation.xls` workbook, shown in Figure 3.9. If you want to use this worksheet with other pairs of variables, follow the instructions in the worksheet for modifying the table area. This worksheet shares some of the design of the covariance worksheet discussed in the previous section.

This worksheet uses the CORREL function in the formula =**CORREL(A2:A11, B2:B11)** in cell E21 to compute the correlation coefficient. Because the covariance, S_X, and S_Y are computed elsewhere in this worksheet, the formula =E18/(E19 * E20) could also be used to compute the correlation coefficient statistic.

4 Basic Probability

Learning Objectives

In this chapter, you learn:

- Basic probability concepts
- Conditional probability
- To use Bayes' theorem to revise probabilities

@ M&R Electronics World

A s the marketing manager for M&R Electronics World, you are analyzing the survey results of an intent-to-purchase study. This study asked the heads of 1,000 households about their intentions to purchase a big-screen television (defined as 36 inches or larger) sometime during the next 12 months. As a follow-up, you plan to survey the same people 12 months later to see whether such a television was purchased. In addition, for households purchasing big-screen televisions, you would like to know whether the television they purchased was a plasma screen, whether they also purchased a digital video recorder (DVR) in the past 12 months, and whether they were satisfied with their purchase of the big-screen television.

You are expected to use the results of this survey to plan a new marketing strategy that will enhance sales and better target those households likely to purchase multiple or more expensive products. What questions can you ask in this survey? How can you express the relationships among the various intent-to-purchase responses of individual households?

In previous chapters, you learned descriptive methods to summarize categorical and numerical variables. In this chapter, you will learn about probability to answer questions such as the following:

- What is the probability that a household is planning to purchase a big-screen television in the next year?
- What is the probability that a household will actually purchase a big-screen television?
- What is the probability that a household is planning to purchase a big-screen television and actually purchases the television?
- Given that the household is planning to purchase a big-screen television, what is the probability that the purchase is made?
- Does knowledge of whether a household *plans* to purchase the television change the likelihood of predicting whether the household *will* purchase the television?
- What is the probability that a household that purchases a big-screen television will purchase a plasma-screen television?
- What is the probability that a household that purchases a big-screen television with a plasma screen will also purchase a DVR?
- What is the probability that a household that purchases a big-screen television will be satisfied with the purchase?

With answers to questions such as these, you can begin to make decisions about your marketing strategy. Should your strategy for selling more big-screen televisions target those households that have indicated an intent to purchase? Should you concentrate on selling plasma screens? Is it likely that households that purchase big-screen televisions with plasma screens can be easily persuaded to also purchase DVRs?

The principles of probability help bridge the worlds of descriptive statistics and inferential statistics. Reading this chapter will help you learn about different types of probabilities, how to compute probabilities, and how to revise probabilities in light of new information. Probability principles are the foundation for the probability distribution, the concept of mathematical expectation, and the binomial and Poisson distributions, topics that are discussed in Chapter 5.

4.1 Basic Probability Concepts

What is meant by the word *probability*? A **probability** is the numeric value representing the chance, likelihood, or possibility a particular event will occur, such as the price of a stock increasing, a rainy day, a defective product, or the outcome five in a single toss of a die. In all these instances, the probability involved is a proportion or fraction whose value ranges between 0 and 1, inclusive. An event that has no chance of occurring (i.e., the **impossible event**) has a probability of 0. An event that is sure to occur (i.e., the **certain event**) has a probability of 1.

There are three types of probability:

- *A priori*
- Empirical
- Subjective

In *a priori* **probability**, the probability of success is based on prior knowledge of the process involved. In the simplest case, where each outcome is equally likely, the chance of occurrence of the event is defined in Equation (4.1).

PROBABILITY OF OCCURRENCE

$$\text{Probability of occurrence} = \frac{X}{T} \qquad (4.1)$$

where

X = number of ways in which the event occurs

T = total number of possible outcomes

Consider a standard deck of cards that has 26 red cards and 26 black cards. The probability of selecting a black card is 26/52 = 0.50 because there are X = 26 black cards and T = 52 total cards. What does this probability mean? If each card is replaced after it is selected, does it mean that 1 out of the next 2 cards selected will be black? No, because you cannot say for certain what will happen on the next several selections. However, you can say that in the long run, if this selection process is continually repeated, the proportion of black cards selected will approach 0.50.

EXAMPLE 4.1

Finding *A Priori* Probabilities

A standard six-sided die has six faces. Each face of the die contains either one, two, three, four, five, or six dots. If you roll a die, what is the probability that you will get a face with five dots?

SOLUTION Each face is equally likely to occur. Because there are six faces, the probability of getting a face with five dots is $\frac{1}{6}$.

The preceding examples use the *a priori* probability approach because the number of ways the event occurs and the total number of possible outcomes are known from the composition of the deck of cards or the faces of the die.

In the **empirical probability** approach, the probabilities are based on observed data, not on prior knowledge of a process. Surveys are often used to generate empirical probabilities. Examples of this type of probability are the proportion of individuals in the Using Statistics scenario who actually purchase a big-screen television, the proportion of registered voters who prefer a certain political candidate, and the proportion of students who have part-time jobs. For example, if you take a survey of students, and 60% state that they have part-time jobs, then there is a 0.60 probability that an individual student has a part-time job.

The third approach to probability, **subjective probability**, differs from the other two approaches because subjective probability differs from person to person. For example, the development team for a new product may assign a probability of 0.6 to the chance of success for the product, even though the president of the company may be less optimistic and assign a probability of 0.3. The assignment of subjective probabilities to various outcomes is usually based on a combination of an individual's past experience, personal opinion, and analysis of a particular situation. Subjective probability is especially useful in making decisions in situations in which you cannot use *a priori* probability or empirical probability.

Events and Sample Spaces

The basic elements of probability theory are the individual outcomes of a variable under study. You need the following definitions to understand probabilities.

EVENT

Each possible outcome of a variable is referred to as an **event**.
A **simple event** is described by a single characteristic.

For example, when you toss a coin, the two possible outcomes are heads and tails. Each of these represents a simple event. When you roll a standard six-sided die in which the six faces of the die contain either one, two, three, four, five, or six dots, there are six possible simple events. An event can be any one of these simple events, a set of them, or a subset of all of them. For example, the event of an *even number of dots* consists of three simple events (i.e., two, four, or six dots).

JOINT EVENT

A **joint event** is an event that has two or more characteristics.

Getting two heads on the toss of two coins is an example of a joint event because it consists of heads on the toss of the first coin and heads on the toss of the second coin.

COMPLEMENT

The **complement** of event A (represented by the symbol A') includes all events that are not part of A.

The complement of a head is a tail because that is the only event that is not a head. The complement of face five is not getting face five. Not getting face five consists of getting face one, two, three, four, or six.

SAMPLE SPACE
The collection of all the possible events is called the **sample space**.

The sample space for tossing a coin consists of heads and tails. The sample space when rolling a die consists of one, two, three, four, five, and six dots. Example 4.2 demonstrates events and sample spaces.

EXAMPLE 4.2

Events and Sample Spaces

TABLE 4.1

Purchase Behavior for Big-Screen Televisions

The Using Statistics scenario on page 199 concerns M&R Electronics World. Table 4.1 presents the results of the sample of 1,000 households in terms of purchase behavior for big-screen televisions.

PLANNED TO PURCHASE	ACTUALLY PURCHASED		
	Yes	No	Total
Yes	200	50	250
No	100	650	750
Total	300	700	1,000

What is the sample space? Give examples of simple events and joint events.

SOLUTION The sample space consists of the 1,000 respondents. Simple events are "planned to purchase," "did not plan to purchase," "purchased," and "did not purchase." The complement of the event "planned to purchase" is "did not plan to purchase." The event "planned to purchase and actually purchased" is a joint event because the respondent must plan to purchase the television *and* actually purchase it.

Contingency Tables and Venn Diagrams

There are several ways in which you can view a particular sample space. One way involves assigning the appropriate events to a **contingency table** (see Section 2.4) such as the one displayed in Table 4.1. You get the values in the cells of the table by subdividing the sample space of 1,000 households according to whether someone planned to purchase and actually purchased the big-screen television set. For example, 200 of the respondents planned to purchase a big-screen television set and subsequently did purchase the big-screen television set.

A second way to present the sample space is by using a **Venn diagram**. This diagram graphically represents the various events as "unions" and "intersections" of circles. Figure 4.1 on page 203 presents a typical Venn diagram for a two-variable situation, with each variable having only two events (A and A', B and B'). The circle on the left (the red one) represents all events that are part of A. The circle on the right (the yellow one) represents all events that are part of B. The area contained within circle A and circle B (center area) is the intersection of A and B (written as $A \cap B$), because it is part of A and also part of B. The total area of the two circles is the union of A and B (written as $A \cup B$) and contains all outcomes that are just part of event A, just part of event B, or part of both A and B. The area in the diagram outside of $A \cup B$ contains outcomes that are neither part of A nor part of B.

FIGURE 4.1

Venn diagram for events
A and B

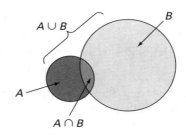

You must define A and B in order to develop a Venn diagram. You can define either event as A or B, as long as you are consistent in evaluating the various events. For the large-screen television example, you can define the events as follows:

$$A = \text{planned to purchase} \qquad B = \text{actually purchased}$$

$$A' = \text{did not plan to purchase} \qquad B' = \text{did not actually purchase}$$

In drawing the Venn diagram in Figure 4.2, you must determine the value of the intersection of A and B so that the sample space can be divided into its parts. $A \cap B$ consists of all 200 households who planned to purchase and actually purchased a big-screen television set. The remainder of event A (planned to purchase) consists of the 50 households who planned to purchase a big-screen television set but did not actually purchase one. The remainder of event B (actually purchased) consists of the 100 households who did not plan to purchase a big-screen television set but actually purchased one. The remaining 650 households represent those who neither planned to purchase nor actually purchased a big-screen television set.

FIGURE 4.2

Venn diagram for the
M&R Electronics World
example

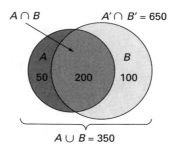

Simple Probability

Now you can answer some of the questions posed in the Using Statistics scenario. Because the results are based on data collected in a survey (refer to Table 4.1), you can use the empirical probability approach.

As stated previously, the most fundamental rule for probabilities is that they range in value from 0 to 1. An impossible event has a probability of 0, and an event that is certain to occur has a probability of 1.

Simple probability refers to the probability of occurrence of a simple event, $P(A)$. A simple probability in the Using Statistics scenario is the probability of planning to purchase a big-screen television. How can you determine the probability of selecting a household that planned to purchase a big-screen television? Using Equation (4.1) on page 200:

$$\text{Probability of occurrence} = \frac{X}{T}$$

$$P(\text{Planned to purchase}) = \frac{\text{Number who planned to purchase}}{\text{Total number of households}}$$

$$= \frac{250}{1,000} = 0.25$$

Thus, there is a 0.25 (or 25%) chance that a household planned to purchase a big-screen television.

Example 4.3 illustrates another application of simple probability.

EXAMPLE 4.3

Computing the Probability that the Big-Screen Television Purchased is a Plasma Screen

TABLE 4.2
Purchase Behavior Regarding Plasma-Screen Televisions and DVR

In the Using Statistics follow-up survey, additional questions were asked of the 300 households that actually purchased big-screen televisions. Table 4.2 indicates the consumers' responses to whether the television purchased was a plasma screen and whether they also purchased a DVR in the past 12 months.

Find the probability that if a household that purchased a big-screen television is randomly selected, the television purchased is a plasma screen.

| | PURCHASED DVR | | |
PURCHASED PLASMA SCREEN	Yes	No	Total
Plasma screen	38	42	80
Not plasma screen	70	150	220
Total	108	192	300

SOLUTION Using the following definitions:

A = purchased a plasma screen B = purchased a DVR

A' = did not purchase a plasma screen B' = did not purchase a DVR

$$P(\text{Plasma screen}) = \frac{\text{Number of plasma-screen televisions}}{\text{Total number of televisions}}$$

$$= \frac{80}{300} = 0.267$$

There is a 26.7% chance that a randomly selected big-screen television purchase is a purchase of a plasma-screen television.

Joint Probability

Whereas simple or marginal probability refers to the probability of occurrence of simple events, **joint probability** refers to the probability of an occurrence involving two or more events. An example of joint probability is the probability that you will get heads on the first toss of a coin and heads on the second toss of a coin.

Referring to Table 4.1, those individuals who planned to purchase and actually purchased a big-screen television consist only of the outcomes in the single cell "yes—planned to purchase *and* yes—actually purchased." Because this group consists of 200 households, the probability of picking a household that planned to purchase *and* actually purchased a big-screen television is

$$P(\text{Planned to purchase } and \text{ actually purchased}) = \frac{\text{Planned to purchase } and \text{ actually purchased}}{\text{Total number of respondents}}$$

$$= \frac{200}{1,000} = 0.20$$

Example 4.4 also demonstrates how to determine joint probability.

EXAMPLE 4.4

Determining the Joint Probability that a Big-Screen Television Customer Purchased a Plasma-Screen Television and a DVR

In Table 4.2, the purchases are cross-classified as plasma screen or not plasma screen and whether or not the household purchased a DVR. Find the probability that a randomly selected household that purchased a big-screen television also purchased a plasma-screen television and a DVR.

SOLUTION Using Equation (4.1) on page 200,

$$P(\text{Planned screen } and \text{ DVR}) = \frac{\text{Number that purchased a plasma screen } and \text{ a DVR}}{\text{Total number of big-screen television purchasers}}$$

$$= \frac{38}{300} = 0.127$$

Therefore, there is a 12.7% chance that a randomly selected household that purchased a big-screen television purchased a plasma-screen television and a DVR.

Marginal Probability

The **marginal probability** of an event consists of a set of joint probabilities. You can determine the marginal probability of a particular event by using the concept of joint probability just discussed. For example, if B consists of two events, B_1 and B_2, then $P(A)$, the probability of event A, consists of the joint probability of event A occurring with event B_1 and the joint probability of event A occurring with event B_2. You use Equation (4.2) to compute marginal probabilities.

> MARGINAL PROBABILITY
>
> $$P(A) = P(A \text{ and } B_1) + P(A \text{ and } B_2) + \cdots + P(A \text{ and } B_k) \qquad \textbf{(4.2)}$$
>
> where $B_1, B_2, \ldots, B_k$ are k mutually exclusive and collectively exhaustive events, defined as follows:
>
> Two events are **mutually exclusive** if both the events cannot occur simultaneously.
> A set of events is **collectively exhaustive** if one of the events must occur.

Heads and tails in a coin toss are mutually exclusive events. The result of a coin toss cannot simultaneously be a head and a tail. Heads and tails in a coin toss are also collectively exhaustive events. One of them must occur. If heads does not occur, tails must occur. If tails does not occur, heads must occur. Being male and being female are mutually exclusive and collectively exhaustive events. No one is both (the two are mutually exclusive), and everyone is one or the other (the two are collectively exhaustive).

You can use Equation (4.2) to compute the marginal probability of "planned to purchase" a big-screen television:

$$P(\text{Planned to purchase}) = P(\text{Planned to purchase } and \text{ purchased})$$
$$+ P(\text{Planned to purchase } and \text{ did not purchase})$$
$$= \frac{200}{1,000} + \frac{50}{1,000}$$
$$= \frac{250}{1,000} = 0.25$$

You get the same result if you add the number of outcomes that make up the simple event "planned to purchase."

General Addition Rule

How do you find the probability of event "*A or B*"? You need to consider the occurrence of either event *A* or event *B* or both *A* and *B*. For example, how can you determine the probability that a household planned to purchase *or* actually purchased a big-screen television? The event "planned to purchase *or* actually purchased" includes all households that planned to purchase and all households that actually purchased the big-screen television. You examine each cell of the contingency table (Table 4.1) to determine whether it is part of this event. From Table 4.1, the cell "planned to purchase *and* did not actually purchase" is part of the event because it includes respondents who planned to purchase. The cell "did not plan to purchase *and* actually purchased" is included because it contains respondents who actually purchased. Finally, the cell "planned to purchase *and* actually purchased" has both characteristics of interest. Therefore, one way to calculate the probability of "planned to purchase *or* actually purchased" is:

$$P(\text{Planned to purchase } or \text{ actually purchased}) = P(\text{Planned to purchase } and \text{ did not actually purchase}) + P(\text{Did not plan to purchase } and \text{ actually purchased}) + P(\text{Planned to purchase } and \text{ actually purchased})$$

$$= \frac{50}{1,000} + \frac{100}{1,000} + \frac{200}{1,000} = \frac{350}{1,000} = 0.35$$

Often, it is easier to determine $P(A \text{ or } B)$, the probability of the event *A or B*, by using the **general addition rule**, defined in Equation (4.3).

GENERAL ADDITION RULE

The probability of *A or B* is equal to the probability of *A* plus the probability of *B* minus the probability of *A and B*.

$$P(A \text{ or } B) = P(A) + P(B) - P(A \text{ and } B) \tag{4.3}$$

Applying Equation (4.3) to the previous example produces the following result:

$$P(\text{Planned to purchase } or \text{ actually purchased}) = P(\text{Planned to purchase}) + P(\text{Actually purchased}) - P(\text{Planned to purchase } and \text{ actually purchased})$$

$$= \frac{250}{1,000} + \frac{300}{1,000} - \frac{200}{1,000}$$

$$= \frac{350}{1,000} = 0.35$$

The general addition rule consists of taking the probability of *A* and adding it to the probability of *B* and then subtracting the probability of the joint event *A and B* from this total because the joint event has already been included in computing both the probability of *A* and the probability of *B*. Referring to Table 4.1, if the outcomes of the event "planned to purchase" are added to those of the event "actually purchased," the joint event "planned to purchase *and* actually purchased" has been included in each of these simple events. Therefore, because this joint event has been double-counted, you must subtract it to provide the correct result. Example 4.5 illustrates another application of the general addition rule.

EXAMPLE 4.5

Using the General Addition Rule for the Households that Purchased Big-Screen Televisions

In Example 4.3, the purchases were cross-classified in Table 4.2 as a plasma screen or not a plasma screen and whether or not the household purchased a DVR. Find the probability that among households that purchased a big-screen television, they purchased a plasma-screen television or a DVR.

SOLUTION Using Equation (4.3),

$$P(\text{Plasma screen } or \text{ DVR}) = P(\text{Plasma screen}) + P(\text{DVR}) - P(\text{Plasma screen } and \text{ DVR})$$

$$= \frac{80}{300} + \frac{108}{300} - \frac{38}{300}$$

$$= \frac{150}{300} = 0.50$$

Therefore, there is a 50.0% chance that a randomly selected household that purchased a big-screen television purchased a plasma-screen television or a DVR.

Problems for Section 4.1

LEARNING THE BASICS

4.1 Two coins are tossed.
a. Give an example of a simple event.
b. Give an example of a joint event.
c. What is the complement of a head on the first toss?

4.2 An urn contains 12 red balls and 8 white balls. One ball is to be selected from the urn.
a. Give an example of a simple event.
b. What is the complement of a red ball?

4.3 Given the following contingency table:

	B	B'
A	10	20
A'	20	40

What is the probability of
a. event A?
b. event A'?
c. event A and B?
d. event A or B?

4.4 Given the following contingency table:

	B	B'
A	10	30
A'	25	35

What is the probability of
a. event A'?
b. event A and B?
c. event A' and B'?
d. event A' or B'?

APPLYING THE CONCEPTS

4.5 For each of the following, indicate whether the type of probability involved is an example of *a priori* probability, empirical probability, or subjective probability.
a. The next toss of a fair coin will land on heads.
b. Italy will win soccer's World Cup the next time the competition is held.
c. The sum of the faces of two dice will be seven.
d. The train taking a commuter to work will be more than 10 minutes late.

4.6 For each of the following, state whether the events created are mutually exclusive and collectively exhaustive. If they are not mutually exclusive and collectively exhaustive, either reword the categories to make them mutually exclusive and collectively exhaustive or explain why that would not be useful.
a. Registered voters in the United States were asked whether they registered as Republicans or Democrats.
b. Each respondent was classified by the type of car he or she drives: American, European, Japanese, or none.
c. People were asked, "Do you currently live in (i) an apartment or (ii) a house?"
d. A product was classified as defective or not defective.

4.7 Which of the following events occur with a probability of zero? For each, state why or why not.
a. A voter in the United States who is registered as a Republican and a Democrat
b. A voter in the United States who is female and registered as a Republican
c. An automobile that is a Ford and a Toyota
d. An automobile that is a Toyota and was manufactured in the United States

4.8 According to an Ipsos poll, the perception of unfairness in the U.S. tax code is spread fairly evenly across income groups, age groups, and education levels. In an April 2006 survey of 1,005 adults, Ipsos reported that almost 60% of all people said the code is unfair, whereas slightly more than 60% of those making more than $50,000 viewed the code as unfair ("People Cry Unfairness," *The Cincinnati Enquirer*, April 16, 2006, p. A8). Suppose that the following contingency table represents the specific breakdown of responses:

| U.S. TAX CODE | INCOME LEVEL | | |
	Less Than $50,000	More Than $50,000	Total
Fair	225	180	405
Unfair	280	320	600
Total	505	500	1,005

a. Give an example of a simple event.
b. Give an example of a joint event.
c. What is the complement of "tax code is fair"?
d. Why is "tax code is fair *and* makes less than $50,000" a joint event?

4.9 Referring to the contingency table in Problem 4.8, if a respondent is selected at random, what is the probability that he or she
a. thinks the tax code is unfair?
b. thinks the tax code is unfair *and* makes less than $50,000?
c. thinks the tax code is unfair *or* makes less than $50,000?
d. Explain the difference in the results in (b) and (c).

✓ SELF Test   **4.10** A yield improvement study at a semiconductor manufacturing facility provided defect data for a sample of 450 wafers. The following table presents a summary of the responses to two questions: "Was a particle found on the die that produced the wafer?" and "Is the wafer good or bad?"

| QUALITY OF WAFER | CONDITION OF DIE | | |
	No Particles	Particles	Totals
Good	320	14	334
Bad	80	36	116
Totals	400	50	450

Source: *Data extracted from S. W. Hall, "Analysis of Defectivity of Semiconductor Wafers by Contingency Table,"* Proceedings Institute of Environmental Sciences, Vol. 1, *1994, pp. 177–183.*

a. Give an example of a simple event.
b. Give an example of a joint event.
c. What is the complement of a good wafer?
d. Why is a "good wafer" and a die "with particles" a joint event?

4.11 Referring to the contingency table in Problem 4.10, if a wafer is selected at random, what is the probability that
a. it was produced from a die with no particles?
b. it is a bad wafer *and* was produced from a die with no particles?
c. it is a bad wafer *or* was produced from a die with no particles?
d. Explain the difference in the results in (b) and (c).

4.12 An experiment was conducted to study the choices made in mutual fund selection. Undergraduate and MBA students were presented with different S&P 500 Index funds that were identical except for fees. Suppose 100 undergraduate students and 100 MBA students were selected. Partial results are shown in the following table:

| FUND | STUDENT GROUP | |
	Undergraduate	MBA
Highest-cost fund	27	18
Not highest-cost fund	73	82

Source: *Data extracted from J. J. Choi, D. Laibson, and B. C. Madrian, Why Does the Law of One Price Fail?* **www.som.yale.edu/faculty/jjc83/fees.pdf.**

If a student is selected at random, what is the probability that he or she
a. selected the highest-cost fund?
b. selected the highest-cost fund *and* is an undergraduate?
c. selected the highest-cost fund *or* is an undergraduate?
d. Explain the difference in the results in (b) and (c).

4.13 Where people turn to for news is different for various age groups. Suppose that a study conducted on this issue (data extracted from P. Johnson, "Young People Turn to the Web for News," *USA Today*, March 23, 2006, p. 9D) was based on 200 respondents who were between the ages of 36 and 50, and 200 respondents who were over age 50. Of the 200 respondents who were between the ages of 36 and 50, 82 got their news primarily from newspapers. Of the 200 respondents who were over age 50, 104 got their news primarily from newspapers. Construct a contingency table or a Venn diagram to evaluate the probabilities. If a respondent is selected at random, what is the probability that he or she
a. got news primarily from newspapers?
b. got news primarily from newspapers *and* is over 50 years old?
c. got news primarily from newspapers *or* is over 50 years old?
d. Explain the difference in the results in (b) and (c).

4.14 A sample of 500 respondents was selected in a large metropolitan area to study consumer behavior. Among the questions asked was "Do you enjoy shopping for clothing?" Of 240 males, 136 answered yes. Of 260 females, 224 answered yes. Construct a contingency table or a Venn

diagram to evaluate the probabilities. What is the probability that a respondent chosen at random
a. enjoys shopping for clothing?
b. is a female *and* enjoys shopping for clothing?
c. is a female *or* enjoys shopping for clothing?
d. is a male *or* a female?

4.15 Each year, ratings are compiled concerning the performance of new cars during the first 90 days of use. Suppose that the cars have been categorized according to whether the car needs warranty-related repair (yes or no) and the country in which the company manufacturing the car is based (United States or not United States). Based on the data collected, the probability that the new car needs warranty repair is 0.04, the probability that the car was man-

ufactured by a U.S.-based company is 0.60, and the probability that the new car needs a warranty repair *and* was manufactured by a U.S.-based company is 0.025. Construct a contingency table or a Venn diagram to evaluate the probabilities of a warranty-related repair. What is the probability that a new car selected at random
a. needs a warranty repair?
b. needs a warranty repair *and* was manufactured by a U.S.-based company?
c. needs a warranty repair *or* was manufactured by a U.S.-based company?
d. needs a warranty repair *or* was not manufactured by a U.S.-based company?

4.2 Conditional Probability

Each example in Section 4.1 involves finding the probability of an event when sampling from the entire sample space. How do you determine the probability of an event if certain information about the events involved is already known?

Computing Conditional Probabilities

Conditional probability refers to the probability of event A, given information about the occurrence of another event B.

CONDITIONAL PROBABILITY
The probability of A given B is equal to the probability of A *and* B divided by the probability of B.

$$P(A \mid B) = \frac{P(A \text{ and } B)}{P(B)} \tag{4.4a}$$

The probability of B given A is equal to the probability of A *and* B divided by the probability of A.

$$P(B \mid A) = \frac{P(A \text{ and } B)}{P(A)} \tag{4.4b}$$

where

$$P(A \text{ and } B) = \text{joint probability of } A \text{ and } B$$
$$P(A) = \text{marginal probability of } A$$
$$P(B) = \text{marginal probability of } B$$

Referring to the Using Statistics scenario involving the purchase of big-screen televisions, suppose you were told that a household planned to purchase a big-screen television. Now, what is the probability that the household actually purchased the television? In this example, the objective is to find $P(\text{Actually purchased} \mid \text{Planned to purchase})$. Here you are given the information that the household planned to purchase the big-screen television. Therefore, the sample space does not consist of all 1,000 households in the survey. It consists of only those households that planned to purchase the big-screen television. Of 250 such households, 200 actually purchased the big-screen television. Therefore, based on Table 4.1 on page 204, the probability that a household actually purchased the big-screen television given that he or she planned to purchase is

$$P(\text{Actually purchased} \mid \text{Planned to purchase}) = \frac{\text{Planned to purchase } and \text{ actually purchased}}{\text{Planned to purchase}}$$

$$= \frac{200}{250} = 0.80$$

You can also use Equation (4.4b) to compute this result:

$$P(B \mid A) = \frac{P(A \text{ and } B)}{P(A)}$$

where

$$A = \text{planned to purchase}$$
$$B = \text{actually purchased}$$

then

$$P(\text{Actually purchased} \mid \text{Planned to purchase}) = \frac{200/1,000}{250/1,000}$$

$$= \frac{200}{250} = 0.80$$

Example 4.6 further illustrates conditional probability.

EXAMPLE 4.6

Finding a Conditional Probability of Purchasing a DVR

Table 4.2 on page 206 is a contingency table for whether the household purchased a plasma-screen television and whether the household purchased a DVR. If a household purchased a plasma-screen television, what is the probability that it also purchased a DVR?

SOLUTION Because you know that the household purchased a plasma-screen television, the sample space is reduced to 80 households. Of these 80 households, 38 also purchased a DVR. Therefore, the probability that a household purchased a DVR, given that the household purchased a plasma-screen television, is:

$$P(\text{Purchased DVR} \mid \text{Purchased plasma screen}) = \frac{\text{Number purchasing plasma screen } and \text{ DVR}}{\text{Number purchasing plasma screen}}$$

$$= \frac{38}{80} = 0.475$$

If you use Equation (4.4b) on page 211:

$$A = \text{Purchased plasma-screen television} \quad B = \text{Purchased DVR}$$

then

$$P(B \mid A) = \frac{P(A \text{ and } B)}{P(A)} = \frac{38/300}{80/300} = 0.475$$

Therefore, given that the household purchased a plasma-screen television, there is a 47.5% chance that the household also purchased a DVR. You can compare this conditional probability to the marginal probability of purchasing a DVR, which is 108/300 = 0.36, or 36%. These results tell you that households that purchased plasma-screen televisions are more likely to purchase DVRs than are households that purchased big-screen televisions that are not plasma-screen televisions.

Decision Trees

In Table 4.1 on page 204, households are classified according to whether they planned to purchase and whether they actually purchased big-screen televisions. A **decision tree** is an alternative to the contingency table. Figure 4.3 represents the decision tree for this example.

FIGURE 4.3

Decision tree for M&R Electronics World example

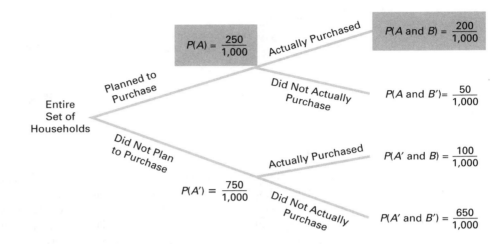

In Figure 4.3, beginning at the left with the entire set of households, there are two "branches" for whether or not the household planned to purchase a big-screen television. Each of these branches has two subbranches, corresponding to whether the household actually purchased or did not actually purchase the big-screen television. The probabilities at the end of the initial branches represent the marginal probabilities of A and A'. The probabilities at the end of each of the four subbranches represent the joint probability for each combination of events A and B. You compute the conditional probability by dividing the joint probability by the appropriate marginal probability.

For example, to compute the probability that the household actually purchased, given that the household planned to purchase the big-screen television, you take P(Planned to purchase *and* actually purchased) and divide by P(Planned to purchase). From Figure 4.3:

$$P(\text{Actually purchased} \mid \text{Planned to purchase}) = \frac{200/1,000}{250/1,000}$$

$$= \frac{200}{250} = 0.80$$

Example 4.7 illustrates how to construct a decision tree.

EXAMPLE 4.7

Forming the Decision Tree for the Households that Purchased Big-Screen Televisions

Using the cross-classified data in Table 4.2 on page 206, construct the decision tree. Use the decision tree to find the probability that a household purchased a DVR, given that the household purchased a plasma-screen television.

SOLUTION The decision tree for purchased a DVR and a plasma-screen television is displayed in Figure 4.4. Using Equation (4.4b) on page 211 and the following definitions,

$$A = \text{Purchased plasma-screen tlelvision}$$

$$B = \text{Purchased DVR}$$

$$P(B \mid A) = \frac{P(A \text{ and } B)}{P(A)} = \frac{38/300}{80/300} = 0.475$$

FIGURE 4.4

Decision tree for purchased a DVR and a plasma-screen television

Independence

In the example concerning the purchase of big-screen televisions, the conditional probability is 200/250 = 0.80 that the selected household actually purchased the big-screen television, given that the household planned to purchase. The simple probability of selecting a household that actually purchased is 300/1,000 = 0.30. This result shows that the prior knowledge that the household planned to purchase affected the probability that the household actually purchased the television. In other words, the outcome of one event is *dependent* on the outcome of a second event.

When the outcome of one event does *not* affect the probability of occurrence of another event, the events are said to be independent. **Independence** can be determined by using Equation (4.5).

INDEPENDENCE

Two events, A and B, are independent if and only if

$$P(A \mid B) = P(A) \qquad\qquad (4.5)$$

where

$P(A \mid B)$ = conditional probability of A given B
$P(A)$ = marginal probability of A

Example 4.8 demonstrates the use of Equation (4.5).

EXAMPLE 4.8

Determining Independence

In the follow-up survey of the 300 households that actually purchased big-screen televisions, the households were asked if they were satisfied with their purchases. Table 4.3 cross-classifies the responses to the satisfaction question with the responses to whether the television was a plasma-screen television.

TABLE 4.3

Satisfaction with Purchase of Big-Screen Televisions

TYPE OF TELEVISION	SATISFIED WITH PURCHASE?		
	Yes	No	Total
Plasma screen	64	16	80
Not plasma screen	176	44	220
Total	240	60	300

Determine whether being satisfied with the purchase and type of television purchased are independent.

SOLUTION For these data,

$$P(\text{Satisfied} \,|\, \text{Plasma screen}) = \frac{64/300}{80/300} = \frac{64}{80} = 0.80$$

which is equal to

$$P(\text{Satisfied}) = \frac{240}{300} = 0.80$$

Thus, being satisfied with the purchase and type of television purchased are independent. Knowledge of one event does not affect the probability of the other event.

Multiplication Rules

The **general multiplication rule** is derived using Equation (4.4a) on page 211:

$$P(A \,|\, B) = \frac{P(A \text{ and } B)}{P(B)}$$

and solving for the joint probability $P(A \text{ and } B)$.

> **GENERAL MULTIPLICATION RULE**
>
> The probability of A and B is equal to the probability of A given B times the probability of B.
>
> $$P(A \text{ and } B) = P(A \,|\, B)P(B) \qquad \qquad \textbf{(4.6)}$$

Example 4.9 demonstrates the use of the general multiplication rule.

EXAMPLE 4.9

Using the Multiplication Rule

Consider the 80 households that purchased plasma-screen televisions. In Table 4.3 on page 214 you see that 64 households are satisfied with their purchase and 16 households are dissatisfied. Suppose two households are randomly selected from the 80 households. Find the probability that both households are satisfied with their purchase.

SOLUTION Here you can use the multiplication rule in the following way. If:

$$A = \text{second household selected is satisfied}$$
$$B = \text{first household selected is satisfied}$$

then, using Equation (4.6),

$$P(A \text{ and } B) = P(A \,|\, B)P(B)$$

The probability that the first household is satisfied with the purchase is 64/80. However, the probability that the second household is also satisfied with the purchase depends on the result of the first selection. If the first household is not returned to the sample after the satisfaction level is determined (i.e., sampling without replacement), the number of households remaining is 79. If the first household is satisfied, the probability that the second is also satisfied is 63/79 because 63 satisfied households remain in the sample. Therefore,

$$P(A \text{ and } B) = \left(\frac{63}{79}\right)\left(\frac{64}{80}\right) = 0.6380$$

There is a 63.80% chance that both of the households sampled will be satisfied with their purchase.

The **multiplication rule for independent events** is derived by substituting $P(A)$ for $P(A \,|\, B)$ in Equation (4.6).

MULTIPLICATION RULE FOR INDEPENDENT EVENTS
If A and B are independent, the probability of A and B is equal to the probability of A times the probability of B.

$$P(A \text{ and } B) = P(A)P(B) \qquad (4.7)$$

If this rule holds for two events, A and B, then A and B are independent. Therefore, there are two ways to determine independence:

1. Events A and B are independent if, and only if, $P(A \mid B) = P(A)$.
2. Events A and B are independent if, and only if, $P(A \text{ and } B) = P(A)P(B)$.

Marginal Probability Using the General Multiplication Rule

In Section 4.1, marginal probability was defined using Equation (4.2) on page 207. You can state the equation for marginal probability by using the general multiplication rule. If

$$P(A) = P(A \text{ and } B_1) + P(A \text{ and } B_2) + \cdots + P(A \text{ and } B_k)$$

then, using the general multiplication rule, Equation (4.8) defines the marginal probability.

MARGINAL PROBABILITY USING THE GENERAL MULTIPLICATION RULE
$$P(A) = P(A \mid B_1)P(B_1) + P(A \mid B_2)P(B_2) + \cdots + P(A \mid B_k)P(B_k) \quad (4.8)$$

where $B_1, B_2, \ldots, B_k$ are k mutually exclusive and collectively exhaustive events.

To illustrate this equation, refer to Table 4.1 on page 204. Let

$$P(A) = \text{probability of ``planned to purchase''}$$
$$P(B_1) = \text{probability of ``actually purchased''}$$
$$P(B_2) = \text{probability of ``did not actually purchase''}$$

Then, using Equation (4.8), the probability of planned to purchase is:

$$P(A) = P(A \mid B_1)P(B_1) + P(A \mid B_2)P(B_2)$$
$$= \left(\frac{200}{300}\right)\left(\frac{300}{1,000}\right) + \left(\frac{50}{700}\right)\left(\frac{700}{1,000}\right)$$
$$= \frac{200}{1,000} + \frac{50}{1,000} = \frac{250}{1,000} = 0.25$$

Problems for Section 4.2

LEARNING THE BASICS

4.16 Given the following contingency table:

	B	B'
A	10	20
A'	20	40

What is the probability of
a. $A \mid B$?
b. $A \mid B'$?
c. $A' \mid B'$?
d. Are events A and B independent?

4.17 Given the following contingency table:

	B	B'
A	10	30
A'	25	35

What is the probability of
a. $A \mid B$?
b. $A' \mid B'$?
c. $A \mid B'$?
d. Are events A and B independent?

4.18 If $P(A \text{ and } B) = 0.4$ and $P(B) = 0.8$, find $P(A \mid B)$.

4.19 If $P(A) = 0.7$, $P(B) = 0.6$, and A and B are independent, find $P(A \text{ and } B)$.

4.20 If $P(A) = 0.3$, $P(B) = 0.4$, and $P(A \text{ and } B) = 0.2$, are A and B independent?

APPLYING THE CONCEPTS

4.21 Where people turn to for news is different for various age groups. Suppose that a study conducted on this issue (data extracted from P. Johnson, "Young People Turn to the Web for News," *USA Today*, March 23, 2006, p. 9D) was based on 200 respondents who were between the ages of 36 and 50 and 200 respondents who were over age 50. Of the 200 respondents who were between the ages of 36 and 50, 82 got their news primarily from newspapers. Of the 200 respondents who were over age 50, 104 got their news primarily from newspapers.

a. Given that a respondent is over age 50, what then is the probability that he or she gets news primarily from newspapers?

b. Given that a respondent gets news primarily from newspapers, what is the probability that he or she is over age 50?

c. Explain the difference in the results in (a) and (b).

d. Are the two events, whether the respondent is over age 50 and whether he or she gets news primarily from newspapers, independent?

✓ **SELF Test** **4.22** A yield improvement study at a semiconductor manufacturing facility provided defect data for a sample of 450 wafers. The following table presents a summary of the responses to two questions: "Were particles found on the die that produced the wafer?" and "Is the wafer good or bad?"

QUALITY OF WAFER	CONDITION OF DIE		
	No Particles	**Particles**	**Totals**
Good	320	14	334
Bad	80	36	116
Totals	400	50	450

Source: *Data extracted from S. W. Hall, "Analysis of Defectivity of Semiconductor Wafers by Contingency Table,"* Proceedings Institute of Environmental Sciences, Vol. 1, *1994, pp. 177–183.*

a. Suppose you know that a wafer is bad. What is the probability that it was produced from a die that had particles?

b. Suppose you know that a wafer is good. What is the probability that it was produced from a die that had particles?

c. Are the two events, a good wafer and a die with no particles, independent? Explain.

4.23 According to an Ipsos poll, the perception of unfairness in the U.S. tax code is spread fairly evenly across income groups, age groups, and education levels. In an April 2006 survey of 1,005 adults, Ipsos reported that almost 60% of all people said the code is unfair, whereas slightly more than 60% of those making more than $50,000 viewed the code as unfair ("People Cry Unfairness," *The Cincinnati Enquirer*, April 16, 2006, p. A8). Suppose that the following contingency table represents the specific breakdown of responses:

	INCOME LEVEL		
	Less Than $50,000	**More Than $50,000**	**Total**
Fair	225	180	405
Unfair	280	320	600
Total	505	500	1,005

a. Given that a respondent earns less than $50,000, what is the probability that he or she said that the tax code is fair?

b. Given that a respondent earns more than $50,000, what is the probability that he or she said that the tax code is fair?

c. Is income level independent of attitude about whether the tax code is fair? Explain.

4.24 An experiment was conducted to study the choices made in mutual fund selection. Undergraduate and MBA students were presented with different S&P 500 Index funds that were identical except for fees. Suppose 100 undergraduate students and 100 MBA students were selected. Partial results are shown in the following table:

FUND	STUDENT GROUP	
	Undergraduate	**MBA**
Highest-cost fund	27	18
Not highest-cost fund	73	82

Source: *Data extracted from J. J. Choi, D. Laibson, and B. C. Madrian, Why Does the Law of One Price Fail?* **www.som.yale.edu/faculty/jjc83/fees.pdf.**

a. Given that a student is an undergraduate, what is the probability that he or she selected the highest-cost fund?

b. Given that a student selected the highest-cost fund, what is the probability that he or she is an undergraduate?

c. Explain the difference in the results in (a) and (b).

d. Are the two events "student group" and "fund selected" independent? Explain.

4.25 A sample of 500 respondents was selected in a large metropolitan area to study consumer behavior, with the following results:

ENJOYS SHOPPING FOR CLOTHING	GENDER		
	Male	**Female**	**Total**
Yes	136	224	360
No	104	36	140
Total	240	260	500

a. Suppose the respondent chosen is a female. What is the probability that she does not enjoy shopping for clothing?

b. Suppose the respondent chosen enjoys shopping for clothing. What is the probability that the individual is a male?

c. Are enjoying shopping for clothing and the gender of the individual independent? Explain.

4.26 Each year, ratings are compiled concerning the performance of new cars during the first 90 days of use. Suppose that the cars have been categorized according to whether the car needs warranty-related repair (yes or no) and the country in which the company manufacturing the car is based (United States or not United States). Based on the data collected, the probability that the new car needs a warranty repair is 0.04, the probability that the car is manufactured by a U.S.-based company is 0.60, and the probability that the new car needs a warranty repair *and* was manufactured by a U.S.-based company is 0.025.

a. Suppose you know that a company based in the United States manufactured a particular car. What is the probability that the car needs warranty repair?

b. Suppose you know that a company based in the United States did not manufacture a particular car. What is the probability that the car needs warranty repair?

c. Are need for warranty repair and location of the company manufacturing the car independent?

4.27 In 37 of the 58 years from 1950 through 2007, the S&P 500 finished higher after the first 5 days of trading. In 32 of those 37 years, the S&P 500 finished higher for the year. Is a good first week a good omen for the upcoming year? The following table gives the first-week and annual performance over this 58-year period:

	S&P 500'S ANNUAL PERFORMANCE	
FIRST WEEK	Higher	Lower
Higher	32	5
Lower	11	10

a. If a year is selected at random, what is the probability that the S&P 500 finished higher for the year?

b. Given that the S&P 500 finished higher after the first five days of trading, what is the probability that it finished higher for the year?

c. Are the two events "first-week performance" and "annual performance" independent? Explain.

d. Look up the performance after the first five days of 2008 and the 2008 annual performance of the S&P 500 at **finance.yahoo.com**. Comment on the results.

4.28 A standard deck of cards is being used to play a game. There are four suits (hearts, diamonds, clubs, and spades), each having 13 faces (ace, 2, 3, 4, 5, 6, 7, 8, 9, 10, jack, queen, and king), making a total of 52 cards. This complete deck is thoroughly mixed, and you will receive the first 2 cards from the deck without replacement.

a. What is the probability that both cards are queens?

b. What is the probability that the first card is a 10 and the second card is a 5 or 6?

c. If you were sampling with replacement, what would be the answer in (a)?

d. In the game of blackjack, the picture cards (jack, queen, king) count as 10 points, and the ace counts as either 1 or 11 points. All other cards are counted at their face value. Blackjack is achieved if 2 cards total 21 points. What is the probability of getting blackjack in this problem?

4.29 A box of nine gloves contains two left-handed gloves and seven right-handed gloves.

a. If two gloves are randomly selected from the box without replacement, what is the probability that both gloves selected will be right-handed?

b. If two gloves are randomly selected from the box without replacement, what is the probability there will be one right-handed glove and one left-handed glove selected?

c. If three gloves are selected with replacement, what is the probability that all three will be left-handed?

d. If you were sampling with replacement, what would be the answers to (a) and (b)?

4.3 Bayes' Theorem

Bayes' theorem is used to revise previously calculated probabilities based on new information. Developed by Thomas Bayes in the eighteenth century (see references 1, 2, and 5), Bayes' theorem is an extension of what you previously learned about conditional probability.

You can apply Bayes' theorem to the situation in which M&R Electronics World is considering marketing a new model of television. In the past, 40% of the televisions introduced by the company have been successful, and 60% have been unsuccessful. Before introducing the television to the marketplace, the marketing research department conducts an extensive study and releases a report, either favorable or unfavorable. In the past, 80% of the successful televisions had received favorable market research reports, and 30% of the unsuccessful televisions had received favorable reports. For the new model of television under consideration, the marketing research department has issued a favorable report. What is the probability that the television will be successful?

Bayes' theorem is developed from the definition of conditional probability. To find the conditional probability of B given A, consider Equation (4.4b) [originally presented on page 211 and shown below]:

$$P(B \mid A) = \frac{P(A \text{ and } B)}{P(A)} = \frac{P(A \mid B)P(B)}{P(A)}$$

Bayes' theorem is derived by substituting Equation (4.8) on page 216 for $P(A)$ in the denominator of Equation (4.4b).

BAYES' THEOREM

$$P(B_i \mid A) = \frac{P(A \mid B_i)P(B_i)}{P(A \mid B_1)P(B_1) + P(A \mid B_2)P(B_2) + \cdots + P(A \mid B_k)P(B_k)} \quad \text{(4.9)}$$

where B_i is the ith event out of k mutually exclusive and collectively exhaustive events.

To use Equation (4.9) for the television-marketing example, let

event S = successful television   event F = favorable report

event S' = unsuccessful television   event F' = unfavorable report

and

$$P(S) = 0.40 \quad P(F \mid S) = 0.80$$

$$P(S') = 0.60 \quad P(F \mid S') = 0.30$$

Then, using Equation (4.9),

$$P(S \mid F) = \frac{P(F \mid S)P(S)}{P(F \mid S)P(S) + P(F \mid S')P(S')}$$

$$= \frac{(0.80)(0.40)}{(0.80)(0.40) + (0.30)(0.60)}$$

$$= \frac{0.32}{0.32 + 0.18} = \frac{0.32}{0.50}$$

$$= 0.64$$

The probability of a successful television, given that a favorable report was received, is 0.64. Thus, the probability of an unsuccessful television, given that a favorable report was received, is $1 - 0.64 = 0.36$. Table 4.4 summarizes the computation of the probabilities, and Figure 4.5 presents the decision tree.

TABLE 4.4

Bayes' Theorem Calculations for the Television-Marketing Example

Event S_i	Prior Probability $P(S_i)$	Conditional Probability $P(F \mid S_i)$	Joint Probability $P(F \mid S_i)P(S_i)$	Revised Probability $P(S_i \mid F)$
S = **successful television**	0.40	0.80	0.32	$P(S \mid F) = 0.32/0.50$ $= 0.64$
S' = **unsuccessful television**	0.60	0.30	$\dfrac{0.18}{0.50}$	$P(S' \mid F) = 0.18/0.50$ $= 0.36$

FIGURE 4.5

Decision tree for
marketing a new
television

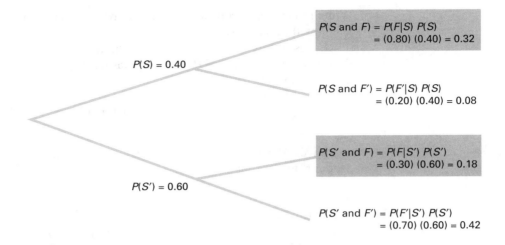

$$P(S \text{ and } F) = P(F|S)\ P(S)$$
$$= (0.80)\ (0.40) = 0.32$$

$$P(S \text{ and } F') = P(F'|S)\ P(S)$$
$$= (0.20)\ (0.40) = 0.08$$

$$P(S' \text{ and } F) = P(F|S')\ P(S')$$
$$= (0.30)\ (0.60) = 0.18$$

$$P(S' \text{ and } F') = P(F'|S')\ P(S')$$
$$= (0.70)\ (0.60) = 0.42$$

$P(S) = 0.40$

$P(S') = 0.60$

Example 4.10 applies Bayes' theorem to a medical diagnosis problem.

EXAMPLE 4.10

**Using Bayes'
Theorem in a
Medical Diagnosis
Problem**

The probability that a person has a certain disease is 0.03. Medical diagnostic tests are available to determine whether the person actually has the disease. If the disease is actually present, the probability that the medical diagnostic test will give a positive result (indicating that the disease is present) is 0.90. If the disease is not actually present, the probability of a positive test result (indicating that the disease is present) is 0.02. Suppose that the medical diagnostic test has given a positive result (indicating that the disease is present). What is the probability that the disease is actually present? What is the probability of a positive test result?

SOLUTION Let

$$\text{event } D = \text{has disease} \qquad \text{event } T = \text{test is positive}$$
$$\text{event } D' = \text{does not have disease} \quad \text{event } T' = \text{test is negative}$$

and

$$P(D) = 0.03 \quad P(T|D) = 0.90$$
$$P(D') = 0.97 \quad P(T|D') = 0.02$$

Using Equation (4.9) on page 219,

$$P(D|T) = \frac{P(T|D)P(D)}{P(T|D)P(D) + P(T|D')P(D')}$$

$$= \frac{(0.90)(0.03)}{(0.90)(0.03) + (0.02)(0.97)}$$

$$= \frac{0.0270}{0.0270 + 0.0194} = \frac{0.0270}{0.0464}$$

$$= 0.582$$

The probability that the disease is actually present, given that a positive result has occurred (indicating that the disease is present), is 0.582. Table 4.5 summarizes the computation of the probabilities, and Figure 4.6 presents the decision tree.

	Prior Probability $P(D_i)$	Conditional Probability $P(T \mid D_i)$	Joint Probability $P(T \mid D_i)P(D_i)$	Revised Probability $P(D_i \mid T)$
TABLE 4.5 Bayes' Theorem Calculations for the Medical Diagnosis Problem				
Event D_i				
D = has disease	0.03	0.90	0.0270	$P(D \mid T) = 0.0270/0.0464$ $= 0.582$
D' = does not have disease	0.97	0.02	0.0194 ―――― 0.0464	$P(D' \mid T) = 0.0194/0.0464$ $= 0.418$

FIGURE 4.6

Decision tree for the medical diagnosis problem

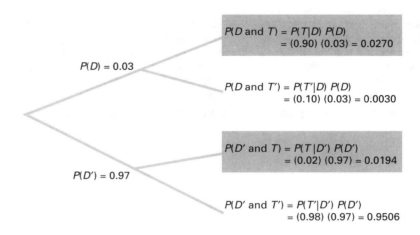

The denominator in Bayes' theorem represents $P(T)$, the probability of a positive test result, which in this case is 0.0464, or 4.64%.

THINK ABOUT THIS   Divine Providence and Spam

If asked, you probably would not guess that the essays *Divine Benevolence: Or, An Attempt to Prove That the Principal End of the Divine Providence and Government Is the Happiness of His Creatures* and *An Essay Towards Solving a Problem in the Doctrine of Chances* were written by the same person. But they were! Don't feel bad if you would not have said they were as your thinking illustrates a modern-day application of Bayesian statistics—spam, or junk mail, filters.

In not guessing that the two essays just named were written by the same person, you probably looked at the words in the titles of the essays and concluded that they were talking about two different things. An implicit rule you used was that word frequencies vary by subject matter. A statistics essay would very likely contain the word *statistics* as well as words such as *chance, problem*, and *solving*. An eighteenth-century essay about theology and religion would be more likely to contain the uppercase forms of *Divine* and *Providence*.

Likewise, there are words you would guess to be very unlikely to appear in either book, such

as technical terms from finance and words that are most likely to appear in both—common words such as *a, and*, and *the*. That words would either be likely and unlikely suggests an application of probability theory. Of course, likely and unlikely are fuzzy concepts and we might occasionally misclassify an essay if we kept things too simple, such as relying solely on the occurrence of the words *Divine* and *Providence*.

For example, a profile of the late Harris Milstead, better known as *Divine,* the star of *Hairspray* and other films, visiting Providence (Rhode Island), would most certainly not be an essay about theology. But if we widened the number of words we examined and found such words as *movie* or the name John Waters (Divine's director in many films), we probably would quickly realize the essay had something to do with twentieth-century cinema and little to do directly with theology and religion.

We can use a similar process to try to classify a new e-mail message in your in-box as either spam or a legitimate message (called "ham" in this context). We would first need to

add a "spam filter" to your e-mail program that has the ability to track word frequencies associated with spam and ham messages as you identify them on a day-to-day basis. This would allow the filter to constantly update the prior probabilities necessary to use Bayes' theorem. With these probabilities, the filter can ask, "What is the probability that an e-mail is spam, given the presence of a certain word?"

Applying the terms of Equation (4.9) on page 219, such a Bayesian spam filter would multiply the probability of finding the word in a spam e-mail, $P(A \mid B)$, by the probability that the e-mail is spam, $P(B)$, and then divide by the probability of finding the word in an e-mail, the denominator in Equation (4.9). Bayesian spam filters also use shortcuts by focusing on a small set of words that have a high probability of being found in a spam message as well as on a small set of other words that have a low probability of being found in a spam message.

As spammers (people who send junk e-mail) learned of these new filters, they tried to outfox them. Having learned that Bayesian filters might be assigning a high $P(A|B)$ value to words such as Viagra commonly found in spam, spammers thought they could fool the filter by misspelling the word as Vi@gr@ or V1agra. What they overlooked was that the misspelled variants were even *more likely* to be found in a spam message than the original word. Thus, the misspelled variants made the job of spotting spam *easier* for the Bayesian filters.

Other spammers tried to fool the filters by adding "good" words, words that would have a low probability of being found in a spam message, or "rare" words, words not frequently encountered in any message. But these spammers overlooked the fact that the conditional probabilities are constantly updated and that words once considered "good" would be soon discarded from the good list by the filter as their

$P(A|B)$ value increased. Likewise as "rare" words grew more common in spam and yet stayed rare in ham, such words acted like the misspelled variants that others had tried earlier.

Even then, and perhaps after reading about Bayesian statistics, spammers thought that they could "break" Bayesian filters by inserting random words in their messages. Those random words would affect the filter by causing it to see many words whose $P(A|B)$ value would be low. The Bayesian filter would begin to label many spam messages as ham and end up being of no practical use. Because the Internet still contains some Web pages and posts that triumph this approach, we will leave it to you to figure out why this method of attack cannot succeed in the long run and why this method is not as initially successful as some would claim.

Today, spammers are still trying to outwit Bayesian filters. Some spammers have decided to eliminate all or most of the words in their messages and replace them with graphics so that Bayesian filters will have very few words to work with. But this approach will fail too, as Bayesian filters are rewritten to consider things other than words in a message. After all, Bayes' theorem concerns *events,* and "graphics present with no text" is as valid an event as "some word *X* present in a message." Other future tricks will ultimately fail for the same reason. (By the way, spam filters use non-Bayestan techniques as well, which make spammers' lives that much more difficult.)

Bayesian spam filters are an example of the unexpected way that applications of statistics can show up in your daily life. You will discover more examples as you read the rest of this book.

Problems for Section 4.3

LEARNING THE BASICS

4.30 If $P(B) = 0.05$, $P(A | B) = 0.80$, $P(B') = 0.95$, and $P(A | B') = 0.40$, find $P(B | A)$.

4.31 If $P(B) = 0.30$, $P(A | B) = 0.60$, $P(B') = 0.70$, and $P(A | B') = 0.50$, find $P(B | A)$.

APPLYING THE CONCEPTS

4.32 In Example 4.10 on page 220, suppose that the probability that a medical diagnostic test will give a positive result if the disease is not present is reduced from 0.02 to 0.01. Given this information,
a. if the medical diagnostic test has given a positive result (indicating that the disease is present), what is the probability that the disease is actually present?
b. if the medical diagnostic test has given a negative result (indicating that the disease is not present), what is the probability that the disease is not present?

4.33 An advertising executive is studying television viewing habits of married men and women during prime-time hours. Based on past viewing records, the executive has determined that during prime time, husbands are watching television 60% of the time. When the husband is watching television, 40% of the time the wife is also watching. When the husband is not watching television, 30% of the time the wife is watching television. Find the probability that
a. if the wife is watching television, the husband is also watching television.
b. the wife is watching television in prime time.

✓ SELF Test **4.34** Olive Construction Company is determining whether it should submit a bid for a new shopping center. In the past, Olive's main competitor, Base Construction Company, has submitted bids 70% of the time. If Base Construction Company does not bid on a job, the probability that Olive Construction Company will get the job is 0.50. If Base Construction Company bids on a job, the probability that Olive Construction Company will get the job is 0.25.
a. If Olive Construction Company gets the job, what is the probability that Base Construction Company did not bid?
b. What is the probability that Olive Construction Company will get the job?

4.35 Laid-off workers who become entrepreneurs because they cannot find meaningful employment with another company are known as *entrepreneurs by necessity. The Wall Street Journal* reports that these entrepreneurs by necessity are less likely to grow into large businesses than are *entrepreneurs by choice* (J. Bailey, "Desire—More Than Need—Builds a Business," *The Wall Street Journal*, May 21, 2001, p. B4). This article states that 89% of the entrepreneurs in the United States are entrepreneurs by choice and 11% are entrepreneurs by necessity. Only 2% of entrepreneurs by necessity expect their new business to employ 20 or more people within five years, whereas 14% of entrepreneurs by choice expect to employ at least 20 people within five years.
a. If an entrepreneur is selected at random, and that individual expects that his or her new business will employ 20 or

more people within five years, what is the probability that this individual is an entrepreneur by choice?

b. Discuss several possible reasons why entrepreneurs by choice are more likely to believe that they will grow their businesses.

4.36 The editor of a textbook publishing company is trying to decide whether to publish a proposed business statistics textbook. Information on previous textbooks published indicates that 10% are huge successes, 20% are modest successes, 40% break even, and 30% are losers. However, before a publishing decision is made, the book will be reviewed. In the past, 99% of the huge successes received favorable reviews, 70% of the moderate successes received favorable reviews, 40% of the break-even books received favorable reviews, and 20% of the losers received favorable reviews.

a. If the proposed textbook receives a favorable review, how should the editor revise the probabilities of the various outcomes to take this information into account?

b. What proportion of textbooks receives favorable reviews?

4.37 A municipal bond service has three rating categories (*A, B,* and *C*). Suppose that in the past year, of the municipal bonds issued throughout the United States, 70% were rated *A*, 20% were rated *B*, and 10% were rated *C*. Of the municipal bonds rated *A*, 50% were issued by cities, 40% by suburbs, and 10% by rural areas. Of the municipal bonds rated *B*, 60% were issued by cities, 20% by suburbs, and 20% by rural areas. Of the municipal bonds rated *C*, 90% were issued by cities, 5% by suburbs, and 5% by rural areas.

a. If a new municipal bond is to be issued by a city, what is the probability that it will receive an *A* rating?

b. What proportion of municipal bonds are issued by cities?

c. What proportion of municipal bonds are issued by suburbs?

4.4 Ethical Issues and Probability

Ethical issues can arise when any statements related to probability are presented to the public, particularly when these statements are part of an advertising campaign for a product or service. Unfortunately, many people are not comfortable with numerical concepts (see reference 4) and tend to misinterpret the meaning of the probability. In some instances, the misinterpretation is not intentional, but in other cases, advertisements may unethically try to mislead potential customers.

One example of a potentially unethical application of probability relates to advertisements for state lotteries. When purchasing a lottery ticket, the customer selects a set of numbers (such as 6) from a larger list of numbers (such as 54). Although virtually all participants know that they are unlikely to win the lottery, they also have very little idea of how unlikely it is for them to select all 6 winning numbers from the list of 54 numbers. They have even less idea of the probability of winning a consolation prize by selecting either 4 or 5 winning numbers.

Given this background, you might consider a recent commercial for a state lottery that stated, "We won't stop until we have made everyone a millionaire" to be deceptive and possibly unethical. Do you think the state has any intention of ever stopping the lottery, given the fact that the state relies on it to bring millions of dollars into the treasury? Is it possible that the lottery can make everyone a millionaire? Is it ethical to suggest that the purpose of the lottery is to make everyone a millionaire?

Another example of a potentially unethical application of probability relates to an investment newsletter promising a 90% probability of a 20% annual return on investment. To make the claim in the newsletter an ethical one, the investment service needs to (a) explain the basis on which this probability estimate rests, (b) provide the probability statement in another format, such as 9 chances in 10, and (c) explain what happens to the investment in the 10% of the cases in which a 20% return is not achieved (e.g., is the entire investment lost?).

These are serious ethical issues. If you were going to write an advertisement for the state lottery that ethically describes the probablity of winning a certain prize, what would you say? If you were gong to write an advertisement for the investment newsletter that ethically states the probability of a 20% return on an investment, what would you say?

USING STATISTICS   @ M&R Electronics World Revisited

As the marketing manager for M&R Electronics World, you analyzed the survey results of an intent-to-purchase study. This study asked the heads of 1,000 households about their intentions to purchase a big-screen television sometime during the next 12 months, and as a follow-up, M&R surveyed the same people 12 months later to see whether such a television was purchased. In addition, for households purchasing big-screen televisions, the survey asked whether the television they purchased was a plasma screen, whether they also purchased a digital video recorder (DVR) in the past 12 months, and whether they were satisfied with their purchase of the big-screen television.

By analyzing the results of these surveys, you were able to uncover many pieces of valuable information that will help you plan a marketing strategy that will enhance sales and better target those households likely to purchase multiple or more expensive products. Whereas only 30% of the households actually purchased a big-screen television, if a household indicated that they planned to purchase a big-screen television in the next 12 months there was an 80% chance that the household actually made the purchase. Thus the marketing strategy should target those households that have indicated an intention to purchase.

You determined that for households which purchased a plasma-screen television, there was a 47.5% chance that the household also purchased a DVR. You then compared this conditional probability to the marginal probability of purchasing a DVR, which was 36%. Thus, households that purchased plasma-screen televisions are more likely to purchase DVRs than are households that purchased big-screen televisions that are not plasma-screen televisions.

You were also able to apply Bayes' theorem to M&R Electronics World's market research reports. The reports investigate a potential new television model prior to its scheduled release. If a favorable report was received, then there was a 64% chance that the new television model would be successful. However, if an unfavorable report was issued, there was only a 16% chance that it would be successful. Therefore, the marketing strategy of M&R needs to pay close attention to whether a report's conclusion is favorable or unfavorable.

SUMMARY

This chapter began by developing the basic concepts of probability. You learned that probability is a numeric value from zero to one that represents the chance, likelihood, or possibility a particular event will occur. In addition to simple probability, you learned about conditional probabilities and independent events. Bayes' theorem was used to revise previously calculated probabilities based on new information. Throughout the chapter, contingency tables, Venn diagrams, and decision trees were used to display information. In the next chapter, important discrete probability distributions such as the binomial and Poisson distributions are developed.

KEY EQUATIONS

Probability of Occurrence

$$\text{Probability of occurrence} = \frac{X}{T} \qquad (4.1)$$

Marginal Probability

$$P(A) = P(A \text{ and } B_1) = P(A \text{ and } B_2) \\ + \cdots + P(A \text{ and } B_k) \qquad (4.2)$$

General Addition Rule

$$P(A \text{ or } B) = P(A) + P(B) - P(A \text{ and } B) \qquad (4.3)$$

Conditional Probability

$$P(A \mid B) = \frac{P(A \text{ and } B)}{P(A)} \qquad (4.4a)$$

$$P(B \mid A) = \frac{P(A \text{ and } B)}{P(B)} \qquad (4.4b)$$

Independence

$$P(A \mid B) = P(A) \qquad \text{(4.5)}$$

General Multiplication Rule

$$P(A \text{ and } B) = P(A \mid B)P(B) \qquad \text{(4.6)}$$

Multiplication Rule for Independent Events

$$P(A \text{ and } B) = P(A)P(B) \qquad \text{(4.7)}$$

Marginal Probability Using the General Multiplication Rule

$$P(A) = P(A \mid B_1)P(B_1) + P(A \mid B_2)P(B_2) + \cdots + P(A \mid B_k)P(B_k) \qquad \text{(4.8)}$$

Bayes' Theorem

$$P(B_i \mid A) = \frac{P(A \mid B_i)P(B_i)}{P(A \mid B_1)P(B_1) + P(A \mid B_2)P(B_2) + \cdots + P(A \mid B_k)P(B_k)} \qquad \text{(4.9)}$$

KEY TERMS

a priori probability   202
Bayes' theorem   218
certain event   202
collectively exhaustive   207
complement   203
conditional probability   211
contingency table   204
decision tree   213
empirical probability   203

event   203
general addition rule   208
general multiplication rule   215
impossible event   202
independence   214
joint event   203
joint probability   206
marginal probability   207

multiplication rule for independent events   215
mutually exclusive   207
probability   202
sample space   204
simple event   203
simple probability   205
subjective probability   203
Venn diagram   204

CHAPTER REVIEW PROBLEMS

CHECKING YOUR UNDERSTANDING

4.38 What are the differences between a priori probability, empirical probability, and subjective probability?

4.39 What is the difference between a simple event and a joint event?

4.40 How can you use the general addition rule to find the probability of occurrence of event A or B?

4.41 What is the difference between mutually exclusive events and collectively exhaustive events?

4.42 How does conditional probability relate to the concept of independence?

4.43 How does the multiplication rule differ for events that are and are not independent?

4.44 How can you use Bayes' theorem to revise probabilities in light of new information?

4.45 In Bayes' theorem, how does the prior probability differ from the revised probability?

APPLYING THE CONCEPTS

4.46 A survey by the Pew Research Center ("Snapshots: Goals of 'Gen next' vs. 'Gen X'," USA Today, March 27, 2007, p. 1A) indicated that 81% of 18- to 25-year-olds had getting rich as a goal as compared to 62% of 26- to 40-year-

olds. Suppose that the survey was based on 500 respondents from each of the two groups.
a. Form a contingency table or a Venn diagram.
b. Give an example of a simple event and a joint event.
c. What is the probability that a randomly selected respondent has a goal of getting rich?
d. What is the probability that a randomly selected respondent has a goal of getting rich and is in the 26- to 40-year-old group?
e. Are the events "age group" and "has getting rich as a goal" independent? Explain.

4.47 The owner of a restaurant serving Continental-style entrées was interested in studying ordering patterns of patrons for the Friday-to-Sunday weekend time period. Records were maintained that indicated the demand for dessert during the same time period. The owner decided to study two other variables, along with whether a dessert was ordered: the gender of the individual and whether a beef entrée was ordered. The results are as follows:

	GENDER		
DESSERT ORDERED	**Male**	**Female**	**Total**
Yes	96	40	136
No	224	240	464
Total	320	280	600

DESSERT ORDERED	BEEF ENTRÉE		
	Yes	**No**	**Total**
Yes	71	65	136
No	116	348	464
Total	187	413	600

A waiter approaches a table to take an order. What is the probability that the first customer to order at the table

a. orders a dessert?

b. orders a dessert *or* a beef entrée?

c. is a female *and* does not order a dessert?

d. is a female *or* does not order a dessert?

e. Suppose the first person that the waiter takes the dessert order from is a female. What is the probability that she does not order dessert?

f. Are gender and ordering dessert independent?

g. Is ordering a beef entrée independent of whether the person orders dessert?

4.48 Unsolicited commercial e-mail messages containing product advertisements, commonly referred to as spam, are routinely deleted before being read by more than 80% of all e-mail users. Furthermore, a small percentage of those reading the spam actually follow through and purchase items. Yet many companies use these unsolicited e-mail advertisements because of the extremely low cost involved. Movies Unlimited, a mail-order video and DVD business in Philadelphia, is one of the more successful companies in terms of generating sales through this form of e-marketing. Ed Weiss, general manager of Movies Unlimited, estimates that somewhere from 15% to 20% of the company's e-mail recipients read the advertisements. Moreover, approximately 15% of those who read the advertisements place orders (S. Forster, "E-Marketers Look to Polish Spam's Rusty Image," *The Wall Street Journal*, May 20, 2002, p. D2).

a. Using Mr. Weiss's lower estimate that the probability a recipient will read the advertisement is 0.15, what is the probability that a recipient will read the advertisement *and* place an order?

b. Movies Unlimited uses a 175,000-customer database to send e-mail advertisements. If an e-mail advertisement is sent to everyone in its customer database, how many customers do you expect will read the advertisement and place an order?

c. If the probability a recipient will read the advertisement is 0.20, what is the probability that a recipient will read the advertisement *and* place an order?

d. What is your answer to (b) if the probability that a recipient will read the advertisement is 0.20?

4.49 An experiment was conducted by James Choi, David Laibson, and Brigitte Madrian to study the choices made in fund selection. Suppose 100 undergraduate students and 100 MBA students were selected. When presented with four

S&P 500 Index funds that were identical except for their fees, undergraduate and MBA students chose the funds as follows:

FUND	STUDENT GROUP	
	Undergraduate	**MBA**
Lowest-cost fund	19	19
Second-lowest-cost fund	37	40
Third-lowest-cost fund	17	23
Highest-cost fund	27	18

Source: *Data extracted from J. J. Choi, D. Laibson, and B. C. Madrian, Why Does the Law of One Price Fail?* www.som.yale.edu/faculty/jjc83/ *fees.pdf.*

If a student is selected at random, what is the probability that he or she

a. selected the lowest- *or* second-lowest cost fund?

b. selected the lowest-cost fund *and* is an undergraduate?

c. selected the lowest-cost fund *or* is an undergraduate?

d. Given that the student is an undergraduate, what is the probability that he or she selected the highest-cost fund?

e. Do you think undergraduate students and graduate students differ in their fund selection? Explain.

4.50 Sport utility vehicles (SUVs), vans, and pickups are generally considered to be more prone to roll over than cars. In 1997, 24.0% of all highway fatalities involved rollovers; 15.8% of all fatalities in 1997 involved SUVs, vans, and pickups, given that the fatality involved a rollover. Given that a rollover was not involved, 5.6% of all fatalities involved SUVs, vans, and pickups (A. Wilde Mathews, "Ford Ranger, Chevy Tracker Tilt in Test," *The Wall Street Journal*, July 14, 1999, p. A2). Consider the following definitions:

$$A = \text{fatality involved an SUV, van, or pickup}$$

$$B = \text{fatality involved a rollover}$$

a. Use Bayes' theorem to find the probability that a fatality involved a rollover, given that the fatality involved an SUV, a van, or a pickup.

b. Compare the result in (a) to the probability that a fatality involved a rollover and comment on whether SUVs, vans, and pickups are generally more prone to rollover accidents than other vehicles.

4.51 Enzyme-linked immunosorbent assay (ELISA) is the most common type of screening test for detecting the HIV virus. A positive result from an ELISA indicates that the HIV virus is present. For most populations, ELISA has a high degree of sensitivity (to detect infection) and specificity (to detect noninfection). (See HIVInsite, at **HIVInsite.ucsf.edu**.) Suppose that the probability a person is infected with the HIV virus for a certain population is 0.015. If the HIV virus is actually present, the probability that the ELISA test will give a positive result is 0.995. If the HIV virus is not actually present, the probability of a positive result from an ELISA is 0.01. If the ELISA has given a positive result, use Bayes' theorem to find the probability that the HIV virus is actually present.

TEAM PROJECT

The data file [Mutual Funds] contains information regarding four categorical variables from a sample of 868 mutual funds. The variables are:

Category—Type of stocks comprising the mutual fund (small cap, mid cap, large cap)

Objective—Objective of stocks comprising the mutual fund (growth or value)

Fees—Sales charges (no or yes)

Risk—Risk-of-loss factor of the mutual fund (low, average, high)

4.52 Construct contingency tables of category and objective, category and fees, category and risk, objective and fees, and fees and risk.

a. For each of these contingency tables, compute all the conditional and marginal probabilities.

b. Based on (a), what conclusions can you reach about whether these variables are independent?

STUDENT SURVEY DATA BASE

4.53 Problem 1.28 describes a survey of 50 undergraduate students (see the file [Undergradsurvey]). For these data, construct contingency tables of gender and major, gender and graduate school intention, gender and employment status, class and graduate school intention, class and employment status, major and graduate school intention, and major and employment status.

a. For each of these contingency tables, compute all the conditional and marginal probabilities.

b. Based on (a), what conclusions can you reach about whether these variables are independent?

4.54 Problem 1.28 describes a survey of 50 undergraduate students (see the file [Undergradsurvey]).

a. Select a sample of 50 undergraduate students at your school and conduct a similar survey for those students.

b. For these data, construct contingency tables of gender and major, gender and graduate school intention, gender and employment status, class and graduate school intention, class and employment status, major and graduate school intention, and major and employment status. For each of these contingency tables, compute all the conditional and marginal probabilities.

c. Based on (b), what conclusions can you reach about whether these variables are independent?

d. Compare the results of (c) to those of Problem 4.53(b).

4.55 Problem 1.29 describes a survey of 40 MBA students (see the file [Gradsurvey]). For these data, construct contingency tables of gender and graduate major, gender and undergraduate major, gender and employment status, graduate major and undergraduate major, and graduate major and employment status.

a. For each of these contingency tables, compute all the conditional and marginal probabilities.

b. Based on (b), what conclusions can you reach about whether these variables are independent?

4.56 Problem 1.29 describes a survey of 40 MBA students (see the file [Gradsurvey]).

a. Select a sample of 40 MBA students from your MBA program and conduct a similar survey for those students.

b. For these data, construct contingency tables of gender and graduate major, gender and undergraduate major, gender and employment status, graduate major and undergraduate major, and graduate major and employment status. For each of these contingency tables, compute all the conditional and marginal probabilities.

c. Based on (b), what conclusions can you reach about whether these variables are independent?

d. Compare the results of (c) to those of Problem 4.55(b).

WEB CASE

Apply your knowledge about contingency tables and the proper application of simple and joint probabilities in this continuing Web Case from Chapter 3.

Visit the EndRun Guaranteed Investment Package (GIP) Web page, at **www.prenhall.com/Springville/ER_ Guaranteed.htm** or open this Web page file from the Student CD-ROM Web Case folder. Read the claims and examine the supporting data. Then answer the following:

1. How accurate is the claim of the probability of success for EndRun's GIP? In what ways is the claim misleading?

How would you calculate and state the probability of having an annual rate of return not less than 15%?

2. What mistake was made in reporting the 7% probability claim? Using the table found on the "Winning Probabilities" Web page, [ER_Guaranteed3.htm], compute the proper probabilities for the group of investors.

3. Are there any probability calculations that would be appropriate for rating an investment service? Why or why not?

REFERENCES

1. Bellhouse, D. R., "The Reverend Thomas Bayes, FRS: A Biography to Celebrate the Tercentenary of His Birth," *Statistical Science* 19 (2004), 3–43.

2. Lowd, D., and C. Meek, "Good Word Attacks on Statistical Spam Filters," presented at the Second Conference on Email and Anti-Spam, CEAS 2005.

3. *Microsoft Excel 2007* (Redmond, WA: Microsoft Corp., 2007).

4. Paulos, J. A., *Innumeracy* (New York: Hill and Wang, 1988).

5. Silberman, S., "The Quest for Meaning," *Wired 8.02*, February 2000.

6. T. Zeller, "The Fight Against V1@gra (and Other Spam)," *The New York Times*, May 21, 2006, pp. B1, B6.

Using Microsoft Excel for Basic Probability

E4.1 Computing Basic Probabilities (all Excel versions)

To compute basic probabilities, open to the **Probabilities** worksheet of the `Probabilities.xls` workbook. Enter event labels and counts in the tinted cells in rows 3 through 6. Figure E4.1 shows a completed worksheet for the "Purchase Behavior for Big-Screen Television" data of Table 4.1 on page 210. Also shown offset in Figure E4.1 are the formulas this worksheet uses to compute the various probabilities.

The worksheet also "computes" the *labels* for the probabilities table with formulas that use the ampersand (**&**) operator to combine parts of a label. For example, the cell A10 formula =**"P(" & B5 & ")"** asks Excel to combine the contents of B5 (**Yes**) to the label **"P("** to get **"P(Yes"** and then to "add" **")"** to get **"P(Yes)"** and form the formula =**"P(Yes)"**–a novel, but acceptable, way of entering the label value **P(Yes)** in a cell.

E4.2 Using Bayes' Theorem (all Excel versions)

You calculate probabilities using Bayes' theorem by making entries in the cell range B5:C6 of the **Bayes** worksheet of the `Bayes.xls` workbook. Figure E4.2 shows a completed worksheet for the television-marketing example shown in Table 4.4 on page 219.

FIGURE E4.1 Probabilities worksheet

FIGURE E4.2 Bayes' theorem worksheet

5 Discrete Probability Distributions

Learning Objectives

In this chapter, you learn:

- The properties of a probability distribution
- To compute the expected value and variance of a probability distribution
- To compute probabilities from the binomial and Poisson distributions
- How to use the binomial and Poisson distributions to solve business problems

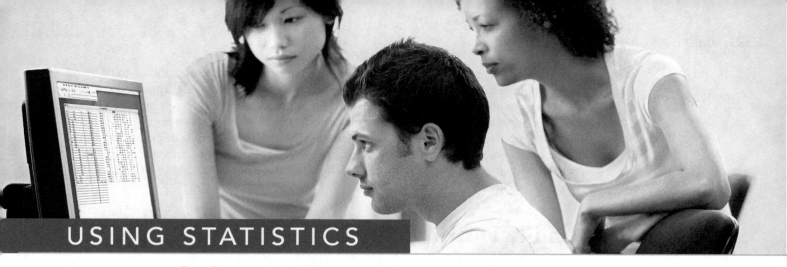

@ Saxon Home Improvement

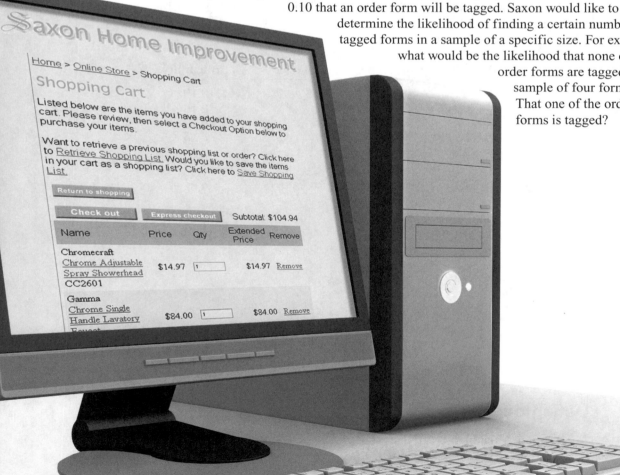

Y ou are an accountant for the Saxon Home Improvement Company which uses a state-of-the-art accounting information system to manage its accounting and financial operations.

Accounting information systems collect, process, store, transform, and distribute financial information to decision makers both internal and external to a business organization. These systems continuously audit accounting information, looking for errors or incomplete or improbable information. For example, when customers of the Saxon Home Improvement Company submit online orders, the company's accounting information system reviews the order forms for possible mistakes. Any questionable invoices are *tagged* and included in a daily *exceptions report*. Recent data collected by the company show that the likelihood is 0.10 that an order form will be tagged. Saxon would like to determine the likelihood of finding a certain number of tagged forms in a sample of a specific size. For example, what would be the likelihood that none of the order forms are tagged in a sample of four forms? That one of the order forms is tagged?

How could the Saxon Home Improvement Company determine the solution to this type of probability problem? One way is to use a model, or small-scale representation, that approximates the process. By using such an approximation, Saxon managers could make inferences about the actual order process. In this case, the Saxon managers can use *probability distributions*, mathematical models suited for solving the type of probability problems the managers are facing. Reading this chapter will help you learn about characteristics of a probability distribution and how to specifically apply the binomial and Poisson distributions to business problems.

5.1 Discrete Probability Distributions: Introductory Concepts

In Section 1.7, a *numerical variable* was defined as a variable that yielded numerical responses, such as the number of magazines you subscribe to or your height. Numerical variables are classified as *discrete* or *continuous*. Continuous numerical variables produce outcomes that come from a measuring process (e.g., your height). Discrete numerical variables produce outcomes that come from a counting process (e.g., the number of magazines you subscribe to). This chapter deals with probability distributions that represent discrete numerical variables.

> **PROBABILITY DISTRIBUTION FOR A DISCRETE RANDOM VARIABLE**
>
> A **probability distribution for a discrete random variable** is a mutually exclusive listing of all the possible numerical outcomes along with the probability of occurrence of each outcome.

For example, Table 5.1 gives the distribution of the number of mortgages approved per week at the local branch office of a bank. The listing in Table 5.1 is collectively exhaustive because all possible outcomes are included. Thus, the probabilities sum to 1. Figure 5.1 is a graphical representation of Table 5.1.

TABLE 5.1

Probability Distribution of the Number of Home Mortgages Approved per Week

Home Mortgages Approved per Week	Probability
0	0.10
1	0.10
2	0.20
3	0.30
4	0.15
5	0.10
6	0.05

FIGURE 5.1

Probability distribution of the number of home mortgages approved per week

Definitions

Random Variable: A variable whose value is determined by the outcome of a random experiment. Symbol is very often 'X'.

Discrete Random Variable: A random variable whose possible values are discrete, i.e. clearly separated individual values.

Discrete Probability Distribution: A table or formula that shows the probability associated with each possible value of a discrete random variable.

EXAMPLE 5.1

A study of the number of cars sold on Sunday at a particular dealership shows that the following probability distribution exists:

let X = # cars sold on Sunday

Probability distribution of X is:

TABLE 5.2

X	P(X)
0	0.1
1	0.1
2	0.4
3	0.3
4	0.1
Total	1.0

EXAMPLE 5.2

A company is in the process of trying to decide whether or not to market a particular new product that it is considering. A market analysis has determined that the probabilities of various acceptance levels are as follows: high with a probability of 0.2, medium with a probability of 0.5, and low with a probability of 0.3. If the company decides to build a local manufacturing facility, the estimated profits over the life of the product if there is high acceptance is $10 million, if there is medium acceptance the profit should be around $3 million and if there is low acceptance there will be a loss of $2 million.

let X = estimated profit over life of product ($ million)

Probability distribution of X is:

TABLE 5.3

Product Acceptance	X	P(X)
High	10	0.2
Medium	3	0.5
Low	−2	0.3
Total		1.0

EXAMPLE 5.3

Toss a fair coin three times. The sample space is composed of eight equally likely outcomes, namely:

S = {HHH HHT HTH THH TTH THT HTT TTT}

let X = # tails

Probability distribution of X is:

TABLE 5.4

X	P(X)
0	1/8 = 0.125
1	3/8 = 0.375
2	3/8 = 0.375
3	1/8 = 0.125
Total	1.000

EXAMPLE 5.4   Roll a fair die. The sample space is composed of 6 equally likely outcomes, namely:

S = {1 2 3 4 5 6}

let X = # rolled

The probability distribution of X is:

TABLE 5.5

X	P(X)
1	1/6 = 0.167
2	1/6 = 0.167
3	1/6 = 0.167
4	1/6 = 0.167
5	1/6 = 0.167
6	1/6 = 0.167
Total	6/6 = 1

EXAMPLE 5.5   Roll two fair dice. The sample space, as seen previously, is composed of 36 equally likely outcomes.

let X = total of the two dice

Probability distribution of X is:

TABLE 5.6

X	P(X)
2	1/36 = 0.028
3	2/36 = 0.056
4	3/36 = 0.083
5	4/36 = 0.111
6	5/36 = 0.139
7	6/36 = 0.167
8	5/36 = 0.139
9	4/36 = 0.111
10	3/36 = 0.083
11	2/36 = 0.056
12	1/36 = 0.028
Total	36/36 = 1

Expected Value of a Discrete Random Variable

The mean, μ, of a probability distribution is the **expected value** of its random variable. To calculate the expected value, you multiply each possible outcome, X, by its corresponding probability, $P(X)$, and then sum these products.

EXPECTED VALUE, μ, OF A DISCRETE RANDOM VARIABLE

$$\mu = E(X) = \sum_{i=1}^{N} X_i P(X_i) \tag{5.1}$$

where

X_i = the ith outcome of the discrete random variable X

$P(X_i)$ = probability of occurrence of the ith outcome of X

For the probability distribution of the number of home mortgages approved per week (Table 5.2), the expected value is computed below using Equation (5.1) and is also shown in Table 5.7.

$$\mu = E(X) = \sum_{i=1}^{N} X_i P(X_i)$$

$$= (0)(0.1) + (1)(0.1) + (2)(0.2) + (3)(0.3) + (4)(0.15) + (5)(0.1) + (6)(0.05)$$

$$= 0 + 0.1 + 0.4 + 0.9 + 0.6 + 0.5 + 0.3$$

$$= 2.8$$

TABLE 5.7

Computing the Expected Value of the Number of Home Mortgages Approved per Week

Home Mortgages Approved per Week (X_i)	$P(X_i)$	$X_i P(X_i)$
0	0.10	$(0)(0.10) = 0.0$
1	0.10	$(1)(0.10) = 0.1$
2	0.20	$(2)(0.20) = 0.4$
3	0.30	$(3)(0.30) = 0.9$
4	0.15	$(4)(0.15) = 0.6$
5	0.10	$(5)(0.10) = 0.5$
6	0.05	$(6)(0.05) = 0.3$
	1.00	$\mu = E(X) = 2.8$

The expected value is 2.8. The expected value of 2.8 for the number of mortgages approved is not a possible outcome because the actual number of mortgages approved in a given week must be an integer value. The expected value represents the *mean* number of mortgages approved per week.

Mean, Variance and Standard Deviation

A discrete probability distribution is equivalent to a population of data. We can calculate any parameters that can be calculated for a population. However, the formulas will look a little different.

I. MEAN OR EXPECTED VALUE:

Formula: $\mu = E(X) = \sum X P(X)$

EXAMPLE 5.1

(Revisit)

A study of the number of cars sold on Sunday at a particular dealership shows that the following probability distribution exists:

let X = # cars sold on Sunday

The mean or expected number of cars that will be sold on Sunday can be calculated as follows:

TABLE 5.8

X	P(X)	XP(X)
0	0.1	0.0
1	0.1	0.1
2	0.4	0.8
3	0.3	0.9
4	0.1	0.4
Total	1.0	2.2

Therefore, the *average* number of cars sold on *infinite* Sunday's is 2.2. Also, we can say that the number of cars the dealer expects to sell on Sunday is 2.2.

Notes: 1. Calculating a mean for a discrete probability distribution is essentially the same as calculating a *weighted mean,* where the probabilities are the weights.

$$\bar{x}_w = \frac{\sum xw}{\sum w} = \frac{\sum xP(x)}{\sum P(x)} = \sum xP(x) \quad \text{since} \quad \sum P(x) = 1$$

2. To calculate the mean on the Casio calculator, enter the data as follows and set up as if calculating a weighted mean of the X data.

Example 5.1:			Example 5.4:	
List 1	**List 2**		**List 1**	**List 2**
0	.1		1	1÷6
1	.1		2	1÷6
2	.4		3	1÷6
3	.3		4	1÷6
4	.1		5	1÷6
			6	1÷6

Xlist: L1
Freq: L2   yields $\bar{x} = 2.2$

Xlist: L1
Freq: L2   yields $\bar{x} = 3.5$

EXAMPLE 5.2

(Revisit)

Referring to the product marketing decision example 5.2:

let X = estimated profit over the life of product ($ million)

TABLE 5.9

Product Acceptance	X	P(X)	XP(X)
High	10	0.2	2.0
Medium	3	0.5	1.5
Low	−2	0.3	−0.6
Total		1.0	2.9

Therefore, the expected profit is $2.9 million.

EXAMPLE 5.3

(Revisit)

Toss a fair coin three times.

let X = # tails

TABLE 5.10

X	P(X)	XP(X)
0	0.125	0.000
1	0.375	0.375
2	0.375	0.750
3	0.125	0.375
Total	1.000	1.5

The average number of tails when a coin is tossed three times, an *infinite* number of times, is 1.5. Also, the expected number of tails if you toss a coin three times is 1.5.

EXAMPLE 5.4

(Revisit)

Roll a fair die.   Let X = # rolled

TABLE 5.11

X	P(X)	XP(X)
1	1/6 = 0.167	1/6
2	1/6 = 0.167	2/6
3	1/6 = 0.167	3/6
4	1/6 = 0.167	4/6
5	1/6 = 0.167	5/6
6	1/6 = 0.167	6/6
Total	6/6 = 1	21/6 = 3.5

If you roll one die infinite times, the average number rolled will be 3.5. Therefore, if you roll a die once, the expected value is 3.5.

EXAMPLE 5.5

(Revisit)

Roll two fair dice.

let X = total of the two dice

TABLE 5.12

X	P(X)	XP(X)
2	1/36 = 0.028	2/36
3	2/36 = 0.056	6/36
4	3/36 = 0.083	12/36
5	4/36 = 0.111	20/36
6	5/36 = 0.139	30/36
7	6/36 = 0.167	42/36
8	5/36 = 0.139	40/36
9	4/36 = 0.111	36/36
10	3/36 = 0.083	30/36
11	2/36 = 0.056	22/36
12	1/36 = 0.028	12/36
Total	36/36 = 1	252/36 = 7

Therefore, if we roll two dice we can expect to get a total of 7.

II. VARIANCE

Formula: $\sigma^2 = \sum (X - \mu)^2 P(X)$ (5.1)

III. STANDARD DEVIATION

Formula: $\sigma = \sqrt{\left(\sum (X - \mu)^2 P(X) \right)}$ (5.2)

Note: We are not interested in showing the use of this formula manually, since if you need to calculate the standard deviation of a random variable you will use your calculator as illustrated above.

Expected Value Decision Making

EXAMPLE 5.7

A fast food company plans to install a new ice-cream dispensing unit in one of two store locations. The company figures that the probability of a unit being successful in location A is 3/4 and the annual profit in this case is $150,000. If it is not successful there will be losses of $80,000. At location B the probability of succeeding is 1/2 but the potential profit and loss are $240,000 and $48,000 respectively.

a) Where should the company locate to maximize expected profit?

SOLUTION X = **Profit**

Location A		Location B	
Profit	Prob.	Profit	Prob.
$150,000	0.75	$240,000	0.5
−$80,000	0.25	−$48,000	0.5

Location A: E(X) = $92,500   Location B: E(X) = $96,000

b) Which location is less risky, i.e. has the lowest relative variability?

$$\text{Location A: } CV = \frac{\sigma}{\mu} \times 100 = \frac{\$99,593}{\$92,500} \times 100 = 108\%$$

$$\text{Location B: } CV = \frac{\sigma}{\mu} \times 100 = \frac{\$144,000}{\$96,000} \times 100 = 150\%$$

Since the difference > 10% smaller, thus Location A is less risky than location B.

EXAMPLE 5.8

An investment advisor sends information to various clients via express delivery companies. In all cases it is important that the client receive the information on the day it is sent. Three companies are capable of providing the delivery service. The following information is available:

TABLE 5.13

Company	Cost	Probability of same day arrival
Can-Express	$22.00	0.99
Can-Parcel	14.00	0.97
Canada Mail	6.00	0.89

The average payoff is $200 when the information arrives on time, but there is no payoff if the delivery is late. Based on maximizing expected profit, which delivery service should be used?

SOLUTION Let X = profit

TABLE 5.14

Can-Express		Can-Parcel		Canada Mail	
X	P(X)	X	P(X)	X	P(X)
178	0.99	186	0.97	194	0.89
−22	0.01	−14	0.03	−6	0.11

The expected values are:

Can-Express: E(X) = $176

Can-Parcel: E(X) = $180

Canada Mail: E(X) = $172

Therefore the company should choose **Can-Parcel.** Since it has the highest expected profit (value).

Variance and Standard Deviation of a Discrete Random Variable

You compute the variance of a probability distribution by multiplying each possible squared difference $[X_i - E(X)]^2$ by its corresponding probability, $P(X_i)$, and then summing the resulting products. Equation (5.2) defines the **variance of a discrete random variable**.

VARIANCE OF A DISCRETE RANDOM VARIABLE

$$\sigma^2 = \sum_{i=1}^{N} [X_i - E(X)]^2 P(X_i) \qquad (5.2)$$

where

$$X_i = \text{the } i\text{th outcome of the discrete random variable } X$$
$$P(X_i) = \text{probability of occurrence of the } i\text{th outcome of } X$$

Equation (5.3) defines the **standard deviation of a discrete random variable**.

STANDARD DEVIATION OF A DISCRETE RANDOM VARIABLE

$$\sigma = \sqrt{\sigma^2} = \sqrt{\sum_{i=1}^{N} [X_i - E(X)]^2 P(X_i)} \qquad (5.3)$$

The variance and the standard deviation of the number of home mortgages approved per week are computed below and in Table 5.15, using Equations (5.2) and (5.3):

$$\sigma^2 = \sum_{i=1}^{N} [X_i - E(X)]^2 P(X_i)$$

$$= (0 - 2.8)^2(0.10) + (1 - 2.8)^2(0.10) + (2 - 2.8)^2(0.20) + (3 - 2.8)^2(0.30)$$
$$+ (4 - 2.8)^2(0.15) + (5 - 2.8)^2(0.10) + (6 - 2.8)^2(0.05)$$

$$= 0.784 + 0.324 + 0.128 + 0.012 + 0.216 + 0.484 + 0.512$$

$$= 2.46$$

TABLE 5.15

Computing the Variance and Standard Deviation of the Number of Home Mortgages Approved per Week

Home Mortgages Approved per Week (X_i)	$P(X_i)$	$X_i P(X_i)$	$[X_i - E(X)]^2 P(X_i)$
0	0.10	$(0)(0.10) = 0.0$	$(0 - 2.8)^2(0.10) = 0.784$
1	0.10	$(1)(0.10) = 0.1$	$(1 - 2.8)^2(0.10) = 0.324$
2	0.20	$(2)(0.20) = 0.4$	$(2 - 2.8)^2(0.20) = 0.128$
3	0.30	$(3)(0.30) = 0.9$	$(3 - 2.8)^2(0.30) = 0.012$
4	0.15	$(4)(0.15) = 0.6$	$(4 - 2.8)^2(0.15) = 0.216$
5	0.10	$(5)(0.10) = 0.5$	$(5 - 2.8)^2(0.10) = 0.484$
6	0.05	$(6)(0.05) = 0.3$	$(6 - 2.8)^2(0.05) = 0.512$
	1.00	$\mu = E(X) = 2.8$	$\sigma^2 = 2.46$

and

$$\sigma = \sqrt{\sigma^2} = \sqrt{2.46} = 1.57$$

Thus, the mean number of mortgages approved per week is 2.8, the variance is 2.46, and the standard deviation is 1.57.

Problems for Section 5.1

LEARNING THE BASICS

5.1 Given the following probability distributions:

Distribution A		Distribution B	
X	P(X)	X	P(X)
0	0.50	0	0.05
1	0.20	1	0.10
2	0.15	2	0.15
3	0.10	3	0.20
4	0.05	4	0.50

a. Compute the expected value for each distribution.
b. Compute the standard deviation for each distribution.
c. Compare the results of distributions A and B.

APPLYING THE CONCEPTS

SELF
Test
5.2 The following table contains the probability distribution for the number of traffic accidents daily in a small city:

Number of Accidents Daily (X)	P(X)
0	0.10
1	0.20
2	0.45
3	0.15
4	0.05
5	0.05

a. Compute the mean number of accidents per day.
b. Compute the standard deviation.

5.3 The manager of a large computer network has developed the following probability distribution of the number of interruptions per day:

Interruptions (X)	P(X)
0	0.32
1	0.35
2	0.18
3	0.08
4	0.04
5	0.02
6	0.01

a. Compute the expected number of interruptions per day.
b. Compute the standard deviation.

5.4 In the carnival game Under-or-Over-Seven, a pair of fair dice is rolled once, and the resulting sum determines whether the player wins or loses his or her bet. For example, the player can bet $1 that the sum will be under 7—that is, 2, 3, 4, 5, or 6. For this bet, the player wins $1 if the result is under 7 and loses $1 if the outcome equals or is greater than 7. Similarly, the player can bet $1 that the sum will be over 7—that is, 8, 9, 10, 11, or 12. Here, the player wins $1 if the result is over 7 but loses $1 if the result is 7 or under. A third method of play is to bet $1 on the outcome 7. For this bet, the player wins $4 if the result of the roll is 7 and loses $1 otherwise.

a. Construct the probability distribution representing the different outcomes that are possible for a $1 bet on under 7.
b. Construct the probability distribution representing the different outcomes that are possible for a $1 bet on over 7.
c. Construct the probability distribution representing the different outcomes that are possible for a $1 bet on 7.
d. Show that the expected long-run profit (or loss) to the player is the same, no matter which method of play is used.

5.5 The number of arrivals per minute at a bank located in the central business district of a large city was recorded over a period of 200 minutes with the following results:

Arrivals	Frequency
0	14
1	31
2	47
3	41
4	29
5	21
6	10
7	5
8	2

a. Compute the expected number of arrivals per minute.
b. Compute the standard deviation.

5.6 The manager of a commercial mortgage department of a large bank has collected data during the past two years concerning the number of commercial mortgages approved per week. The results from these two years (104 weeks) indicated the following:

Number of Commercial Mortgages Approved	Frequency
0	13
1	25
2	32
3	17
4	9
5	6
6	1
7	1

a. Compute the expected number of mortgages approved per week.
b. Compute the standard deviation.

DISCRETE PROBABILITY DISTRIBUTION

5.7 At the 2nd Cup coffee shop they offer free refills. The following information has been gathered by studying many customers.

# refills	Prob.
0	0.3
1	0.4
2	0.2
3	0.1

Calculate the mean and standard deviation of the number of refills.

5.8 The director of admissions at Expected University has predicted the probability distribution of applications for the coming year based on past experience.

# applicants	Prob.
1000	0.6
1200	0.3
1500	0.1

a. What is the expected number of applicants for the coming year?
b. What is the standard deviation?

5.9 After consulting the sales reps, a marketing manager has decided that the following table represents the potential profits they might make next year for one of the company's products.

Profit	Prob.
$50,000	0.02
35,000	0.12
20,000	0.50
10,000	0.25
0	0.08
−10,000	0.03

What is the expected profit?

5.10 The Chancit Marketing Company is considering the distribution of a new item. They think there is a 20% chance that the item will be successful, in which case they will make $1,000,000 revenue. There is a 40% chance that they will break even and the other possibility is that there will be virtually no revenues. The distribution expenses in all cases will be $200,000. What is the expected net profit from the distribution of this item?

5.11 A mail order magazine service has the exclusive subscription rights to a certain magazine. Subscriptions can be reserved for one, two, three, or five years. A study of the subscriber list for other similar magazines reveals that the following information regarding the probabilities of sub-

scription length would be appropriate: there are five time as many one year subscriptions as five year subscriptions and that the number of two year and three year subscriptions are each one fifth of the total.

The mail order service company receives a fee of $2.00 for a one year subscription, $3.50 for each two year subscription and an additional dollar for every year over two years.

a. What is the probability distribution of subscription fees?
b. What is the expected total fee revenue from 125 new subscriptions?

5.12 A financial analyst for Petrified Paper Products has submitted the following probability distributions of profit for three investment proposals. The company has sufficient funds to consider only one of the proposals.

Project 1		Project 2		Project 3	
Profit	Prob.	Profit	Prob.	Profit	Prob.
−5,000	0.1	−2,000	0.10	−3,000	0.10
0	0.1	0	0.15	2,000	0.20
2,000	0.2	2,000	0.30	4,000	0.40
4,000	0.3	4,000	0.30	6,000	0.25
6,000	0.3	7,000	0.15	8,000	0.05

a. Based on expected profit, which proposal should be selected?
b. Which proposal has the lowest relative variability, i.e. risk?

5.13 An export company may ship goods to country A at a cost of $2,000, country B at a cost of $3,000 or country C at a cost of $5,000. The revenues earned by selling the goods in these countries are $5,000, $7,000 and $10,000, respectively. Currently the countries are all involved in wars and only 70% of shipments have been arriving at the destination country. The remainder are being lost at sea.

Based on expected values, to which country would you ship the next shipment of goods?

5.14 B. F. Retread, a tire manufacturer, wants to select one of the feasible designs for a new longer-wearing radial tire. The manufacturing cost of each type of tire is shown below.

Tire Design	Fixed Cost/year	Variable Cost per Tire
A	$60,000	$30
B	90,000	20
C	120,000	15

There are 3 possible levels of annual demand: 4,000 tires, 7,000 tires and 10,000 tires. The respective probabilities are 0.3, 0.5 and 0.2. The selling price will be $80 for A, $75 for B and $75 for C. Based on expected profit, which design should be produced?

5.15 The normal weekly demand of a certain perishable product sold by QMS Inc. is given by the following distribution:

Demand	Probability
8	0.1
9	0.2
10	0.3
11	0.3
12	0.1

The product costs QMS $3 each. The product sells for $10 each. If not sold by the end of the week, the leftover units must be scrapped.

The supplier only has 10 or 11 units available for QMS to purchase. How many would you recommend QMS purchase based on expected profit?

5.2 Binomial Distribution

The next two sections use mathematical models to solve business problems.

> MATHEMATICAL MODEL
> A **mathematical model** is a mathematical expression that represents a variable of interest.

When a mathematical expression is available, you can compute the exact probability of occurrence of any particular outcome of the variable.

The **binomial distribution** is one of the most useful mathematical models. You use the binomial distribution when the discrete random variable is the number of events of interest in a sample of n observations. The binomial distribution has four basic properties:

- The sample consists of a fixed number of observations, n.
- Each observation is classified into one of two mutually exclusive and collectively exhaustive categories.

Characteristics of a Binomial Experiment

1. The experiment consists of 'n' repetitions (trials) of some action.
   or
   A sample of 'n' items are selected from a large population.
2. Each trial will result in one of 2 possible outcomes called *success* or *failure*, where success is when the outcome of interest occurs.
   or
   Each item in the sample will either possess a certain characteristic (success) or it will not (failure).
3. The probability of success on each trial or selection is the same and is given the symbol 'π'. The probability of failure is therefore $(1 - \pi)$. Note that this condition implies that the trials are *independent*.

The random variable associated with a binomial experiment is:

$$X = \# \text{ of successes}$$

To calculate the probability that X takes on a specific value we use the

Binomial Probability Distribution Function:

$$P(X = x) = \frac{n!}{x!(n-x)!} \pi^2 (1 - \pi)^{n-x}$$

where   n = # of trials or sample size

π = probability of success on each trial

n! = n factorial

= n(n-1)(n-2)(n-3) . . . 3•2•1

Example: 6! = 6•5•4•3•2•1 = 720

EXAMPLE 5.9   Toss a coin 6 times. Find the probability of getting 2 tails.

SOLUTION X = # of tails

$n = 6$

$\pi = 0.5$

$$P(X = 2) = \frac{6!}{2!(6-2)!}(0.5)^2(1-0.5)^{6-2} = 0.2344$$

Note: The part of the binomial formula $\dfrac{n!}{x!(n-x)!}$ calculates the number of outcomes where there are x successes in n trials. For example, if a coin is tossed 6 times, there will be $\dfrac{6!}{(2!(6-2)!}= 15$ possible outcomes that have exactly 2 tails. These outcomes are:

TTHHHH	THTHHH	THHTHH	THHHTH	THHHHT
HTTHHH	HTHTHH	HTHHTH	HTHHHT	
HHTTHH	HHTHTH	HHTHHT		
HHHTTH	HHHTHT			
HHHHTT				

The factor $\dfrac{n!}{x!(n-x)!}$ is often given the shorthand symbol $_nC_x$.

Using the CASIO calculator to obtain the probability value (refer to 'Calculator Lesson 4').

STAT F5(DIST)   **F5**(BINM)   **F1**(Bpd)   then select the following options.

Data   : **F2**(Var)
x   : **2 EXE**
Numtrial : **6 EXE**
p   : **0.5**

Now key **EXE** or **F1**(Calc)

Results: Binomial P.D.

p(x = 2) = 0.23437

EXAMPLE 5.10   Roll a die 10 times. Find the probability of getting three 5's ?

SOLUTION X = # of 5's
$n = 10$
$\pi = 1/6$

$$P(X = 3) = \frac{10!}{3!(10-3)!}\left(\frac{1}{6}\right)^3\left(1-\frac{1}{6}\right)^{10-3} = 0.1550$$

Using the CASIO calculator to obtain the probability value.

STAT F5(DIST)   **F5**(BINM)   **F1**(Bpd)   then select the following options.

Data   : **F2**(Var)
x   : **3**
Numtrial : **10**
p   : **1 ÷ 6**

Results: Binomial P.D.

p(x = 3) = 0.15504

EXAMPLE 5.11   A survey of people in the 30 and under 40 age bracket shows that 43 percent of them have investments in mutual funds. In a particular condominium there are 18 adults in this age bracket. What is the probability that:

a. 5 of them will have investments in mutual funds?

SOLUTION X = # of people in their 30's with investments in mutual funds

$$n = 18$$

$$\pi = 0.43$$

$$P(X = 5) = \frac{18!}{5!(18-5)!}(0.43)^5(1-0.43)^{18-5} = 0.0845$$

Using the CASIO calculator to obtain the probability value.

STAT F5(DIST)   **F5**(BINM)   **F1**(Bpd)   then select the following options.

Data   : **F2**(Var)
x   : **5**
Numtrial : **18**
p   : **0.43**

Results: Binomial P.D.

p(x = 5) = 0.084449

b. at most 2 of these people will have investments in mutual funds?

SOLUTION $P(X \le 2) = P(X = 0) + P(X = 1) + P(X = 2)$
$$= 0.00004 + 0.00055 + 0.00351 = 0.0041$$

Using the CASIO calculator to obtain the probability value.

STAT F5(DIST)   **F5**(BINM)   **F1**(Bcd)   then select the following options.

Data   : **F2**(Var)
x   : **2**
Numtrial : **18**
p   : **0.43**

Results: Binomial C.D.

p(x < 2) = 4.1007E.03

which is 0.0041007

c. more than 10 of these people will have investments in mutual funds?

SOLUTION $P(X > 10) = 1 - P(X \ge 10)$
$$= 1 - 0.9049 = 0.0951$$

Explanation:

X	P(X)
0	0.00004
1	0.00055
2	0.00351
3	0.0141
4	0.0400
5	0.0844
6	0.1380
7	0.1785
8	0.1852
9	0.1552
10	0.1054
11	0.0578
12	0.0254
13	0.0089
14	0.0024
15	0.00048
16	0.00007
17	0.00001
18	0.00000
Total	1

d. from 3 to 9 of these people will have investments in mutual funds?

SOLUTION $P(3 \leq X \leq 9) = P(3) + P(4) + \ldots + P(9)$
$$= P(X \leq 9) - P(X \leq 2)$$
$$= 0.7996 - 0.0041 = 0.795$$

Binomial Template

You will notice that a similar style is used to present all the answers to the sample examples above. You are *not* to follow this style exactly however, since you will be using a calculator or computer to determine the probability value. Your answers should look like the following template:

X = # of _____
                     (successes)

n = _____

π = _____
     (dec.)

P(_____) = P(X symbol #) = _____ = 0._ _ _ _
    (words*)   (calculator or SPSS input)   (4 dec.)

* If the question does not directly say what the number is.

EXAMPLE 5.12

Determining
$P(X = 3)$, Given
$n = 4$ and $\pi = 0.1$

If the likelihood of a tagged order form is 0.1, what is the probability that there are three tagged order forms in the sample of four?

SOLUTION Using binomial template and casio calculator, the probability of three tagged orders from a sample of four is

$$X = \text{Number of tagged order forms}$$
$$n = 4$$
$$\pi = 0.1$$

$$P(X = 3) = \text{Bpd } (3, 4, 0.1)$$
$$= 0.0036 \quad \text{(Note: round to 4 decimals)}$$

Examples 5.2 and 5.3 show the computations for other values of X.

EXAMPLE 5.13

Determining $P(X \geq 3)$, Given $n = 4$ and $\pi = 0.1$

If the likelihood of a tagged order form is 0.1, what is the probability that there are three or more (i.e., at least three) tagged order forms in the sample of four?

SOLUTION In Example 5.1, you found that the probability of *exactly* three tagged order forms from a sample of four is 0.0036. To compute the probability of *at least* three tagged order forms, you need to add the probability of three tagged order forms to the probability of four tagged order forms. The probability of four tagged order forms is

$$X = \text{Number of tagged order forms}$$
$$n = 4$$
$$\pi = 0.1$$

$$P(X \geq 3) = 1 - P(X \leq 2)$$
$$= 1 - \text{Bcd}\,(2, 4, 0.1)$$
$$= 1 - 0.9963$$
$$= 0.0037$$

There is a 0.37% chance that there will be at least three tagged order forms in a sample of four.

EXAMPLE 5.14

Determining $P(X < 3)$, Given $n = 4$ and $\pi = 0.1$

If the likelihood of a tagged order form is 0.1, what is the probability that there are less than three tagged order forms in the sample of four?

SOLUTION The probability that there are less than three tagged order forms is

$$X = \text{Number of tagged order forms}$$
$$n = 4$$
$$\pi = 0.1$$

$$P(X < 3) = P(X = 0) + P(X = 1) + P(X = 2)$$

Using Equation (5.5) on page 254, these probabilities are

$$P(X = 0) = \text{Bpd}\,(0, 4, 0.1) = 0.6561$$
$$P(X = 1) = \text{Bpd}\,(1, 4, 0.1) = 0.2916$$
$$P(X = 2) = \text{Bpd}\,(2, 4, 0.1) = 0.0486$$

Therefore, $P(X < 3) = 0.6561 + 0.2916 + 0.0486 = 0.9963$. $P(X < 3)$ could also be calculated from its complement, $P(X \leq 2)$, as follows:

$$P(X < 3) = P(X \leq 2)$$
$$= \text{Bcd}\,(2, 4, 0.1)$$
$$= 0.9963$$

Computations such as those in Example 5.14 can become tedious, especially as n gets large. To avoid computational drudgery, you can find many binomial probabilities directly from Table E.6 (in Appendix E), a portion of which is reproduced in Table 5.16. Table E.6 provides binomial probabilities for $X = 0, 1, 2, \ldots, n$ for various selected combinations of n and π. For example, to find the probability of exactly two events of interest in a sample of four when the probability of an event is 0.1, you first find $n = 4$ and then look in the row $X = 2$ and column $\pi = 0.10$. The result is 0.0486.

TABLE 5.16

Finding a Binomial
Probability for
$n = 4$, $X = 2$, and
$\pi = 0.1$

				π	
n	X	**0.01**	**0.02**	**....**	**0.10**
4	0	0.9606	0.9224	....	0.6561
	1	0.0388	0.0753	....	0.2916
	2	0.0006	0.0023	....	0.0486
	3	0.0000	0.0000	....	0.0036
	4	0.0000	0.0000	....	0.0001

Source: *Table E.6.*

You can also compute the binomial probabilities given in Table E.6 by using Microsoft Excel
or Minitab as shown in Figures 5.2 and 5.3 (note that Minitab uses the letter p instead of π to
denote the probability of an event of interest).

FIGURE 5.2

Microsoft Excel
worksheet for computing
binomial probabilities

*See Section E5.2 to create
this.*

	A	B	
1	**Tagged Orders**		
2			
3	**Data**		
4	Sample size	4	
5	Probability of an event of interest	0.1	
6			
7	**Statistics**		
8	Mean	0.4	=B4 * B5
9	Variance	0.36	=B8 * (1 - B5)
10	Standard deviation	0.6	=SQRT(B9)
11			
12	**Binomial Probabilities Table**		
13	X	P(X)	
14	0	0.6561	=BINOMDIST(A14, $B$4, $B$5, FALSE)
15	1	0.2916	=BINOMDIST(A15, $B$4, $B$5, FALSE)
16	2	0.0486	=BINOMDIST(A16, $B$4, $B$5, FALSE)
17	3	0.0036	=BINOMDIST(A17, $B$4, $B$5, FALSE)
18	4	0.0001	=BINOMDIST(A18, $B$4, $B$5, FALSE)

FIGURE 5.3

Minitab results for
computing binomial
probabilities

```
Binomial with n = 4 and p = 0.1

x    P( X = x )
0       0.6561
1       0.2916
2       0.0486
3       0.0036
4       0.0001
```

The shape of a binomial probability distribution depends on the values of n and π.
Whenever $\pi = 0.5$, the binomial distribution is symmetrical, regardless of how large or small
the value of n. When $\pi \neq 0.5$, the distribution is skewed. The closer π is to 0.5 and the larger
the number of observations, n, the less skewed the distribution becomes. For example, the distribution of the number of tagged order forms is highly skewed to the right because $\pi = 0.1$
and $n = 4$ (see Figure 5.4).

FIGURE 5.4

Microsoft Excel
histogram of the
binomial probability
distribution with $n = 4$
and $\pi = 0.1$

*See Section E5.2 and E2.9 to
create this.*

Binomial Probability Histogram

(histogram showing P(X) on the y-axis from 0 to 0.7, and X on the x-axis from 0 to 4, labeled "Number of tagged order forms")

The Mean or Expected Value of a Binomial Random Variable

The mean of a binomial random variable can be calculated using the formula shown previously for calculating the mean of a discrete random variable, namely:

$$\mu = E(X) = \sum XP(X)$$

EXAMPLE 5.15

Refer to the mutual funds example 5.15. We will get the following:

TABLE 5.17

X	P(X)	XP(X)
0	0.00004	0
1	0.00055	0.00055
2	0.00351	0.00702
3	0.0141	0.0423
4	0.0400	0.1600
5	0.0844	0.4220
6	0.1380	0.8280
7	0.1785	1.2495
8	0.1852	1.4816
9	0.1552	1.3968
10	0.1054	1.0540
11	0.0578	0.6358
12	0.0254	0.3048
13	0.0089	0.1157
14	0.0024	0.0336
15	0.00048	0.0072
16	0.00007	0.00112
17	0.00001	0.00017
18	0.00000	0.00000
Total	1	7.74016

From these calculations, we see that: $\mu = E(X) = 7.74$ people

i.e. If infinite groups of 18 people were selected, and the number who had investments in mutual funds was determined for each group, and then the average number of people who had investments in mutual funds was calculated: the average would be 7.74 people.

You will note that it was quite tedious calculating the mean in this fashion. Even if we were to input the data in 2 lists in the calculator and calculate the mean using the weighted method of calculating, it would still take some time. However, it can be shown that for any binomial distribution, the following formula applies:

$$\mu = E(X) = n\pi \qquad\qquad 5.3$$

Now referring back to the example:

$$\mu = E(X) = n\pi = 18(0.43) = 7.74 \; people$$

The Standard Deviation of a Binomial Random Variable

The standard deviation can also be calculated using the methods shown in the discrete random variable section 5.1, however, there is a simple formula that can be used for all binomial distributions. The formula is:

$$\sigma = \sqrt{n\pi(1 - \pi)} \qquad\qquad 5.4$$

Now referring back to Example 5.16:

$$\sigma = \sqrt{n\pi(1-\pi)} = \sqrt{18 \times 0.43(1-0.43)} = 2.10 \; people$$

The mean (or expected value) of the binomial distribution is equal to the product of n and π. Instead of using Equation (5.1) to compute the mean of the probability distribution, you use Equation (5.6) to compute the mean for variables that follow the binomial distribution.

MEAN OF THE BINOMIAL DISTRIBUTION

The mean, μ, of the binomial distribution is equal to the sample size, n, multiplied by the probability of an event of interest, π.

$$\mu = E(X) = n\pi \qquad\qquad (5.6)$$

On the average, over the long run, you theoretically expect $\mu = E(X) = n\pi = (4)(0.1) = 0.4$ tagged order form in a sample of four orders.

The standard deviation of the binomial distribution is calculated using Equation (5.7).

STANDARD DEVIATION OF THE BINOMIAL DISTRIBUTION

$$\sigma = \sqrt{\sigma^2} = \sqrt{Var(X)} = \sqrt{n\pi(1-\pi)} \qquad\qquad (5.7)$$

The standard deviation of the number of tagged order forms is

$$\sigma = \sqrt{4(0.1)(0.9)} = 0.60$$

You get the same result if you use Equation (5.3).

Example 5.16 applies the binomial distribution to service at a fast-food restaurant.

EXAMPLE 5.16

Computing Binomial Probabilities

Accuracy in taking orders at a drive-through window is important for fast-food chains. Each month, *QSR Magazine*, **www.qsrmagazine.com**, publishes the results of its surveys. Accuracy is measured as the percentage of orders that are filled correctly. In a recent month, the percentage of orders filled correctly at McDonald's was approximately 91%. If a sample of three orders is taken, what are the mean and standard deviation of the binomial distribution for the number of orders filled correctly? Suppose that you go to the drive-through window at McDonald's and place an order. Two friends of yours independently place orders at the drive-through window at the same McDonald's. What are the probabilities that all three, that none of the three, and that at least two of the three orders will be filled correctly?

SOLUTION Because there are three orders and the probability of a correct order is 0.91, $n = 3$ and $\pi = 0.91$. Using Equations (5.6) and (5.7),

$$\mu = E(X) = n\pi = 3(0.91) = 2.73$$
$$\sigma = \sqrt{\sigma^2} = \sqrt{Var(X)} = \sqrt{n\pi(1-\pi)}$$
$$= \sqrt{3(0.91)(0.09)}$$
$$= \sqrt{0.2457} = 0.4957$$

Using Equation (5.5),

$$P(X = 3) = \text{Bpd}\,(3, 3, 0.91)$$
$$= 0.7536$$

$$P(X = 0) = \text{Bpd}(0, 3, 0.91)$$
$$= 0.0007$$
$$P(X = 2) = \text{Bpd}(2, 3, 0.91)$$
$$= 0.2236$$
$$P(X \geq 2) = P(X = 2) + P(X = 3)$$
$$= 0.2236 + 0.7536$$
$$= 0.9772$$

or

$$P(X \geq 2) = 1 - P(X \leq 1)$$
$$= 1 - \text{Bcd}(1, 3, 0.91)$$
$$= 1 - 0.0228$$
$$= 0.9772$$

The mean number of orders filled correctly in a sample of three orders is 2.73, and the standard deviation is 0.4957. The probability that all three orders are filled correctly is 0.7536, or 75.36%. The probability that none of the orders are filled correctly is 0.0007, or 0.07%. The probability that at least two orders are filled correctly is 0.9772, or 97.72%.

In this section, you have been introduced to the binomial distribution. The binomial distribution is an important mathematical model in many business situations.

CALCULATOR LESSON 4

CASIO FX-9750G, CFX-9850GB, OR FX-9750GII CALCULATOR

Lesson 4—Binomial Probabilities

Note: The following instructions refer to examples in the notes on the Binomial Probability Distribution.

The Casio calculator has *two* Binomial probability functions programmed into its memory. These are:

i. **Bpd** which stands for **B**inomial **p**robability **d**istribution. This function calculates a Binomial probability of the form:

$$P(X = \#)$$

ii. **Bcd** which stands for **B**inomial **c**umulative **d**istribution. This function calculates a Binomial probability of the form:

$$P(X \leq \#)$$

A. Individual values of X—using the built-in **Bpd** distribution function

EXAMPLE 5.9
(Revisit)

$P(X = 2)$ where n = 6 and $\pi = 0.5$

STAT F5(DIST)   **F5**(BINM)   **F1**(Bpd)   then select the following options

Data	: **F2**(Var) ▼ (Note: Do not key EXE now)
x	: **2 EXE**
Numtrial	: **6 EXE**
p	: **.5 EXE**

Now key **EXE** or **F1**(Calc)

The calculator will now show the result 0.23437

To calculate another Binomial probability key **EXE** and enter new values where necessary.

B. Cumulative values of X—using the built-in **Bcd** distribution function

EXAMPLE 5.11a
(Revisit)

$P(X \leq 2)$ where n = 18 and π = 0.43

STAT F5(DIST)   **F5**(BINM)   **F2**(Bcd)   then select the following options

Data	: **F2**(Var) ▼ (Note: Do not key EXE now)
x	: **2 EXE**
Numtrial	: **18 EXE**
p	: **.43 EXE**

Now key **EXE** or **F1**(Calc)

The calculator will now show the result 4.1007 E –03 which is scientific notation for the value 0.0041. E –03 means that you should move the decimal point 3 places to the left.

EXAMPLE 5.11c
(Revisit)

$P(X > 10) = 1 - P(X \leq 10)$ where n = 18 and π = 0.43

You must *first* calculate $P(X \leq 10)$

STAT F5(DIST)   **F5**(BINM)   **F2**(Bcd)   then select the following options

Data	: **F2**(Var) ▼ (Note: Do not key EXE now)
x	: **10 EXE**
Numtrial	: **18 EXE**
p	: **.43 EXE**

Now key **EXE** or **F1**(Calc)

The calculator will now show the result 0.90494.

Therefore, $P(X > 10) = 1 - P(X \leq 10) = 1 - 0.9049 = 0.0951$

EXAMPLE 5.11d
(Revisit)

$P(3 \leq X \leq 9) = P(X \leq 9) - P(X \leq 2)$ where n = 18 and π = 0.43

You will have to calculate the two cumulative probabilities separately and then record the results and subtract the appropriate values to get the final result 0.7955.

Problems for Section 5.2

APPLYING THE CONCEPTS

Binomial Template:

X = # of _____
                    (successes)

n = _____

π = _____
        (dec.)

P(_____) = P(X symbol #) =
    (words*)

_____ = 0._ _ _ _
  (calculator or SPSS input)   (4 dec.)

* If the question does not directly say what the number is.

5.16 The increase or decrease in the price of a stock between the beginning and the end of a trading day is assumed to be an equally likely random event. What is the probability that a stock will show an increase in its closing price on five consecutive days?

5.17 Sixty percent of Americans read their employment contract, including the fine print ("Snapshots," **usatoday.com**, January 20, 2004). Assume that the number of employees who read every word of their contract can be modeled using the binomial distribution. For a group of five employees, what is the probability that

a. all five will have read every word of their contract?
b. at least three will have read every word of their contract?
c. less than two will have read every word of their contract?
d. What are your answers in (a) through (c) if the probability is 0.80 that an employee reads every word of their contract?

 5.18 A student is taking a multiple-choice exam in which each question has four choices. Assuming that she has no knowledge of the correct answers to any of the questions, she has decided on a strategy in which she will place four balls (marked *A*, *B*, *C*, and *D*) into a box. She randomly selects one ball for each question and replaces the ball in the box. The marking on the ball will determine her answer to the question. There are five multiple-choice questions on the exam. What is the probability that she will get

a. five questions correct?
b. at least four questions correct?
c. no questions correct?
d. no more than two questions correct?

5.19 The commission rate commercial airlines pay travel agents has been declining for several years. In an attempt by travel agencies to raise revenue, many agencies are now charging their customers a ticket fee, typically between $10 and $25. According to the American Society of Ticket Agents, about 90% of travel agents charge customers fees when purchasing an airline ticket (Kortney Stringer, "American Air Fees for Travel Agents to Be Cut Again," *The Wall Street Journal*, August 20, 2001, B2).

a. Is the 90% figure quoted by the American Society of Ticket Agents best classified as *a priori* classical probability, empirical classical probability, or subjective probability?
b. You select a random sample of 10 travel agencies. Assume that the number of the 10 travel agencies charging a ticket fee is distributed as a binomial random variable. What are the mean and standard deviation of this distribution?
c. What assumptions are necessary in (b)?

5.20 Referring to problem 5.19, compute the probability that of the 10 travel agencies:

a. zero charge ticket fees?
b. exactly one charges ticket fees?
c. two or fewer charge ticket fees?
d. three or more charge ticket fees?

 5.21 When a customer places an order with Rudy's On-Line Office Supplies, a computerized accounting information system (AIS) automatically checks to see if the customer has exceeded his or her credit limit. Past records indicate that the probability of customers exceeding their credit limit is 0.05. Suppose that, on a given day, 20 customers place orders. Assume that the number of customers that the AIS detects as having exceeded their credit limit is distributed as a binomial random variable.

a. What are the mean and standard deviation of the number of customers exceeding their credit limits?
b. What is the probability that zero customers will exceed their limit?
c. What is the probability that one customer will exceed his or her limit?
d. What is the probability that two or more customers will exceed their limits?

5.22 The broadcast networks introduce new television shows each fall. In an attempt to get viewers interested in the new shows, television commercials are aired during the summer as part of a promotional campaign conducted prior to the fall debuts. The networks then conduct surveys to see what percentage of the viewing public is *aware* of the shows. According to network sources, in the fall of 2001, 68% of viewers aged 18–49 were aware of the new series *Criminal Intent*, whereas only 24% of viewers aged 18–49 were aware of *Inside Schwartz* (Joe Flint, "Viewers Awareness of New Shows Rises," *The Wall Street Journal*, August 20, 2001, B7). Suppose that a random sample of 20 viewers aged 18–49 is selected. What is the probability that:

a. less than five of the viewers are aware of *Criminal Intent*?
b. 10 or more are aware of *Criminal Intent*?
c. all 20 are aware of *Criminal Intent*?

5.23 A new public school is presently being built in your community. The classrooms will include chairs that have a small table attached on the right or left side. The school is trying to determine how many left-handed tables should be included in each classroom. If only 7% of the population is left-handed, what is the probability that in a class of 25 students:

a. two will be left-handed?   (0.2770)
b. more than three will be left-handed?   (0.0936)
c. What is the expected number of left-handed children in a class of 25?   (1.75 children)

5.24 The quality inspector for a company that produces heptium computer chips has determined that 3% of the production is defective. The company does not perform final product inspection, but instead agrees to replace any defective chip found by any customer and will give the customer a $5 discount on their next order.

a. If a customer orders 30 heptium chips, what is the probability that 3 or more defective chips will be included in the order?   (0.0601)
b. What is the expected number of defective chips in the above order?   (0.9 def.)

c. Another customer assembles computer motherboards, each with 7 heptium chips. If any chip fails, then the motherboard fails. What is the probability that a motherboard will fail? (0.1920)

5.25 According to a well-known accounting firm, the chances of your tax return being audited by Revenue Canada are about 9 in 1000 if your income is less than $50,000. The chances increase to 22 in 1000 if your income is more than $50,000. You are presently employed by an accounting firm and have prepared tax returns for 58 clients with income under $50,000 and for 42 clients with income over $50,000.
a. What is the probability that at most 3 of the clients with incomes under $50,000 will be audited? (0.9981)
b. What is the probability that at least 4 of your clients that have incomes over $50,000 will be audited? (0.0135)

5.26 A salesperson has to sell a minimum of 50 cars in a month in order to get a bonus. One particular salesperson has sold 43 cars so far this month. Today he has appointments with 9 prospective customers. Based on past experience he has a 55% chance of selling a car to any customer. What is the probability that he will earn his bonus today? (0.1495)

5.27 A certain soft drink manufacturer believes that 40% of the people that drink cola prefer their brand. A random sample of 60 cola drinkers was surveyed. If the manufacturer is correct:
a. What is the probability that less than half of those surveyed will prefer the manufacturer's product? (0.9254)
b. What is the probability that at least the expected number of people will prefer the manufacturer's product? (0.5489)

LEARNING THE BASICS

5.28 If $n = 5$ and $\pi = 0.40$, what is the probability that
a. $X = 4$?
b. $X \leq 3$?
c. $X < 2$?
d. $X > 1$?

5.29 Determine the following:
a. For $n = 4$ and $\pi = 0.12$, what is $P(X = 0)$?
b. For $n = 10$ and $\pi = 0.40$, what is $P(X = 9)$?
c. For $n = 10$ and $\pi = 0.50$, what is $P(X = 8)$?
d. For $n = 6$ and $\pi = 0.83$, what is $P(X = 5)$?

APPLYING THE CONCEPTS

5.30 The increase or decrease in the price of a stock between the beginning and the end of a trading day is assumed to be an equally likely random event. What is the probability that a stock will show an increase in its closing price on five consecutive days?

5.31 A recent article in *Quality Progress* (Dennis R. Owens, "The Probability of Reoccurrence: P(r)," April 2007, 40, p. 88) discusses a manufacturing company assessing the chance that its product will fail. The article identifies six independent events that can cause a failure. The probability of each of these events failing is quite low, 0.05, but for a product to ultimately be a success, it must not experience a failure in any of the six events.
a. Use the binomial probability distribution to calculate the probability that a product will ultimately be successful (i.e., that it will not fail).
b. If the probabilities of the six events are not all equal, how could you calculate the probability in (a)?

5.32 A student is taking a multiple-choice exam in which each question has four choices. Assuming that she has no knowledge of the correct answers to any of the questions, she has decided on a strategy in which she will place four balls (marked *A*, *B*, *C*, and *D*) into a box. She randomly selects one ball for each question and replaces the ball in the box. The marking on the ball will determine her answer to the question. There are five multiple-choice questions on the exam. What is the probability that she will get
a. five questions correct?
b. at least four questions correct?
c. no questions correct?
d. no more than two questions correct?

SELF Test **5.33** In Example 5.16, you and two friends decided to go to McDonald's. Instead, suppose that you went to KFC, which last month filled 86.1% of the orders correctly. What is the probability that
a. all three orders will be filled correctly?
b. none of the three will be filled correctly?
c. at least two of the three will be filled correctly?
d. What are the mean and standard deviation of the binomial distribution used in (a) through (c)? Interpret these values.

5.34 When a customer places an order with Rudy's On-Line Office Supplies, a computerized accounting information system (AIS) automatically checks to see if the customer has exceeded his or her credit limit. Past records indicate that the probability of customers exceeding their credit limit is 0.05. Suppose that, on a given day, 20 customers place orders. Assume that the number of customers that the AIS detects as having exceeded their credit limit is distributed as a binomial random variable.
a. What are the mean and standard deviation of the number of customers exceeding their credit limits?
b. What is the probability that 0 customers will exceed their limits?
c. What is the probability that 1 customer will exceed his or her limit?
d. What is the probability that 2 or more customers will exceed their limits?

5.3 Poisson Probability Distribution

Many studies are based on counts of the times a particular event occurs in a given *area of opportunity*. An **area of opportunity** is a continuous unit or interval of time, volume, or any physical area in which there can be more than one occurrence of an event. Examples are the surface defects on a new refrigerator, the number of network failures in a day, the number of people arriving at a bank, and the number of fleas on the body of a dog.

Characteristics of a Poisson Experiment

1. The experiment consists of observing some situation for a period of *time*.

   or

   An *amount of space* is inspected or analyzed. SPACE may be length, area, volume or weight.

2. In each infinitesimally small amount of time or space there will either be one success or no successes, where success is when the outcome of interest occurs. The successes must occur *randomly*. Note that this condition implies that the successes are *independent* of each other.

3. The average rate of success for the amount of time or space we are interested in is given the symbol λ (lambda).

The **random variable** associated with a Poisson experiment is:

$$X = \# \text{ of successes IN a certain amount of time or space.}$$

To calculate the probability that X takes on a specific value we use the

Poisson Probability Distribution Function:

$$P(X = x) = \frac{e^{-\lambda}\lambda^{x}}{x!} \qquad (5.5)$$

where $e = 2.718281828459\ldots$ (a mathematical constant)

Note: On your calculator there is an 'e^{x}' key. Try calculating 'e^{1}'.

EXAMPLE 5.17   Records have been kept for the past several months and they show that customers arrive to use a certain banking machine at an average rate of 15 per hour.

a. What is the probability that 12 customers will use the machine in the next hour?

SOLUTION X = # of customers at the bank machine IN 1 hour

$\lambda = 15 / \text{hour}$

$P(X = 12) = \text{Ppd}(12, 15) = 0.0829$

b. What is the probability that there will be less than 3 customers in the next 10 minutes?

SOLUTION X = # of customers at the bank machine IN 10 minutes

$\lambda = 15 / \text{hour} = 2.5 / 10 \text{ minutes}$

$P(X < 3) = P(X \leq 2)$

$= \text{Pcd}(2, 2.5) = 0.5438$

a. What is the probability that there will be more than 40 customers in the next 2 hours?

SOLUTION X = # of customers at the bank machine IN 2 hours

λ = 5 / hour = 30 / 2 hours

$P(X > 40) = 1 - P(X \leq 40) = 1 - $ Pcd (40, 30)

$= 1 - 0.9677 = 0.0323$

EXAMPLE 5.18

It has been noted that potholes on the 401 highway occur randomly. An inspection of a 200 km stretch of the 401 indicated that there were 450 potholes. Today the pothole repair work crew will repair 3 km. of the highway. What is the probability that they will repair at least 6 potholes?

SOLUTION X = # of potholes IN 3 km.

λ = 450 / 200 km = 2.25 / km = 6.75 / 3 km.

$P(X \geq 6) = 1 - P(X \leq 5) = 1 - $ Pcd (5, 6.75)

$= 1 - 0.3338 = 0.6662$

Consider the number of customers arriving during the lunch hour at a bank located in the central business district in a large city. You are interested in the number of customers that arrive each minute. Does this situation match the four properties of the Poisson distribution given above? First, the *event* of interest is a customer arriving, and the *given area of opportunity* is defined as a 1-minute interval. Will zero customers arrive, one customer arrive, two customers arrive, and so on? Second, it is reasonable to assume that the probability that a customer arrives during a particular 1-minute interval is the same as the probability for all the other 1-minute intervals. Third, the arrival of one customer in any 1-minute interval has no effect on (i.e., is independent of) the arrival of any other customer in any other 1-minute interval. Finally, the probability that two or more customers will arrive in a given time period approaches zero as the time interval becomes small. For example, the probability is virtually zero that two customers will arrive in a time interval of 0.01 second. Thus, you can use the Poisson distribution to determine probabilities involving the number of customers arriving at the bank in a 1-minute time interval during the lunch hour.

The Poisson distribution has one parameter, called λ (the Greek lowercase letter *lambda*), which is the mean or expected number of events per unit. The variance of a Poisson distribution is also equal to λ, and the standard deviation is equal to $\sqrt{\lambda}$. The number of events, X, of the Poisson random variable ranges from 0 to infinity (∞).

Equation (5.8) presents the mathematical expression for the Poisson distribution for computing the probability of X events, given that λ events are expected.

POISSON DISTRIBUTION

$$P(X) = \frac{e^{-\lambda}\lambda^X}{X!}$$ (5.8)

where

$P(X)$ = the probability of X events in an area of opportunity

λ = expected number of events

e = mathematical constant approximated by 2.71828

X = number of events ($X = 0, 1, 2, \ldots, \infty$)

To demonstrate the Poisson distribution, suppose that the mean number of customers who arrive per minute at the bank during the noon-to-1 p.m. hour is equal to 3.0. What is the probability that in a given minute, exactly two customers will arrive? And what is the probability that more than two customers will arrive in a given minute?

Using Equation (5.8) and $\lambda = 3$, the probability that in a given minute exactly two customers will arrive is

$$P(X = 2) = \text{Ppd}\,(2, 3) = 0.2240$$

To determine the probability that in any given minute more than two customers will arrive,

$$P(X > 2) = P(X = 3) + P(X = 4) + \cdots + P(X = \infty)$$

Because in a probability distribution, all the probabilities must sum to 1, the terms on the right side of the equation $P(X > 2)$ also represent the complement of the probability that X is less than or equal to 2 [i.e., $1 - P(X \le 2)$]. Thus,

$$P(X > 2) = 1 - P(X \le 2) = 1 - [P(X = 0) + P(X = 1) + P(X = 2)]$$

Now, using Equation (5.8),

$$P(X > 2) = 1 - [\text{Ppd}\,(0, 3) + \text{Ppd}\,(1, 3) + \text{Ppd}\,(2, 3)]$$
$$= 1 - [0.0498 + 0.1494 + 0.2240]$$
$$= 1 - 0.4232 = 0.5768$$

Thus, there is a 57.68% chance that more than two customers will arrive in the same minute.

To avoid drudgery involved in these computations, you can find Poisson probabilities directly from Table E.7 (in Appendix E), a portion of which is reproduced in Table 5.18. Table E.7 provides the probabilities that the Poisson random variable takes on values of $X = 0, 1, 2, \ldots$, for selected values of the parameter λ. To find the probability that exactly two customers will arrive in a given minute when the mean number of customers arriving is 3.0 per minute, you can read the probability corresponding to the row $X = 2$ and column $\lambda = 3.0$ from the table. The result is 0.2240, as demonstrated in Table 5.18.

TABLE 5.18

Finding a Poisson Probability for $\lambda = 3$

X	2.1	2.2	$\lambda \ldots$	3.0
0	.1225	.1108	....	.0498
1	.2572	.2438	....	.1494
2	.2700	.2681	....	.2240
3	.1890	.1966	....	.2240
4	.0992	.1082	....	.1680
5	.0417	.0476	....	.1008
6	.0146	.0174	....	.0504
7	.0044	.0055	....	.0216
8	.0011	.0015	....	.0081
9	.0003	.0004	....	.0027
10	.0001	.0001	....	.0008
11	.0000	.0000	....	.0002
12	.0000	.0000	....	.0001

Source: *Table E.7.*

You can also compute the Poisson probabilities given in Table E.7 by using Microsoft Excel or Minitab, as illustrated in Figures 5.5 and 5.6.

FIGURE 5.5

Microsoft Excel worksheet for computing Poisson probabilities with $\lambda = 3$

See Section E5.3 to create this.

	A	B	C	D	E
1	**Customer Arrivals Analysis**				
2					
3		**Data**			
4	**Mean/Expected number of events of interest:**				3
5					
6	**Poisson Probabilities Table**				
7	**X**	**P(X)**			
8	0	0.049787	=POISSON(A8, $E$4, FALSE)		
9	1	0.149361	=POISSON(A9, $E$4, FALSE)		
10	2	0.224042	=POISSON(A10, $E$4, FALSE)		
11	3	0.224042	=POISSON(A11, $E$4, FALSE)		
12	4	0.168031	=POISSON(A12, $E$4, FALSE)		
13	5	0.100819	=POISSON(A13, $E$4, FALSE)		
14	6	0.050409	=POISSON(A14, $E$4, FALSE)		
15	7	0.021604	=POISSON(A15, $E$4, FALSE)		
16	8	0.008102	=POISSON(A16, $E$4, FALSE)		
17	9	0.002701	=POISSON(A17, $E$4, FALSE)		
18	10	0.000810	=POISSON(A18, $E$4, FALSE)		
19	11	0.000221	=POISSON(A19, $E$4, FALSE)		
20	12	0.000055	=POISSON(A20, $E$4, FALSE)		
21	13	0.000013	=POISSON(A21, $E$4, FALSE)		
22	14	0.000003	=POISSON(A22, $E$4, FALSE)		
23	15	0.000001	=POISSON(A23, $E$4, FALSE)		
24	16	0.000000	=POISSON(A24, $E$4, FALSE)		
25	17	0.000000	=POISSON(A25, $E$4, FALSE)		
26	18	0.000000	=POISSON(A26, $E$4, FALSE)		
27	19	0.000000	=POISSON(A27, $E$4, FALSE)		
28	20	0.000000	=POISSON(A28, $E$4, FALSE)		

FIGURE 5.6

Minitab results for computing Poisson probabilities with $\lambda = 3$

```
Poisson with mean = 3

x     P( X = x )
0      0.049787
1      0.149361
2      0.224042
3      0.224042
4      0.168031
5      0.100819
6      0.050409
7      0.021604
8      0.008102
9      0.002701
10     0.000810
11     0.000221
12     0.000055
13     0.000013
14     0.000003
15     0.000001
```

EXAMPLE 5.19

Computing Poisson Probabilities

The number of work-related injuries per month in a manufacturing plant is known to follow a Poisson distribution with a mean of 2.5 work-related injuries a month. What is the probability that in a given month no work-related injuries occur? That at least one work-related injury occurs?

SOLUTION Using Equation (5.8) with $\lambda = 2.5$ (or using Table E.7 or Microsoft Excel or Minitab), the probability that in a given month no work-related injuries occur is

$$P(X = 0) = \text{Ppd}\,(0, 2.5) = 0.0821$$

The probability that there will be no work-related injuries in a given month is 0.0821 or 8.21%. Thus,

$$P(X \geq 1) = 1 - P(X = 0)$$
$$= 1 - 0.0821$$
$$= 0.9179$$

The probability that there will be at least one work-related injury is 0.9179 or 91.79%.

CALCULATOR LESSON 5

CASIO FX-9750G, CFX-9850GB, OR FX-9750GII CALCULATOR

Lesson 5—Poisson Probabilities

Note: The following instructions refer to examples in the notes on the Poisson Probability Distribution.

The Casio calculator has *two* Poisson probability functions programmed into its memory. These are:

i. **Ppd** which stands for **P**oisson **p**robability **d**istribution. This function calculates a Poisson probability of the form:

$$P(X = \#)$$

ii. **Pcd** which stands for **P**oisson **c**umulative **d**istribution. This function calculates a Poisson probability of the form:

$$P(X \leq \#)$$

A. Individual values of X—using the built-in **Ppd** distribution function

EXAMPLE 5.13a
(Revisit)

$P(X = 12)$ where $\lambda = 15$

STAT F5(DIST)   **F6**(×)   **F1**(POISN)   **F1**(Ppd)   then select the following options

Data   : **F2**(Var) ▼ (Note: Do not key EXE now)
x   : **12 EXE**
μ   : **15 EXE**   (Note: the calc. Uses the 'μ' symbol instead of 'λ')

Now key **EXE** or **F1**(Calc)

The calculator will now show the result 0.082859

To calculate another Poisson probability key **EXE** and enter new values where necessary.

B. Cumulative values of X—using the built-in **Pcd** distribution function

EXAMPLE 5.13b
(Revisit)

$P(X < 3) = P(X \leq 2)$ where $\lambda = 2.5$

STAT F5(DIST) **F6**(×) **F1**(POISN) **F2**(Pcd)   then select the following options

Data   : **F2**(Var) ▼ (Note: Do not key EXE now)
x   : **2 EXE**
μ   : **2.5 EXE**

Now key **EXE** or **F1**(Calc)

The calculator will now show the result 0.54381

EXAMPLE 5.13c
(Revisit)

$P(X > 40) = 1 - P(X \leq 40)$ where $\lambda = 30$

You must *first* calculate $P(X \leq 40)$

STAT F5(DIST) **F5**(BINM) **F2**(Bcd)   then select the following options

Data   : **F2**(Var) ▼ (Note: Do not key EXE now)
x   : **40 EXE**
μ   : **30 EXE**

Now key **EXE** or **F1**(Calc)

The calculator will now show the result 0.96769

Therefore, $P(X > 40) = 1 - P(X \leq 40) = 1 - 0.9677 = 0.0323$

Problems for Section 5.3

APPLYING THE CONCEPTS

Poisson Template:

X = # of _____ IN _____
             (successes)   (time or space)

λ = _____ = _____
      (given)   (new—if needed)

P(_____) = P(X symbol #) =
     (words*)

_____ = 0._ _ _ _
(calculator or SPSS input)   (4 dec.)

* If the question does not directly say what the number is.

5.35 Assume that the number of network errors experienced in a day on a local area network (LAN) is distributed as a Poisson random variable. The mean number of network errors experienced in a day is 2.4. What is the probability that in any given day
a. zero network errors will occur?
b. exactly one network error will occur?
c. two or more network errors will occur?
d. less than three network errors will occur?

SELF **5.36** The quality control manager of Marilyn's
Test Cookies is inspecting a batch of chocolate-chip cookies that has just been baked. If the production process is in control, the mean number of chip parts per cookie is 6.0. What is the probability that in any particular cookie being inspected
a. less than five chip parts will be found?
b. exactly five chip parts will be found?
c. five or more chip parts will be found?
d. either four or five chip parts will be found?

5.37 Refer to Problem 5.36. How many cookies in a batch of 100 should the manager expect to discard if company policy requires that all chocolate-chip cookies sold have at least four chocolate-chip parts?

5.38 The U.S. Department of Transportation maintains statistics for mishandled bags per 1,000 airline passengers. In 2007, airlines had mishandled 7 bags per 1,000 passengers (data extracted from R. Yu, "Airline Performance Nears 20 Year Low," *USA Today*, April 8, 2008, p. B1). What is the probability that in the next 1,000 passengers, airlines will have
a. no mishandled bags?
b. at least one mishandled bag?
c. at least two mishandled bags?

5.39 The U.S. Department of Transportation also maintains statistics for consumer complaints per 100,000 airline passengers. In 2007, consumer complaints were 1.42 per 100,000 passengers (data extracted from R. Yu, "Airline

Performance Nears 20 Year Low," *USA Today*, April 8, 2008, p. B1). What is the probability that in the next 100,000 passengers, there will be
a. no complants?
b. at least one complaint?
c. at least two complaints?

5.40 Based on past experience, it is assumed that the number of flaws per foot in rolls of grade 2 paper follows a Poisson distribution with a mean of 1 flaw per 5 feet of paper (0.2 flaw per foot). What is the probability that in a
a. 1-foot roll, there will be at least 2 flaws?
b. 12-foot roll, there will be at least 1 flaw?
c. 50-foot roll, there will be greater than or equal to 5 flaws and less than or equal to 15 flaws?

5.41 J.D. Power and Associates calculates and publishes various statistics concerning car quality. The initial quality score measures the number of problems per new car sold. For 2008 model cars, Ford had 1.12 problems per car. Dodge had 1.41 problems per car (S. Carty, "Ford Moves Up in Quality Survey," *USA Today*, June 5, 2008, p. 3B). Let the random variable X be equal to the number of problems with a newly purchased 2008 Ford.
a. What assumptions must be made in order for X to be distributed as a Poisson random variable? Are these assumptions reasonable?
Making the assumptions as in (a), if you purchased a 2008 Ford, what is the probability that the new car will have
b. zero problems?
c. two or less problems?
d. Give an operational definition for *problem*. Why is the operational definition important in interpreting the initial quality score?

5.42 Refer to Problem 5.41. If you purchased a 2008 Dodge, what is the probability that the new car will have
a. zero problems?
b. two or less problems?
c. Compare your answers in (a) and (b) to those for the Ford in Problem 5.41(b) and (c).

5.43 Refer to Problem 5.41. The same article reported that in 2007, Ford had 1.27 problems per car, and Dodge had 1.32 problems per car. If you purchased a 2007 Ford, what is the probability that the new car will have
a. zero problems?
b. two or less problems?
c. Compare your answers in (a) and (b) to those for the 2008 Ford in Problem 5.41(b) and (c).

5.44 Refer to Problem 5.43. If you purchased a 2007 Dodge, what is the probability that the new car will have
a. zero problems?
b. two or less problems?
c. Compare your answers in (a) and (b) to those for the 2008 Dodge in Problem 5.42(a) and (b).

5.45 A toll-free phone number is available from 9 a.m. to 9 p.m. for your customers to register complaints about a product purchased from your company. Past history indicates that an average of 0.4 calls are received per minute.
a. What properties must be true about the situation described here in order to use the Poisson distribution to calculate probabilities concerning the number of phone calls received in a 1-minute period?
Assuming that this situation matches the properties discussed in (a), what is the probability that during a 1-minute period
b. zero phone calls will be received?
c. three or more phone calls will be received?
d. What is the maximum number of phone calls that will be received in a 1-minute period 99.99% of the time?

5.46 A taxicab company has found that, on the average, two accidents occur in a month. The accidents appear to occur randomly. Find the probability of there being 5 or more accidents during a given month.   (0.0527)

5.47 Customers arrive randomly at a service desk at an average rate of 2 every five minutes. Find the probability that:
a. None arrive in a five minute period.   (0.1353)
b. More than four arrive in a ten minute period.   (0.3712)

5.48 Bankruptcies of convenience stores in Toronto occur randomly at an average rate of 4.5 per year. Find the probability that:
a. there will be no corner store bankruptcies in the next four months.   (0.2231)
b. there will be at most 3 corner store bankruptcies this year.   (0.3423)

5.49 Flaws in plate glass used for large office buildings occur randomly at an average of 1 per 10 square feet. What is the probability that a 6 ft. by 10 ft. sheet of this type of glass will contain:
a. less than 2 flaws?   (0.0174)
b. at least 1 flaw?   (0.9975)

5.50 A data entry typist makes an average of 2 errors per page. If the errors occur randomly, what is the probability that:
a. there will be one error on the next page?   (0.2707)
b. there will be more than 5 errors on the next 2 pages?   (0.2149)

5.51 Two students have started a business to seal driveways during the summer months. They rent a pickup truck and a power sprayer. With this they will use a tar based spray to seal asphalt driveways. Past experience has shown that the best time to sign up customers is to ring their doorbells between 5:00 and 8:00 p.m. on any weekday evening. Any jobs that they obtain will be completed the next day. In the months of June, July and August they find that they get an average 2 customers per hour ringing doorbells.

a. What is the probability that they will get from 5 to 9 jobs in an evening of soliciting?   (0.6310)

b. They charge $25 per driveway. If the truck costs $50 per day, and the spraying equipment costs $20 per day and the material to seal one driveway costs $5, what is the probability that they will make a profit on any given day?   (0.8488)

5.52 J.D. Power & Associates calculates and publishes various statistics concerning car quality. The Initial Quality score measures the number of problems per new car sold. For 2003 model cars, the Lexus was the top brand with 1.63 problems per car. Korea's Kia came in last with 5.09 problems per car (L. Hawkins, "Finding a Car That's Built to Last?" *The Wall Street Journal*, July 9, 2003, D1, D5). Let the random variable X be equal to the number of problems with a newly purchased Lexus.

a. What assumptions must be made in order for X to be distributed as a Poisson random variable? Are these assumptions reasonable?

Making the assumptions as in (a), if you purchased a 2003 Lexus, what is the probability that the new car will have:

b. zero problems?

c. two or fewer problems?

5.53 Refer to problem 5.52. If you purchased a 2003 Kia, what is the probability that the new car will have:

a. zero problems?

b. two or fewer problems?

c. Compare your answers in (a) and (b) to those for the Lexus in problem 5.52 (b) and (c).

5.54 In 2004, both Lexus and Kia improved their performance (D. Hakim, "Hyundai Near Top of a Quality Ranking," *The New York Times*, April 29, 2004, C.8). Lexus had 0.87 problems per car and Korea's Kia had 1.53 problems per car. If you purchased a 2004 Lexus, what is the probability that the new car will have:

a. zero problems?

b. two or fewer problems?

c. compare your answers in (a) and (b) to those of the 2003 Lexus in problem 5.52 (b) and (c).

5.55 Refer to problem 5.54. If you purchased a 2004 Kia, what is the probability that the new car will have:

a. zero problems?

b. two or fewer problems?

c. Compare your answers in (a) and (b) to those for the 2003 Kia in problem 5.53 (a) and (b).

USING STATISTICS @ Saxon Home Improvement Revisited

In the Using Statistics scenario, you were an accountant for the Saxon Home Improvement Company. The company's accounting information system automatically reviews order forms from online customers for possible mistakes. Any questionable invoices are tagged and included in a daily exceptions report. Knowing that the probability that an order will be tagged is 0.10, you were able to use the binomial distribution to determine the chance of finding a certain number of tagged forms in a sample of size 4. There was a 65.6% chance that none of the forms would be tagged, a 29.2% chance that one would be tagged, and a 5.2% chance that two or more would be tagged. You were also able to determine that on average, you would expect 0.4 forms to be tagged and the standard deviation of the number of tagged order forms would be 0.6. Now that you have learned the mechanics of using the binomial distribution for a known probability of 0.10 and a sample size of four, you will be able to apply the same approach to any given probability and sample size. Thus, you will be able to make inferences about the online ordering process and, more importantly, evaluate any changes or proposed changes to the process.

SUMMARY

In this chapter, you have studied mathematical expectation and two important discrete probability distributions, the binomial and Poisson distributions. In the following chapter, you will study the most important continuous distribution, the normal distribution.

To help decide what probability distribution to use for a particular situation, you need to ask the following question:

• Is there a fixed number of observations, n, each of which is classified as an event of interest or not an event of interest, or is there an area of opportunity? If there is a fixed number of observations, n, each of which is classified as an event of interest or not an event of interest, you use the binomial distribution. If there is an area of opportunity, you use the Poisson distribution.

KEY EQUATIONS

Expected Value, μ, of a Discrete Random Variable

$$\mu = E(X) = \sum_{i=1}^{N} X_i P(X_i) \tag{5.1}$$

Variance of a Discrete Random Variable

$$\sigma^2 = \sum_{i=1}^{N} [X_i - E(X)]^2 P(X_i) \tag{5.2}$$

Standard Deviation of a Discrete Random Variable

$$\sigma = \sqrt{\sigma^2} = \sqrt{\sum_{i=1}^{N} [X_i - E(X)]^2 P(X_i)} \tag{5.3}$$

Combinations

$$_nC_X = \frac{n!}{X!(n-X)!} \tag{5.4}$$

Binomial Distribution

$$P(X) = \frac{n!}{X!(n-X)!} \pi^X (1-\pi)^{n-X} \tag{5.5}$$

Mean of the Binomial Distribution

$$\mu = E(X) = n\pi \tag{5.6}$$

Standard Deviation of the Binomial Distribution

$$\sigma = \sqrt{\sigma^2} = \sqrt{Var(X)} = \sqrt{n\pi(1-\pi)} \tag{5.7}$$

Poisson Distribution

$$P(X) = \frac{e^{-\lambda}\lambda^X}{X!} \tag{5.8}$$

KEY TERMS

area of opportunity 254
binomial distribution 242
expected value 234
mathematical model 242

probability distribution for a discrete
   random variable 232
random variable 232

standard deviation of a discrete random variable 239
variance of a discrete random variable
   239

CHAPTER REVIEW PROBLEMS

CHECKING YOUR UNDERSTANDING

5.56 What is the meaning of the expected value of a probability distribution?

5.57 What are the four properties that must be present in order to use the binomial distribution?

5.58 What are the four properties that must be present in order to use the Poisson distribution?

APPLYING THE CONCEPTS

5.59 Darwin Head, a 35-year-old sawmill worker, won $1 million and a Chevrolet Malibu Hybrid by scoring 15 goals within 24 seconds at the Vancouver Canucks National Hockey League game (B. Ziemer, "Darwin Evolves into an Instant Millionaire," *Vancouver Sun*, February 28, 2008, p.1). Head said he would use the money to pay off his mortgage and provide for his children and had no plans to quit his job. The contest was part of the Chevrolet Malibu Million Dollar Shootout, sponsored by General Motors Canadian Division. Did GM-Canada risk the $1 million? No! GM-Canada purchased event insurance from a company specializing in promotions at sporting events like a half-court basketball shot or a hole-in-one giveaway at the local charity golf outing. The event insurance company estimates the probability of a contestant winning the contest, and for a modest charge, insures the event. The promoters pay the insurance premium but take on no added risk as the insurance company will make the large payout in the unlikely event that a contestant wins. To see how it works, suppose that the insurance company estimates that the probability a contestant would win a million dollar shootout is 0.001 and that the insurance company charges $4,000.

a. Calculate the expected value of the profit made by the insurance company.

b. Many call this kind of situation a win-win opportunity for the insurance company and the promoter. Do you agree? Explain.

5.60 Between 1872 and 2000, stock prices rose in 74% of the years (M. Hulbert, "The Stock Market Must Rise in 2002? Think Again," *The New York Times*, December 6, 2001, Business, p. 6). Based on this information, and assuming a binomial distribution, what do you think the probability is that the stock market will rise

a. next year?

b. the year after next?

c. in four of the next five years?

d. in none of the next five years?

e. For this situation, what assumption of the binomial distribution might not be valid?

5.61 The mean cost of a phone call handled by an automated customer-service system is $0.45. The mean cost of a phone call passed on to a "live" operator is $5.50. However, as more and more companies have implemented automated systems, customer annoyance with such systems has grown. Many customers are quick to leave the automated system when given an option such as "Press zero to talk to a customer-service representative." According to the Center for Client Retention, 40% of all callers to automated customer-service systems automatically opt to go to a live operator when given the chance (J. Spencer, "In Search of the Operator," *The Wall Street Journal*, May 8, 2002, p. D1).

If 10 independent callers contact an automated customer-service system, what is the probability that

a. 0 will automatically opt to talk to a live operator?

b. exactly 1 will automatically opt to talk to a live operator?

c. 2 or less will automatically opt to talk to a live operator?

d. all 10 will automatically opt to talk to a live operator?

e. If all 10 automatically opt to talk to a live operator, do you think that the 40% value given in the article applies to this particular system? Explain.

5.62 One theory concerning the Dow Jones Industrial Average is that it is likely to increase during U.S. presidential election years. From 1964 through 2004, the Dow Jones Industrial Average increased in 9 of the 11 U.S. presidential election years. Assuming that this indicator is a random event with no predictive value, you would expect that the indicator would be correct 50% of the time.

a. What is the probability of the Dow Jones Industrial Average increasing in 9 or more of the 11 U.S. presidential election years if the true probability of an increase in the Dow Jones Industrial Average is 0.50?

b. From 1964 to 2004, the Dow Jones Industrial Average increased in 74% of the years. What is the probability that the Dow Jones Industrial Average will increase in 9 or more of the 11 U.S. presidential election years if the probability of an increase in the Dow Jones Industrial Average in any year is 0.74?

5.63 Errors in a billing process often lead to customer dissatisfaction and ultimately hurt bottom line profits. An article in *Quality Progress* (L. Tatikonda, "A Less Costly Billing Process," January, 2008, pp. 30–38) discussed a company where 40% of the bills prepared contained an error. If 10 bills are processed, what is the probability that:

a. 0 bills will contain an error?

b. exactly 1 bill will contain an error?

c. 2 or more bills will contain an error?

d. What are the mean and the standard deviation of the probability distribution?

5.64 Refer to Problem 5.63. Suppose that a quality improvement initiative has reduced the percentage of bills containing an error to 20%. If 10 bills are processed, what is the probability that:

a. 0 bills will contain an error?

b. exactly 1 bill will contain an error?

c. 2 or more bills will contain an error?

d. What are the mean and the standard deviation of the probability distribution?

e. Compare the results of (a) through (c) to those of Problem 5.63 (a) through (c).

5.65 A study by the Center for Financial Services Innovation showed that only 64% of U.S. income earners aged 15 and older had a bank account (A. Carrns, "Banks Court a New Client," *The Wall Street Journal*, March 16, 2007, p. D1).

If a random sample of 20 U.S. income earners aged 15 and older is selected, what is the probability that

a. all 20 have a bank account?

b. no more than 15 have a bank account?

c. more than 10 have a bank account?

d. What assumptions did you have to make to answer (a) through (c)?

5.66 One of the retail industry's biggest frustrations is customers who abuse the return and exchange policies

(S. Kang, "New Return Policy: Retailers Say 'No' to Serial Exchangers," *The Wall Street Journal*, November 29, 2004, pp. B1, B3). In a recent year, returns were 13% of sales in department stores. Consider a sample of 20 customers who make a purchase at a department store. Use the binomial model to answer the following questions:

a. What is the expected value, or mean, of the binomial distribution?

b. What is the standard deviation of the binomial distribution?

c. What is the probability that none of the 20 customers will make a return?

d. What is the probability that no more than 2 of the customers will make a return?

e. What is the probability that 3 or more of the customers will make a return?

5.67 Refer to Problem 5.40. In the same year, returns were 1% of sales in grocery stores.

a. What is the expected value, or mean, of the binomial distribution?

b. What is the standard deviation of the binomial distribution?

c. What is the probability that none of the 20 customers will make a return?

d. What is the probability that no more than 2 of the customers will make a return?

e. What is the probability that 3 or more of the customers will make a return?

f. Compare the results of (a) through (e) to those of Problem 5.40 (a) through (e).

5.68 One theory concerning the S&P 500 index is that if it increases during the first five trading days of the year, it is likely to increase during the entire year. From 1950 through 2007, the S&P 500 index had these early gains in 38 years. In 32 of these 38 years, the S&P 500 index increased for the entire year. Assuming that this indicator is a random event with no predictive value, you would expect that the indicator would be correct 50% of the time. What is the probability of the S&P 500 index increasing in 32 or more years if the true probability of an increase in the S&P 500 index is

a. 0.50?

b. 0.70?

c. 0.90?

d. Based on the results of (a) through (c), what do you think is the probability that the S&P 500 index will increase if there is an early gain in the first five trading days of the year? Explain.

5.69 *Spurious correlation* refers to the apparent relationship between variables that either have no true relationship or are related to other variables that have not been measured. One widely publicized stock market indicator in the United States that is an example of spurious correlation is the relationship between the winner of the National Football League Super Bowl and the performance of the Dow Jones Industrial Average in that year. The indicator states that when a team representing the National Football Conference wins the Super Bowl, the Dow Jones Industrial Average will increase in that year. When a team representing the American Football Conference wins the Super Bowl, the Dow Jones Industrial Average will decline in that year. Since the first Super Bowl was held in 1967 through 2007, the indicator has been correct 32 out of 41 times. Assuming that this indicator is a random event with no predictive value, you would expect that the indicator would be correct 50% of the time.

a. What is the probability that the indicator would be correct 32 or more times in 41 years?

b. What does this tell you about the usefulness of this indicator?

5.70 Worldwide golf ball sales total more than $1 billion annually. One reason for such a large number of golf ball purchases is that golfers lose them at a rate of 4.5 per 18-hole round ("Snapshots," **www.usatoday.com**, January 29, 2004). Assume that the number of golf balls lost in an 18-hole round is distributed as a Poisson random variable.

a. What assumptions need to be made so that the number of golf balls lost in an 18-hole round is distributed as a Poisson random variable?

Making the assumptions given in (a), what is the probability that

b. 0 balls will be lost in an 18-hole round?

c. 5 or less balls will be lost in an 18-hole round?

d. 6 or more balls will be lost in an 18-hole round?

5.71 According to a Virginia Tech survey, college students make an average of 11 calls per day on their cellphone. Moreover, 80% of the students surveyed indicated that their parents pay their cellphone expenses (Jean Elliot, "Professor Researches Cell Phone Usage among Students," **www.physorg.com**, February 26, 2007).

a. What distribution can you use to model the number of calls a student makes in a day?

b. If you select a student at random, what is the probability that he or she makes more than 10 calls in a day? More than 15? More than 20?

c. If you select a random sample of 10 students, what distribution can you use to model the proportion of students who have parents that pay their cellphone expenses?

d. Using the distribution selected in (c), what is the probability that all 10 have parents that pay their cellphone expenses? At least 9? At least 8?

MANAGING THE *SPRINGVILLE HERALD*

The *Herald* marketing department is seeking to increase home-delivery sales through an aggressive direct-marketing campaign that includes mailings, discount coupons, and telephone solicitations. Feedback from these efforts indicates that getting their newspapers delivered early in the morning is a very important factor for both prospective as well as existing subscribers. After several brainstorming sessions, a team consisting of members from the marketing and circulation departments decided that guaranteeing newspaper delivery by a specific time could be an important selling point in retaining and getting new subscribers. The team concluded that the *Herald* should offer a guarantee that customers will receive their newspapers by a certain time or else that day's issue is free.

To assist the team in setting a guaranteed delivery time, Al Leslie, the research director, determined that the circulation department had data that showed the percentage of newspapers yet undelivered every quarter hour from 6 A.M. to 8 A.M. Jan Shapiro remembered that customers were asked on their subscription forms at what time they would be looking for their copy of the *Herald* to be delivered. These data were subsequently combined and posted on an internal *Herald* Web page. (See `Circulation_Data.htm` in the Herald Case folder on the Student CD-ROM or go to **www.prenhall.com/HeraldCase/Circulation_Data.htm**).

EXERCISES

Review the internal data and propose a reasonable time (to the nearest quarter hour) to guarantee delivery. To help explore the effects of your choice, calculate the following probabilities:

SH5.1 If a sample of 50 customers is selected on a given day, what is the probability, given your selected delivery time, that
   a. less than 3 customers will receive a free newspaper?
   b. 2, 3, or 4 customers will receive a free newspaper?
   c. more than 5 customers will receive a free newspaper?

SH5.2 Consider the effects of improving the newspaper delivery process so that the percentage of newspapers that go undelivered by your guaranteed delivery time decreases by 2%. If a sample of 50 customers is selected on a given day, what is the probability, given your selected delivery time (and the delivery improvement), that
   a. less than 3 customers will receive a free newspaper?
   b. 2, 3, or 4 customers will receive a free newspaper?
   c. more than 5 customers will receive a free newspaper?

REFERENCES

1. Bernstein, P. L., *Against the Gods: The Remarkable Story of Risk* (New York: Wiley, 1996).
2. Emery, D. R., J. D. Finnerty, and J. D. Stowe, *Corporate Financial Management*, 3rd ed. (Upper Saddle River, NJ: Prentice Hall, 2007).
3. Kirk, R. L., ed., *Statistical Issues: A Reader for the Behavioral Sciences* (Belmont, CA: Wadsworth, 1972).
4. Levine, D. M., P. Ramsey, and R. Smidt, *Applied Statistics for Engineers and Scientists Using Microsoft Excel and Minitab* (Upper Saddle River, NJ: Prentice Hall, 2001).
5. *Microsoft Excel 2007* (Redmond, WA: Microsoft Corp., 2007).
6. *Minitab Version 15* (State College, PA: Minitab, Inc., 2006).
7. Moscove, S. A., M. G. Simkin, and N. A. Bagranoff, *Core Concepts of Accounting Information Systems*, 10th ed. (New York: Wiley, 2007).

APPENDIX A5a

A5.1 MICROSOFT EXCEL

For Expected Value of a Discrete Random Variable

Open the **Expected Value.xls** file. This worksheet already contains the entries for a home mortgage approval example and uses the SUM and SQRT (square root) functions to calculate statistics. To adapt this worksheet to other problems:

- If you have more or less than seven outcomes, first add or delete table rows by selecting the cell range **A5:E5** and then either **Insert → Cells** or **Edit → Delete**. (If a box of options appears, choose **Shift cells down** if adding cells or choose **Shift cells up** if deleting.)
- If adding rows, copy the formulas in cell range C4:E4 down through the new table rows.
- Enter a corrected list of X values in column A starting with **1** in cell A5.
- Enter the new values for P(X) in column B.

For Binomial Probabilities

Open the **Binomial.xls** Excel file. This worksheet already contains the entries for a tagged orders example. The worksheet uses the BINOMDIST function to calculate binomial probabilities (see section G.6 for additional information).

To adapt this worksheet to other problems:

- If you have more or less than three outcomes, first add or delete table rows by selecting **row 15** and then either **Insert → Rows** or **Edit → Delete**.
- If adding rows, copy the entries in cell range A14:B14 down through the entire table to update the table.
- Enter the new sample size and probability of success values in cells B4 and B5.

OR See section G.6 (**Binomial**) if you want PHStat2 to produce this worksheet for you.

For Poisson Probabilities

Open the **Poisson.xls** Excel file. This worksheet already contains the entries for a bank arrivals example. The worksheet uses the POISSON function to calculate Poisson probabilities (see section G.7 for additional information).

To adapt this worksheet to other problems:

- If you need more than 20 successes, first add table rows by selecting **row 9** and then **Insert → Rows**. Next, copy the entries in cell range A8:B8 down through the entire table to update the table.
- Enter the new **Average/Expected number of successes** value in cell E4.

OR See section G.7 (**Poisson**) if you want PHStat2 to produce this worksheet for you.

Using Microsoft Excel for Discrete Probability Distributions

E5.1 Computing the Expected Value of a Discrete Random Variable

You compute the expected value of a discrete random variable by making entries in the **Discrete** worksheet of the **Expected Value.xls** workbook. This worksheet uses the SUM and SQRT (square root) functions to calculate its statistics.

Figure E5.1 shows a completed worksheet using the mortgage probability distribution of Table 5.1. To adapt this worksheet to other problems that have more or less than seven outcomes, first select the cell range **A5:E5**. To add table rows, right-click and click **Insert**. (If a box of options appears, click **Shift cells down** and then click **OK**.) Then, copy the formulas in cell range C4:E4 down through the new table rows and enter the new X and $P(X)$ values in columns A and B.

To delete table rows, right-click and click **Delete**. (If a box of options appears, click **Shift cells up** and then click **OK**.) Enter a corrected list of X values starting with **1** in cell A5 in column A and enter the new $P(X)$ values in column B.

E5.2 Computing Binomial Probabilities

You compute binomial probabilities by making entries in the **Binomial** worksheet of the **Binomial.xls** workbook. This worksheet (shown in Figure 5.2) already contains the entries for the tagged orders example of Section 5.2. To adapt this worksheet to other problems, change the **Sample size** and **Probability of an event of interest** values in cells B4 and B5. If your problem has a sample size other than 4, first

select **row 15** and then add or delete rows one at a time by right-clicking row 15 and clicking either **Insert** or **Delete** and adjusting the X values in column A. (If you inserted rows, you will also have to copy formulas down to those new rows.)

The worksheet features the **BINOMDIST(X, n, π, cumulative)** function in which X is the number of events of interest, n is the sample size, π is the probability of an event of interest, and *cumulative* is a True or False value. When *cumulative* is **True**, the function computes the probability of X or fewer events of interest; when *cumulative* is **False**, the function computes the probability of exactly X events of interest.

E5.3 Computing Poisson Probabilities

You compute Poisson probabilities by making entries in the **Poisson** worksheet of the **Poisson.xls** workbook. This worksheet (shown in Figure 5.18) already contains the entries for the bank customer arrivals problem of Section 5.3. To adapt this worksheet to other problems, change the **Mean/Expected number of events of interest value** in cell **E4**.

The worksheet features the **POISSON(X, lambda, cumulative)** function in which X is the number of events of interest, *lambda* is the average or expected number of events of interest, and *cumulative* is a True or False value. When *cumulative* is **True**, the function computes the probability of X or fewer events of interest; when *cumulative* is **False**, the function computes the probability of exactly X events of interest.

	A	B	C	D	E	F	G	H	
1	**Discrete Random Variable Probability Distribution**								
2							**Statistics**		
3	X	P(X)	X*P(X)	[X-E(X)]^2	[X-E(X)]^2*P(X)		Expected value	2.8	=SUM(C:C)
4	0	0.10	0	7.84	0.784		Variance	2.46	=SUM(E:E)
5	1	0.10	0.1	3.24	0.324		Standard deviation	1.57	=SQRT(H4)
6	2	0.20	0.4	0.64	0.128				
7	3	0.30	0.9	0.04	0.012		X*P(X)	[X - E(X)]^2	[X - E(X)]^2*P(X)
8	4	0.15	0.6	1.44	0.216		=A4 * B4	=(A4 - $H$3)^2	=D4 * B4
9	5	0.10	0.5	4.84	0.484		=A5 * B5	=(A5 - $H$3)^2	=D5 * B5
10	6	0.05	0.3	10.24	0.512		=A6 * B6	=(A6 - $H$3)^2	=D6 * B6
							=A7 * B7	=(A7 - $H$3)^2	=D7 * B7
							=A8 * B8	=(A8 - $H$3)^2	=D8 * B8
							=A9 * B9	=(A9 - $H$3)^2	=D9 * B9
							=A10 * B10	=(A10 - $H$3)^2	=D10 * B10

FIGURE E5.1 Discrete worksheet

6 The Normal Distribution

Learning Objectives

In this chapter, you learn:

• To compute probabilities from the normal distribution
• How to use the normal distribution to solve business problems
• To use the normal probability plot to determine whether a set of data is approximately normally distributed

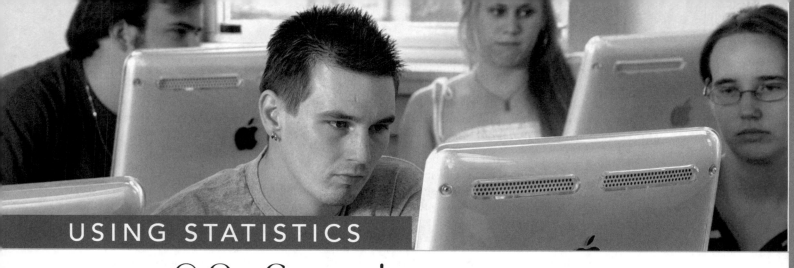

USING STATISTICS

@ OurCampus!

You are a designer for the OurCampus! Web site, which targets college students. To attract and retain customers, you need to make sure that the home page downloads quickly. Both the design of the home page and the load on the company's Web servers affect the download time. To check how fast the home page loads, you open a Web browser on a PC at the corporate offices of OurCampus! and measure the download time—the amount of time in seconds that pass from first linking to the Web site until the home page is fully displayed.

Past data indicate that the mean download time is 7 seconds and that the standard deviation is 2 seconds. Approximately two-thirds of the download times are between 5 and 9 seconds, and about 95% of the download times are between 3 and 11 seconds. In other words, the download times are distributed as a bell-shaped curve, with a clustering around the mean of 7 seconds. How could you use this information to answer questions about the download times of the current home page?

In Chapter 5, Saxon Home Improvement Company managers wanted to be able to solve problems about the number of tagged items in a given sample size. As an OurCampus! Web designer, you face a different task, one that involves a continuous measurement because a download time could be any value and not just a whole number. How can you answer questions about this *continuous numerical variable*, such as:

- What proportion of the home page downloads take more than 10 seconds?
- How many seconds elapse before 10% of the downloads are complete?
- How many seconds elapse before 99% of the downloads are complete?
- How would redesigning the home page to download faster affect the answers to these questions?

As in Chapter 5, you can use a probability distribution as a model. Reading this chapter will help you learn about characteristics of continuous probability distributions and how to use the normal distribution to solve business problems.

6.1 Continuous Probability Distributions

A **continuous probability density function** is the mathematical expression that defines the distribution of the values for a continuous random variable. Figure 6.1 graphically displays three continuous probability density functions.

FIGURE 6.1

Three continuous distributions

Values of *X*
Panel A
Normal Distribution

Values of *X*
Panel B
Uniform Distribution

Values of *X*
Panel C
Exponential Distribution

Panel A depicts a normal distribution. The normal distribution is symmetrical and bell shaped, implying that most values tend to cluster around the mean, which, due to the distribution's symmetrical shape, is equal to the median. Although the values in a normal distribution can range from negative infinity to positive infinity, the shape of the distribution makes it very unlikely that extremely large or extremely small values will occur.

Panel B depicts a **uniform distribution** where each value has an equal probability of occurrence anywhere in the range between the smallest value, *a*, and the largest value, *b*. Sometimes referred to as the **rectangular distribution**, the uniform distribution is symmetrical and therefore the mean equals the median.

Panel C illustrates an **exponential distribution**. This distribution is skewed to the right, making the mean larger than the median. The range for an exponential distribution is zero to positive infinity, but the distribution's shape makes the occurrence of extremely large values unlikely.

6.2 The Normal Distribution

The **normal distribution** (sometimes referred to as the *Gaussian distribution*) is the most common continuous distribution used in statistics. The normal distribution is vitally important in statistics for three main reasons:

- Numerous continuous variables common in business have distributions that closely resemble the normal distribution.

- The normal distribution can be used to approximate various discrete probability distributions.
- The normal distribution provides the basis for *classical statistical inference* because of its relationship to the *Central Limit Theorem*.

The normal distribution is represented by the classic bell shape shown in Panel A of Figure 6.1. In the normal distribution, you can calculate the probability that various values occur within certain ranges or intervals. However, the *exact* probability of a *particular value* from a continuous distribution such as the normal distribution is zero. This property distinguishes continuous variables, which are measured, from discrete variables, which are counted. As an example, time (in seconds) is measured and not counted. Therefore, you can determine the probability that the download time for a home page on a Web browser is between 7 and 10 seconds, or the probability that the download time is between 8 and 9 seconds, or the probability that the download time is between 7.99 and 8.01 seconds. However, the probability that the download time is *exactly* 8 seconds is zero.

The normal distribution has several important theoretical properties:

- It is symmetrical and thus its mean and median are equal.
- It is bell shaped in its appearance.
- Its interquartile range is equal to 1.33 standard deviations. Thus, the middle 50% of the values are contained within an interval of two-thirds of a standard deviation below the mean and two-thirds of a standard deviation above the mean.
- It has an infinite range ($-\infty < X < \infty$).

In practice, many variables have distributions that closely resemble the theoretical properties of the normal distribution. The data in Table 6.1 represent the thickness (in inches) of 10,000 brass washers manufactured by a large company. The continuous variable of interest, thickness, can be approximated by the normal distribution. The measurements of the thickness of the 10,000 brass washers cluster in the interval 0.0190 to 0.0192 inch and distribute symmetrically around that grouping, forming a bell-shaped pattern.

TABLE 6.1

Thickness of 10,000 Brass Washers

Thickness (inches)	Relative Frequency
< 0.0180	48/10,000 = 0.0048
0.0180 < 0.0182	122/10,000 = 0.0122
0.0182 < 0.0184	325/10,000 = 0.0325
0.0184 < 0.0186	695/10,000 = 0.0695
0.0186 < 0.0188	1,198/10,000 = 0.1198
0.0188 < 0.0190	1,664/10,000 = 0.1664
0.0190 < 0.0192	1,896/10,000 = 0.1896
0.0192 < 0.0194	1,664/10,000 = 0.1664
0.0194 < 0.0196	1,198/10,000 = 0.1198
0.0196 < 0.0198	695/10,000 = 0.0695
0.0198 < 0.0200	325/10,000 = 0.0325
0.0200 < 0.0202	122/10,000 = 0.0122
0.0202 or above	48/10,000 = 0.0048
Total	1.0000

Figure 6.2 shows the relative frequency histogram and polygon for the distribution of the thickness of 10,000 brass washers. For these data, the first three theoretical properties of the normal distribution are approximately satisfied. However, the fourth one, having an infinite range, does not hold. The thickness of the washer cannot possibly be zero or below, nor can a washer be so thick that it becomes unusable. From Table 6.1, you see that only 48 out of every 10,000 brass washers manufactured are expected to have a thickness of 0.0202 inch or more, whereas an equal number are expected to have a thickness under 0.0180 inch. Thus, the chance of randomly getting a washer so thin or so thick is 0.0048 + 0.0048 = 0.0096, less than 1 in 100.

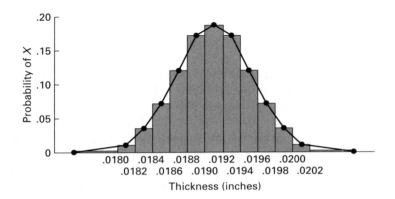

The mathematical expression representing a continuous probability density function is denoted by the symbol $f(X)$. For the normal distribution, the **normal probability density function** is given in Equation (6.1).

NORMAL PROBABILITY DENSITY FUNCTION

$$f(X) = \frac{1}{\sqrt{2\pi}\sigma} e^{-(1/2)[(X-\mu)/\sigma]^2}$$ **(6.1)**

where

e = the mathematical constant approximated by 2.71828

π = the mathematical constant approximated by 3.14159

μ = the mean

σ = the standard deviation

X = any value of the continuous variable, where $-\infty < X < \infty$

Because e and π are mathematical constants, the probabilities of the random variable X are dependent only on the two parameters of the normal distribution—the mean, μ, and the standard deviation, σ. Every time you specify a *particular combination* of μ and σ, a *different* normal probability distribution is generated. Figure 6.3 illustrates three different normal distributions.

FIGURE 6.3

Three normal
distributions

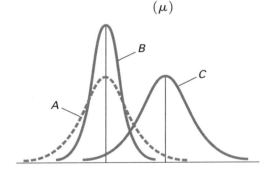

Distributions A and B have the same mean   but have different standard deviations. Distributions A and C have the same standard deviation (σ) but have different means. Distributions B and C differ with respect to both μ and σ.

The mathematical expression in Equation (6.1) is computationally tedious and requires integral calculus. Fortunately, normal probability tables are available, and you *never* need to use Equation (6.1) to make computations of normal distribution probabilities. The first step in finding normal probabilities is to use the **transformation formula**, given in Equation (6.2), to convert any normal random variable, X, to a **standardized normal random variable**, Z.

TRANSFORMATION FORMULA

The Z value is equal to the difference between X and the mean, μ, divided by the standard deviation, σ.

$$Z = \frac{X - \mu}{\sigma}$$

(6.2)

CALCULATOR LESSON 6

CASIO FX-9750G, CFX-9850GB, OR FX-9750GII CALCULATOR

Lesson 6—Normal Distribution

The Casio calculator has *two* Normal probability functions programmed into its memory. These are:

i. **Ncd** which stands for **N**ormal **c**umulative **d**istribution. This function calculates a Normal probability of the form:

$$P(X \le \#)$$

ii. **InvN** which stands for **I**nverse **N**ormal. This function calculates an 'x' value, i.e.?, for a known Normal probability of the form:

$$P(X \le ?) = \text{given probability}$$

EXAMPLE 6.1

Suppose that the weights of adults are normally distributed with a mean of 170.0 lbs. and a standard deviation of 25.0 lbs.

a. What is the probability that a person weighs from 150 to 190 lbs.?

> **Solution:** X = a person's weight
> μ = 170.0 lbs.
> σ = 25.0 lbs.

STAT   F5(DIST)   **F1**(NORM)   **F2**(Ncd)   then select the following options

Lower   : **150 EXE**
Upper   : **190 EXE**
σ : **25 EXE**
μ : **170 EXE**

Now key **EXE** or **F1**(Calc)

The calculator will now show the result 0.57628

i.e. P(150 ≤ X ≤ 190) = 0.5763

b. What is the probability that a person weighs less than 140 lbs.?

Lower   : **–100 EXE**
Upper   : **140 EXE**
σ : **25 EXE**
μ : **170 EXE**

Now key **EXE** or **F1**(Calc)

The calculator will now show the result 0.11506

i.e. P(X < 140) = 0.1151

Note: To represent $-\infty$ use any value less than: $\mu - 6\sigma$
To represent ∞ use any value more than: $\mu + 6\sigma$

c. What is the probability that a person weighs at least 160 lbs.?

Lower   : **160 EXE**
Upper   : **1000 EXE**
σ : **25 EXE**
μ : **170 EXE**

$P(X \geq 160) = 0.6554$

d. What is the maximum weight of the lightest 15% of the adult population?

$P(X \leq ?) = 0.15$

STAT F5(DIST) **F1**(NORM) **F3**(InvN)   then select the following options

Area   : **.15 EXE**
σ : **25 EXE**
μ : **170 EXE**

Now key **EXE** or **F1**(Calc)   The calculator will now show the result   144.09

i.e. The lightest 15% of adults weigh at most 144.1 lbs.

e. What is the minimum weight to be in the heaviest 30% of the adult population?

$P(X \geq ?) = 0.3$

STAT F5(DIST) **F1**(NORM) **F3**(InvN)   then select the following options

Area   : **.7 EXE**
σ : **25 EXE**
μ : **170 EXE**

Now key **EXE** or **F1**(Calc)   The calculator will now show the result 183.11

i.e. The heaviest 30% weigh at least 183.1 lbs.

Note: When using the InvN function, the *Area* value that is required is the area to the *LEFT* of the desired X value.

Problems for Section 6.2

NORMAL PROBABILITY EXERCISES

Normal Template:

X = _____

μ =
         } Normal
σ =

P(_____) = P(X symbol #) =
   (words*)

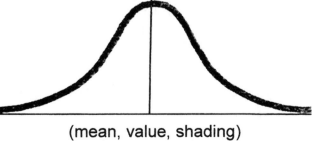

(mean, value, shading)

_____ = 0._ _ _ _
   (calculator or SPSS input)   (4 dec.)

Inverse Normal Template:

X = _____

μ =
                    } Normal
σ =

P(_____) = P(X symbol ?) = 0._____
  (words*)   (given)

? = _____ = _____
        (calculator or SPSS input)   (same dec. as μ)

Concluding statement.

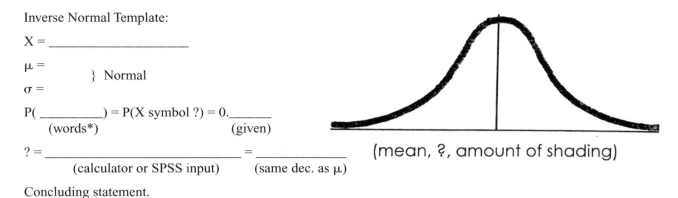

(mean, ?, amount of shading)

6.1 The lifetime of a certain brand of tire is normally distributed with a mean of 90,000 km. and standard deviation of 8,000 km. The tire carries a warranty for 80,000 km.

a. What is the probability that the tire you recently purchased will last more than 100,000 km.?

b. What percent of this brand of tire will fail before the warranty expires?

c. What should the mileage warranty be so that only 4% of the tires need to be replaced under warranty?

6.2 A firm's marketing manager believes that total sales for next year can be represented by a normal distribution, with a mean of $2.5 million and a standard deviation of $300,000. The firm has fixed costs of $1.8 million.

a. What is the probability that the firm's sales will be less than $3.0 million?

b. What is the probability that the firm will have sufficient sales to cover fixed costs?

c. What is the probability that the firm's sales will be within $150,000 of the expected, i.e. mean, sales?

d. Determine the sales level that has only a 9% chance of being exceeded.

6.3 The owner of a convenience store has copies of the local newspaper delivered early each morning. The demand for papers is normally distributed with a mean of 75 and a standard deviation of 16.

a. What is the probability that the newspapers will be sold out if the owner orders 65 copies?

b. How many copies should be ordered so that the probability of selling out is at most 15%?

6.4 In the movie Forest Gump, the public school required an IQ of at least 80 to be admitted.

a. If IQ test scores are normally distributed with a mean of 100 and a standard deviation of 16, what percent of children would qualify for admittance to the school?

b. If the public school wished to have only 5% of all children not qualify for admittance, what minimum IQ test score should be required for admittance?

6.5 An investment broker reports that the annual returns on common stock and municipal bonds are both normally distributed. The stocks have a mean return of 12.4% with a standard deviation of 20.6%. On the other hand the bonds have a mean return of 5.2% with a standard deviation of 8.6%.

a. If you are a conservative investor and just don't like to lose money, which type of investment should you choose?

b. If you are more ambitious an investor and would like to have the best chance of making more than 15%, which investment should you choose?

c. What minimum return would a stock have to earn to be rated in the top 20% of stocks in term of return?

6.6 At a certain university the cumulative grade point average (CGPA) of first year students usually averages 2.73 with a standard deviation 0.37. It has been found that the marks are usually approximately normally distributed.

a. What is the probability that a student will have a CGPA that is between 2.00 and 3.00?

b. What percent of students will be on probation, i.e. their CGPA is less than 2.00?

c. Academic scholarships are awarded to the top 1% of first year students. What minimum CGPA is needed to receive a scholarship?

APPLYING THE CONCEPTS

6.7 During 2001, 61.3% of U.S. households purchased ground coffee and spent an average of $36.16 on ground coffee during the year ("Annual Product Preference Study," *Progressive Grocer*, May 1, 2002, 31). Consider the annual ground coffee expenditures for households purchasing ground coffee, assuming that these expenditures are approximately distributed as a normal random variable with a mean of $36.16 and a standard deviation of $10.00.

a. Find the probability that a household spent less than $25.00.

b. Find the probability that a household spent more than $50.00.

c. What proportion of the households spent between $30.00 and $40.00?

d. 99% of the households spent less than what amount?

6.8 Toby's Trucking Company determined that on an annual basis the distance traveled per truck is normally distributed with a mean of 50.0 thousand miles and a standard deviation of 12.0 thousand miles.
a. What proportion of trucks can be expected to travel between 34.0 and 50.0 thousand miles in the year?
b. What percentage of trucks can be expected to travel either below 30.0 or above 60.0 thousand miles in the year?
c. How many miles will be traveled by at least 80% of the trucks?
d. What are your answers to (a) through (c) if the standard deviation is 10.0 thousand miles?

6.9 The breaking strength of plastic bags used for packaging produce is normally distributed with a mean of 5 pounds per square inch and a standard deviation of 1.5 pounds per square inch. What proportion of the bags have a breaking strength of
a. less than 3.17 pounds per square inch?
b. at least 3.6 pounds per square inch?
c. between 5 and 5.5 pounds per square inch?
d. Between what two values symmetrically distributed around the mean will 95% of the breaking strengths fall?

6.10 A set of final examination grades in an introductory statistics course is normally distributed with a mean of 73 and a standard deviation of 8.
a. What is the probability of getting a grade of 91 or less on this exam?

b. What is the probability that a student scored between 65 and 89?
c. There is a 5% chance that a student taking the test scores higher than what grade?
d. If the professor grades on a curve (gives A's to the top 10% of the class regardless of the score), are you better off with a grade of 81 on this exam or a grade of 68 on a different exam where the mean is 62 and the standard deviation is 3? Show your answer statistically and explain.

6.11 A statistical analysis of 1,000 long-distance telephone calls made from the headquarters of the Bricks and Clicks Computer Corporation indicates that the length of these calls is normally distributed with $\mu = 240$ seconds and $\sigma = 40$ seconds.
a. What is the probability that a call lasted less than 180 seconds?
b. What is the probability that a particular call lasted between 180 and 300 seconds?
c. What is the probability that a call lasted between 110 and 180 seconds?
d. What is the length of a particular call if only 1% of all calls are shorter?

6.2 The Normal Distribution (continued)

Although the original data for the random variable X had mean μ and standard deviation σ, the standardized random variable, Z, will always have mean $\mu = 0$ and standard deviation $\sigma = 1$.

Any set of normally distributed values can be converted to its standardized form. Then you can determine the desired probabilities by using Table E.2, the **cumulative standardized normal distribution**. To see how the transformation formula is applied and the results are used to find probabilities from Table E.2, recall from the Using Statistics scenario that past data indicate that the time to download the Web page is normally distributed, with a mean, $\mu = 7$ seconds and a standard deviation, $\sigma = 2$ seconds. From Figure 6.4, you see that every measurement, X, has a corresponding standardized measurement, Z, computed from the transformation formula [Equation (6.2)]. Therefore, a download time of 9 seconds is equivalent to 1 standardized unit (i.e., 1 standard deviation above the mean) because

$$Z = \frac{9 - 7}{2} = +1$$

FIGURE 6.4
Transformation of scales

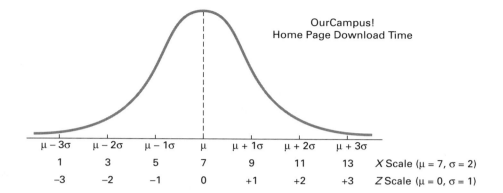

A download time of 1 second is equivalent to 3 standardized units (3 standard deviations) below the mean because

$$Z = \frac{1 - 7}{2} = -3$$

Thus, the standard deviation is the unit of measurement. In other words, a time of 9 seconds is 2 seconds (i.e., 1 standard deviation) higher, or *slower*, than the mean time of 7 seconds. Similarly, a time of 1 second is 6 seconds (i.e., 3 standard deviations) lower, or *faster*, than the mean time.

To further illustrate the transformation formula, suppose that the home page of another Web site has a download time that is normally distributed, with a mean, $\mu = 4$ seconds, and a standard deviation, $\sigma = 1$ second. This distribution is illustrated in Figure 6.5.

Comparing these results with those of the OurCampus! Web site, you see that a download time of 5 seconds is 1 standard deviation above the mean download time because

$$Z = \frac{5 - 4}{1} = +1$$

FIGURE 6.5
A different
transformation of scales

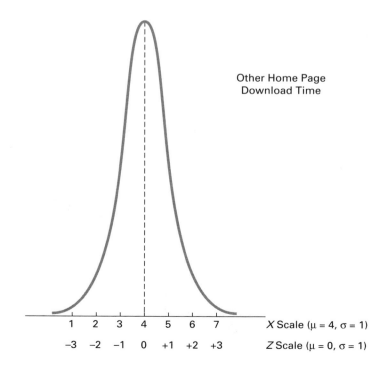

A time of 1 second is 3 standard deviations below the mean download time because

$$Z = \frac{1 - 4}{1} = -3$$

Suppose you wanted to find the probability that the download time for the OurCampus! site is less than 9 seconds. First, you use Equation (6.2) on page 271 to transform $X = 9$ to standardized Z units. Because $X = 9$ is one standard deviation above the mean, $Z = +1.00$. Next, you use Table E.2, a portion of which is shown below in Table 6.2, to find the cumulative area under the normal curve less than (i.e., to the left of) $Z = +1.00$. To read the probability or area under the curve less than $Z = +1.00$, you scan down the Z column from Table E.2 until you locate the Z value of interest (in 10ths) in the Z row for 1.0. Next, you read across this row until you intersect the column that contains the 100ths place of the Z value. Therefore, in the body of the table, the tabulated probability for $Z = 1.00$ corresponds to the intersection of the row $Z = 1.0$ with the column $Z = .00$, as shown in Table 6.2. This probability is 0.8413. As illustrated in Figure 6.6, there is an 84.13% chance that the download time will be less than 9 seconds.

TABLE 6.2

Finding a Cumulative Area Under the Normal Curve

					Cumulative Probabilities					
Z	**.00**	**.01**	**.02**	**.03**	**.04**	**.05**	**.06**	**.07**	**.08**	**.09**
0.0	.5000	.5040	.5080	.5120	.5160	.5199	.5239	.5279	.5319	.5359
0.1	.5398	.5438	.5478	.5517	.5557	.5596	.5636	.5675	.5714	.5753
0.2	.5793	.5832	.5871	.5910	.5948	.5987	.6026	.6064	.6103	.6141
0.3	.6179	.6217	.6255	.6293	.6331	.6368	.6406	.6443	.6480	.6517
0.4	.6554	.6591	.6628	.6664	.6700	.6736	.6772	.6808	.6844	.6879
0.5	.6915	.6950	.6985	.7019	.7054	.7088	.7123	.7157	.7190	.7224
0.6	.7257	.7291	.7324	.7357	.7389	.7422	.7454	.7486	.7518	.7549
0.7	.7580	.7612	.7642	.7673	.7704	.7734	.7764	.7794	.7823	.7852
0.8	.7881	.7910	.7939	.7967	.7995	.8023	.8051	.8078	.8106	.8133
0.9	.8159	.8186	.8212	.8238	.8264	.8289	.8315	.8340	.8365	.8389
1.0	.8413	.8438	.8461	.8485	.8508	.8531	.8554	.8577	.8599	.8621

Source: *Extracted from Table E.2.*

FIGURE 6.6

Determining the area less than *Z* from a cumulative standardized normal distribution

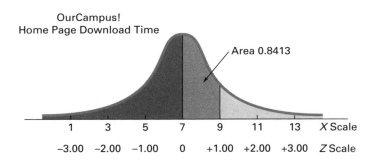

However, for the other home page, you see that a time of 5 seconds is 1 standardized unit above the mean time of 4 seconds. Thus, the probability that the download time will be less than 5 seconds is also 0.8413. Figure 6.7 shows that regardless of the value of the mean, μ, and standard deviation, σ, of a normally distributed variable, Equation (6.2) can transform the problem to Z values.

FIGURE 6.7

Demonstrating a transformation of scales for corresponding cumulative portions under two normal curves

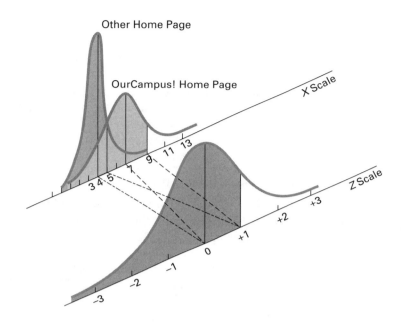

Now that you have learned to use Table E.2 with Equation (6.2), you can answer many questions related to the OurCampus! home page, using the normal distribution.

EXAMPLE 6.1

Finding $P(X > 9)$

What is the probability that the download time will be more than 9 seconds?

SOLUTION The probability that the download time will be less than 9 seconds is 0.8413 (see Figure 6.6 above). Thus, the probability that the download time will be more than 9 seconds is the *complement* of less than 9 seconds, $1 - 0.8413 = 0.1587$. Figure 6.8 illustrates this result.

FIGURE 6.8
Finding $P(X > 9)$

EXAMPLE 6.2

Finding $P(7 < X < 9)$

What is the probability that the download time will be between 7 and 9 seconds?

SOLUTION From Figure 6.6, you can see that the probability that a download time is less than 9 seconds is 0.8413. Now you must determine the probability that the download time will be under 7 seconds and subtract this from the probability that the download time is under 9 seconds. Figure 6.9 illustrates this result.

FIGURE 6.9
Finding $P(7 < X < 9)$

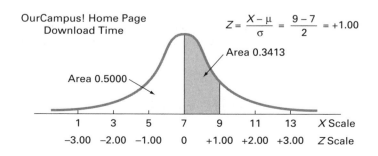

Using Equation (6.2),

$$Z = \frac{7 - 7}{2} = 0.00$$

Using Table E.2 or Table 6.2, the area under the normal curve less than the mean of $Z = 0.00$ is 0.5000. (Because the mean and the median are the same for normally distributed data, 50% of the download times are less than 7 seconds.) Hence, the area under the curve between $Z = 0.00$ and $Z = 1.00$ is $0.8413 - 0.5000 = 0.3413$.

EXAMPLE 6.3

Finding
$P(X < 7 \text{ or } X > 9)$

What is the probability that the download time will be under 7 seconds or over 9 seconds?

SOLUTION From Figure 6.9, the probability that the download time is between 7 and 9 seconds is 0.3413. The probability that the download time is under 7 seconds or over 9 seconds is its complement, $1 - 0.3413 = 0.6587$.

Another way to view this problem, is to separately calculate the probability of a download time of less than 7 seconds and the probability of a download time of greater than 9 seconds and then add these two probabilities together. Figure 6.10 illustrates this result. Because the mean is seven seconds, 50% of download times are under 7 seconds. From Example 6.1, the probability that the download time is greater than 9 seconds is 0.1587. Hence, the probability that a download time is under 7 or over 9 seconds, $P(X < 7 \text{ or } X > 9)$, is $0.5000 + 0.1587 = 0.6587$.

FIGURE 6.10

Finding
$P(X < 7 \text{ or } X > 9)$

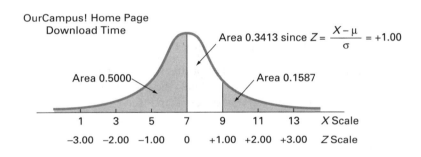

EXAMPLE 6.4

Finding
$P(5 < X < 9)$

What is the probability that the download time will be between 5 and 9 seconds—that is, $P(5 < X < 9)$?

SOLUTION In Figure 6.11, you can see that the area of interest is located between two values, 5 and 9.

FIGURE 6.11

Finding $P(5 < X < 9)$

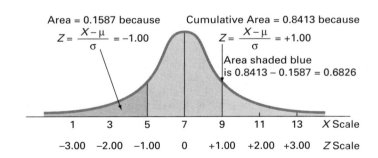

In Example 6.1, you already found that the area under the normal curve less than 9 seconds is 0.8413. To find the area under the normal curve less than 5 seconds,

$$Z = \frac{5 - 7}{2} = -1.00$$

Using Table E.2, you look up $Z = -1.00$ and find 0.1587. Thus, the probability that the download time will be between 5 and 9 seconds is $0.8413 - 0.1587 = 0.6826$, as displayed in Figure 6.11.

The result of Example 6.4 enables you to state that for any normal distribution, 68.26% of the values will fall within ± 1 standard deviation of the mean. From Figure 6.12, 95.44% of the values will fall within ± 2 standard deviations of the mean. Thus, 95.44% of the download times are between 3 and 11 seconds. From Figure 6.13, 99.73% of the values are within ± 3 standard deviations above or below the mean. Thus, 99.73% of the download times are between 1 and 13 seconds. Therefore, it is unlikely (0.0027, or only 27 in 10,000) that a download time will be so fast or so slow that it will take under 1 second or more than 13 seconds. In general, you can use 6σ (that is, 3 standard deviations below the mean to 3 standard deviations above the mean) as a practical approximation of the range for normally distributed data.

FIGURE 6.12
Finding $P(3 < X < 11)$

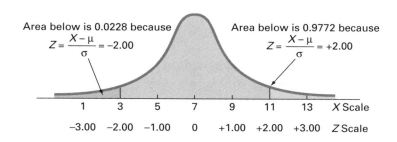

FIGURE 6.13
Finding $P(1 < X < 13)$

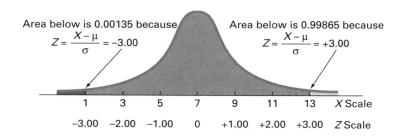

Figures 6.11, 6.12, and 6.13 illustrate how the values of a normal distribution cluster near the mean. For any normal distribution:

- Approximately 68.26% of the values fall within ± 1 standard deviation of the mean.
- Approximately 95.44% of the values fall within ± 2 standard deviations of the mean.
- Approximately 99.73% of the values fall within ± 3 standard deviations of the mean.

This result is the justification for the empirical rule presented on page 163. The accuracy of the empirical rule improves as a data set follows the normal distribution more closely.

EXAMPLE 6.5

Finding $P(X < 3.5)$

What is the probability that a download time will be under 3.5 seconds?

SOLUTION To calculate the probability that a download time will be under 3.5 seconds, you need to examine the shaded lower-left tail region of Figure 6.14.

FIGURE 6.14
Finding $P(X < 3.5)$

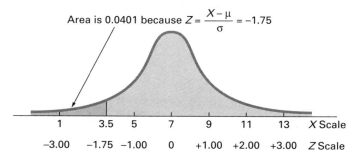

To determine the area under the curve below 3.5 seconds, you first calculate

$$Z = \frac{X - \mu}{\sigma} = \frac{3.5 - 7}{2} = -1.75$$

You then look up the Z value of -1.75 by matching the appropriate Z row (-1.7) with the appropriate Z column $(.05)$, as shown in Table 6.3 (which is extracted from Table E.2). The resulting probability or area under the curve less than -1.75 standard deviations below the mean is 0.0401.

TABLE 6.3

Finding a Cumulative Area Under the Normal Curve

| | | | | | Cumulative Probabilities | | | | |
Z	.00	.01	.02	.03	.04	.05	.06	.07	.08	.09
.	.	.	.	.	.		.	.	.	.
.	.	.	.	.	.		.	.	.	.
.	.	.	.	.	.		.	.	.	.
−1.7	.0446	.0436	.0427	.0418	.0409	.0401	.0392	.0384	.0375	.0367
−1.6	.0548	.0537	.0526	.0516	.0505	.0495	.0485	.0475	.0465	.0455

Source: *Extracted from Table E.2.*

Examples 6.1 through 6.5 require you to use the normal table to find an area under the normal curve that corresponds to a specific X value. There are many circumstances in which you want to find the X value that corresponds to a specific area. Examples 6.6 and 6.7 illustrate such situations.

EXAMPLE 6.6

Finding the X Value for a Cumulative Probability of 0.10

How much time (in seconds) will elapse before 10% of the downloads are complete?

SOLUTION Because 10% of the home pages are expected to download in under X seconds, the area under the normal curve less than this value is 0.1000. Using the body of Table E.2, you search for the area or probability of 0.1000. The closest result is 0.1003, as shown in Table 6.4 (which is extracted from Table E.2).

TABLE 6.4

Finding a Z Value Corresponding to a Particular Cumulative Area (0.10) Under the Normal Curve

| | | | | | Cumulative Probabilities | | | | |
Z	.00	.01	.02	.03	.04	.05	.06	.07	.08	.09
.	.	.	.	.	.	.	.	.		.
.	.	.	.	.	.	.	.	.		.
.	.	.	.	.	.	.	.	.		.
−1.5	.0668	.0655	.0643	.0630	.0618	.0606	.0594	.0582	.0571	.0559
−1.4	.0808	.0793	.0778	.0764	.0749	.0735	.0721	.0708	.0694	.0681
−1.3	.0968	.0951	.0934	.0918	.0901	.0885	.0869	.0853	.0838	.0823
−1.2	.1151	.1131	.1112	.1093	.1075	.0156	.0138	.1020	.1003	.0985

Source: *Extracted from Table E.2.*

Working from this area to the margins of the table, the Z value corresponding to the particular Z row (-1.2) and Z column $(.08)$ is -1.28 (see Figure 6.15).

FIGURE 6.15

Finding Z to determine X

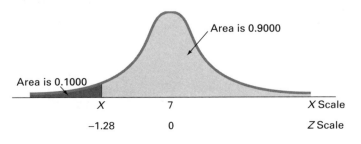

Once you find Z, you use the transformation formula Equation (6.2) on page 273 to determine the X value, as follows. Let

$$Z = \frac{X - \mu}{\sigma}$$

then

$$X = \mu + Z\sigma$$

Substituting $\mu = 7$, $\sigma = 2$, and $Z = -1.28$,

$$X = 7 + (-1.28)(2) = 4.44 \text{ seconds}$$

Thus, 10% of the download times are 4.44 seconds or less.

In general, you use Equation (6.3) for finding an X value.

FINDING AN X VALUE ASSOCIATED WITH KNOWN PROBABILITY

The X value is equal to the mean μ plus the product of the Z value and the standard deviation σ.

$$X = \mu + Z\sigma \qquad \textbf{(6.3)}$$

To find a *particular* value associated with a known probability, follow these steps:

1. Sketch the normal curve and then place the values for the mean and X on the X and Z scales.
2. Find the cumulative area less than X.
3. Shade the area of interest.
4. Using Table E.2, determine the Z value corresponding to the area under the normal curve less than X.
5. Using Equation (6.3), solve for X:

$$X = \mu + Z\sigma$$

EXAMPLE 6.7

Finding the X Values that Include 95% of the Download Times

FIGURE 6.16

Finding Z to determine X_L

What are the lower and upper values of X, symmetrically distributed around the mean, that include 95% of the download times?

SOLUTION First, you need to find the lower value of X (called X_L). Then you find the upper value of X (called X_U). Because 95% of the values are between X_L and X_U, and because X_L and X_U are equally distant from the mean, 2.5% of the values are below X_L (see Figure 6.16).

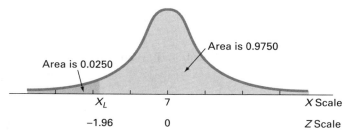

Although X_L is not known, you can find the corresponding Z value because the area under the normal curve less than this Z is 0.0250. Using the body of Table 6.5, you search for the probability 0.0250.

TABLE 6.5

Finding a Z Value Corresponding to a Cumulative Area of 0.025 Under the Normal Curve

					Cumulative Area				
Z	**.00**	**.01**	**.02**	**.03**	**.04**	**.05**	**.06**	**.07**	**.08**	**.09**
.	.	.	.	.	.	.	.	.	.
.	.	.	.	.	.	.	.	.	.
.	.	.	.	.	.	.	.	.	.
−2.0	.0228	.0222	.0217	.0212	.0207	.0202	.0197	.0192	.0188	.0183
−1.9	.0287	.0281	.0274	.0268	.0262	.0256	.0250	.0244	.0239	.0233
−1.8	.0359	.0351	.0344	.0336	.0329	.0232	.0314	.0307	.0301	.0294

Source: *Extracted from Table E.2.*

Working from the body of the table to the margins of the table, you see that the Z value corresponding to the particular Z row (−1.9) and Z column (.06) is −1.96.

Once you find Z, the final step is to use Equation (6.3) on page 283 as follows:

$$X = \mu + Z\sigma$$
$$= 7 + (-1.96)(2)$$
$$= 7 - 3.92$$
$$= 3.08 \text{ seconds}$$

You use a similar process to find X_U. Because only 2.5% of the home page downloads take longer than X_U seconds, 97.5% of the home page downloads take less than X_U seconds. From the symmetry of the normal distribution, the desired Z value, as shown in Figure 6.17, is +1.96 (because Z lies to the right of the standardized mean of 0). You can also extract this Z value from Table 6.6. You can see that 0.975 is the area under the normal curve less than the Z value of +1.96.

FIGURE 6.17

Finding Z to determine X_U

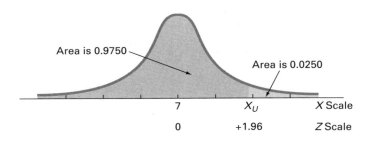

TABLE 6.6

Finding a Z Value Corresponding to a Cumulative Area of 0.975 Under the Normal Curve

					Cumulative Area				
Z	**.00**	**.01**	**.02**	**.03**	**.04**	**.05**	**.06**	**.07**	**.08**	**.09**
.	.	.	.	.	.	.	.	.	.
.	.	.	.	.	.	.	.	.	.
.	.	.	.	.	.	.	.	.	.
+ 1.8	.9641	.9649	.9656	.9664	.9671	.9678	.9686	.9693	.9699	.9706
+ 1.9	.9713	.9719	.9726	.9732	.9738	.9744	.9750	.9756	.9761	.9767
+ 2.0	.9772	.9778	.9783	.9788	.9793	.9798	.9803	.9808	.9812	.9817

Source: *Extracted from Table E.2.*

Using Equation (6.3) on page 281,

$$X = \mu + Z\sigma$$
$$= 7 + (+1.96)(2)$$
$$= 7 + 3.92$$
$$= 10.92 \text{ seconds}$$

Therefore, 95% of the download times are between 3.08 and 10.92 seconds.

You can also use Microsoft Excel or Minitab to compute normal probabilities. Figure 6.18 below illustrates a Microsoft Excel worksheet for Examples 6.5 and 6.6 and Figure 6.19 illustrates Minitab results for Examples 6.1 and 6.6.

FIGURE 6.18

Microsoft Excel worksheet for computing normal probabilities

See Section E6.1 to create this.

	A	B	
1	**Normal Probabilities**		
2			
3	**Common Data**		
4	**Mean**	7	
5	**Standard Deviation**	2	
6			
7	**Probability for X <=**		
8	**X Value**	3.5	
9	**Z Value**	-1.75	=STANDARDIZE(B8, B4, B5)
10	**P(X<=3.5)**	0.0401	=NORMDIST(B8, B4, B5, TRUE)
11			
12	**Find X and Z Given Cum. Pctage.**		
13	**Cumulative Percentage**	10.00%	
14	**Z Value**	-1.2816	=NORMSINV(B13)
15	**X Value**	4.4369	=NORMINV(B13, B4, B5)

VISUAL EXPLORATIONS   Exploring the Normal Distribution

You can use the Visual Explorations Normal Distribution procedure to see the effects of changes in the mean and standard deviation on the area under a normal distribution curve.

Open the `Visual Explorations.xla` add-in workbook and select **VisualExplorations → Normal Distribution** (Excel 97–2003) or **Add-Ins → VisualExplorations → Normal Distribution** (Excel 2007). You will see a normal curve for the Using Statistics home page download example and a floating control panel that allows you to adjust the shape of the curve and the shaded area under the curve (see illustration at right). Use the control panel spinner buttons to change the values for the mean, standard deviation, and *X* value, while noting their effects on the probability of *X* <= value and the corresponding shaded area under the curve (see illustration at right). If you prefer, you can select the **Z Values** option button to see the normal curve labeled with *Z* values.

Click the **Reset** button to reset the control panel values or click **Help** for additional information about the prob-

lem. Click **Finish** when you are done exploring. (Review Section E1.8 for more information on using add-ins, if necessary.)

FIGURE 6.19

Minitab results for normal probabilities

Cumulative Distribution Function

Normal with mean = 7 and standard deviation = 2

```
x   P( X <= x )
9      0.841345
```

Inverse Cumulative Distribution Function

Normal with mean = 7 and standard deviation = 2

```
P( X <= x )        x
       0.1   4.43690
```

THINK ABOUT THIS | What Is Normal?

Ironically the statistician who popularized the use of "normal" to describe the distribution discussed in Section 6.2 was someone who saw the distribution as anything but the everyday, anticipated occurrence that the adjective normal usually suggests.

Starting with an 1894 paper, Karl Pearson argued that measurements of phenomena do not naturally or "normally" conform to the classic bell shape. Pearson believed that individuals in populations could show true variability, and that variability in the measurement of individuals in populations reflected true variability and not errors made in measurement. While this principle underlies statistics today, Pearson's point of view was radical to contemporaries who saw the world as standardized and normal. Pearson changed minds by showing that some populations are naturally skewed (coining that word in

passing) and he helped put to rest the notion that the normal distribution underlies all phenomena.

Today, unfortunately, people still make the type of mistake that Pearson refuted. One of us recalls the story about a small college class of three students in which the professor announced one student would get an A, one would get a B, and one would get a C "because grades need to be normally distributed." (That the professor was describing a uniform distribution was a double irony.) As a student, you have probably heard many discussions about grade inflation (undoubtedly a phenomena at many schools). But, have you ever realized that an argument offered as "proof" of this inflation—that there are "too few" low grades because grades are skewed towards A's and B's—wrongly implies that grades should be "normally" distributed. By the time you finish reading this book, you may

realize that because college students represent small nonrandom samples, there are plenty of reasons to suspect that the distribution of grades would not be "normal."

Misunderstandings about the normal distribution can be found both in business and in the public sector through the years. These misunderstandings have caused a number of business blunders as well as sparked some famous public policy debates. As you continue to study this chapter, make sure you understand the "normal" distribution and the assumptions that must hold for its proper use. Not verifying whether these assumptions hold is another common error made by decision makers using this distribution. And most importantly, always remember that the name *normal* distribution does not mean to suggest normal in the everyday (*dare we say "normal"*) sense of the word!

Problems for Section 6.2

LEARNING THE BASICS

6.12 Given a standardized normal distribution (with a mean of 0 and a standard deviation of 1, as in Table E.2), what is the probability that
a. Z is less than 1.57?
b. Z is greater than 1.84?
c. Z is between 1.57 and 1.84?
d. Z is less than 1.57 or greater than 1.84?

6.13 Given a standardized normal distribution (with a mean of 0 and a standard deviation of 1, as in Table E.2), what is the probability that
a. Z is between -1.57 and 1.84?
b. Z is less than -1.57 or greater than 1.84?
c. What is the value of Z if only 2.5% of all possible Z values are larger?
d. Between what two values of Z (symmetrically distributed around the mean) will 68.26% of all possible Z values be contained?

6.14 Given a standardized normal distribution (with a mean of 0 and a standard deviation of 1, as in Table E.2), what is the probability that
a. Z is less than 1.08?
b. Z is greater than -0.21?
c. Z is less than -0.21 or greater than the mean?
d. Z is less than -0.21 or greater than 1.08?

6.15 Given a standardized normal distribution (with a mean of 0 and a standard deviation of 1, as in Table E.2), determine the following probabilities:
a. $P(Z > 1.08)$
b. $P(Z < -0.21)$

c. $P(-1.96 < Z < -0.21)$
d. What is the value of Z if only 15.87% of all possible Z values are larger?

6.16 Given a normal distribution with $\mu = 100$ and $\sigma = 10$, what is the probability that
a. $X > 75$?
b. $X < 70$?
c. $X < 80$ or $X > 110$?
d. 80% of the values are between what two X values (symmetrically distributed around the mean)?

6.17 Given a normal distribution with $\mu = 50$ and $\sigma = 4$, what is the probability that
a. $X > 43$?
b. $X < 42$?
c. 5% of the values are less than what X value?
d. 60% of the values are between what two X values (symmetrically distributed around the mean)?

APPLYING THE CONCEPTS

6.18 In a recent year, about two-thirds of U.S. households purchased ground coffee. Consider the annual ground coffee expenditures for households purchasing ground coffee, assuming that these expenditures are approximately distributed as a normal random variable with a mean of $45.16 and a standard deviation of $10.00.
a. Find the probability that a household spent less than $25.00.
b. Find the probability that a household spent more than $50.00.

c. What proportion of the households spent between $30.00 and $40.00?

d. 99% of the households spent less than what amount?

SELF **6.19** Toby's Trucking Company determined that
Test the distance traveled per truck per year is normally distributed, with a mean of 50.0 thousand miles and a standard deviation of 12.0 thousand miles.

a. What proportion of trucks can be expected to travel between 34.0 and 50.0 thousand miles in the year?

b. What percentage of trucks can be expected to travel either below 30.0 or above 60.0 thousand miles in the year?

c. How many miles will be traveled by at least 80% of the trucks?

d. What are your answers to (a) through (c) if the standard deviation is 10.0 thousand miles?

6.20 The breaking strength of plastic bags used for packaging produce is normally distributed, with a mean of 5 pounds per square inch and a standard deviation of 1.5 pounds per square inch. What proportion of the bags have a breaking strength of

a. less than 3.17 pounds per square inch?

b. at least 3.6 pounds per square inch?

c. between 5 and 5.5 pounds per square inch?

d. 95% of the breaking strengths will be contained between what two values symmetrically distributed around the mean?

6.21 A set of final examination grades in an introductory statistics course is normally distributed, with a mean of 73 and a standard deviation of 8.

a. What is the probability of getting a grade below 91 on this exam?

b. What is the probability that a student scored between 65 and 89?

c. The probability is 5% that a student taking the test scores higher than what grade?

d. If the professor grades on a curve (i.e., gives A's to the top 10% of the class, regardless of the score), are you better off with a grade of 81 on this exam or a grade of 68 on a different exam, where the mean is 62 and the standard deviation is 3? Show your answer statistically and explain.

6.22 A statistical analysis of 1,000 long-distance telephone calls made from the headquarters of the Bricks and Clicks Computer Corporation indicates that the length of these calls is normally distributed, with $\mu = 240$ seconds and $\sigma = 40$ seconds.

a. What is the probability that a call lasted less than 180 seconds?

b. What is the probability that a call lasted between 180 and 300 seconds?

c. What is the probability that a call lasted between 110 and 180 seconds?

d. What is the length of a call if only 1% of all calls are shorter?

6.23 According to the American Society for Quality, a certified quality engineer (CQE) is a professional who understands the principles of product and service quality evaluation and control. In a 2007 survey, the mean salary of 1,190 CQEs was $71,093, with a standard deviation of $17,871 (H. Lindborg, "Navigate Your Career Path With QP's Annual Salary Survey," *Quality Progress*, December, 2007, pp. 21–50). Assume that the salaries of CQEs is approximately normally distributed. For a randomly selected CQE, what is the probability that he or she has a salary

a. below $50,000?

b. above $75,000?

c. above $100,000?

6.24 Many manufacturing problems involve the matching of machine parts, such as shafts that fit into a valve hole. A particular design requires a shaft with a diameter of 22.000 mm, but shafts with diameters between 21.900 mm and 22.010 mm are acceptable. Suppose that the manufacturing process yields shafts with diameters normally distributed, with a mean of 22.002 mm and a standard deviation of 0.005 mm. For this process, what is

a. the proportion of shafts with a diameter between 21.90 mm and 22.00 mm?

b. the probability that a shaft is acceptable?

c. the diameter that will be exceeded by only 2% of the shafts?

d. What would be your answers in (a) through (c) if the standard deviation of the shaft diameters was 0.004 mm?

6.3 Evaluating Normality

As discussed in Section 6.2, many continuous variables used in business closely follow a normal distribution. This section presents two approaches for determining whether a set of data can be approximated by the normal distribution:

1. Compare the characteristics of the data with the theoretical properties of the normal distribution.
2. Construct a normal probability plot.

Comparing Data Characteristics to Theoretical Properties

The normal distribution has several important theoretical properties:

- It is symmetrical; thus, the mean and median are equal.
- It is bell shaped; thus, the empirical rule applies.

- The interquartile range equals 1.33 standard deviations.
- The range is approximately equal to 6 standard deviations.

In actual practice, a continuous variable may have characteristics that approximate these theoretical properties. However, many continuous variables are neither normally distributed nor approximately normally distributed. For such variables, the descriptive characteristics of the data do not match well with the properties of a normal distribution. One approach to determining whether a data set follows a normal distribution is to compare the characteristics of the data with the corresponding properties from an underlying normal distribution, as follows:

- Construct charts and observe their appearance. For small- or moderate-sized data sets, construct a stem-and-leaf display or a boxplot. For large data sets, plot a histogram or polygon.
- Compute descriptive numerical measures and compare the characteristics of the data with the theoretical properties of the normal distribution. Compare the mean and median. Is the interquartile range approximately 1.33 times the standard deviation? Is the range approximately 6 times the standard deviation?
- Evaluate how the values in the data are distributed. Determine whether approximately two-thirds of the values lie between the mean and ±1 standard deviation. Determine whether approximately four-fifths of the values lie between the mean and ±1.28 standard deviations. Determine whether approximately 19 out of every 20 values lie between the mean and ±2 standard deviations.

Do the returns in 2006 discussed in Chapters 2 and 3 have the properties of the normal distribution? Figure 6.20 displays descriptive statistics for these data, and Figure 6.21 presents a boxplot.

FIGURE 6.20

Microsoft Excel descriptive statistics for the 2006 returns

See Section E3.1 to create this.

	A	B
1	*Return 2006*	
2		
3	Mean	12.5142
4	Standard Error	0.2136
5	Median	13.1000
6	Mode	16.6000
7	Standard Deviation	6.2916
8	Sample Variance	39.5840
9	Kurtosis	0.0200
10	Skewness	-0.2982
11	Range	44.0000
12	Minimum	-9.0000
13	Maximum	35.0000
14	Sum	10862.3000
15	Count	868.0000
16	Largest(1)	35.0000
17	Smallest(1)	-9.0000

FIGURE 6.21

Minitab boxplot for the 2006 returns

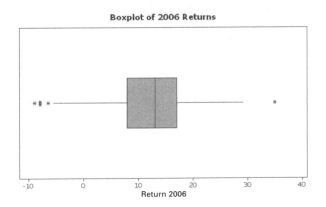

Boxplot of 2006 Returns

From Figures 6.20 and 6.21 and from an ordered array of the 2006 returns (not shown here), you can make the following statements:

1. The mean of 12.5142 is slightly lower than the median of 13.1. (In a normal distribution, the mean and median are equal.)
2. The boxplot appears symmetrical, with four lower outliers at -9.0, -8.0, -8.0, and -6.5 and one upper outlier at 35.0. (The normal distribution is symmetrical.)
3. The interquartile range of 9.2 is approximately 1.46 standard deviations. (In a normal distribution, the interquartile range is 1.33 standard deviations.)
4. The range of 44 is equal to 6.99 standard deviations. (In a normal distribution, the range is approximately six standard deviations.)
5. 72.2% of the returns are within ± 1 standard deviation of the mean. (In a normal distribution, 68.26% of the values lie between the mean ± 1 standard deviation.)
6. 87.0% of the returns are within ± 1.28 standard deviations of the mean. (In a normal distribution, 80% of the values lie between the mean ± 1.28 standard deviations.)

Based on these statements and the criteria given, the 2006 returns are slightly left-skewed and contain more values closer to the mean than expected. The range is higher than would be expected in a normal distribution, but this is mostly due to the single outlier at 35.0. You can conclude that the data characteristics of the 2006 returns do not greatly differ from the theoretical properties of a normal distribution.

Constructing the Normal Probability Plot

A **normal probability plot** is a graphical approach for evaluating whether data are normally distributed. One common approach is called the **quantile-quantile plot**. In this method, you first transform each ordered value to a Z value. For example, if you have a sample of $n = 19$, the Z value for the smallest value corresponds to a cumulative area of $\dfrac{1}{n+1} = \dfrac{1}{19+1} = \dfrac{1}{20} = 0.05$.

The Z value for a cumulative area of 0.05 (from Table E.2) is -1.65. Table 6.7 illustrates the entire set of Z values for a sample of $n = 19$.

TABLE 6.7

Ordered Values and Corresponding Z Values for a Sample of $n = 19$

Ordered Value	Z Value	Ordered Value	Z Value
1	-1.65	11	0.13
2	-1.28	12	0.25
3	-1.04	13	0.39
4	-0.84	14	0.52
5	-0.67	15	0.67
6	-0.52	16	0.84
7	-0.39	17	1.04
8	-0.25	18	1.28
9	-0.13	19	1.65
10	0.00		

To construct the quantile-quantile plot, the Z values are plotted on the X axis, and the corresponding values of the variable are plotted on the Y axis. If the data are normally distributed, the values will plot along an approximately straight line. (Minitab uses a different approach that plots the original values on the X axis and a theoretical percentage score based on the normal distribution on the Y axis. Once again, if the data are normally distributed, the values will plot along an approximately straight line.)

Figure 6.22 illustrates the typical shape of normal probability plots for a left-skewed distribution (Panel A), a normal distribution (Panel B), and a right-skewed distribution (Panel C). If the data are left-skewed, the curve will rise more rapidly at first and then level off. If the data are normally distributed, the points will plot along an approximately straight line. If the data are right-skewed, the data will rise more slowly at first and then rise at a faster rate for higher values of the variable being plotted.

FIGURE 6.22

Normal probability plots for a left-skewed distribution, a normal distribution, and a right-skewed distribution

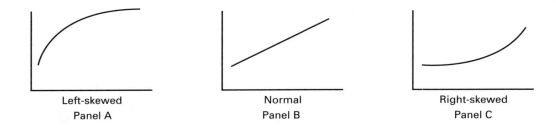

Figure 6.23 shows a Microsoft Excel quantile-quantile normal probability plot and Figure 6.24 displays a Minitab normal probability plot for the 2006 returns.

FIGURE 6.23

Microsoft Excel normal probability plot for 2006 returns

FIGURE 6.24

Minitab normal probability plot for 2006 returns

Figures 6.23 and 6.24 show that the 2006 returns approximate a straight line with the exception of a few outliers at the lower and upper ends of the distribution. Thus, it is reasonable for you to conclude that the 2006 returns do not depart greatly from a normal distribution.

Problems for Section 6.3

LEARNING THE BASICS

6.25 Show that for a sample of $n = 39$, the smallest and largest Z values are -1.96 and $+1.96$, and the middle (i.e., 20th) Z value is 0.00.

6.26 For a sample of $n = 6$, list the six Z values.

APPLYING THE CONCEPTS

✓**SELF** **6.27** The data in the file Chicken contains the
Test total fat, in grams per serving, for a sample of 20 chicken sandwiches from fast-food chains. The data are as follows:

7 8 4 5 16 20 20 24 19 30 23 30 25 19 29 29 30 30 40 56

Source: *Data extracted from "Fast Food: Adding Health to the Menu,"* Consumer Reports, *September 2004, pp. 28–31.*

Decide whether the data appear to be approximately normally distributed by
a. comparing data characteristics to theoretical properties.
b. constructing a normal probability plot.

6.28 As player salaries have increased, the cost of attending games has increased dramatically. The data in the file BBCost (data extracted from **teammarketing.com**, March 29, 2008) represent the cost of four tickets, two beers, four soft drinks, four hot dogs, two game programs, two baseball caps, and the parking fee for one car for each of the 30 major league teams. Decide whether the data appear to be approximately normally distributed by
a. comparing data characteristics to theoretical properties.
b. constructing a normal probability plot.

6.29 The data in the file Property Taxes contain the property taxes per capita for the fifty states and the District of Columbia. Decide whether the data appear to be approximately normally distributed by
a. comparing data characteristics to theoretical properties.
b. constructing a normal probability plot.

6.30 The number of shares traded daily on the New York Stock Exchange (NYSE) is referred to as the *volume* of trading. During the first three months of 2008, daily volume ranged from 1.976 billion to 4.312 billion. The daily value of the stocks traded ranged from $70.688 billion to $153.062 (NYSE Group, **www.nyse.com**, April 2, 2008). The file NYSE contains the date, volume (in billions), and value (in

billions of U.S. dollars) for the first three months of 2008. Decide whether the volume of trades appear to be approximately normally distributed by
a. comparing data characteristics to theoretical properties.
b. constructing a normal probability plot.
c. constructing a histogram.
d. Repeat (a) through (c) using the value data.

6.31 One operation of a mill is to cut pieces of steel into parts that will later be used as the frame for front seats in an automotive plant. The steel is cut with a diamond saw and requires the resulting parts to be within ± 0.005 inch of the length specified by the automobile company. The data come from a sample of 100 steel parts and are stored in the file Steel. The measurement reported is the difference, in inches, between the actual length of the steel part, as measured by a laser measurement device, and the specified length of the steel part. Decide whether the data appear to be approximately normally distributed by
a. comparing data characteristics to theoretical properties.
b. constructing a normal probability plot.

6.32 The data in the file Savings Rate are the yields for a money market account, a one-year certificate of deposit (CD), and a five-year CD for 38 banks in south Florida, as of March 28, 2008 (data extracted from **Bankrate.com**, March 28, 2008). For each of the three types of investments, decide whether the data appear to be approximately normally distributed by
a. comparing data characteristics to theoretical properties.
b. constructing a normal probability plot.

6.33 The following data, stored in the file Utility, represent the electricity costs in dollars during July 2008 for a random sample of 50 two-bedroom apartments in a large city:

96	171	202	178	147	102	153	197	127	82
157	185	90	116	172	111	148	213	130	165
141	149	206	175	123	128	144	168	109	167
95	163	150	154	130	143	187	166	139	149
108	119	183	151	114	135	191	137	129	158

Decide whether the data appear to be approximately normally distributed by
a. comparing data characteristics to theoretical properties.
b. constructing a normal probability plot.

USING STATISTICS

@ OurCampus! Revisited

In the Using Statistics scenario, you were a Web-page designer for OurCampus! The home page must download quickly but still be flashy enough to attract and retain the college student customers using OurCampus! By running experiments in the corporate offices, you determined that the amount of time in seconds that pass from first linking to the Web site until the home page is fully displayed was a bell-shaped distribution with a mean download time of 7 seconds and standard deviation of 2 seconds. Using the normal distribution, you were able to calculate that approximately 84% of the download times are 9 seconds or less, and 95% of the download times are between 3.08 and 10.92 seconds.

Now that you understand how to calculate probabilities from the normal distribution, you can evaluate download times of home pages with different designs. For example, if the standard deviation remained at 2 seconds, lowering the mean to 6 seconds would shift the entire distribution lower by one second. Thus, approximately 84% of the download times would be 8 seconds or less, and 95% of the download times would be between 2.08 and 9.92 seconds. Another change that could reduce long download times would be lowering the variation. For example, consider the case where the mean remained at the original 7 seconds but the standard deviation was reduced to 1 second. Again, approximately 84% of the download times would be 8 seconds or less, and 95% of the download times would be between 5.04 and 8.96 seconds.

SUMMARY

In this and the previous chapter, you have learned about mathematical models called probability distributions and how they can be used to solve business problems. In Chapter 5, you used discrete probability distributions in situations where the outcomes come from a counting process (e.g., the number of courses you are enrolled in, or the number of tagged order forms in a report generated by an accounting information system). In this chapter, you learned about continuous probability distributions where the outcomes come from a measuring process (e.g., your height, or the download time of a Web page). Continuous probability distributions come in all kinds of shapes, but the most common and most important in business is the normal distribution. The normal distribution is symmetrical thus its mean

and median are equal. It is also bell-shaped and approximately 68.26% of its observations are within one standard deviation of the mean, approximately 95.44% of its observations are within two standard deviations of the mean, and approximately 99.73% of its observations are within three standard deviations of the mean. Although many data sets in business are closely approximated by the normal distribution, do not think that all data can be approximated using the normal distribution. In Section 6.3, you learned various methods used to evaluate normality in order to determine whether or not the normal distribution is a reasonable mathematical model to use in specific situations. In Chapter 7, the normal distribution is used in developing the subject of statistical inference.

KEY EQUATIONS

Normal Probability Density Function

$$f(X) = \frac{1}{\sqrt{2\pi}\sigma} e^{-(1/2)[(X-\mu)/\sigma]^2}$$ (6.1)

Transformation Formula

$$Z = \frac{X - \mu}{\sigma}$$ (6.2)

Finding an X Value Associated with Known Probability

$$X = \mu + Z\sigma$$ (6.3)

KEY TERMS

continuous probability density
    function 270
cumulative standardized normal
    distribution 276
exponential distribution 270

normal distribution 270
normal probability density
    function 272
normal probability plot 289
quantile-quantile plot 289

rectangular distribution 270
standardized normal random
    variable 272
transformation formula 272
uniform distribution 270

CHAPTER REVIEW PROBLEMS

CHECKING YOUR UNDERSTANDING

6.34 Why is it that only one normal distribution table such as Table E.2 is needed to find any probability under the normal curve?

6.35 How do you find the area between two values under the normal curve?

6.36 How do you find the X value that corresponds to a given percentile of the normal distribution?

6.37 What are some of the distinguishing properties of a normal distribution?

6.38 How does the shape of the normal distribution differ from those of the uniform and exponential distributions?

6.39 How can you use the normal probability plot to evaluate whether a set of data is normally distributed?

APPLYING THE CONCEPTS

6.40 An industrial sewing machine uses ball bearings that are targeted to have a diameter of 0.75 inch. The lower and upper specification limits under which the ball bearings can operate are 0.74 inch and 0.76 inch, respectively. Past experience has indicated that the actual diameter of the ball bearings is approximately normally distributed, with a mean of 0.753 inch and a standard deviation of 0.004 inch. What is the probability that a ball bearing is
a. between the target and the actual mean?
b. between the lower specification limit and the target?
c. above the upper specification limit?
d. below the lower specification limit?
e. 93% of the diameters are greater than what value?

6.41 The fill amount of soft drink bottles is normally distributed, with a mean of 2.0 liters and a standard deviation of 0.05 liter. If bottles contain less than 95% of the listed net content (1.90 liters, in this case), the manufacturer may be subject to penalty by the state office of consumer affairs. Bottles that have a net content above 2.10 liters may cause excess spillage upon opening. What proportion of the bottles will contain
a. between 1.90 and 2.0 liters?
b. between 1.90 and 2.10 liters?
c. below 1.90 liters or above 2.10 liters?

d. 99% of the bottles contain at least how much soft drink?
e. 99% of the bottles contain an amount that is between which two values (symmetrically distributed) around the mean?

6.42 In an effort to reduce the number of bottles that contain less than 1.90 liters, the bottler in Problem 6.30 sets the filling machine so that the mean is 2.02 liters. Under these circumstances, what are your answers in (a) through (e)?

6.43 An orange juice producer buys all his oranges from a large orange grove. The amount of juice squeezed from each of these oranges is approximately normally distributed, with a mean of 4.70 ounces and a standard deviation of 0.40 ounce.
a. What is the probability that a randomly selected orange will contain between 4.70 and 5.00 ounces of juice?
b. What is the probability that a randomly selected orange will contain between 5.00 and 5.50 ounces of juice?
c. 77% of the oranges will contain at least how many ounces of juice?
d. 80% of the oranges contain between what two values (in ounces of juice), symmetrically distributed around the population mean?

6.44 Data concerning 71 of the best-selling domestic beer in the United States are located in the file **Domesticbeer**. The values for three variables are included: percentage alcohol, number of calories per 12 ounces, and number of carbohydrates (in grams) per 12 ounces. For each of the three variables, decide whether the data appear to be approximately normally distributed. Support your decision through the use of appropriate statistics and graphs.
Source: *Data extracted from* **www.Beer100.com**, *May 4, 2007.*

6.45 The evening manager of a restaurant was very concerned about the length of time some customers were waiting in line to be seated. She also had some concern about the seating times—that is, the length of time between when a customer is seated and the time he or she leaves the restaurant. Over the course of one week, 100 customers (no more than 1 per party) were randomly selected, and their waiting and seating times (in minutes) were recorded in the file **Wait**.
a. Think about your favorite restaurant. Do you think waiting times more closely resemble a uniform, exponential, or normal distribution?

b. Again, think about your favorite restaurant. Do you think seating times more closely resemble a uniform, exponential, or normal distribution?

c. Construct a histogram and a normal probability plot of the waiting times. Do you think these waiting times more closely resemble a uniform, exponential, or normal distribution?

d. Construct a histogram and a normal probability plot of the seating times. Do you think these seating times more closely resemble a uniform, exponential, or normal distribution?

6.46 At the end of 2007, all the major stock market indexes had posted gains in the previous 12 months. The mean one-year return for stocks in the S&P 500, a group of 500 very large companies, was 3.5%. The mean one-year return for the Nasdaq, a group of 3,200 small and medium-sized companies, was 9.8%. Historically, the one-year returns are approximately normal, the standard deviation in the S&P 500 is approximately 20%, and the standard deviation in the Nasdaq is approximately 30%.

a. What is the probability that a stock in the S&P 500 gained 25% or more in 2007? gained 50% or more?

b. What is the probability that a stock in the S&P 500 lost money in 2007? lost 25% or more? lost 50% or more?

c. Repeat (a) and (b) for a stock in the Nasdaq.

d. Write a short summary on your findings. Be sure to include a discussion of the risks associated with a large standard deviation.

6.47 *The New York Times* reported (L. J. Flynn, "Tax Surfing," March 25, 2002, p. C10) that the mean time to download the home page for the Internal Revenue Service, **www.irs.gov**, is 0.8 second. Suppose that the download time is normally distributed with a standard deviation of 0.2 second. What is the probability that a download time is

a. less than 1 second?

b. between 0.5 and 1.5 seconds?

c. above 0.5 second?

d. 99% of the download times are above how many seconds?

e. 95% of the download times are between what two values, symmetrically distributed around the mean?

6.48 The same article mentioned in Problem 6.47 also reported that the mean download time for the H&R Block Web site, **www.hrblock.com**, is 2.5 seconds. Suppose that the download time is normally distributed with a standard deviation of 0.5 second. What is the probability that a download time is

a. less than 1 second?

b. between 0.5 and 1.5 seconds?

c. above 0.5 second?

d. 99% of the download times are above how many seconds?

e. Compare the results for the IRS site computed in Problem 6.36 to those of the H&R Block site.

6.49 When obtaining a mortgage, the borrower will pay closing costs to the lender. These costs vary from bank to

bank, and from state to state. **Bankrate.com** conducted a survey in all fifty states to identify average closing costs on a $200,000 loan, assuming a 20-percent down payment and good credit. The file **Closing** includes the average rate for all fifty states and the District of Columbia for 2006, along with the state rank.

Source: *Data extracted from "Closing Cost Survey,"* **www.bankrate.com**, *May 15, 2007.*

a. Is the distribution of state closing costs approximately distributed as a normal random variable?

b. The variable "RANK 2006" includes 51 numbers, 1, 2, 3, . . . , 51. What type of distribution does this column of numbers resemble? Construct a graphical display that supports your answer.

6.50 (Class Project) According to Burton G. Malkiel, the daily changes in the closing price of stock follow a *random walk*—that is, these daily events are independent of each other and move upward or downward in a random manner—and can be approximated by a normal distribution. To test this theory, use either a newspaper or the Internet to select one company traded on the NYSE, one company traded on the American Stock Exchange, and one company traded on the Nasdaq and then do the following:

1. Record the daily closing stock price of each of these companies for six consecutive weeks (so that you have 30 values per company).

2. Record the daily changes in the closing stock price of each of these companies for six consecutive weeks (so that you have 30 values per company).

For each of your six data sets, decide whether the data are approximately normally distributed by

a. examining the stem-and-leaf display, histogram or polygon, and boxplot.

b. comparing data characteristics to theoretical properties.

c. constructing a normal probability plot.

d. Discuss the results of (a) through (c). What can you say about your three stocks with respect to daily closing prices and daily changes in closing prices? Which, if any, of the data sets are approximately normally distributed?

Note: *The random-walk theory pertains to the daily changes in the closing stock price, not the daily closing stock price.*

TEAM PROJECTS

The data file **Mutual Funds** contains information regarding nine variables from a sample of 868 mutual funds. The variables are:

   Category—Type of stocks comprising the mutual fund (small cap, mid cap, large cap)

   Objective—Objective of stocks comprising the mutual fund (growth or value)

   Assets—In millions of dollars

   Fees—Sales charges (no or yes)

   Expense ratio—Ratio of expenses to net assets, in percentage

   Return 2006—Twelve-month return in 2006

Three-year return—Annualized return, 2004–2006
Five-year return—Annualized return, 2002–2006
Risk—Risk-of-loss factor of the mutual fund (low, average, high)

6.51 For the expense ratio, three-year return, and five-year return, decide whether the data are approximately normally distributed by
a. comparing data characteristics to theoretical properties.
b. constructing a normal probability plot.

STUDENT SURVEY DATA BASE

6.52 Problem 1.28 describes a survey of 50 undergraduate students (see the file `Undergradsurvey`). For these data, for each numerical variable, decide whether the data are approximately normally distributed by
a. comparing data characteristics to theoretical properties.
b. constructing a normal probability plot.

6.53 Problem 1.28 describes a survey of 50 undergraduate students (see the file `Undergradsurvey`).

a. Select a sample of 50 undergraduate students and conduct a similar survey for those students.
b. For the data collected in (a), repeat (a) and (b) of Problem 6.41.
c. Compare the results of (b) to those of Problem 6.52.

6.54 Problem 1.29 describes a survey of 40 MBA students (see the file `Gradsurvey`). For these data, for each numerical variable, decide whether the data are approximately normally distributed by
a. comparing data characteristics to theoretical properties.
b. constructing a normal probability plot.

6.55 Problem 1.29 describes a survey of 40 MBA students (see the file `Gradsurvey`).
a. Select a sample of 40 graduate students and conduct a similar survey for those students.
b. For the data collected in (a), repeat (a) and (b) of Problem 6.53.
c. Compare the results of (b) to those of Problem 6.54.

MANAGING THE *SPRINGVILLE HERALD*

The production department of the newspaper has embarked on a quality improvement effort. Its first project relates to the blackness of the newspaper print. Each day, a determination needs to be made concerning how black the newspaper is printed. Blackness is measured on a standard scale in which the target value is 1.0. Data collected over the past year indicate that the blackness is approximately normally distributed, with a mean of 1.005 and a standard deviation of 0.10. Each day, one spot on the first newspaper printed is chosen, and the blackness of the spot is measured. The blackness of the newspaper is considered acceptable if the blackness of a spot is between 0.95 and 1.05.

EXERCISES

SH6.1 Assuming that the distribution has not changed from what it was in the past year, what is the probability that the blackness of the spot is

a. less than 1.0?
b. between 0.95 and 1.0?
c. between 1.0 and 1.05?
d. less than 0.95 or greater than 1.05?

SH6.2 The objective of the production team is to reduce the probability that the blackness is below 0.95 or above 1.05. Should the team focus on process improvement that lowers the mean to the target value of 1.0 or on process improvement that reduces the standard deviation to 0.075? Explain.

WEB CASE

Apply your knowledge about the normal distribution in this Web Case, which extends the Using Statistics scenario from this chapter.

To satisfy concerns of potential advertisers, the management of OurCampus! has undertaken a research project to learn the amount of time it takes users to download a complex video features page. The marketing department has collected data and has made some claims based on the assertion that the data follow a normal distribution. These data and conclusions can be found in a report located on the internal Web page **www.prenhall.com/Springville/**

Our_DownloadResearch.htm (or in the file with the same name in the Student CD-ROM Web Case folder).

Read this marketing report and then answer the following:

1. Can the collected data be approximated by the normal distribution?
2. Review and evaluate the conclusions made by the OurCampus! marketing department. Which conclusions are correct? Which ones are incorrect?
3. If OurCampus! could improve the mean time by five minutes, how would the probabilities change?

REFERENCES

1. Gunter, B., "Q-Q Plots," *Quality Progress* (February 1994), 81–86.

2. Levine, D. M., P. Ramsey, and R. Smidt, *Applied Statistics for Engineers and Scientists Using Microsoft Excel and Minitab* (Upper Saddle River, NJ: Prentice Hall, 2001).

3. *Microsoft Excel 2007* (Redmond, WA: Microsoft Corp., 2007).

4. Miller, J., "Earliest Known Uses of Some of the Words of Mathematics," **http://members.aol.com/jeff570/n.html**.

5. *Minitab for Windows Version 15* (State College, PA: Minitab, Inc., 2006).

6. Pearl, R., "Karl Pearson, 1857–1936," *Journal of the American Statistical Association*, 31 (1936), 653–664.

7. Pearson, E. S., "Some Incidents in the Early History of Biometry and Statistics, 1890–94," *Biometrika*, 52 (1965), 3–18.

8. Walker, H., "The Contributions of Karl Pearson," *Journal of the American Statistical Association*, 53 (1958), 11–22.

A6.1 MICROSOFT EXCEL

For Normal Probabilities

Open the **Normal.xls** file, shown in Figure 6.18. This work-sheet solves the problems for Examples 6.6 and 6.7. Open the similar **Normal Expanded.xls** file to solve problems similar to Examples 6.3 and 6.4 as well as Examples 6.6 and 6.7. Both worksheets use the STANDARDIZE, NORMDIST, NORMSINV, and NORMINV functions to calculate normal probabilities and related values (see section G.8 for additional information).

To adapt this worksheet to other problems, change the **Mean, Standard Deviation, X Values**, and **Cumulative Percentage** values in the aqua-tinted cells.

OR see section G.8 **(Normal)** if you want PHStat2 to produce a worksheet for you.

For Normal Probability Plot

There are no Microsoft Excel commands that directly produce a Normal Probability Plot. If you want PHStat2 to produce a Normal Probability Plot, see section G.9.

SPSS—Version 15 Lesson 3

Lesson 6—The Normal Distribution

INTRODUCTION

Normal probabilities are calculated using the **CDF.NORMAL** function in the **Transform / Compute variable...** menu.

Inverse normal calculations are performed by the **IDF.NORMAL** function.

CDF.NORMAL

Note: You must have entered at least one data value in the SPSS input spreadsheet in order to perform a calculation. Therefore, key in a '1' in the first case of var00001.

Example 1:

The weights of adults are normally distributed with a mean of 170.0 pounds and a standard deviation of 25.0 pounds. What is the probability that a randomly selected person will weigh:

    a) at most 160 pounds?

Solution: X = weights of adults
            $\mu = 170.0$
            $\sigma = 25.0$

            $P(X \leq 160) = ?$

            To get this answer using SPSS use the following:

Transform / Compute Variable... key in any name in the Target Variable box, suppose 'ans1a'

Now scroll down the **Function group** list and highlight **CDF & Noncentral CDF** and then highlight **Cdf.Normal** in the **Functions and Special Variables** list and then click the ▲ to place the function in the **Numeric Expression** box.

You will now have the function **CDF.NORMAL(?,?,?)** in the Numeric Expression box. Key in **160, 170, 25** in place of the ?,?,? (see the Compute Variable window below) then click **OK.**

Note: CDF.NORMAL will always give the area to the left of the indicated X (quant) value.

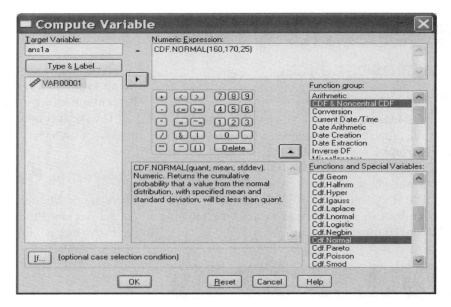

If you put the cursor on the first case of the ans1a variable, the answer .344578258389676 appears in the edit line. However, only 2 decimals appear for the answer shown under the ans1a variable. Now change to Variable View and select 4 decimals. The answer is now shown as '.3446'.

Example: (cont'd)

b) more than 200 pounds?

Solution: $P(X > 200) = 1 - P(X \le 200) = ?$

To get this answer using SPSS use the following:

Transform / Compute Variable... key in 'ans1b' in the **Target Variable** box.

Now insert '**1 −**' in the **Numeric Expressions** box before the CDF.NORMAL function that was placed there for example (a) that is currently in the numeric expressions box.

Type in **200** over the previous X value of 160. (See the Compute Variable window below.) Then click **OK.**

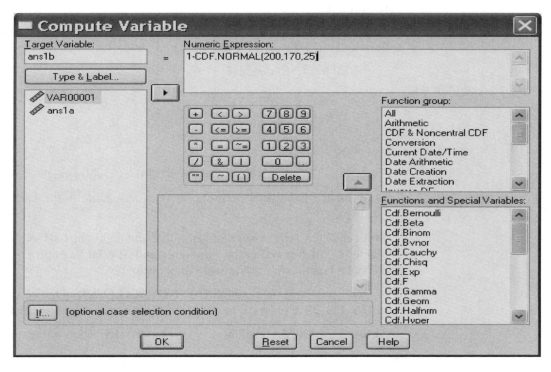

The answer now appears in the ans1b variable column. If you change the number of decimals to 4 you will get the final answer of '.1151'.

Example: (cont'd)

c) between 140 and 165 pounds?

Solution: $P(140 < X < 165) = P(X < 165) - P(X < 140)$

To get this answer using SPSS use the following:

Transform Compute key in any name in the **Target Variable** box, suppose 'ans1c'.

Again highlight **Cdf.Normal** and click the ▲ (to place the CDF.NORMAL function in the **Numeric Expression** box). Key in **165, 170, 25** in place of the ?,?,? Then key in '–' and once again click the ▲ (to place another CDF.NORMAL function in the **Numeric Expression** box). Key in **140,170, 25** in place of the ?,?,? (See the Compute Variable window below.) Then click **OK.**

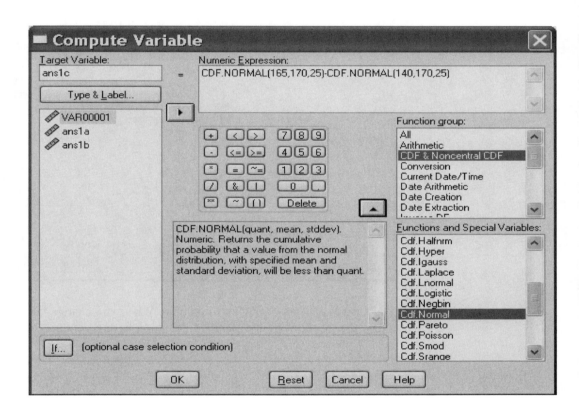

The 4 decimal answer of '.3057' appears in ans1c column.

Example: (cont'd)

d) The lightest 15% of adults weigh at most ___ pounds?

Solution: $P(X \le ?) = 0.15$

To get this answer using SPSS use the following:

Transform / Compute Variable... key in any name in the **Target Variable** box, suppose 'ans1d'. Delete any previous expressions in the **Numeric expressions** box.

Now scroll down the **Function group** list and highlight **Inverse DF** and then highlight **Idf.Normal** in the Functions and Special Variables list and then click the ▲ (to place the IDF.NORMAL function in the **Numeric Expression** box).

You will now have the function **IDF.NORMAL(?,?,?)** in the numeric expressions box. Key in **.15, 170, 25** in place of the ?,?,? (See the Compute Variable window below.) Then click **OK.**

Note: IDF.NORMAL solves for an unknown X value based on the:

    i. **left** area (prob)
    ii. mean
    iii. standard deviation

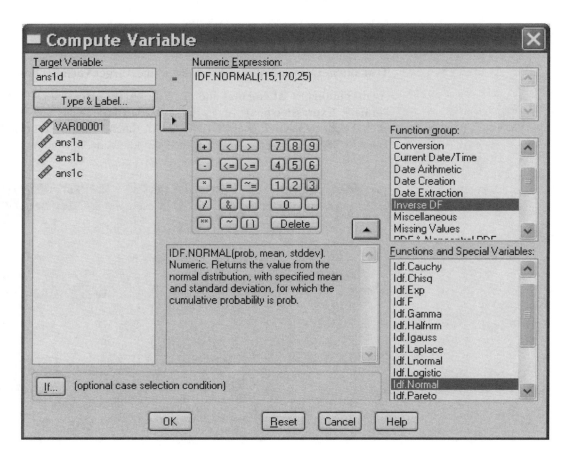

The answer appears in the ans1d column. When you change the number of decimals to '1' (since the given mean and standard deviation have 1 decimal), then the final result will be '144.1' pounds.

Using Microsoft Excel to Compute Probabilities from the Normal Distribution

E6.1 Computing Normal Probabilities

You compute normal probabilities by using either the **Normal** or **Normal Expanded** worksheets of the **Normal.xls** workbook. The **Normal** worksheet, shown in Figure 6.18, contains the entries to solve the Example 6.5 and 6.6 problems. Change the **Mean, Standard Deviation, X Value**, and/or **Cumulative Percentage** to solve similar problems. Use the **Normal Expanded** worksheet (part of which is shown in Figure E6.1) to compute all types of normal probabilities. In these worksheets, the STANDARDIZE function returns the Z value for a specific X value, mean, and standard deviation; the NORMDIST function returns the area or probability of less than a given X value for a specific mean and standard deviation; the NORMSINV function returns the Z value for a given probability of less than a given X, and the NORMINV function returns the X value for a given probability, mean, and standard deviation.

FIGURE E6.1 Normal Expanded worksheet (columns A and B)

E6.2 Creating Normal Probability Plots

There are no Microsoft Excel features that directly create normal probability plots.

7 Sampling and Sampling Distributions

Learning Objectives

In this chapter, you learn:

- To distinguish between different sampling methods
- The concept of the sampling distribution
- To compute probabilities related to the sample mean and the sample proportion
- The importance of the Central Limit Theorem

@ Oxford Cereals

Oxford Cereals fills thousands of boxes of cereal during an eight-hour shift. As the plant operations manager, you are responsible for monitoring the amount of cereal placed in each box. To be consistent with package labeling, boxes should contain a mean of 368 grams of cereal. Because of the speed of the process, the cereal weight varies from box to box, causing some boxes to be underfilled and others overfilled. If the process is not working properly, the mean weight in the boxes could vary too much from the label weight of 368 grams to be acceptable.

Because weighing every single box is too time-consuming, costly, and inefficient, you must take a sample of boxes. For each sample you select, you plan to weigh the individual boxes and calculate a sample mean. You need to determine the probability that such a sample mean could have been randomly selected from a population whose mean is 368 grams. Based on your analysis, you will have to decide whether to maintain, alter, or shut down the cereal-filling process.

In Chapter 6, you used the normal distribution to study the distribution of download times for the OurCampus! Web site. In this chapter, you need to make a decision about the cereal-filling process, based on the weights of a sample of cereal boxes packaged at Oxford Cereals. You will learn different methods of sampling and about sampling distributions and how to use them to solve business problems.

7.1 Types of Sampling Methods

In Section 1.3, a sample was defined as the portion of a population that has been selected for analysis. Rather than selecting every item in the population, statistical sampling procedures focus on collecting a small representative group of the larger population. The results of the sample are then used to estimate characteristics of the entire population. There are three main reasons for selecting a sample:

- Selecting a sample is less time-consuming than selecting every item in the population.
- Selecting a sample is less costly than selecting every item in the population.
- An analysis of a sample is less cumbersome and more practical than an analysis of the entire population.

The sampling process begins by defining the **frame**. The frame is a listing of items that make up the population. Frames are data sources such as population lists, directories, or maps. Samples are drawn from frames. Inaccurate or biased results can occur if a frame excludes certain portions of the population. Using different frames to generate data can lead to dissimilar conclusions.

After you select a frame, you draw a sample from the frame. As illustrated in Figure 7.1, there are two kinds of samples: nonprobability samples and probability samples.

FIGURE 7.1
Types of samples

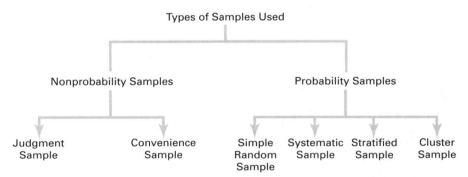

In a **nonprobability sample**, you select the items or individuals without knowing their probabilities of selection. Thus, the theory of statistical inference that has been developed for probability sampling cannot be applied to nonprobability samples. A common type of nonprobability sampling is **convenience sampling**. In convenience sampling, items selected are easy, inexpensive, or convenient to sample. For example, if you were sampling tires stacked in a warehouse, it would be much more convenient to sample tires that were at the top of a stack than tires that were at the bottom of a stack. In many cases, participants in the sample select themselves. For example, many companies conduct surveys by giving visitors to their Web site the opportunity to complete survey forms and submit them electronically. The responses to these surveys can provide large amounts of data quickly and inexpensively, but the sample consists of self-selected Web users. For many studies, only a nonprobability sample such as a judgment sample is available. In a **judgment sample**, you get the opinions of preselected experts in the subject matter. Although the experts may be well informed, you cannot generalize their results to the general public.

Nonprobability samples can have certain advantages, such as convenience, speed, and low cost. However, their lack of accuracy due to selection bias and the fact that the results cannot be used for statistical inference more than offset these advantages.

In a **probability sample**, you select the items based on known probabilities. Whenever possible, you should use probability sampling methods. Probability samples allow you to make unbiased inferences about the population of interest. The four types of probability samples most commonly used are simple random, systematic, stratified, and cluster samples. These sampling methods vary in their cost, accuracy, and complexity.

Simple Random Samples

In a **simple random sample**, every item from a frame has the same chance of selection as every other item. In addition, every sample of a fixed size has the same chance of selection as every other sample of that size. Simple random sampling is the most elementary random sampling technique. It forms the basis for the other random sampling techniques.

With simple random sampling, you use n to represent the sample size and N to represent the frame size. You number every item in the frame from 1 to N. The chance that you will select any particular member of the frame on the first selection is $1/N$.

You select samples with replacement or without replacement. **Sampling with replacement** means that after you select an item, you return it to the frame, where it has the same probability of being selected again. Imagine that you have a fishbowl containing N business cards. On the first selection, you select the card for Judy Craven. You record pertinent information and replace the business card in the bowl. You then mix up the cards in the bowl and select the second card. On the second selection, Judy Craven has the same probability of being selected again, $1/N$. You repeat this process until you have selected the desired sample size, n. However, usually you do not want the same item to be selected again.

Sampling without replacement means that once you select an item, you cannot select it again. The chance that you will select any particular item in the frame—for example, the business card for Judy Craven—on the first draw is $1/N$. The chance that you will select any card not previously selected on the second draw is now 1 out of $N - 1$. This process continues until you have selected the desired sample of size n.

Regardless of whether you have sampled with or without replacement, "fishbowl" methods of sample selection have a major drawback—the ability to thoroughly mix the cards and randomly select the sample. As a result, fishbowl methods are not very useful. You need to use less cumbersome and more scientific methods of selection.

One such method uses a **table of random numbers** (see Table E.1 in Appendix E) for selecting the sample. A table of random numbers consists of a series of digits listed in a randomly generated sequence. Because the numeric system uses 10 digits (0, 1, 2, . . . , 9), the chance that you will randomly generate any particular digit is equal to the probability of generating any other digit. This probability is 1 out of 10. Hence, if you generate a sequence of 800 digits, you would expect about 80 to be the digit 0, 80 to be the digit 1, and so on. Because every digit or sequence of digits in the table is random, the table can be read either horizontally or vertically. The margins of the table designate row numbers and column numbers. The digits themselves are grouped into sequences of five in order to make reading the table easier.

To use Table E.1 instead of a fishbowl for selecting the sample, you first need to assign code numbers to the individual items of the frame. Then you generate the random sample by reading the table of random numbers and selecting those individuals from the frame whose assigned code numbers match the digits found in the table. You can better understand the process of sample selection by studying Example 7.1.

| **EXAMPLE 7.1**

Selecting a Simple Random Sample by Using a Table of Random Numbers | A company wants to select a sample of 32 full-time workers from a population of 800 full-time employees in order to collect information on expenditures concerning a company-sponsored dental plan. How do you select a simple random sample?

SOLUTION The company decides to conduct an e-mail survey. Assuming that not everyone will respond to the survey, you need to send more than 32 surveys to get the necessary 32 responses. Assuming that 8 out of 10 full-time workers will respond to such a survey (i.e., a response rate of 80%), you decide to send 40 surveys. Because you want to send the 40 surveys to 40 different individuals, you should sample without replacement.

The frame consists of a listing of the names and e-mail addresses of all $N = 800$ full-time employees taken from the company personnel files. Thus, the frame is a complete listing of the |

population. To select the random sample of 40 employees from this frame, you use a table of random numbers. Because the frame size (800) is a three-digit number, each assigned code number must also be three digits so that every full-time worker has an equal chance of selection. You assign a code of 001 to the first full-time employee in the population listing, a code of 002 to the second full-time employee in the population listing, and so on, until a code of 800 is assigned to the Nth full-time worker in the listing. Because $N = 800$ is the largest possible coded value, you discard all three-digit code sequences greater than 800 (i.e., 801 through 999 and 000).

To select the simple random sample, you choose an arbitrary starting point from the table of random numbers. One method you can use is to close your eyes and strike the table of random numbers with a pencil. Suppose you used this procedure and you selected row 06, column 05, of Table 7.1 (which is extracted from Table E.1) as the starting point. Although you can go in any direction, in this example you read the table from left to right, in sequences of three digits, without skipping.

TABLE 7.1

Using a Table of Random Numbers

					Column			
		00000	00001	11111	11112	22222	22223	33333	33334
	Row	12345	67890	12345	67890	12345	67890	12345	67890
	01	49280	88924	35779	00283	81163	07275	89863	02348
	02	61870	41657	07468	08612	98083	97349	20775	45091
	03	43898	65923	25078	86129	78496	97653	91550	08078
	04	62993	93912	30454	84598	56095	20664	12872	64647
	05	33850	58555	51438	85507	71865	79488	76783	31708
Begin	06	97340	03364	88472	04334	63919	36394	11095	92470
selection	07	70543	29776	10087	10072	55980	64688	68239	20461
(row 06,	08	89382	93809	00796	95945	34101	81277	66090	88872
column 05)	09	37818	72142	67140	50785	22380	16703	53362	44940
	10	60430	22834	14130	96593	23298	56203	92671	15925
	11	82975	66158	84731	19436	55790	69229	28661	13675
	12	39087	71938	40355	54324	08401	26299	49420	59208
	13	55700	24586	93247	32596	11865	63397	44251	43189
	14	14756	23997	78643	75912	83832	32768	18928	57070
	15	32166	53251	70654	92827	63491	04233	33825	69662
	16	23236	73751	31888	81718	06546	83246	47651	04877
	17	45794	26926	15130	82455	78305	55058	52551	47182
	18	09893	20505	14225	68514	46427	56788	96297	78822
	19	54382	74598	91499	14523	68479	27686	46162	83554
	20	94750	89923	37089	20048	80336	94598	26940	36858
	21	70297	34135	53140	33340	42050	82341	44104	82949
	22	85157	47954	32979	26575	57600	40881	12250	73742
	23	11100	02340	12860	74697	96644	89439	28707	25815
	24	36871	50775	30592	57143	17381	68856	25853	35041
	25	23913	48357	63308	16090	51690	54607	72407	55538

Source: Data extracted from The Rand Corporation, A Million Random Digits with 100,000 Normal Deviates *(Glencoe, IL: The Free Press, 1955) and displayed in Table E.1 in Appendix E.*

The individual with code number 003 is the first full-time employee in the sample (row 06 and columns 05–07), the second individual has code number 364 (row 06 and columns 08–10), and the third individual has code number 884. Because the highest code for any employee is 800, you discard the number 884. Individuals with code numbers 720, 433, 463, 363, 109, 592, 470, and 705 are selected third through tenth, respectively.

You continue the selection process until you get the required sample size of 40 full-time employees. If any three-digit sequence repeats during the selection process, you discard the repeating sequence because you are sampling without replacement.

Systematic Samples

In a **systematic sample**, you partition the N items in the frame into n groups of k items, where

$$k = \frac{N}{n}$$

You round k to the nearest integer. To select a systematic sample, you choose the first item to be selected at random from the first k items in the frame. Then, you select the remaining $n - 1$ items by taking every kth item thereafter from the entire frame.

If the frame consists of a listing of prenumbered checks, sales receipts, or invoices, a systematic sample is faster and easier to take than a simple random sample. A systematic sample is also a convenient mechanism for collecting data from telephone books, class rosters, and consecutive items coming off an assembly line.

To take a systematic sample of $n = 40$ from the population of $N = 800$ full-time employees, you partition the frame of 800 into 40 groups, each of which contains 20 employees. You then select a random number from the first 20 individuals and include every twentieth individual after the first selection in the sample. For example, if the first random number you select is 008, your subsequent selections are 028, 048, 068, 088, 108, . . . , 768, and 788.

Although they are simpler to use, simple random sampling and systematic sampling are generally less efficient than other, more sophisticated, probability sampling methods. Even greater possibilities for selection bias and lack of representation of the population characteristics occur when using systematic samples than with simple random samples. If there is a pattern in the frame, you could have severe selection biases. To overcome the potential problem of disproportionate representation of specific groups in a sample, you can use either stratified sampling methods or cluster sampling methods.

Stratified Samples

In a **stratified sample**, you first subdivide the N items in the frame into separate subpopulations, or **strata**. A stratum is defined by some common characteristic, such as gender or year in school. You select a simple random sample within each of the strata and combine the results from the separate simple random samples. Stratified sampling is more efficient than either simple random sampling or systematic sampling because you are ensured of the representation of items across the entire population. The homogeneity of items within each stratum provides greater precision in the estimates of underlying population parameters.

EXAMPLE 7.2 Selecting a Stratified Sample	A company wants to select a sample of 32 full-time workers from a population of 800 full-time employees in order to estimate expenditures from a company-sponsored dental plan. Of the full-time employees, 25% are managers and 75% are nonmanagerial workers. How do you select the stratified sample in order for the sample to represent the correct percentage of managers and nonmanagerial workers?

SOLUTION If you assume an 80% response rate, you need to send 40 surveys to get the necessary 32 responses. The frame consists of a listing of the names and e-mail addresses of all $N = 800$ full-time employees included in the company personnel files. Because 25% of the full-time employees are managers, you first separate the frame into two strata: a subpopulation listing of all 200 managerial-level personnel and a separate subpopulation listing of all 600 full-time nonmanagerial workers. Because the first stratum consists of a listing of 200 managers, you assign three-digit code numbers from 001 to 200. Because the second stratum contains a listing of 600 nonmanagerial workers, you assign three-digit code numbers from 001 to 600.

To collect a stratified sample proportional to the sizes of the strata, you select 25% of the overall sample from the first stratum and 75% of the overall sample from the second stratum. You take two separate simple random samples, each of which is based on a distinct random starting point from a table of random numbers (Table E.1). In the first sample, you select 10 managers from the listing of 200 in the first stratum, and in the second sample, you select 30 nonmanagerial workers from the listing of 600 in the second stratum. You then combine the results to reflect the composition of the entire company.

Cluster Samples

In a **cluster sample**, you divide the N items in the frame into several clusters so that each cluster is representative of the entire population. **Clusters** are naturally occurring designations, such as counties, election districts, city blocks, households, or sales territories. You then take a random sample of one or more clusters and study all items in each selected cluster. If clusters are large, a probability-based sample taken from a single cluster is all that is needed.

Cluster sampling is often more cost-effective than simple random sampling, particularly if the population is spread over a wide geographic region. However, cluster sampling often requires a larger sample size to produce results as precise as those from simple random sampling or stratified sampling.

Problems for Section 7.1

LEARNING THE BASICS

7.1 For a population containing $N = 902$ individuals, what code number would you assign for
a. the first person on the list?
b. the fortieth person on the list?
c. the last person on the list?

7.2 For a population of $N = 902$, verify that by starting in row 05, column 01 of the table of random numbers (Table E.1), you need only six rows to select a sample of $n = 60$ *without* replacement.

7.3 Given a population of $N = 93$, starting in row 29, column 01 of the table of random numbers (Table E.1), and reading across the row, select a sample of $n = 15$
a. *without* replacement.
b. *with* replacement.

APPLYING THE CONCEPTS

7.4 For a study that consists of personal interviews with participants (rather than mail or phone surveys), explain why simple random sampling might be less practical than some other sampling methods.

7.5 You want to select a random sample of $n = 1$ from a population of three items (which are called A, B, and C). The rule for selecting the sample is: Flip a coin; if it is heads, pick item A; if it is tails, flip the coin again; this time, if it is heads, choose B; if it is tails, choose C. Explain why this is a probability sample but not a simple random sample.

7.6 A population has four members (called A, B, C, and D). You would like to select a random sample of $n = 2$, which you decide to do in the following way: Flip a coin; if it is heads, the sample will be items A and B; if it is tails, the sample will be items C and D. Although this is a random sample, it is not a simple random sample. Explain why. (If you did Problem 7.5, compare the procedure described there with the procedure described in this problem.)

7.7 The registrar of a college with a population of $N = 4,000$ full-time students is asked by the president to conduct a survey to measure satisfaction with the quality of life on campus. The following table contains a breakdown of the 4,000 registered full-time students, by gender and class designation:

	Class Designation				
Gender	Fr.	So.	Jr.	Sr.	Total
Female	700	520	500	480	2,200
Male	560	460	400	380	1,800
Total	1,260	980	900	860	4,000

The registrar intends to take a probability sample of $n = 200$ students and project the results from the sample to the entire population of full-time students.
a. If the frame available from the registrar's files is an alphabetical listing of the names of all $N = 4,000$ registered full-time students, what type of sample could you take? Discuss.
b. What is the advantage of selecting a simple random sample in (a)?
c. What is the advantage of selecting a systematic sample in (a)?
d. If the frame available from the registrar's files is a listing of the names of all $N = 4,000$ registered full-time students compiled from eight separate alphabetical lists, based on the gender and class designation breakdowns shown in the class designation table, what type of sample should you take? Discuss.
e. Suppose that each of the $N = 4,000$ registered full-time students lived in one of the 10 campus dormitories. Each dormitory accommodates 400 students. It is college policy to fully integrate students by gender and class designation in each dormitory. If the registrar is able to compile a listing of all students by dormitory, explain how you could take a cluster sample.

7.8 Prenumbered sales invoices are kept in a sales journal. The invoices are numbered from 0001 to 5000.
a. Beginning in row 16, column 01, and proceeding horizontally in Table E.1, select a simple random sample of 50 invoice numbers.
b. Select a systematic sample of 50 invoice numbers. Use the random numbers in row 20, columns 05–07, as the starting point for your selection.
c. Are the invoices selected in (a) the same as those selected in (b)? Why or why not?

7.9 Suppose that 5,000 sales invoices are separated into four strata. Stratum 1 contains 50 invoices, stratum 2 contains 500 invoices, stratum 3 contains 1,000 invoices, and stratum 4 contains 3,450 invoices. A sample of 500 sales invoices is needed.
a. What type of sampling should you do? Why?
b. Explain how you would carry out the sampling according to the method stated in (a).
c. Why is the sampling in (a) not simple random sampling?

7.2 Evaluating Survey Worthiness

Surveys are used to collect data. Nearly every day, you read or hear about survey or opinion poll results in newspapers, on the Internet, or on radio or television. To identify surveys that lack objectivity or credibility, you must critically evaluate what you read and hear by examining the worthiness of the survey. First, you must evaluate the purpose of the survey, why it was conducted, and for whom it was conducted.

The second step in evaluating the worthiness of a survey is to determine whether it was based on a probability or nonprobability sample (as discussed in Section 7.1). You need to remember that the only way to make valid statistical inferences from a sample to a population is through the use of a probability sample. Surveys that use nonprobability sampling methods are subject to serious, perhaps unintentional, biases that may make the results meaningless.

Survey Error

Even when surveys use random probability sampling methods, they are subject to potential errors. There are four types of survey errors:

- Coverage error
- Nonresponse error
- Sampling error
- Measurement error

Well-designed surveys reduce or minimize these four types of errors, often at considerable cost.

Coverage Error The key to proper sample selection is an adequate frame. Remember, a frame is an up-to-date list of all the items from which you will select the sample. **Coverage error** occurs if certain groups of items are excluded from this frame so that they have no chance of being selected in the sample. Coverage error results in a **selection bias.** If the frame is inadequate because certain groups of items in the population were not properly included, any random probability sample selected will only provide an estimate of the characteristics of the frame, not the *actual* population.

Nonresponse Error Not everyone is willing to respond to a survey. In fact, research has shown that individuals in the upper and lower economic classes tend to respond less frequently to surveys than do people in the middle class. **Nonresponse error** arises from the failure to collect data on all items in the sample and results in a **nonresponse bias.** Because you cannot always assume that persons who do not respond to surveys are similar to those who do, you need to follow up on the nonresponses after a specified period of time. You should make several attempts to convince such individuals to complete the survey. The follow-up responses are then compared to the initial responses in order to make valid inferences from the survey. The mode of response you use affects the rate of response. The personal interview and the telephone interview usually produce a higher response rate than does the mail survey—but at a higher cost.

Sampling Error A sample is selected because it is simpler, less costly, and more efficient. However, chance dictates which individuals or items will or will not be included in the sample. **Sampling error** reflects the variation, or "chance differences," from sample to sample, based on the probability of particular individuals or items being selected in the particular samples.

When you read about the results of surveys or polls in newspapers or magazines, there is often a statement regarding a margin of error, such as "the results of this poll are expected to be within ±4 percentage points of the actual value." This **margin of error** is the sampling error. You can reduce sampling error by taking larger sample sizes, although this also increases the cost of conducting the survey.

Measurement Error In the practice of good survey research, you design a questionnaire with the intention of gathering meaningful information. But you have a dilemma here: Getting meaningful measurements is often easier said than done. Consider the following proverb:

A person with one watch always knows what time it is;

A person with two watches always searches to identify the correct one;

A person with ten watches is always reminded of the difficulty in measuring time.

Unfortunately, the process of measurement is often governed by what is convenient, not what is needed. The measurements you get are often only a proxy for the ones you really desire. Much attention has been given to measurement error that occurs because of a weakness in question wording. A question should be clear, not ambiguous. Furthermore, in order to avoid *leading questions*, you need to present them in a neutral manner.

Three sources of **measurement error** are ambiguous wording of questions, the Hawthorne effect, and respondent error. As an example of ambiguous wording, in November 1993, the U.S. Department of Labor reported that the unemployment rate in the United States had been underestimated for more than a decade because of poor questionnaire wording in the Current Population Survey. In particular, the wording had led to a significant undercount of women in the labor force. Because unemployment rates are tied to benefit programs such as state unemployment compensation, survey researchers had to rectify the situation by adjusting the questionnaire wording.

The "Hawthorne effect" occurs when the respondent feels obligated to please the interviewer. Proper interviewer training can minimize the Hawthorne effect.

Respondent error occurs as a result of an overzealous or underzealous effort by the respondent. You can minimize this error in two ways: (1) by carefully scrutinizing the data and then recontacting those individuals whose responses seem unusual and (2) by establishing a program of recontacting a small number of randomly chosen individuals in order to determine the reliability of the responses.

Ethical Issues

Ethical considerations arise with respect to the four types of potential errors that can occur when designing surveys: coverage error, nonresponse error, sampling error, and measurement error. Coverage error can result in selection bias and becomes an ethical issue if particular groups or individuals are *purposely* excluded from the frame so that the survey results are more favorable to the survey's sponsor. Nonresponse error can lead to nonresponse bias and becomes an ethical issue if the sponsor knowingly designs the survey so that particular groups or individuals are less likely than others to respond. Sampling error becomes an ethical issue if the findings are purposely presented without reference to sample size and margin of error so that the sponsor can promote a viewpoint that might otherwise be truly insignificant. Measurement error becomes an ethical issue in one of three ways: (1) a survey sponsor chooses leading questions that guide the responses in a particular direction; (2) an interviewer, through mannerisms and tone, purposely creates a Hawthorne effect or otherwise guides the responses in a particular direction; or (3) a respondent willfully provides false information.

Ethical issues also arise when the results of nonprobability samples are used to form conclusions about the entire population. When you use a nonprobability sampling method, you need to explain the sampling procedures and state that the results cannot be generalized beyond the sample.

THINK ABOUT THIS   Probability Sampling vs. Web-Based Surveys

In Sections 7.1 and 7.2, you learned that statistical inferences about populations can only be made by analyzing data collected from probability samples. This type of sampling has been the "gold standard" in survey research for more than fifty years. Companies using surveys based on probability sampling typically make a great effort (and spend large sums) to deal with coverage error, nonresponse error, sampling error, and measurement error.

A recent article (T. Crampton, "About Online Surveys, Traditional Pollsters Are Somewhat Disappointed," **http://www.nytimes.com/2007/05/31/business media**), reported that some survey companies are offering an Internet alternative to traditional surveys based on random sampling. YouGov, a British company, is planning to introduce Internet-based polling in the United States for the 2008 presidential election.

YouGov uses a large panel of respondents who answer questions online. These panelists supposedly come from a diverse group with special efforts made to include people who are less likely to use the Internet. In addition, panelists are paid to participate. This method of sampling (and the fact that respondents are paid and are not volunteers) makes Web-based sampling scientifically unacceptable to traditional pollsters.

Despite these concerns, YouGov has partnered with Polimetrix, an online company based in Palo Alto, California, to conduct surveys in the United States. The founder of Polimetrix, Professor Douglas Rivers of Stanford University, claims that the margin of error of Polimetrix polls is similar to telephone polls. YouGov's chief executive, Nadhim Zahawi, points out that modern technology, such as cell phones, has made old-fashioned polls more unreliable due to the increased difficulty of contacting people at home. In fact, a recent article (M. Thee, "Cellphones Challenge Poll Sampling," *The New York Times*, December 7, 2007, p. A27) indicated that cell-phone-only households make up 16% of the households in the United States.

However, Leendert de Voogd, managing director of TSN Opinion in Brussels, believes that "Internet polling is like the Wild West, with no rules, no sheriff, and no reference points." He believes that only polling with probability sampling will deliver valid results. On the other hand, Professor Anthony King of the University of Essex does not believe that Internet polling fails to reflect a nation's population. According to Professor King, "There is no evidence to suggest that people who use the Internet are fundamentally different from those without it. One mad, awful lady living in a poor neighborhood without Internet does not differ much from her mad, awful friend next door who goes online." Perhaps only time will tell who is right.

Problems for Section 7.2

APPLYING THE CONCEPTS

7.10 "A survey indicates that the vast majority of college students own their own personal computers." What information would you want to know before you accepted the results of this survey?

7.11 A simple random sample of $n = 300$ full-time employees is selected from a company list containing the names of all $N = 5,000$ full-time employees in order to evaluate job satisfaction.
a. Give an example of possible coverage error.
b. Give an example of possible nonresponse error.
c. Give an example of possible sampling error.
d. Give an example of possible measurement error.

7.12 Business professor Thomas Callarman traveled to China more than a dozen times from 2000 to 2005. He warns people about believing everything they read about surveys conducted in China and gives two specific reasons. Callarman stated, "First, things are changing so rapidly that what you hear today may not be true tomorrow. Second, the people who answer the surveys may tell you what they think you want to hear, rather than what they really believe" (T. E. Callarman, "Some Thoughts on China," *Decision Line*, March, 2006, pp. 1, 43–44).

a. List the four types of survey error discussed in this section.
b. Which of the types of survey errors in (a) are the basis for Professor Callarman's two reasons to question the surveys being conducted in China?

7.13 A recent survey of college freshmen investigated the amount of involvement their parents have with decisions concerning their education. When asked about the decision to go to college, 84% said their parents' involvement was about right, 10.3% said too much, and 5.7% said too little. When it came to selecting individual courses, 72.5% said their parents' involvement was about right, 3.5% said too much, and 24.0% said too little (M. B. Marklein, "Study: Colleges Shouldn't Fret Over Hands-On Parents," **usatoday.com**, January 23, 2008). What additional information would you want to know about the survey before you accepted the results of the study?

7.14 Seventy-three percent of Americans say now is a bad time to find a quality job, according to a Gallup Poll taken May 16, 2008. ("Americans' Job Market Worries," *The Gallup Poll*, **galluppoll.com**, May 16, 2008.) What additional information would you want to know before you accepted the results of the survey?

7.3 Sampling Distributions

In many applications, you want to make inferences that are based on statistics calculated from samples to estimate the values of population parameters. In the next two sections, you will learn about how the sample mean (a statistic) is used to estimate the population mean (a parameter) and how the sample proportion (a statistic) is used to estimate the population proportion (a parameter). Your main concern when making a statistical inference is drawing conclusions about a population, *not* about a sample. For example, a political pollster is interested in the sample results only as a way of estimating the actual proportion of the votes that each candidate will receive from the population of voters. Likewise, as plant operations manager for Oxford Cereals, you are only interested in using the sample mean weight calculated from a sample of cereal boxes for estimating the mean weight contained in a population of boxes.

In practice, you select a single random sample of a predetermined size from the population. Hypothetically, to use the sample statistic to estimate the population parameter, you could examine *every* possible sample of a given size that could occur. A **sampling distribution** is the distribution of the results if you actually selected all possible samples. The single result you obtain in practice is just one of the results in the sampling distribution.

7.4 Sampling Distribution of the Mean

In Chapter 3, several measures of central tendency, including the mean, median, and mode, were discussed. Undoubtedly, the mean is the most widely used measure of central tendency. The sample mean is often used to estimate the population mean. The **sampling distribution of the mean** is the distribution of all possible sample means if you select all possible samples of a given size.

The Unbiased Property of the Sample Mean

The sample mean is **unbiased** because the mean of all the possible sample means (of a given sample size, n) is equal to the population mean, μ. A simple example concerning a population of four administrative assistants demonstrates this property. Each assistant is asked to type the same page of a manuscript. Table 7.2 presents the number of errors. This population distribution is shown in Figure 7.2.

TABLE 7.2

Number of Errors Made by Each of Four Administrative Assistants

Administrative Assistant	Number of Errors
Ann	$X_1 = 3$
Bob	$X_2 = 2$
Carla	$X_3 = 1$
Dave	$X_4 = 4$

FIGURE 7.2

Number of errors made by a population of four administrative assistants

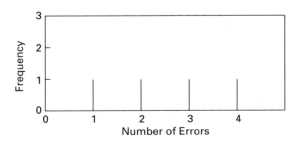

When you have the data from a population, you compute the mean by using Equation (7.1).

POPULATION MEAN

The population mean is the sum of the values in the population divided by the population size, N.

$$\mu = \frac{\sum_{i=1}^{N} X_i}{N} \tag{7.1}$$

You compute the population standard deviation, σ, using Equation (7.2):

POPULATION STANDARD DEVIATION

$$\sigma = \sqrt{\frac{\sum_{i=1}^{N} (X_i - \mu)^2}{N}} \tag{7.2}$$

Thus, for the data of Table 7.2,

$$\mu = \frac{3 + 2 + 1 + 4}{4} = 2.5 \text{ errors}$$

and

$$\sigma = \sqrt{\frac{(3 - 2.5)^2 + (2 - 2.5)^2 + (1 - 2.5)^2 + (4 - 2.5)^2}{4}} = 1.12 \text{ errors}$$

If you select samples of two administrative assistants *with* replacement from this population, there are 16 possible samples ($N^n = 4^2 = 16$). Table 7.3 lists the 16 possible sample outcomes. If you average all 16 of these sample means, the mean of these values, $\mu_{\bar{X}}$, is equal to 2.5, which is also the mean of the population μ.

TABLE 7.3

All 16 Samples of $n = 2$ Administrative Assistants from a Population of $N = 4$ Administrative Assistants When Sampling with Replacement

Sample	Administrative Assistants	Sample Outcomes	Sample Means
1	Ann, Ann	3, 3	$\bar{X}_1 = 3$
2	Ann, Bob	3, 2	$\bar{X}_2 = 2.5$
3	Ann, Carla	3, 1	$\bar{X}_3 = 2$
4	Ann, Dave	3, 4	$\bar{X}_4 = 3.5$
5	Bob, Ann	2, 3	$\bar{X}_5 = 2.5$
6	Bob, Bob	2, 2	$\bar{X}_6 = 2$
7	Bob, Carla	2, 1	$\bar{X}_7 = 1.5$
8	Bob, Dave	2, 4	$\bar{X}_8 = 3$
9	Carla, Ann	1, 3	$\bar{X}_9 = 2$
10	Carla, Bob	1, 2	$\bar{X}_{10} = 1.5$
11	Carla, Carla	1, 1	$\bar{X}_{11} = 1$
12	Carla, Dave	1, 4	$\bar{X}_{12} = 2.5$
13	Dave, Ann	4, 3	$\bar{X}_{13} = 3.5$
14	Dave, Bob	4, 2	$\bar{X}_{14} = 3$
15	Dave, Carla	4, 1	$\bar{X}_{15} = 2.5$
16	Dave, Dave	4, 4	$\bar{X}_{16} = 4$
			$\mu_{\bar{X}} = 2.5$

Because the mean of the 16 sample means is equal to the population mean, the sample mean is an unbiased estimator of the population mean. Therefore, although you do not know how close the sample mean of any particular sample selected comes to the population mean, you are at least assured that the mean of all the possible sample means that could have been selected is equal to the population mean.

Standard Error of the Mean

Figure 7.3 illustrates the variation in the sample means when selecting all 16 possible samples. In this small example, although the sample means vary from sample to sample, depending on which two administrative assistants are selected, the sample means do not vary as much as the individual values in the population. That the sample means are less variable than the individual values in the population follows directly from the fact that each sample mean averages together all the values in the sample. A population consists of individual outcomes that can take on a wide range of values, from extremely small to extremely large. However, if a sample contains an extreme value, although this value will have an effect on the sample mean, the effect is reduced because the value is averaged with all the other values in the sample. As the sample size increases, the effect of a single extreme value becomes smaller because it is averaged with more values.

FIGURE 7.3

Sampling distribution of the mean, based on all possible samples containing two administrative assistants

Source: Data are from Table 7.3

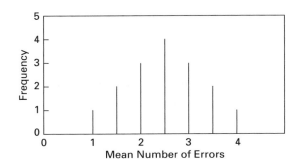

The value of the standard deviation of all possible sample means, called the **standard error of the mean**, expresses how the sample means vary from sample to sample. Equation (7.3) defines the standard error of the mean when sampling *with* replacement or *without* replacement from large or infinite populations.

STANDARD ERROR OF THE MEAN

The standard error of the mean, $\sigma_{\bar{X}}$, is equal to the standard deviation in the population, σ, divided by the square root of the sample size, n.

$$\sigma_{\bar{X}} = \frac{\sigma}{\sqrt{n}} \tag{7.3}$$

Therefore, as the sample size increases, the standard error of the mean decreases by a factor equal to the square root of the sample size.

You can also use Equation (7.3) as an approximation of the standard error of the mean when the sample is selected without replacement if the sample contains less than 5% of the entire population. Example 7.3 computes the standard error of the mean for such a situation.

EXAMPLE 7.3	Returning to the cereal-filling process described in the Using Statistics scenario on page 297, if you randomly select a sample of 25 boxes without replacement from the thousands of boxes filled during a shift, the sample contains far less than 5% of the population. Given that the standard deviation of the cereal-filling process is 15 grams, compute the standard error of the mean.
Computing the Standard Error of the Mean	

SOLUTION Using Equation (7.3) with $n = 25$ and $\sigma = 15$, the standard error of the mean is

$$\sigma_{\bar{X}} = \frac{\sigma}{\sqrt{n}} = \frac{15}{\sqrt{25}} = \frac{15}{5} = 3$$

The variation in the sample means for samples of $n = 25$ is much less than the variation in the individual boxes of cereal (i.e., $\sigma_{\bar{X}} = 3$ while $\sigma = 15$).

Sampling from Normally Distributed Populations

Now that the concept of a sampling distribution has been introduced and the standard error of the mean has been defined, what distribution will the sample mean, $\overline{X}$, follow? If you are sampling from a population that is normally distributed with mean, μ, and standard deviation, σ, then regardless of the sample size, n, the sampling distribution of the mean is normally distributed, with mean, $\mu_{\overline{X}} = \mu$, and standard error of the mean, $\sigma_{\overline{X}} = \sigma/\sqrt{n}$.

In the simplest case, if you take samples of size $n = 1$, each possible sample mean is a single value from the population because

$$\overline{X} = \frac{\sum\limits_{i=1}^{n} X_i}{n} = \frac{X_1}{1} = X_1$$

Therefore, if the population is normally distributed, with mean, μ, and standard deviation, σ, the sampling distribution of $\overline{X}$ for samples of $n = 1$ must also follow the normal distribution, with mean $\mu_{\overline{X}} = \mu$ and standard error of the mean $\sigma_{\overline{X}} = \sigma/\sqrt{1} = \sigma$. In addition, as the sample size increases, the sampling distribution of the mean still follows a normal distribution, with $\mu_{\overline{X}} = \mu$, but the standard error of the mean decreases, so that a larger proportion of sample means are closer to the population mean. Figure 7.4 below illustrates this reduction in variability. Note that 500 samples of 1, 2, 4, 8, 16, and 32 were randomly selected from a normally distributed population. From the polygons in Figure 7.4, you can see that, although the sampling distribution of the mean is approximately[1] normal for each sample size, the sample means are distributed more tightly around the population mean as the sample size increases.

[1]Remember that "only" 500 samples out of an infinite number of samples have been selected, so that the sampling distributions shown are only approximations of the true population distributions.

FIGURE 7.4

Sampling distributions of the mean from 500 samples of sizes $n = 1, 2, 4, 8, 16,$ and 32 selected from a normal population

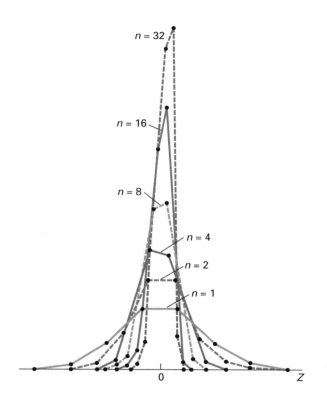

To further examine the concept of the sampling distribution of the mean, consider the Using Statistics scenario. The packaging equipment that is filling 368-gram boxes of cereal is set so that the amount of cereal in a box is normally distributed, with a mean of 368 grams. From past experience, you know the population standard deviation for this filling process is 15 grams.

If you randomly select a sample of 25 boxes from the many thousands that are filled in a day and the mean weight is computed for this sample, what type of result could you expect? For example, do you think that the sample mean could be 368 grams? 200 grams? 365 grams?

The sample acts as a miniature representation of the population, so if the values in the population are normally distributed, the values in the sample should be approximately normally distributed. Thus, if the population mean is 368 grams, the sample mean has a good chance of being close to 368 grams.

How can you determine the probability that the sample of 25 boxes will have a mean below 365 grams? From the normal distribution (Section 6.2), you know that you can find the area below any value X by converting to standardized Z values:

$$Z = \frac{X - \mu}{\sigma}$$

In the examples in Section 6.2, you studied how any single value, X, differs from the population mean. Now, in this example, you want to study how a sample mean, $\overline{X}$ differs from the population mean. Substituting $\overline{X}$ for X, $\mu_{\overline{X}}$ for μ, and $\sigma_{\overline{X}}$ for σ in the equation above results in Equation (7.4).

FINDING Z FOR THE SAMPLING DISTRIBUTION OF THE MEAN

The Z value is equal to the difference between the sample mean, $\overline{X}$, and the population mean, μ, divided by the standard error of the mean, $\sigma_{\overline{X}}$.

$$Z = \frac{\overline{X} - \mu_{\overline{X}}}{\sigma_{\overline{X}}} = \frac{\overline{X} - \mu}{\dfrac{\sigma}{\sqrt{n}}} \tag{7.4}$$

To find the area below 365 grams, from Equation (7.4),

$$Z = \frac{\overline{X} - \mu_{\overline{X}}}{\sigma_{\overline{X}}} = \frac{365 - 368}{\dfrac{15}{\sqrt{25}}} = \frac{-3}{3} = -1.00$$

The area corresponding to $Z = -1.00$ in Table E.2 is 0.1587. Therefore, 15.87% of all the possible samples of 25 boxes have a sample mean below 365 grams.

The preceding statement is not the same as saying that a certain percentage of *individual* boxes will have less than 365 grams of cereal. You compute that percentage as follows:

$$Z = \frac{X - \mu}{\sigma} = \frac{365 - 368}{15} = \frac{-3}{15} = -0.20$$

The area corresponding to $Z = -0.20$ in Table E.2 is 0.4207. Therefore, 42.07% of the *individual* boxes are expected to contain less than 365 grams. Comparing these results, you see that many more *individual boxes* than *sample means* are below 365 grams. This result is explained by the fact that each sample consists of 25 different values, some small and some large. The averaging process dilutes the importance of any individual value, particularly when the sample size is large. Thus, the chance that the sample mean of 25 boxes is far away from the population mean is less than the chance that a *single* box is far away.

Examples 7.4 and 7.5 show how these results are affected by using different sample sizes.

EXAMPLE 7.4

The Effect of Sample Size *n* on the Computation of $\sigma_{\bar{X}}$

How is the standard error of the mean affected by increasing the sample size from 25 to 100 boxes?

SOLUTION If $n = 100$ boxes, then using Equation (7.3) on page 314:

$$\sigma_{\bar{X}} = \frac{\sigma}{\sqrt{n}} = \frac{15}{\sqrt{100}} = \frac{15}{10} = 1.5$$

The fourfold increase in the sample size from 25 to 100 reduces the standard error of the mean by half—from 3 grams to 1.5 grams. This demonstrates that taking a larger sample results in less variability in the sample means from sample to sample.

EXAMPLE 7.5

The Effect of Sample Size *n* on the Clustering of Means in the Sampling Distribution

If you select a sample of 100 boxes, what is the probability that the sample mean is below 365 grams?

SOLUTION Using Equation (7.4) on page 316,

$$Z = \frac{\bar{X} - \mu_{\bar{X}}}{\sigma_{\bar{X}}} = \frac{365 - 368}{\dfrac{15}{\sqrt{100}}} = \frac{-3}{1.5} = -2.00$$

From Table E.2, the area less than $Z = -2.00$ is 0.0228. Therefore, 2.28% of the samples of 100 boxes have means below 365 grams, as compared with 15.87% for samples of 25 boxes.

Sometimes you need to find the interval that contains a fixed proportion of the sample means. You need to determine a distance below and above the population mean containing a specific area of the normal curve. From Equation (7.4) on page 316,

$$Z = \frac{\bar{X} - \mu}{\dfrac{\sigma}{\sqrt{n}}}$$

Solving for $\bar{X}$ results in Equation (7.5).

FINDING $\bar{X}$ FOR THE SAMPLING DISTRIBUTION OF THE MEAN

$$\bar{X} = \mu + Z\frac{\sigma}{\sqrt{n}} \qquad\qquad (7.5)$$

Example 7.6 illustrates the use of Equation (7.5).

EXAMPLE 7.6

Determining the Interval That Includes a Fixed Proportion of the Sample Means

In the cereal-fill example, find an interval symmetrically distributed around the population mean that will include 95% of the sample means based on samples of 25 boxes.

SOLUTION If 95% of the sample means are in the interval, then 5% are outside the interval. Divide the 5% into two equal parts of 2.5%. The value of Z in Table E.2 corresponding to an area of 0.0250 in the lower tail of the normal curve is -1.96, and the value of Z corresponding to a cumulative area of 0.9750 (i.e., 0.0250 in the upper tail of the normal curve) is $+1.96$. The lower value of $\bar{X}$ (called $\bar{X}_L$) and the upper value of $\bar{X}$ (called $\bar{X}_U$) are found by using Equation (7.5):

$$\bar{X}_L = 368 + (-1.96)\frac{15}{\sqrt{25}} = 368 - 5.88 = 362.12$$

$$\bar{X}_U = 368 + (1.96)\frac{15}{\sqrt{25}} = 368 + 5.88 = 373.88$$

Therefore, 95% of all sample means based on samples of 25 boxes are between 362.12 and 373.88 grams.

Sampling from Non-Normally Distributed Populations—The Central Limit Theorem

Thus far in this section, only the sampling distribution of the mean for a normally distributed population has been considered. However, in many instances, either you know that the population is not normally distributed or it is unrealistic to assume that the population is normally distributed. An important theorem in statistics, the Central Limit Theorem, deals with this situation.

THE CENTRAL LIMIT THEOREM

The **Central Limit Theorem** states that as the sample size (i.e., the number of values in each sample) gets *large enough*, the sampling distribution of the mean is approximately normally distributed. This is true regardless of the shape of the distribution of the individual values in the population.

What sample size is large enough? A great deal of statistical research has gone into this issue. As a general rule, statisticians have found that for many population distributions, when the sample size is at least 30, the sampling distribution of the mean is approximately normal. However, you can apply the Central Limit Theorem for even smaller sample sizes if the population distribution is approximately bell shaped. In the uncommon case in which the distribution is extremely skewed or has more than one mode, you may need sample sizes larger than 30 to ensure normality.

Figure 7.5 illustrates the application of the Central Limit Theorem to different populations. The sampling distributions from three different continuous distributions (normal, uniform, and exponential) for varying sample sizes ($n = 2, 5, 30$) are displayed.

FIGURE 7.5

Sampling distribution of the mean for different populations for samples of $n = 2$, 5, and 30

See Section E7.2 to create a simulated sampling distribution.

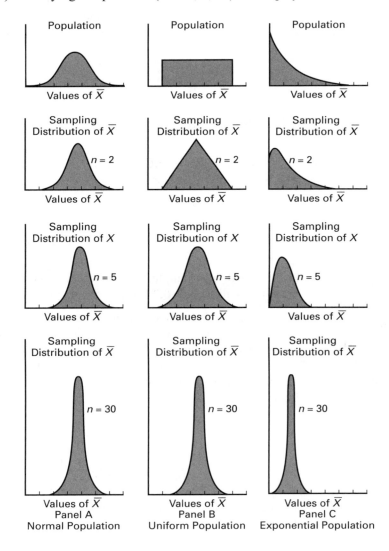

In each of the panels, because the sample mean has the property of being unbiased, the mean of any sampling distribution is always equal to the mean of the population.

Panel A of Figure 7.5 shows the sampling distribution of the mean selected from a normal population. As mentioned earlier in this section, when the population is normally distributed, the sampling distribution of the mean is normally distributed for any sample size. [You can measure the variability by using the standard error of the mean, Equation (7.3), on page 308.]

Panel B of Figure 7.5 depicts the sampling distribution from a population with a uniform (or rectangular) distribution (see Section 6.1). When samples of size $n = 2$ are selected, there is a peaking, or *central limiting*, effect already working. For $n = 5$, the sampling distribution is bell shaped and approximately normal. When $n = 30$, the sampling distribution looks very similar to a normal distribution. In general, the larger the sample size, the more closely the sampling distribution will follow a normal distribution. As with all cases, the mean of each sampling distribution is equal to the mean of the population, and the variability decreases as the sample size increases.

Panel C of Figure 7.5 presents an exponential distribution (see Section 6.1). This population is extremely right-skewed. When $n = 2$, the sampling distribution is still highly right-skewed but less so than the distribution of the population. For $n = 5$, the sampling distribution is slightly right-skewed. When $n = 30$, the sampling distribution looks approximately normal. Again, the mean of each sampling distribution is equal to the mean of the population, and the variability decreases as the sample size increases.

Using the results from the normal, uniform, and exponential distributions, you can reach the following conclusions regarding the Central Limit Theorem:

- For most population distributions, regardless of shape, the sampling distribution of the mean is approximately normally distributed if samples of at least size 30 are selected.
- If the population distribution is fairly symmetric, the sampling distribution of the mean is approximately normal for samples as small as size 5.
- If the population is normally distributed, the sampling distribution of the mean is normally distributed, regardless of the sample size.

The Central Limit Theorem is of crucial importance in using statistical inference to draw conclusions about a population. It allows you to make inferences about the population mean without having to know the specific shape of the population distribution.

VISUAL EXPLORATIONS   Exploring Sampling Distributions

Use the Visual Explorations **Two Dice Probability** procedure to observe the effects of simulated throws on the frequency distribution of the sum of the two dice. Open the **Visual Explorations.xla** add-in workbook and select **VisualExplorations ➔ Two Dice Probability** (Excel 97-2003) or **Add-Ins ➔ VisualExplorations ➔ Two Dice Probability** (Excel 2007). The procedure produces a worksheet that contains an empty frequency distribution table and histogram and a floating control panel (see right).

Click the **Tally** button to tally a set of throws in the frequency distribution table and histogram. Optionally, use the spinner buttons to adjust the number of throws per tally (round). Click the **Help** button for more information about this simulation. Click **Finish** when you are done with this exploration.

Problems for Section 7.4

LEARNING THE BASICS

7.15 Given a normal distribution with $\mu = 100$ and $\sigma = 10$, if you select a sample of $n = 25$, what is the probability that $\bar{X}$ is
a. less than 95?
b. between 95 and 97.5?
c. above 102.2?
d. There is a 65% chance that $\bar{X}$ is above what value?

7.16 Given a normal distribution with $\mu = 50$ and $\sigma = 5$, if you select a sample of $n = 100$, what is the probability that $\bar{X}$ is
a. less than 47?
b. between 47 and 49.5?
c. above 51.1?
d. There is a 35% chance that $\bar{X}$ is above what value?

APPLYING THE CONCEPTS

Central Limit Theorem Template:

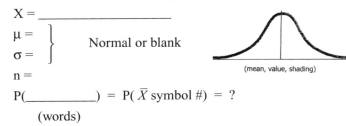

$X =$ _____

$\left.\begin{array}{l} \mu = \\ \sigma = \end{array}\right\}$ Normal or blank

$n =$

$P(\underline{\qquad}) = P(\bar{X} \text{ symbol } \#) = ?$

  (words)

Info about $\bar{X}$

1. $\mu_{\bar{x}} = \mu =$

2. $\sigma_{\bar{x}} = \dfrac{\sigma}{\sqrt{n}} =$

3. a) Original population is normal, therefore $\bar{X}$ is normal.

   OR

   b) Original population is not normal, but $\bar{X}$ is normal because n ≥ 30.

$P(\bar{X} \text{ symbol } \#) =$ _____ $= 0.\_\_\_\_$
         (calc. or SPSS input)   (4 dec.)

7.17 For each of the following three populations, indicate what the sampling distribution for samples of 25 would consist of:
a. Travel expense vouchers for a university in an academic year
b. Absentee records (days absent per year) in 2007 for employees of a large manufacturing company
c. Yearly sales (in gallons) of unleaded gasoline at service stations located in a particular state

7.18 The following data represent the number of days absent per year in a population of six employees of a small company:

         1   3   6   7   9   10

a. Assuming that you sample without replacement, select all possible samples of $n = 2$ and construct the sampling distribution of the mean. Compute the mean of all the sample means and also compute the population mean. Are they equal? What is this property called?
b. Repeat (a) for all possible samples of $n = 3$.
c. Compare the shape of the sampling distribution of the mean in (a) and (b). Which sampling distribution has less variability? Why?
d. Assuming that you sample with replacement, repeat (a) through (c) and compare the results. Which sampling distributions have the least variability—those in (a) or (b)? Why?

7.19 The diameter of a brand of Ping-Pong balls is approximately normally distributed, with a mean of 1.30 inches and a standard deviation of 0.04 inch. If you select a random sample of 16 Ping-Pong balls,
a. what is the sampling distribution of the mean?
b. what is the probability that the sample mean is less than 1.28 inches?
c. what is the probability that the sample mean is between 1.31 and 1.33 inches?
d. The probability is 60% that the sample mean will be between what two values, symmetrically distributed around the population mean?

7.20 The U.S. Census Bureau announced that the median sales price of new houses sold in February 2008 was $244,100, whereas the mean sales price was $296,400 (**www.census.gov/newhomesales**, March 28, 2008). Assume that the standard deviation of the prices is $90,000.
a. If you select samples of $n = 2$, describe the shape of the sampling distribution of $\bar{X}$.
b. If you select samples of $n = 100$, describe the shape of the sampling distribution of $\bar{X}$.
c. If you select a random sample of $n = 100$, what is the probability that the sample mean will be less than $300,000?
d. If you select a random sample of $n = 100$, what is the probability that the sample mean will be between $275,000 and $290,000?

7.21 Time spent using e-mail per session is normally distributed, with $\mu = 8$ minutes and $\sigma = 2$ minutes. If you select a random sample of 25 sessions,
a. what is the probability that the sample mean is between 7.8 and 8.2 minutes?
b. what is the probability that the sample mean is between 7.5 and 8 minutes?
c. If you select a random sample of 100 sessions, what is the probability that the sample mean is between 7.8 and 8.2 minutes?
d. Explain the difference in the results of (a) and (c).

7.22 The amount of time a bank teller spends with each customer has a population mean, μ, of 3.10 minutes and standard deviation, σ, of 0.40 minute. If you select a random sample of 16 customers,

a. what is the probability that the mean time spent per customer is at least 3 minutes?

b. there is an 85% chance that the sample mean is less than how many minutes?

c. What assumption must you make in order to solve (a) and (b)?

d. If you select a random sample of 64 customers, there is an 85% chance that the sample mean is less than how many minutes?

PROBABILITY DISTRIBUTIONS—REVIEW EXERCISES

7.23 A manufacturing company anticipates that its daily demand for electric power during the next few months will fluctuate around a mean of 100.0 kilowatts. Based on past results, the daily power usage distribution should be normally distributed with a standard deviation of 10.0 kilowatts.

a. What is the probability that the demand for electric power on a given day will range from 90.0 to 125.0 kilowatts? (0.8351)

b. What is the level of usage that will be exceeded only 20 percent of the time? (108.4 kw)

7.24 The defects in an automatic weaving process occur randomly at an average rate of 0.0025 per square metre and a standard deviation of 0.05 per square metre.The process has just been set up to run 1000 square meters of fabric. What is the probability that there will be at least 4 defects in this fabric? (0.2424)

7.25 The occurrence of the first breakdown of an automatic washing machine is normally distributed with a mean of 5.9 years and a standard deviation of 1.5 years. How long (full years) should these washing machines be guaranteed so that no more than 10% would require repairs during the warrantee period? (4 years)

7.26 A large company is currently evaluating 14 cost-reducing proposals submitted by employees. Past experience has shown that 30 percent of such proposals are implemented by the company.

a. What is the probability that more than 5 proposals will be implemented? (0.2195)

b. What is the probability that at least half of the proposals will be implemented? (0.0933)

c. What is the expected number of proposals implemented? (4.2)

7.27 The manufacturer of a quartz travel clock claims that, on average, its clocks deviate from perfect time by an average of 30 seconds in a month, with a standard deviation of 10 seconds. The test group that works for a consumer magazine purchased 40 of these clocks and found that the average deviation from perfect time was 35 seconds after one month.

a. If the manufacturer's claim is correct, what is the probability that the average deviation from perfect time for the 40 clocks would be 35 seconds or more? (0.0008)

b. If the average clock deviates by 33 seconds from perfect in one month, what is the probability that the average deviation from perfect time for the 40 clocks would be 35 seconds or more? (0.1030)

7.28 The Executours Corp. offers tours of the city to visiting businesspersons and uses a 12-passenger luxury bus. From past experience 10% of the people who make advance reservations will cancel at the last minute, therefore, Executours usually takes 13 reservations. For what percent of tours will they have enough seats for the passengers who show up for the tour? (74.6%)

7.29 The number of man-hours required by the Victory Construction Co. to assemble its prefabricated 2-bedroom house is normally distributed with a mean of 400 man-hours and a standard deviation of 40 man-hours.

a. The probability is 0.9 that the assembly of a house will take less than how many hours? (451 hours)

b. What is the probability that assembly of a house will take more than 420 man-hours? (0.3085)

7.30 There are two major steps in the production of solar covers for swimming pools. First, a 1 metre wide continuous strip of plastic air bubble material is produced. Then the material is cut to the required length (in this case 10 metres) and an appropriate number of these strips are sewn together to produce a solar cover.

Records kept by the quality control department indicate that on average:

i. there is 1 puncture in every 1,000 m^2 of plastic material.

ii. there is 1 sewing defect for every 1,500 m. of sewing.

For a 4 m. by 10 m. solar cover:

a. What is the probability that the cover will not have a puncture? (0.9608)

b. What is the probability that the cover will not have a sewing defect? (0.9802)

7.31 In an attempt to improve sales, the management of a large chain of fast food restaurants has decided to implement a Reward/Reprimand system based on monthly sales figures. The initial standards have been set up as follows:

i. Reward the mangers of restaurants that have placed in the top 15% of sales for the month.

ii. Reprimand managers with sales less than $180,000 for the month.

For the month just past, the sales figures for the 4,350 restaurants were normally distributed with a mean of $230,000 and a standard deviation of $22,000.

a. How many managers will be reprimanded? (50)

b. What will be the minimum sales that will qualify for a reward? ($252,802)

7.32 A checkout counter is considered 'over-occupied' if more than 8 customers arrive within a five-minute period. The average number of customers per hour is 78.
a. What is the probability that in one minute at most two customers arrive?　(0.8571)
b. What is the probability that the counter is 'over-occupied' in a five-minute period?　(0.2084)

7.33A From past experience, an airline has found that the luggage weight for individual air travelers on their trans-Atlantic route averages 40 kilograms with a standard deviation of 10 kg. The plane consistently is booked with 100 passengers. The pilot insists on loading an extra 500 litres of fuel whenever the total luggage weight exceeds 4200 kg. On what percent of the flights will the extra fuel be required? (2.28%)

7.33B The manufacturing process for automobile windshields involves placing a plastic adhesive film between two panes of glass. Then high pressure is applied to bond the three layers. The glass is then cut and bent to the required shape.

Quality standards require that there are no bubbles in order for a windshield to be considered suitable for installation into an automobile. Also the glass must withstand an impact of 10 kg. dropped from a height of 3 metres. The thickness of the finished windshield must be from 3.2 to 3.4 mm.

The High-Lite Glass Company makes rectangular windshield glass in sheets that are 2 metres wide by 1.5 metres high. Their process usually averages 0.39 bubbles per sheet. Usually, only 3% of the windshields made from their glass fail the impact test.

One particular auto manufacturer just ordered 20 sheets of glass, which will be enough to make 60 windshields which are 2 metres wide by 0.5 metres high.
a. What is the probability that a finished windshield will have no bubbles?　(.8781)
b. What is the probability that at least 57 of the windshields will be able to withstand the impact test? (.8943)

7.34 The Long-Life Tire Co. claims that their Super-All-Season tire lasts an average of 110,000 km. It is known that the tire life is normally distributed with a standard deviation of 2800 km. Your company has just purchased all new tires for its fleet of 10 cars. Assuming that the manufacturer's claim is true:
a. What is the probability that a tire will last longer than 112,000 km?
b. What is the probability that the tires for your company car will last an average of at least 112,000 km?
c. What is the probability that the average life of all the tires purchased by your company will be at least 112,000 km?
d. What is the probability that all the tires of your car will last more than 112,000 km?

7.35 A sand and gravel dealer has received an order for five hundred 10.0 kg. bags of sand. Presently the company has 5150 kg. of sand available.

A specialized sand-bag filling machine will be used to fill the bags. The machine can fill 100 bags per hour. The weight of sand in each bag will be normally distributed with a standard deviation of 0.3 kg. The sand bag's mean weight can be adjusted by the filling machine operator.

If the mean weight is set at 10.25 kg, how many of the 500 bags are expected to meet the customer's expectations?　(399 bags)

7.36 An automobile battery has a mean life of 1200 days with a standard deviation of 100 days. If the battery lifetimes are normally distributed, how long should the manufacturer make the guarantee in order to replace at most 10% of the batteries under warranty?　(1072 days)

7.37 A hardware store chain has just received a truckload of 5000 electric drills. Before accepting the shipment, the purchasing manager will test a random selection of 10 drills. The drills will be tested for maximum power consumption and the shipment will be rejected if the mean consumption is more than the 300 watts indicated on the product label. Suppose that the maximum power consumption of the drills in the shipment is normally distributed and averages only 295 watts with a standard deviation of 12 watts.
a. What is the probability that the shipment will be rejected?　(0.0938)
b. How many of the drills in the shipment are expected to exceed the maximum power consumption indicated on the label?　(1692 drills)

7.38 The quality control manager of Marilyn's Cookies is inspecting a batch of chocolate-chip cookies that has just been baked. If the production process is operating properly, the average number of chocolate chips per cookie is 6.76 with a standard deviation of 2.6 chocolate chips. What percent of the cookies will have less than 4 chocolate chips? (9.52%)

7.39 A student is about to write his marketing final exam that consists of 30 multiple-choice questions, each of which has 5 possible answers. If he has done no studying and has no common sense regarding marketing, and thus has to guess the answer to each question, what is the probability that he will pass the exam?　(0.0002)

7.40 The time to get an oil change at a certain car dealership averages 42.3 minutes with a standard deviation of 8.6 minutes.
a. There are 45 cars booked for oil changes today. What is the probability that the jobs can be done in an average of 38 minutes or less?　(0.0004)
b. Suppose 90 oil changes were done in one particular week. There is a 95% chance that the mean time was more than _____ minutes.　(40.8)

7.41 Table A at the bottom of this page appeared in the Nov. 2000 issue of Quality Progress magazine. Assume that the salary distributions for all categories of analysts are normal.

a. What is the probability that an analyst with 3.1 to 6 years experience in the quality field will earn more than $60,000? (0.2051)

b. What is the 3rd quartile salary of analysts with 10.1 to 20 years experience in the quality field? ($60,702)

7.42 The following table appeared in the Autumn 2003 issue of Canadian Social Trends.

	Total '000	Too many demands/ hours	Risk of accident/ injury	Poor interpersonal relations	Threat of layoff/ job loss	Having to learn computer skills	Other
				%			
Work arrangements							
Class of worker							
All workers	16,800	34	13	15	13	11	6
Self-employed	2,800	37	12	10	8	11	10
Employees	14,000	34	13	16	14	11	6
Employees only							
Hours of work							
All employees[1]	14,000	34	13	16	14	11	6
Full-time	11,500	37	14	17	15	12	6
30-35 hours/week	1,900	29	11	15	15	11	6
36-40 hours/week	6,100	33	14	17	16	12	6
41 or more hours/week	3,600	47	16	18	13	13	6
Part-time	2,300	20	9	11	10	7	5
1-15 hours/week	900	16	6	10	8	4E	4E
16-29 hours/week	1,400	22	11	12	11	9	5
Work schedules							
Regular daytime	9,500	35	11	15	14	12	6
Rotating shift	1,800	35	24	20	16	11	5
Regular evening or night	1,400	27	16	16	12	5	4
Irregular/split shift	900	35	17	16	13	11	5E
Other/on call	300	21	11E	15E	13E	F	9E

1. Full-time and part-time employees.
E High sampling variability.
F Sample too small to provide reliable estimate.
Source: Statistics Canada, General Social Survey, 2000.

Living in one particular neighbourhood are 183 full-time workers that work 36–40 hours per week.

a. What is the probability that more than 15% of them worry about the risk of accident or injury? (0.3366)

b. In a sample of 120 rotating shift workers, what is the relative variability of the number who worry about the threat of layoff or job loss?

PROBABILITY DISTRIBUTIONS— COMBINATION QUESTIONS

7.43 In the 1840's, Lambert Quetelet recorded data on an entire regiment of 5,732 soldiers. According to the records of Monsieur Quetelet:

- soldiers' chest measurements were normal with a mean of 39.80 inches and a standard deviation of 2.05 inches
- 12% of soldiers reported that they suffered from skin rash, and
- on average, 25 soldiers reported to Sick Bay each day.

a. What percentage of the soldiers in this regiment could be expected to have had chest measurements less than 38.5 inches? (26.3%)

b. Twenty-five percent of the soldiers had a chest measurement below what size? (38.42")

c. In a group of fifty soldiers, what is the probability that more than four of them suffered from skin rash? (.7320)

d. In a group of forty soldiers, what is the probability that no more than eight of them suffered from skin rash? (.9557)

e. What is the probability that exactly 30 soldiers reported to Sick Bay on a particular day? (0.0454)

f. What is the probability that a maximum of 200 soldiers reported to Sick Bay in a week? (.9710)

g. In a sample of 35 randomly selected soldiers, what is the probability that the average chest measurement of the soldiers in this sample was at least 40.5 inches? (.0217)

7.44 There are 12 agents in one office of a certain real estate firm. Much of the business in this office is conducted by taking a prospective customer out to view a particular property. The time to drive to and view a property is normally distributed and averages 47.3 minutes with a standard deviation of 11.7 minutes. Past studies have shown that twenty-six (26) percent of customers that visit properties with an agent will eventually buy a property being shown by that agent. On average each agent visits 3.6 properties a day, with a standard deviation of 1.9 visits. All of the above activities are independent of each other.

a. What is the probability that an agent will visit at least 7 properties over the next three days? (0.9128)

Table A. Salary by Job Title and Number of Years' Experience in the Quality Field for Respondents Who Work in the United States

	Minimum	Maximum	Standard deviation	Count	Mean	Median
Analyst						
Less than 1 year	$50,000	$64,000	$ 7,095	3	$56,333	$55,000
1 to 3 years	22,000	70,000	13,414	29	43,835	42,300
3.1 to 6 years	28,500	85,000	14,148	34	48,351	45,000
6.1 to 10 years	30,000	98,000	16,221	26	50,438	44,000
10.1 to 20 years	26,800	85,000	14,780	36	50,733	53,000
More than 20 years	21,000	83,000	18,851	9	54,111	55,000
No experience	42,000	77,000	11,404	6	58,731	58,000

b. What is the probability that the average time of the next 50 property viewings will be less than 45 minutes   (0.0823)

c. A particular agent currently has 17 prospective customers that are being shown properties for sale. What is the probability that less than 4 of these customers will eventually buy a property being shown by the agent?   (0.3186)

d. Eighty-two (82) percent of property visits will take what range of time, centered at the mean? (from 31.6 to 63.0 minutes)

7.45 For the Seashell gas station in your neighbourhood, records indicate that the number of customers arriving in any 5-minute interval averages 0.94 customers, with a standard deviation of 0.97 customers. Sixty-five (65) percent of the customers use a credit card to pay for their purchase. There are 8 pumps at this service station. The time that a car is parked at a pump is normally distributed with a mean of 6.35 minutes and a standard deviation of 2.10 minutes. All the above activities are independent of each other.

a. Ninety-four (94) percent of the customers will be parked for what maximum amount of time?   (9.62 minutes)

b. For 12 randomly selected customers, what is the probability that at least 10 of them will pay using a credit card? (0.1513)

c. What is the probability that more than 5 customers will arrive in a 15-minute period?   (0.0669)

d. What is the probability that the average parked time for the next 40 customers is less than 6 minutes?   (0.1459)

7.46 There are 12 brokers in one office of a certain broker-age firm. Much of the business in this office is conducted by telephone. The duration of a telephone call is normally distributed and averages 7.45 minutes with a standard deviation of 1.7 minutes. Past studies have shown that fifty-seven (57) percent of telephone calls result in a buy or sell order. On average each broker receives 1.6 calls every 20 minutes, with a standard deviation of 1.3 calls. All of the above activities are independent of each other.

a. What is the probability that a broker will receive at least 4 calls in the next hour?   (0.7058)

b. What is the probability that the average duration of the next 40 calls will be less than 7 minutes?   (0.0471)

c. For 9 randomly selected calls, what is the probability that at least 7 of them result in a buy or sell order? (0.1796)

d. Ninety-two (92) percent of the calls will last for what minimum amount of time?   (5.06 min.)

7.47 During the month of December at Reader's Bookstore, the average number of customers entering the store is 7.84 every 20 minutes with a standard deviation of 2.8 customers. The time to get through the check-out counter is approximately normally distributed with a mean of 5.6 minutes and a standard deviation of 1.9 minutes. Fifteen percent of cus-tomers are first-time shoppers and 25% of all customers use their debit card to pay for their books.

a. Presently there are 40 customers in the store. What is the probability that more than three quarters of them will have shopped at Reader's before?   (0.9328)

b. What is the probability that a customer will take less than 4 minutes to check-out?   (0.1999)

c. What is the probability that more than 10 customers will enter the store in the next half-hour?   (0.6271)

d. Ten percent of the customers will take longer than _____ to check-out.   (8.0 min.)

7.48 New houses are being built and sold at record paces in the GTA this year. It was reported on the radio last week that on the average one new home was sold every six minutes. In February 3,215 new houses were sold in the GTA region, of which 80% were located in the '905' area code municipalities.

The prices of new homes being built and sold this year are also at record high levels. The average price of a 2-bedroom home was $212,000 with a standard deviation of $5,300. The mean and standard deviation of the prices of 3-bedroom homes were $276,000 and $10,700, respectively. For 4-bedroom homes the corresponding figures were $328,000 and $24,800. All the price data sets were normally distributed.

The figures also showed that 32% of homes being built this year had 2 bedrooms, 45% had 3 bedrooms, 15% had 4 bed-rooms, and the remainder were equal amounts of 5 and 6 bedroom homes. The time to build a 3-bedroom home aver-aged 205 days, with a standard deviation of 12 days. The sizes of 3-bedroom homes were normally distributed with a mean of 2,540 ft^2 and a standard deviation of 175 ft^2.

In Mississauga, just west of Winston Churchill Blvd., a large new community of 2400 houses is being built on a 3 square kilometer (3,000,000 m^2) area. Only 10% of the houses will be bungalows, i.e. one storey. All others will be 2-storey houses. The bungalows are to be randomly dis-tributed throughout the community.

(Note: All figures above, except those in the 1st paragraph, also apply to the Mississauga community.)

a. What is the probability that a 2-bedroom home will cost more than $225,000?

b. On one street in the Mississauga development there are 23 houses. What is the probability that at most five of them have 4-bedrooms?

c. One developer is building fifty-three 3-bedroom homes in the new Mississauga community. What is the probabil-ity that the mean time to construct these homes will be less than 200 days?

d. What is the probability that 12 new homes will be sold in an hour?

e. One developer in the new Mississauga community has a special deal this weekend on 3-bedroom houses. There will be a $20,000 price discount on the largest 15% of houses. How big a 3-bedroom house do you have to buy to get this discount?

f. What is the expected number of bedrooms in new homes being built this year?

g. What is the probability that there would be at least 3 bungalows in a 10,000 m² area in the new development in Mississauga?

7.49 The production process used to produce 500 ft. spools of electrical cable operates continuously, 24 hours a day, and is capable of producing approximately 6 spools per day. The time required to produce one spool is normally distributed with a mean of 4.23 hours and a standard deviation of 0.45 hours. Defects occur in the wire at an average rate of 1 per 1000 feet. As a result, 61% of all spools have no defects. The machine used to produce the wire, needs to be adjusted an average of 4 times per day with a standard deviation of 2 times per day.

a. What is the probability that in a week's production, i.e. 42 spools, there will be at least 35 spools without defects?

b. What is the probability that a spool can be produced in less than 4 hours?

c. What is the probability that the wire producing machine will need to be adjusted at most once in an 8 hour shift?

d. What is the probability that the average time to produce the next 15 spools will be more than 4.1 hours?

e. Seventy-eight (78) percent of spools will be produced within what range of time, centered at the mean?

7.5 Sampling Distribution of the Proportion

Consider a categorical variable that has only two categories, such as the customer prefers your brand or the customer prefers the competitor's brand. Of interest is the proportion of items belonging to one of the categories—for example, the proportion of customers that prefers your brand. The population proportion, represented by π, is the proportion of items in the entire population with the characteristic of interest. The sample proportion, represented by p, is the proportion of items in the sample with the characteristic of interest. The sample proportion, a statistic, is used to estimate the population proportion, a parameter. To calculate the sample proportion, you assign the two possible outcomes scores of 1 or 0 to represent the presence or absence of the characteristic. You then sum all the 1 and 0 scores and divide by n, the sample size. For example, if, in a sample of five customers, three preferred your brand and two did not, you have three 1s and two 0s. Summing the three 1s and two 0s and dividing by the sample size of 5 gives you a sample proportion of 0.60.

SAMPLE PROPORTION

$$p = \frac{X}{n} = \frac{\text{Number of items having the characteristic of interest}}{\text{Sample size}} \qquad (7.6)$$

The sample proportion, p, takes on values between 0 and 1. If all items have the characteristic, you assign each a score of 1, and p is equal to 1. If half the items have the characteristic, you assign half a score of 1 and assign the other half a score of 0, and p is equal to 0.5. If none of the items have the characteristic, you assign each a score of 0, and p is equal to 0.

In Section 7.4, you learned that the sample mean, $\overline{X}$, is an unbiased estimator of the population mean, μ. Similarly, the statistic p is an unbiased estimator of the population proportion, π.

By analogy to the sampling distribution of the mean whose standard error is $\sigma_{\overline{X}} = \dfrac{\sigma}{\sqrt{n}}$, the **standard error of the proportion**, σ_p, is given in Equation (7.7).

STANDARD ERROR OF THE PROPORTION

$$\sigma_p = \sqrt{\frac{\pi(1 - \pi)}{n}} \qquad (7.7)$$

The **sampling distribution of the proportion** follows the binomial distribution, as discussed in Section 5.2. However, you can use the normal distribution to approximate the binomial distribution when $n\pi$ and $n(1 - \pi)$ are each at least 5. In most cases in which inferences are made about the proportion, the sample size is substantial enough to meet the conditions for using the normal approximation (see reference 1). Therefore, in many instances, you can use the normal distribution to estimate the sampling distribution of the proportion. Substituting p for $\bar{X}$, π for μ, and $\sqrt{\dfrac{\pi(1-\pi)}{n}}$ for $\dfrac{\sigma}{\sqrt{n}}$ in Equation (7.4) on page 316 results in Equation (7.8).

FINDING Z FOR THE SAMPLING DISTRIBUTION OF THE PROPORTION

$$Z = \frac{p - \pi}{\sqrt{\dfrac{\pi(1 - \pi)}{n}}} \tag{7.8}$$

To illustrate the sampling distribution of the proportion, suppose that the manager of the local branch of a bank determines that 40% of all depositors have multiple accounts at the bank. If you select a random sample of 200 depositors, the probability that the sample proportion of depositors with multiple accounts is less than 0.30 is calculated as follows: Because $n\pi = 200(0.40) = 80 \geq 5$ and $n(1 - \pi) = 200(0.60) = 120 \geq 5$, the sample size is large enough to assume that the sampling distribution of the proportion is approximately normally distributed. Using Equation (7.8),

$$Z = \frac{p - \pi}{\sqrt{\dfrac{\pi(1 - \pi)}{n}}}$$

$$= \frac{0.30 - 0.40}{\sqrt{\dfrac{(0.40)(0.60)}{200}}} = \frac{-0.10}{\sqrt{\dfrac{0.24}{200}}} = \frac{-0.10}{0.0346}$$

$$= -2.89$$

Using Table E.2, the area under the normal curve less than -2.89 is 0.0019. Therefore, if the true proportion of items of interest in the population is 0.40, then only 0.19% of the samples of $n = 200$ would be expected to have sample proportions less than 0.30.

Problems for Section 7.5

LEARNING THE BASICS

7.50 In a random sample of 64 people, 48 are classified as "successful."
a. Determine the sample proportion, p, of "successful" people.
b. If the population proportion is 0.70, determine the standard error of the proportion.

7.51 A random sample of 50 households was selected for a telephone survey. The key question asked was, "Do you or any member of your household own a cellular telephone with a built-in camera?" Of the 50 respondents, 15 said yes and 35 said no.
a. Determine the sample proportion, p, of households with cellular telephones with built-in cameras.
b. If the population proportion is 0.40, determine the standard error of the proportion.

N N Y N N Y N Y N Y N N Y N Y Y N N N Y
N Y N N N N Y N N Y Y N N N Y N N Y N N

7.52 The following data represent the responses (Y for yes and N for no) from a sample of 40 college students to the question "Do you currently own shares in any stocks?"
a. Determine the sample proportion, p, of college students who own shares of stock.
b. If the population proportion is 0.30, determine the standard error of the proportion.

APPLYING THE CONCEPTS

✓ **SELF Test** **7.53** A political pollster is conducting an analysis of sample results in order to make predictions on election night. Assuming a two-candidate election, if a specific candidate receives at least 55% of the vote in the sample, then that candidate will be forecast as the winner of the election. If you select a random sample of 100 voters, what is the probability that a candidate will be forecast as the winner when

a. the true percentage of her vote is 50.1%?

b. the true percentage of her vote is 60%?

c. the true percentage of her vote is 49% (and she will actually lose the election)?

d. If the sample size is increased to 400, what are your answers to (a) through (c)? Discuss.

7.54 You plan to conduct a marketing experiment in which students are to taste one of two different brands of soft drink. Their task is to correctly identify the brand tasted. You select a random sample of 200 students and assume that the students have no ability to distinguish between the two brands. (Hint: If an individual has no ability to distinguish between the two soft drinks, then each brand is equally likely to be selected.)

a. What is the probability that the sample will have between 50% and 60% of the identifications correct?

b. The probability is 90% that the sample percentage is contained within what symmetrical limits of the population percentage?

c. What is the probability that the sample percentage of correct identifications is greater than 65%?

d. Which is more likely to occur—more than 60% correct identifications in the sample of 200 or more than 55% correct identifications in a sample of 1,000? Explain.

7.55 An online quiz available at **www.pewinternet.org/quiz** divides up people according to their usage of the computer. In a survey of 4,001 respondents, 8% were classified as productivity enhancers who are comfortable with technology and use the Internet for its practical value (M. Himowitz, "How to Tell What Kind of Tech User You Are," *Newsday*, May 27, 2007, p. F6). Suppose you select a sample of 400 students at your school, and the population proportion of productivity enhancers is 0.08.

a. What is the probability that in the sample, less than 10% of the students will be productivity enhancers?

b. What is the probability that in the sample, between 6% and 10% of the students will be productivity enhancers?

c. What is the probability that in the sample, more than 5% of the students will be productivity enhancers?

d. If a sample of 100 is taken, how does this change your answers to (a) through (c)?

7.56 Companies often make flextime scheduling available to help recruit and keep women employees who have children at home. Other workers sometimes view these flextime schedules as unfair. An article in *USA Today* indicates that 25% of male employees state that they have to pick up the slack for moms working flextime schedules (D. Jones, "Poll Finds Resentment of Flextime," **usatoday.com**, May 11, 2007). Suppose you select a random sample of 100 male employees working for companies offering flextime.

a. What is the probability that 25% or fewer male employees will indicate that they have to pick up the slack for moms working flextime?

b. What is the probability that 20% or fewer will indicate that they have to pick up the slack for moms working flextime?

c. If a random sample of 500 is taken, how does this change your answers to (a) and (b)?

7.57 According to Gallup's poll on personal finances, 46% of U.S. workers say they feel they will have enough money to live comfortably when they retire. (*The Gallup Poll*, **galluppoll.com**, May 6, 2008.) If you select a random sample of 200 U.S. workers,

a. what is the probability that the sample will have between 45% and 55% who say they have enough money to live comfortably now and expect to do so in the future?

b. the probability is 90% that the sample percentage will be contained within what symmetrical limits of the population percentage?

c. the probability is 95% that the sample percentage will be contained within what symmetrical limits of the population percentage?

7.58 New research shows (J. O'Donnell, "Gen Y Sits on Top of Consumer Food Chain," *USA Today*, October 11, 2006, p. 3B) that members of generation Y (people born from 1982 to 2000) have a great say in household purchases. Specifically, 68% of Gen Y people have a say in computer purchases. Suppose you select a sample of 100 Gen Y respondents.

a. What is the probability that the sample percentage will be contained between 65% and 75%?

b. The probability is 90% that the sample percentage will be contained within what symmetrical limits of the population percentage?

c. The probability is 95% that the sample percentage will be contained within what symmetrical limits of the population percentage?

d. Suppose you selected a sample of 400 respondents. How does this change your answers in (a) through (c)?

7.59 Yahoo HotJobs reported that 56% of full-time office workers believe that dressing-down can affect jobs, salaries, or promotions (J. Yang and K. Carter, "Dress Can Affect Size of Paycheck," **usatoday.com**, May 9, 2007).

a. Suppose that you take a sample of 100 full-time workers. If the true population proportion of workers who believe that dressing-down can affect jobs, salaries, or promotions is 0.56, what is the probability that less than half in your sample hold that same belief?

b. Suppose that you take a sample of 500 full-time workers. If the true population proportion of workers who believe that dressing-down can affect jobs, salaries, or promotions is 0.56, what is the probability that less than half in your sample hold that same belief?

c. Discuss the effect of sample size on the sampling distribution of the proportion in general, and the effect on the probabilities in (a) and (b).

USING STATISTICS   @ Oxford Cereals Revisited

As the plant operations manager for Oxfords Cereals, you were responsible for monitoring the amount of cereal placed in each box. To be consistent with package labeling, boxes should contain a mean of 368 grams of cereal. Thousands of boxes are produced during a shift, and thus weighing every single box was determined to be too time-consuming, costly, and inefficient. Instead a sample of boxes was selected. Based on your analysis of the sample, you had to decide whether to maintain, alter, or shut down the process.

Using the concept of the sampling distribution of the mean, you were able to determine probabilities that such a sample mean could have been randomly selected from a population with a mean of 368 grams. Specifically, if a sample of size $n = 25$ is selected from a population with a mean of 368 and standard deviation of 15, you calculated that the probability of selecting a sample with a mean of 365 grams or less to be 15.87%. If a larger sample size is selected, the sample mean should be closer to the population mean. This result was illustrated when you calculated the probability if the sample size were increased to $n = 100$. Using the larger sample size, you determined that the probability of selecting a sample with a mean of 365 grams or less to be 2.28%.

SUMMARY

You have learned that in many business situations the population is so large that you cannot gather information on every item. Instead, statistical sampling procedures focus on collecting a small representative group of the larger population. The results of the sample are then used to estimate characteristics of the entire population. Selecting a sample is less time-consuming, less costly, and more practical than an analysis of the entire population.

In this chapter, you studied four common sampling methods—simple random, systematic, stratified, and clus-

ter. You also studied the sampling distribution of the sample mean, the Central Limit Theorem, and the sampling distribution of the sample proportion. You learned that the sample mean is an unbiased estimator of the population mean, and the sample proportion is an unbiased estimator of the population proportion. In the next four chapters, the techniques of confidence intervals and tests of hypotheses commonly used for statistical inference are discussed.

KEY EQUATIONS

Population Mean

$$\mu = \frac{\sum_{i=1}^{N} X_i}{N} \tag{7.1}$$

Population Standard Deviation

$$\sigma = \sqrt{\frac{\sum_{i=1}^{N} (X_i - \mu)^2}{N}} \tag{7.2}$$

Standard Error of the Mean

$$\sigma_{\bar{X}} = \frac{\sigma}{\sqrt{n}} \tag{7.3}$$

Finding Z for the Sampling Distribution of the Mean

$$Z = \frac{\bar{X} - \mu_{\bar{X}}}{\sigma_{\bar{X}}} = \frac{\bar{X} - \mu}{\frac{\sigma}{\sqrt{n}}} \tag{7.4}$$

Finding $\bar{X}$ for the Sampling Distribution of the Mean

$$\bar{X} = \mu + Z\frac{\sigma}{\sqrt{n}} \tag{7.5}$$

Sample Proportion

$$p = \frac{X}{n} \tag{7.6}$$

Standard Error of the Proportion

$$\sigma_p = \sqrt{\frac{\pi(1 - \pi)}{n}} \qquad (7.7)$$

Finding Z for the Sampling Distribution of the Proportion

$$Z = \frac{p - \pi}{\sqrt{\dfrac{\pi(1 - \pi)}{n}}} \qquad (7.8)$$

KEY TERMS

Central Limit Theorem   318
cluster   308
cluster sample   308
convenience sampling   304
coverage error   309
frame   304
judgment sample   304
margin of error   310
measurement error   310
nonprobability sample   304

nonresponse bias   309
nonresponse error   309
probability sample   304
sampling distribution   312
sampling distribution of the
  mean   312
sampling distribution of the
  proportion   325
sampling error   310
sampling with replacement   305

sampling without replacement   305
selection bias   309
simple random sample   305
standard error of the mean   314
standard error of the proportion   325
strata   307
stratified sample   307
systematic sample   307
table of random numbers   305
unbiased   312

CHAPTER REVIEW PROBLEMS

CHECKING YOUR UNDERSTANDING

7.60 Why is the sample mean an unbiased estimator of the population mean?

7.61 Why does the standard error of the mean decrease as the sample size, n, increases?

7.62 Why does the sampling distribution of the mean follow a normal distribution for a large enough sample size, even though the population may not be normally distributed?

7.63 What is the difference between a population and a sampling distribution?

7.64 Under what circumstances does the sampling distribution of the proportion approximately follow the normal distribution?

7.65 What is the difference between probability and non-probability sampling?

7.66 What are some potential problems with using "fish-bowl" methods to select a simple random sample?

7.67 What is the difference between sampling *with* replacement versus *without* replacement?

7.68 What is the difference between a simple random sample and a systematic sample?

7.69 What is the difference between a simple random sample and a stratified sample?

7.70 What is the difference between a stratified sample and a cluster sample?

APPLYING THE CONCEPTS

7.71 An industrial sewing machine uses ball bearings that are targeted to have a diameter of 0.75 inch. The lower and upper specification limits under which the ball bearing can operate are 0.74 inch (lower) and 0.76 inch (upper). Past experience has indicated that the actual diameter of the ball bearings is approximately normally distributed, with a mean of 0.753 inch and a standard deviation of 0.004 inch. If you select a random sample of 25 ball bearings, what is the probability that the sample mean is
a. between the target and the population mean of 0.753?
b. between the lower specification limit and the target?
c. greater than the upper specification limit?
d. less than the lower specification limit?
e. The probability is 93% that the sample mean diameter will be greater than what value?

7.72 The fill amount of bottles of a soft drink is normally distributed, with a mean of 2.0 liters and a standard deviation of 0.05 liter. If you select a random sample of 25 bottles, what is the probability that the sample mean will be
a. between 1.99 and 2.0 liters?
b. below 1.98 liters?
c. greater than 2.01 liters?
d. The probability is 99% that the sample mean amount of soft drink will be at least how much?
e. The probability is 99% that the sample mean amount of soft drink will be between which two values (symmetrically distributed around the mean)?

7.73 An orange juice producer buys all his oranges from a large orange grove that has one variety of orange. The amount of juice squeezed from these oranges is approximately normally distributed, with a mean of 4.70 ounces and a standard deviation of 0.40 ounce. Suppose that you select a sample of 25 oranges.

a. What is the probability that the sample mean amount of juice will be at least 4.60 ounces?

b. The probability is 70% that the sample mean amount of juice will be contained between what two values symmetrically distributed around the population mean?

c. The probability is 77% that the sample mean amount of juice will be greater than what value?

7.74 In his management information systems textbook, Professor David Kroenke raises an interesting point: "If 98% of our market has Internet access, do we have a responsibility to provide non-Internet materials to that other 2%?" (D. M. Kroenke, *Using MIS*, Upper Saddle River, NJ: Prentice Hall, 2007, p. 29a). Suppose that 98% of the customers in your market have Internet access and you select a random sample of 500 customers. What is the probability that the sample has

a. greater than 99% with Internet access?

b. between 97% and 99% with Internet access?

c. less than 97% with Internet access?

7.75 International mutual funds reported strong earnings in 2007. The population of international mutual funds earned a mean return of 14.52% in 2007 (*The Wall Street Journal*, January 2, 2008, p. R8). Assume that the returns for international mutual funds were distributed as a normal random variable, with a mean of 14.57 and a standard deviation of 20. If you selected a random sample of 10 funds from this population, what is the probability that the sample would have a mean return

a. less than 0—that is, a loss?

b. between 0 and 20?

c. greater than 10?

7.76 The same article as in Problem 7.75 reported that long-term treasury bonds had a mean return of 7.81% during this time. Assume that the returns for the long-term treasury bonds were distributed as a normal random variable, with a mean of 7.81 and a standard deviation of 10. If you select an individual treasury bond from this population, what is the probability that it would have a return

a. less than 0—that is, a loss?

b. between 0 and 20?

c. greater than 10?

If you selected a random sample of 10 treasury bonds from this population, what is the probability that the sample would have a mean return

d. less than 0—that is, a loss?

e. between 0 and 20?

f. greater than 10?

g. Compare your results in parts (d) through (f) to (a) through (c).

h. Compare your results in parts (d) through (f) to Problem 7.75 (a) through (c).

7.77 Telephone interviews have traditionally been the number one tool in political polling. Recently, many have argued that Internet polling is faster and less expensive and produces a higher response rate. Dr. Doug Usher, a leading authority on political polling, agrees that the telephone poll is still the gold standard in political polls due to its superior statistical reliability even though it is getting harder to reach people via the telephone with the growing use of caller ID and the fact that many younger people no longer have landlines (D. Usher, "The Internet's Unfulfilled Promise for Political Polling," **www.mysterypollster.com**, June 30, 2005). What concerns, if any, do you have on Internet polling?

7.78 A survey sponsored by The American Dietetic Association and the agribusiness giant ConAgra found that 53% of office workers take 30 minutes or less for lunch each day. Approximately 37% take 30 to 60 minutes, and 10% take more than an hour ("Snapshots," **usatoday.com**, April 26, 2006).

a. What additional information would you want to know before you accepted the results of the survey?

b. Discuss the four types of survey errors in the context of this survey.

c. One of the types of survey errors discussed in part (b) should have been measurement error. Explain how the root cause of measurement error in this survey could be the Hawthorne effect.

7.79 In a survey conducted by AOL and the Associated Press, less than 25% of adults use instant messaging (IM), and almost 75% of adults who use IM use e-mail more often than IM. The survey also showed that almost 50% of teens use IM, and almost 75% of teens who use IM use IM more often than e-mail (M. Levitt, "Bridging the Collaboration Age Gap with Unified Communications and Web 2.0," *KM World*, June 2007, p. 10).

a. What other information would you want to know before you used the results of this survey?

b. Suppose you work for AOL and wanted to investigate IM and e-mail usage by AOL users. Define the population, frame, and sampling method you would use.

7.80 (Class Project) The table of random numbers is an example of a uniform distribution because each digit is equally likely to occur. Starting in the row corresponding to the day of the month in which you were born, use the table of random numbers (Table E.1) to take one digit at a time.

Select five different samples each of $n = 2, n = 5$, and $n = 10$. Compute the sample mean of each sample. Develop a frequency distribution of the sample means for the results of the entire class, based on samples of sizes $n = 2, n = 5$, and $n = 10$.

What can be said about the shape of the sampling distribution for each of these sample sizes?

7.81 (Class Project) Toss a coin 10 times and record the number of heads. If each student performs this experiment five times, a frequency distribution of the number of heads can be developed from the results of the entire class. Does this distribution seem to approximate the normal distribution?

7.82 (Class Project) The number of cars waiting in line at a car wash is distributed as follows:

Number of Cars	Probability
	0.25
1	0.40
2	0.20
3	0.10
4	0.04
5	0.01

You can use the table of random numbers (Table E.1) to select samples from this distribution by assigning numbers as follows:
1. Start in the row corresponding to the day of the month in which you were born.
2. Select a two-digit random number.
3. If you select a random number from 00 to 24, record a length of 0; if from 25 to 64, record a length of 1; if from 65 to 84, record a length of 2; if from 85 to 94, record a length of 3; if from 95 to 98, record a length of 4; if 99, record a length of 5.

Select samples of $n = 2, n = 5$, and $n = 10$. Compute the mean for each sample. For example, if a sample of size 2 results in the random numbers 18 and 46, these would correspond to lengths of 0 and 1, respectively, producing a sample mean of 0.5. If each student selects five different sam-

ples for each sample size, a frequency distribution of the sample means (for each sample size) can be developed from the results of the entire class. What conclusions can you reach concerning the sampling distribution of the mean as the sample size is increased?

7.83 (Class Project) Using Table E.1, simulate the selection of different-colored balls from a bowl as follows:
1. Start in the row corresponding to the day of the month in which you were born.
2. Select one-digit numbers.
3. If a random digit between 0 and 6 is selected, consider the ball white; if a random digit is a 7, 8, or 9, consider the ball red.

Select samples of $n = 10, n = 25$, and $n = 50$ digits. In each sample, count the number of white balls and compute the proportion of white balls in the sample. If each student in the class selects five different samples for each sample size, a frequency distribution of the proportion of white balls (for each sample size) can be developed from the results of the entire class. What conclusions can you reach about the sampling distribution of the proportion as the sample size is increased?

7.84 (Class Project) Suppose that step 3 of Problem 7.83 uses the following rule: "If a random digit between 0 and 8 is selected, consider the ball to be white; if a random digit of 9 is selected, consider the ball to be red." Compare and contrast the results in this problem and those in Problem 7.83.

MANAGING THE *SPRINGVILLE HERALD*

Continuing its quality improvement effort first described in the Chapter 6 "Managing the *Springville Herald*" case, the production department of the newspaper has been monitoring the blackness of the newspaper print. As before, blackness is measured on a standard scale in which the target value is 1.0. Data collected over the past year indicate that the blackness is approximately normally distributed, with a mean of 1.005 and a standard deviation of 0.10.

EXERCISE

SH7.1   Each day, 25 spots on the first newspaper printed are chosen, and the blackness of the spots is measured. Assuming that the distribution has not

changed from what it was in the past year, what is the probability that the mean blackness of the spots is
a. less than 1.0?
b. between 0.95 and 1.0?
c. between 1.0 and 1.05?
d. less than 0.95 or greater than 1.05?
e. Suppose that the mean blackness of today's sample of 25 spots is 0.952. What conclusion can you reach about the blackness of today's newspaper based on this result? Explain.

WEB CASE

Apply your knowledge about sampling distributions in this Web Case, which reconsiders the Oxford Cereals Using Statistics scenario.

The advocacy group Consumers Concerned About Cereal Cheaters (CCACC) suspects that cereal companies, including

Oxford Cereals, are cheating consumers by packaging cereals at less than labeled weights. Visit the organization's home page at **www.prenhall.com/Springville/ConsumersConcerned. htm** (or open the `ConsumersConcerned.htm` file in the Student CD-ROM Web Case folder), examine their claims and supporting data, and then answer the following:

1. Are the data collection procedures that the CCACC uses to form its conclusions flawed? What procedures could the group follow to make their analysis more rigorous?

2. Assume that the two samples of five cereal boxes (one sample for each of two cereal varieties) listed on the CCACC Web site were collected randomly by organization members. For each sample, do the following:
   a. Calculate the sample mean.
   b. Assume that the standard deviation of the process is 15 grams and a population mean is 368 grams. Calculate the percentage of all samples for each process that have a sample mean less than the value you calculated in (a).
   c. Again, assuming that the standard deviation is 15 grams, calculate the percentage of individual boxes of cereal that have a weight less than the value you calculated in (a).

3. What, if any, conclusions can you form by using your calculations about the filling processes of the two different cereals?

4. A representative from Oxford Cereals has asked that the CCACC take down its page discussing shortages in Oxford Cereals boxes. Is that request reasonable? Why or why not?

5. Can the techniques discussed in this chapter be used to prove cheating in the manner alleged by the CCACC? Why or why not?

REFERENCES

1. Cochran, W. G., *Sampling Techniques*, 3rd ed. (New York: Wiley, 1977).

2. Gallup, G. H., *The Sophisticated Poll-Watcher's Guide* (Princeton, NJ: Princeton Opinion Press, 1972).

3. Goleman, D., "Pollsters Enlist Psychologists in Quest for Unbiased Results," *The New York Times*, September 7, 1993, pp. C1, C11.

4. Hahn, G., and W. Meeker, *Statistical Intervals, A Guide for Practioners* (New York: John Wiley and Sons, Inc., 1991).

5. *Microsoft Excel 2007* (Redmond, WA: Microsoft Corp., 2007).

6. *Minitab for Windows Version 15* (State College, PA: Minitab, Inc., 2006).

7. Rand Corporation, *A Million Random Digits with 100,000 Normal Deviates* (New York: The Free Press, 1955).

Using Microsoft Excel for Sampling and Sampling Distributions

E7.1 Creating Simple Random Samples Without Replacement

No Microsoft Excel features directly create simple random samples.

E7.2 Creating Simulated Sampling Distributions

You create simulated sampling distributions by first using the ToolPak Random Number Generation procedure to create a worksheet of multiple random samples and then adding formulas to that worksheet to compute the sample means and other appropriate measures.

To start, select **Tools → Data Analysis** and in the Data Analysis dialog box, click **Random Number Generation** and then click **OK**. In the Random Number Generation dialog box (shown at right), enter the number of samples as the **Number of Variables** and enter the sample size of each sample as the **Number of Random Numbers**. Select the type of distribution from the **Distribution** drop-down list and make entries in the Parameters area, the contents of which vary according to the distribution selected. (If you select the

Discrete option, you will need to be opened to a worksheet that contains a table of X and $P(X)$ values and enter the range of the table as the **Value and Probability Input Range**.) To finish, click **New Worksheet Ply** and then **OK**.

8

Statistical Applications in Quality Management

Learning Objectives

In this chapter, you learn:

- How to construct various control charts
- Which control chart to use for a particular type of data
- The basic themes of total quality management and Deming's 14 points
- The basic aspects of Six Sigma

USING STATISTICS

@ Beachcomber Hotel

Y ou find yourself managing the Beachcomber Hotel, one of the resorts owned by T.C. Resort Properties. You want to continually improve the quality of service that your guests receive so that overall guest satisfaction increases. To help you achieve this improvement, T.C. Resort Properties has provided its managers with training in Six Sigma. In order to meet the business objective of increasing the return rate of guests at your hotel, you have decided to focus on the critical first impressions of the service that your hotel provides. Is the assigned hotel room ready when a guest checks in? Are all expected amenities, such as extra towels and a complimentary guest basket, in the room when the guest first walks in? Are the video-entertainment center and high-speed Internet access working properly? And do guests receive their luggage in a reasonable amount of time?

To study these guest satisfaction issues, you have embarked on an improvement project that focuses on the readiness of the room and the time it takes to deliver luggage. You would like to learn the following:

- Are the proportion of rooms ready and the time required to deliver luggage to the rooms acceptable?
- Are the proportion of rooms ready and the luggage delivery time consistent from day to day, or are they increasing or decreasing?
- On the days when the proportion of rooms that are not ready or the time to deliver luggage is greater than normal, are these due to a chance occurrence, or are there fundamental flaws in the processes used to make rooms ready and to deliver luggage?

C ompanies manufacturing products, as well as those providing services, such as the Beachcomber Hotel in the "Using Statistics" scenario, realize that quality is essential for survival in the global economy. Among the areas in which quality has an impact on our everyday work and personal lives are the design, production, and reliability of our automobiles; the services provided by hotels, banks, schools, retailing operations, and mail-order companies; the continuous improvement in computer chips that makes for faster and more powerful computers; and the availability of new technology and equipment that has led to improved diagnosis of illnesses and the improved delivery of health care services.

In this chapter you will learn how to develop and analyze control charts, a statistical tool that is widely used for quality improvement. You will then learn how business and organizations around the world are using control charts as part of two important quality improvement approaches, total quality management (TQM) and Six Sigma.

8.1 The Theory of Control Charts

A **process** is the value-added transformation of inputs to outputs. Control charts, developed by Walter Shewhart in the 1920s, are commonly used statistical tools for monitoring and improving processes. The inputs and outputs of a process can involve machines, materials, methods, measurement, people, and the environment. Each of the inputs is a source of variability. Variability in the output can result in poor service and poor product quality, both of which often decrease customer satisfaction.

The **control chart** is used to analyze a process in which data are collected sequentially over time. You can use a control chart to study past performance, to evaluate present conditions, or to predict future outcomes. Control charts are used at the beginning of quality improvement efforts to study an existing process (called Phase 1 control charts). Information gained from analyzing Phase I control charts forms the basis for process improvement. After improvements to the process are implemented, control charts are then used to monitor the processes to ensure that the improvements continue (called Phase 2 control charts).

Different types of control charts allow you to analyze different types of critical-to-quality (CTQ in Six Sigma lingo—see Section 8.4) variables—for categorical variables, such as the proportion of hotel rooms that are nonconforming in terms of the availability of amenities and the working order of all appliances in the room; and for continuous variables, such as the length of time required for delivering luggage to the room.

In addition to providing a visual display of data representing a process, a principal focus of a control chart is the attempt to separate special causes of variation from common causes of variation.

> **Special causes of variation** represent large fluctuations or patterns in the data that are not part of a process. These fluctuations are often caused by unusual events and represent either problems to correct or opportunities to exploit. Some organizations refer to special causes of variation as **assignable causes of variation**.

> **Common causes of variation** represent the inherent variability that exists in a process. These fluctuations consist of the numerous small causes of variability that operate randomly or by chance. Some organizations refer to common causes of variation as **chance causes of variation**.

One experiment that is useful to help you appreciate the distinction between common and special causes of variation was developed by Walter Shewhart (see reference 16) more than 80 years ago. The experiment requires that you repeatedly write the letter A over and over again in a horizontal line across a piece of paper:

AAAAAAAAAAAAAAAAA

When you do this, you immediately notice that the A's are all similar but not exactly the same. In addition, you may notice some difference in the size of the A's from letter to letter. This difference is due to common cause variation. Nothing special happened that caused the differences in the size of the A's. You probably would have a hard time trying to explain why the largest A is bigger than the smallest A. These types of differences almost certainly represent common cause variation.

However, if you did the experiment over again, but wrote half of the A's with your right hand and the other half of the A's with your left hand, you would almost certainly see a very big difference in the A's written with each hand. In this case, which hand was used to write the A's is the source of the special cause variation.

The distinction between the two causes of variation is crucial because special causes of variation are not part of a process and are correctable or exploitable without changing the process. Common causes of variation, however, can be reduced only by changing the process. Such systemic changes are the responsibility of management.

Control charts allow you to monitor a process and identify the presence or absence of special causes. By doing so, control charts help prevent two types of errors. The first type of error involves the belief that an observed value represents special cause variation when it is due to the common cause variation of the process. Treating common cause variation as special cause variation often results in overadjusting a process. This overadjustment, known as **tampering**, increases the variation in the process. The second type of error involves treating special cause variation as common cause variation. This error results in not taking immediate corrective action when necessary. Although both of these types of errors can occur even when using a control chart, they are far less likely.

To construct a control chart, you collect samples from the output of a process over time. The samples used for constructing control charts are known as **subgroups**. For each subgroup (i.e., sample), you calculate a sample statistic. Commonly used statistics include the sample proportion for a categorical variable, and the mean and range of a numerical variable (see Section 8.2). You then plot the values over time and add control limits to the chart. The most typical form of a control chart sets control limits that are within ± 3 standard deviations[1] of the statistical measure of interest. Equation (8.1) defines, in general, the upper and lower control limits for control charts.

[1]Recall from Section 6.2 that in the normal distribution, $\mu \pm 3\sigma$ includes almost all (99.73%) of the values in the population.

CONSTRUCTING CONTROL LIMITS

$$\text{Process mean } \pm 3 \text{ standard deviations} \qquad \textbf{(8.1)}$$

so that

Upper control limit (UCL) = process mean $+3$ standard deviations

Lower control limit (LCL) = process mean -3 standard deviations

When these control limits are set, you evaluate the control chart by trying to find any pattern that might exist in the values over time and by determining whether any points fall outside the control limits. Figure 8.1 illustrates three different patterns.

FIGURE 8.1

Three control chart patterns

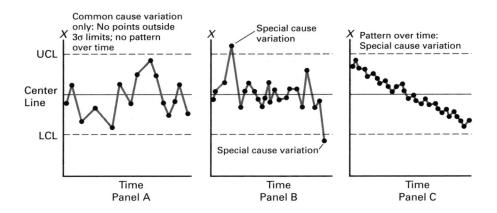

In Panel A of Figure 8.1, there is no apparent pattern in the values over time, and there are no points that fall outside the 3 standard deviation control limits. The process appears stable and contains only common cause variation. Panel B, on the contrary, contains two points that fall outside the 3 standard deviation control limits. You should investigate these points to try to determine the special causes that led to their occurrence. Although Panel C does not have any points outside the control limits, it has a series of consecutive points above the mean value (the center line) as well as a series of consecutive points below the mean value. In addition, a long-term overall downward trend is clearly visible. You should investigate the situation to try to determine what may have caused this pattern.

Detecting a pattern is not always so easy. The following simple rule can help you to detect a trend or a shift in the mean level of a process:

- Eight or more *consecutive* points that lie above the center line or eight or more *consecutive* points that lie below the center line[2]

[2]This rule is often referred to as the runs rule. A similar rule used by some companies is called the trend rule: Eight or more consecutive points that increase in value or eight or more consecutive points that decrease in value. Some statisticians (see reference 5) have criticized the trend rule. It should only be used with extreme caution.

A process whose control chart indicates an out-of-control condition (i.e., a point outside the control limits or a series of points that exhibits a pattern) is said to be out of control. An **out-of-control process** contains both common causes of variation and special causes of variation. Because special causes of variation are not part of the process design, an out-of-control process is unpredictable. When you determine that a process is out of control, you must identify the special causes of variation that are producing the out-of-control conditions. If the special causes are detrimental to the quality of the product or service, you need to implement plans to eliminate this source of variation. When a special cause increases quality, you should change the process so that the special cause is incorporated into the process design. Thus, this beneficial special cause now becomes a common cause source of variation, and the process is improved.

A process whose control chart does not indicate any out-of-control conditions is said to be in control. An **in-control process** contains only common causes of variation. Because these sources of variation are inherent to the process itself, an in-control process is predictable. In-control processes are sometimes said to be in a **state of statistical control**. When a process is in control, you must determine whether the amount of common cause variation in the process is small enough to satisfy the customers of the products or services. If the common cause variation is small enough to consistently satisfy the customer, you then use control charts to monitor the process on a continuing basis to make sure the process remains in control. If the common cause variation is too large, you need to alter the process itself.

Quality Control Charts

We will only be studying two charts, namely X-bar and R charts. Also, the only out-of-control indications that we will be concerned with are:

a. A point above the UCL on the range chart.
b. A point above the UCL or a point below the LCL on the X-bar chart.

In a real life setting, if there is an indication that the process is out-of-control, the people monitoring the process will find an 'Assignable Cause' for this situation. They will then take appropriate steps to make changes in the process so that this instability does not occur again in the future. It is these changes that will result in the improvement of quality.

In order to establish the centre-lines and the upper and lower control limits for the X-bar and R charts we need some initial sample data. Usually the results of from 10 to 30 samples are used. The following two examples will illustrate the formulas and techniques for setting up X-bar and R chart limits. It should be noted that all the formulas shown are based on the assumption that the population of measurements would fit a *normal* distribution.

EXAMPLE 8.1

A chocolate company monitors the weights of its chocolate bars. One particular bar will have a label indicating that it is a 60 gm. Bar. In order to monitor the bar weights, every hour a sample of 4 bars is taken and the bars are weighed. The results of the first 15 samples are shown below.

TABLE 8.1

Sample	Bar 1	Bar 2	Bar 3	Bar 4	Mean	Range
1	60.2	60.4	60.1	60.5	60.300	0.4
2	60.6	60.2	60.7	60.6	60.525	0.5
3	60.2	60.2	60.5	60.7	60.400	0.5
4	60.1	60.1	60.6	60.4	60.300	0.5
5	60.3	60.6	60.3	60.1	60.325	0.5
6	60.5	60.4	60.3	60.1	60.250	0.4
7	60.5	60.4	60.5	60.2	60.400	0.3
8	60.3	60.5	60.2	60.3	60.325	0.3
9	60.5	60.1	60.0	60.5	60.275	0.5
10	60.7	60.4	60.4	60.5	60.500	0.3
11	60.0	60.3	60.7	60.3	60.325	0.7
12	60.2	60.7	60.3	60.6	60.450	0.5
13	60.6	60.0	60.6	60.2	60.350	0.6
14	59.9	60.1	60.3	60.6	60.200	0.7
15	60.5	60.2	60.5	60.5	60.425	0.3

Weight of a bar (grams)

First we calculate the R-chart values using the control factors as follows:

$$\bar{R} = 0.47$$
$$UCL_R = D_4\bar{R} = 2.282(0.47) = 1.07$$
$$LCL_R = D_3\bar{R} = 0(0.47) = 0$$

We now check the sample ranges to see if any values are higher than 1.07. There are none. We now proceed to calculate the X-bar chart values.

$$\bar{\bar{X}} = 60.3567$$
$$UCL_{\bar{X}} + \bar{\bar{X}} + A_2\bar{R} = 60.3567 + (0.729)(0.47) = 60.6993$$
$$LCL_{\bar{X}} = \bar{\bar{X}} - A_2\bar{R} = 60.3567 - (0.729)(0.47) = 60.0141$$

We now check the sample means to see if any values are higher than 60.6993 or lower than 60.0141. There are none. This process is **in control**, i.e. stable, and we have established the control chart limits for future samples of this product.

If in the initial samples used to set up the control charts, points are found to be out-of-control, then we will assume that an assignable cause can be found to account for this problem. In the meantime, the sample data for any point that is out-of-control is removed from the calculations, are the control chart values are recalculated. The following example will illustrate the appropriate procedure to follow.

EXAMPLE 8.2

A company is concerned about a particular measurement. The results of 24 samples of 5 items are shown below.

TABLE 8.2

Sample results							
Sample	Item 1	Item 2	Item 3	Item 4	Item 5	Mean	Range
1	10.65	10.70	10.65	10.65	10.85	10.70	0.20
2	10.75	10.85	10.75	10.85	10.65	10.77	0.20
3	10.75	10.80	10.80	10.70	10.75	10.76	0.10
4	10.60	10.70	10.70	10.75	10.65	10.68	0.15
5	10.70	10.75	10.65	10.85	10.80	10.75	0.20
6	10.60	10.75	10.75	10.85	10.70	10.73	0.25
7	10.60	10.80	10.70	10.75	10.75	10.72	0.20
8	10.75	10.80	10.65	10.75	10.70	10.73	0.15
9	10.65	10.80	10.85	10.85	10.75	10.78	0.20
10	10.60	10.70	10.60	10.80	10.65	10.67	0.20
11	10.80	10.75	10.90	10.50	10.85	10.76	0.40
12	10.85	10.75	10.85	10.65	10.70	10.76	0.20
13	10.70	10.70	10.75	10.75	10.70	10.72	0.05
14	10.65	10.70	10.85	10.75	10.60	10.71	0.25
15	10.75	10.80	10.75	10.80	10.65	10.75	0.15
16	10.90	10.80	10.80	10.75	10.85	10.82	0.15
17	10.75	10.70	10.85	10.70	10.80	10.76	0.15
18	10.75	10.70	10.60	10.70	10.60	10.67	0.15
19	10.65	10.65	10.85	10.65	10.70	10.70	0.20
20	10.55	10.55	10.60	10.50	10.60	10.56	0.10
21	10.50	10.55	10.65	10.80	10.80	10.66	0.30
22	10.80	10.65	10.75	10.65	10.65	10.70	0.15
23	10.65	10.60	10.65	10.60	10.70	10.64	0.10
24	10.65	10.70	10.70	10.60	10.65	10.66	0.10

First calculate the R-chart values:

$$\bar{R} = 0.179$$
$$UCL_R = D_4\bar{R} = 2.114(0.179) = 0.378$$
$$LCL_R = D_3\bar{R} = 0(0.179) = 0$$

Now we look at the sample ranges and find that sample 11 with R = 0.40 is out-of-control. We will assume that an assignable cause for this can be found and in the meantime we **remove** sample 11 and recalculate the R-chart values.

$$\bar{R} = 0.170$$

We now get:
$$UCL_R = D_4\bar{R} = 2.114(0.170) = 0.360$$
$$LCL_R = D_3\bar{R} = 0(0.170) = 0$$

Once again we check the sample ranges and this time there are no ranges that are out-of-control.

Now we calculate the X-bar chart values (with sample 11 having been removed from the data.)

$$\bar{\bar{X}} = 10.713$$

We get:
$$UCL_{\bar{X}} = \bar{\bar{X}} + A_2\bar{R} = 10.713 + (0.577)(0.170) = 10.811$$
$$LCL_{\bar{X}} = \bar{\bar{X}} - A_2\bar{R} = 10.713 - (0.577)(0.170) = 10.615$$

We now check the sample means and find that sample 16 with $\bar{X} = 10.82$ and sample 20 with $\bar{X} = 10.56$ are out-of-control. Once again we assume that assignable causes can be found to account for these out-of-control results, and in the meantime we **remove** samples 16 and 20.

Since the R-chart values above have been calculated including samples 16 and 20, these results are no longer valid. We must recalculate new R-chart values before recalculating new X-bar chart values.

$$\bar{R} = 10.174$$

We now get:
$$UCL_R = D_4\bar{R} = 2.114(0.174) = 0.368$$
$$LCL_R = D_3\bar{R} = 0(0.174) = 0$$

We now once again check the sample ranges for any out-of-control points. There are none. We therefore proceed to the X-bar chart values.

$$\bar{\bar{X}} = 10.715$$

We get:
$$UCL_{\bar{X}} = \bar{\bar{X}} + A_2\bar{R} = 10.715 + (0.577)(0.174) = 10.815$$
$$LCL_{\bar{X}} = \bar{\bar{X}} - A_2\bar{R} = 10.715 - (0.577)(0.174) = 10.616$$

Once again we check the sample means and find that none of the remaining samples are out-of-control. We now have determined the appropriate X-bar and R-chart control limits.

8.2 Total Quality Management

An increased interest in improving the quality of products and services in the United States occurred as a reaction to improvements of Japanese industry that began as early as 1950. Individuals such as W. Edwards Deming, Joseph Juran, and Kaoru Ishikawa developed an approach that focuses on continuous improvement of products and services through an increased emphasis on statistics, process improvement, and optimization of the total system. This approach, widely known as **total quality management (TQM)**, is characterized by these themes:

- The primary focus is on process improvement.
- Most of the variation in a process is due to the system and not the individual.
- Teamwork is an integral part of a quality management organization.
- Customer satisfaction is a primary organizational goal.
- Organizational transformation must occur in order to implement quality management.
- Fear must be removed from organizations.
- Higher quality costs less, not more, but requires an investment in training.

In the 1980s, the federal government of the United States increased its efforts to encourage the improvement of quality in American business. Congress passed the Malcolm Baldrige National Improvement Act of 1987 and began awarding the Malcolm Baldrige Award to companies making the greatest strides in improving quality and customer satisfaction. Deming became a prominent consultant to many Fortune 500 companies, including Ford, General Motors, and Procter & Gamble. Many companies adopted some or all the basic themes of TQM.

Today, many quality improvement systems are in place in organizations worldwide. Although most organizations no longer use the name TQM, the underlying philosophy and statistical methods used in today's quality improvement systems are consistent with TQM and the work of Deming. This holistic approach to quality is captured in **Deming's 14 points for management** listed here:

1. Create constancy of purpose for improvement of product and service.
2. Adopt the new philosophy.

3. Cease dependence on inspection to achieve quality.
4. End the practice of awarding business on the basis of price tag alone. Instead, minimize total cost by working with a single supplier.
5. Improve constantly and forever every process for planning, production, and service.
6. Institute training on the job.
7. Adopt and institute leadership.
8. Drive out fear.
9. Break down barriers between staff areas.
10. Eliminate slogans, exhortations, and targets for the workforce.
11. Eliminate numerical quotas for the workforce and numerical goals for management.
12. Remove barriers that rob people of pride of workmanship. Eliminate the annual rating or merit system.
13. Institute a vigorous program of education and self-improvement for everyone.
14. Put everyone in the company to work to accomplish the transformation.

Points 1, 2, 5, 7, and 14 focus on the need for organizational transformation and the responsibility of top management to assert leadership in committing to the transformation. Without this commitment, any improvements obtained will be limited.

One aspect of the improvement process is illustrated by the **Shewhart-Deming cycle**, shown in Figure 8.2. The Shewhart-Deming cycle represents a continuous cycle of "plan, do, study, and act." The first step, planning, represents the initial design phase for planning a change in a manufacturing or service process. This step involves teamwork among individuals from different areas within an organization. The second step, doing, involves implementing the change, preferably on a small scale. The third step, studying, involves analyzing the results, using statistical methods to determine what was learned. The fourth step, acting, involves the acceptance of the change, its abandonment, or further study of the change under different conditions.

FIGURE 8.2
Shewhart-Deming cycle

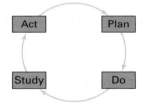

Point 3, cease dependence on inspection to achieve quality, implies that any inspection whose purpose is to improve quality is too late because the quality is already built into the product. It is better to focus on making it right the first time. Among the difficulties involved in inspection (besides high costs) are the failure of inspectors to agree on the operational definitions for nonconforming items and the problem of separating good and bad items. The following example illustrates the difficulties inspectors face.

Suppose your job involves proofreading the sentence in Figure 8.3, with the objective of counting the number of occurrences of the letter F. Perform this task and record the number of occurrences of the letter F that you discover.

FIGURE 8.3

An example of a proofreading process

Source: *Adapted from W. W. Scherkenbach*, The Deming Route to Quality and Productivity: Road Maps and Roadblocks *(Washington, DC: CEEP Press, 1986).*

FINISHED FILES ARE THE RESULT OF YEARS OF SCIENTIFIC STUDY COMBINED WITH THE EXPERIENCE OF MANY YEARS

People usually see either three F's or six F's. The correct number is six F's. The number you see depends on the method you use to examine the sentence. You are likely to find three F's if you read the sentence phonetically and six F's if you count the number of F's carefully. The point of the exercise is to show that, if such a simple process as counting F's leads to inconsistency of inspectors' results, what will happen when a much more complicated process fails to provide clear operational definitions?

Point 4, end the practice of awarding business on the basis of price tag alone, focuses on the idea that there is no real long-term meaning to price without knowledge of the quality of the product. In addition, minimizing the number of entities in the supply chain will reduce the variation involved.

Points 6 and 13 refer to training and reflect the needs of all employees. Continuous learning is critical for quality improvement within an organization. In particular, management needs to understand the differences between special causes and common causes of variation so that proper action is taken in each circumstance.

Points 8 through 12 relate to the evaluation of employee performance. Deming believed that an emphasis on targets and exhortations places an improper burden on the workforce. Workers cannot produce beyond what the system allows. It is management's job to *improve* the system, not to raise the expectations on workers beyond the system's capability.

Although Deming's points are thought provoking, some have criticized his approach for lacking a formal, objective accountability. Many managers of large organizations, used to seeing financial analyses of policy changes, need a more prescriptive approach.

8.3 Six Sigma

Six Sigma is a quality improvement system originally developed by Motorola in the mid-1980s. After seeing the huge financial successes at Motorola, GE, and other early adopters of Six Sigma, many companies worldwide have now instituted Six Sigma to improve efficiency, cut costs, eliminate defects, and reduce product variation. Six Sigma offers a more prescriptive and systematic approach to process improvement than TQM. It is also distinguished from other quality improvement systems by its clear focus on achieving bottom-line results in a relatively short three- to six-month period of time.

The name Six Sigma comes from the fact that it is a managerial approach designed to create processes that result in no more than 3.4 defects per million. The Six Sigma approach assumes that processes are designed so that the upper and lower specification limits are six standard deviations away from the mean. Then, if the processes are monitored correctly with control charts, the worst possible scenario is for the mean to shift to within 4.5 standard deviations from the nearest specification limit. The area under the normal curve less than 4.5 standard deviations below the mean is approximately 3.4 out of a million. (Table E.2 reports this probability as 0.000003398.)

The DMAIC Model

To guide managers in their task of improving short- and long-term results, Six Sigma uses a five-step process known as the **DMAIC model**—named for the five steps in the process:

- *Define* The problem is defined, along with the costs, the benefits, and the impact on the customer.
- *Measure* Important characteristics relating to the quality of the service or product are identified and discussed. Variables measuring these characteristics are defined and called **critical-to-quality (CTQ)** variables. Operational definitions for all the CTQ variables are then developed. In addition, the measurement procedure is verified so that it is consistent over repeated measurements.

- *Analyze* The root causes of *why* defects occur are determined, and variables in the process causing the defects are identified. Data are collected to determine benchmark values for each process variable. This analysis often uses control charts (discussed in Sections 8.2–8.3).
- *Improve* The importance of each process variable on the CTQ variable is studied using designed experiments. The objective is to determine the best level for each variable.
- *Control* The objective is to maintain the benefits for the long term by avoiding potential problems that can occur when a process is changed.

The Define phase of a Six Sigma project consists of the development of a project charter, performing a SIPOC analysis, and identifying the customers for the output of the process. The development of a project charter involves forming a table of business objectives and indicators for all potential Six Sigma projects. Importance ratings are assigned by top management, projects are prioritized, and the most important project is selected. A **SIPOC analysis** is used to identify the **S**uppliers to the process, list the **I**nputs provided by the suppliers, flowchart the **P**rocess, list the process **O**utputs, and identify the **C**ustomers of the process. This is followed by a Voice of the Customer analysis that involves market segmentation in which different types of users of the process are identified and the circumstances of their use of the process are identified. Statistical methods used in the *Define* phase include tables and charts, descriptive statistics, and control charts.

In the *Measure* phase of a Six Sigma project, members of a team identify the CTQ variables that measure important quality characteristics. Next, operational definitions (see Section 1.3) of each CTQ variable are developed so that everyone will have a firm understanding of the CTQ. Then studies are undertaken to ensure that there is a valid measurement system for the CTQ that is consistent across measurements. Finally, baseline data are collected to determine the capability and stability of the current process. Statistical methods used in the *Measure* phase include tables and charts, descriptive statistics, the normal distribution, the Analysis of Variance, and control charts.

The *Analyze* phase of a Six Sigma project focuses on the factors that affect the central tendency, variation, and shape of each CTQ variable. Factors are identified, and the relationships between the factors and the CTQs are analyzed. Statistical methods used in the *Analyze* phase include tables and charts, descriptive statistics, the Analysis of Variance, regression analysis, and control charts.

In the *Improve* phase of a Six Sigma project, team members carry out designed experiments to actively intervene in a process. The objective of the experiments is to determine the settings of the factors that will optimize the central tendency, variation, and shape of each CTQ variable. Statistical methods used in the *Improve* phase include tables and charts, descriptive statistics, regression analysis, hypothesis testing, the Analysis of Variance, and designed experiments.

The *Control* phase of a Six Sigma project focuses on the maintenance of improvements that have been made in the Improve phase. A risk abatement plan is developed to identify elements that can cause damage to a process. Statistical methods used in the *Control* phase include tables and charts, descriptive statistics, and control charts.

Roles in a Six Sigma Organization

Six Sigma requires that the employees of an organization have well-defined roles. The roles of senior executive (C.E.O. or president), executive committee, champion, process owner, master black belt, black belt, and green belt are critical to Six Sigma. More importantly, everyone must be properly trained in order to successfully fulfill their roles' tasks and responsibilities.

The role of the **senior executive** is critical for Six Sigma's ultimate success. The most successful, highly publicized Six Sigma efforts have all had unwavering, clear, and committed leadership from top management. Although Six Sigma concepts and processes can be initiated at lower levels, high-level success cannot be achieved without the leadership of the senior executive.

The members of the **executive committee** consist of the top management of an organization. They need to operate at the same level of commitment to Six Sigma as the senior executive.

Champions take a strong sponsorship and leadership role in conducting and implementing Six Sigma projects. They work closely with the executive committee, the black belt assigned to their project, and the master black belt overseeing their project. A champion should be a member of the executive committee, or at least someone who reports directly to a member of the executive committee. He or she should have enough influence to remove obstacles or provide resources without having to go higher in the organization.

A **process owner** is the manager of a process. He or she has responsibility for the process and has the authority to change the process on her or his signature. The process owner should be identified and involved immediately in all Six Sigma projects relating to his or her own area.

A **master black belt** takes on a leadership role in the implementation of the Six Sigma process and as an advisor to senior executives. The master black belt must use his or her skills while working on projects that are led by black belts and green belts. A master black belt has successfully led many teams through complex Six Sigma projects. He or she is a proven change agent, leader, facilitator, and technical expert in Six Sigma.

A **black belt** works full-time on Six Sigma projects. A black belt is mentored by a master black belt, but may report to a manager for his or her tour of duty as a black belt. Ideally, a black belt works well in a team format, can manage meetings, is familiar with statistics and systems theory, and has a focus on the customer.

A **green belt** is an individual who works on Six Sigma projects part-time (approximately 25%), either as a team member for complex projects or as a project leader for simpler projects. Most managers in a mature Six Sigma organization are green belts. Green belt certification is a critical prerequisite for advancement into upper management in a Six Sigma organization.

Recent research indicates that more than 80% of the top 100 publicly traded companies in the United States use Six Sigma. So, you do need to be aware of the distinction between master black belt, black belt, and green belt if you are to function effectively in a Six Sigma organization.

In a Six Sigma organization, 25% to 50% of the organization will be green belts, only 6% to 12% of the organization need to be black belts, and only 1% of the organization need to be master black belts (reference 9). Individual companies, professional organizations such as the American Society for Quality, and universities such as the University of Miami offer certification programs for green belt, black belt, and master black belt.

USING STATISTICS @ Beachcomber Hotel Revisited

In the Using Statistics scenario, you were the manager of the Beachcomber Hotel. After being trained in Six Sigma, you decided to focus on two critical first impressions: Is the room ready when a guest checks in? And, do guests receive their luggage in a reasonable amount of time?

You constructed a p chart on the proportion of rooms not ready at check in. The p chart indicated that the check-in process was in control and that, on average, the proportion of rooms not ready was approximately 0.08 (i.e., 8%). You then constructed $\overline{X}$ and R charts for the amount of time required to deliver luggage. Although there was a considerable amount of variability around the overall average of approximately 9.5 minutes, you determined that the luggage delivery process was also in control.

You have learned that an in control process contains common causes but no special causes. Improvements in the outcomes of in control processes must come from changes in the actual processes. Thus, if you want to reduce the proportion of rooms not ready at check in, and/or lower the mean luggage delivery time, then you will need to change the check-in process and/or the luggage delivery process. From your knowledge of Six Sigma and statistics, you know that during the *Improve* phase of the DMAIC model, you will be able to perform and analyze experiments using different process designs. Hopefully you will discover better process designs which will lead to a higher percentage of rooms being ready on time and/or quicker luggage delivery times. These improvements should ultimately lead to greater guest satisfaction.

SUMMARY

In this chapter you have learned how to use control charts to distinguish between common causes and special causes of variation. For categorical data, you learned how to construct and analyze *p* charts. For numerically measured variables, you learned how to construct and analyze $\overline{X}$ and *R* charts. The chapter also discussed managerial approaches used to improve the quality of products and services, including TQM and Six Sigma.

KEY EQUATIONS

Constructing Control Limits

Process mean ± 3 standard deviations

Upper control limit (UCL) = process mean
$\qquad\qquad\qquad\qquad +3$ standard deviations

Lower control limit (LCL) = process mean
$\qquad\qquad\qquad\qquad -3$ standard deviations   **(8.1)**

Control Limits for the *p* Chart

$$\overline{p} \pm 3\sqrt{\frac{\overline{p}(1 - \overline{p})}{\overline{n}}}$$

$$\text{UCL} = \overline{p} + 3\sqrt{\frac{\overline{p}(1 - \overline{p})}{\overline{n}}}$$

$$\text{LCL} = \overline{p} - 3\sqrt{\frac{\overline{p}(1 - \overline{p})}{\overline{n}}} \qquad\qquad \textbf{(8.2)}$$

KEY TERMS

CHAPTER REVIEW PROBLEMS

CHECKING YOUR UNDERSTANDING

8.1 What is the difference between common cause variation and special cause variation?

8.2 What should you do to improve a process when special causes of variation are present?

8.3 What should you do to improve a process when only common causes of variation are present?

8.4 What is the difference between attribute control charts and variables control charts?

8.5 Why are $\overline{X}$ and R charts used together?

8.6 What principles did you learn from the red bead experiment?

APPLYING THE CONCEPTS

8.7 A survey sponsored by the American Society for Quality found that master black belts make around $23,000 more a year, on average, than black belts. A partial listing of the survey results concerning annual salaries is given below.

Title	Sample Size	Mean	Standard Deviation
Black belt	194	85,465	18,894
Master black belt	131	108,879	21,946

Source: *Data extracted from H. Lindborg, "Navigate Your Career Path with QP's Annual Salary Survey,"* Quality Progress, *December 2007, pp. 21–50.*

a. Discuss the role of a black belt in a Six Sigma organization.
b. Discuss the role of a master black belt in a Six Sigma organization.
c. Assuming that the population variances are equal, construct and interpret a 95% confidence interval estimate of the difference between the population mean salary of master black belts and black belts. (*Hint:* Use Equation 10.2.)

8.8 According to the American Society for Quality, customers in the United States consistently rate service quality lower than product quality (American Society for Quality, *The Quarterly Quality Report*, **www.asq.org**, May 16, 2006). For example, products in the beverage, personal care and cleaning industries, and major appliance sectors all received very high customer satisfaction ratings. At the other extreme, services provided by airlines, banks, and insurance companies all received low customer satisfaction ratings.

a. Why do you think service quality consistently rates lower than product quality?
b. What are the similarities and differences between measuring service quality and product quality?
c. Do Deming's 14 points apply to both products and services?
d. Can Six Sigma be used for both products and services?

8.9 Six Flags Amusement Parks lost $133 million on revenue of $1.09 billion in 2005. To turn things around, Six Flags CEO Mark Shapiro is focusing on big problems (such as cutting long-term debt) and small details (such as cleaner restrooms and grounds). His attention to providing clean parks is part of his overall strategy to get entire families to enjoy their day in the park so much that they want to return (data extracted from L. Petrecca, "Six Flags CEO Waves the Signal Flag for Families," **usatoday.com**, June 13, 2006). Suppose that you have been hired as a summer intern at a large amusement park. Every day, your task is to conduct 200 exit interviews in the parking lot when customers leave. You need to construct questions to address the cleanliness of the park and the customers' intent to return again. When you begin to construct a short questionnaire, you remember the control chart material you learned in a statistics course, and you decide to write questions that will provide you with data to graph on control charts. After collecting data for 30 days, you plan to construct the control charts.

a. Write a question that will allow you to develop a control chart of customers' perceptions of cleanliness of the park.
b. Give examples of common cause variation and special cause variation for the control chart.
c. If the control chart is in control, what does that indicate and what do you do next?
d. If the control chart is out of control, what does that indicate and what do you do next?
e. Repeat (a) through (d), this time addressing the customers' intent to return to the park.
f. After the initial 30 days, assuming that the charts indicate in-control processes or that the root sources of special cause variation have been corrected, explain how the charts can be used on a daily basis to monitor and improve the quality in the park.

8.10 Researchers at Miami University in Oxford, Ohio, investigated the use of p charts to monitor the market share of a product and to document the effectiveness of marketing promotions. Market share is defined as the company's proportion of the total number of products sold in a category. If a p chart based on a company's market share indicates an in-control process, then the company's share in the marketplace is deemed to be stable and consistent over time. In the example given in the article, the RudyBird Diskette Company collected daily sales data from a nationwide retail audit service. The first 30 days of data in the accompanying table (see the file Rudybird) indicate the total number of cases of computer disks sold and the number of RudyBird diskettes sold. The final 7 days of data were taken after RudyBird launched a major in-store promotion. A control chart was used to see if the in-store promotion would result in special cause variation in the marketplace.

a. Construct a p chart using data from the first 30 days (prior to the promotion) to monitor the market share for RudyBird Diskettes.
b. Is the market share for RudyBird in control before the start of the in-store promotion?
c. On your control chart, extend the control limits generated in (b) and plot the proportions for days 31 through 37. What effect, if any, did the in-store promotion have on RudyBird's market share?

Cases Sold Before the Promotion

Day	Total	RudyBird	Day	Total	RudyBird
1	154	35	16	177	56
2	153	43	17	143	43
3	200	44	18	200	69
4	197	56	19	134	38
5	194	54	20	192	47
6	172	38	21	155	45
7	190	43	22	135	36
8	209	62	23	189	55
9	173	53	24	184	44
10	171	39	25	170	47
11	173	44	26	178	48
12	168	37	27	167	42
13	184	45	28	204	71
14	211	58	29	183	64
15	179	35	30	169	43

Cases Sold After the Promotion

Day	Total	RudyBird
31	201	92
32	177	76
33	205	85
34	199	90
35	187	77
36	168	79
37	198	97

Source: *Data extracted from C. T. Crespy, T. C. Krehbiel, and J. M. Stearns, "Integrating Analytic Methods into Marketing Research Education: Statistical Control Charts as an Example,"* Marketing Education Review, *5, Spring 1995, pp. 11–23.*

8.11 The manufacturer of Boston and Vermont asphalt shingles constructed control charts and analyzed several quality characteristics. One characteristic of interest is the strength of the sealant on the shingle. During each day of production, three shingles are tested for their sealant strength. (Thus, a subgroup is operationally defined as one day of production, and the sample size for each subgroup is 3.) Separate pieces are cut from the upper and lower portions of a shingle and then reassembled to simulate shingles on a roof. A timed heating process is used to simulate the sealing process. The sealed shingle pieces are pulled apart, and the amount of force (in pounds) required to break the sealant bond is measured and recorded. This variable is called the *sealant strength*. The data file Sealant contains sealant strength measurements on 25 days of production for Boston shingles and 19 days for Vermont shingles.

For the Boston shingles,

a. construct a control chart for the range.
b. construct a control chart for the mean.
c. is the process in control?

d. Repeat (a) through (c), using the 19 production days for Vermont shingles.

8.12 A professional basketball player has embarked on a program to study his ability to shoot foul shots. On each day in which a game is not scheduled, he intends to shoot 100 foul shots. He maintains records over a period of 40 days of practice, with the results stored in the file **Foulspc**:

a. Construct a p chart for the proportion of successful foul shots. Do you think that the player's foul-shooting process is in statistical control? If not, why not?

b. What if you were told that the player used a different method of shooting foul shots for the last 20 days? How might this information change your conclusions in (a)?

c. If you knew the information in (b) prior to doing (a), how might you do the analysis differently?

8.13 The funds-transfer department of a bank is concerned with turnaround time for investigations of funds-transfer payments. A payment may involve the bank as a remitter of funds, a beneficiary of funds, or an intermediary in the payment. An investigation is initiated by a payment inquiry or a query by a party involved in the payment or any department affected by the flow of funds. When a query is received, an investigator reconstructs the transaction trail of the payment and verifies that the information is correct and that the proper payment is transmitted. The investigator then reports the results of the investigation, and the transaction is considered closed. It is important that investigations are closed rapidly, preferably within the same day. The number of new investigations and the number and proportion closed on the same day that the inquiry was made are in the file **Fundtran**.

a. Construct a control chart for these data.

b. Is the process in a state of statistical control? Explain.

c. Based on the results of (a) and (b), what should management do next to improve the process?

8.14 A branch manager of a brokerage company is concerned with the number of undesirable trades made by her sales staff. A trade is considered undesirable if there is an error on the trade ticket. Trades with errors are canceled and resubmitted. The cost of correcting errors is billed to the brokerage company. The branch manager wants to know whether the proportion of undesirable trades is in a state of statistical control so she can plan the next step in a quality improvement process. Data were collected for a 30-day period, with the results stored in the file **Trade**.

a. Construct a control chart for these data.

b. Is the process in control? Explain.

c. Based on the results of (a) and (b), what should the manager do next to improve the process?

8.15 As chief operating officer of a local community hospital, you have just returned from a three-day seminar on quality and productivity. It is your intention to implement many of the ideas that you learned at the seminar. You have decided to construct control charts for the upcoming month for the proportion of rework in the laboratory (based on 1,000 daily samples), and time (in hours) between receipt of a specimen at the laboratory and completion of the work (based on a subgroup of 10 specimens per day). The data collected are summarized in the file **Hospadm**. You are to make a presentation to the chief executive officer of the hospital and the board of directors. Prepare a report that summarizes the conclusions drawn from analyzing control charts for these variables. In addition, recommend additional variables to measure and monitor by using control charts.

8.16 For a period of four weeks, record your pulse rate (in beats per minute) just after you get out of bed in the morning and also before you go to sleep at night. Construct $\overline{X}$ and R charts and determine whether your pulse rate is in a state of statistical control. Discuss.

8.17 (Class Project) Use the table of random numbers (Table E.1) to simulate the selection of different-colored balls from an urn, as follows:

1. Start in the row corresponding to the day of the month in which you were born plus the last two digits of the year in which you were born. For example, if you were born October 3, 1986, you would start in row 3 + 86 = 89. If your total exceeds 100, subtract 100 from the total.

2. Select two-digit random numbers.

3. If you select a random number from 00 to 94, consider the ball to be white; if the random number is from 95 to 99, consider the ball to be red.

Each student is to select 100 such two-digit random numbers and report the number of "red balls" in the sample. Construct a control chart for the proportion of red balls. What conclusions can you draw about the system of selecting red balls? Are all the students part of the system? Is anyone outside the system? If so, what explanation can you give for someone who has too many red balls? If a bonus were paid to the top 10% of the students (the 10% with the fewest red balls), what effect would that have on the rest of the students? Discuss.

THE HARNSWELL SEWING MACHINE COMPANY CASE

PHASE 1

For more than 40 years, the Harnswell Sewing Machine Company has manufactured industrial sewing machines. The company specializes in automated machines called pattern tackers that sew repetitive patterns on such mass-produced products as shoes, garments, and seat belts. Aside from the sales of machines, the company sells machine parts. Because the company's products have a reputation for being superior, Harnswell is able to command a price premium for its product line.

Recently, the operations manager, Natalie York, purchased several books relating to quality at a local bookstore. After reading them, she considered the feasibility of beginning a quality program at the company. At the current time, the company has no formal quality program. Parts are 100% inspected at the time of shipping to a customer or installation in a machine, yet Natalie has always wondered why inventory of certain parts (in particular, the half-inch cam rollers) invariably falls short before a full year lapses, even though 7,000 pieces have been produced for a demand of 5,000 pieces per year.

After a great deal of reflection and with some apprehension, Natalie has decided that she will approach John Harnswell, the owner of the company, about the possibility of beginning a program to improve quality in the company, starting with a trial project in the machine parts area. As she is walking to Mr. Harnswell's office for the meeting, she has second thoughts about whether this is such a good idea. After all, just last month, Mr. Harnswell told her, "Why do you need to go to graduate school for your master's degree in business? That is a waste of your time and will not be of any value to the Harnswell Company. All those professors are just up in their ivory towers and don't know a thing about running a business, like I do."

As she enters his office, Mr. Harnswell, ever courteous to her, invites Natalie to sit down across from him. "Well, what do you have on your mind this morning?" Mr. Harnswell asks her in an inquisitive tone. She begins by starting to talk about the books that she has just completed reading and about how she has some interesting ideas for making production even better than it is now and improving profits. Before she can finish, Mr. Harnswell has started to answer. "Look, everything has been fine since I started this company in 1968. I have built this company up from nothing to one that employs more than 100 people. Why do you want to make waves? Remember, if it ain't broke, don't fix it." With that he ushers her from his office with the admonishment of, "What am I going to do with you if you keep coming up with these ridiculous ideas?"

EXERCISES

HS8.1 Based on what you have read, which of Deming's 14 points of management are most lacking in the Harnswell Sewing Machine Company? Explain.

HS8.2 What changes, if any, do you think that Natalie York might be able to institute in the company? Explain.

DO NOT CONTINUE UNTIL YOU HAVE COMPLETED THE PHASE 1 EXERCISES.

PHASE 2

Natalie slowly walks down the hall after leaving Mr. Harnswell's office, feeling rather downcast. He just won't listen to anyone, she thinks. As she walks, Jim Murante, the shop foreman, comes up beside her. "So," he says, "did you really think that he would listen to you? I've been here more than 25 years. The only way he listens is if he is shown something that worked after it has already been done. Let's see what we can plan together."

Natalie and Jim decide to begin by investigating the production of the cam rollers, which are precision-ground parts. The last part of the production process involves the grinding of the outer diameter. After grinding, the part mates with the cam groove of the particular sewing pattern. The half-inch rollers technically have an engineering specification for the outer diameter of the roller of 0.5075 inch (the specifications are actually metric, but in factory floor jargon, they are referred to as half-inch), plus a tolerable error of 0.0003 inch on the lower side. Thus, the outer diameter is allowed to be between 0.5072 and 0.5075 inch. Anything larger is reclassified into a different and less costly category, and anything smaller is unusable for anything other than scrap.

The grinding of the cam roller is done on a single machine with a single tool setup and no change in the grinding wheel after initial setup. The operation is done by Dave Martin, the head machinist, who has 30 years of experience in the trade and specific experience producing the cam roller part. Because production occurs in batches, Natalie and Jim sample five parts produced from each batch. Table HS8.1 presents data collected over 30 batches (stored in the file **Harnswell**).

EXERCISE

HS8.3 **a.** Is the process in control? Why?
b. What recommendations do you have for improving the process?

DO NOT CONTINUE UNTIL YOU HAVE COMPLETED THE PHASE 2 EXERCISE.

TABLE HS8.1

Diameter of Cam Rollers (in Inches)

Batch	Cam Roller 1	2	3	4	5
1	.5076	.5076	.5075	.5077	.5075
2	.5075	.5077	.5076	.5076	.5075
3	.5075	.5075	.5075	.5075	.5076
4	.5075	.5076	.5074	.5076	.5073
5	.5075	.5074	.5076	.5073	.5076
6	.5076	.5075	.5076	.5075	.5075
7	.5076	.5076	.5076	.5075	.5075
8	.5075	.5076	.5076	.5075	.5074
9	.5074	.5076	.5075	.5075	.5076
10	.5076	.5077	.5075	.5075	.5075
11	.5075	.5075	.5075	.5076	.5075
12	.5075	.5076	.5075	.5077	.5075
13	.5076	.5076	.5073	.5076	.5074
14	.5075	.5076	.5074	.5076	.5075
15	.5075	.5075	.5076	.5074	.5073
16	.5075	.5074	.5076	.5075	.5075
17	.5075	.5074	.5075	.5074	.5072
18	.5075	.5075	.5076	.5075	.5076
19	.5076	.5076	.5075	.5075	.5076
20	.5075	.5074	.5077	.5076	.5074
21	.5075	.5074	.5075	.5075	.5075
22	.5076	.5076	.5075	.5076	.5074
23	.5076	.5076	.5075	.5075	.5076
24	.5075	.5076	.5075	.5076	.5075
25	.5075	.5075	.5075	.5075	.5074
26	.5077	.5076	.5076	.5074	.5075
27	.5075	.5075	.5074	.5076	.5075
28	.5077	.5076	.5075	.5075	.5076
29	.5075	.5075	.5074	.5075	.5075
30	.5076	.5075	.5075	.5076	.5075

PHASE 3

Natalie examines the $\overline{X}$ and R charts developed from the data presented in Table HS8.1. The R chart indicates that the process is in control, but the $\overline{X}$ chart reveals that the mean for batch 17 is outside the LCL. This immediately gives her cause for concern because low values for the roller diameter could mean that parts have to be scrapped. Natalie goes to see Jim Murante, the shop foreman, to try to find out what had happened to batch 17. Jim looks up the production records to determine when this batch was produced. "Aha!" he exclaims. "I think I've got the answer! This batch was produced on that really cold morning we had last month. I've been after Mr. Harnswell for a long time to let us install an automatic thermostat here in the shop so that the place doesn't feel so cold when we get here in the morning. All he ever tells me is that people aren't as tough as they used to be."

Natalie stands there almost in shock. She realizes that what happened is that, rather than standing idle until the environment and the equipment warmed to acceptable temperatures, the machinist opted to manufacture parts that might have to be scrapped. In fact, Natalie recalls that a major problem occurred on that same day, when several other expensive parts had to be scrapped. Natalie says to Jim, "We just have to do something. We can't let this go on now that we know what problems it is potentially causing." Natalie and Jim decide to take enough money out of petty cash to get the thermostat without having to fill out a requisition requiring Mr. Harnswell's signature. They install the thermostat and set the heating control so that the heat turns on a half hour before the shop opens each morning.

EXERCISES

HS8.4   What should Natalie now do concerning the cam roller data? Explain.

HS8.5   Explain how the actions of Natalie and Jim to avoid this particular problem in the future have resulted in quality improvement.

DO NOT CONTINUE UNTIL YOU HAVE COMPLETED THE PHASE 3 EXERCISES.

PHASE 4

Because corrective action was taken to eliminate the special cause of variation, Natalie removes the data for batch 17 from the analysis. The control charts for the remaining days indicate a stable system, with only common causes of variation operating on the system. Then, Natalie and Jim sit down with Dave Martin and several other machinists to try to determine all the possible causes for the existence of oversized and scrapped rollers. Natalie is still troubled by the data. After all, she wants to find out whether the process is giving oversizes (which are downgraded) and undersizes (which are scrapped). She thinks about which tables and charts might be most helpful.

EXERCISE

HS8.6   **a.** Construct a frequency distribution and a stem-and-leaf display of the cam roller diameters. Which one do you prefer?

       b. Based on your results in (a), construct all appropriate graphs of the cam roller diameters.

       c. Write a report, expressing your conclusions concerning the cam roller diameters. Be sure to discuss the diameters as they relate to the specifications.

DO NOT CONTINUE UNTIL YOU HAVE COMPLETED THE PHASE 4 EXERCISE.

PHASE 5

Natalie notices immediately that the overall mean diameter with batch 17 eliminated is 0.507527, which is higher than the specification value. Thus, the mean diameter of the rollers produced is so high that they will be downgraded in value. In fact, 55 of the 150 rollers sampled (36.67%) are above the specification value. If this percentage is extrapolated to the full year's production, 36.67% of the 7,000 pieces manufactured, or 2,567, could not be sold as half-inch rollers, leaving only 4,433 available for sale. "No wonder we often have shortages that require costly emergency runs," she thinks. She also notes that not one diameter is below the lower specification of 0.5072, so not one of the rollers had to be scrapped.

Natalie realizes that there has to be a reason for all this. Along with Jim Murante, she decides to show the results to Dave Martin, the head machinist. Dave says that the results don't surprise him that much. "You know," he says, "there is only 0.0003 inch in diameter that I'm allowed in variation.

If I aim for exactly halfway between 0.5072 and 0.5075, I'm afraid that I'll make a lot of short pieces that will have to be scrapped. I know from way back when I first started here that Mr. Harnswell and everybody else will come down on my head if they start seeing too many of those scraps. I figure that if I aim at 0.5075, the worst thing that will happen will be a bunch of downgrades, but I won't make any pieces that have to be scrapped."

EXERCISES

HS8.7 What approach do you think the machinist should take in terms of the diameter he should aim for? Explain.

HS8.8 What do you think that Natalie should do next? Explain.

MANAGING *THE SPRINGVILLE HERALD*

PHASE 1

An advertising production team is charged with reducing the number and dollar amount of the advertising errors, with initial focus on the ran-in-error category. The team collects data, including the number of ads with errors, on a Monday-to-Saturday basis. Table SH8.1 includes the total number of ads and the number containing errors for a period of one month (see the file SH8-1). (Sundays are excluded because a special type of production is used for that day.)

EXERCISES

SH8.1 What is the first thing that the team from the advertising production department should do to reduce the number of errors? Explain.

SH8.2 **a.** Construct the appropriate control chart for these data.

b. Is the process in a state of statistical control? Explain.

c. What should the team recommend as the next step to improve the process?

DO NOT CONTINUE UNTIL YOU HAVE COMPLETED THE PHASE 1 EXERCISES.

PHASE 2

The advertising production team examines the *p* chart developed from the data of Table SH8.1. Using the rules for determining out-of-control points, they observe that day 8 is above the UCL. Upon investigation, they determine that on that day, there was an employee from another work area assigned to the processing of the ads because several employees were out ill. The group brainstorms ways of avoiding the problem in the future and recommends that a team of people from other work areas receive training on the work done by this

TABLE SH8.1

Number of Ads with Errors and Daily Number of Display Ads

Day	Number of Ads with Errors	Total Number of Ads	Day	Number of Ads with Errors	Total Number of Ads
1	4	228	14	5	245
2	6	273	15	7	266
3	5	239	16	2	197
4	3	197	17	4	228
5	6	259	18	5	236
6	7	203	19	4	208
7	8	289	20	3	214
8	14	241	21	8	258
9	9	263	22	10	267
10	5	199	23	4	217
11	6	275	24	9	277
12	4	212	25	7	258
13	3	207			

area. Members of this team can then cover the processing of the ads by rotating in one- or two-hour shifts.

EXERCISES

SH8.3 What should the advertising production team now do concerning the data of Table SH8.1? Explain.

SH8.4 Explain how the actions of the team to avoid this particular problem in the future have resulted in quality improvement.

SH8.5 In addition to the number of ads with errors, what other information concerning errors on a daily basis should the team collect?

DO NOT CONTINUE UNTIL YOU HAVE COMPLETED THE PHASE 2 EXERCISES.

PHASE 3

A print production team also is charged with improving the quality of the *Herald*. The team has chosen the blackness of the print of the newspaper as its first project. Blackness is measured on a device that records the results on a standard scale, where the blacker the spot, the higher the blackness measure. The blackness of the print should be approximately 1.0. The lower and upper specifications for blackness are 0.8 and 1.2, respectively. Five spots on the first newspaper printed each day are randomly selected, and the blackness of each spot is measured. Table SH8.2 presents the results for 25 days (stored in the file SH8-2).

EXERCISE

SH8.6 **a.** Construct the appropriate control charts for these data.
b. Is the process in a state of statistical control? Explain.
c. What should the team recommend as the next step to improve the process?

TABLE SH8.2

Newsprint Blackness for 25 Consecutive Days

| | Spot | | | | | | Spot | | | | |
Day	1	2	3	4	5	Day	1	2	3	4	5
1	0.96	1.01	1.12	1.07	0.97	14	1.03	0.89	1.03	1.12	1.03
2	1.06	1.00	1.02	1.16	0.96	15	0.96	1.12	0.95	0.88	0.99
3	1.00	0.90	0.98	1.18	0.96	16	1.01	0.87	0.99	1.04	1.16
4	0.92	0.89	1.01	1.16	0.90	17	0.98	0.85	0.99	1.04	1.16
5	1.02	1.16	1.03	0.89	1.00	18	1.03	0.82	1.21	0.98	1.08
6	0.88	0.92	1.03	1.16	0.91	19	1.02	0.84	1.15	0.94	1.08
7	1.05	1.13	1.01	0.93	1.03	20	0.90	1.02	1.10	1.04	1.08
8	0.95	0.86	1.14	0.90	0.95	21	0.96	1.05	1.01	0.93	1.01
9	0.99	0.89	1.00	1.15	0.92	22	0.89	1.04	0.97	0.99	0.95
10	0.89	1.18	1.03	0.96	1.04	23	0.96	1.00	0.97	1.04	0.95
11	0.97	1.13	0.95	0.86	1.06	24	1.01	0.98	1.04	1.01	0.92
12	1.00	0.87	1.02	0.98	1.13	25	1.01	1.00	0.92	0.90	1.11
13	0.96	0.79	1.17	0.97	0.95						

REFERENCES

1. Arndt, M., "Quality Isn't Just for Widgets," *Business Week*, July 22, 2002, pp. 72–73.
2. Automotive Industry Action Group (AIAG), *Statistical Process Control Reference Manual* (Chrysler, Ford, and General Motors Quality and Supplier Assessment Staff, 1995).
3. Bothe, D. R., *Measuring Process Capability* (New York: McGraw-Hill, 1997).
4. Cyger, M. "The Last Word-Riding the Bandwagon," *iSixSigma Magazine*, November/December 2006.
5. Davis, R. B., and T. C. Krehbiel, "Shewhart and Zone Control Charts under Linear Trend," *Communications in Statistics: Simulation and Computation*, 2002, 31(1), pp. 91–96.
6. Deming, W. E., *The New Economics for Business, Industry, and Government* (Cambridge, MA: MIT Center for Advanced Engineering Study, 1993).
7. Deming, W. E., *Out of the Crisis* (Cambridge, MA: MIT Center for Advanced Engineering Study, 1986).
8. Gabor, A., *The Man Who Discovered Quality* (New York: Time Books, 1990).
9. Gitlow, H., and D. Levine, *Six Sigma for Green Belts and Champions* (Upper Saddle River, NJ: Financial Times/Prentice Hall, 2005).
10. Gitlow, H., D. Levine, and E. Popovich, *Design for Six Sigma for Green Belts and Champions* (Upper Saddle River, NJ: Financial Times/Prentice Hall, 2006).
11. Hahn, G. J., N. Doganaksoy, and R. Hoerl, "The Evolution of Six Sigma," *Quality Engineering*, 12 (2000): 317–326.
12. Lemak, D. L. , N. P. Mero, and R. Reed, " When Quality Works: A Premature Post-Mortem on TQM," *Journal of Business and Management*, 8 (2002): 391–407.

13. Levine, D. M., *Statistics for Six Sigma for Green Belts with Minitab and JMP* (Upper Saddle River, NJ: Financial Times/Prentice Hall, 2006).

14. *Microsoft Excel 2007* (Redmond, WA: Microsoft Corp., 2007).

15. Scherkenbach, W. W., *The Deming Route to Quality and Productivity: Road Maps and Roadblocks* (Washington, DC: CEEP Press, 1987).

16. Shewhart, W. A., *Economic Control of the Quality of Manufactured Product* (New York: Van Nostrand-Reinhard, 1931, reprinted by the American Society for Quality Control, Milwaukee, 1980).

17. Snee, R. D., "Impact of Six Sigma on Quality," *Quality Engineering*, 12 (2000): ix–xiv.

18. Vardeman, S. B., and J. M. Jobe, *Statistical Methods for Quality Assurance: Basics, Measurement, Control, Capability and Improvement* (New York: Springer-Verlag, 2009).

19. Walton, M., *The Deming Management Method* (New York: Perigee Books, 1986).

Using Microsoft Excel for Control Charts

E8.1 Computing Control Limits for *p* Charts

You compute control limits for *p* charts by making entries in the **pChartData** worksheet of the `p Chart.xls` workbook.

Open to that worksheet and enter time period data into column A, the sample/subgroup size for each time period in column B, and the number of nonconforming items for each time period in column C. Then select the preexisting formulas in the cell range D2:G2 and copy them down through all data rows. (Before you enter your data, these cells will display the message #DIV/0!. This is not an error.)

The formulas that you copy are shown in Figure E8.1. The cell D2 formula computes a point to be plotted on the *p* chart. The cell E2 formula displays the lower control limit value, the cell F2 formula displays the center values, and the G2 formula displays the upper control limit. As you copy the formulas in these last three columns, the same set of three values appears in every row to facilitate creating a *p* chart as explained in Section E8.2.

	D	E	F	G
1	p	LCL	Center	UCL
2	=C2/B2	= pCalcs!$B$12	=pCalcs!$B$13	=pCalcs!$B$14

FIGURE E8.1   pChartData worksheet formulas

As you complete this worksheet by copying formulas, you also complete the **pCalcs** worksheet that summarizes the control limits formulas. You make no entries into the pCalcs worksheet; its data come from summarizing your entries in the pChartData worksheet.

	A	B	
1	**p Chart Summary**		
2			
3	Intermediate Calculations		
4	Sum of Subgroup Sizes	5600	=SUM(pChartData!B:B)
5	Number of Subgroups Taken	28	=COUNT(pChartData!B:B)
6	Average Sample/Subgroup Size	200	=B4/B5
7	Average Proportion of Nonconforming Items	0.0827	=SUM(pChartData!C:C)/B4
8	Three Standard Deviations	0.0584	=3 * SQRT(B7 * (1 - B7)/B6)
9	Preliminary Lower Control Limit	0.0243	=B7 - B8
10			
11	**p Chart Control Limits**		
12	**Lower Control Limit**	0.0243	=IF(B9 > 0, B9, 0)
13	**Center**	0.0827	=B7
14	**Upper Control Limit**	0.1411	=B7 + B8

FIGURE E8.2   pCalcs worksheet

E8.2 Creating *p* Charts: Overview

You create *p* charts by using Excel charting features with your completed **pChartData** and **pCalcs** worksheets (discussed in the previous section).

E8.2A Creating *p* Charts (Excel 97–2003)

Open to your completed **pChartData** worksheet. Select **Insert → Chart** and make the following entries in the Wizard Step dialog boxes:

Wizard Step 1 Click **XY (Scatter)** from the Standard Types Chart type box and then select the first choice in the bottom row of Chart sub-type choices, labeled as Scatter with data points connected by lines.

Wizard Step 2 Click the **Data Range** tab. Enter the column A cell range of your time period data followed by the columns D through G cell range that contain the formulas as the **Data Range**. Because you are entering a data range composed of two nonadjacent areas, you must separate the two cell ranges with a comma. For example, if your pChartData worksheet contained entries in rows 2 through 29, you would enter **A1:A29,D1:G29** as the Data Range. Click the **Columns** option after you have entered your Data Range.

Wizard Step 3 Click the **Titles** tab. Enter a title as the **Chart title** and enter appropriate values for the **Value (X) axis** and **Value (Y) axis** titles. Click, in turn, the **Axes**, **Gridlines**, **Legend**, and **Data Labels** tabs and use the formatting settings that are given in Section E2.3A.

At this point, the UCL, Center, and LCL lines of your *p* chart will be missing labels and be incorrectly formatted. You can correct these errors using the following instructions.

To add labels for the control chart and center lines. Display the Drawing toolbar by selecting **View → Toolbars → Drawing**. For each line, click the **Text Box icon** and drag the mouse to draw a box to hold a label. (Figure E8.3 shows the Excel 2003 Text Box icon selected; the icons in other Excel versions are similar.) Type the label (UCL, pBar, or LCL). If necessary, you can adjust the size of the box by clicking and dragging one of the corner circle handles. If necessary, you can adjust the position of the box by clicking and dragging the halo around the text box.

FIGURE E8.3   Text Box icon of the Drawing toolbar (Excel 2003)

To eliminate data point markers from the control chart and center lines. For each line, right-click the line and select **Format Data Series** from the shortcut menu. In the **Marker Options** panel, select the **None** option and then click **Close**.

To reformat the UCL and LCL lines. For each line, right-click the line and select **Format Data Series** from the shortcut menu. In the **Patterns** tab of the Format Data Series Data dialog box, select the first dashed line choice from the **Style drop-down** list box in the **Line** group, select the **None** option in the **Marker** group and click **OK**.

To reformat the center line. Right-click the line and select **Format Data Series** from the shortcut menu. In the **Patterns** tab of the Format Data Series Data dialog box, select a red color from the **Color** drop-down list in the **Line** group, select the **None** option in the **Marker** group, and click **OK**.

E8.2B Creating *p* Charts (Excel 2007)

Open to your completed **pChartData** worksheet and select the column A and columns D through G data. To select these nonadjacent areas together, hold down the **Ctrl** key while selecting the ranges. Then select **Insert → Scatter → Scatter with Straight Lines and Markers**. Finish by relocating your chart to a chart sheet and customizing your chart using the instructions in Section E.2.3B. At this point, the UCL, Center, and LCL lines of your *p* chart will be missing labels and be incorrectly formatted. You can correct these errors using the following instructions.

To add labels for the control chart and center lines. For each line, click **Insert → Text Box** and drag the mouse to draw a box to hold a label. Right-click in the box and select **Edit Test** from the shortcut menu. Type the label (UCL, pBar, or LCL) and click outside the text box. If necessary, you can adjust the size of the box by clicking and dragging one of the corner circle handles. If necessary, you can adjust the position of the box by clicking and dragging the box.

To reformat the UCL and LCL lines. For each line, right-click the line and select **Format Data Series** from the shortcut menu. In the **Line Style** panel, select one of the choices from the **Dash type** drop-down list. In the **Marker Options** panel, select the **None** option and then click **Close**.

To reformat the center line. Right-click the line and select **Format Data Series** from the shortcut menu. In the **Line**

panel, select one of the red choices from the **Color** drop-down list. In the **Marker Options** panel, select the **None** option and then click **Close**.

E8.3 Computing Control Limits for R and $\overline{X}$ Charts

You compute control limits for R and $\overline{X}$ charts by making entries in the **RXChartData** and **RXCalcs** worksheets in the `RandXBarChart.xls` workbook.

Open to the **RXChartData** worksheet of the `RandXBarChart.xls` workbook. Enter the time period, $\overline{X}$, and range data into columns A, B, and C, respectively. If you have only the raw data for each time period, you first need to compute the mean and range for each time period. If necessary, use the AVERAGE function to compute the mean. Use the MAX and MIN functions to determine the largest and smallest value and then subtract the smallest value from the largest value to compute the range.

With columns A through C completed, select the preexisting formulas in the cell range D2:I2 and copy them down through all data rows. (Before you enter your data, these cells will display the message #DIV/0!. This is not an error.) The formulas that you copy compute the control limit and center lines for both the R and $\overline{X}$ chart. These formulas are similar to the pChartData worksheet formulas discussed in Section E8.1.

After copying these formulas, open to the **RXCalcs** worksheet (to which the formulas refer). Enter the sample/subgroup size in cell B4. Use Table E.9 to look up the proper values for the D_3, D_4, and A_2 factors and enter those values in cells B8, B9, and B18, respectively, to complete the worksheet. Figure E8.4 shows a completed RXCalcs worksheet for the R and $\overline{X}$ charts shown in Figures 8.1 and 8.2.

	A	B	
1	**R and XBar Chart Summary**		
2			
3	**Data**		
4	**Sample/Subgroup Size**	5	
5			
6	R Chart Intermediate Calculations		
7	RBar	3.4821	=AVERAGE(RXChartData!C:C)
8	D3 Factor	0	
9	D4 Factor	2.114	
10			
11	**R Chart Control Limits**		
12	**Lower Control Limit**	0.0000	=B8 * B7
13	**Center**	3.4821	=B7
14	**Upper Control Limit**	7.3613	=B9 * B7
15			
16	XBar Chart Intermediate Calculations		
17	Average of Subgroup Averages	9.4779	=AVERAGE(RXChartData!B:B)
18	A2 Factor	0.577	
19	A2 Factor * RBar	2.0092	=B18 * B7
20			
21	**XBar Chart Control Limits**		
22	**Lower Control Limit**	7.4687	=B17 - B19
23	**Center**	9.4779	=B17
24	**Upper Control Limit**	11.4871	=B17 + B19

FIGURE E8.4   RXCalcs worksheet

E8.4 Creating *R* and $\overline{X}$ Charts: Overview

You create *R* or $\overline{X}$ charts by using Excel charting features with your completed RXChartData and RXCalcs worksheets (see previous section).

E8.4A Creating *R* and $\overline{X}$ Charts (Excel 97–2003)

Open to your completed **RXChartData** worksheet. Select **Insert → Chart** and make the following entries in the Wizard Step dialog boxes:

Wizard Step 1 Click **XY (Scatter)** from the **Standard Types Chart type** box and then select the first choice in the bottom row of **Chart sub-type** choices, labeled as **Scatter with data points connected by lines**.

Wizard Step 2 Click the **Data Range** tab. To create an *R* chart, enter the column A cell range of your time period data followed by the columns C through F cell range that contain the formulas as the **Data Range**. To create an $\overline{X}$ chart, enter the column A and B cell range followed by the columns G through I cell range that contain the formulas as the **Data Range**. Because you are entering a data range composed of two nonadjacent areas, you must separate the two cell ranges with a comma. For example, if your RXChartData worksheet contained entries in rows 2 through 29, you would enter **A1:A29,C1:F29** if creating an *R* chart or **A1:B29,G1:I29** if creating an $\overline{X}$ chart. Click the **Columns** option after you have entered your Data Range.

Wizard Step 3 Click the **Titles** tab. Enter a title as the **Chart title** and enter appropriate values for the **Value (X) axis** and **Value (Y) axis** titles. Click, in turn, the **Axes, Gridlines, Legend,** and **Data Labels** tabs and use the formatting settings that are given in Section E2.3A on page 119.

At this point, the UCL, Center, and LCL lines of your *R* or $\overline{X}$ chart will be missing labels and be incorrectly formatted. Use the Section E8.2A instructions for correcting *p* chart format errors to correct your *R* or $\overline{X}$ chart.

E8.4B Creating *R* and $\overline{X}$ Charts (Excel 2007)

Open to your completed **RXChartData** worksheet. To create an *R* chart, select the column A and columns C through F data. To create an $\overline{X}$ chart, select the columns A and B and columns G through I data. To select these nonadjacent areas together, hold down the **Ctrl** key while selecting the ranges. Then select **Insert → Scatter → Scatter with Straight Lines and Markers**. Finish by relocating your chart to a chart sheet and customizing your chart, using the instructions in Section E.2.3B.

At this point, the UCL, Center, and LCL lines of your *R* or $\overline{X}$ chart will be missing labels and be incorrectly formatted. Use the Section E8.2B instructions for correcting *p* chart format errors to correct your *R* or $\overline{X}$ chart.

9 Confidence Interval Estimation

Learning Objectives

In this chapter, you learn:

- To construct and interpret confidence interval estimates for the mean and the proportion
- How to determine the sample size necessary to develop a confidence interval for the mean or proportion

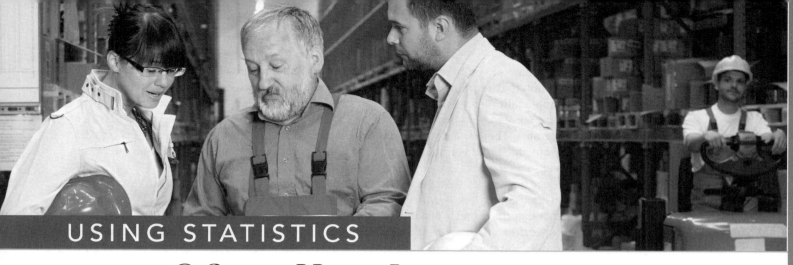

@ Saxon Home Improvement

Saxon Home Improvement distributes home improvement supplies in the northeastern United States. As a company accountant, you are responsible for the accuracy of the integrated inventory management and sales information system. You could review the contents of each and every record to check the accuracy of this system, but such a detailed review would be time-consuming and costly. A better approach is to use statistical inference techniques to draw conclusions about the population of all records from a relatively small sample collected during an audit. At the end of each month, you could select a sample of the sales invoices to estimate the following:

- The mean dollar amount listed on the sales invoices for the month.
- The proportion of invoices that contain errors that violate the internal control policy of the warehouse.

How accurate are the results from the samples and how do you use this information? Are the sample sizes large enough to give you the information you need?

I n Section 7.4, you used the Central Limit Theorem and knowledge of the population distribution to determine the percentage of sample means that are within certain distances of the population mean. For instance, in the cereal-fill example used throughout Chapter 7 (see Example 7.6), you can conclude that 95% of all sample means are between 362.12 and 373.88 grams. This is an example of *deductive* reasoning because the conclusion is based on taking something that is true in general (for the population) and applying it to something specific (the sample means).

To get the results that Saxon Home Improvement needs requires *inductive* reasoning. Inductive reasoning lets you use some specifics to make broader generalizations. You cannot guarantee that the broader generalizations are absolutely correct, but with a careful choosing of the specifics and a rigorous methodology, you can get useful conclusions. As a Saxon accountant, you need to use inferential statistics, the process of using sample results (the "some specifics") to *estimate* ("the making of the broader generalization") unknown population parameters such as a population mean or a population proportion. Note that statisticians use the word *estimate* in the same sense of the everyday usage, something you are reasonably certain about, but cannot flatly say is absolutely correct.

You estimate population parameters using either point estimates or interval estimates. A **point estimate** is the value of a single sample statistic. A **confidence interval estimate** is a range of numbers, called an interval, constructed around the point estimate. The confidence interval is constructed such that the probability that the population parameter is located somewhere within the interval is known.

Suppose you want to estimate the mean GPA of all the students at your university. The mean GPA for all the students is an unknown population mean, denoted by μ. You select a sample of students and find that the sample mean is 2.80. The sample mean, $\overline{X} = 2.80$, is a point estimate of the population mean, μ. How accurate is 2.80? To answer this question, you must construct a confidence interval estimate.

Recall that the sample mean, $\overline{X}$, is a point estimate of the population mean, μ. However, the sample mean varies from sample to sample because it depends on the items selected in the sample. By taking into account the known variability from sample to sample (see Section 7.4 on the sampling distribution of the mean), you can develop the interval estimate for the population mean. The interval constructed should have a specified confidence of correctly estimating the value of the population parameter, μ. In other words, there is a specified confidence that μ is somewhere in the range of numbers defined by the interval.

Suppose that after studying this chapter, you find that a 95% confidence interval for the mean GPA at your university is $(2.75 \le \mu \le 2.85)$. You can interpret this interval estimate by stating that you are 95% confident that the mean GPA at your university is between 2.75 and 2.85. There is a 5% chance that the mean GPA is below 2.75 or above 2.85.

After learning about the confidence interval for the mean, you will learn how to develop an interval estimate for the population proportion. Then you will learn how large a sample to select when constructing confidence intervals.

9.1 Confidence Interval Estimation for the Mean (σ Known)

In Section 7.4, you used the Central Limit Theorem and knowledge of the population distribution to determine the percentage of sample means that are within certain distances of the population mean. Suppose that in the cereal-fill example, you wished to estimate the population mean using the information from a single sample. Thus, rather than taking $\mu \pm (1.96)(\sigma/\sqrt{n})$ to find the upper and lower limits around μ, as in Section 7.4, you substitute the sample mean, $\overline{X}$, for the unknown μ and use $\overline{X} \pm (1.96)(\sigma/\sqrt{n})$ as an interval to estimate the unknown μ. Although in practice you select a single sample of n values and compute the mean, $\overline{X}$, in order to understand the full meaning of the interval estimate, you need to examine a hypothetical set of all possible samples of n values.

Suppose that a sample of $n = 25$ boxes has a mean of 362.3 grams. The interval developed to estimate μ is $362.3 \pm (1.96)(15)/(\sqrt{25})$ or 362.3 ± 5.88. The estimate of μ is

$$356.42 \le \mu \le 368.18$$

Because the population mean, μ (equal to 368), is included within the interval, this sample results in a correct statement about μ (see Figure 9.1).

FIGURE 9.1

Confidence interval estimates for five different samples of $n = 25$ taken from a population where $\mu = 368$ and $\sigma = 15$

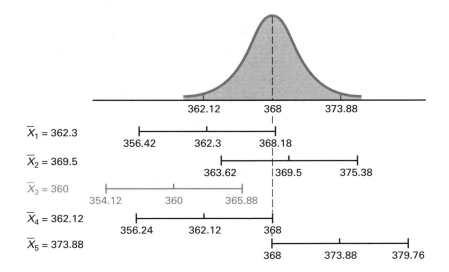

To continue this hypothetical example, suppose that for a different sample of $n = 25$ boxes, the mean is 369.5. The interval developed from this sample is

$$369.5 \pm (1.96)(15)/(\sqrt{25})$$

or 369.5 ± 5.88. The estimate is

$$363.62 \leq \mu \leq 375.38$$

Because the population mean, μ (equal to 368), is also included within this interval, this statement about μ is correct.

Now, before you begin to think that correct statements about μ are always made by developing a confidence interval estimate, suppose a third hypothetical sample of $n = 25$ boxes is selected and the sample mean is equal to 360 grams. The interval developed here is $360 \pm (1.96)(15)/(\sqrt{25})$, or 360 ± 5.88. In this case, the estimate of μ is

$$354.12 \leq \mu \leq 365.88$$

This estimate is *not* a correct statement because the population mean, μ, is not included in the interval developed from this sample (see Figure 8.1). Thus, for some samples, the interval estimate of μ is correct, but for others it is incorrect. In practice, only one sample is selected, and because the population mean is unknown, you cannot determine whether the interval estimate is correct. To resolve this dilemma of sometimes having an interval that provides a correct estimate and sometimes having an interval that provides an incorrect estimate, you need to determine the proportion of samples producing intervals that result in correct statements about the population mean, μ. To do this, consider two other hypothetical samples: the case in which $\overline{X} = 362.12$ grams and the case in which $\overline{X} = 373.88$ grams. If $\overline{X} = 362.12$, the interval is $362.12 \pm (1.96)(15)/(\sqrt{25})$, or 362.12 ± 5.88. This leads to the following interval:

$$356.24 \leq \mu \leq 368.00$$

Because the population mean of 368 is at the upper limit of the interval, the statement is a correct one (see Figure 9.1).

When $\overline{X} = 373.88$, the interval is $373.88 \pm (1.96)(15)/(\sqrt{25})$, or 373.88 ± 5.88. The interval estimate for the mean is

$$368.00 \leq \mu \leq 379.76$$

In this case, because the population mean of 368 is included at the lower limit of the interval, the statement is correct.

In Figure 9.1, you see that when the sample mean falls anywhere between 362.12 and 373.88 grams, the population mean is included *somewhere* within the interval. In Example 7.6 you found that 95% of the sample means fall between 362.12 and 373.88 grams. Therefore, 95% of all samples of $n = 25$ boxes have sample means that will result in intervals that include the population mean.

Because, in practice, you select only one sample of size n, and μ is unknown, you never know for sure whether your specific interval includes the population mean. However, if you take all possible samples of n and compute their 95% confidence intervals, 95% of the intervals will include the population mean, and only 5% of them will not. In other words, you have 95% confidence that the population mean is somewhere in your interval.

Consider once again the first sample discussed in this section. A sample of $n = 25$ boxes had a sample mean of 362.3 grams. The interval constructed to estimate μ is:

$$362.3 \pm (1.96)(15)/(\sqrt{25})$$

$$362.3 \pm 5.88$$

$$356.42 \leq \mu \leq 368.18$$

The interval from 356.42 to 368.18 is referred to as a 95% confidence interval. The following contains an interpretation of the interval that most business professionals will understand. (For a technical discussion of different ways to interpret confidence interval.)

> "I am 95% confident that the mean amount of cereal in the population of boxes is somewhere between 356.42 and 368.18 grams."

To assist in your understanding of the meaning of the confidence interval, the following example concerns the order-filling process at a Web site. Filling orders consists of several steps including receiving an order, picking the parts of the order, checking the order, packing, and shipping the order. The data in the file **Order** consists of the time in minutes to fill orders for a population of 200 on a recent day. Although in practice, the population characteristics are rarely known, for this population of orders, the mean μ is known to be equal to 69.637 minutes and the standard deviation σ is known to be equal to 10.411 minutes. To illustrate how the sample mean and sample standard deviation can vary from one sample to another, 20 different samples of $n = 10$ were selected from the population of 200 orders and the sample mean and sample standard deviation (and other statistics) were calculated for each sample using Minitab. Figure 9.2 shows these results.

FIGURE 9.2

Minitab sample statistics and 95% confidence intervals for 20 samples of $n = 10$ selected from the population of 200 orders

Variable	Count	Mean	StDev	Minimum	Median	Maximum	Range	95% CI
Sample 1	10	74.15	13.39	56.10	76.85	97.70	41.60	(67.6973, 80.6027)
Sample 2	10	61.10	10.60	46.80	61.35	79.50	32.70	(54.6473, 67.5527)
Sample 3	10	74.36	6.50	62.50	74.50	84.00	21.50	(67.9073, 80.8127)
Sample 4	10	70.40	12.80	47.20	70.95	84.00	36.80	(63.9473, 76.8527)
Sample 5	10	62.18	10.85	47.10	59.70	84.00	36.90	(55.7273, 68.6327)
Sample 6	10	67.03	9.68	51.10	69.60	83.30	32.20	(60.5773, 73.4827)
Sample 7	10	69.03	8.81	56.60	68.85	83.70	27.10	(62.5773, 75.4827)
Sample 8	10	72.30	11.52	54.20	71.35	87.00	32.80	(65.8473, 78.7527)
Sample 9	10	68.18	14.10	50.10	69.95	86.20	36.10	(61.7273, 74.6327)
Sample 10	10	66.67	9.08	57.10	64.65	86.10	29.00	(60.2173, 73.1227)
Sample 11	10	72.42	9.76	59.60	74.65	86.10	26.50	(65.9673, 78.8727)
Sample 12	10	76.26	11.69	50.10	80.60	87.00	36.90	(69.8073, 82.7127)
Sample 13	10	65.74	12.11	47.10	62.15	86.10	39.00	(59.2873, 72.1927)
Sample 14	10	69.99	10.97	51.00	73.40	84.60	33.60	(63.5373, 76.4427)
Sample 15	10	75.76	8.60	61.10	75.05	87.80	26.70	(69.3073, 82.2127)
Sample 16	10	67.94	9.19	56.70	67.70	87.80	31.10	(61.4873, 74.3927)
Sample 17	10	71.05	10.48	50.10	71.15	86.20	36.10	(64.5973, 77.5027)
Sample 18	10	71.68	7.96	55.60	72.35	82.60	27.00	(65.2273, 78.1327)
Sample 19	10	70.97	9.83	54.40	70.05	84.60	30.20	(64.5173, 77.4227)
Sample 20	10	74.48	8.80	62.00	76.25	85.70	23.70	(68.0273, 80.9327)

From Figure 9.2, you can see the following:

1. The sample statistics differ from sample to sample. The sample means vary from 61.10 to 76.26 minutes, the sample standard deviations vary from 6.50 to 14.10 minutes, the sample medians vary from 59.70 to 76.85 minutes, and the sample ranges vary from 21.50 to 41.60 minutes.
2. Some of the sample means are greater than the population mean of 69.637 minutes, and some of the sample means are less than the population mean.
3. Some of the sample standard deviations are greater than the population standard deviation of 10.411 minutes, and some of the sample standard deviations are less than the population standard deviation.
4. The variation in the sample range from sample to sample is much more than the variation in the sample standard deviation.

The fact that sample statistics vary from sample to sample is called sampling error. Sampling error is the variation that occurs due to selecting a single sample from the population. The size of the sampling error is primarily based on the amount of variation in the population and on the sample size. Larger samples have less sampling error than small samples, but will cost more.

The last column of Figure 9.2 contains 95% confidence interval estimates of the population mean order-filling time based on the results of those 20 samples of $n = 10$. Begin by examining the first sample selected. The sample mean is 74.15 minutes, and the interval estimate for the population mean is 67.6973 to 80.6027 minutes. In a typical study, you would not know for sure whether this interval estimate is correct because you rarely know the value of the population mean. However, for this example *concerning the order-filling times*, the population mean is known to be 69.637 minutes. If you examine the interval 67.6973 to 80.6027 minutes, you see that the population mean of 69.637 minutes is located *between* these lower and upper limits. Thus, the first sample provides a correct estimate of the population mean in the form of an interval estimate. Looking over the other 19 samples, you see that similar results occur for all the other samples *except* for samples 2, 5, and 12. For each of the intervals generated (other than samples 2, 5, and 12), the population mean of 69.637 minutes is located *somewhere* within the interval.

For sample 2, the sample mean is 61.10 minutes, and the interval is 54.6473 to 67.5527 minutes; for sample 5, the sample mean is 62.18, and the interval is between 55.7273 and 68.6327; whereas for sample 12, the sample mean is 76.26, and the interval is between 69.8073 and 82.7127 minutes. The population mean of 69.637 minutes is *not* located within any of these intervals, and the estimate of the population mean made using these intervals is incorrect.

In some situations, you might want a higher degree of confidence (such as 99%) of including the population mean within the interval. In other cases, you might accept less confidence (such as 90%) of correctly estimating the population mean. In general, the **level of confidence** is symbolized by $(1 - \alpha) \times 100\%$, where α is the proportion in the tails of the distribution that is outside the confidence interval. The proportion in the upper tail of the distribution is $\alpha/2$, and the proportion in the lower tail of the distribution is $\alpha/2$. You use Equation (9.1) to construct a $(1 - \alpha) \times 100\%$ confidence interval estimate of the mean with σ known.

CONFIDENCE INTERVAL FOR THE MEAN (σ KNOWN)

$$\overline{X} \pm Z_{\alpha/2} \frac{\sigma}{\sqrt{n}}$$

or

$$\overline{X} - Z_{\alpha/2} \frac{\sigma}{\sqrt{n}} \leq \mu \leq \overline{X} + Z_{\alpha/2} \frac{\sigma}{\sqrt{n}} \tag{9.1}$$

where $Z_{\alpha/2}$ is the value corresponding to an upper-tail probability of $\alpha/2$ from the standardized normal distribution (i.e., a cumulative area of $1 - \alpha/2$).

The value of $Z_{\alpha/2}$ needed for constructing a confidence interval is called the **critical value** for the distribution. 95% confidence corresponds to an α value of 0.05. The critical Z value corresponding to a cumulative area of 0.975 is 1.96 because there is 0.025 in the upper tail of the distribution and the cumulative area less than $Z = 1.96$ is 0.975.

There is a different critical value for each level of confidence, $1 - \alpha$. A level of confidence of 95% leads to a Z value of 1.96 (see Figure 9.3). 99% confidence corresponds to an α value of 0.01. The Z value is approximately 2.58 because the upper-tail area is 0.005 and the cumulative area less than $Z = 2.58$ is 0.995 (see Figure 9.4).

FIGURE 9.3

Normal curve for determining the Z value needed for 95% confidence

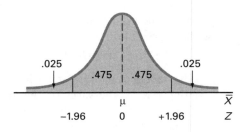

FIGURE 9.4

Normal curve for determining the Z value needed for 99% confidence

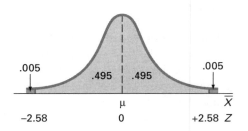

Now that various levels of confidence have been considered, why not make the confidence level as close to 100% as possible? Before doing so, you need to realize that any increase in the level of confidence is achieved only by widening (and making less precise) the confidence interval. There is no "free lunch" here. You would have more confidence that the population mean is within a broader range of values; however, this might make the interpretation of the confidence interval less useful. The trade-off between the width of the confidence interval and the level of confidence is discussed in greater depth in the context of determining the sample size in Section 9.4. Example 9.1 illustrates the application of the confidence interval estimate.

EXAMPLE 9.1

Estimating the Mean Paper Length With 95% Confidence

A paper manufacturer has a production process that operates continuously throughout an entire production shift. The paper is expected to have a mean length of 11 inches, and the standard deviation of the length is 0.02 inch. At periodic intervals, a sample is selected to determine whether the mean paper length is still equal to 11 inches or whether something has gone wrong in the production process to change the length of the paper produced. You select a random sample of 100 sheets, and the mean paper length is 10.998 inches. Construct a 95% confidence interval estimate for the population mean paper length.

SOLUTION Using Equation (9.1) on page 363, with $Z_{\alpha/2} = 1.96$ for 95% confidence,

$$\bar{X} \pm Z_{\alpha/2} \frac{\sigma}{\sqrt{n}} = 10.998 \pm (1.96)\frac{0.02}{\sqrt{100}}$$

$$= 10.998 \pm 0.00392$$

$$10.99408 \leq \mu \leq 11.00192$$

Thus, with 95% confidence, you conclude that the population mean is between 10.99408 and 11.00192 inches. Because the interval includes 11, the value indicating that the production process is working properly, you have no reason to believe that anything is wrong with the production process.

To see the effect of using a 99% confidence interval, examine Example 9.2.

EXAMPLE 9.2

Estimating the Mean Paper Length with 99% Confidence

Construct a 99% confidence interval estimate for the population mean paper length.

SOLUTION Using Equation (9.1) on page 363, with $Z_{\alpha/2} = 2.58$ for 99% confidence,

$$\overline{X} \pm Z_{\alpha/2} \frac{\sigma}{\sqrt{n}} = 10.998 \pm (2.58) \frac{0.02}{\sqrt{100}}$$

$$= 10.998 \pm 0.00516$$

$$10.99284 \le \mu \le 11.00316$$

Once again, because 11 is included within this wider interval, you have no reason to believe that anything is wrong with the production process.

As discussed in Section 7.4, the sampling distribution of the sample mean $\overline{X}$ is normally distributed if the population for your characteristic of interest X is a normal distribution. And, if the population of X is not a normal distribution, the Central Limit Theorem almost always ensures that $\overline{X}$ is normally distributed when n is large. However, when dealing with a small sample size and a population of X that is not a normal distribution, the sampling distribution of $\overline{X}$ is not normally distributed and therefore the confidence interval discussed in this section is inappropriate. In practice, however, as long as the sample size is large enough and the population is not very skewed, you can use the confidence interval defined in Equation (9.1) to estimate the population mean when σ is known. To assess the assumption of normality, you can evaluate the shape of the sample data by using a histogram, stem-and-leaf display, boxplot, or normal probability plot.

Can You Ever *Really* Know Sigma?

This section discusses the concept of the confidence interval estimate, how to develop it, and how to interpret it. The discussion limited itself to the case where the population standard deviation, sigma, is known. But, can you ever *really* know sigma? Probably not, but it is much easier to explain the confidence interval estimate using an example where the population standard deviation, sigma, is known. If sigma is known, then you can use the normal distribution, which you are already familiar with from Chapters 6 and 7. In Section 9.2, you will learn how to construct confidence interval estimates when sigma is not known, and you will use the *t* distribution instead of the normal distribution.

In virtually all real-world business applications, you do not know the standard deviation of the population. If, for a particular case, you knew the population standard deviation, you would also already know (or could compute) the population mean. Why is that so? You could only know the population standard deviation if you have access to all of the population data. And if you knew all of the population data, you could compute the population mean. There would be no need to employ the *inductive* reasoning of inferential statistics to estimate the population mean.

So why study the confidence interval estimate of the mean when sigma is known? Because it is a good way to understand the confidence interval concept—a very important concept to know when studying the rest of this book.

Problems for Section 9.1

LEARNING THE BASICS

9.1 If $\overline{X} = 85, \sigma = 8$, and $n = 64$, construct a 95% confidence interval estimate of the population mean, μ.

9.2 If $\overline{X} = 125, \sigma = 24$ and $n = 36$, construct a 99% confidence interval estimate of the population mean, μ.

APPLYING THE CONCEPTS

9.3 A market researcher selects a simple random sample of $n = 100$ customers from its population of two million customers. After analyzing the sample, she states that she has 95% confidence that the mean annual income of its two million customers is between $70,000 and $85,000. Explain the meaning of this statement.

9.4 If you were to collect a set of data, either from an entire population or from a random sample taken from that population:
a. Which statistical measure would you compute first: the mean or the standard deviation? Explain.
b. What does your answer to (a) tell you about the "practicality" of using the confidence interval estimate formula given in Equation (9.1)?

9.5 Consider the confidence interval estimate discussed in Problem 9.3. Suppose that the population mean annual income is $71,000. Is the confidence interval estimate stated in Problem 9.3 correct? Explain.

9.6 You are working as an assistant to the dean of institutional research at your university. She wants to survey members of the alumni association who obtained their baccalaureate degrees 5 years ago to learn what their starting salaries were in their first full-time job after receiving their degrees. A sample of 100 alumni is to be randomly selected from the list of 2,500 graduates in that class. If her goal is to construct a 95% confidence interval estimate of the population mean starting salary, why is it unlikely that you will be able to use Equation (9.1) on page 363 for this purpose? Explain.

9.2 Confidence Interval Estimation for the Mean (σ Unknown)

Just as the mean of the population, μ, is usually unknown, you virtually never know the standard deviation of the population, σ. Therefore, you need to construct a confidence interval estimate of μ, using the sample statistic S as an estimate of the population parameter σ.

Student's t Distribution

At the beginning of the twentieth century, William S. Gosset, a statistician for Guinness Breweries in Ireland (see reference 4), wanted to make inferences about the mean when σ was unknown. Because Guinness employees were not permitted to publish research work under their own names, Gosset adopted the pseudonym "Student." The distribution that he developed is known as **Student's t distribution** and is commonly referred to as the t distribution.

If the random variable X is normally distributed, then the following statistic has a t distribution with $n - 1$ **degrees of freedom**:

$$t = \frac{\overline{X} - \mu}{\frac{S}{\sqrt{n}}}$$

This expression has the same form as the Z statistic in Equation (7.4) on page 316, except that S is used to estimate the unknown σ.

Properties of the t Distribution

The t distribution looks very similar to the standardized normal distribution. Both distributions are symmetrical and bell shaped with means and medians equal to zero. However, the t distribution has more area in the tails and less in the center than does the standardized normal distribution (see Figure 9.5). Because S is used to estimate the unknown σ, the values of t are more variable than those for Z.

FIGURE 9.5

Standardized normal distribution and t distribution for 5 degrees of freedom

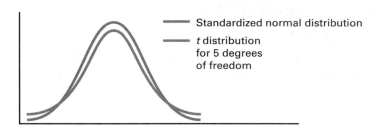

Standardized normal distribution

t distribution for 5 degrees of freedom

The degrees of freedom, $n - 1$, are directly related to the sample size, n. The concept of *degrees of freedom* is discussed further on page 368. As the sample size and degrees of freedom increase, S becomes a better estimate of σ, and the t distribution gradually approaches the standardized normal distribution, until the two are virtually identical. With a sample size of about 120 or more, S estimates σ precisely enough so that there is little difference between the t and Z distributions.

As stated earlier, the t distribution assumes that the random variable X is normally distributed. In practice, however, when the sample size is large enough and the population is not very skewed, in most cases you can use the t distribution to estimate the population mean when σ is unknown. When dealing with a small sample size and a skewed population distribution, the confidence interval estimate may not provide a valid estimate of the population mean. To assess the assumption of normality, you can evaluate the shape of the sample data by using a histogram, stem-and-leaf display, boxplot, or normal probability plot. However, the usefulness of any of these graphs to evaluate normality is limited when you have a small sample size.

You find the critical values of t for the appropriate degrees of freedom from the table of the t distribution (see Table E.3). The columns of the table present the most commonly needed cumulative probabilities and corresponding upper-tail areas. The rows of the table represent the degrees of freedom. The critical t values are found in the cells of the table. For example, with 99 degrees of freedom, if you want 95% confidence, you find the appropriate value of t, as shown in Table 9.1. The 95% confidence level means that 2.5% of the values (an area of 0.025) are in each tail of the distribution. Looking in the column for a cumulative probability of 0.975 and an upper-tail area of 0.025 in the row corresponding to 99 degrees of freedom gives you a critical value for t of 1.9842 (see Figure 9.6). Because t is a symmetrical distribution with a mean of 0, if the upper-tail value is $+1.9842$, the value for the lower-tail area (lower 0.025) is -1.9842. A t value of -1.9842 means that the probability that t is less than -1.9842 is 0.025, or 2.5%.

TABLE 9.1

Determining the Critical Value from the t Table for an Area of 0.025 in Each Tail with 99 Degrees of Freedom

		Cumulative Probabilities					
	.75	.90	.95	.975	.99	.995
			Upper Tail Areas				
Degrees of Freedom	.25	.10	.05	.025	.01	.005
1	1.0000	3.0777	6.3138	12.7062	31.8207	63.6574
2	0.8165	1.8856	2.9200	4.3027	6.9646	9.9248
3	0.7649	1.6377	2.3534	3.1824	4.5407	5.8409
4	0.7407	1.5332	2.1318	2.7764	3.7469	4.6041
5	0.7267	1.4759	2.0150	2.5706	3.3649	4.0322
.	.	.	.	.	.	.
.	.	.	.	.	.	.
.	.	.	.	.	.	.
96	0.6771	1.2904	1.6609	1.9850	2.3658	2.6280
97	0.6770	1.2903	1.6607	1.9847	2.3654	2.6275
98	0.6770	1.2902	1.6606	1.9845	2.3650	2.6269
99	0.6770	1.2902	1.6604	1.9842	2.3646	2.6264
100	0.6770	1.2901	1.6602	1.9840	2.3642	2.6259

Source: *Extracted from Table E.3.*

FIGURE 9.6

t distribution with 99 degrees of freedom

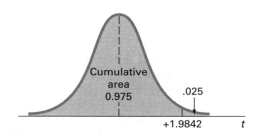

Cumulative area 0.975

.025

+1.9842 t

Note that for a 95% confidence interval, you will always use a cumulative probability of 0.975 and an upper-tail area of 0.025. Similarly, for a 99% confidence interval, use 0.995 and 0.005, and for a 90% confidence interval use 0.95 and 0.05.

The Concept of Degrees of Freedom

In Chapter 3, you learned that the numerator of the sample variance, S^2 [see Equation (3.4)], requires the computation of

$$\sum_{i=1}^{n}(X_i - \overline{X})^2$$

In order to compute S^2, you first need to know $\overline{X}$. Therefore, only $n - 1$ of the sample values are free to vary. This means that you have $n - 1$ degrees of freedom. For example, suppose a sample of five values has a mean of 20. How many values do you need to know before you can determine the remainder of the values? The fact that $n = 5$ and $\overline{X} = 20$ also tells you that

$$\sum_{i=1}^{n}X_i = 100$$

because

$$\frac{\sum_{i=1}^{n}X_i}{n} = \overline{X}$$

Thus, when you know four of the values, the fifth one is *not* free to vary because the sum must add to 100. For example, if four of the values are 18, 24, 19, and 16, the fifth value must be 23 so that the sum equals 100.

The Confidence Interval Statement

Equation (9.2) defines the $(1 - \alpha) \times 100\%$ confidence interval estimate for the mean with σ unknown.

CONFIDENCE INTERVAL FOR THE MEAN (σ UNKNOWN)

$$\overline{X} \pm t_{\alpha/2}\frac{S}{\sqrt{n}}$$

or

$$\overline{X} - t_{\alpha/2}\frac{S}{\sqrt{n}} \leq \mu \leq \overline{X} + t_{\alpha/2}\frac{S}{\sqrt{n}} \tag{9.2}$$

where $t_{\alpha/2}$ is the critical value corresponding to an upper-tail probability of $\alpha/2$ from the t distribution with $n - 1$ degrees of freedom (i.e., a cumulative area of $1 - \alpha/2$).

To illustrate the application of the confidence interval estimate for the mean when the standard deviation, σ, is unknown, recall the Using Statistics scenario presented earlier. As an accountant for Saxon Home Improvement, you want to estimate the mean dollar amount listed on the sales invoices for the month. You select a sample of 100 sales invoices from the population of sales invoices during the month, and the sample mean of the 100 sales invoices is

$110.27, with a sample standard deviation of $28.95. For 95% confidence, the critical value from the t distribution (as shown in Table 9.1 on page 367) is 1.9842. Using Equation (9.2),

$$\bar{X} \pm t_{\alpha/2}\frac{S}{\sqrt{n}}$$

$$= 110.27 \pm (1.9842)\frac{28.95}{\sqrt{100}}$$

$$= 110.27 \pm 5.74$$

$$\$104.53 \leq \mu \leq \$116.01$$

A Casio calculator worksheet for these data is presented in Figure 9.7.

FIGURE 9.7

Estimate for the Mean Sales Invoice Amount

From the **Main Menu** select:

STAT F4(INTR) **F2**(t) **F1**(1-S)   then enter the following items:

1-Sample ZInterval
Data   : **F2(Var)**   ▼
C-Level   : **0.95**   **EXE**
$\bar{x}$: **110.27**   **EXE**
sx   : **28.95**   **EXE**
n   : **100**   **EXE**
Save Res   : **None**

Now key **EXE** or **F1**(Calc)

The calculator will now show the results:

1-Sample tInterval
Left   = 104.525692
Right   = 116.014308
$\bar{x}$ = 110.27
Sx   = 28.95
n   = 100

The 95% confidence Interval is $104.525692 \leq \mu \leq 116.014308$

Thus, with 95% confidence, you conclude that the mean amount of all the sales invoices is between $104.53 and $116.01. The 95% confidence level indicates that if you selected all possible samples of 100 (something that is never done in practice), 95% of the intervals developed would include the population mean somewhere within the interval. The validity of this confidence interval estimate depends on the assumption of normality for the distribution of the amount of the sales invoices. With a sample of 100, the normality assumption is not overly restrictive (see the Central Limit Theorem), and the use of the t distribution is likely appropriate. Example 9.3 further illustrates how you construct the confidence interval for a mean when the population standard deviation is unknown.

EXAMPLE 9.3

Estimating the Mean Force Required to Break Electric Insulators

A manufacturing company produces electric insulators. If the insulators break when in use, a short circuit is likely. To test the strength of the insulators, you carry out destructive testing to determine how much *force* is required to break the insulators. You measure force by observing how many pounds are applied to the insulator before it breaks. Table 9.2 lists 30 values from this experiment, which are located in the file Force. Construct a 95% confidence interval estimate for the population mean force required to break the insulator.

TABLE 9.2

Force (in Pounds) Required to Break the Insulator

1,870	1,728	1,656	1,610	1,634	1,784	1,522	1,696	1,592	1,662
1,866	1,764	1,734	1,662	1,734	1,774	1,550	1,756	1,762	1,866
1,820	1,744	1,788	1,688	1,810	1,752	1,680	1,810	1,652	1,736

SOLUTION Figure 9.8 shows that the sample mean is $\overline{X} = 1{,}723.4$ pounds and the sample standard deviation is $S = 89.55$ pounds. Using Equation (9.2) on page 368 to construct the confidence interval, you need to determine the critical value from the t table using the row for 29 degrees of freedom. For 95% confidence, you use the column corresponding to an upper-tail area of 0.025 and a cumulative probability of 0.975. From Table E.3, you see that $t_{\alpha/2} = 2.0452$. Thus, using $\overline{X} = 1{,}723$, $S = 89.55$, $n = 30$, and $t_{\alpha/2} = 2.0452$,

$$\overline{X} \pm t_{\alpha/2} \frac{S}{\sqrt{n}}$$

$$= 1{,}723.4 \pm (2.0452)\frac{89.55}{\sqrt{30}}$$

$$= 1{,}723.4 \pm 33.4$$

$$1{,}690.0 \le \mu \le 1{,}756.8$$

FIGURE 9.8

SSPS confidence interval estimate for the mean amount of force required to break electric insulators

SSPS output

			Statistic	Statistic
		Descriptives		
Force	Mean		1723.40	16.350
	95% Confidence	**Lower Bound**	**1689.96**	
	Interval for Mean	**Upper Bound**	**1756.84**	
	5% Trimmed Mean		1726.00	
	Median		1735.00	
	Variance		8019.352	
	Std. Deviation		89.551	
	Minimum		1522	
	Maximum		1870	
	Range		348	
	Interquartile Range		125	
	Skewness		−.367	.427
	Kurtosis		−.244	.833

You conclude with 95% confidence that the mean breaking force required for the population of insulators is between 1,690.0 and 1,756.8 pounds. The validity of this confidence interval estimate depends on the assumption that the force required is normally distributed. Remember, however, that you can slightly relax this assumption for large sample sizes. Thus, with a sample of 30, you can use the t distribution even if the amount of force required is only slightly left-skewed. From the normal probability plot displayed in Figure 9.9 or the boxplot displayed in Figure 9.10, the amount of force required appears only slightly left-skewed. Thus, the t distribution is appropriate for these data.

FIGURE 9.9

SSPS normal probability plot for the amount of force required to break electric insulators

FIGURE 9.10

SSPS boxplot for the amount of force required to break electric insulators

The interpretation of the confidence interval when σ is unknown is the same as when σ is known. To illustrate the fact that the confidence interval for the mean varies more when σ is unknown, return to the example concerning the order-filling times discussed in Section 9.1. Suppose that, in this case, you do not know the population standard deviation. Figure 9.11 shows the results for each of 20 samples of $n = 10$ orders.

FIGURE 9.11

Minitab confidence interval estimates of the mean for 20 samples of $n = 10$ selected from the population of 200 orders with σ unknown

Variable	N	Mean	StDev	SE Mean	95% CI
Sample 1	10	71.64	7.58	2.40	(66.22, 77.06)
Sample 2	10	67.22	10.95	3.46	(59.39, 75.05)
Sample 3	10	67.97	14.83	4.69	(57.36, 78.58)
Sample 4	10	73.90	10.59	3.35	(66.33, 81.47)
Sample 5	10	67.11	11.12	3.52	(59.15, 75.07)
Sample 6	10	68.12	10.83	3.43	(60.37, 75.87)
Sample 7	10	65.80	10.85	3.43	(58.03, 73.57)
Sample 8	10	77.58	11.04	3.49	(69.68, 85.48)
Sample 9	10	66.69	11.45	3.62	(58.50, 74.88)
Sample 10	10	62.55	8.58	2.71	(56.41, 68.69)
Sample 11	10	71.12	12.82	4.05	(61.95, 80.29)
Sample 12	10	70.55	10.52	3.33	(63.02, 78.08)
Sample 13	10	65.51	8.16	2.58	(59.67, 71.35)
Sample 14	10	64.90	7.55	2.39	(59.50, 70.30)
Sample 15	10	66.22	11.21	3.54	(58.20, 74.24)
Sample 16	10	70.43	10.21	3.23	(63.12, 77.74)
Sample 17	10	72.04	6.25	1.98	(67.57, 76.51)
Sample 18	10	73.91	11.29	3.57	(65.83, 81.99)
Sample 19	10	71.49	9.76	3.09	(64.51, 78.47)
Sample 20	10	70.15	10.84	3.43	(62.39, 77.91)

From Figure 9.11, observe that the standard deviation of the samples varies from 6.25 (sample 17) to 14.83 (sample 3). Thus, the width of the confidence interval developed varies from 8.94 in sample 17 to 21.22 in sample 3. Because you know that the population mean order time $\mu = 69.637$ minutes, you can see that the interval for sample 8 $(69.68 - 85.48)$ and the interval for sample 10 $(56.41 - 68.69)$ do not correctly estimate the population mean. All the other intervals correctly estimate the population mean. Once again, remember that in practice you select only one sample and you have no way of knowing for sure whether this one sample provides a confidence interval that includes the population mean.

Problems for Section 9.2

LEARNING THE BASICS

9.7 If $\overline{X} = 75, S = 24$, and $n = 36$, and assuming that the population is normally distributed, construct a 95% confidence interval estimate of the population mean, μ.

9.8 Determine the critical value of t in each of the following circumstances:
a. $1 - \alpha = 0.95, n = 10$
b. $1 - \alpha = 0.99, n = 10$
c. $1 - \alpha = 0.95, n = 32$
d. $1 - \alpha = 0.95, n = 65$
e. $1 - \alpha = 0.90, n = 16$

9.9 Assuming that the population is normally distributed, construct a 95% confidence interval estimate for the population mean for each of the following samples:

Sample A: 1, 1, 1, 1, 8, 8, 8, 8
Sample B: 1, 2, 3, 4, 5, 6, 7, 8

Explain why these two samples produce different confidence intervals even though they have the same mean and range.

9.10 Assuming that the population is normally distributed, construct a 95% confidence interval for the population mean, based on the following sample of size $n = 7$: 1, 2, 3, 4, 5, 6, and 20. Change the number 20 to 7 and recalculate the confidence interval. Using these results, describe the effect of an outlier (i.e., an extreme value) on the confidence interval.

APPLYING THE CONCEPTS

9.11 A stationery store wants to estimate the mean retail value of greeting cards that it has in its inventory. A random sample of 100 greeting cards indicates a mean value of $2.55 and a standard deviation of $0.44.
a. Assuming a normal distribution, construct a 95% confidence interval estimate of the mean value of all greeting cards in the store's inventory.
b. Suppose there were 2,500 greeting cards in the store's inventory. How are the results in (a) useful in assisting the store owner to estimate the total value of her inventory?

 9.12 Southside Hospital in Bay Shore, New York, commonly conducts stress tests to study the heart muscle after a person has a heart attack. Members of the diagnostic imaging department conducted a quality improvement project to try to reduce the turnaround time for stress tests. Turnaround time is defined as the time from when the test is ordered to when the radiologist signs off on the test results. Initially, the mean turnaround time for a stress test was 68 hours. After incorporating changes into the stress-test process, the quality improvement team collected a sample of 50 turnaround times. In this sample, the mean turnaround time was 32 hours, with a standard deviation of 9 hours (data extracted from E. Godin, D. Raven, C. Sweetapple, and F. R. Del Guidice, "Faster Test Results," *Quality Progress*, January 2004, 37(1), pp. 33–39).
a. Construct a 95% confidence interval estimate for the population mean turnaround time.
b. Interpret the interval constructed in (a).
c. Do you think the quality improvement project was a success?

9.13 The U.S. Department of Transportation requires tire manufacturers to provide tire performance information on the sidewall of the tire to better inform prospective customers when making purchasing decisions. One very important measure of tire performance is the tread wear index, which indicates the tire's resistance to tread wear compared with a tire graded with a base of 100. This means that a tire with a grade of 200 should last twice as long, on average, as a tire graded with a base of 100. A consumer organization wants to estimate the actual tread wear index of a brand name of tires that claims "graded 200" on the sidewall of the tire. A random sample of $n = 18$ indicates a sample mean tread wear index of 195.3 and a sample standard deviation of 21.4.
a. Assuming that the population of tread wear indexes is normally distributed, construct a 95% confidence interval estimate of the population mean tread wear index for tires produced by this manufacturer under this brand name.
b. Do you think that the consumer organization should accuse the manufacturer of producing tires that do not meet the performance information provided on the sidewall of the tire? Explain.
c. Explain why an observed tread wear index of 210 for a particular tire is not unusual, even though it is outside the confidence interval developed in (a).

9.14 The data in the file Movieprices contain the price for two tickets with online service charges, large popcorn, and two medium soft drinks at a sample of six theater chains:

$36.15 $31.00 $35.05 $40.25 $33.75 $43.00

Source: *Data extracted from K. Kelly, "The Multiplex Under Siege,"* The Wall Street Journal, *December 24–25, 2005, pp. P1, P5.*

a. Construct a 95% confidence interval estimate for the population mean price for two tickets with online service charges, large popcorn, and two medium soft drinks, assuming a normal distribution.

b. Interpret the interval constructed in (a).

9.15 The data in the file Sedans represents the overall miles per gallon (MPG) of 2008 sedans priced under $20,000.

31, 27, 27, 28, 28, 28, 25, 25, 26, 25, 33, 23, 24

Source: *Data extracted from "Vehicle Ratings,"* Consumer Reports, *April 2008, p. 32.*

a. Construct a 95% confidence interval estimate for the population mean miles per gallon of 2008 sedans (4 cylinder) priced under $20,000 assuming a normal distribution.

b. Interpret the interval constructed in (a).

c. Compare the results in (a) to those in Problem 9.16(a).

9.16 The data in the file SUV represents the overall miles per gallon (MPG) of 2009 SUVs priced under $30,000.

23, 20, 21, 22, 18, 18, 17, 17, 19, 19, 19,
17, 21, 18, 18, 18, 17, 17, 16, 20, 16, 22

Source: *Extracted from "Vehicle Ratings,"* Consumer Reports, *April 2008, p. 40.*

a. Construct a 95% confidence interval estimate for the population mean miles per gallon of 2008 SUVs priced under $30,000 assuming a normal distribution.

b. Interpret the interval constructed in (a).

c. Compare the results in (a) to those in Problem 9.15(a).

9.17 The data in the file Chicken represent the total fat, in grams per serving, for a sample of 20 chicken sandwiches from fast-food chains. The data are as follows:

| 7 | 8 | 4 | 5 | 16 | 20 | 20 | 24 | 19 | 30 |
| 23 | 30 | 25 | 19 | 29 | 29 | 30 | 30 | 40 | 56 |

Source: *Data extracted from "Fast Food: Adding Health to the Menu,"* Consumer Reports, *September 2004, pp. 28–31.*

a. Construct a 95% confidence interval for the population mean total fat, in grams per serving.

b. Interpret the interval constructed in (a).

c. What assumption must you make about the population distribution in order to construct the confidence interval estimate in (a)?

d. Do you think that the assumption needed in order to construct the confidence interval estimate in (a) is valid? Explain.

9.18 One of the major measures of the quality of service provided by any organization is the speed with which it responds to customer complaints. A large family-held department store selling furniture and flooring, including carpet, had undergone a major expansion in the past several years. In particular, the flooring department had expanded from 2 installation crews to an installation supervisor, a measurer, and 15 installation crews. Last year, there were 50 complaints concerning carpet installation. The following data, also in the file Furniture, represent the number of days between the receipt of a complaint and the resolution of the complaint:

54	5	35	137	31	27	152	2	123	81	74	27
11	19	126	110	110	29	61	35	94	31	26	5
12	4	165	32	29	28	29	26	25	1	14	13
13	10	5	27	4	52	30	22	36	26	20	23
33	68										

a. Construct a 95% confidence interval estimate of the population mean number of days between the receipt of a complaint and the resolution of the complaint.

b. What assumption must you make about the population distribution in order to construct the confidence interval estimate in (a)?

c. Do you think that the assumption needed in order to construct the confidence interval estimate in (a) is valid? Explain.

d. What effect might your conclusion in (c) have on the validity of the results in (a)?

9.19 In New York State, savings banks are permitted to sell a form of life insurance called savings bank life insurance (SBLI). The approval process consists of underwriting, which includes a review of the application, a medical information bureau check, possible requests for additional medical information and medical exams, and a policy compilation stage in which the policy pages are generated and sent to the bank for delivery. The ability to deliver approved policies to customers in a timely manner is critical to the profitability of this service to the bank. During a period of one month, a random sample of 27 approved policies was selected, and the total processing time, in days, was as shown below and stored in the file Insurance :

| 73 | 19 | 16 | 64 | 28 | 28 | 31 | 90 | 60 | 56 | 31 | 56 | 22 | 18 |
| 45 | 48 | 17 | 17 | 17 | 91 | 92 | 63 | 50 | 51 | 69 | 16 | 17 |

a. Construct a 95% confidence interval estimate of the population mean processing time.

b. What assumption must you make about the population distribution in order to construct the confidence interval estimate in (a)?

c. Do you think that the assumption needed in order to construct the confidence interval estimate in (a) is valid? Explain.

9.20 The data in the file $\boxed{\text{Dark Chocolate}}$ represent the cost per ounce ($) for a sample of fourteen dark chocolate bars.

> 0.68 0.72 0.92 1.14 1.42 0.94 0.77
> 0.57 1.51 0.57 0.55 0.86 1.41 0.90

Source: *Data extracted from "Dark Chocolate: Which Bars Are Best?"* Consumer Reports, *September 2007, p. 8.*

a. Construct a 95% confidence interval estimate for the population cost per ounce ($) of dark chocolate bars.
b. What assumption do you need to make about the population distribution to construct the interval in (a)?
c. Given the data presented, do you think the assumption needed in (a) is valid? Explain.

9.21 One operation of a mill is to cut pieces of steel into parts that are used later in the frame for front seats in an automobile. The steel is cut with a diamond saw and requires the resulting parts to be within ±0.005 inch of the length specified by the automobile company. The measurement reported from a sample of 100 steel parts (and stored in the file $\boxed{\text{Steel}}$) is the difference, in inches, between the actual length of the steel part, as measured by a laser measurement device, and the specified length of the steel part. For example, the first observation, −0.002, represents a steel part that is 0.002 inch shorter than the specified length.

a. Construct a 95% confidence interval estimate of the population mean difference between the actual length of the steel part and the specified length of the steel part.
b. What assumption must you make about the population distribution in order to construct the confidence interval estimate in (a)?
c. Do you think that the assumption needed in order to construct the confidence interval estimate in (a) is valid? Explain.
d. Compare the conclusions reached in (a) with those of Problem 2.26.

9.3 Confidence Interval Estimation for the Proportion

This section extends the concept of the confidence interval to categorical data. Here you are concerned with estimating the proportion of items in a population having a certain characteristic of interest. The unknown population proportion is represented by the Greek letter π. The point estimate for π is the sample proportion, $p = X/n$, where n is the sample size and X is the number of items in the sample having the characteristic of interest. Equation (9.3) defines the confidence interval estimate for the population proportion.

CONFIDENCE INTERVAL ESTIMATE FOR THE PROPORTION

$$p \pm Z_{\alpha/2}\sqrt{\frac{p(1-p)}{n}}$$

or

$$p - Z_{\alpha/2}\sqrt{\frac{p(1-p)}{n}} \leq \pi \leq p + Z_{\alpha/2}\sqrt{\frac{p(1-p)}{n}} \tag{9.3}$$

where

$$p = \text{sample proportion} = \frac{X}{n} = \frac{\text{Number of items having the characteristic}}{\text{Sample size}}$$

π = population proportion

$Z_{\alpha/2}$ = critical value from the standardized normal distribution

n = sample size

Note: To use this interval, the sample size n must be large enough to ensure that both X and $n - X$ are greater than 5.

You can use the confidence interval estimate of the proportion defined in Equation (9.3) to estimate the proportion of sales invoices that contain errors (see the Using Statistics scenario). Suppose that in a sample of 100 sales invoices, 10 contain errors. Thus, for these data, $p = X/n = 10/100 = 0.10$. Using Equation (9.3) and $Z_{\alpha/2} = 1.96$ for 95% confidence,

$$p \pm Z_{\alpha/2}\sqrt{\frac{p(1 - p)}{n}}$$

$$= 0.10 \pm (1.96)\sqrt{\frac{(0.10)(0.90)}{100}}$$

$$= 0.10 \pm (1.96)(0.03)$$

$$= 0.10 \pm 0.0588$$

$$0.0412 \leq \pi \leq 0.1588$$

Therefore, you have 95% confidence that between 4.12% and 15.88% of all the sales invoices contain errors. Figure 9.12 shows a Casio calculator worksheet for these data and Figure 9.13 shows Minitab results.

FIGURE 9.12

Casio calculator FX 9750G or FX9750GII worksheet to construct a confidence interval estimate for the proportion of sales invoices that contain errors

Proportion of In-Error Sales Invoices

From the **Main Menu** select:

STAT F4(INTR) **F1**(z) **F1**(1-p)   then enter the following items:

1-Prop ZInterval

C-Level	**: 0.95**	**EXE**
x	**: 10**	**EXE**
n	**: 100**	**EXE**
Save Res	: None	

Now key **EXE** or **F1**(Calc)

The calculator will now show the results:

1-Prop ZInterval

Left	= 0.04120108
Right	= 0.15879892
p	= 0.1
n	= 100

The 95% confidence interval is $0.04120108 \leq \pi \leq 0.15879892$

FIGURE 9.13

Minitab confidence interval estimate for the proportion of sales invoices that contain errors

```
Sample   X    N   Sample p          95% CI
1       10  100  0.100000   (0.041201, 0.158799)

Using the normal approximation.
```

Example 9.4 illustrates another application of a confidence interval estimate for the proportion.

EXAMPLE 9.4

Estimating the Proportion of Nonconforming Newspapers Printed

The operations manager at a large newspaper wants to estimate the proportion of newspapers printed that have a nonconforming attribute, such as excessive ruboff, improper page setup, missing pages, or duplicate pages. A random sample of $n = 200$ newspapers is selected from all the newspapers printed during a single day. In this sample, 35 contain some type of nonconformance. Construct and interpret a 90% confidence interval for the proportion of newspapers printed during the day that have a nonconforming attribute.

SOLUTION Using Equation (9.3),

$$p = \frac{X}{n} = \frac{35}{200} = 0.175, \text{ and with a 90\% level of confidence } Z_{\alpha/2} = 1.645$$

$$p \pm Z_{\alpha/2}\sqrt{\frac{p(1-p)}{n}}$$

$$= 0.175 \pm (1.645)\sqrt{\frac{(0.175)(0.825)}{200}}$$

$$= 0.175 \pm (1.645)(0.0269)$$

$$= 0.175 \pm 0.0442$$

$$0.1308 \leq \pi \leq 0.2192$$

You conclude with 90% confidence that between 13.08% and 21.92% of the newspapers printed on that day have some type of nonconformance.

Equation (9.3) contains a Z statistic because you can use the normal distribution to approximate the binomial distribution when the sample size is sufficiently large. In Example 9.4, the confidence interval using Z provides an excellent approximation for the population proportion because both X and $n - X$ are greater than 5. However, if you do not have a sufficiently large sample size, you should use the binomial distribution rather than Equation (9.3) (see references 1, 2, and 7). The exact confidence intervals for various sample sizes and proportions of successes have been tabulated by Fisher and Yates and can be computed using Minitab.

Problems for Section 9.3

LEARNING THE BASICS

9.22 If $n = 200$ and $X = 50$, construct a 95% confidence interval estimate of the population proportion.

9.23 If $n = 400$ and $X = 25$, construct a 99% confidence interval estimate of the population proportion.

APPLYING THE CONCEPTS

SELF Test **9.24** The telephone company wants to estimate the proportion of households that would purchase an additional telephone line if it were made available at a substantially reduced installation cost. A random sample of 500 households is selected. The results indicate that 135 of the households would purchase the additional telephone line at a reduced installation cost.

a. Construct a 99% confidence interval estimate of the population proportion of households that would purchase the additional telephone line.

b. How would the manager in charge of promotional programs concerning residential customers use the results in (a)?

9.25 CareerBuilder.com surveyed 1,124 moms who were currently employed full-time. Of the women surveyed, 281 said that they were dissatisfied with their work-life balance, and 495 said that they would take a pay cut to spend more time with their kids (data extracted from D. Jones, "Poll Finds Resentment of Flextime," **usatoday.com** May 11, 2007).

a. Construct a 95% confidence interval estimate for the population proportion of moms employed full-time who are dissatisfied with their work-life balance.

b. Construct a 95% confidence interval estimate for the population proportion of moms employed full-time who would take a pay cut to spend more time with their kids.

c. Write a short summary of the information derived from (a) and (b).

9.26 In a survey conducted for American Express, 27% of small business owners indicated that they never check in with the office when on vacation (data extracted from "Snapshots," **usatoday.com**, April 18, 2006). The article did not disclose the sample size used in the study.

a. Suppose that the survey was based on 500 small business owners. Construct a 95% confidence interval estimate for the population proportion of small business owners who never check in with the office when on vacation.

b. Suppose that the survey was based on 1,000 small business owners. Construct a 95% confidence interval estimate for the population proportion of small business owners who never check in with the office when on vacation.

c. Discuss the effect of sample size on the confidence interval estimate.

9.27 The start of the twenty-first century saw many corporate scandals and many individuals lost faith in business. In a 2007 poll conducted by the New York City-based Edelman Public Relations firm, 57% of respondents say they trust business to "do what is right." This percentage was the highest in the annual survey since 2001 (data extracted from G. Colvin, "Business is Back!" *Fortune*, May 14, 2007, pp. 40–48).

a. Construct a 95% confidence interval estimate of the population proportion of individuals who trust business to "do what is right" assuming that the poll surveyed:
  1. 100 individuals.
  2. 200 individuals.
  3. 300 individuals.

b. Discuss the effect that sample size has on the width of confidence intervals.

c. Interpret the intervals in (a).

9.28 A survey of 705 workers (data extracted from "Snapshots," *USA Today*, March 21, 2006, p. 1B) were asked how much they used the Internet at work. 423 said they used it within limits, and 183 said that they did not use the Internet at work.

a. Construct a 95% confidence interval estimate for the proportion of all workers who use the Internet within limits.

b. Construct a 95% confidence interval estimate for the proportion of all workers who did not use the Internet at work.

9.29 The utility of mobile devices raises new questions about the intrusion of work into personal life. In a recent survey by **CareerJournal.com** (data extracted from P. Kitchen, "Can't Turn It Off," *Newsday*, October 20, 2006, pp. F4–F5), 158 of 473 employees responded that they typically took work with them on vacation and 85 responded that there are unwritten and unspoken expectations that they stay connected.

a. Construct a 95% confidence interval estimate for the population proportion of employees who typically take work with them on vacation.

b. Construct a 95% confidence interval estimate for the population proportion of employees who said that there are unwritten and unspoken expectations that they stay connected.

c. Interpret the intervals in (a) and (b).

d. Explain the difference in the results in (a) and (b).

9.4 Determining Sample Size

In each confidence interval developed so far in this chapter, the sample size was reported along with the results with little discussion of the width of the resulting confidence interval. In the business world, sample sizes are determined prior to data collection to ensure that the confidence interval is narrow enough to be useful in making decisions. Determining the proper sample size is a complicated procedure, subject to the constraints of budget, time, and the amount of acceptable sampling error. In the Saxon Home Improvement example, if you want to estimate the mean dollar amount of the sales invoices, you must determine in advance how large a sampling error to allow in estimating the population mean. You must also determine, in advance, the level of confidence (i.e., 90%, 95%, or 99%) to use in estimating the population parameter.

Sample Size Determination for the Mean

To develop an equation for determining the appropriate sample size needed when constructing a confidence interval estimate of the mean, recall Equation (9.1):

$$\bar{X} \pm Z_{\alpha/2} \frac{\sigma}{\sqrt{n}}$$

The amount added to or subtracted from $\overline{X}$ is equal to half the width of the interval. This quantity represents the amount of imprecision in the estimate that results from sampling error. The **sampling error**[1], e, is defined as

$$e = Z_{\alpha/2} \frac{\sigma}{\sqrt{n}}$$

Solving for n gives the sample size needed to construct the appropriate confidence interval estimate for the mean. "Appropriate" means that the resulting interval will have an acceptable amount of sampling error.

SAMPLE SIZE DETERMINATION FOR THE MEAN

The sample size, n, is equal to the product of the $Z_{\sigma/2}$ value squared and the standard deviation, σ, squared, divided by the square of the sampling error, e.

$$n = \frac{Z_{a/2}^2 \sigma^2}{e^2} \tag{9.4}$$

To compute the sample size, you must know three factors:

1. The desired confidence level, which determines the value of $Z_{\alpha/2}$, the critical value from the standardized normal distribution[2]
2. The acceptable sampling error, e
3. The standard deviation, σ

In some business-to-business relationships that require estimation of important parameters, legal contracts specify acceptable levels of sampling error and the confidence level required. For companies in the food or drug sectors, government regulations often specify sampling errors and confidence levels. In general, however, it is usually not easy to specify the three factors needed to determine the sample size. How can you determine the level of confidence and sampling error? Typically, these questions are answered only by the subject matter expert (i.e., the individual most familiar with the variables under study). Although 95% is the most common confidence level used, if more confidence is desired, then 99% might be more appropriate; if less confidence is deemed acceptable, then 90% might be used. For the sampling error, you should think not of how much sampling error you would like to have (you really do not want any error) but of how much you can tolerate when reaching conclusions from the confidence interval.

In addition to specifying the confidence level and the sampling error, you need an estimate of the standard deviation. Unfortunately, you rarely know the population standard deviation, σ. In some instances, you can estimate the standard deviation from past data. In other situations, you can make an educated guess by taking into account the range and distribution of the variable. For example, if you assume a normal distribution, the range is approximately equal to 6σ (i.e., $\pm 3\sigma$ around the mean) so that you estimate σ as the range divided by 6. If you cannot estimate σ in this way, you can conduct a small-scale study and estimate the standard deviation from the resulting data.

To explore how to determine the sample size needed for estimating the population mean, consider again the audit at Saxon Home Improvement. In Section 9.2, you selected a sample of 100 sales invoices and constructed a 95% confidence interval estimate of the population mean sales invoice amount. How was this sample size determined? Should you have selected a different sample size?

Suppose that, after consultation with company officials, you determine that a sampling error of no more than $\pm\$5$ is desired, along with 95% confidence. Past data indicate that the standard deviation of the sales amount is approximately $25. Thus, $e = \$5, \sigma = \$25$, and $Z_{\alpha/2} = 1.96$ (for 95% confidence). Using Equation (9.4),

$$n = \frac{Z_{\alpha/2}^2 \sigma^2}{e^2} = \frac{(1.96)^2(25)^2}{(5)^2}$$

$$= 96.04$$

Because the general rule is to slightly oversatisfy the criteria by rounding the sample size up to the next whole integer, you should select a sample of size 97. Thus, the sample of size $n = 100$ used is close to what is necessary to satisfy the needs of the company, based on the estimated standard deviation, desired confidence level, and sampling error. Because the calculated sample standard deviation is slightly higher than expected, $28.95 compared to $25.00, the confidence interval is slightly wider than desired. Figure 9.14 shows a Microsoft Excel worksheet to determine the sample size.

FIGURE 9.14

Microsoft Excel worksheet for determining sample size for estimating the mean sales invoice amount for the Saxon Home Improvement Company

See Section E9.4 to create this.

	A	B	
1	**For Mean Sales Invoice Amount**		
2			
3	**Data**		
4	**Population Standard Deviation**	25	
5	**Sampling Error**	5	
6	**Confidence Level**	95%	
7			
8	Intemediate Calculations		
9	Z Value	-1.9600	=NORMSINV((1 - B6)/2)
10	Calculated Sample Size	96.0365	=((B9 * B4)/B5)^2
11			
12	Result		
13	**Sample Size Needed**	97	=ROUNDUP(B10, 0)

Example 9.5 illustrates another application of determining the sample size needed to develop a confidence interval estimate for the mean.

EXAMPLE 9.5

Determining the Sample Size for the Mean

Returning to Example 9.3, suppose you want to estimate the population mean force required to break the insulator to within ±25 pounds with 95% confidence. On the basis of a study taken the previous year, you believe that the standard deviation is 100 pounds. Find the sample size needed.

SOLUTION Using Equation (9.4) on page 378 and $e = 25, \sigma = 100$, and $Z_{\alpha/2} = 1.96$ for 95% confidence,

$$n = \frac{Z_{\alpha/2}^2 \sigma^2}{e^2} = \frac{(1.96)^2(100)^2}{(25)^2}$$

$$= 61.47$$

Therefore, you should select a sample size of 62 insulators because the general rule for determining sample size is to always round up to the next integer value in order to slightly oversatisfy the criteria desired. An actual sampling error slightly larger than 25 will result if the sample standard deviation calculated in this sample of 62 is greater than 100 and slightly smaller if the sample standard deviation is less than 100.

Sample Size Determination for the Proportion

So far in this section, you have learned how to determine the sample size needed for estimating the population mean. Now suppose that you want to determine the sample size necessary for estimating a population proportion.

To determine the sample size needed to estimate a population proportion, π, you use a method similar to the method for a population mean. Recall that in developing the sample size for a confidence interval for the mean, the sampling error is defined by

$$e = Z_{\alpha/2} \frac{\sigma}{\sqrt{n}}$$

When estimating a proportion, you replace σ with $\sqrt{\pi(1 - \pi)}$. Thus, the sampling error is

$$e = Z_{\alpha/2} \sqrt{\frac{\pi(1 - \pi)}{n}}$$

Solving for n, you have the sample size necessary to develop a confidence interval estimate for a proportion.

SAMPLE SIZE DETERMINATION FOR THE PROPORTION

The sample size n is equal to the product of $Z_{\alpha/2}$ squared, the population proportion, π, and 1 minus the population proportion, π, divided by the square of the sampling error, e.

$$n = \frac{Z_{\alpha/2}^2 \pi(1 - \pi)}{e^2} \qquad (9.5)$$

To determine the sample size, you must know three factors:

1. The desired confidence level, which determines the value of $Z_{\alpha/2}$, the critical value from the standardized normal distribution
2. The acceptable sampling error (or margin of error), e
3. The population proportion, π

In practice, selecting these quantities requires some planning. Once you determine the desired level of confidence, you can find the appropriate $Z_{\alpha/2}$ value from the standardized normal distribution. The sampling error, e, indicates the amount of error that you are willing to tolerate in estimating the population proportion. The third quantity, π, is actually the population parameter that you want to estimate! Thus, how do you state a value for what you are trying to determine?

Here you have two alternatives. In many situations, you may have past information or relevant experience that provide an educated estimate of π. Or, if you do not have past information or relevant experience, you can try to provide a value for π that would never *underestimate* the sample size needed. Referring to Equation (9.5), you can see that the quantity $\pi(1 - \pi)$ appears in the numerator. Thus, you need to determine the value of π that will make the quantity $\pi(1 - \pi)$ as large as possible. When $\pi = 0.5$, the product $\pi(1 - \pi)$ achieves its maximum value. To show this result, consider the following values of π, along with the accompanying products of $\pi(1 - \pi)$:

When $\pi = 0.9$, then $\pi(1 - \pi) = (0.9)(0.1) = 0.09$
When $\pi = 0.7$, then $\pi(1 - \pi) = (0.7)(0.3) = 0.21$
When $\pi = 0.5$, then $\pi(1 - \pi) = (0.5)(0.5) = 0.25$
When $\pi = 0.3$, then $\pi(1 - \pi) = (0.3)(0.7) = 0.21$
When $\pi = 0.1$, then $\pi(1 - \pi) = (0.1)(0.9) = 0.09$

Therefore, when you have no prior knowledge or estimate of the population proportion, π, you should use $\pi = 0.5$ for determining the sample size. Using $\pi = 0.5$ produces the largest possible sample size and results in the narrowest and most precise confidence interval. This increased precision comes at the cost of spending more time and money for an increased sample size. Also, note that if you use $\pi = 0.5$ and the proportion is different from 0.5, you will overestimate the sample size needed, because you will get a confidence interval narrower than originally intended.

Returning to the Saxon Home Improvement Using Statistics scenario, suppose that the auditing procedures require you to have 95% confidence in estimating the population proportion of sales invoices with errors to within ± 0.07. The results from past months indicate that the largest proportion has been no more than 0.15. Thus, using Equation (9.5) and $e = 0.07$, $\pi = 0.15$, and $Z_{\alpha/2} = 1.96$ for 95% confidence,

$$n = \frac{Z_{\alpha/2}^2 \pi (1 - \pi)}{e^2}$$

$$= \frac{(1.96)^2 (0.15)(0.85)}{(0.07)^2}$$

$$= 99.96$$

Because the general rule is to round the sample size up to the next whole integer to slightly oversatisfy the criteria, a sample size of 100 is needed. Thus, the sample size needed to satisfy the requirements of the company, based on the estimated proportion, desired confidence level, and sampling error, is equal to the sample size taken. The actual confidence interval is narrower than required because the sample proportion is 0.10, whereas 0.15 was used for π in Equation (9.5). Figure 9.15 shows a Microsoft Excel worksheet for determining sample size.

FIGURE 9.15

Microsoft Excel worksheet for determining sample size for estimating the proportion of sales invoices with errors for the Saxon Home Improvement Company

See Section E9.5 to create this.

	A	B	
1	**For Proportion of In-Error Sales Invoices**		
2			
3	**Data**		
4	**Estimate of True Proportion**	0.15	
5	**Sampling Error**	0.07	
6	**Confidence Level**	95%	
7			
8	**Intermediate Calculations**		
9	Z Value	-1.9600	=NORMSINV((1 - B6)/2)
10	Calculated Sample Size	99.9563	=(B9^2 * B4 * (1 - B4))/B5^2
11			
12	**Result**		
13	**Sample Size Needed**	100	=ROUNDUP(B10, 0)

Example 9.6 provides another application of determining the sample size for estimating the population proportion.

EXAMPLE 9.6

Determining the Sample Size for the Population Proportion

You want to have 90% confidence of estimating the proportion of office workers who respond to e-mail within an hour to within ± 0.05. Because you have not previously undertaken such a study, there is no information available from past data. Determine the sample size needed.

SOLUTION Because no information is available from past data, assume that $\pi = 0.50$. Using Equation (9.5) on page 380 and $e = 0.05$, $\pi = 0.50$, and $Z_{a/2} = 1.645$ for 90% confidence,

$$n = \frac{Z_{\alpha/2}^2 \pi (1 - \pi)}{e^2}$$

$$= \frac{(1.645)^2 (0.50)(0.50)}{(0.05)^2}$$

$$= 270.6$$

Therefore, you need a sample of 271 office workers to estimate the population proportion to within ± 0.05 with 90% confidence.

Problems for Section 9.4

LEARNING THE BASICS

9.30 If you want to be 95% confident of estimating the population mean to within a sampling error of ± 5 and the standard deviation is assumed to be 15, what sample size is required?

9.31 If you want to be 99% confident of estimating the population mean to within a sampling error of ± 20 and the standard deviation is assumed to be 100, what sample size is required?

9.32 If you want to be 99% confident of estimating the population proportion to within a sampling error of ± 0.04, what sample size is needed?

9.33 If you want to be 95% confident of estimating the population proportion to within a sampling error of ± 0.02 and there is historical evidence that the population proportion is approximately 0.40, what sample size is needed?

APPLYING THE CONCEPTS

✓SELF Test 9.34 A survey is planned to determine the mean annual family medical expenses of employees of a large company. The management of the company wishes to be 95% confident that the sample mean is correct to within $\pm \$50$ of the population mean annual family medical expenses. A previous study indicates that the standard deviation is approximately $400.
a. How large a sample size is necessary?
b. If management wants to be correct to within $\pm \$25$, how many employees need to be selected?

9.35 If the manager of a paint supply store wants to estimate the mean amount of paint in a 1-gallon can to within ± 0.004 gallon with 95% confidence and also assumes that the standard deviation is 0.02 gallon, what sample size is needed?

9.36 If a quality control manager wants to estimate the mean life of lightbulbs to within ± 20 hours with 95% confidence and also assumes that the population standard deviation is 100 hours, how many lightbulbs need to be selected?

9.37 If the inspection division of a county weights and measures department wants to estimate the mean amount of soft-drink fill in 2-liter bottles to within ± 0.01 liter with 95% confidence and also assumes that the standard deviation is 0.05 liter, what sample size is needed?

9.38 A consumer group wants to estimate the mean electric bill for the month of July for single-family homes in a large city. Based on studies conducted in other cities, the standard deviation is assumed to be $25. The group wants to estimate the mean bill for July to within $\pm \$5$ with 99% confidence.

a. What sample size is needed?
b. If 95% confidence is desired, how many homes need to be selected?

9.39 An advertising agency that serves a major radio station wants to estimate the mean amount of time that the station's audience spends listening to the radio daily. From past studies, the standard deviation is estimated as 45 minutes.
a. What sample size is needed if the agency wants to be 90% confident of being correct to within ± 5 minutes?
b. If 99% confidence is desired, how many listeners need to be selected?

9.40 A growing niche in the restaurant business is gourmet-casual breakfast, lunch, and brunch. Chains in this group include Le Peep, Good Egg, Eggs & I, First Watch, and Eggs Up Grill. The mean per-person check for First Watch is approximately $7, and the mean per-person check for Eggs Up Grill is $6.50 (data extracted from J. Hayes, "Competition Heats Up as Breakfast Concepts Eye Growth," *Nation's Restaurant News*, April 24, 2006, pp. 8, 66).
a. Assuming a standard deviation of $2.00, what sample size is needed to estimate the mean per-person check for Good Egg to within $\pm \$0.25$ with 95% confidence?
b. Assuming a standard deviation of $2.50, what sample size is needed to estimate the mean per-person check for Good Egg to within $\pm \$0.25$ with 95% confidence?
c. Assuming a standard deviation of $3.00, what sample size is needed to estimate the mean per-person check for Good Egg to within $\pm \$0.25$ with 95% confidence?
d. Discuss the effect of variation on selecting the sample size needed.

9.41 What proportion of people hit snags with online transactions? According to a poll conducted by Harris Interactive, 89% hit snags with online transactions (data extracted from "Snapshots: Top Online Transaction Trouble," *USA Today*, April 4, 2006, p. 1D).
a. To conduct a follow-up study that would provide 95% confidence that the point estimate is correct to within ± 0.04 of the population proportion, how large a sample size is required?
b. To conduct a follow-up study that would provide 99% confidence that the point estimate is correct to within ± 0.04 of the population proportion, how many people need to be sampled?
c. To conduct a follow-up study that would provide 95% confidence that the point estimate is correct to within ± 0.02 of the population proportion, how large a sample size is required?
d. To conduct a follow-up study that would provide 99% confidence that the point estimate is correct to within ± 0.02 of the population proportion, how many people need to be sampled?

e. Discuss the effects of changing the desired confidence level and the acceptable sampling error on sample size requirements.

9.42 A poll of 1,286 young adult cellphone users was conducted in March 2006. These cellphone users, aged 18 to 29, were actively engaged in multiple uses of their cellphones. The data suggest that 707 took still pictures with their phones, 604 played games, and 360 used the Internet (data extracted from "Poll: Cellphones Are Annoying but Invaluable," **usatoday.com**, April 3, 2006). Construct a 95% confidence interval estimate of the population proportion of young adults that used their cellphone to

a. take still pictures.

b. play games.

c. use the Internet.

d. You have been asked to update the results of this study. Determine the sample size necessary to estimate the population proportions in (a) through (c) to within ±0.02 with 95% confidence.

9.43 A study of 658 CEOs conducted by the Conference Board reported that 250 stated that their company's greatest concern was sustained and steady top-line growth (data extracted from "Snapshots: CEOs' Greatest Concerns," *USA Today*, May 8, 2006, p. 1D).

a. Construct a 95% confidence interval for the proportion of CEOs whose greatest concern was sustained and steady top-line growth.

b. Interpret the interval constructed in (a).

c. To conduct a follow-up study to estimate the population proportion of CEOs whose greatest concern was sustained and steady top-line growth to within ±0.01 with 95% confidence, how many CEOs would you survey?

9.44 In 2007, oil companies posted huge profits and consumers paid record high prices at the gas pump. The president of Shell Oil stated that "we know for a fact that the favorability rating of oil companies today ranges from 10–15%" (data extracted from D. J. Lynch, "Shell Oil Tries Different Path to Engage Public Opinion," **usatoday.com**, May 14, 2007).

a. If you conduct a follow-up study to estimate the population proportion of individuals who view oil companies favorably, would you use a π of 0.10, 0.15, or 0.50 in the sample size formula? Discuss.

b. Using your answer to (a), find the sample size necessary to estimate the population proportion to within ±0.03 with 95% certainty.

9.45 The Department of Commerce announced that the national rental vacancy rate during the first quarter of 2007 was 10.1%. The report noted that the proportion of rentals vacant was 0.101 and with 95% confidence a margin of error of 0.004 (data extracted from R. R. Callis and L. B. Cavanaugh, "Census Bureau Reports on Residential Vacancies and Homeownership," *United States Department of Commerce News*, April 27, 2007, p.1).

a. Construct a 95% confidence interval estimate for the national rental vacancy rate.

b. Interpret the interval found in (a).

c. If the estimate reported was constructed using the methods in this section, what sample size was used?

9.5 Confidence Interval Estimation and Ethical Issues

Ethical issues relating to the selection of samples and the inferences that accompany them can occur in several ways. The major ethical issue relates to whether confidence interval estimates are provided along with the point estimates. To provide a point estimate without also including the confidence interval limits (typically set at 95%), the sample size used, and an interpretation of the meaning of the confidence interval in terms that a person untrained in statistics can understand raises ethical issues. Failure to include a confidence interval estimate might mislead the user of the results into thinking that the point estimate is all that is needed to predict the population characteristic with certainty. Thus, it is important that you indicate the interval estimate in a prominent place in any written communication, along with a simple explanation of the meaning of the confidence interval. In addition, you should highlight the sample size and sampling error.

One of the most common areas where ethical issues concerning confidence intervals occurs is in the publication of the results of political polls. Often, the results of the polls are highlighted on the front page of the newspaper, and the sampling error involved along with the methodology used is printed on the page where the article is continued, often in the middle of the newspaper. To ensure an ethical presentation of statistical results, the confidence levels, sample size, sampling error, and confidence limits should be made available for all surveys and other statistical studies.

USING STATISTICS @ Saxon Home Improvement Revisited

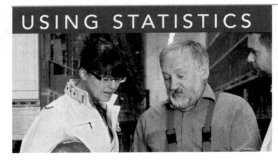

In the Using Statistics scenario, you were an accountant for Saxon Home Improvement, a distributor of home improvement supplies in the northeastern United States. You were responsible for the accuracy of the integrated inventory management and sales information system. You used confidence interval estimation techniques to draw conclusions about the population of all records from a relatively small sample collected during an audit.

At the end of the month, you collected a random sample of 100 sales invoices and made the following inferences:

- With 95% confidence, you concluded that the mean amount of all the sales invoices is between $104.53 and $116.01.
- With 95% confidence, you concluded that between 4.12% and 15.88% of all the sales invoices contain errors.

These estimates provide an interval of values that you believe contain the true population parameters. If these intervals are too wide (i.e., the sampling error is too large) for the types of decisions Saxon Home Improvement needs to make, you will need to take a larger sample. You can use the sample size formulas in Section 9.4 to determine the number of sales invoices to sample to ensure that the size of the sampling error is acceptable.

SUMMARY

This chapter discusses confidence intervals for estimating the characteristics of a population, along with how you can determine the necessary sample size. You learned how to apply these methods to numerical and categorical data. Table 9.3 provides a list of topics covered in this chapter.

To determine what equation to use for a particular situation, you need to answer two questions:

- Are you developing a confidence interval or are you determining sample size?
- Do you have a numerical variable or do you have a categorical variable?

The next three chapters develop a hypothesis-testing approach to making decisions about population parameters.

TABLE 9.3

Summary of Topics in Chapter 9

Type of Analysis	Type of Data	
	Numerical	**Categorical**
Confidence interval for a population parameter	Confidence interval estimate for the mean (Sections 9.1 and 9.2)	Confidence interval estimate for the proportion (Section 9.3)
Determining sample size	Sample size determination for the mean (Section 9.4)	Sample size determination for the proportion (Section 9.4)

KEY EQUATIONS

Confidence Interval for the Mean (σ Known)

$$\bar{X} \pm Z_{\alpha/2} \frac{\sigma}{\sqrt{n}}$$

or

$$\bar{X} - Z_{\alpha/2} \frac{\sigma}{\sqrt{n}} \leq \mu \leq \bar{X} + Z_{\alpha/2} \frac{\sigma}{\sqrt{n}} \quad (9.1)$$

Confidence Interval for the Mean (σ Unknown)

$$\bar{X} \pm t_{\alpha/2} \frac{S}{\sqrt{n}}$$

or

$$\bar{X} - t_{\alpha/2} \frac{S}{\sqrt{n}} \leq \mu \leq \bar{X} + t_{\alpha/2} \frac{S}{\sqrt{n}} \quad (9.2)$$

Confidence Interval Estimate for the Proportion

$$p \pm Z_{\alpha/2}\sqrt{\frac{p(1-p)}{n}}$$

or

$$p - Z_{\alpha/2}\sqrt{\frac{p(1-p)}{n}} \le \pi \le p + Z_{\alpha/2}\sqrt{\frac{p(1-p)}{n}} \quad (9.3)$$

Sample Size Determination for the Mean

$$n = \frac{Z_{\alpha/2}^2 \sigma^2}{e^2} \quad (9.4)$$

Sample Size Determination for the Proportion

$$n = \frac{Z_{\alpha/2}^2 \pi(1-\pi)}{e^2} \quad (9.5)$$

KEY TERMS

confidence interval estimate 360	level of confidence 363	sampling error 378
critical value 364	margin of error 378	Student's *t* distribution 366
degrees of freedom 366	point estimate 360	

CHAPTER REVIEW PROBLEMS

CHECKING YOUR UNDERSTANDING

9.46 Why can you never really have 100% confidence of correctly estimating the population characteristic of interest?

9.47 When are you able to use the *t* distribution to develop the confidence interval estimate for the mean?

9.48 Why is it true that for a given sample size, *n*, an increase in confidence is achieved by widening (and making less precise) the confidence interval?

9.49 Why is the sample size needed to determine the proportion smaller when the population proportion is 0.20 than when the population proportion is 0.50?

APPLYING THE CONCEPTS

9.50 You work in the corporate office for a nationwide convenience store franchise that operates nearly 10,000 stores. The per-store daily customer count has been steady at 900 for some time (i.e., the mean number of customers in a store in one day is 900). To increase the customer count, the franchise is considering cutting coffee prices by approximately half. The 12-ounce size will now be $.59 instead of $.99, and the 16-ounce size will be $.69 instead of $1.19. Even with this reduction in price, the franchise will have a 40% gross margin on coffee. To test the new initiative, the franchise has reduced coffee prices in a sample of 34 stores, where customer counts have been running almost exactly at the national average of 900. After four weeks, the sample stores stabilize at a mean customer count of 974 and a standard deviation of 96. This increase seems like a substantial amount to you, but it also seems like a pretty small sample. Is there some way to get a feel for what the mean per-store count in all the stores will be if you cut coffee prices nationwide? Do you think reducing coffee prices is a good strategy for increasing the mean customer count?

9.51 Companies are spending more time screening applicants than in the past. A study of 102 recruiters conducted by ExecuNet found that 77 did Internet research on candidates (data extracted from P. Kitchen, "Don't Let Any 'Digital Dirt' Bury Your Job Prospects," *Newsday*, August 21, 2005, p. A59).
a. Construct a 95% confidence interval estimate of the population proportion of recruiters who do Internet research on candidates.
b. Based on (a), is it correct to conclude that more than 70% of recruiters do Internet research on candidates?
c. Suppose that the study uses a sample size of 400 recruiters and 302 did Internet research on candidates. Construct a 95% confidence interval estimate of the population proportion of recruiters who do Internet research on candidates.
d. Based on (c), is it correct to conclude that more than 70% of recruiters do Internet research on candidates?
e. Discuss the effect of sample size on your answers to (a) through (d).

9.52 A market researcher for a consumer electronics company wants to study the television viewing habits of residents of a particular area. A random sample of 40 respondents is selected, and each respondent is instructed to keep a detailed record of all television viewing in a particular week. The results are as follows:
- Viewing time per week: $\overline{X} = 15.3$ hours, $S = 3.8$ hours.
- 27 respondents watch the evening news on at least 3 weeknights.
a. Construct a 95% confidence interval estimate for the mean amount of television watched per week in this city.
b. Construct a 95% confidence interval estimate for the population proportion who watch the evening news on at least 3 weeknights per week.

Suppose that the market researcher wants to take another survey in a different city. Answer these questions:

c. What sample size is required to be 95% confident of estimating the population mean to within ± 2 hours and assumes that the population standard deviation is equal to 5 hours?

d. How many respondents need to be selected to be 95% confident of being within ± 0.035 of the population proportion who watch the evening news on at least 3 weeknights if no previous estimate is available?

e. Based on (c) and (d), how many respondents should the market researcher select if a single survey is being conducted?

9.53 The real estate assessor for a county government wants to study various characteristics of single-family houses in the county. A random sample of 70 houses reveals the following:

- Heated area of the houses (in square feet): $\overline{X} = 1,759$, $S = 380$.
- 42 houses have central air-conditioning.

a. Construct a 99% confidence interval estimate of the population mean heated area of the houses.

b. Construct a 95% confidence interval estimate of the population proportion of houses that have central air-conditioning.

9.54 The personnel director of a large corporation wishes to study absenteeism among clerical workers at the corporation's central office during the year. A random sample of 25 clerical workers reveals the following:

- Absenteeism: $\overline{X} = 9.7$ days, $S = 4.0$ days.
- 12 clerical workers were absent more than 10 days.

a. Construct a 95% confidence interval estimate of the mean number of absences for clerical workers during the year.

b. Construct a 95% confidence interval estimate of the population proportion of clerical workers absent more than 10 days during the year.

Suppose that the personnel director also wishes to take a survey in a branch office. Answer these questions:

c. What sample size is needed to have 95% confidence in estimating the population mean absenteeism to within ± 1.5 days if the population standard deviation is estimated to be 4.5 days?

d. How many clerical workers need to be selected to have 90% confidence in estimating the population proportion to within ± 0.075 if no previous estimate is available?

e. Based on (c) and (d), what sample size is needed if a single survey is being conducted?

9.55 The market research director for Dotty's Department Store wants to study women's spending on cosmetics. A survey of the store's credit card holders is designed in order to estimate the proportion of women who purchase their cosmetics primarily from Dotty's Department Store and the mean yearly amount that women spend on cosmetics. A pre-

vious survey found that the standard deviation of the amount women spend on cosmetics in a year is approximately $18.

a. What sample size is needed to have 99% confidence of estimating the population mean to within $\pm\$5$?

b. How many of the store's credit card holders need to be selected to have 90% confidence of estimating the population proportion to within ± 0.045?

9.56 The owner of a restaurant that serves continental food wants to study characteristics of his customers. He decides to focus on two variables: the amount of money spent by customers and whether customers order dessert. The results from a sample of 60 customers are as follows:

- Amount spent: $\overline{X} = \$38.54, S = \$7.26$.
- 18 customers purchased dessert.

a. Construct a 95% confidence interval estimate of the population mean amount spent per customer in the restaurant.

b. Construct a 90% confidence interval estimate of the population proportion of customers who purchase dessert.

The owner of a competing restaurant wants to conduct a similar survey in her restaurant. This owner does not have access to the information of the owner of the first restaurant. Answer the following questions:

c. What sample size is needed to have 95% confidence of estimating the population mean amount spent in her restaurant to within $\pm\$1.50$, assuming that the standard deviation is estimated to be $8?

d. How many customers need to be selected to have 90% confidence of estimating the population proportion of customers who purchase dessert to within ± 0.04?

e. Based on your answers to (c) and (d), how large a sample should the owner take?

9.57 The manufacturer of "Ice Melt" claims its product will melt snow and ice at temperatures as low as $0°$ Fahrenheit. A representative for a large chain of hardware stores is interested in testing this claim. The chain purchases a large shipment of 5-pound bags for distribution. The representative wants to know with 95% confidence, within ± 0.05, what proportion of bags of Ice Melt perform the job as claimed by the manufacturer.

a. How many bags does the representative need to test? What assumption should be made concerning the population proportion? (This is called *destructive testing*; that is, the product being tested is destroyed by the test and is then unavailable to be sold.)

b. The representative tests 50 bags, and 42 of them do the job as claimed. Construct a 95% confidence interval estimate for the population proportion that will do the job as claimed.

c. How can the representative use the results of (b) to determine whether to sell the Ice Melt product?

9.58 A manufacturing company produces steel housings for electrical equipment. The main component part of the housing is a steel trough that is made out of a 14-gauge steel coil. It is produced using a 250-ton progressive punch press with a wipe-down operation that puts two 90-degree forms in the flat steel to make the trough. The distance from one side of the form to the other is critical because of weatherproofing in outdoor applications. The widths (in inches) and stored in the file Trough from a sample of 49 troughs follows:

8.312 8.343 8.317 8.383 8.348 8.410 8.351 8.373 8.481 8.422

8.476 8.382 8.484 8.403 8.414 8.419 8.385 8.465 8.498 8.447

8.436 8.413 8.489 8.414 8.481 8.415 8.479 8.429 8.458 8.462

8.460 8.444 8.429 8.460 8.412 8.420 8.410 8.405 8.323 8.420

8.396 8.447 8.405 8.439 8.411 8.427 8.420 8.498 8.409

a. Construct a 95% confidence interval estimate of the mean width of the troughs.
b. Interpret the interval developed in (a).
c. Do you think the assumption needed to construct the confidence interval estimate in (a) in valid?

9.59 A quality characteristic of interest for a tea-bag-filling process is the weight of the tea in the individual bags. In this example, the label weight on the package indicates that the mean amount is 5.5 grams of tea in a bag. If the bags are underfilled, two problems arise. First, customers may not be able to brew the tea to be as strong as they wish. Second, the company may be in violation of the truth-in-labeling laws. On the other hand, if the mean amount of tea in a bag exceeds the label weight, the company is giving away product. Getting an exact amount of tea in a bag is problematic because of variation in the temperature and humidity inside the factory, differences in the density of the tea, and the extremely fast filling operation of the machine (approximately 170 bags per minute). The following data (stored in the file Teabags) are the weights, in grams, of a sample of 50 tea bags produced in one hour by a single machine:

5.65 5.44 5.42 5.40 5.53 5.34 5.54 5.45 5.52 5.41

5.57 5.40 5.53 5.54 5.55 5.62 5.56 5.46 5.44 5.51

5.47 5.40 5.47 5.61 5.53 5.32 5.67 5.29 5.49 5.55

5.77 5.57 5.42 5.58 5.58 5.50 5.32 5.50 5.53 5.58

5.61 5.45 5.44 5.25 5.56 5.63 5.50 5.57 5.67 5.36

a. Construct a 99% confidence interval estimate of the population mean weight of the tea bags.
b. Is the company meeting the requirement set forth on the label that the mean amount of tea in a bag is 5.5 grams?
c. Do you think the assumption needed to construct the confidence interval estimate in (a) is valid?

9.60 The manufacturer of Boston and Vermont asphalt shingles provides its customers with a 20-year warranty on most of its products. To determine whether a shingle will last as long as the warranty period, accelerated-life testing is conducted at the manufacturing plant. Accelerated-life testing exposes the shingle to the stresses it would be subject to in a lifetime of normal use via a laboratory experiment that takes only a few minutes to conduct. In this test, a shingle is repeatedly scraped with a brush for a short period of time,

and the shingle granules removed by the brushing are weighed (in grams). Shingles that experience low amounts of granule loss are expected to last longer in normal use than shingles that experience high amounts of granule loss. In this situation, a shingle should experience no more than 0.8 grams of granule loss if it is expected to last the length of the warranty period. The file Granule contains a sample of 170 measurements made on the company's Boston shingles and 140 measurements made on Vermont shingles.

a. For the Boston shingles, construct a 95% confidence interval estimate of the mean granule loss.
b. For the Vermont shingles, construct a 95% confidence interval estimate of the mean granule loss.
c. Do you think the assumption needed to construct the confidence interval estimates in (a) and (b) is valid?
d. Based on the results of (a) and (b), what conclusions can you reach concerning the mean granule loss of the Boston and Vermont shingles?

9.61 The manufacturer of Boston and Vermont asphalt shingles knows that product weight is a major factor in the customer's perception of quality. The last stage of the assembly line packages the shingles before they are placed on wooden pallets. Once a pallet is full (a pallet for most brands holds 16 squares of shingles), it is weighed, and the measurement is recorded. The file Pallet contains the weight (in pounds) from a sample of 368 pallets of Boston shingles and 330 pallets of Vermont shingles.

a. For the Boston shingles, construct a 95% confidence interval estimate of the mean weight.
b. For the Vermont shingles, construct a 95% confidence interval estimate of the mean weight.
c. Do you think the assumption needed to construct the confidence interval estimates in (a) and (b) is valid?
d. Based on the results of (a) and (b), what conclusions can you reach concerning the mean weight of the Boston and Vermont shingles?

REPORT WRITING EXERCISES

9.62 Referring to the results in Problem 9.58 concerning the width of a steel trough, write a report that summarizes your conclusions.

TEAM PROJECT

9.63 Refer to the team project. Construct all appropriate confidence interval estimates of the population characteristics of low-risk, average-risk, and high-risk mutual funds. Include these estimates in a report to the vice president for research at the financial investment service (The data are stored in the Mutual Funds file).

STUDENT SURVEY DATABASE

9.64 Problem 1.28 describes a survey of 50 undergraduate students (see the file Undergradsurvey).
a. For these data, for each variable, construct a 95% confidence interval estimate of the population characteristic.
b. Write a report that summarizes your conclusions.

9.65 Problem 1.28 describes a survey of 50 undergraduate students (see the file Undergradsurvey).
a. Select a sample of 50 undergraduate students at your school and conduct a similar survey for those students.
b. For the data collected in (a), repeat (a) and (b) of Problem 8.64.
c. Compare the results of (b) to those of Problem 9.64.

9.66 Problem 1.29 describes a survey of 40 MBA students (see the file Gradsurvey).

a. For these data, for each variable, construct a 95% confidence interval estimate of the population characteristic.
b. Write a report that summarizes your conclusions.

9.67 Problem 1.29 describes a survey of 40 MBA students (see the file Gradsurvey).
a. Select a sample of 40 graduate students in your MBA program and conduct a similar survey for those students.
b. For the data collected in (a), repeat (a) and (b) of Problem 9.66.
c. Compare the results of (b) to those of Problem 9.66.

MANAGING THE *SPRINGVILLE HERALD*

The marketing department has been considering ways to increase the number of new subscriptions and increase the rate of retention among customers who agreed to a trial subscription. Following the suggestion of Assistant Manager Lauren Adler, the department staff designed a survey to help determine various characteristics of readers of the newspaper who were not home-delivery subscribers. The survey consists of the following 10 questions:

1. Do you or a member of your household ever purchase the *Springville Herald*?
   (1) Yes   (2) No
   [If the respondent answers no, the interview is terminated.]

2. Do you receive the *Springville Herald* via home delivery?
   (1) Yes   (2) No
   [If no, skip to question 4.]

3. Do you receive the *Springville Herald*:
   (1) Monday–Saturday (2) Sunday only (3) Every day
   [If every day, skip to question 9.]

4. How often during the Monday–Saturday period do you purchase the *Springville Herald*?
   (1) Every day
   (2) Most days
   (3) Occasionally or never

5. How often do you purchase the *Springville Herald* on Sundays?
   (1) Every Sunday
   (2) 2–3 Sundays per month
   (3) No more than once a month

6. Where are you most likely to purchase the *Springville Herald*?
   (1) Convenience store
   (2) Newsstand/candy store
   (3) Vending machine
   (4) Supermarket
   (5) Other

7. Would you consider subscribing to the *Springville Herald* for a trial period if a discount were offered?
   (1) Yes   (2) No
   [If no, skip to question 9.]

8. The *Springville Herald* currently costs $0.50 Monday–Saturday and $1.50 on Sunday, for a total of $4.50 per week. How much would you be willing to pay per week to get home delivery for a 90-day trial period?

9. Do you read a daily newspaper other than the *Springville Herald*?
   (1) Yes   (2) No

10. As an incentive for long-term subscribers, the newspaper is considering the possibility of offering a card that would provide discounts at certain restaurants in the Springville area to all subscribers who pay in advance for six months of home delivery. Would you want to get such a card under the terms of this offer?
   (1) Yes   (2) No

The group agreed to use a random-digit dialing method to poll 500 local households by telephone. Using this approach, the last four digits of a telephone number are randomly selected to go with an area code and exchange (the first 6 digits of a 10-digit telephone number). Only those pairs of area codes and exchanges that were for the Springville city area were used for this survey.

Of the 500 households selected, 94 households either refused to participate, could not be contacted after repeated attempts, or represented telephone numbers that were not in service. The summary results are as follows:

Households That Purchase the *Springville Herald*	Frequency
Yes	352
No	54

Households with Home Delivery	Frequency
Yes	136
No	216

Type of Home Delivery Subscription	Frequency
Monday–Saturday	18
Sunday only	25
7 days a week	93

Purchase Behavior of Nonsubscribers for Monday–Saturday Editions	Frequency
Every day	78
Most days	95
Occasionally or never	43

Purchase Behavior of Nonsubscribers for Sunday Editions	Frequency
Every Sunday	138
2–3 Sundays a month	54
No more than once a month	24

Nonsubscribers' Purchase Location	Frequency
Convenience store	74
Newsstand/candy store	95
Vending machine	21
Supermarket	13
Other locations	13

Would Consider Trial Subscription If Offered a Discount	Frequency
	46
No	170

Rate ($) Willing to Pay per Week (data file SH9) for a 90-Day Home-Delivery Trial Subscription

4.15	3.60	4.10	3.60	3.60	3.60	4.40	3.15	4.00	3.75	4.00
3.25	3.75	3.30	3.75	3.65	4.00	4.10	3.90	3.50	3.75	3.00
3.40	4.00	3.80	3.50	4.10	4.25	3.50	3.90	3.95	4.30	4.20
3.50	3.75	3.30	3.85	3.20	4.40	3.80	3.40	3.50	2.85	3.75
3.80	3.90									

Read a Daily Newspaper Other Than the *Springville Herald*	Frequency
Yes	138
No	214

Would Prepay Six Months to Receive a Restaurant Discount Card	Frequency
Yes	66
No	286

EXERCISES

SH9.1 Some members of the marketing department are concerned about the random-digit dialing method used to collect survey responses. Prepare a memorandum that examines the following issues:

- The advantages and disadvantages of using the random-digit dialing method.
- Possible alternative approaches for conducting the survey and their advantages and disadvantages.

SH9.2 Analyze the results of the survey of Springville households. Write a report that discusses the marketing implications of the survey results for the *Springville Herald*.

WEB CASE

Apply your knowledge about confidence interval estimation in this Web Case, which extends the OurCampus! Web Case from Chapter 6.

Among its other features, the OurCampus! Web site allows customers to purchase OurCampus! LifeStyles merchandise online. To handle payment processing, the management of OurCampus! has contracted with the following firms:

- PayAFriend (PAF): an online payment system with which customers and businesses such as OurCampus! register in order to exchange payments in a secure and convenient manner without the need for a credit card.
- Continental Banking Company (Conbanco): a processing services provider that allows OurCampus! customers to pay for merchandise using nationally recognized credit cards issued by a financial institution.

To reduce costs, the management is considering eliminating one of these two payment systems. However, Virginia Duffy of the sales department suspects that customers use the two forms of payment in unequal numbers and that customers display different buying behaviors when using the two forms of payment. Therefore, she would like to first determine:

a. The proportion of customers using PAF and the proportion of customers using a credit card to pay for their purchases.

b. The mean purchase amount when using PAF and the mean purchase amount when using a credit card.

Assist Ms. Duffy by preparing an appropriate analysis based on a random sample of 50 transactions that she has prepared and placed in an internal file on the OurCampus! Web site, **www.prenhall.com/Springville/OurCampus_PymtSample. htm** or open **OurCampus_PymtSample.htm** from the Student CD-ROM Web Case folder. Summarize your findings and determine whether Ms. Duffy's conjectures about OurCampus! customer purchasing behaviors are correct. If you want the sampling error to be no more than $3 when estimating the mean purchase amount, is Ms. Duffy's sample large enough to perform a valid analysis?

REFERENCES

1. Cochran, W. G., *Sampling Techniques*, 3rd ed. (New York: Wiley, 1977).

2. Fisher, R. A., and F. Yates, *Statistical Tables for Biological, Agricultural and Medical Research*, 5th ed. (Edinburgh: Oliver & Boyd, 1957).

3. Hahn, G., and W. Meeker, *Statistical Intervals, A Guide for Practioners* (New York: John Wiley and Sons, Inc., 1991).

4. Kirk, R. E., ed., *Statistical Issues: A Reader for the Behavioral Sciences* (Belmont, CA: Wadsworth, 1972).

5. Larsen, R. L., and M. L. Marx, *An Introduction to Mathematical Statistics and Its Applications*, 4th ed. (Upper Saddle River, NJ: Prentice Hall, 2006).

6. *Microsoft Excel 2007* (Redmond, WA: Microsoft Corp., 2007).

7. *Minitab for Windows Version 15* (State College, PA: Minitab, Inc., 2006).

8. Snedecor, G. W., and W. G. Cochran, *Statistical Methods*, 7th ed. (Ames, IA: Iowa State University Press, 1980).

CALCULATOR LESSON 7A

**CFX-9850GB
CALCULATOR
EXAMPLE 9.7**

Lesson 7A—Confidence Intervals

1-Sample Z Interval (Using sample statistics)

A certain population is known to have a standard deviation of 4.0. A sample of 40 has been chosen and the mean is 9.7. Construct a 95% confidence interval estimate for the mean.

Solution: From the **Main Menu** select:

STAT   **F4**(INTR)   **F1**(Z)   **F1**(1-S)   then enter the following items:

(Note: Only use the **EXE** key after a new data entry. Otherwise, use the cursor ▼ arrow. If you accidentally hit the wrong key, use **AC/ON** or **EXIT** to go back.)

1-Sample ZInterval

Data	: **F2**(Var)	▼
C-Level	: **.95**	**EXE (Notice the decimal point.)**
σ	: **4**	**EXE**
$\bar{x}$	: **9.7**	**EXE**
n	: **40**	**EXE**

Now key **EXE** or **F1**(Calc)

The calculator will now show the results:

1-Sample ZInterval

Left	=8.4604
Right	=10.939
$\bar{x}$	=9.7
n	=40

This shows that the 95% confidence interval estimate for the population mean is 8.46 to 10.94. This shows the numerical result only. You must remember to write up the complete answer as shown in class.

EXAMPLE 9.8

1-Sample Z Interval (Using raw data)

A random survey of 8 dry-cleaning outlets indicated that the amount of GST collected from each outlet on the previous day was: $70, 65, 76, 52, 80, 71, 59 and $63. Use this information to estimate the mean daily amount of GST collected by all dry cleaning outlets if the amounts are known to be normally distributed with a standard deviation of $5. Determine the 90% confidence interval estimate.

Solution:

First enter the data into **List 1**

Now, from the **Main Menu** select:

STAT   **F4**(INTR)   **F1**(Z)   **F1**(1-S)   then enter the following items:

1-Sample ZInterval

Data	: **F1**(List)	▼
C-Level	: **.90**	**EXE**
σ	: **5**	**EXE**
List	: **List1**	**EXE**
Freq	: **1**	**EXE**

Now key **EXE** or **F1**(Calc)

The calculator will now show the results:

1-Sample ZInterval
Left	=64.092
Right	=69.907
$\bar{x}$	=67
xσn-1	=9.1339
n	=8

This shows that the 90% confidence interval estimate for the population mean is $64.09 to $69.91. This shows the numerical result only. You must remember to write up the complete answer as shown in class.

EXAMPLE 9.9   **1-Sample t Interval** (Using sample statistics)

Management at a bank wish to estimate the mean amount of time customers spend at the automated teller machine (ATM). They believe the times to be normally distributed. A random sample of 20 customers has been selected and the sample mean time was 255 seconds with a standard deviation of 33 seconds. Construct a 95% confidence interval estimate for the mean time at the ATM machine per customer.

Solution: From the **Main Menu** select:

STAT   F4(INTR)   **F2**(t)   **F1**(1-S)   then enter the following items:

(Note: Only use the **EXE** key after a new data entry. Otherwise, use the cursor ▼ arrow. If you accidentally hit the wrong key, use **AC/ON** or **EXIT** to go back.)

1-Sample tInterval
Data	: F2(Var)	▼
C-Level	: .95	**EXE**
$\bar{x}$	: 255	**EXE**
xσ-1	: 33	**EXE**
n	: 20	**EXE**

Now key **EXE** or **F1**(Calc)

The calculator will now show the results:

1-Sample tInterval
Left	=239.55
Right	=270.44
x	=255
xσn-1	=33
n	=20

This shows that the 95% confidence interval estimate for the population mean is 240 to 270 sec. This shows the numerical result only. You must remember to write up the complete answer as shown in class.

EXAMPLE 9.10   **1-Sample t Interval** (Using raw data)

A random survey of 8 dry-cleaning outlets indicated that the amount of GST collected from each outlet on the previous day was: $70, 65, 76, 52, 80, 71, 59 and $63. Use this information to estimate the mean daily amount of GST collected by all dry cleaning outlets if the amounts are known to be normally distributed. Determine the 90% confidence interval estimate.

Solution:

First enter the data into **List 1**

Now, from the **Main Menu** select:

STAT   **F4**(INTR)   **F2**(t)   **F1**(1-S)   then enter the following items:

1-Sample tInterval
Data	**: F1**(List)	▼
C-Level	**: .90**	**EXE**
List	**: List1**	▼
Freq	**: 1**	**EXE**

Now key **EXE** or **F1**(Calc)

The calculator will now show the results:

1-Sample tInterval
Left	=60.882
Right	=73.117
$\bar{x}$	=67
xσn-1	=9.1339
n	=8

This shows that the 90% confidence interval estimate for the population mean is $60.88 to $73.12. This shows the numerical result only. You must remember to write up the complete answer as shown in class.

EXAMPLE 9.11

1-Proportion Z Interval

A bank manager wants to estimate the proportion of all the bank's customers who use the ATM to pay bills. A random sample of 80 customers has been selected and it was found that 43 of them use the ATM to pay bills. Determine the 99% confidence interval estimate for the proportion of all the bank's customers who use the ATM to pay bills.

Solution: From the **Main Menu** select:

STAT   **F4**(INTR)   **F1**(Z)   **F3**(1-P)   then enter the following items:

1-Prop ZInterval
C-Level	**: .99**	**EXE**
x	**: 43**	**EXE**
n	**: 80**	**EXE**

Now key **EXE** or **F1**(Calc)

The calculator will now show the results:

1-Prop ZInterval
Left	=0.39391
Right	=0.68108
$\hat{p}$	=0.5375
n	=80

This shows that the 99% confidence interval estimate for the population proportion is 0.394 to 0.681. This shows the numerical result only. You must remember to write up the complete answer as shown in class.

CALCULATOR LESSON 7B

**CASIO FX-9750GII
CALCULATOR
EXAMPLE 9.12**

Lesson 7B—Confidence Interval

1-Sample Z Interval (Using sample statistics)

A certain population is known to have a standard deviation of 4.0. A sample of 40 has been chosen and the mean is 9.7. Construct a 95% confidence interval estimate for the mean.

Solution: From the **Main Menu** select:

STAT F4(INTR) **F1**(Z) **F1**(1-S)   then enter the following items:

(Note: Only use the **EXE** key after a new data entry. Otherwise, use the cursor ▼ arrow. If you accidentally hit the wrong key, use **AC/ON** or **EXIT** to go back.)

1-Sample ZInterval

Data	: **F2**(Var)	▼
C-Level	: **.95**	**EXE**
σ	: **4**	**EXE**
$\bar{x}$	: **9.7**	**EXE**
n	: **40**	**EXE**
Save Res	: None(press **F1**)	

Now key **EXE** or **F1**(Calc)

The calculator will now show the results:

1-Sample ZInterval

Left	=8.46040994
Right	=10.9395901
$\bar{x}$	=9.7
n	=40

This shows that the 95% confidence interval estimate for the population mean is 8.46 to 10.94. This shows the numerical result only. You must remember to write up the complete answer as shown in class.

EXAMPLE 9.13

1-Sample Z Interval (Using raw data)

A random survey of 8 dry-cleaning outlets indicated that the amount of GST collected from each outlet on the previous day was: $70, 65, 76, 53, 75, 71, 59 and $67. Use this information to estimate the mean daily amount of GST collected by all dry cleaning outlets if the amounts are known to be normally distributed with a standard deviation of $5. Determine the 90% confidence interval estimate.

Solution:

First enter the data into **List 1**

Now, from the **Main Menu** select:

STAT F4(INTR) **F1**(Z) **F1**(1-S)   then enter the following items:

1-Sample ZInterval

Data	: **F1**(List)	▼
C-Level	: **.90**	**EXE**
σ	: **5**	**EXE**
List	: **List1**	**EXE (Press F1 and answer the question)**
Freq	: **1 (F1)**	**EXE (Note: If the data given is a weighted data, then enter the weight values in a list, in that case you would select list(F2)**

Save Res   : None

Now key **EXE** or **F1**(Calc)

The calculator will now show the results:

1-Sample ZInterval

Left	=64.0922821
Right	=69.9077179
$\bar{x}$	=67
Sx	=9.13392421
n	=8

This shows that the 90% confidence interval estimate for the population mean is $64.09 to $69.91. This shows the numerical result only. You must remember to write up the complete answer as shown in class.

EXAMPLE 9.14   **1-Sample t Interval** (Using sample statistics)

Management at a bank wish to estimate the mean amount of time customers spend at the automated teller machine (ATM). They believe the times to be normally distributed. A random sample of 20 customers has been selected and the sample mean time was 255 seconds with a standard deviation of 33 seconds. Construct a 95% confidence interval estimate for the mean time at the ATM machine per customer.

Solution: From the **Main Menu** select:

STAT   F4(INTR)   **F2**(t)   **F1**(1-S)   then enter the following items:

(Note: Only use the **EXE** key after a new data entry. Otherwise, use the cursor ▼ arrow. If you accidentally hit the wrong key, use **AC/ON** or **EXIT** to go back.)

1-Sample tInterval

Data	: **F2**(Var)	▼
C-Level	: **0.95**	**EXE**
$\bar{x}$	: **255**	**EXE**
sx	: **33**	**EXE**
n	: **20**	**EXE**

Save Res   : None

Now key **EXE** or **F1**(Calc)

The calculator will now show the results:

1-Sample tInterval

Left	=239.555525
Right	=270.444475
$\bar{x}$	=255
Sx	=33
n	=20

This shows that the 95% confidence interval estimate for the population mean is 240 to 270 sec. This shows the numerical result only. You must remember to write up the complete answer as shown in class.

EXAMPLE 9.15

1-Sample t Interval (Using raw data)

A random survey of 8 dry-cleaning outlets indicated that the amount of GST collected from each outlet on the previous day was: $70, 65, 76, 53, 75, 71, 59 and $67. Use this information to estimate the mean daily amount of GST collected by all dry cleaning outlets if the amounts are known to be normally distributed. Determine the 90% confidence interval estimate.

Solution:

First enter the data into **List 1**

Now, from the **Main Menu** select:

STAT   F4(INTR)   **F2**(t)   **F1**(1-S)   then enter the following items:

1-Sample tInterval
Data   : **F1**(List)   ▼
C-Level   : **0.90**   **EXE**
List   : **List1**   ▼
Freq   : **1**   **EXE**
Save Res   : None

Now key **EXE** or **F1**(Calc)

The calculator will now show the results:

1-Sample tInterval
  Left   =60.8817807
  Right   =73.1182193
  $\bar{x}$ =67
  sx   =9.13392421
  n   =8

This shows that the 90% confidence interval estimate for the population mean is $60.88 to $73.12. This shows the numerical result only. You must remember to write up the complete answer as shown in class.

EXAMPLE 9.16

1-Proportion Z Interval

A bank manager wants to estimate the proportion of all the bank's customers who use the ATM to pay bills. A random sample of 80 customers has been selected and it was found that 43 of them use the ATM to pay bills. Determine the 99% confidence interval estimate for the proportion of all the bank's customers who use the ATM to pay bills.

Solution: From the **Main Menu** select:

STAT   F4(INTR)   **F1**(Z)   **F3**(1-P)   then enter the following items:

1-Prop ZInterval
C-Level   : **0.99** **EXE**
x   : **43**   **EXE**
n   : **80**   **EXE**
Save Res   : None

Now key **EXE** or **F1**(Calc)

The calculator will now show the results:

1-Prop ZInterval

Left	=0.39391231
Right	=0.68108768
$\hat{p}$	=0.5375
n	=80

This shows that the 99% confidence interval estimate for the population proportion is 0.394 to 0.681. This shows the numerical result only. You must remember to write up the complete answer as shown in class.

Using Microsoft Excel for Confidence Interval Estimation

E9.1 Computing the Confidence Interval Estimate for the Mean (σ Known)

You compute the confidence interval estimate for the mean (σ known) by making entries in the **CIE_SK** worksheet of the **CIE sigma known.xls** workbook. This worksheet uses the **NORMSINV($P < X$)** and **CONFIDENCE(1-*confidence level, population standard deviation, sample size*)** functions to compute the Z value and interval half width for the Example 9.1 mean paper length problem. To adapt this worksheet to other problems, change the population standard deviation, sample mean, sample size, and confidence level values in the tinted cells B4 through B7, and enter a new title in cell A1.

E9.2 Computing the Confidence Interval Estimate for the Mean (σ Unknown)

You compute the confidence interval estimate for the mean (σ unknown) by making entries in the **CIE_SU** worksheet of the **CIE sigma unknown.xls** workbook. The worksheet (see Figure 9.7) uses the **TINV(1-*confidence level, degrees of freedom*)** function to determine the critical value from the t distribution and compute the interval half width for the Section 9.2 Saxon Home Improvement Company example. To adapt this worksheet to other problems, change the sample statistics and confidence level values in the tinted cells B4 through B7, and enter a new title in cell A1.

E9.3 Computing the Confidence Interval Estimate for the Proportion

You compute the confidence interval estimate for the proportion by making entries in the **CIE_P** worksheet of the **CIE Proportion.xls** workbook. The worksheet (see Figure 9.12) uses the **NORMSINV($P < X$)** function to determine

the Z value and uses the square root function to compute the standard error of the proportion for the Section 9.3 Saxon Home Improvement Company example. To adapt this worksheet to other problems, change the sample size, number of successes, and confidence level values in the tinted cells B4, B5, and B6, and enter a new title in cell A1.

E9.4 Computing the Sample Size Needed for Estimating the Mean

You compute the sample size needed for estimating the mean by making entries in the **SampleSize_M** worksheet of the **Sample Size Mean.xls** workbook. The worksheet (see Figure 9.14) uses the **NORMSINV($P < X$)** function to compute the Z value and uses the **ROUNDUP(*value*)** function to round up the sample size needed to the next higher integer for the Section 9.4 Saxon Home Improvement Company example. To adapt this worksheet to other problems, change the population standard deviation, sampling error, and confidence level values in the tinted cells B4, B5, and B6, and enter a new title in cell A1.

E9.5 Computing the Sample Size Needed for Estimating the Proportion

You compute the sample size needed for estimating the proportion by making entries in the **SampleSize_P** worksheet of the **Sample Size Proportion.xls** workbook. The worksheet (see Figure 9.15) uses the **ROUNDUP(*value*)** function to round up the sample size needed to the next higher integer for the Section 9.4 Saxon Home Improvement Company example. To adapt this worksheet to other problems, change the estimate of true proportion, sampling error, and confidence level values in the tinted cells B4 through B6, and enter a new title in cell A1.

10 Fundamentals of Hypothesis Testing: One-Sample Tests

Learning Objectives

In this chapter, you learn:

- The basic principles of hypothesis testing
- How to use hypothesis testing to test a mean or proportion
- The assumptions of each hypothesis-testing procedure, how to evaluate them, and the consequences if they are seriously violated
- How to avoid the pitfalls involved in hypothesis testing
- Ethical issues involved in hypothesis testing

@ Oxford Cereals, Part II

As in Chapter 7, you again find yourself as plant operations manager for Oxford Cereals. You are responsible for monitoring the amount in each cereal box filled. Company specifications require a mean weight of 368 grams per box. It is your responsibility to adjust the process when the mean fill weight in the population of boxes differs from 368 grams. How can you rationally make the decision whether or not to adjust the process when it is impossible to weigh every single box as it is being filled? You begin by selecting and weighing a random sample of 25 cereal boxes. After computing a sample mean, how do you proceed?

I n Chapter 7, you learned methods to determine whether a sample mean is consistent with a known population mean. In this Oxford Cereals scenario, you seek to use a sample mean to validate a claim about the population mean, a somewhat different problem. For this type of problem, you use an inferential method called **hypothesis testing**. Hypothesis testing requires that you state a claim unambiguously. In this scenario, the claim is that the population mean is 368 grams. You examine a sample statistic to see if it better supports the stated claim, called the *null hypothesis*, or the mutually exclusive alternative (for this scenario, that the population mean is not 368 grams).

In this chapter, you will learn several applications of hypothesis testing. You will learn how to make inferences about a population parameter by *analyzing differences* between the results observed, the sample statistic, and the results you would expect to get if an underlying hypothesis were actually true. For the Oxford Cereals scenario, hypothesis testing would allow you to infer one of the following:

- The mean weight of the cereal boxes in the sample is a value consistent with what you would expect if the mean of the entire population of cereal boxes is 368 grams.
- The population mean is not equal to 368 grams because the sample mean is significantly different from 368 grams.

10.1 Fundamentals of Hypothesis-Testing Methodology

Hypothesis testing typically begins with some theory, claim, or assertion about a particular parameter of a population. For example, your initial hypothesis about the cereal example is that the process is working properly, so the mean fill is 368 grams, and no corrective action is needed.

The Null and Alternative Hypotheses

The hypothesis that the population parameter is equal to the company specification is referred to as the null hypothesis. A **null hypothesis** is always one of status quo and is identified by the symbol H_0. Here the null hypothesis is that the filling process is working properly, and therefore the mean fill is the 368-gram specification provided by Oxford Cereals. This is stated as

$$H_0: \mu = 368$$

Even though information is available only from the sample, the null hypothesis is written in terms of the population. Remember, your focus is on the population of all cereal boxes. The sample statistic is used to make inferences about the entire filling process. One inference may be that the results observed from the sample data indicate that the null hypothesis is false. If the null hypothesis is considered false, something else must be true.

Whenever a null hypothesis is specified, an alternative hypothesis is also specified, and it must be true if the null hypothesis is false. The **alternative hypothesis**, H_1, is the opposite of the null hypothesis, H_0. This is stated in the cereal example as

$$H_1: \mu \neq 368$$

The alternative hypothesis represents the conclusion reached by rejecting the null hypothesis. The null hypothesis is rejected when there is sufficient evidence from the sample information that the null hypothesis is false. In the cereal example, if the weights of the sampled boxes are sufficiently above or below the expected 368-gram mean specified by Oxford Cereals, you reject the null hypothesis in favor of the alternative hypothesis that the mean fill is different from 368 grams. You stop production and take whatever action is necessary to correct the problem. If the null hypothesis is not rejected, you should continue to believe in the status quo, that the process is working correctly and therefore no corrective action is necessary. In this second circumstance, you have not proven that the process is working correctly. Rather, you have failed to prove that it is working incorrectly, and therefore you continue your belief (although unproven) in the null hypothesis.

In hypothesis testing, you reject the null hypothesis when the sample evidence suggests that it is far more likely that the alternative hypothesis is true. However, failure to reject the null hypothesis is not proof that it is true. You can never prove that the null hypothesis is correct because the decision is based only on the sample information, not on the entire population. Therefore, if you fail to reject the null hypothesis, you can only conclude that there is insufficient evidence to warrant its rejection. The following key points summarize the null and alternative hypotheses:

- The null hypothesis, H_0, represents the status quo or the current belief in a situation.
- The alternative hypothesis, H_1, is the opposite of the null hypothesis and represents a research claim or specific inference you would like to prove.
- If you reject the null hypothesis, you have statistical proof that the alternative hypothesis is correct.
- If you do not reject the null hypothesis, you have failed to prove the alternative hypothesis. The failure to prove the alternative hypothesis, however, does not mean that you have proven the null hypothesis.
- The null hypothesis, H_0, always refers to a specified value of the population parameter (such as μ), not a sample statistic (such as $\overline{X}$).
- The statement of the null hypothesis always contains an equal sign regarding the specified value of the population parameter (e.g., $H_0: \mu = 368$ grams).
- The statement of the alternative hypothesis never contains an equal sign regarding the specified value of the population parameter (e.g., $H_1: \mu \neq 368$ grams).

EXAMPLE 10.1

The Null and Alternative Hypotheses

You are the manager of a fast-food restaurant. You want to determine whether the waiting time to place an order has changed in the past month from its previous population mean value of 4.5 minutes. State the null and alternative hypotheses.

SOLUTION The null hypothesis is that the population mean has not changed from its previous value of 4.5 minutes. This is stated as

$$H_0: \mu = 4.5$$

The alternative hypothesis is the opposite of the null hypothesis. Because the null hypothesis is that the population mean is 4.5 minutes, the alternative hypothesis is that the population mean is not 4.5 minutes. This is stated as

$$H_1: \mu \neq 4.5$$

The Critical Value of the Test Statistic

The logic of hypothesis testing involves determining how likely the null hypothesis is to be true by considering the information gathered in a sample. In the Oxford Cereal Company scenario, the null hypothesis is that the mean amount of cereal per box in the entire filling process is 368 grams (the population parameter specified by the company). You select a sample of boxes from the filling process, weigh each box, and compute the sample mean. This statistic is an estimate of the corresponding parameter (the population mean, μ). Even if the null hypothesis is true, the statistic (the sample mean, $\overline{X}$) is likely to differ from the value of the parameter (the population mean, μ) because of variation due to sampling. However, you expect the sample statistic to be close to the population parameter if the null hypothesis is true. If the sample statistic is close to the population parameter, you have insufficient evidence to reject the null hypothesis. For example, if the sample mean is 367.9, you conclude that the population mean has not changed (i.e., $\mu = 368$) because a sample mean of 367.9 is very close to the hypothesized value of 368. Intuitively, you think that it is likely that you could get a sample mean of 367.9 from a population whose mean is 368.

However, if there is a large difference between the value of the statistic and the hypothesized value of the population parameter, you conclude that the null hypothesis is false. For example, if the sample mean is 320, you conclude that the population mean is not 368 (i.e., $\mu \neq 368$), because the sample mean is very far from the hypothesized value of 368. In such a case, you conclude that it is very unlikely to get a sample mean of 320 if the population mean is really 368. Therefore, it is more logical to conclude that the population mean is not equal to 368. Here you reject the null hypothesis.

Unfortunately, the decision-making process is not always so clear-cut. Determining what is "very close" and what is "very different" is arbitrary without clear definitions. Hypothesis-testing methodology provides clear definitions for evaluating differences. Furthermore, it enables you to quantify the decision-making process by computing the probability of getting a given sample result if the null hypothesis is true. You calculate this probability by determining the sampling distribution for the sample statistic of interest (e.g., the sample mean) and then computing the particular **test statistic** based on the given sample result. Because the sampling distribution for the test statistic often follows a well-known statistical distribution, such as the standardized normal distribution or t distribution, you can use these distributions to help determine whether the null hypothesis is true.

Regions of Rejection and Nonrejection

The sampling distribution of the test statistic is divided into two regions, a **region of rejection** (sometimes called the critical region) and a **region of nonrejection** (see Figure 10.1). If the test statistic falls into the region of nonrejection, you do not reject the null hypothesis. In the Oxford Cereals scenario, you conclude that there is insufficient evidence that the population mean fill is different from 368 grams. If the test statistic falls into the rejection region, you reject the null hypothesis. In this case, you conclude that the population mean is not 368 grams.

FIGURE 10.1

Regions of rejection and nonrejection in hypothesis testing

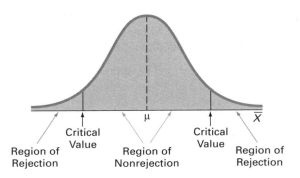

The region of rejection consists of the values of the test statistic that are unlikely to occur if the null hypothesis is true. These values are much more likely to occur if the null hypothesis is false. Therefore, if a value of the test statistic falls into this *rejection region*, you reject the null hypothesis because that value is unlikely if the null hypothesis is true.

To make a decision concerning the null hypothesis, you first determine the **critical value** of the test statistic. The critical value divides the nonrejection region from the rejection region. Determining this critical value depends on the size of the rejection region. The size of the rejection region is directly related to the risks involved in using only sample evidence to make decisions about a population parameter.

Risks in Decision Making Using Hypothesis Testing

When using a sample statistic to make decisions about a population parameter, there is a risk that you will reach an incorrect conclusion. You can make two different types of errors when applying hypothesis testing, Type I and Type II errors.

A **Type I error** occurs if you reject the null hypothesis, H_0, when it is true and should not be rejected. The probability of a Type I error occurring is α.
A **Type II error** occurs if you do not reject the null hypothesis, H_0, when it is false and should be rejected. The probability of a Type II error occurring is β.

In the Oxford Cereals scenario, you make a Type I error if you conclude that the population mean fill is *not* 368 when it *is* 368. This error causes you to adjust the filling process even though the process is working properly. Thus, a Type I error is a "false alarm." You make a Type II error if you conclude that the population mean fill *is* 368 when it is *not* 368. Here, you would allow the process to continue without adjustment even though adjustments are needed. Thus, a Type II error represents a "missed opportunity."

The Level of Significance (α) The probability of committing a Type I error, denoted by α (the lowercase Greek letter *alpha*), is referred to as the **level of significance** of the statistical test. Traditionally, you control the Type I error by deciding the risk level, α, that you are willing to have of rejecting the null hypothesis when it is true. Because you specify the level of significance before the hypothesis test is performed, the risk of committing a Type I error, α, is directly under your control. Traditionally, you select levels of 0.01, 0.05, or 0.10. The choice of a particular risk level for making a Type I error depends on the cost of making a Type I error. After you specify the value for α, you can then determine the critical values that divide the rejection and nonrejection regions. You know the size of the rejection region because α is the probability of rejection when the null hypothesis is true. From this, you can then determine the critical value or values that divide the rejection and nonrejection regions.

The Confidence Coefficient The complement of the probability of a Type I error, $(1 - \alpha)$, is called the confidence coefficient. When multiplied by 100%, the confidence coefficient yields the confidence level that was studied when constructing confidence intervals (see Section 9.1).

> The **confidence coefficient**, $(1 - \alpha)$, is the probability that you will not reject the null hypothesis, H_0, when it is true and should not be rejected. The **confidence level** of a hypothesis test is $(1 - \alpha) \times 100\%$.

In terms of hypothesis testing, the confidence coefficient represents the probability of concluding that the value of the parameter as specified in the null hypothesis is plausible when it is true. In the Oxford Cereals scenario, the confidence coefficient measures the probability of concluding that the population mean fill is 368 grams when it is actually 368 grams.

The β Risk The probability of committing a Type II error is denoted by β (the lowercase Greek letter *beta*). Unlike a Type I error, which you control by the selection of α, the probability of making a Type II error depends on the difference between the hypothesized and actual values of the population parameter. Because large differences are easier to find than small ones, if the difference between the hypothesized and actual value of the population parameter is large, β is small. For example, if the population mean is 330 grams, there is a small chance (β) that you will conclude that the mean has not changed from 368. However, if the difference between the hypothesized and actual values of the parameter is small, β is large. For example, if the population mean is actually 367 grams, there is a large chance (β) that you will conclude that the mean is still 368 grams.

The Power of a Test The complement of the probability of a Type II error, $(1 - \beta)$, is called the power of a statistical test.

> The **power of a statistical test**, $(1 - \beta)$, is the probability that you will reject the null hypothesis when it is false and should be rejected.

In the Oxford Cereals scenario, the power of the test is the probability that you will correctly conclude that the mean fill amount is not 368 grams when it actually is not 368 grams.

Risks in Decision Making: A Delicate Balance Table 10.1 illustrates the results of the two possible decisions (do not reject H_0 or reject H_0) that you can make in any hypothesis test. You can make a correct decision or make one of two types of errors.

TABLE 10.1

Hypothesis Testing and Decision Making

	Actual Situation	
Statistical Decision	**H_0 True**	**H_0 False**
Do not reject H_0	Correct decision Confidence $= (1 - \alpha)$	Type II error $P(\text{Type II error}) = \beta$
Reject H_0	Type I error $P(\text{Type I error}) = \alpha$	Correct decision Power $= (1 - \beta)$

One way to reduce the probability of making a Type II error is by increasing the sample size. Large samples generally permit you to detect even very small differences between the hypothesized values and the actual population parameters. For a given level of α, increasing the sample size decreases β and therefore increases the power of the test to detect that the null hypothesis, H_0, is false. However, there is always a limit to your resources, and this affects the decision as to how large a sample you can take. Thus, for a given sample size, you must consider the trade-offs between the two possible types of errors. Because you can directly control the risk of Type I error, you can reduce this risk by selecting a smaller value for α. For example, if the negative consequences associated with making a Type I error are substantial, you could select $\alpha = 0.01$ instead of 0.05. However, when you decrease α, you increase β, so reducing the risk of a Type I error results in an increased risk of a Type II error. However, if you wish to reduce β, you could select a larger value for α. Therefore, if it is important to try to avoid a Type II error, you can select α of 0.05 or 0.10 instead of 0.01.

In the Oxford Cereals scenario, the risk of a Type I error involves concluding that the mean fill amount has changed from the hypothesized 368 grams when it actually has not changed. The risk of a Type II error involves concluding that the mean fill amount has not changed from the hypothesized 368 grams when it actually has changed. The choice of reasonable values for α and β depends on the costs inherent in each type of error. For example, if it is very costly to change the cereal-fill process, you would want to be very confident that a change is needed before making any changes. In this case, the risk of a Type I error is more important, and you would choose a small α. However, if you want to be very certain of detecting changes from a mean of 368 grams, the risk of a Type II error is more important, and you would choose a higher level of α.

10.2 Z Test of Hypothesis for the Mean (σ Known)

Now that you have been introduced to hypothesis testing, recall that in the Using Statistics scenario on page 401, Oxford Cereals wants to determine whether the cereal-fill process is working properly (i.e., whether the mean fill throughout the entire packaging process remains at the specified 368 grams, and no corrective action is needed). To evaluate the 368-gram requirement, you take a random sample of 25 boxes, weigh each box, and then evaluate the difference between the sample statistic and the hypothesized population parameter by comparing the mean weight (in grams) from the sample to the expected mean of 368 grams specified by the company. The null and alternative hypotheses are

$$H_0: \mu = 368$$

$$H_1: \mu \neq 368$$

When the standard deviation, σ, is known (which rarely occurs), you use the **Z test for the mean** if the population is normally distributed. If the population is not normally distributed, you can still use the Z test if the sample size is large enough for the Central Limit Theorem to take effect (see Section 7.4). Equation (10.1) defines the Z_{STAT} test statistic for determining the difference between the sample mean, $\overline{X}$, and the population mean, μ, when the standard deviation, σ, is known.

Z TEST FOR THE MEAN (σ KNOWN)

$$Z_{STAT} = \frac{\overline{X} - \mu}{\dfrac{\sigma}{\sqrt{n}}}$$

(10.1)

In Equation (10.1), the numerator measures the difference between the observed sample mean, $\overline{X}$, and the hypothesized mean, μ. The denominator is the standard error of the mean, so Z_{STAT} represents the difference between $\overline{X}$ and μ in standard error units.

The Critical Value Approach to Hypothesis Testing

In the critical value approach to hypothesis testing, the observed value of the Z_{STAT} test statistic from Equation (10.1) is compared to critical values. The critical values are expressed as standardized *Z* values (i.e., in standard error units). For example, if you use a level of significance of 0.05, the size of the rejection region is 0.05. Because the rejection region is divided into the two tails of the distribution (this is called a **two-tail test**), you divide the 0.05 into two equal parts of 0.025 each. A rejection region of 0.025 in each tail of the normal distribution results in a cumulative area of 0.025 below the lower critical value and a cumulative area of 0.975 below the upper critical value (i.e., an area of 0.025 in the upper tail). According to the cumulative standardized normal distribution table (Table E.2), the critical values that divide the rejection and nonrejection regions are −1.96 and +1.96. Figure 10.2 illustrates that if the mean is actually 368 grams, as H_0 claims, the values of the Z_{STAT} test statistic have a standardized normal distribution centered at $Z = 0$ (which corresponds to an $\overline{X}$ value of 368 grams). Values of Z_{STAT} greater than +1.96 or less than −1.96 indicate that $\overline{X}$ is sufficiently different from the hypothesized $\mu = 368$ that it is unlikely that such an $\overline{X}$ value would occur if H_0 were true.

FIGURE 10.2

Testing a hypothesis about the mean (σ known) at the 0.05 level of significance

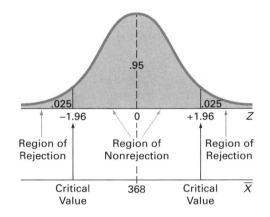

Therefore, the decision rule is

Reject H_0 if $Z_{STAT} > +1.96$

or if $Z_{STAT} < -1.96$;

otherwise, do not reject H_0.

Suppose that the sample of 25 cereal boxes indicates a sample mean, $\overline{X}$, of 372.5 grams, and the population standard deviation, σ, is 15 grams. Using Equation (10.1),

$$Z_{STAT} = \frac{\overline{X} - \mu}{\dfrac{\sigma}{\sqrt{n}}} = \frac{372.5 - 368}{\dfrac{15}{\sqrt{25}}} = +1.50$$

Because $Z_{STAT} = +1.50$ is between −1.96 and +1.96, you do not reject H_0 (see Figure 10.3). You continue to believe that the mean fill amount is 368 grams. To take into account the possibility of a Type II error, you state the conclusion as "there is insufficient evidence that the mean fill is different from 368 grams."

FIGURE 10.3

Testing a hypothesis about the mean cereal weight (σ known) at the 0.05 level of significance

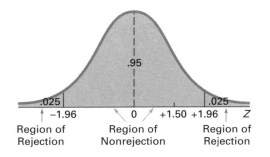

Exhibit 10.1 provides a summary of the critical value approach to hypothesis testing.

EXHIBIT 10.1 THE SIX-STEP METHOD OF HYPOTHESIS TESTING

1. State the null hypothesis, H_0, and the alternative hypothesis, H_1.
2. Choose the level of significance, α, and the sample size, n. The level of significance is based on the relative importance of the risks of committing Type I and Type II errors in the problem.
3. Determine the appropriate test statistic and sampling distribution.
4. Determine the critical values that divide the rejection and nonrejection regions.
5. Collect the sample data and compute the value of the test statistic.
6. Make the statistical decision and state the managerial conclusion. If the test statistic falls into the nonrejection region, you do not reject the null hypothesis. If the test statistic falls into the rejection region, you reject the null hypothesis. The managerial conclusion is written in the context of the real-world problem.

EXAMPLE 10.2

Applying the Six-Step Method of Hypothesis Testing at Oxford Cereals

State the six-step method of hypothesis testing at Oxford Cereals.

SOLUTION

Step 1: State the null and alternative hypotheses. The null hypothesis, H_0, is always stated as a mathematical expression using population parameters. In testing whether the mean fill is 368 grams, the null hypothesis states that μ equals 368. The alternative hypothesis, H_1, is also stated as a mathematical expression using population parameters. Therefore, the alternative hypothesis states that μ is not equal to 368 grams.

Step 2: Choose the level of significance and the sample size. You choose the level of significance, α, according to the relative importance of the risks of committing Type I and Type II errors in the problem. The smaller the value of α, the less risk there is of making a Type I error. In this example, making a Type I error means that you conclude that the population mean is not 368 grams when it is 368 grams. Thus, you will take corrective action on the filling process even though the process is working properly. Here, $\alpha = 0.05$ is selected. The sample size, n, is 25.

Step 3: Select the appropriate test statistic. Because σ is known from information about the filling process, you use the normal distribution and the Z_{STAT} test statistic.

Step 4: Determine the rejection region. Critical values for the appropriate test statistic are selected so that the rejection region contains a total area of α when H_0 is true and the nonrejection region contains a total area of $1 - \alpha$ when H_0 is true. Because $\alpha = 0.05$ in the cereal example, the critical values of the Z_{STAT} test statistic are -1.96 and $+1.96$. The rejection region is therefore $Z_{STAT} < -1.96$ or $Z_{STAT} > +1.96$. The nonrejection region is $-1.96 \leq Z_{STAT} \leq +1.96$.

Step 5: Collect the sample data and compute the value of the test statistic. In the cereal example, $\overline{X} = 372.5$, and the value of the test statistic is $Z_{STAT} = +1.50$.

Step 6: State the statistical decision and the managerial conclusion. First, determine whether the test statistic has fallen into the rejection region or the nonrejection region. For the cereal example, $Z_{STAT} = +1.50$ is in the region of nonrejection because $-1.96 \leq Z_{STAT} = +1.50 \leq +1.96$. Because the test statistic falls into the nonrejection region, the statistical decision is to not reject the null hypothesis, H_0. The managerial conclusion is that insufficient evidence exists to prove that the mean fill is different from 368 grams. No corrective action on the filling process is needed.

EXAMPLE 10.3

Testing and Rejecting a Null Hypothesis

You are the manager of a fast-food restaurant. You want to determine whether the population mean waiting time to place an order has changed in the past month from its previous population mean value of 4.5 minutes. From past experience, you can assume that the population is normally distributed with a population standard deviation of 1.2 minutes. You select a sample of 25 orders during a one-hour period. The sample mean is 5.1 minutes. Use the six-step approach listed in Exhibit 10.1 on page 408 to determine whether there is evidence at the 0.05 level of significance that the population mean waiting time to place an order has changed in the past month from its previous population mean value of 4.5 minutes.

SOLUTION

Step 1: The null hypothesis is that the population mean has not changed from its previous value of 4.5 minutes:

$$H_0: \mu = 4.5$$

The alternative hypothesis is the opposite of the null hypothesis. Because the null hypothesis is that the population mean is 4.5 minutes, the alternative hypothesis is that the population mean is not 4.5 minutes:

$$H_1: \mu \neq 4.5$$

Step 2: You have selected a sample of $n = 25$. The level of significance is 0.05 (i.e., $\alpha = 0.05$).

Step 3: Because σ is assumed known, you use the normal distribution and the Z_{STAT} test statistic.

Step 4: Because $\alpha = 0.05$, the critical values of the Z_{STAT} test statistic are -1.96 and $+1.96$. The rejection region is $Z_{STAT} < -1.96$ or $Z_{STAT} > +1.96$. The nonrejection region is $-1.96 \leq Z_{STAT} \leq +1.96$

Step 5: You collect the sample data and compute $\overline{X} = 5.1$. Using Equation (10.1) on page 407, you compute the test statistic:

$$Z_{STAT} = \frac{\overline{X} - \mu}{\dfrac{\sigma}{\sqrt{n}}} = \frac{5.1 - 4.5}{\dfrac{1.2}{\sqrt{25}}} = +2.50$$

Step 6: Because $Z_{STAT} = +2.50 > +1.96$, you reject the null hypothesis. You conclude that there is evidence that the population mean waiting time to place an order has changed from its previous value of 4.5 minutes. The mean waiting time for customers is longer now than it was last month.

The *p*-Value Approach to Hypothesis Testing

Most software packages, including Microsoft Excel and SPSS, compute the *p*-value when performing a test of hypothesis.

The ***p*-value** is the probability of getting a test statistic equal to or more extreme than the sample result, given that the null hypothesis, H_0, is true. The *p*-value is often referred to as the *observed level of significance*.

The decision rules for rejecting H_0 in the *p*-value approach are

- If the *p*-value is greater than or equal to α, do not reject the null hypothesis.
- If the *p*-value is less than α, reject the null hypothesis.

Many people confuse these rules, mistakenly believing that a high *p*-value is grounds for rejection. You can avoid this confusion by remembering the following mantra:

If the *p*-value is low, then reject H_0.

To understand the *p*-value approach, consider the Oxford Cereals scenario. You tested whether the mean fill was equal to 368 grams. The test statistic resulted in a Z_{STAT} value of $+1.50$, and you did not reject the null hypothesis because $+1.50$ was less than the upper critical value of $+1.96$ and more than the lower critical value of -1.96.

To use the *p*-value approach for the *two-tail test*, you find the probability of getting a test statistic Z_{STAT} that is equal to or *more extreme than* 1.50 standard error units from the center of a standardized normal distribution. In other words, you need to compute the probability of a Z_{STAT} value greater than $+1.50$, along with the probability of a Z_{STAT} value less than -1.50. Table E.2 shows that the probability of a Z_{STAT} value below -1.50 is 0.0668. The probability of a value below $+1.50$ is 0.9332, and the probability of a value above $+1.50$ is $1 - 0.9332 = 0.0668$. Therefore, the *p*-value for this two-tail test is $0.0668 + 0.0668 = 0.1336$ (see Figure 10.4). Thus, the probability of a test statistic equal to or more extreme than the sample result is 0.1336. Because 0.1336 is greater than $\alpha = 0.05$, you do not reject the null hypothesis.

FIGURE 10.4

Finding a *p*-value for a two-tail test

In this example, the observed sample mean is 372.5 grams, 4.5 grams above the hypothesized value, and the *p*-value is 0.1336. Thus, if the population mean is 368 grams, there is a 13.36% chance that the sample mean differs from 368 grams by at least 4.5 grams (i.e., is ≥ 372.5 grams or ≤ 363.5 grams). Therefore, even though 372.5 is above the hypothesized value of 368, a result as extreme as or more extreme than 372.5 is not highly unlikely when the population mean is 368.

Unless you are dealing with a test statistic that follows the normal distribution, you will only be able to approximate the *p*-value from the tables of the distribution. However, Microsoft Excel and SPSS routinely compute the *p*-values in each hypothesis-testing procedure. Once you under-

FIGURE 10.5

Casio Calculator FX-9750GII results for the cereal-fill example

Cereal-Filling Process Hypothesis Test

From the **Main Menu** select:

STAT   F3(test)   **F1**(Z)   **F1**(1-S)   then enter the following items:

(**Note:** Only use the **EXE** key after a new entry. Otherwise, use the cursor ▼ arrow. If you accidentally hit the wrong key, use **AC/ON** or **EXIT** to go back.)

1-Sample ZTest
Data	: **F2**(Var)	▼
μ	: **F1**($\neq \mu0$)	▼
$\mu0$	: **368**	**EXE**
σ	: **15**	**EXE**
$\bar{x}$	: **372.5**	**EXE**
n	: **25**	**EXE**
Save Res	: None	

Now key **EXE** or **F1**(CALC) or **F6**(DRAW)

If you select **F6**(DRAW), you will see a normal distribution.

If you select either **EXE** or **F1**(Calc), the calculator will now show the results:

1-Sample ZTest

μ $\neq 368$
z $= 1.5$
p $= 0.1336144$
$\bar{x}$ $= 372.5$
n $= 25$

Statistical Decision: Do not reject the null hypothesis.

To find z critical value:

From the **Main Menu** select:

STAT   **F5**(dist)   **F1**(Norm)   **F3**(InvN)   then enter the following items:

Using calculator fx-9750GII	Using calculator fx-9750G Plus
Inverse Normal	**Inverse Normal**
Data : **F2**(Var) ▼	Area : **0.05 ÷ 2** **EXE**
Tail : **F3**(CNTR) ▼	σ : **1** **EXE**
Area : **1–0.05** **EXE**	μ : **0** **EXE**
σ : **1** **EXE**	
μ : **0** **EXE**	Now key **EXE** or **F1**(CALC)
Save Res : **None** **EXE**	
	The calculator will now show the results:
Now key **EXE** or **F1**(CALC)	
	Inverse Normal:
The calculator will now show the results:	**X = −1.959964**
	Note: For this model, when using the
Inverse Normal:	**InvN function, the *Area* value that is**
X₁ Inv = −1.959964	**required is the area to the *LEFT* of the**
X₂ Inv = 1.95996398	**desired X value.**

stand the *p*-value approach, and assuming that you are using software such as Microsoft Excel or SPSS, you can just use the *p*-value approach instead of the critical value approach.

Figure 10.5 shows a Casio calculator worksheet for the cereal-filling example discussed in this section.

Exhibit 10.2 provides a summary of the *p*-value approach for hypothesis testing.

EXHIBIT 10.2 THE FIVE-STEP *p*-VALUE APPROACH TO HYPOTHESIS TESTING

1. State the null hypothesis, H_0, and the alternative hypothesis, H_1.
2. Choose the level of significance, α, and the sample size, n. The level of significance is based on the relative importance of the risks of committing Type I and Type II errors in the problem.
3. Determine the appropriate test statistic and the sampling distribution.
4. Collect the sample data, compute the value of the test statistic, and compute the *p*-value.
5. Make the statistical decision and state the managerial conclusion. If the *p*-value is greater than or equal to α, you do not reject the null hypothesis. If the *p*-value is less than α, you reject the null hypothesis. Remember the mantra: If the *p*-value is low, then H_0 must go. The managerial conclusion is written in the context of the real-world problem.

EXAMPLE 10.4

Testing and Rejecting a Null Hypothesis, Using the *p*-Value Approach

You are the manager of a fast-food restaurant. You want to determine whether the population mean waiting time to place an order has changed in the past month from its previous value of 4.5 minutes. From past experience, you can assume that the population standard deviation is 1.2 minutes. You select a sample of 25 orders during a one-hour period. The sample mean is 5.1 minutes. Use the five-step *p*-value approach of Exhibit 10.2 to determine whether there is evidence that the population mean waiting time to place an order has changed in the past month from its previous population mean value of 4.5 minutes.

SOLUTION

Step 1: The null hypothesis is that the population mean has not changed from its previous value of 4.5 minutes:

$$H_0: \mu = 4.5$$

The alternative hypothesis is the opposite of the null hypothesis. Because the null hypothesis is that the population mean is 4.5 minutes, the alternative hypothesis is that the population mean is not 4.5 minutes:

$$H_1: \mu \neq 4.5$$

Step 2: You have selected a sample of $n = 25$ and you have chosen a 0.05 level of significance (i.e., $\alpha = 0.05$).

Step 3: Select the appropriate test statistic. Because σ is assumed known, you use the normal distribution and the Z_{STAT} test statistic.

Step 4: You collect the data and compute $\overline{X} = 5.1$. Using Equation (10.1) on page 407, you compute the test statistic as follows:

$$Z_{STAT} = \frac{\overline{X} - \mu}{\dfrac{\sigma}{\sqrt{n}}} = \frac{5.1 - 4.5}{\dfrac{1.2}{\sqrt{25}}} = +2.50$$

To find the probability of getting a Z_{STAT} test statistic that is equal to or more extreme than 2.50 standard error units from the center of a standardized normal distribution, you compute the probability of a Z_{STAT} value greater than $+2.50$ along with the probability of a Z_{STAT} value less than -2.50. From Table E.2, the probability of a Z_{STAT} value below -2.50 is 0.0062. The probability of a value below $+2.50$ is 0.9938. Therefore, the probability of a value above $+2.50$ is $1 - 0.9938 = 0.0062$. Thus, the *p*-value for this two-tail test is $0.0062 + 0.0062 = 0.0124$.

Step 5: Because the *p*-value $= 0.0124 < \alpha = 0.05$, you reject the null hypothesis. You conclude that there is evidence that the population mean waiting time to place an order has changed from its previous population mean value of 4.5 minutes. The mean waiting time for customers is longer now than it was last month.

A Connection Between Confidence Interval Estimation and Hypothesis Testing

This chapter and Chapter 9 discuss the two major components of statistical inference: confidence interval estimation and hypothesis testing. Although they are based on the same set of concepts, they are used for different purposes. In Chapter 9, confidence intervals were used to estimate parameters. In this chapter, hypothesis testing is used for making decisions about specified values of population parameters. Hypothesis tests are used when trying to prove that a parameter is less than, more than, or not equal to a specified value. Proper interpretation of a confidence interval, however, can also indicate whether a parameter is less than, more than, or not equal to a specified value. For example, in this section, you tested whether the population mean fill amount was different from 368 grams by using Equation (10.1):

$$Z_{STAT} = \frac{\overline{X} - \mu}{\dfrac{\sigma}{\sqrt{n}}}$$

Instead of testing the null hypothesis that $\mu = 368$ grams, you can reach the same conclusion by constructing a confidence interval estimate of μ. If the hypothesized value of $\mu = 368$ is contained within the interval, you do not reject the null hypothesis because 368 would not be considered an unusual value. However, if the hypothesized value does not fall into the interval, you reject the null hypothesis because "$\mu = 368$ grams" is then considered an unusual value. Using Equation (9.1) on page 363 and the following data:

$$n = 25, \overline{X} = 372.5 \text{ grams}, \sigma = 15 \text{ grams}$$

for a confidence level of 95% (i.e., $\alpha = 0.05$),

$$\overline{X} \pm Z_{\alpha/2} \frac{\sigma}{\sqrt{n}}$$

$$372.5 \pm (1.96)\frac{15}{\sqrt{25}}$$

$$372.5 \pm 5.88$$

so that

$$366.62 \le \mu \le 378.38$$

Because the interval includes the hypothesized value of 368 grams, you do not reject the null hypothesis. There is insufficient evidence that the mean fill amount over the entire filling process is not 368 grams. You reached the same decision by using two-tail hypothesis testing.

Can You Ever *Really* Know Sigma? Part II

This section discussed the fundamentals of hypothesis testing. Just as in Chapter 9 when confidence intervals were developed, using an example in which the population standard deviation σ is known makes it much easier to explain the fundamentals of hypothesis testing. With a known population standard deviation, you can use the normal distribution and compute *p*-values from the tables of the normal distribution.

In virtually all situations, you do not know the standard deviation of the population. If you did, you would also know the population mean and therefore would not need to test a hypothesis about it. So, use this section to understand the fundamentals of hypothesis testing, but don't think that, in practice, you will ever know the population standard deviation σ.

CALCULATOR LESSON 8A

CFX-9850GB CALCULATOR

EXAMPLE 10.5

Lesson 8A—Z-Test of a Single Mean

A company that makes batteries for computers needs to make sure that the voltage of these batteries is not too low or too high. The ideal voltage for the QMS model battery, which is used in many computers, is 5.60 volts. The process that is used to make these batteries is also used to many other models of batteries with different voltages. It is known that the standard deviation of the process is 0.18 volts and that the voltages will fit a normal distribution. The process has just been set up to produce 1 million QMS batteries. Before too many are produced the batteries need to be checked to see if the average voltage is close to 5.60 volts. A sample of 25 QMS batteries is tested and the average voltage was 5.65 volts. Should the process be allowed to continue production of the QMS battery or should it be adjusted? Use a 5% level of significance.

Solution: From the **Main Menu** select:

STAT   F3(test)   **F1**(Z)   **F1**(1-S)   then enter the following items:

(Note: Only use the **EXE** key after a new entry. Otherwise, use the cursor ▼ arrow. If you accidentally hit the wrong key, use **AC/ON** or **EXIT** to go back.)

1-Sample ZTest

Data	: **F2**(Var)	▼
μ	: **F1**($\neq\mu 0$)	▼
$\mu 0$	: **5.60**	**EXE**
σ	: **.18**	**EXE**
$\bar{x}$	: **5.65**	**EXE**
n	: **25**	**EXE**

Now key **EXE** or **F1**(Calc)

The calculator will now show the results:

1-Sample ZTest

μ	$\neq 5.6$
z	$=1.3888$
p	$=0.16486$
x	$=5.65$
n	$=25$

Since the p-value > 0.05, the conclusion is to not reject the null hypothesis. In other words the process does not need to be adjusted.

EXAMPLE 10.6

A company that sells a brand of soft drink with a label of 355 ml. is suspected of cheating its purchasers. The consumers understand that it is not necessary that every can contain 355 ml. but the average should be at least 355 ml. They believe that the average amount in the cans is less than 355 ml. A group of concerned consumers has approached a consumer advocate who has found out that the bottling process that fills this type of can has a standard deviation of 2 ml. and that the volume of soft drink in the cans will fit a normal distribution. To obtain evidence a sample of 4 cases of 24 cans was measured carefully and the mean volume was found to be 354.5 ml. At the 5% level of significance, does this evidence support the claim of the consumers?

Solution: From the **Main Menu** select:

STAT   F3(test)   **F1**(Z)   **F1**(1-S)   then enter the following items:

1-Sample ZTest

Data	: **F2**(Var)	▼
μ	: **F2**($<\mu 0$)	▼
$\mu 0$	: **355**	**EXE**
σ	: **2**	**EXE**
$\bar{x}$	: **354.5**	**EXE**
n	: **96**	**EXE**

Now key **EXE** or **F1**(Calc)

The calculator will now show the results:

1-Sample ZTest

μ   <355
z   = −2.4494
p   =7.1529E-03 (=0.0071529)
$\bar{x}$ =354.5
n   =96

Since the p-value < 0.05, the conclusion is to *reject* the null hypothesis. In other words the evidence supports the consumers claim.

EXAMPLE 10.7   In the past an automobile manufacturer has been using seatbelts that could withstand a breaking force of 1000 kgs. New legislation has dictated that seatbelts should be able to withstand an average of at least 1500 kgs. One supplier has approached the manufacturer with a claim that their seatbelts have an average breaking strength that is significantly higher than 1500 kgs. The standard deviation of their process is known to be 48 kgs. In order to test the claim, the automobile manufacturer has purchased 60 of these seatbelts and has determined that their mean breaking strength is 1517 kgs. At the 1% level of significance, should the auto company accept the seatbelt manufacturer's claim?

Solution: From the **Main Menu** select:

STAT F3(test) **F1**(Z) **F1**(1-S)   then enter the following items:

Data   : **F2**(Var) ▼
μ   : **F3**(>μ0) ▼
μ0   : **1500**   **EXE**
σ   : **48**   **EXE**
$\bar{x}$: **1517**   **EXE**
n   : **60**   **EXE**

Now key **EXE** or **F1**(Calc)

The calculator will now show the results:

1-Sample ZTest

μ   >1500
z   =2.7433
p   =3.0406E-03 (=.0030406)
$\bar{x}$ =1517
n   =60

Since the p-value < 0.01, the conclusion is to *reject* the null hypothesis. In other words the evidence supports the seatbelt manufacturer's claim.

EXAMPLE 10.8   A researcher is asked to test the hypothesis that the average price of a 2-star (CAA rating) motel room has decreased since last year. Last year a study has shown that the prices of all room were normally distributed with an average of $89.50 and a standard deviation of $2.80. A random sample of twelve 2-star motels has yielded the following information on room prices: $85.00, 92.50, 87.50, 89.90, 90.00, 82.50, 87.50, 90.00, 85.00, 89.00, 91.50 and $87.50. If it is believed that the standard deviation of the population of room prices has not changed since last year and the prices are still normally distributed, at the 5% level of significance, what conclusion should the researcher make?

Solution:

First enter the data into **List 1**

Now, from the **Main Menu** select:

STAT F3(test) F1(Z) **F1**(1-S)   then enter the following items:

Data	: **F1**(List)	▼
μ	: **F2**($<μ0$)	▼
μ0	: **89.50**	**EXE**
σ	: **2.80**	**EXE**
List	: **List1**	**EXE**
Freq	: **1**	**EXE**

Now key **EXE** or **F1**(Calc)

The calculator will now show the results:

1-Sample ZTest

μ	<89.5
z	$= -1.6598$
p	$=0.048469$
$\bar{x}$	$=88.158$
xσn-1	$=2.9202$
n	$=12$

Since the p-value < 0.05, the conclusion is to *reject* the null hypothesis. In other words the evidence indicates that the mean price of a 2-star motel room has decreased this year and is lower than last year's mean of $89.50.

CALCULATOR LESSON 8B

CASIO FX-9750GII CALCULATOR

Lesson 8—Z-Test of a Single Mean

EXAMPLE 10.9

A company that makes batteries for computers needs to make sure that the voltage of these batteries is not too low or too high. The ideal voltage for the QMS model battery, which is used in many computers, is 5.60 volts. The process that is used to make these batteries is also used to many other models of batteries with different voltages. It is known that the standard deviation of the process is 0.18 volts and that the voltages will fit a normal distribution. The process has just been set up to produce 1 million QMS batteries. Before too many are produced the batteries need to be checked to see if the average voltage is close to 5.60 volts. A sample of 25 QMS batteries is tested and the average voltage was 5.65 volts. Should the process be allowed to continue production of the QMS battery or should it be adjusted? Use a 5% level of significance.

Solution: From the **Main Menu** select:

STAT **F3**(test) **F1**(Z) **F1**(1-S) then enter the following items:

(Note: Only use the **EXE** key after a new entry. Otherwise, use the cursor ▼ arrow. If you accidentally hit the wrong key, use **AC/ON** or **EXIT** to go back.)

1-Sample ZTest

Data	: **F2**(Var)	▼
μ	: **F1**($≠μ0$)	▼
μ0	: **5.60**	**EXE**
σ	: **0.18**	**EXE**
$\bar{x}$	: **5.65**	**EXE**
n	: **25**	**EXE**
Save Res	: None	

Now key **EXE** or **F1**(Calc) or **F6**(DRAW)

If you select **F6**(DRAW), you will see a normal distribution.

If you select either **EXE** or **F1**(Calc), the calculator will now show the results:

1-Sample ZTest

μ	$\neq 5.6$
z	$=1.3888$
p	$=0.16486$
$\bar{x}$	$=5.65$
n	$=25$

Since the p-value > 0.05, the conclusion is to *not reject* the null hypothesis. In other words the process does not need to be adjusted.

EXAMPLE 10.10   A company that sells a brand of soft drink with a label of 355 ml. is suspected of cheating its purchasers. The consumers understand that it is not necessary that every can contain 355 ml. but the average should be at least 355 ml. They believe that the average amount in the cans is less than 355 ml. A group of concerned consumers has approached a consumer advocate who has found out that the bottling process that fills this type of can has a standard deviation of 2 ml. and that the volume of soft drink in the cans will fit a normal distribution. To obtain evidence a sample of 4 cases of 24 cans was measured carefully and the mean volume was found to be 354.5 ml. At the 5% level of significance, does this evidence support the claim of the consumers?

Solution: From the **Main Menu** select:

STAT **F3**(test) **F1**(Z) **F1**(1-S)   then enter the following items:

1-Sample ZTest

Data	**: F2**(Var)	▼
μ	**: F2**($<\mu 0$)	▼
$\mu 0$	**: 355**	**EXE**
σ	**: 2**	**EXE**
$\bar{x}$	**: 354.5**	**EXE**
n	**: 96**	**EXE**
Save Res	: None	

Now key **EXE** or **F1**(Calc) or **F6**(DRAW)

If you select **F6**(DRAW), you will see a normal distribution.

If you select either **EXE** or **F1**(Calc), the calculator will now show the results:

1-Sample ZTest

μ	<355
z	$=-2.4494$
p	$=7.1529\text{E-}03$ $(=0.0071529)$
$\bar{x}$	$=354.5$
n	$=25$

Since the p-value < 0.05, the conclusion is to *reject* the null hypothesis. In other words the evidence supports the consumers claim.

EXAMPLE 10.11   In the past an automobile manufacturer has been using seatbelts that could withstand a breaking force of 1000 kgs. New legislation has dictated that seatbelts should be able to withstand an average of at least 1500 kgs. One supplier has approached the manufacturer with a claim that their seatbelts have an average breaking strength that is significantly higher than 1500 kgs. The standard deviation of their process is known to be 48 kgs. In order to test the claim, the automobile manufacturer has purchased 60 of these seatbelts and has determined that their mean breaking strength is 1517 kgs. At the 1% level of significance, should the auto company accept the seatbelt manufacturer's claim?

Solution: From the **Main Menu** select:

STAT **F3**(test) **F1**(Z) **F1**(1-S)   then enter the following items:

Data	: F2(Var)	▼
μ	: F3(>μ0)	▼
μ0	: 1500	EXE
σ	: 48	EXE
$\bar{x}$	: 1517	EXE
n	: 60	EXE
Save Res	: None	

Now key **EXE** or **F1**(Calc) or **F6**(DRAW)

If you select **F6**(DRAW), you will see a normal distribution.

If you select either **EXE** or **F1**(Calc), the calculator will now show the results:

1-Sample ZTest

μ	>1500
z	=2.7433
p	=3.0406E-03 (=.0030406)
$\bar{x}$	=1517
n	=60

Since the p-value < 0.01, the conclusion is to *reject* the null hypothesis. In other words the evidence supports the seatbelt manufacturer's claim.

EXAMPLE 10.12   A researcher is asked to test the hypothesis that the average price of a 2-star (CAA rating) motel room has decreased since last year. Last year a study has shown that the prices were normally distributed with an average of $89.50 and a standard deviation of $2.80. A random sample of twelve 2-star motels has yielded the following information on room prices: $85.00, 92.50, 87.50, 89.90, 90.00, 82.50, 87.50, 90.00, 85.00, 89.00, 91.50 and $87.50. If it is believed that the standard deviation of room prices has not changed since last year and the prices are still normally distributed, at the 5% level of significance, what conclusion should the researcher make?

Solution:

First enter the data into **List 1**

Now, from the **Main Menu** select:

STAT F3(test) **F1**(Z) **F1**(1-S)   then enter the following items:

Data	: F1(List)	▼
μ	: F2(<μ0)	▼
μ0	: 89.50	EXE
σ	: 2.80	EXE
List	: List1	EXE
Freq	: 1	EXE
Save Res	: None	

Now key **EXE** or **F1**(Calc) or **F6**(DRAW)

If you select **F6**(DRAW), you will see a normal distribution.

If you select either **EXE** or **F1**(Calc), the calculator will now show the results:

1-Sample ZTest

μ	<89.5
z	= −1.6598
p	=0.048469
$\bar{x}$	=88.158
sx	=2.9202
n	=12

Since the p-value < 0.05, the conclusion is to *reject* the null hypothesis. In other words the evidence indicates that the mean price of a 2-star motel room has decreased this year and is lower than last year's mean of $89.50.

Problems for Section 10.1

LEARNING THE BASICS

10.1 For $H_0: \mu = 100$, $H_1: \mu \neq 100$, and for a sample of size n, why is β larger if the actual value of μ is 90 than if the actual value of μ is 75?

10.2 If you use a 0.05 level of significance in a (two-tail) hypothesis test, what will you decide if $Z_{STAT} = +2.21$?

10.3 If you use a 0.10 level of significance in a (two-tail) hypothesis test, what is your decision rule for rejecting a null hypothesis that the population mean is 500 if you use the *Z* test?

10.4 If you use a 0.01 level of significance in a (two-tail) hypothesis test, what is your decision rule for rejecting $H_0: \mu = 12.5$ if you use the *Z* test?

10.5 What is your decision in Problem 10.4 if $Z_{STAT} = -2.61$?

10.6 What is the *p*-value if, in a two-tail hypothesis test, $Z_{STAT} = +2.00$?

10.7 In Problem 10.6, what is your statistical decision if you test the null hypothesis at the 0.10 level of significance?

10.8 What is the *p*-value if, in a two-tail hypothesis test, $Z_{STAT} = -1.38$?

APPLYING THE CONCEPTS

10.9 In the U.S. legal system, a defendant is presumed innocent until proven guilty. Consider a null hypothesis, H_0, that the defendant is innocent, and an alternative hypothesis, H_1, that the defendant is guilty. A jury has two possible decisions: Convict the defendant (i.e., reject the null hypothesis) or do not convict the defendant (i.e., do not reject the null hypothesis). Explain the meaning of the risks of committing either a Type I or Type II error in this example.

10.10 Suppose the defendant in Problem 10.9 is presumed guilty until proven innocent, as in some other judicial systems. How do the null and alternative hypotheses differ from those in Problem 10.9? What are the meanings of the risks of committing either a Type I or Type II error here?

10.11 The U.S. Food and Drug Administration (FDA) is responsible for approving new drugs. Many consumer groups feel that the approval process is too easy and, therefore, too many drugs are approved that are later found to be unsafe. On the other hand, a number of industry lobbyists are pushing for a more lenient approval process so that pharmaceutical companies can get new drugs approved more easily and quickly (data extracted from R. Sharpe, "FDA Tries to Find Right Balance on Drug Approvals," *The Wall Street Journal*, April 20, 1999, p. A24). Consider a null hypothesis that a new, unapproved drug is unsafe and an alternative hypothesis that a new, unapproved drug is safe.
a. Explain the risks of committing a Type I or Type II error.
b. Which type of error are the consumer groups trying to avoid? Explain.
c. Which type of error are the industry lobbyists trying to avoid? Explain.
d. How would it be possible to lower the chances of both Type I and Type II errors?

SELF Test **10.12** As a result of complaints from both students and faculty about lateness, the registrar at a large university wants to adjust the scheduled class times to allow for adequate travel time between classes and is ready to undertake a study. Until now, the registrar has believed that there should be 20 minutes between scheduled classes. State the null hypothesis, H_0, and the alternative hypothesis, H_1.

10.13 Do students at your school study more, less, or about the same as at other business schools? *Business Week* reported that at the top 50 business schools, students studied an average of 14.6 hours (data extracted from "Cracking the Books," SPECIAL REPORT/Online Extra, **www.businessweek.com**, March 19, 2007). Set up a hypothesis test to try to prove that the mean number of hours studied at your school is different from the 14.6 hour benchmark reported by *Business Week*.
a. State the null and alternative hypotheses.
b. What is a Type I error for your test?
c. What is a Type II error for your test?

10.14 The manager of a paint supply store wants to determine whether the amount of paint contained in 1-gallon cans purchased from a nationally known manufacturer actually averages 1 gallon. State the null and alternative hypotheses.

10.15 The quality control manager at a lightbulb factory needs to determine whether the mean life of a large shipment of lightbulbs is equal to the specified value of 375 hours. State the null and alternative hypotheses.

10.3 *t* Test of Hypothesis for the Mean (σ Unknown)

In virtually all hypothesis-testing situations concerning the population mean, μ, you do not know the population standard deviation, σ. Instead, you use the sample standard deviation, S. If you assume that the population is normally distributed, then the sampling distribution of the mean follows a *t* distribution with $n - 1$ degrees of freedom and you use the **t test for the mean**. If the population is not normally distributed, you can still use the *t* test if the sample size is large enough for the Central Limit Theorem to take effect (see Section 7.4). Equation (10.2) defines the test statistic for determining the difference between the sample mean, $\overline{X}$, and the population mean, μ, when using the sample standard deviation, S.

t TEST OF HYPOTHESIS FOR THE MEAN (σ UNKNOWN)

$$t_{STAT} = \frac{\overline{X} - \mu}{\dfrac{S}{\sqrt{n}}} \qquad (10.2)$$

where the t_{STAT} test statistic follows a *t* distribution having $n - 1$ degrees of freedom.

To illustrate the use of this *t* test, return to the Using Statistics scenario concerning the Saxon Home Improvement company. Over the past five years, the mean amount per sales invoice is $120. As an accountant for the company, you need to inform the finance department if this amount changes. In other words, the hypothesis test is used to try to prove that the mean amount per sales invoice is increasing or decreasing.

The Critical Value Approach

To perform this two-tail hypothesis test, you use the six-step method listed in Exhibit 10.1.

Step 1: $H_0: \mu = \$120$

$H_1: \mu \neq \$120$

The alternative hypothesis contains the statement you are trying to prove. If the null hypothesis is rejected, then there is statistical proof that the population mean amount per sales invoice is no longer $120. If the statistical conclusion is "do not reject H_0," then you will conclude that there is insufficient evidence to prove that the mean amount differs from the long-term mean of $120.

Step 2: You have selected a sample of $n = 12$. You decide to use $\alpha = 0.05$.

Step 3: Because σ is unknown, you use the *t* distribution and the t_{STAT} test statistic. You must assume that the population of sales invoices is normally distributed.

Step 4: For a given sample size, n, the test statistic t_{STAT} follows a *t* distribution with $n - 1$ degrees of freedom. The critical values of the *t* distribution with $12 - 1 = 11$ degrees of freedom are found in Table E.3, as illustrated in Table 10.2 and Figure 10.6. The alternative hypothesis, $H_1: \mu \neq \$120$ is two-tail. Thus, the area in the rejection region of the *t* distribution's left (lower) tail is 0.025, and the area in the rejection region of the *t* distribution's right (upper) tail is also 0.025.

From the *t* table as given in Table E.3, a portion of which is shown in Table 10.2, the critical values are ± 2.2010. The decision rule is

$$\text{Reject } H_0 \text{ if } t_{STAT} < -t_{\alpha/2} = -2.2010$$

$$\text{or if } t_{STAT} > t_{\alpha/2} = +2.2010;$$

$$\text{otherwise, do not reject } H_0.$$

Step 5: A random sample of 12 sales invoices is selected. The dollar amounts for the 12 invoices are given below (and in the file **Invoices**):

| 108.98 | 152.22 | 111.45 | 110.59 | 127.46 | 107.26 |
| 93.32 | 91.97 | 111.56 | 75.71 | 128.58 | 135.11 |

TABLE 10.2

Determining the Critical Value from the *t* Table for an Area of 0.025 in Each Tail with 11 Degrees of Freedom

	Cumulative Probabilities					
	.75	.90	.95	.975	.99	.995
	Upper-Tail Areas					
Degrees of Freedom	.25	.10	.05	.025	.01	.005
1	1.0000	3.0777	6.3138	12.7062	31.8207	63.6574
2	0.8165	1.8856	2.9200	4.3027	6.9646	9.9248
3	0.7649	1.6377	2.3534	3.1824	4.5407	5.8409
4	0.7407	1.5332	2.1318	2.7764	3.7469	4.6041
5	0.7267	1.4759	2.0150	2.5706	3.3649	4.0322
6	0.7176	1.4398	1.9432	2.4469	3.1427	3.7074
7	0.7111	1.4149	1.8946	2.3646	2.9980	3.4995
8	0.7064	1.3968	1.8595	2.3060	2.8965	3.3554
9	0.7027	1.3830	1.8331	2.2622	2.8214	3.2498
10	0.6998	1.3722	1.8125	2.2281	2.7638	3.1693
11	0.6974	1.3634	1.7959	2.2010	2.7181	3.1058

Source: *Extracted from Table E.3.*

FIGURE 10.6

Testing a hypothesis about the mean (σ unknown) at the 0.05 level of significance with 11 degrees of freedom

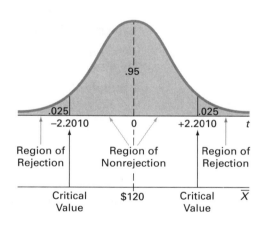

Using Equations (3.1) and (3.5), or Microsoft Excel or Minitab as shown in Figures 10.7 and 10.8,

$$\bar{X} = \frac{\sum\limits_{i=1}^{n} X_i}{n} = \$112.85 \quad \text{and} \quad S = \sqrt{\frac{\sum\limits_{i=1}^{n}(X_i - \bar{X})^2}{n-1}} = \$20.80$$

From Equation (10.2) on page 420,

$$t_{STAT} = \frac{\bar{X} - \mu}{\dfrac{S}{\sqrt{n}}} = \frac{112.85 - 120}{\dfrac{20.80}{\sqrt{12}}} = -1.1908$$

Step 6: Because $-2.2010 < t_{STAT} = -1.1908 < 2.2010$, you do not reject H_0. You have insufficient evidence to conclude that the mean amount per sales invoice differs from

$120. You should inform the finance department that the audit suggests that the mean amount per invoice has not changed.

The *p*-Value Approach

Step 1–3: These steps are the same as in the critical value approach on page 408.

Step 4: From the Casio calculator worksheet of Figure 10.7 or from the Minitab results of Figure 10.8, $t_{STAT} = -1.19$ and the *p*-value $= 0.259$.

FIGURE 10.7

Casio calculator FX 9750GII results for the *t* test of sales invoices

t-Test for the hypothesis of the Mean

From the **Main Menu** select:

STAT   F3(test)   **F2**(t)   **F1**(1-S)   then enter the following items:

(Note: Only use the **EXE** key after a new entry. Otherwise, use the cursor ▼ arrow. If you accidentally hit the wrong key, use **AC/ON** or **EXIT** to go back.)

1-Sample tTest

Data	**: F2**(Var)	▼
μ	**: F1**($\neq$μ0)	▼
μ0	**: 120**	**EXE**
$\bar{x}$	**: 112.85**	**EXE**
sx	**: 20.8**	**EXE**
n	**: 12**	**EXE**
Save Res	: None	

Now key **EXE** or **F1**(CALC) or **F6**(DRAW)

If you select **F6**(DRAW), you will see a normal distribution.

If you select either **EXE** or **F1**(Calc), the calculator will now show the results:

1-Sample tTest

μ	$\neq$ 120
t	$= -1.1907849$
p	$= 0.25880033$
$\bar{x}$	$= 112.85$
n	$= 12$

Statistical Decision: Do not reject the null hypothesis.

To find t critical value:

Two ways of finding the t critical value:

(1)   Using the Casio Calculator fx-9750GII
Note: Fx-9750G Plus does not have this option, therefore you have to use the t-table on page iii.

From the **Main Menu** select:

STAT   F6(DIST)   **F2**(t)   **F3**(Invt)   then enter the following items:

Inverse Student-t

Data	**: F2**(Var)	▼
Area	**: 0.05 $\div$ 2**	
df	**: 12–1**	**EXE**
Save Res	: None	

Now key **EXE** or **F1**(CALC)

The calculator will now show the results:

Inverse Student-t
x-Inv $= 2.20098516$

(2) Using the t table on page iii.

df	0.25	0.1	0.05	0.025	0.01	0.005
	T Table		Upper Tail Areas			
1	1.000	3.078	6.314	12.706	31.821	63.657
2	0.816	1.886	2.920	4.303	6.965	9.925
3	0.765	1.638	2.353	3.182	4.541	5.841
4	0.741	1.533	2.132	2.776	3.747	4.604
5	0.727	1.476	2.015	2.571	3.365	4.032
6	0.718	1.440	1.943	2.447	3.143	3.707
7	0.711	1.415	1.895	2.365	2.998	3.499
8	0.706	1.397	1.860	2.306	2.896	3.355
9	0.703	1.383	1.833	2.262	2.821	3.250
10	0.700	1.372	1.812	2.228	2.764	3.169
11	0.697	1.363	1.796	2.201	2.718	3.106

FIGURE 10.8

Minitab results for the *t* test of sales invoices

```
Test of mu = 120 vs not = 120


Variable   N    Mean   StDev   SE Mean      95% CI         T      P
Amount     12  112.85  20.80    6.00    (99.64, 126.07)  -1.19  0.259
```

Step 5: The Casio calculator results in Figure 10.7 and the Minitab results in Figure 10.8 give the *p*-value for this two-tail test as 0.259. Because the *p*-value of 0.259 is greater than $\alpha = 0.05$, you do not reject H_0. The data provide insufficient evidence to conclude that the mean amount per sales invoice differs from $120. You should inform the finance department that the audit suggests that the mean amount per invoice has not changed. The *p*-value indicates that if the null hypothesis is true, the probability that a sample of 12 invoices could have a sample mean that differs by $7.15 or more from the stated $120 is 0.259. In other words, if the mean amount per sales invoice is truly $120, then there is a 25.9% chance of observing a sample mean below $112.85 or above $127.15.

In the preceding example, it is incorrect to state that there is a 25.9% chance that the null hypothesis is true. This misinterpretation of the *p*-value is sometimes used by those not properly trained in statistics. Remember that the *p*-value is a conditional probability, calculated by *assuming* that the null hypothesis is true. In general, it is proper to state the following:

> If the null hypothesis is true, there is a (*p*-value)*100% chance of observing a test statistic at least as contradictory to the null hypothesis as the sample result.

Checking the Normality Assumption

You use the *t* test when the population standard deviation, σ, is not known and is estimated using the sample standard deviation, *S*. To use the *t* test, you assume that the data represent a random sample from a population that is normally distributed. In practice, as long as the sample size is not very small and the population is not very skewed, the *t* distribution provides a good approximation to the sampling distribution of the mean when σ is unknown.

There are several ways to evaluate the normality assumption necessary for using the *t* test. You can observe how closely the sample statistics match the normal distribution's theoretical properties. You can also use a histogram, stem-and-leaf display, boxplot, or normal probability plot. For details on evaluating normality, see Section 6.3.

Figure 10.9 presents descriptive statistics generated by SPSS. Figure 10.10 is an SPSS boxplot. Figure 10.11 is an SPSS normal probability plot.

FIGURE 10.9

SPSS descriptive statistics for the sales invoice data

SPSS output

Statistics

Sales Invoice		
N	Valid	12
Mean		112.8508
Median		111.0200
Mode		75.71[a]
Std. Deviation		20.79799
Variance		432.556
Skewness		.134
Std. Error of Skewness		.637
Kurtosis		.173
Std. Error of Kurtosis		1.232
Range		76.51
Minimum		75.71
Maximum		152.22
Sum		1354.21
Percentiles	25	96.8050
	50	111.0200
	75	128.3000

a. *Multiple modes exist. The smallest value is shown.*

FIGURE 10.10

SPSS boxplot for the sales invoice data

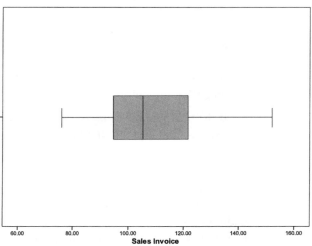

Boxplot of Invoice Amount

FIGURE 10.11

SPSS normal probability plot for the sales invoice data

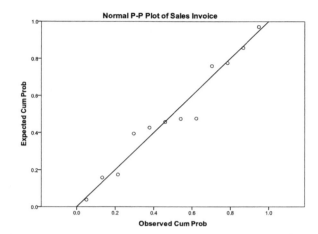

The mean is very close to the median and the points on the normal probability plot appear to be increasing approximately in a straight line. The boxplot appears approximately symmetrical. Thus, you can assume that the population of sales invoices is approximately normally distributed. The normality assumption is valid, and therefore the auditor's results are valid.

The t test is a **robust** test. It does not lose power if the shape of the population departs somewhat from a normal distribution, particularly when the sample size is large enough to enable the test statistic t to be influenced by the Central Limit Theorem (see Section 7.4). However, you can reach erroneous conclusions and can lose statistical power if you use the t test incorrectly. If the sample size, n, is small (i.e., less than 30) and you cannot easily make the assumption that the underlying population is at least approximately normally distributed, then *nonparametric* testing procedures are more appropriate (see references 1 and 2).

CALCULATOR LESSON 9A

CFX-9850GB CALCULATOR

EXAMPLE 10.13

Lesson 9A—t-Test of a Single Mean

A new winter ice-gripping tire has been developed. It will sell in a high price range and it is hoped that the manufacturer can claim that they will last more than 80,000 km on average. The manufacturer is certain that the mileages will be normally distributed. A random sample of 50 tires has been tested and they lasted an average of 81,200 km with a standard deviation of 5,400 km. Use a 5% level of significance.

Solution: From the **Main Menu** select:

STAT   F3(test)   **F2**(t)   **F1**(1-S)   then enter the following items:

(Note: Only use the **EXE** key after a new data entry. Otherwise, use the cursor ▼ arrow. If you accidentally hit the wrong key, use **AC/^{ON}** or **EXIT** to go back.)

1-Sample tTest

Data   : **F2**(Var)   ▼
μ : **F3**(>)   ▼

μ_0	: 80000	EXE
$\bar{x}$	: 81200	EXE
$x\sigma n\text{-}1$	: 5400	EXE
n	: 50	EXE

Now key **EXE** or **F1**(Calc)

The calculator will now show the results:

1-Sample tTest

μ	>80000
t	=1.5713
p	=0.061268
$\bar{x}$	=81200
$x\sigma n\text{-}1$	=5400
n	=50

Since the p-value > 0.05, the conclusion is to *not reject* the null hypothesis. In other words, there is insufficient evidence to indicate that the tires last more then 80,000 km on average.

EXAMPLE 10.14   A researcher is asked to test the hypothesis that the average price of a 2-star (CAA rating) motel room has decreased since last year. Last year a study has shown that the prices were normally distributed with an average of $89.50. A random sample of twelve 2-star motels has yielded the following information on room prices: $85.00, 92.50, 87.50, 89.90, 90.00, 82.50, 87.50, 90.00, 85.00, 89.00, 91.50 and $87.50. If it is believed that the distribution of room prices is normal, at the 5% level of significance, what conclusion should the researcher make?

Solution:

First enter the data into **List 1**

Now, from the **Main Menu** select:

STAT   F3(test)   **F2**(t)   **F1**(1-S)   then enter the following items:

1-Sample tTest

Data	: **F1**(List)	▼
μ	: **F2**(<)	▼
μ_0	: 89.50	EXE
List	: List1	▼
Freq	: 1	EXE

Now key **EXE** or **F1**(Calc)

The calculator will now show the results:

1-Sample tTest

μ	<89.5
t	= −1.5915
p	=0.069901
$\bar{x}$	=88.158
$x\sigma n\text{-}1$	=2.9202
n	=12

Since the p-value > 0.05, the conclusion is to *not reject* the null hypothesis. In other words the evidence does not indicate that the mean price of a 2-star motel room has decreased this year.

CALCULATOR LESSON 9B

CASIO FX-9750GII CALCULATOR

Lesson 9B—t-Test of a Single Mean

EXAMPLE 10.15

A new winter ice-gripping tire has been developed. It will sell in a high price range and it is hoped that the manufacturer can claim that they will last more than 80,000 km on average. The manufacturer is certain that the mileages will be normally distributed. A random sample of 50 tires has been tested and they lasted an average of 81,200 km with a standard deviation of 5,400 km. Use a 5% level of significance.

Solution: From the **Main Menu** select:

STAT   F3(test)   **F2**(t)   **F1**(1-S)   then enter the following items:

(Note: Only use the **EXE** key after a new data entry. Otherwise, use the cursor ▼ arrow. If you accidentally hit the wrong key, use **AC/ON** or **EXIT** to go back.)

1-Sample tTest

Data	: **F2**(Var)	▼
μ	: **F3**(>)	▼
μ_0	: **80000**	**EXE**
$\bar{x}$	: **81200**	**EXE**
sx	: **5400**	**EXE**
n	: **50**	**EXE**
Save Res	: None	

Now key **EXE** or **F1**(Calc) or **F6**(DRAW)

If you select **F6**(DRAW), you will see a normal distribution.

If you select either **EXE** or **F1**(Calc), the calculator will now show the results:

1-Sample tTest

μ	>80000
t	=1.5713484
p	=0.061268
$\bar{x}$	=81200
Sx	=5400
n	=50

Since the p-value > 0.05, the conclusion is to *not reject* the null hypothesis. In other words the tires do not average more than 80,000 km.

EXAMPLE 10.16

A researcher is asked to test the hypothesis that the average price of a 2-star (CAA rating) motel room has decreased since last year. Last year a study has shown that the prices were normally distributed with an average of \$89.50. A random sample of twelve 2-star motels has yielded the following information on room prices: \$85.00, 92.50, 87.50, 89.90, 90.00, 82.50, 87.50, 90.00, 85.00, 89.00, 91.50 and \$87.50. If it is believed that the distribution of room prices is normal, at the 5% level of significance, what conclusion should the researcher make?

Solution:

First enter the data into **List 1**

Now, from the **Main Menu** select:

STAT   F3(test)   **F2**(t)   **F1**(1-S)   then enter the following items:

1-Sample tTest

Data	: **F1**(List)	▼
μ	: **F2**(<)	▼

μ_0	: 89.50	EXE
List	: List1	(Press F1 to enter list number)
Freq	: 1	EXE
Save Res	: None	

Now key **EXE** or **F1**(Calc) or **F6**(DRAW)

If you select **F6**(DRAW), you will see a normal distribution.

If you select either **EXE** or **F1**(Calc), the calculator will now show the results:

1-Sample tTest

μ	<89.5
t	=−1.5915
p	=0.069901
$\bar{x}$	=88.158
sx	=2.9202
n	=12

Since the p-value > 0.05, the conclusion is to *not reject* the null hypothesis. In other words the evidence does not indicate that the mean price of a 2-star motel room has decreased this year.

Problems for Section 10.3

LEARNING THE BASICS

10.16 If, in a sample of $n = 16$ selected from a normal population, $\bar{X} = 56$ and $S = 12$, what is the value of t_{STAT} if you are testing the null hypothesis $H_0: \mu = 50$?

10.17 In Problem 10.16, how many degrees of freedom are there in the t test?

10.18 In Problems 10.16 and 10.17, what are the critical values of t if the level of significance, α, is 0.05 and the alternative hypothesis, H_1, is $\mu \neq 50$?

10.19 In Problems 10.16, 10.17, and 10.18, what is your statistical decision if the alternative hypothesis, H_1, is $\mu \neq 50$?

10.20 If, in a sample of $n = 16$ selected from a left-skewed population, $\bar{X} = 65$ and $S = 21$, would you use the t test to test the null hypothesis $H_0: \mu = 60$? Discuss.

10.21 If, in a sample of $n = 160$ selected from a left-skewed population, $\bar{X} = 65$ and $S = 21$, would you use the t test to test the null hypothesis $H_0: \mu = 60$? Discuss.

APPLYING THE CONCEPTS

✓ SELF Test 10.22 You are the manager of a restaurant for a fast-food franchise. Last month, the mean waiting time at the drive-through window for branches in your geographical region, as measured from the time a customer places an order until the time the customer receives the order, was 3.7 minutes. You select a random sample of 64 orders. The sample mean waiting time is 3.57 minutes, with a sample standard deviation of 0.8 minute.
a. At the 0.05 level of significance, is there evidence that the population mean waiting time is different from 3.7 minutes?

b. Because the sample size is 64, do you need to be concerned about the shape of the population distribution when conducting the t test in (a)? Explain.

10.23 A manufacturer of chocolate candies uses machines to package candies as they move along a filling line. Although the packages are labeled as 8 ounces, the company wants the packages to contain a mean of 8.17 ounces so that virtually none of the packages contain less than 8 ounces. A sample of 50 packages is selected periodically, and the packaging process is stopped if there is evidence that the mean amount packaged is different from 8.17 ounces. Suppose that in a particular sample of 50 packages, the mean amount dispensed is 8.159 ounces, with a sample standard deviation of 0.051 ounce.
a. Is there evidence that the population mean amount is different from 8.17 ounces? (Use a 0.05 level of significance.)
b. Determine the p-value and interpret its meaning.

10.24 The data in the file **MoviePrices** contain prices (in dollars) for two tickets, with online service charges, large popcorn, and two medium soft drinks at a sample of six theater chains:

36.15 31.00 35.05 40.25 33.75 43.00

Source: *Data extracted from K. Kelly, "The Multiplex Under Siege," The Wall Street Journal, December 24–25, 2005, pp. P1, P5.*

a. At the 0.05 level of significance, is there evidence that the mean price for two tickets, with online service charges, large popcorn, and two medium soft drinks, is different from $35?
b. Determine the p-value in (a) and interpret its meaning.
c. What assumption must you make about the population distribution in order to conduct the t test in (a) and (b)?

d. Because the sample size is 6, do you need to be concerned about the shape of the population distribution when conducting the *t* test in (a)? Explain.

10.25 In New York State, savings banks are permitted to sell a form of life insurance called savings bank life insurance (SBLI). The approval process consists of underwriting, which includes a review of the application, a medical information bureau check, possible requests for additional medical information and medical exams, and a policy compilation stage in which the policy pages are generated and sent to the bank for delivery. The ability to deliver approved policies to customers in a timely manner is critical to the profitability of this service. During a period of one month, a random sample of 27 approved policies is selected, and the total processing time, in days, is recorded (as stored in the `Insurance` file):

73 19 16 64 28 28 31 90 60 56 31 56 22 18
45 48 17 17 17 91 92 63 50 51 69 16 17

a. In the past, the mean processing time was 45 days. At the 0.05 level of significance, is there evidence that the mean processing time has changed from 45 days?
b. What assumption about the population distribution is needed in order to conduct the *t* test in (a)?
c. Use a boxplot or a normal probability plot to evaluate the assumption made in (b).
d. Do you think that the assumption needed in order to conduct the *t* test in (a) is valid? Explain.

10.26 The following data (see the `Drink` file) represent the amount of soft-drink filled in a sample of 50 consecutive 2-liter bottles. The results, listed horizontally in the order of being filled, were:

2.109 2.086 2.066 2.075 2.065 2.057 2.052 2.044 2.036 2.038

2.031 2.029 2.025 2.029 2.023 2.020 2.015 2.014 2.013 2.014

2.012 2.012 2.012 2.010 2.005 2.003 1.999 1.996 1.997 1.992

1.994 1.986 1.984 1.981 1.973 1.975 1.971 1.969 1.966 1.967

1.963 1.957 1.951 1.951 1.947 1.941 1.941 1.938 1.908 1.894

a. At the 0.05 level of significance, is there evidence that the mean amount of soft drink filled is different from 2.0 liters?
b. Determine the *p*-value in (a) and interpret its meaning.
c. In (a), you assumed that the distribution of the amount of soft drink filled was normally distributed. Evaluate this assumption using a boxplot or a normal probability plot.
d. Do you think that the assumption needed in order to conduct the *t* test in (a) is valid? Explain.
e. Examine the values of the 50 bottles in their sequential order, as given in the problem. Is there a pattern to the results? If so, what impact might this pattern have on the validity of the results in (a)?

10.27 One of the major measures of the quality of service provided by any organization is the speed with which it responds to customer complaints. A large family-held department store selling furniture and flooring, including

carpet, had undergone a major expansion in the past several years. In particular, the flooring department had expanded from 2 installation crews to an installation supervisor, a measurer, and 15 installation crews. Last year there were 50 complaints concerning carpet installation. The following data (stored in the `Furniture` file) represent the number of days between the receipt of a complaint and the resolution of the complaint:

54   5   35 137   31 27 152   2 123 81   74 27
11   19 126 110 110 29   61 35 94 31   26   5
12   4 165 32   29 28   29 26 25   1   14 13
13   10   5 27   4 52   30 22 36 26   20 23
33   68

a. The installation supervisor claims that the mean number of days between the receipt of a complaint and the resolution of the complaint is 20 days. At the 0.05 level of significance, is there evidence that the claim is not true (i.e., that the mean number of days is different from 20)?
b. What assumption about the population distribution is needed in order to conduct the *t* test in (a)?
c. Use a boxplot or a normal probability plot to evaluate the assumption made in (b).
d. Do you think that the assumption needed in order to conduct the *t* test in (a) is valid? Explain.

10.28 A manufacturing company produces steel housings for electrical equipment. The main component part of the housing is a steel trough that is made out of a 14-gauge steel coil. It is produced using a 250-ton progressive punch press with a wipe-down operation that puts two 90-degree forms in the flat steel to make the trough. The distance from one side of the form to the other is critical because of weatherproofing in outdoor applications. The company requires that the width of the trough be between 8.31 inches and 8.61 inches. The file `Trough` contains the widths of the troughs, in inches, for a sample of *n* = 49.

8.312 8.343 8.317 8.383 8.348 8.410 8.351 8.373 8.481 8.422

8.476 8.382 8.484 8.403 8.414 8.419 8.385 8.465 8.498 8.447

8.436 8.413 8.489 8.414 8.481 8.415 8.479 8.429 8.458 8.462

8.460 8.444 8.429 8.460 8.412 8.420 8.410 8.405 8.323 8.420

8.396 8.447 8.405 8.439 8.411 8.427 8.420 8.498 8.409

a. At the 0.05 level of significance, is there evidence that the mean width of the troughs is different from 8.46 inches?
b. What assumption about the population distribution is needed in order to conduct the *t* test in (a)?
c. Evaluate the assumption made in (b).
d. Do you think that the assumption needed in order to conduct the *t* test in (a) is valid? Explain.

10.29 One operation of a steel mill is to cut pieces of steel into parts that are used in the frame for front seats in an automobile. The steel is cut with a diamond saw and requires the resulting parts to be within ±0.005 inch of the length specified by the automobile company. The data in the file

Steel come from a sample of 100 steel parts. The measurement reported is the difference, in inches, between the actual length of the steel part, as measured by a laser measurement device, and the specified length of the steel part. For example, a value of -0.002 represents a steel part that is 0.002 inch shorter than the specified length.

a. At the 0.05 level of significance, is there evidence that the mean difference is not equal to 0.0 inches?
b. Construct a 95% confidence interval estimate of the population mean. Interpret this interval.
c. Compare the conclusions reached in (a) and (b).
d. Because $n = 100$, do you have to worry about the normality assumption needed for the t test and t interval?

10.30 In Problem 3.93 on page 186, you were introduced to a tea-bag-filling operation. An important quality characteristic of interest for this process is the weight of the tea in the individual bags. The data in the file Teabags are provided in an ordered array of the weight, in grams, of a sample of 50 tea bags produced during an eight-hour shift.

a. Is there evidence that the mean amount of tea per bag is different from 5.5 grams (use $\alpha = 0.01$)?
b. Construct a 99% confidence interval estimate of the population mean amount of tea per bag. Interpret this interval.
c. Compare the conclusions reached in (a) and (b).

10.31 Although many people think they can put a meal on the table in a short period of time, a recent article reported that they end up spending about 40 minutes doing so (data extracted from N. Hellmich, "Americans Go for the Quick Fix for Dinner," *USA Today*, February 14, 2006). Suppose another study is conducted to test the validity of this statement. A sample of 25 people is selected, and the length of time to prepare and cook dinner (in minutes) is recorded, with the following results (stored in the file Dinner).

44.0 51.9 49.7 40.0 55.5 33.0 43.4 41.3 45.2 40.7 41.1 49.1 30.9
45.2 55.3 52.1 55.1 38.8 43.1 39.2 58.6 49.8 43.2 47.9 46.6

a. Is there evidence that the population mean time to prepare and cook dinner is different from 40 minutes? Use the p-value approach and a level of significance of 0.05.
b. What assumption about the population distribution is needed in order to conduct the t test in (a)?
c. Make a list of the various ways you could evaluate the assumption noted in (b).
d. Evaluate the assumption noted in (b) and determine whether the t test in (a) is valid.

10.4 One-Tail Tests

In Section 10.1, hypothesis testing was used to examine the question of whether the population mean amount of cereal filled is 368 grams. The alternative hypothesis ($H_1: \mu \neq 368$) contains two possibilities: Either the mean is less than 368 grams, or the mean is more than 368 grams. For this reason, the rejection region is divided into the two tails of the sampling distribution of the mean. In Section 10.3, once again a two-tail test was used to determine whether the mean amount per invoice had changed from $120.

In contrast to these two examples, many situations require an alternative hypothesis that focuses on a *particular direction*. For example, the population mean is *less than* a specified value. One such situation involves the service time at the drive-through window of a fast-food restaurant. The speed with which customers are served is of critical importance to the success of the service (see **www.qsrmagazine.com/reports/drive-thru_time_study**). In a recent study, McDonald's had a mean service time of 163.9 seconds, which was the fourth best in the industry. Suppose that McDonald's has embarked on a quality improvement effort to reduce the service time and has developed improvements to the service process at the drive-through. The new process will be tested in a sample of 25 stores. Because McDonald's would only want to institute the new process in all of its stores if it resulted in *decreased* drive-through time, the entire rejection region is located in the lower tail of the distribution.

The Critical Value Approach

You wish to determine whether the new drive-through process has a mean that is less than 163.9 seconds. To perform this one-tail hypothesis test, you use the six-step method listed in Exhibit 10.1.

Step 1:
$$H_0: \mu \geq 163.9$$
$$H_1: \mu < 163.9$$

The alternative hypothesis contains the statement you are trying to prove. If the conclusion of the test is "reject H_0," there is statistical proof that the mean drive-through time is less than the drive-through time in the old process. This would be reason to change the drive-through process for the entire population of stores. If the conclusion of the test is "do not reject H_0," then there is insufficient evidence to prove that the mean drive-through time in the new process is significantly less than the drive-through time in the old process. If this occurs, there would be insufficient reason to institute the new drive-through process in the population of stores.

Step 2: You have selected a sample size of $n = 25$ stores. You decide to use $\alpha = 0.05$.

Step 3: Because σ is unknown, you use the t distribution and the t_{STAT} test statistic. You must assume that the service time is normally distributed.

Step 4: The rejection region is entirely contained in the lower tail of the sampling distribution of the mean because you want to reject H_0 only when the sample mean is significantly less than 163.9 seconds. When the entire rejection region is contained in one tail of the sampling distribution of the test statistic, the test is called a **one-tail** or **directional test**. If the alternative hypothesis includes the *less than* sign, the critical value of t is negative. As shown in Table 10.3 and Figure 10.12, because the entire rejection region is in the lower tail of the t distribution and contains an area of 0.05, owing to the symmetry of the t distribution, the critical value of the t test statistic with $25 - 1 = 24$ degrees of freedom is -1.7109.

The decision rule is

$$\text{Reject } H_0 \text{ if } t_{STAT} < -1.7109;$$

$$\text{otherwise, do not reject } H_0.$$

TABLE 10.3

Determining the Critical Value from the t Table for an Area of 0.05 in the Lower Tail with 24 Degrees of Freedom

	Cumulative Probabilities					
	.75	.90	.95	.975	.99	.995
	Upper-Tail Areas					
Degrees of Freedom	.25	.10	.05	.025	.01	.005
1	1.0000	3.0777	6.3138	12.7062	31.8207	63.6574
2	0.8165	1.8856	2.9200	4.3027	6.9646	9.9248
3	0.7649	1.6377	2.3534	3.1824	4.5407	5.8409
.	.	.	.	.	.	.
.	.	.	.	.	.	.
.	.	.	.	.	.	.
23	0.6853	1.3195	1.7139	2.0687	2.4999	2.8073
24	0.6848	1.3178	1.7109	2.0639	2.4922	2.7969
25	0.6844	1.3163	1.7081	2.0595	2.4851	2.7874

Source: *Extracted from Table E.3.*

FIGURE 10.12

One-tail test of hypothesis for a mean (σ known) at the 0.05 level of significance

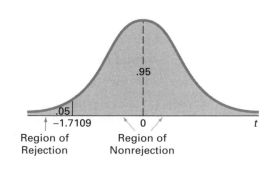

Step 5: You select a sample of 25 stores and find that the sample mean service time at the drive-through equals 152.7 seconds and the sample standard deviation equals 20 seconds. Using $n = 25, \overline{X} = 152.7, S = 20$, and Equation (10.2),

$$t_{STAT} = \frac{\overline{X} - \mu}{\frac{S}{\sqrt{n}}} = \frac{152.7 - 163.9}{\frac{20}{\sqrt{25}}} = -2.80$$

Step 6: Because $t_{STAT} = -2.80 < -1.7109$, you reject the null hypothesis (see Figure 10.12). You conclude that the mean service time at the drive-through is below 163.9 seconds. There is sufficient evidence to change the drive-through process for the entire population of stores.

The *p*-Value Approach

Use the five steps listed in Exhibit 10.2 to illustrate the *t* test for the drive-through time study using the *p*-value approach.

Step 1–3: These steps are the same as in the critical value approach.

Step 4: $t_{STAT} = -2.80$ (see step 5 of the critical value approach). Because the alternative hypothesis indicates a rejection region entirely in the *lower* tail of the sampling distribution, to compute the *p*-value you need to find the probability that the *t*-value will be *less than* the t_{STAT} test statistic of -2.80. From Figure 10.13, the *p*-value is 0.0050.

FIGURE 10.13

Casio calculator FX-9750GII *t* test results for the drive-through time study

t-Test for the hypothesis of the Mean Service Time at Drive Through Study

From the **Main Menu** select:

STAT   F3(test)   **F2**(t)   **F1**(1-S)   then enter the following items:

(Note: Only use the **EXE** key after a new entry. Otherwise, use the cursor ▼ arrow. If you accidentally hit the wrong key, use **AC/ON** or **EXIT** to go back.)

1-Sample tTest
Data	: **F2**(Var)	▼
μ	: **F2**($<\mu0$)	▼
μ0	: **163.9**	**EXE**
$\overline{x}$	: **152.7**	**EXE**
sx	: **20**	**EXE**
n	: **25**	**EXE**
Save Res	: None	

Now key **EXE** or **F1**(CALC) or **F6**(DRAW)

If you select **F6**(DRAW), you will see a normal distribution.

If you select either **EXE** or **F1**(Calc), the calculator will now show the results:

1-Sample tTest
μ	<163.9
t	$=-2.8$
p	$=4.9646E-03$ (which is 0.004946)
$\overline{x}$	$=152.7$
n	$=25$

Statistical Decision: Do not reject the null hypothesis.

To find t critical value:

Two ways of finding the t critical value:

(1)   Using the Casio Calculator fx-9750GII
       Note: Fx-9750G Plus does not have this option, therefore you
       have to use the t-table on page iii.

From the **Main Menu** select:

STAT **F6**(DIST) **F2**(t) **F3**(Invt)   then enter the following items:

Inverse Student-t
Data   : **F2**(Var)   ▼
Area   : **0.05**
df   : **25–1**   **EXE**
Save Res   : None

Now key **EXE** or **F1**(CALC)

The calculator will now show the results:

Inverse Student-t
x-Inv = 1.71088208

(2)   Using the t table on page iii.

df	T Table Upper Tail Areas					
	0.25	0.1	0.05	0.025	0.01	0.005
1	1.000	3.078	6.314	12.706	31.821	63.657
2	0.816	1.886	2.920	4.303	6.965	9.925
3	0.765	1.638	2.353	3.182	4.541	5.841
4	0.741	1.533	2.132	2.776	3.747	4.604
5	0.727	1.476	2.015	2.571	3.365	4.032
6	0.718	1.440	1.943	2.447	3.143	3.707
7	0.711	1.415	1.895	2.365	2.998	3.499
8	0.706	1.397	1.860	2.306	2.896	3.355
9	0.703	1.383	1.833	2.262	2.821	3.250
10	0.700	1.372	1.812	2.228	2.764	3.169
11	0.697	1.363	1.796	2.201	2.718	3.106
12	0.695	1.356	1.782	2.179	2.681	3.055
13	0.694	1.350	1.771	2.160	2.650	3.012
14	0.692	1.345	1.761	2.145	2.624	2.977
15	0.691	1.341	1.753	2.131	2.602	2.947
16	0.690	1.337	1.746	2.120	2.583	2.921
17	0.689	1.333	1.740	2.110	2.567	2.898
18	0.688	1.330	1.734	2.101	2.552	2.878
19	0.688	1.328	1.729	2.093	2.539	2.861
20	0.687	1.325	1.725	2.086	2.528	2.845
21	0.686	1.323	1.721	2.080	2.518	2.831
22	0.686	1.321	1.717	2.074	2.508	2.819
23	0.685	1.319	1.714	2.069	2.500	2.807
24	0.685	1.318	1.711	2.064	2.492	2.797

Step 5: The *p*-value of 0.005 is less than $\alpha = 0.05$ (see Figure 10.14). You reject H_0, and conclude that the mean service time at the drive-through is less than 163.9 seconds. There is sufficient evidence to change the drive-through process for the entire population of stores.

FIGURE 10.14

Determining the *p*-value for a one-tail test

EXAMPLE 10.17

A One-Tail Test for the Mean

A company that manufactures chocolate bars is particularly concerned that the mean weight of a chocolate bar is not greater than 6.03 ounces. A sample of 50 chocolate bars is selected, and the sample mean is 6.034 ounces and the sample standard deviation is 0.02 ounces. Using the $\alpha = 0.01$ level of significance, is there evidence that the population mean weight of the chocolate bars is greater than 6.03 ounces?

SOLUTION Using the critical value approach,

Step 1:
$$H_0: \mu \leq 6.03$$
$$H_1: \mu > 6.03$$

Step 2: You have selected a sample size of $n = 50$. You decide to use $\alpha = 0.01$.

Step 3: Because σ is unknown, you use the t distribution and the t_{STAT} test statistic.

Step 4: The rejection region is entirely contained in the upper tail of the sampling distribution of the mean because you want to reject H_0 only when the sample mean is significantly greater than 6.03 ounces. Because the entire rejection region is in the upper tail of the t distribution and contains an area of 0.01, the critical value of the t distribution with $50 - 1 = 49$ degrees of freedom is 2.4049 (see Table E.3).

The decision rule is

$$\text{Reject } H_0 \text{ if } t_{STAT} > 2.4049;$$

$$\text{otherwise, do not reject } H_0.$$

Step 5: You select a sample of 50 chocolate bars, and the sample mean weight is 6.034 ounces. Using $n = 50, \overline{X} = 6.034, S = 0.02$, and Equation (10.2) on page 420,

$$t_{STAT} = \frac{\overline{X} - \mu}{\dfrac{S}{\sqrt{n}}} = \frac{6.034 - 6.03}{\dfrac{0.02}{\sqrt{50}}} = 1.414$$

Step 6: Because $t_{STAT} = 1.414 < 2.4049$, or using Microsoft Excel or Minitab, the p-value is $0.0818 > 0.01$, you do not reject the null hypothesis. There is insufficient evidence to conclude that the population mean weight is greater than 6.03 ounces.

To perform one-tail tests of hypotheses, you must properly formulate H_0 and H_1. A summary of the null and alternative hypotheses for one-tail tests is as follows:

- The null hypothesis, H_0, represents the status quo or the current belief in a situation.
- The alternative hypothesis, H_1, is the opposite of the null hypothesis and represents a research claim or specific inference you would like to prove.
- If you reject the null hypothesis, you have statistical proof that the alternative hypothesis is correct.
- If you do not reject the null hypothesis, then you have failed to prove the alternative hypothesis. The failure to prove the alternative hypothesis, however, does not mean that you have proven the null hypothesis.
- The null hypothesis always refers to a specified value of the *population parameter* (such as μ), not to a *sample statistic* (such as $\overline{X}$).
- The statement of the null hypothesis *always* contains an equal sign regarding the specified value of the parameter (e.g., $H_0: \mu \geq 163.9$).
- The statement of the alternative hypothesis *never* contains an equal sign regarding the specified value of the parameter (e.g., $H_1: \mu < 163.9$).

Problems for Section 10.4

LEARNING THE BASICS

10.32 In a one-tail hypothesis test where you reject H_0 only in the *upper* tail, what is the p-value if $Z_{STAT} = +2.00$?

10.33 In Problem 10.32, what is your statistical decision if you test the null hypothesis at the 0.05 level of significance?

10.34 In a one-tail hypothesis test where you reject H_0 only in the *lower* tail, what is the p-value if $Z_{STAT} = -1.38$?

10.35 In Problem 10.34, what is your statistical decision if you test the null hypothesis at the 0.01 level of significance?

10.36 In a one-tail hypothesis test where you reject H_0 only in the *lower* tail, what is the p-value if $Z_{STAT} = +1.38$?

10.37 In Problem 10.36, what is the statistical decision if you test the null hypothesis at the 0.01 level of significance?

10.38 In a one-tail hypothesis test where you reject H_0 only in the *upper* tail, what is the critical value of the *t*-test statistic with 10 degrees of freedom at the 0.01 level of significance?

10.39 In Problem 10.38, what is your statistical decision if $t_{STAT} = +2.39$?

10.40 In a one-tail hypothesis test where you reject H_0 only in the *lower* tail, what is the critical value of the t_{STAT} test statistic with 20 degrees of freedom at the 0.01 level of significance?

10.41 In Problem 10.40, what is your statistical decision if $t_{STAT} = -1.15$?

APPLYING THE CONCEPTS

SELF Test 10.42 The Glen Valley Steel Company manufactures steel bars. If the production process is working properly, it turns out steel bars that are normally distributed with mean length of *at least* 2.8 feet. Longer steel bars can be used or altered, but shorter bars must be scrapped. You select a sample of 25 bars, and the mean length is 2.73 feet and the sample standard deviation is 0.20 foot. Do you need to adjust the production equipment?
a. If you test the null hypothesis at the 0.05 level of significance, what decision do you make using the critical value approach to hypothesis testing?
b. If you test the null hypothesis at the 0.05 level of significance, what decision do you make using the p-value approach to hypothesis testing?
c. Interpret the meaning of the p-value in this problem.
d. Compare your conclusions in (a) and (b).

10.43 You are the manager of a restaurant that delivers pizza to college dormitory rooms. You have just changed your delivery process in an effort to reduce the mean time between the order and completion of delivery from the current 25 minutes. A sample of 36 orders using the new delivery process yields a sample mean of 22.4 minutes and a sample standard deviation of 6 minutes.

a. Using the six-step critical value approach, at the 0.05 level of significance, is there evidence that the population mean delivery time has been reduced below the previous population mean value of 25 minutes?
b. At the 0.05 level of significance, use the five-step p-value approach.
c. Interpret the meaning of the p-value in (b).
d. Compare your conclusions in (a) and (b).

10.44 Children in the United States account directly for $36 billion in sales annually. When their indirect influence over product decisions from stereos to vacations is considered, the total economic spending affected by children in the United States is $290 billion. It is estimated that by age 10, a child makes an average of more than five trips a week to a store (data extracted from M. E. Goldberg, G. J. Gorn, L. A. Peracchio, and G. Bamossy, "Understanding Materialism Among Youth," *Journal of Consumer Psychology*, 2003, 13(3), pp. 278–288). Suppose that you want to prove that children in your city average more than five trips a week to a store. Let μ represent the population mean number of times children in your city make trips to a store.
a. State the null and alternative hypotheses.
b. Explain the meaning of the Type I and Type II errors in the context of this scenario.
c. Suppose that you carry out a similar study in the city in which you live. You take a sample of 100 children and find that the mean number of trips to the store is 5.47 and the sample standard deviation of the number of trips to the store is 1.6. At the 0.01 level of significance, is there evidence that the population mean number of trips to the store is greater than 5 per week?
d. Interpret the meaning of the p-value in (c).

10.45 The waiting time to check out of a supermarket has had a population mean of 10.73 minutes. Recently, in an effort to reduce the waiting time, the supermarket has experimented with a system in which there is a single waiting line with multiple checkout servers. A sample of 100 customers was selected, and their mean waiting time to check out was 9.52 minutes with a sample standard deviation of 5.8 minutes.
a. At the 0.05 level of significance, using the critical value approach to hypothesis testing, is there evidence that the population mean waiting time to check out is less than 10.73 minutes?
b. At the 0.05 level of significance, using the p-value approach to hypothesis testing, is there evidence that the population mean waiting time to check out is less than 10.73 minutes?
c. Interpret the meaning of the p-value in this problem.
d. Compare your conclusions in (a) and (b).

10.5 Z Test of Hypothesis for the Proportion

In some situations, you want to test a hypothesis about the proportion of events of interest in the population, π, rather than testing the population mean. To begin, you select a random sample and compute the **sample proportion**, $p = X/n$. You then compare the value of this statistic to the hypothesized value of the parameter, π, in order to decide whether to reject the null hypothesis. If the number of events of interest (X) and the number of events that are not of interest $(n - X)$ are each at least five, the sampling distribution of a proportion approximately follows a normal distribution. You use the **Z test for the proportion** given in Equation (10.3) to perform the hypothesis test for the difference between the sample proportion, p, and the hypothesized population proportion, π.

Z TEST FOR THE PROPORTION

$$Z_{STAT} = \frac{p - \pi}{\sqrt{\dfrac{\pi(1 - \pi)}{n}}} \tag{10.3}$$

where

$$p = \text{sample proportion} = \frac{X}{n} = \frac{\text{Number of events of interest in the sample}}{\text{Sample size}}$$

$\pi = $ hypothesized proportion of events of interest in the population

The Z_{STAT} test statistic approximately follows a standardized normal distribution when X and $(n - X)$ are each at least 5.

Alternatively, by multiplying the numerator and denominator by n, you can write the Z_{STAT} test statistic in terms of the number of events of interest, X, as shown in Equation (10.4).

Z TEST FOR THE PROPORTION IN TERMS OF THE NUMBER OF EVENTS OF INTEREST

$$Z_{STAT} = \frac{X - n\pi}{\sqrt{n\pi(1 - \pi)}} \tag{10.4}$$

The Critical Value Approach

To illustrate the Z test for a proportion, consider a survey that sought to determine whether customer service is better or worse at e-commerce sites than it is at physical stores (data extracted from "Consumers Happier With E-Commerce," *USA Today Snapshots*, March 13, 2007, p. 1B). Of 1,100 respondents, 561 stated that customer service was better at e-commerce sites than at physical stores. For this survey, the null and alternative hypotheses are stated as follows:

H_0: $\pi = 0.50$ (i.e., half of all consumers believe that customer service is better at e-commerce sites than at physical stores)

H_1: $\pi \neq 0.50$ (i.e., either less than half or more than half of all consumers believe that customer service is better at e-commerce sites than at physical stores)

Because you are interested in determining whether the population proportion of consumers who believe that customer service is better at e-commerce sites than at physical stores is less than or more than 0.50, you use a two-tail test. If you select the $\alpha = 0.05$ level of significance, the rejection and nonrejection regions are set up as in Figure 10.15, and the decision rule is

Reject H_0 if $Z_{STAT} < -1.96$ or if $Z_{STAT} > +1.96$;

otherwise, do not reject H_0.

FIGURE 10.15

Two-tail test of hypothesis for the proportion at the 0.05 level of significance

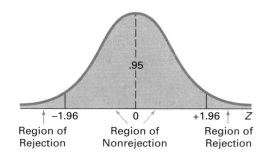

Because 561 of the 1,100 respondents stated that customer service was better at e-commerce sites than at physical stores,

$$p = \frac{561}{1,100} = 0.51$$

Using Equation (10.3),

$$Z_{STAT} = \frac{p - \pi}{\sqrt{\dfrac{\pi(1 - \pi)}{n}}} = \frac{0.51 - 0.50}{\sqrt{\dfrac{0.50(1 - 0.50)}{1,100}}} = \frac{0.01}{0.0151} = 0.6633$$

or, using Equation (10.4),

$$Z_{STAT} = \frac{X - n\pi}{\sqrt{n\pi(1 - \pi)}} = \frac{561 - (1,100)(0.50)}{\sqrt{1,100(0.50)(0.50)}} = \frac{11}{16.5831} = 0.6633$$

Because $-1.96 < Z_{STAT} = 0.6633 < 1.96$, you do not reject H_0. There is insufficient evidence to prove that the population proportion of all consumers who believe that customer service is better at e-commerce sites than at physical stores is not 0.50. Figure 10.16 presents a Casio calculator worksheet and Figure 10.17 presents Minitab results for these data.

FIGURE 10.16

Casio calculator FX-9750GII results for the survey of whether customer service is better or worse at e-commerce sites than it is at physical stores

Z-Test for the hypothesis for the proportion

From the **Main Menu** select:

STAT **F3**(test) **F1**(Z) **F3**(1-p)   then enter the following items:

(**Note:** Only use the **EXE** key after a new entry. Otherwise, use the cursor ▼ arrow. If you accidentally hit the wrong key, use **AC/ON** or **EXIT** to go back.)

1-Prop ZTest
Prop	: **F2**($\neq$p0)	▼
p0	: **0.5**	**EXE**
x	: **561**	**EXE**
n	: **1100**	**EXE**
Save Res	: None	

Now key **EXE** or **F1**(CALC) or **F6**(DRAW)

If you select **F6** (DRAW), you will see a normal distribution.

If you select either **EXE** or **F1**(Calc), the calculator will now show the results:

1-Prop ZTest
Prop	$\neq$0.5
z	=0.66332495
p	=0.50712245
$\bar{p}$	=0.51
n	=1100

Statistical Decision: Do not reject the null hypothesis.

To find z critical value:

From the **Main Menu** select:

STAT **F5**(dist) **F1**(Norm) **F3**(InvN)   then enter the following items:

Using calculator fx-9750GII	Using calculator fx-9750G Plus
Inverse Normal	**Inverse Normal**
Data : **F2**(Var) ▼	Area : **0.05 ÷ 2** **EXE**
Tail : **F3**(CNTR) ▼	σ : **1** **EXE**
Area : **1−0.05** **EXE**	μ : **0** **EXE**
σ : **1** **EXE**	Now key **EXE** or **F1**(CALC)
μ : **0** **EXE**	The calculator will now show the results:
Save Res : **None** **EXE**	
Now key **EXE** or **F1**(CALC)	**Inverse Normal:**
	X = −1.959964
The calculator will now show the results:	**Note: For this model, when using the**
	InvN function, the *Area* value that is
Inverse Normal:	**required is the area to the *LEFT* of the**
X₁ Inv = −1.959964	**desired X value.**
X₂ Inv = 1.95996398	

FIGURE 10.17
Minitab results for the survey of whether customer service is better or worse at e-commerce sites than it is at physical stores

```
Sample    X     N   Sample p       95% CI        Z-Value  P-Value
1        561  1100  0.510000  (0.480458, 0.539542)  0.66    0.507

Using the normal approximation.
```

The *p*-Value Approach

As an alternative to the critical value approach, you can compute the *p*-value. For this two-tail test in which the rejection region is located in the lower tail and the upper tail, you need to find the area below a Z value of -0.66 and above a Z value of $+0.66$. Figures 10.16 and 10.17 report a *p*-value of 0.507. Because this value is greater than the selected level of significance $(\alpha = 0.05)$, you do not reject the null hypothesis.

EXAMPLE 10.18

Testing a Hypothesis for a Proportion

A fast-food chain has developed a new process to ensure that orders at the drive-through are filled correctly. The previous process filled orders correctly 85% of the time. Based on a sample of 100 orders using the new process, 94 were filled correctly. At the 0.01 level of significance, can you conclude that the new process has increased the proportion of orders filled correctly?

SOLUTION The null and alternative hypotheses are

H_0: $\pi \leq 0.85$ (i.e., the population proportion of orders filled correctly using the new process is less than or equal to 0.85)

H_1: $\pi > 0.85$ (i.e., the population proportion of orders filled correctly using the new process is greater than 0.85)

Using Equation (10.3) on page 436,

$$p = \frac{X}{n} = \frac{94}{100} = 0.94$$

$$Z_{STAT} = \frac{p - \pi}{\sqrt{\dfrac{\pi(1 - \pi)}{n}}} = \frac{0.94 - 0.85}{\sqrt{\dfrac{0.85(1 - 0.85)}{100}}} = \frac{0.09}{0.0357} = 2.52$$

The *p*-value for $Z_{STAT} > 2.52$ is 0.0059.

   Using the critical value approach, you reject H_0 if $Z_{STAT} > 2.33$. Using the *p*-value approach, you reject H_0 if the *p*-value < 0.01. Because $Z_{STAT} = 2.52 > 2.33$ or the *p*-value $= 0.0059 < 0.01$, you reject H_0. You have evidence that the new process has increased the proportion of correct orders above 0.85.

CALCULATOR LESSON 10A

CFX-9850GB CALCULATOR

EXAMPLE 10.19

Lesson 10A—Z-Test of a Single Proportion

A bank manager wants to test the hypothesis that less than 60% of all the bank's customers use the ATM to pay some of their bills. A random sample of 80 customers has been selected and it was found that 43 of them use the ATM to pay some bills. Use the 10% significance level.

Solution: From the **Main Menu** select:

STAT **F3**(test) **F1**(Z) **F3**(1-P)   then enter the following items:

(Note: Only use the **EXE** key after a new data entry. Otherwise, use the cursor ▼ arrow. If you accidentally hit the wrong key, use **AC/ON** or **EXIT** to go back.)

1-Prop ZTest

Prop	: **F2**(<)	▼
p0	: **0.6**	**EXE**
x	: **43**	**EXE**
n	: **80**	**EXE**

Now key **EXE** or **F1**(Calc)

The calculator will now show the results:

1-Prop ZTest
μ <0.6
z = −1.141
p =0.12691
$\hat{p}$ =0.5375
n =80

Since the p-value > 0.05, the conclusion is to *not reject* the null hypothesis. In other words the bank manager cannot say that less than 60% of its customers use ATM to pay some bills.

CALCULATOR LESSON 10B

CASIO FX9750GII CALCULATOR

EXAMPLE 10.20

Lesson 10B—Z-Test of a Single Proportion

A bank manager wants to test the hypothesis that less than 60% of all the bank's customers use the ATM to pay some of their bills. A random sample of 80 customers has been selected and it was found that 43 of them use the ATM to pay some bills. Use the 10% significance level.

Solution: From the **Main Menu** select:

STAT **F3**(test) **F1**(Z) **F3**(1-P)   then enter the following items:

(Note: Only use the **EXE** key after a new data entry. Otherwise, use the cursor ▼ arrow. If you accidentally hit the wrong key, use **AC/ON** or **EXIT** to go back.)

1-Prop ZTest

Prop	: F2(<)	▼
p0	: 0.6	**EXE**
x	: 43	**EXE**
n	: 80	**EXE**

Save Res : None

Now key **EXE** or **F1**(Calc) or **F6**(DRAW)

If you select **F6**(DRAW), you will see a normal distribution.

If you select either **EXE** or **F1**(Calc), the calculator will now show the results:

1-Prop ZTest

μ <0.6

z   = −1.141

p   =0.12691

$\hat{p}$ =0.5375

n   =80

Since the p-value > 0.05, the conclusion is to *not reject* the null hypothesis. In other words the bank manager cannot say that less than 60% of its customers use ATM to pay some bills.

Problems for Section 10.5

LEARNING THE BASICS

10.46 If, in a random sample of 400 items, 88 are defective, what is the sample proportion of defective items?

10.47 In Problem 10.46, if the null hypothesis is that 20% of the items in the population are defective, what is the value of Z_{STAT}?

10.48 In Problems 10.46 and 10.47, suppose you are testing the null hypothesis H_0: $\pi = 0.20$ against the two-tail alternative hypothesis H_1: $\pi \neq 0.20$ and you choose the level of significance $\alpha = 0.05$. What is your statistical decision?

APPLYING THE CONCEPTS

10.49 Late payment of medical claims can add to the cost of health care. An article (M. Freudenheim, "The Check Is Not in the Mail," *The New York Times*, May 25, 2006, pp. C1, C6) reported that for one insurance company, 85.1% of the claims were paid in full when first submitted. Suppose that the insurance company developed a new payment system in an effort to increase this percentage. A sample of 200 claims processed under this system revealed that 180 of the claims were paid in full when first submitted.

a. At the 0.05 level of significance, is there evidence that the population proportion of claims processed under this new system is higher than the article reported for the previous system?

b. Compute the *p*-value and interpret its meaning.

10.50 Online magazines make it easy for readers to link to an advertiser's Web site directly from an advertisement placed in the digital magazine. A recent survey indicated that 56% of online magazine readers have clicked on an advertisement and linked directly to the advertiser's Web site. The survey was based on a sample size of $n = 6,403$ (data extracted from "Metrics," *EContent*, January/February, 2007, p. 20).

a. Use the five-step *p*-value approach to try to determine whether there is evidence that more than half of all the readers of online magazines have linked to an advertiser's Web site. (Use the 0.05 level of significance.)

b. Suppose that the sample size was only $n = 100$, and as before, 56% of the online magazine readers indicated that they had clicked on an advertisement to link directly to the advertiser's Web site. Use the five-step *p*-value approach to try to determine whether there is evidence that more than half of all the readers of online magazines have linked to an advertiser's Web site. (Use the 0.05 level of significance.)

c. Discuss the effect that sample size has on hypothesis testing.

d. What do you think your chances are of rejecting any null hypothesis concerning a population proportion if a sample size of $n = 20$ is used?

10.51 One of the issues facing organizations is increasing diversity throughout the organization. One of the ways to evaluate an organization's success at increasing diversity is to compare the percentage of employees in the organization in a particular position with a specific background to the percentage in a particular position with that specific background in the general workforce. Recently, a large academic medical center determined that 9 of 17 employees in a particular position were female whereas 55% of the employees for this position in the general workforce were female. At the 0.05 level of significance, is there evidence that the proportion of females in this position at this medical center is different from what would be expected in the general workforce?

10.52 Sixty-five percent of 1,000 respondents aged 24 to 35 reported that they preferred to "look for a job in a place where I would like to live" rather than "look for the best job I can find, the place where I live is secondary" (data extracted from L. Belkin, "What Do Young Jobseekers Want? (Something Other Than a Job)," *The New York Times*, September 6, 2007, p. G2). At the 0.05 level of significance, is there evidence that the proportion of all young jobseekers aged 24 to 35 who preferred to "look for a job in a place where I would like to live" rather than "look for the best job I can find, the place where I live is secondary" is different from 60%?

10.53 One of the biggest issues facing e-retailers is the ability to reduce the proportion of customers who cancel their transactions after they have selected their products. It has been estimated that about half of prospective customers cancel their transactions after they have selected their products (data extracted from B. Tedeschi, "E-Commerce, a Cure for Abandoned Shopping Carts: A Web Checkout System That Eliminates the Need for Multiple Screens," *The New York Times*, February 14, 2005, p. C3). Suppose that a company changed its Web site so that customers could use a single-page checkout process rather than multiple pages. A sample of 500 customers who had selected their products were provided with the new checkout system. Of these 500 customers, 210 cancelled their transactions after they had selected their products.

a. At the 0.01 level of significance, is there evidence that the population proportion of customers who select products and then cancel their transaction is less than 0.50 with the new system?

b. Suppose that a sample of $n = 100$ customers (instead of $n = 500$ customers) were provided with the new checkout system and that 42 of those customers cancelled their transactions after they had selected their products. At the 0.01 level of significance, is there evidence that the population proportion of customers who select products and then cancel their transaction is less than 0.50 with the new system?

c. Compare the results of (a) and (b) and discuss the effect that sample size has on the outcome, and, in general, in hypothesis testing.

10.54 A recent study by the Pew Internet and American Life Project (**pewinternet.org**) found that Americans had a complex and ambivalent attitude toward technology (data extracted from M. Himowitz, "How to Tell What Kind of Tech User You Are," *Newsday*, May 27, 2007, p. F6). The study reported that 8% of the respondents were "Omnivores" who are gadget lovers, text messengers, and online gamers who often had their own blogs, Web pages, video makers, and YouTube posters. You believe that the percentage of students at your school who are Omnivores is greater than 8% and you plan to carry out a study to prove that this is so.

a. State the null and alternative hypothesis.

You select a sample of 200 students at your school and find that 30 students can be classified as Omnivores.

b. Use either the six-step critical value hypothesis-testing approach or the five-step p-value approach to determine at the 0.05 level of significance whether there is evidence that the percentage of Omnivores at your school is greater than 8%.

10.6 Potential Hypothesis-Testing Pitfalls and Ethical Issues

To this point, you have studied the fundamental concepts of hypothesis testing. You have used hypothesis testing to analyze differences between sample statistics and hypothesized population parameters in order to make business decisions concerning the underlying population characteristics. You have also learned how to evaluate the risks involved in making these decisions.

When planning to carry out a hypothesis test based on a survey, research study, or designed experiment, you must ask several questions to ensure that you use proper methodology. You need to raise and answer questions such as the following in the planning stage:

1. What is the goal of the survey, study, or experiment? How can you translate the goal into a null hypothesis and an alternative hypothesis?
2. Is the hypothesis test a two-tail test or one-tail test?
3. Can you select a random sample from the underlying population of interest?

4. What types of data will you collect in the sample? Are the variables numerical or categorical?
5. At what level of significance should you conduct the hypothesis test?
6. Is the intended sample size large enough to achieve the desired power of the test for the level of significance chosen?
7. What statistical test procedure should you use and why?
8. What conclusions and interpretations can you reach from the results of the hypothesis test?

Failing to consider these questions early in the planning process can lead to biased or incomplete results. Proper planning can help ensure that the statistical study will provide objective information needed to make good business decisions.

Statistical Significance versus Practical Significance You need to make the distinction between the existence of a statistically significant result and its practical significance in the context within a field of application. Sometimes, due to a very large sample size, you may get a result that is statistically significant but has little practical significance. For example, suppose that prior to a national marketing campaign focusing on a series of expensive television commercials, you believe that the proportion of people who recognize your brand is 0.30. At the completion of the campaign, a survey of 20,000 people indicates that 6,168 recognized your brand. A one-tail test trying to prove that the proportion is now greater than 0.30 results in a p-value of 0.0047 and the correct statistical conclusion is that the proportion of consumers recognizing your brand name has now increased. Was the campaign successful? The result of the hypothesis test indicates a statistically significant increase in brand awareness, but is this increase practically important? The population proportion is now estimated at $6{,}168/20{,}000 = 0.3084$, or 30.84%. This increase is less than 1% more than the hypothesized value of 30%. Did the large expenses associated with the marketing campaign produce a result with a meaningful increase in brand awareness? Because of the minimal real-world impact an increase of less than 1% has on the overall marketing strategy and the huge expenses associated with the marketing campaign, you should conclude that the campaign was not successful. On the other hand, if the campaign increased brand awareness by 20%, you could conclude that the campaign was successful.

Reporting of Findings In conducting research, you should document both good and bad results. You should not just report the results of hypothesis tests that show statistical significance but omit those for which there is insufficient evidence in the findings. In instances in which there is insufficient evidence to reject H_0, you must make it clear that this does not prove that the null hypothesis is true. What the result does indicate is that with the sample size used, there is not enough information to *disprove* the null hypothesis.

Ethical Issues You also need to distinguish between poor research methodology and unethical behavior. Ethical considerations arise when the hypothesis-testing process is manipulated. Some of the areas where ethical issues can arise include the use of human subjects in experiments, data collection method, the type of test (one-tail or two-tail test), the choice of the level of significance, the cleansing and discarding of data, and the failure to report pertinent findings.

USING STATISTICS @ Oxford Cereals, Part II Revisited

As the plant operations manager for Oxford Cereals, you were responsible for the cereal-filling process. It was your responsibility to adjust the process when the mean fill weight in the population of boxes deviated from the company specifications of 368 grams. Since weighing all the cereal boxes would be too time-consuming and impractical, you needed to select and weigh a sample of boxes and conduct a hypothesis test.

You determined that the null hypothesis should be that the population mean fill was 368 grams. If the weights of the sampled boxes were sufficiently above or below the expected 368-gram mean specified by Oxford Cereals, you would reject the null hypothesis in favor of the alternative hypothesis that the mean fill was different from 368 grams. If this happened, you would stop production and take whatever action is necessary to correct the problem. If the null hypothesis was not rejected, you would continue to believe in the status quo, that the process was working correctly, and therefore take no corrective action.

Before proceeding, you considered the risks involved with hypothesis tests known as Type I and Type II errors. If you rejected a true null hypothesis, then you would make a Type I error and conclude that the population mean fill was not 368 when it actually was 368. This error would result in adjusting the filling process even though the process was working properly. If you did not reject a false null hypothesis, then you would make a Type II error and conclude that the population mean fill was 368 when it actually was not 368. Here, you would allow the process to continue without adjustment even though the process was not working properly.

After collecting a random sample of 25 cereal boxes, you used the six-step critical value approach to hypothesis testing. Because the test statistic fell into the nonrejection region, you did not reject the null hypothesis. You concluded that there was insufficient evidence to prove that the mean fill differed from 368 grams. No corrective action on the filling process was needed.

SUMMARY

This chapter presented the foundation of hypothesis testing. You learned how to perform tests on the population mean and on the population proportion. The chapter developed both the critical value approach and the *p*-value approach to hypothesis testing.

In deciding which test to use, you should ask the following question:

Does the test involve a numerical variable or a categorical variable? If the test involves a categorical variable, use the *Z* test for the proportion. If the test involves a numerical variable, use the *t* test for the mean.

TABLE 10.4

Summary of Topics in Chapter 10

	Type of Data	
Type of Analysis	**Numerical**	**Categorical**
Hypothesis test concerning a single parameter	*t* test of hypothesis for the mean (Section 10.3)	*Z* test of hypothesis for the proportion (Section 10.5)

KEY EQUATIONS

***Z* Test for the Mean (σ Known)**

$$Z_{STAT} = \frac{\bar{X} - \mu}{\dfrac{\sigma}{\sqrt{n}}} \qquad (10.1)$$

***t* Test for the Mean (σ Unknown)**

$$t_{STAT} = \frac{\bar{X} - \mu}{\dfrac{S}{\sqrt{n}}} \qquad (10.2)$$

Z Test for the Proportion

$$Z_{STAT} = \frac{p - \pi}{\sqrt{\dfrac{\pi(1 - \pi)}{n}}}$$

(10.3)

Z Test for the Proportion in Terms of the Number of Events of Interest

$$Z_{STAT} = \frac{X - n\pi}{\sqrt{n\pi(1 - \pi)}}$$

(10.4)

KEY TERMS

α (level of significance)   405
alternative hypothesis (H_1) 402
β risk   405
confidence coefficient   405
confidence level   405
critical value   404
directional test   431
hypothesis testing   402

level of significance (α) 405
null hypothesis (H_0) 402
one-tail test   431
p-value   409
power of a statistical test   405
region of nonrejection   404
region of rejection   404
robust   425

sample proportion   436
t test for the mean   420
test statistic   404
two-tail test   407
Type I error   404
Type II error   404
Z test for the mean   406
Z test for the proportion   436

CHAPTER REVIEW PROBLEMS

CHECKING YOUR UNDERSTANDING

10.55 What is the difference between a null hypothesis, H_0, and an alternative hypothesis, H_1?

10.56 What is the difference between a Type I error and a Type II error?

10.57 What is meant by the power of a test?

10.58 What is the difference between a one-tail test and a two-tail test?

10.59 What is meant by a p-value?

10.60 How can a confidence interval estimate for the population mean provide conclusions to the corresponding two-tail hypothesis test for the population mean?

10.61 What is the six-step critical value approach to hypothesis testing?

10.62 What is the five-step p-value approach to hypothesis testing?

APPLYING THE CONCEPTS

10.63 An article in *Marketing News* (T. T. Semon, "Consider a Statistical Insignificance Test," *Marketing News*, February 1, 1999) argued that the level of significance used when comparing two products is often too low—that is, sometimes you should be using an α value greater than 0.05. Specifically, the article recounted testing the proportion of potential customers with a preference for product 1 over product 2. The null hypothesis was that the population pro-

portion of potential customers preferring product 1 was 0.50, and the alternative hypothesis was that it was not equal to 0.50. The p-value for the test was 0.22. The article suggested that, in some cases, this should be enough evidence to reject the null hypothesis.

a. State the null and alternative hypotheses for this example in statistical terms.
b. Explain the risks associated with Type I and Type II errors in this case.
c. What would be the consequences if you rejected the null hypothesis for a p-value of 0.22?
d. Why do you think the article suggested raising the value of α?
e. What would you do in this situation?
f. What is your answer in (e) if the p-value equals 0.12? What if it equals 0.06?

10.64 La Quinta Motor Inns developed a computer model to help predict the profitability of sites that are being considered as locations for new hotels. If the computer model predicts large profits, La Quinta buys the proposed site and builds a new hotel. If the computer model predicts small or moderate profits, La Quinta chooses not to proceed with that site (data extracted from S. E. Kimes and J. A. Fitzsimmons, "Selecting Profitable Hotel Sites at La Quinta Motor Inns," *Interfaces*, Vol. 20, March–April 1990, pp. 12–20). This decision-making procedure can be expressed in the hypothesis-testing framework. The null hypothesis is that the site is not a profitable location. The alternative hypothesis is that the site is a profitable location.

a. Explain the risks associated with committing a Type I error in this case.

b. Explain the risks associated with committing a Type II error in this case.

c. Which type of error do you think the executives at La Quinta Motor Inns are trying hard to avoid? Explain.

d. How do changes in the rejection criterion affect the probabilities of committing Type I and Type II errors?

10.65 In 2006, Visa wanted to move away from its long-running television advertising theme of "Visa, it's everywhere you want to be." During the Winter Olympics, Visa featured Olympians in commercials with a broader message, including security, check cards, and payment technologies such as contactless processing. One of the first commercials featured snowboarder Lindsey Jacobellis being coached to calm down before a big race by imagining that her Visa Check Card got stolen. A key metric for the success of television advertisements is the proportion of viewers who "like the ads a lot." Harris Ad Research Service conducted a study of 903 adults who viewed the new Visa advertisement and reported that 54 indicated that they "like the ad a lot." According to Harris, the proportion of a typical television advertisement receiving the "like the ad a lot" score is 0.21 (data extracted from T. Howard, "Visa to Change Strategies in Upcoming Ads," **usatoday.com**, January 23, 2006).

a. Use the six-step critical value approach to hypothesis testing and a 0.05 level of significance to try to prove that the new Visa ad is less successful than a typical television advertisement.

b. Use the five-step *p*-value approach to hypothesis testing and a 0.05 level of significance to try to prove that the new Visa ad is less successful than a typical television advertisement.

c. Compare the results of (a) and (b).

10.66 The owner of a gasoline station wants to study gasoline purchasing habits by motorists at his station. He selects a random sample of 60 motorists during a certain week, with the following results:
- The amount purchased was $\overline{X} = 11.3$ gallons, $S = 3.1$ gallons.
- 11 motorists purchased premium-grade gasoline.

a. At the 0.05 level of significance, is there evidence that the population mean purchase was different from 10 gallons?

b. Determine the *p*-value in (a).

c. At the 0.05 level of significance, is there evidence that fewer than 20% of all the motorists at the station purchased premium-grade gasoline?

d. What is your answer to (a) if the sample mean equals 10.3 gallons?

e. What is your answer to (c) if 7 motorists purchased premium-grade gasoline?

10.67 An auditor for a government agency is assigned the task of evaluating reimbursement for office visits to physicians paid by Medicare. The audit was conducted on a sample of 75 of the reimbursements, with the following results:

- In 12 of the office visits, an incorrect amount of reimbursement was provided.
- The amount of reimbursement was $\overline{X} = \$93.70$, $S = \$34.55$.

a. At the 0.05 level of significance, is there evidence that the population mean reimbursement was less than $100?

b. At the 0.05 level of significance, is there evidence that the proportion of incorrect reimbursements in the population was greater than 0.10?

c. Discuss the underlying assumptions of the test used in(a).

d. What is your answer to (a) if the sample mean equals $90?

e. What is your answer to (b) if 15 office visits had incorrect reimbursements?

10.68 A bank branch located in a commercial district of a city has developed an improved process for serving customers during the noon-to-1:00 P.M. lunch period. The waiting time (defined as the time the customer enters the line until he or she reaches the teller window) of all customers during this hour is recorded over a period of 1 week. A random sample of 15 customers (see the data file Bank1) is selected, and the results are as follows:

4.21	5.55	3.02	5.13	4.77	2.34	3.54	3.20
4.50	6.10	0.38	5.12	6.46	6.19	3.79	

a. At the 0.05 level of significance, is there evidence that the population mean waiting time is less than 5 minutes?

b. What assumption about the population distribution is needed in order to conduct the *t* test in (a)?

c. Use a boxplot or a normal probability plot to evaluate the assumption made in (b).

d. Do you think that the assumption needed in order to conduct the *t* test in (a) is valid? Explain.

e. As a customer walks into the branch office during the lunch hour, she asks the branch manager how long she can expect to wait. The branch manager replies, "Almost certainly not longer than 5 minutes." On the basis of the results of (a), evaluate this statement.

10.69 A manufacturing company produces electrical insulators. If the insulators break when in use, a short circuit is likely to occur. To test the strength of the insulators, destructive testing is carried out to determine how much *force* is required to break the insulators. Force is measured by observing the number of pounds of force applied to the insulator before it breaks. The following data (stored in the Force file) are from 30 insulators subject to this testing:

1,870 1,728 1,656 1,610 1,634 1,784 1,522 1,696 1,592 1,662
1,866 1,764 1,734 1,662 1,734 1,774 1,550 1,756 1,762 1,866
1,820 1,744 1,788 1,688 1,810 1,752 1,680 1,810 1,652 1,736

a. At the 0.05 level of significance, is there evidence that the population mean force is greater than 1,500 pounds?

b. What assumption about the population distribution is needed in order to conduct the *t* test in (a)?

c. Use a histogram, boxplot, or a normal probability plot to evaluate the assumption made in (b).

d. Do you think that the assumption needed in order to conduct the *t* test in (a) is valid? Explain.

10.70 An important quality characteristic used by the manufacturer of Boston and Vermont asphalt shingles is the amount of moisture the shingles contain when they are packaged. Customers may feel that they have purchased a product lacking in quality if they find moisture and wet shingles inside the packaging. In some cases, excessive moisture can cause the granules attached to the shingle for texture and coloring purposes to fall off the shingle, resulting in appearance problems. To monitor the amount of moisture present, the company conducts moisture tests. A shingle is weighed and then dried. The shingle is then reweighed, and, based on the amount of moisture taken out of the product, the pounds of moisture per 100 square feet are calculated. The company would like to show that the mean moisture content is less than 0.35 pound per 100 square feet. The data file **Moisture** includes 36 measurements (in pounds per 100 square feet) for Boston shingles and 31 for Vermont shingles.

a. For the Boston shingles, is there evidence at the 0.05 level of significance that the population mean moisture content is less than 0.35 pound per 100 square feet?

b. Interpret the meaning of the *p*-value in (a).

c. For the Vermont shingles, is there evidence at the 0.05 level of significance that the population mean moisture content is less than 0.35 pound per 100 square feet?

d. Interpret the meaning of the *p*-value in (c).

e. What assumption about the population distribution is needed in order to conduct the *t* tests in (a) and (c)?

f. Use a histogram, boxplot, or a normal probability plot to evaluate the assumption made in (a) and (c).

g. Do you think that the assumption needed in order to conduct the *t* tests in (a) and (c) is valid? Explain.

10.71 Studies conducted by the manufacturer of Boston and Vermont asphalt shingles have shown product weight to be a major factor in the customer's perception of quality. Moreover, the weight represents the amount of raw materials being used and is therefore very important to the company from a cost standpoint. The last stage of the assembly line packages the shingles before the packages are placed on wooden pallets. Once a pallet is full (a pallet for most brands holds 16 squares of shingles), it is weighed, and the measurement is recorded. The data file **Pallet** contains the weight (in pounds) from a sample of 368 pallets of Boston shingles and 330 pallets of Vermont shingles.

a. For the Boston shingles, is there evidence that the population mean weight is different from 3,150 pounds?

b. Interpret the meaning of the *p*-value in (a).

c. For the Vermont shingles, is there evidence that the population mean weight is different from 3,700 pounds?

d. Interpret the meaning of the *p*-value in (c).

e. In (a) through (d), do you have to worry about the normality assumption? Explain.

10.72 The manufacturer of Boston and Vermont asphalt shingles provides its customers with a 20-year warranty on most of its products. To determine whether a shingle will last as long as the warranty period, accelerated-life testing is conducted at the manufacturing plant. Accelerated-life testing exposes the shingle to the stresses it would be subject to in a lifetime of normal use in a laboratory setting via an experiment that takes only a few minutes to conduct. In this test, a shingle is repeatedly scraped with a brush for a short period of time, and the shingle granules removed by the brushing are weighed (in grams). Shingles that experience low amounts of granule loss are expected to last longer in normal use than shingles that experience high amounts of granule loss. The data file **Granule** contains a sample of 170 measurements made on the company's Boston shingles and 140 measurements made on Vermont shingles.

a. For the Boston shingles, is there evidence that the population mean granule loss is different from 0.50 gram?

b. Interpret the meaning of the *p*-value in (a).

c. For the Vermont shingles, is there evidence that the population mean granule loss is different from 0.50 gram?

d. Interpret the meaning of the *p*-value in (c).

e. In (a) through (d), do you have to worry about the normality assumption? Explain.

REPORT WRITING EXERCISES

10.73 Referring to the results of Problems 10.70 through 10.72 concerning Boston and Vermont shingles, write a report that evaluates the moisture level, weight, and granule loss of the two types of shingles.

MANAGING THE *SPRINGVILLE HERALD*

Continuing its monitoring of the blackness of the newspaper print, first described in the Chapter 6 Managing the *Springville Herald* case, the production department of the newspaper wants to ensure that the mean blackness of the print for all newspapers is at least 0.97 on a standard scale in which the target value is 1.0. A random sample of 50 newspapers was selected, and the blackness of one spot on each of the 50 newspapers is measured (and stored in the **SH9** file).

```
0.854  1.023  1.005  1.030  1.219  0.977  1.044  0.778  1.122  1.114
1.091  1.086  1.141  0.931  0.723  0.934  1.060  1.047  0.800  0.889
1.012  0.695  0.869  0.734  1.131  0.993  0.762  0.814  1.108  0.805
1.223  1.024  0.884  0.799  0.870  0.898  0.621  0.818  1.113  1.286
1.052  0.678  1.162  0.808  1.012  0.859  0.951  1.112  1.003  0.972
```

Calculate the sample statistics and determine whether there is evidence that the population mean blackness is less than 0.107. Write a memo to management that summarizes your conclusions.

WEB CASE

Apply your knowledge about hypothesis testing in this Web Case, which continues the cereal-fill-packaging dispute Web Case from Chapter 7.

In response to the negative statements made by the Consumers Concerned About Cereal Cheaters (CCACC) in the Chapter 7 Web Case, Oxford Cereals recently conducted an experiment concerning cereal packaging. The company claims that the results of the experiment refute the CCACC allegations that Oxford Cereals has been cheating consumers by packaging cereals at less than labeled weights. Review the Oxford Cereals' press release and supporting documents that describe the experiment at the company's Web site, **www.prenhall.com/Springville/OC_FullUp.htm**, or open OC_FullUp.htm

from the Student CD-ROM Web Case folder, and then answer the following:

1. Are the results of the experiment valid? Why or why not? If you were conducting the experiment, is there anything you would change?
2. Do the results support the claim that Oxford Cereals is not cheating its customers?
3. Is the claim of the Oxford Cereals CEO that many cereal boxes contain *more* than 368 grams surprising? Is it true?
4. Could there ever be a circumstance in which the results of the Oxford Cereals experiment *and* the CCACC's results are both correct? Explain.

REFERENCES

1. Bradley, J. V., *Distribution-Free Statistical Tests* (Upper Saddle River, NJ: Prentice Hall, 1968).
2. Daniel, W., *Applied Nonparametric Statistics*, 2nd ed. (Boston: Houghton Mifflin, 1990).
3. *Microsoft Excel 2007* (Redmond, WA: Microsoft Corp., 2007).
4. *Minitab for Windows Version 15* (State College, PA: Minitab, Inc., 2006).

APPENDIX E10

Using Microsoft Excel for One-Sample Tests

E10.1 Using the *Z* Test for the Mean (σ Known)

You perform the *Z* test for the mean (σ known) by making entries in either the **ZMean_TT** (see Figure 10.5 or **ZMean_All** worksheets of the Z Mean.xls workbook. These worksheets use the **NORMSINV($P < X$)** function to determine the lower and upper critical values and use the **NORMSDIST(Z *value*)** function to compute the *p*-values from the *Z* value calculated in cell B12. The worksheets also use the **IF(*comparison, what to do if comparison holds, what to do if comparison fails*)** function to determine whether or not you should reject the null hypothesis. (Although shown as two lines in Figure 10.5, the function is entered as a single, continuous line.)

The **ZMean_TT** worksheet applies the two-tail *Z* test to the Example 10.2 cereal-filling process. The similar **ZMean_All** worksheet includes the two-tail test, the upper one-tail test, and the lower one-tail test on one worksheet. To adapt these worksheets to other problems, change the null hypothesis, level of significance, population standard deviation, sample size, and sample mean values, in the tinted cells B4 through B8, as is necessary.

E10.2 Using the *t* Test for the Mean (σ Unknown)

You perform the *t* test for the mean (σ unknown) by making entries in either the **TMean_TT** (see Figure 10.7) or

TMean_All worksheets of the T Mean.xls workbook. These worksheets use the **TINV(1-*confidence level, degrees of freedom*)** function to determine the lower and upper critical values and use the **TDIST(ABS(*t*), *degrees of freedom, tails*)** function in which **ABS(*t*)** is the absolute value of the t_{STAT} test statistic, and *tails* is either 1, for a one-tail test, or 2, for a two-tail test, to compute the *p*-values. The worksheets also use the IF function to determine whether or not you should reject the null hypothesis.

The **TMean_TT** worksheet applies the two-tail *t* test to the Section 10.2 sales invoices example. The similar **TMean_All** worksheet includes the two-tail test, the upper one-tail test, and the lower one-tail test on one worksheet. To adapt these worksheets to other problems, change the null hypothesis, level of significance, sample size, sample mean, and sample standard deviation values, in the tinted cells B4 through B8, as is necessary.

E10.3 Using the *Z* Test for the Proportion

You perform the *Z* test for the proportion by making entries in either the **ZProp_TT** (see Figure 10.16) or **ZProp_All** worksheets of the Z Proportion.xls workbook. These worksheets use the **NORMSINV(*P* < *X*)** function to determine the lower and upper critical values and use the **NORMSDIST(Z *value*)** function to compute the *p*-values. The worksheets also use the IF function to determine whether or not you should reject the null hypothesis.

The **ZProp_TT** worksheet applies the two-tail *Z* test to the Section 10.4 example concerning customer satisfaction. The **ZProp_All** worksheet includes the two-tail test, the upper one-tail test, and the lower one-tail test on one worksheet. To adapt these worksheets to other problems, enter the appropriate null hypothesis, level of significance, number of items of interest, and sample size, in the tinted cells B4 through B7, as is necessary.

11

Two-Sample Tests and One-Way ANOVA

Learning Objectives

In this chapter, you learn how to use hypothesis testing for comparing the difference between:

- The means of two independent populations
- The means of two related populations
- The proportions of two independent populations
- The variances of two independent populations
- The means of more than two populations

@ BLK Foods

Does the type of display used in a supermarket affect the sales of products? As the regional sales manager for BLK Foods, you want to compare the sales volume of BLK Cola when the product is placed in the normal shelf location to the sales volume when the product is featured in a special end-aisle display. To test the effectiveness of the end-aisle displays, you select 20 stores from the BLK supermarket chain that all experience similar storewide sales volumes. You then randomly assign 10 of the 20 stores to sample 1 and 10 to sample 2. The managers of the 10 stores in sample 1 place the BLK Cola in the normal shelf location alongside the other cola products. The 10 stores in sample 2 use the special end-aisle promotional display. At the end of one week, the sales of BLK Cola are recorded. How can you determine whether sales of BLK Cola using the end-aisle displays are the same as those when the cola is placed in the normal shelf location? How can you decide if the variability in BLK cola sales from store to store is the same for the two types of displays? How could you use the answers to these questions to improve sales of BLK Cola?

H ypothesis testing provides a *confirmatory* approach to data analysis. In Chapter 10, you learned a variety of commonly used hypothesis-testing procedures that relate to a single sample of data selected from a single population. In this chapter, you learn how to extend hypothesis testing to procedures that compare statistics from samples of data selected from two or more populations. One such extension would be asking the question, "Are the mean weekly sales of BLK Cola when using the normal shelf location equal to the mean weekly sales of BLK Cola when placed in an end-aisle display?"

11.1 Comparing the Means of Two Independent Populations

Z Test for the Difference Between Two Means

Suppose that you take a random sample of n_1 from the first population and a random sample of n_2 from the second population, and the data collected in each sample are from a numerical variable. In the first population, the mean is represented by the symbol μ_1 and the standard deviation is represented by the symbol σ_1. In the second population, the mean is represented by the symbol μ_2 and the standard deviation is represented by the symbol σ_1.

The test statistic used to determine the difference between the population means is based on the difference between the sample means $(\overline{X}_1 - \overline{X}_2)$. If you assume that the samples are randomly and independently selected from populations that are normally distributed, this statistic follows the standardized normal distribution. If the populations are not normally distributed, the Z test is still appropriate if the sample sizes are large enough (typically n_1 and $n_2 \geq 30$; see the Central Limit Theorem). Equation (11.1) defines the **Z test for the difference between two means.**

Z TEST FOR THE DIFFERENCE BETWEEN TWO MEANS

$$Z = \frac{(\overline{X}_1 - \overline{X}_2) - (\mu_1 - \mu_2)}{\sqrt{\dfrac{\sigma_1^2}{n_1} + \dfrac{\sigma_2^2}{n_2}}}$$

(11.1)

where

$\overline{X}_1$ = mean of the sample taken from population 1

μ_1 = mean of population 1

σ_1^2 = variance of population 1

n_1 = size of the sample taken from population 1

$\overline{X}_2$ = mean of the sample taken from population 2

μ_2 = mean of population 2

σ_2^2 = variance of population 2

n_2 = size of the sample taken from population 2

The test statistic Z follows a standardized normal distribution.

Pooled-Variance t Test for the Difference Between Two Means

Suppose that you take a random sample of n_1 from the first population and a random sample of n_2 from the second population. The data collected in each sample are from a numerical variable. In the first population, the mean is represented by the symbol μ_1 and the standard deviation is represented by the symbol σ_1. In the second population, the mean is represented by the symbol μ_2 and the standard deviation is represented by the symbol σ_2.

In almost all cases, the variances of the two populations are not known. The only information you usually have are the sample means and the sample variances. If you assume that the samples are randomly and independently selected from populations that are normally distributed and that the population variances are equal (i.e., $\sigma_1^2 = \sigma_2^2$), you can use a **pooled-variance t test** to determine whether there is a significant difference between the means of the two populations. If the populations are not normally distributed, the pooled-variance t test is still appropriate if the sample sizes are large enough (typically n_1 and $n_2 \geq 30$; see the Central Limit Theorem in Section 7.4).

To test the null hypothesis of no difference in the means of two independent populations:

$$H_0: \mu_1 = \mu_2 \quad \text{or} \quad \mu_1 - \mu_2 = 0$$

against the alternative that the means are not the same

$$H_1: \mu_1 \neq \mu_2 \quad \text{or} \quad \mu_1 - \mu_2 \neq 0$$

you use the pooled-variance t-test statistic t_{STAT} shown in Equation (11.1). The pooled-variance t test gets its name from the fact that the test statistic pools or combines the two sample variances S_1^2 and S_2^2 to compute S_p^2, the best estimate of the variance common to both populations under the assumption that the two population variances are equal.[1]

[1]When the two sample sizes are equal (i.e., $n_1 = n_2$), the equation for the pooled variance can be simplified to

$$S_p^2 = \frac{S_1^2 + S_2^2}{2}$$

POOLED-VARIANCE t TEST FOR THE DIFFERENCE BETWEEN TWO MEANS

$$t_{STAT} = \frac{(\overline{X}_1 - \overline{X}_2) - (\mu_1 - \mu_2)}{\sqrt{S_p^2\left(\dfrac{1}{n_1} + \dfrac{1}{n_2}\right)}}$$

where

$$S_p^2 = \frac{(n_1 - 1)S_1^2 + (n_2 - 1)S_2^2}{(n_1 - 1) + (n_2 - 1)} \tag{11.1}$$

and

S_p^2 = pooled variance

$\overline{X}_1$ = mean of the sample taken from population 1

S_1^2 = variance of the sample taken from population 1

n_1 = size of the sample taken from population 1

$\overline{X}_2$ = mean of the sample taken from population 2

S_2^2 = variance of the sample taken from population 2

n_2 = size of the sample taken from population 2

The t_{STAT} test statistic follows a t distribution with $n_1 + n_2 - 2$ degrees of freedom.

For a given level of significance α, in a two-tail test, you reject the null hypothesis if the computed t_{STAT} test statistic is greater than the upper-tail critical value from the t distribution or if the computed t_{STAT} test statistic is less than the lower-tail critical value from the t distribution. Figure 11.1 displays the regions of rejection.

FIGURE 11.1

Regions of rejection and nonrejection for the pooled-variance t test for the difference between the means (two-tail test)

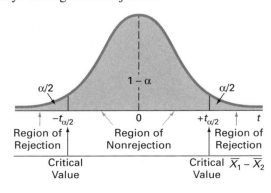

In a one-tail test in which the rejection region is in the lower tail, you reject the null hypothesis if the computed t_{STAT} test statistic is less than the lower-tail critical value from the t distribution. In a one-tail test in which the rejection region is in the upper tail, you reject the null hypothesis if the computed t_{STAT} test statistic is greater than the upper-tail critical value from the t distribution.

To demonstrate the use of the pooled-variance t test, return to the Using Statistics scenario. You want to determine whether the mean weekly sales of BLK Cola are the same when using a normal shelf location and when using an end-aisle display. There are two populations of interest. The first population is the set of all possible weekly sales of BLK Cola *if* all the BLK supermarkets used the normal shelf location. The second population is the set of all possible weekly sales of BLK Cola *if* all the BLK supermarkets used the end-aisle displays. The first sample contains the weekly sales of BLK Cola from the 10 stores selected to use the normal shelf location, and the second sample contains the weekly sales of BLK Cola from the 10 stores selected to use the end-aisle display. Table 11.1 contains the cola sales (in number of cases) for the two samples (see the `Cola` file).

TABLE 11.1

Comparing BLK Cola Weekly Sales from Two Different Display Locations (in Number of Cases)

Display Location									
Normal					**End-Aisle**				
22	34	52	62	30	52	71	76	54	67
40	64	84	56	59	83	66	90	77	84

The null and alternative hypotheses are

$$H_0: \mu_1 = \mu_2 \quad \text{or} \quad \mu_1 - \mu_2 = 0$$

$$H_1: \mu_1 \neq \mu_2 \quad \text{or} \quad \mu_1 - \mu_2 \neq 0$$

Assuming that the samples are from normal populations having equal variances, you can use the pooled-variance t test. The t_{STAT} test statistic follows a t distribution with $10 + 10 - 2 = 18$ degrees of freedom. Using $\alpha = 0.05$ level of significance, you divide the rejection region into the two tails for this two-tail test (i.e., two equal parts of 0.025 each). Table E.3 shows that the critical values for this two-tail test are $+2.1009$ and -2.1009. As shown in Figure 11.2, the decision rule is:

$$\text{Reject } H_0 \text{ if } t_{STAT} > +2.1009$$

$$\text{or if } t_{STAT} < -2.1009;$$

$$\text{otherwise do not reject } H_0.$$

FIGURE 11.2

Two-tail test of hypothesis for the difference between the means at the 0.05 level of significance with 18 degrees of freedom

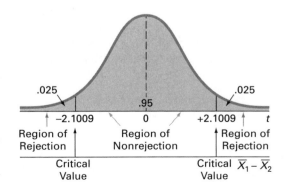

From Figure 11.3, the computed t_{STAT} test statistic for this test is -3.045 and the p-value is 0.0070.

FIGURE 11.3

SPSS *t*-test results for the two display locations

Group Statistics					
Display		**N**	**Mean**	**Std. Deviation**	**Std. Error Mean**
Weekly Sales	Normal	10	50.30	18.726	5.922
	End-Aisle	10	72.00	12.543	3.967

		Levene's Test for Equality of Variances		t-test for Equality of Means						
									95% Confidence Interval of the Difference	
		F	**Sig.**	**t**	**df**	**Sig. (2-tailed)**	**Mean Difference**	**Std. Error Difference**	**Lower**	**Upper**
Weekly Sales	Equal variances assumed	1.745	.203	−3.045	18	.007	−21.700	7.127	−36.674	−6.726
	Equal variances not assumed			−3.045	15.723	.008	−21.700	7.127	−36.831	−6.569

Using Equation (11.1) on page 453 and the descriptive statistics provided in Figure 11.3,

$$t_{STAT} = \frac{(\overline{X}_1 - \overline{X}_2) - (\mu_1 - \mu_2)}{\sqrt{S_p^2\left(\dfrac{1}{n_1} + \dfrac{1}{n_2}\right)}}$$

where

$$S_p^2 = \frac{(n_1 - 1)S_1^2 + (n_2 - 1)S_2^2}{(n_1 - 1) + (n_2 - 1)}$$

$$= \frac{9(350.6778) + 9(157.3333)}{9 + 9} = 254.0056$$

Therefore,

$$t_{STAT} = \frac{(50.3 - 72.0) - 0.0}{\sqrt{254.0056\left(\dfrac{1}{10} + \dfrac{1}{10}\right)}} = \frac{-21.7}{\sqrt{50.801}} = -3.0446$$

You reject the null hypothesis because $t_{STAT} = -3.045 < -2.1009$. The *p*-value (as computed from Microsoft Excel or Minitab) is 0.0070. In other words, the probability that $t_{STAT} > 3.0446$ or $t_{STAT} < -3.0446$ is equal to 0.0070. This *p*-value indicates that if the population means are equal, the probability of observing a difference this large or larger in the two sample means is only 0.0070. Because the *p*-value is less than $\alpha = 0.05$, there is sufficient evidence to reject the null hypothesis. You can conclude that the mean sales are different for the normal shelf location and the end-aisle location. Based on these results, the sales are lower for the normal location (i.e., higher for the end-aisle location). Example 11.1 provides another application of the pooled-variance *t* test.

EXAMPLE 11.1

Testing for the Difference in the Mean Delivery Times

A local pizza restaurant and a local branch of a national chain are located across the street from a college campus. The local pizza restaurant advertises that they deliver to the dormitories faster than the national chain. In order to determine whether this advertisement is valid, you and some friends have decided to order 10 pizzas from the local pizza restaurant and 10 pizzas from the national chain, all at different times. The delivery times in minutes (see the `Pizzatime` file) are shown in Table 11.2:

TABLE 11.2

Delivery Times (in minutes) for Local Pizza Restaurant and National Pizza Chain

Local		Chain	
16.8	18.1	22.0	19.5
11.7	14.1	15.2	17.0
15.6	21.8	18.7	19.5
16.7	13.9	15.6	16.5
17.5	20.8	20.8	24.0

At the 0.05 level of significance, is there evidence that the mean delivery time for the local pizza restaurant is less than the mean delivery time for the national pizza chain?

SOLUTION Because you want to know whether the mean is *lower* for the local pizza restaurant than for the national pizza chain, you have a one-tail test with the following null and alternative hypotheses:

$H_0: \mu_1 \geq \mu_2$ (The mean delivery time for the local pizza restaurant is equal to or greater than the mean delivery time for the national pizza chain.)

$H_1: \mu_1 < \mu_2$ (The mean delivery time for the local pizza restaurant is less than the mean delivery time for the national pizza chain.)

Figure 11.4 displays SPSS results of the pooled t test for these data.

FIGURE 11.4

SPSS results of the pooled t test for the pizza delivery time data

Group Statistics

Pizzarestaurant		N	Mean	Std. Deviation	Std. Error Mean
Delivery Time	Local Pizza restaurant	10	16.700	3.0955	.9789
	National Pizza Chain	10	18.880	2.8662	.9064

Independent Samples Test

		Levene's Test for Equality of Variances		t-test for Equality of Means					95% Confidence Interval of the Difference	
		F	Sig.	t	df	Sig. (2-tailed)	Mean Difference	Std. Error Difference	Lower	Upper
Delivery Time	Equal variances assumed	.001	.980	−1.634	18	.120	−2.1800	1.3341	−4.9828	.6228
	Equal variances not assumed			−1.634	17.894	.120	−2.1800	1.3341	−4.9840	.6240

Using Equation (11.1),

$$t_{STAT} = \frac{(\bar{X}_1 - \bar{X}_2) - (\mu_1 - \mu_2)}{\sqrt{S_p^2 \left(\dfrac{1}{n_1} + \dfrac{1}{n_2} \right)}}$$

where

$$S_p^2 = \frac{(n_1 - 1)S_1^2 + (n_2 - 1)S_2^2}{(n_1 - 1) + (n_2 - 1)}$$

$$= \frac{9(9.5822) + 9(8.2151)}{9 + 9} = 8.8987$$

Therefore,

$$t_{STAT} = \frac{(16.7 - 18.88) - 0.0}{\sqrt{8.8987 \left(\dfrac{1}{10} + \dfrac{1}{10} \right)}} = \frac{-2.18}{\sqrt{1.7797}} = -1.6341$$

You do not reject the null hypothesis because $t_{STAT} = -1.634 > -1.7341$. The p-value (as computed from SPSS) is 0.06. This p-value indicates that the probability that $t_{STAT} < -1.6341$ is equal to 0.06. In other words, if the population means are equal, the probability that the sample mean delivery time for the local pizza restaurant is at least 2.18 minutes faster than the national chain is 0.06. Because the p-value is greater than $\alpha = 0.05$, there is insufficient evidence to reject the null hypothesis. Based on these results, there is insufficient evidence for the local pizza restaurant to make the advertising claim that they have a faster delivery time.

In testing for the difference between the means, you assume that the populations are normally distributed with equal variances. For situations in which the two populations have equal variances, the pooled-variance t test is **robust** (or not sensitive) to moderate departures from the assumption of normality, provided that the sample sizes are large. In such situations, you can use the pooled-variance t test without serious effects on its power. However, if you cannot assume that both populations are normally distributed, you have two choices. You can use a nonparametric procedure, such as the Wilcoxon rank sum test (see references 1 and 2), that does not depend on the assumption of normality for the two populations, or you can use a normalizing transformation (see reference 9) on each of the outcomes and then use the pooled-variance t test.

To check the assumption of normality in each of the two populations, observe the boxplot of the sales for the two display locations in Figure 11.5. For these two small samples, there appears to be only moderate departure from normality, so the assumption of normality needed for the t test is not seriously violated.

Separate-Variance t Test for the Difference Between Two Means

In testing for the difference between the means of two independent populations when the population variances are assumed to be equal, the sample variances are pooled together into a common estimate S_p^2. However, if you cannot make this assumption, then the pooled-variance t test is inappropriate. In this case, you should use the **separate-variance t test** developed by Satterthwaite. This test procedure includes the two separate sample variances in the computation of the t-test statistic. Although the computations for the separate-variance t test are complicated, you can use Microsoft Excel or SPSS to perform the test.

Figure 11.6 illustrates SPSS results for this separate-variance t test. Note that Excel rounds the degrees of freedom.

FIGURE 11.5

Minitab boxplot for the sales for two display locations

(Microsoft Excel users, see Section E3.3.)

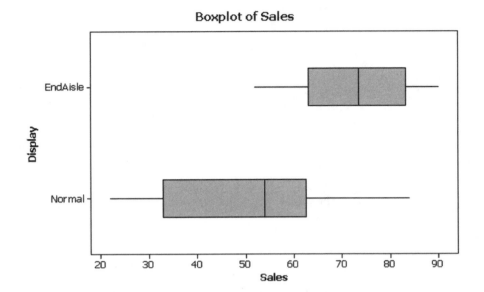

FIGURE 11.6

SPSS results of the separate-variance *t* test for the display location data

See Section E11.4 to create this.

Group Statistics

Display		N	Mean	Std. Deviation	Std. Error Mean
Weekly Sales	Normal	10	50.30	18.726	5.922
	End-Aisle	10	72.00	12.543	3.967

Independent Samples Test

		Levene's Test for Equality of Variances		t-test for Equality of Means					95% Confidence Interval of the Difference	
		F	Sig.	t	df	Sig. (2-tailed)	Mean Difference	Std. Error Difference	Lower	Upper
Weekly Sales	Equal variances assumed	1.745	.203	−3.045	18	.007	−21.700	7.127	−36.674	−6.726
	Equal variances not assumed			−3.045	15.723	.008	−21.700	7.127	−36.831	−6.569

In Figure 11.6 the test statistic $t_{STAT} = -3.045$ and the *p*-value is $0.008 < 0.05$. Thus, the results for the separate-variance *t* test are almost exactly the same as those of the pooled-variance *t* test. The assumption of equality of population variances had no real effect on the results. Sometimes, however, the results from the pooled-variance and separate-variance *t* tests conflict because the assumption of equal variances is violated. Therefore, it is important that you evaluate the assumptions and use those results as a guide in appropriately selecting a test procedure. In Section 11.4, the *F* test is used to determine whether there is evidence of a difference in the two population variances. The results of that test can help you determine which of the *t* tests—pooled-variance or separate-variance—is more appropriate.

THINK ABOUT THIS | "This Call May Be Monitored . . ."

If you have ever used a telephone to seek customer service, you've probably heard at least once a message that begins "this call may be monitored . . ." Most of the time the message explains the monitoring is for "quality assurance purposes," but do companies really monitor your calls to improve quality?

From one of our previous students, we've learned that a certain large financial corporation really does monitor calls for quality purposes. This student was asked to develop an improved training program for a call center that was hiring people to answer phone calls customers make about outstanding loans. For feedback and evaluation, she planned to randomly select phone calls received by each new employee and rate the employee on ten aspects of the call including did the employee maintain a pleasant tone with the customer?

Who You Gonna Call?

She presented her plan to her boss for approval, but her boss, remembering the words of a famous statistician, said, "In God we trust, all others must bring data." That is, her boss wanted proof that her new training program would improve customer service. Faced with such a request, who would you call? She called one of us. "Hey professor, you'll never believe why I called. I work for a large company and in the project I am currently working on, I have to put some of the statistics you taught us to work! Can you help?" The answer was "Yes" and together they formulated this test:

- Randomly assign the 60 most recent hires into two training programs. Half would go through the preexisting training program, and half would be trained using the new program.

- At the end of the first month, compare the mean score for the 30 employees in the new training program against the mean score for the 30 employees in the preexisting training program.

She listened as her professor explained, "What you are trying to prove is that the mean score from the new training program is higher than the mean score from the current program. You can make the null hypothesis that the means are equal, and see if you can reject it in favor of the alternative that the mean score from the new program is higher."

"Or, as you used to say, 'if the p-value is low, H_0 must go!'—yes, I do remember!" she replied. Her professor chuckled and said, "Yes, that's correct. And if you can reject H_0, you will have the proof to present to your boss." She thanked him for his help and got back to work with the newfound confidence that she would be able to successfully apply the t test that compares the means of two independent populations.

CALCULATOR LESSON 11A

CFX-9850GB CALCULATOR

Lesson 11A—Z-Test and t-Test of Two Means

EXAMPLE 11.2

A company that makes bolts that are used on an automotive component uses two machines to make these bolts. It has been determined by past studies that the standard deviation of the bolt diameters made by machine 1 is 0.025 mm. and the standard deviation of the bolt diameters of machine 2 is 0.022 mm. Both machines have a dial to set for the desired diameter. Recently the company used both machines to fill a large order. The customer found that many of the bolts from a certain package were too large and made a complaint. It was determined that the package in question was made by machine 2. The manufacturer decided to take samples of the bolts from both machines to test to see whether the mean diameter of the bolts from machine 2 was significantly larger than the mean diameter from machine 1 when the dial was set to the same diameter on each machine. The sample of 100 bolts from machine 1 had a mean diameter of 5.02 mm and a sample of 100 bolts from machine 2 had a mean diameter of 5.09 mm. At the 5% level of significance what is the conclusion?

Solution: From the **Main Menu** select:

STAT **F3**(test) **F1**(Z) **F2**(2-S)   then enter the following items:

2-Sample ZTest

Data	: **F2**(Var)	▼
μ1	: **F2**(<μ2)	▼
σ1	: **0.025**	**EXE**
σ2	: **0.022**	**EXE**
$\bar{x}$1	: **5.023**	**EXE**
n1	: **100**	**EXE**
$\bar{x}$2	: **5.031**	**EXE**
n2	: **100**	**EXE**

Now key **EXE** or **F1**(Calc)

The calculator will now show the results:

2-Sample ZTest

$\mu 1$	$< \mu 2$
z	$= -2.4022$
p	$=8.1465\text{E-}03$ $(=0.0081465)$
$\bar{x}1$	$=5.023$
$\bar{x}2$	$=5.031$
n1	$=100$
n2	$=100$

Since the p-value < 0.05, the conclusion is to *reject* the null hypothesis. In other words the mean diameter of bolts produced by machine 2 is greater than the mean of machine 1.

EXAMPLE 11.3

A work team has developed a new process to assemble a certain component. They would like to know if this new process has significantly reduced the time to assemble the component. They have taken samples of 50 components produced by the existing process and 40 components produced by the new process. The mean and standard deviation of the assembly times for the existing process were 73.2 minutes and 3.6 minutes, respectively. The mean time was 71.4 minutes with a standard deviation of 3.2 minutes for the components assembled by the new process. Assume that the times for both processes are normally distributed with the same variance. At the 1% level of significance, does this evidence indicate that the new process is quicker than the old process?

Solution: Let sample 1 be the existing process sample, and sample 2 the new process. From the **Main Menu** select:

STAT **F3**(test) **F2**(t) **F2**(2-S)   then enter the following items:

2-Sample tTest

Data	: **F2**(Var)	▼
$\mu 1$	: **F3**($>\mu 2$)	▼
$\bar{x}1$	**: 73.2**	**EXE**
x1_n-1	**: 3.6**	**EXE**
n1	**: 50**	**EXE**
$\bar{x}12$	**: 71.4**	**EXE**
x2σn-1	**: 3.2**	**EXE**
n2	**: 40**	**EXE**
Pooled	: **F1**(On)	**EXE**

(Note: if you select **F1(On)**, you are using the t-test-pooled-variance procedure)
if you select **F2(OFF)**, you are using the t-test-separate variance.

The calculator will now show the results:

2-Sample tTest

$\mu 1$	$> \mu 2$
t	$=2.4749$
p	$=7.6215\text{E-}03$ $(=0.0076215)$
df	$=88$
1	$=73.2$
2	$=71.4$
$\bar{x}1$σn-1	$=3.6$
$\bar{x}2$σn-1	$=3.2$
xPσn-1	$=3.4284$
n1	$=50$
n2	$=40$

Since the p-value < 0.01, the conclusion is to reject the null hypothesis. In other words the evidence does indicate that the average time to assemble the component by the new process is less than the average time to assemble the component by the existing process, i.e. the new process is faster.

EXAMPLE 11.4   We wish to determine if there is a difference in the braking distances for two types of tires. Use the 5% level of significance and assume that the braking distances for each type of tire are normally distributed with the same variance. Based on the data for the samples of tires shown, at the 5% level of significance, should we conclude that there is a difference in the mean braking distance?

Braking distance (metres)

Tire A	Tire B
83	75
79	84
82	76
84	83
80	85
81	78
	83

Solution: Enter the data for Tire A in List 1 and the data for Tire B in List 2. From the **Main Menu** select:

STAT F3(test) **F2**(t) **F2**(2-S)   then enter the following items:

2-Sample tTest

Data	: **F1**(List)	▼
μ1	: **F1**($\neq$μ2)	▼
List1	: **F1**(List1)	▼
List2	: **F2**(List2)	▼
Freq	: **1**	▼
Freq	: **1**	▼
Pooled	: **F1**(On)	**EXE**

The calculator will now show the results:

2-Sample tTest

μ1	$\neq$μ2
t	=0.50699
p	=0.62216
df	=11
$\bar{x}1$	=81.5
$\bar{x}2$	=80.571
x1σn-1	=1.8708
x2σn-1	=4.1173
xPσn-1	=3.292
n1	=6
n2	=7

Since the p-value > 0.05, the conclusion is to *not reject* the null hypothesis. In other words the evidence does not indicate that the average stopping distance is different for the two types of tires.

C A L C U L A T O R   L E S S O N   1 1 B

CASIO FX-9750GII CALCULATOR

Lesson 11B—Z-Test and t-Test of Two Means

EXAMPLE 11.5

A company that makes bolts that are used on an automotive component uses two machines to make these bolts. It has been determined by past studies that the standard deviation of the bolt diameters made by machine 1 is 0.025 mm. and the standard deviation of the bolt diameters of machine 2 is 0.022 mm. Both machines have a dial to set for the desired diameter. Recently they used both machines to fill a large order. The customer found that many of the bolts from a certain package were too large and made a complaint. It was determined that the package in question was made by machine 2. The manufacturer decided to take samples of the bolts from both machines to test to see whether the mean diameter of the bolts from machine 2 was significantly larger than the mean diameter from machine 1 when the dial was set to the same diameter on each machine. The sample of 100 bolts from machine 1 had a mean diameter of 5.02 mm and a sample of 100 bolts from machine 2 had a mean diameter of 5.09 mm when the dial on both machines was set at 5.00 mm. At the 5% level of significance what is the conclusion?

Solution: From the **Main Menu** select:

STAT   F3(test)   **F1**(Z)   **F2**(2-S)   then enter the following items:

2-Sample ZTest

Data	: **F2**(Var)	▼
$\mu 1$	: **F2**($<\mu 2$)	▼
$\sigma 1$	: **0.025**	**EXE**
$\sigma 2$	: **0.022**	**EXE**
$\bar{x}1$	: **5.023**	**EXE**
n1	: **100**	**EXE**
$\bar{x}2$	: **5.031**	**EXE**
n2	: **100**	**EXE**
Save Res	: NONE	

Now key **EXE** or **F1**(Calc) or **F6**(DRAW)

If you select **F6**(DRAW), you will see a normal distribution.

If you select either **EXE** or **F1**(Calc), the calculator will now show the results:

2-Sample ZTest

$\mu 1$	$<\mu 2$
z	$=-2.4022$
p	$=8.1465E-03$ $(=0.0081465)$
$\bar{x}1$	$=5.023$
$\bar{x}2$	$=5.031$
n1	$=100$
n2	$=100$

Since the p-value < 0.05, the conclusion is to *reject* the null hypothesis. In other words the mean diameter of bolts produced by machine 2 is greater than the mean of machine 1.

EXAMPLE 11.6

A work team has developed a new process to assemble a certain component. They would like to know if this new process has significantly reduced the time to assemble the component. They have taken samples of 50 components produced by the existing process and 40 components produced by the new process. The mean and standard deviation of the assembly times for the existing process were 73.2 minutes and 3.6 minutes, respectively. The mean time was 71.4 minutes with a standard deviation of 3.2 minutes for the components assembled by the new process. Assume that the times for both processes are normally distributed with the same variance. At the 1% level of significance, does this evidence indicate that the new process is quicker than the old process?

Solution: Let sample 1 be the existing process sample, and sample 2 the new process. From the **Main Menu** select:

STAT   F3(test) **F2**(t) **F2**(2-S)   then enter the following items:

2-Sample tTest

Data	: **F2**(Var)	▼
μ1	: **F3**(>μ2)	▼
$\bar{x}$1	: **73.2**	**EXE**
sx1	: **3.6**	**EXE**
n1	: **50**	**EXE**
$\bar{x}$2	: **71.4**	**EXE**
sx2	: **3.2**	**EXE**
n2	: **40**	**EXE**
Pooled	: **F1**(On)	**EXE**
Save Res	: None	

Now key **EXE** or **F1**(Calc) or **F6**(DRAW)

If you select **F6**(DRAW), you will see a normal distribution.

If you select either **EXE** or **F1**(Calc), the calculator will now show the results:

2-Sample tTest

μ1	>μ2
t	=2.4749
p	=7.6215E-03 (=0.0076215)
df	=88
$\bar{x}$1	=73.2
$\bar{x}$2	=71.4
sx1	=3.6
sx2	=3.2
sp	=3.4284
n1	=50
n2	=40

Since the p-value < 0.01, the conclusion is to *reject* the null hypothesis. In other words the evidence does indicate that the average time to assemble the component by the new process is less than the average time to assemble the component by the existing process, i.e. the new process is faster.

EXAMPLE 11.7   We wish to determine if there is a difference in the braking distances for two types of tires. Use the 5% level of significance and assume that the braking distances for each type of tire are normally distributed with the same variance. Based on the data for the samples of tires shown, at the 5% level of significance, should we conclude that there is a difference in the mean braking distance?

Braking distance (metres)	
Tire A	Tire B
83	75
79	84
82	76
84	83
80	85
81	78
	83

Solution: Enter the data for Tire A in List 1 and the data for Tire B in List 2. From the **Main Menu** select:

STAT F3(test) **F2**(t) **F2**(2-S)   then enter the following items:

2-Sample tTest

Data	: **F1**(List)	▼
μ1	: **F1**($\neq$μ2)	▼
List1	: **F1**(List1)	▼
List2	: **F1**(List2)	▼
Freq	: **1**	▼
Freq	: **1**	▼
Pooled	: **F1**(On)	**EXE**
Save Res	: None	

Now key **EXE** or **F1**(Calc) or **F6**(DRAW)

If you select **F6**(DRAW), you will see a normal distribution.

If you select either **EXE** or **F1**(Calc), the calculator will now show the results:

2-Sample tTest

μ1	$\neq$μ2
t	=0.50699
p	=0.62216
df	=11
$\bar{x}1$	=81.5
$\bar{x}2$	=80.571
sx1	=1.8708
sx2	=4.1173
sp	=3.292
n1	=6
n2	=7

Since the p-value > 0.05, the conclusion is to *not reject* the null hypothesis. In other words the evidence does not indicate that the average stopping distance is different for the two types of tires.

SPSS—VERSION 16—Two Independent Samples T-Test

We will use the scenario, "Delivery Times for Local Pizza Restaurant and National Pizza Chain" (Example 11.1), to demonstrate how to perform two independent samples T test using SPSS.

A local pizza restaurant located close to a college campus advertises that their delivery time to a college dormitory is less than for a local branch of a national pizza chain. In order to determine whether this advertisement is valid, you and some friends have decided to order 10 pizzas from the local pizza restaurant and 10 pizzas from the national chain, all at different times. The data is shown below:

Local	Chain
16.8	22.0
11.7	15.2
15.6	18.7
16.7	15.6
17.5	20.8
18.1	19.5
14.1	17.0
21.8	19.5
13.9	16.5
20.8	24.0

At the 0.05 level of significance, is there evidence that the mean delivery time is lower for the local pizza restaurant than for the national pizza chain?

Solution:

Performing an Independent-Samples T test on SPSS—Version 16

Step 1: Open the SPSS Data Editor.

Click **"cancel"** to cancel the SPSS opening window.

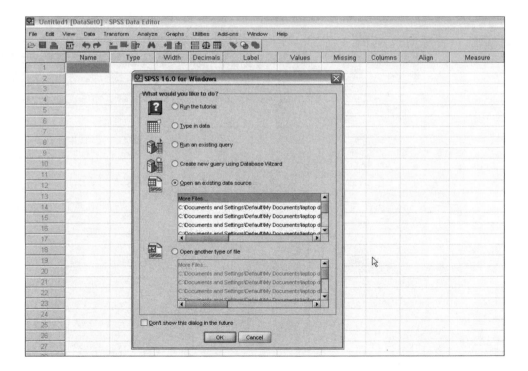

Step 2: Define the variables and give the variables a label.

Click **"Variable View"** (at the bottom of the window) to go to the variable view window to define the variables and fix the data at zero or one decimal places.

- Enter the first variable name -"Restaurant" and then click **values.** Key **"1"** in the value box and key **"Local Pizza Restaurant"** in the Label box, and then click **Add.** Similarly enter "2" for **"National Pizza Chain".**

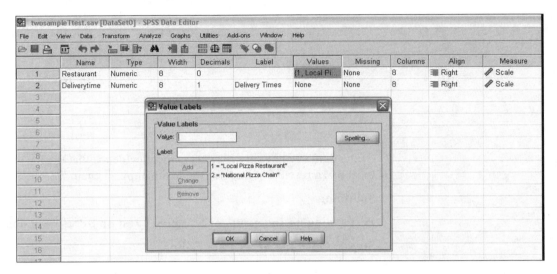

- Enter the second variable name – "Deliverytime" and label it as "Delivery Times".

Step 3: Create a SPSS data file.

Click **"Data View"** to return to the data view window. Now, enter the raw data on page 416 into the respective column of variables.

	Restaurant	Deliverytime	var	var	var	var
1	1	16.8				
2	1	11.7				
3	1	15.6				
4	1	16.7				
5	1	17.5				
6	1	18.1				
7	1	14.1				
8	1	21.8				
9	1	13.9				
10	1	20.8				
11	2	22.0				
12	2	15.2				
13	2	18.7				
14	2	15.6				
15	2	20.8				
16	2	19.5				
17	2	17.0				
18	2	19.5				
19	2	16.5				
20	2	24.0				
21						

After you have entered all the data, save it as "twosampleTtest.sav" (or any filename).

Step 3: Perform Two independent samples t-test.

Make the following menu selections:

Analyze → Compare Means → Independent-Samples T test

At this point, the **Independent Samples T Test** dialog box will appear. Make these entries in the **Independent-Samples T Test** dialog box:

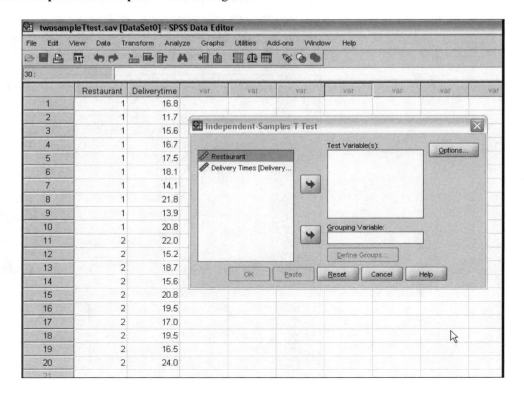

- Highlight on the **"Delivery Times"** variable and click on the arrow key (→). The variable will automatically fall into the **Test Variable(s)** box.

- Highlight on the **"Restaurant"** variable and click on the arrow key (→). The variable will automatically fall into the **Grouping Variable** box.

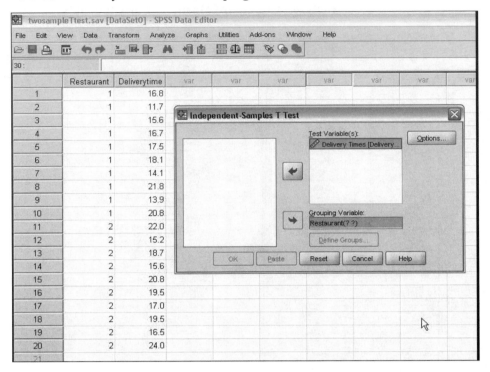

- Next, click on the **Define Groups** button. In the "Define Groups" window, select **Use specified values** by entering "1" for Group 1 and "2" for Group 2. The values of "1" and "2" depend on how you define the two groups at the beginning when you define the variables. Then click on **continue** button to return to the "Independent-Samples T Test" window.

- Click on the **Ok** button to obtain the SPSS results.

Step 3: Go to **SPSS Viewer** to obtain your SPSS results.

SPSS output: T-Test

Group Statistics

	Restaurant	N	Mean	Std. Deviation	Std. Error Mean
Delivery Times	Local Pizza Restaurant	10	16.700	3.0955	.9789
	National Pizza Chain	10	18.880	2.8662	.9064

Independent Samples Test

		Levene's Test for Equality of Variances		t-test for Equality of Means					95% Confidence Interval of the Difference	
		F	Sig.	t	df	Sig. (2-tailed)	Mean Difference	Std. Error Difference	Lower	Upper
Delivery Times	Equal variances assumed	.001	.980	−1.634	18	.120	−2.1800	1.3341	−4.9828	.6228
	Equal variances not assumed			−1.634	17.894	.120	−2.1800	1.3341	−4.9840	.6240

Problems for Section 11.1

LEARNING THE BASICS

11.1 If you have samples of $n_1 = 12$ and $n_2 = 15$, in performing the pooled-variance t test, how many degrees of freedom do you have?

11.2 Assume that you have a sample of $n_1 = 8$, with the sample mean $\overline{X}_1 = 42$, and a sample standard deviation of $S_1 = 4$, and you have an independent sample of $n_2 = 15$ from another population with a sample mean of $\overline{X}_2 = 34$ and the sample standard deviation $S_2 = 5$.

a. What is the value of the pooled-variance t_{STAT} test statistic for testing $H_0: \mu_1 = \mu_2$?
b. In finding the critical value $t_{\alpha/2}$, how many degrees of freedom are there?
c. Using the level of significance $\alpha = 0.01$, what is the critical value for a one-tail test of the hypothesis $H_0: \mu_1 \le \mu_2$ against the alternative $H_1: \mu_1 > \mu_2$?
d. What is your statistical decision?

11.3 What assumptions about the two populations are necessary in Problem 11.2?

11.4 Referring to Problem 11.2, construct a 95% confidence interval estimate of the population mean difference between μ_1 and μ_2.

11.5 Referring to Problem 11.2, if $n_1 = 5$ and $n_2 = 4$, how many degrees of freedom do you have?

11.6 Referring to Problem 11.2, if $n_1 = 5$ and $n_2 = 4$, at the 0.01 level of significance, is there evidence that $\mu_1 > \mu_2$?

APPLYING THE CONCEPTS

11.7 According to a recent study, when shopping online for luxury goods, men spend a mean of \$2,401 as compared to women who spend a mean of \$1,527 (data extracted from R. A. Smith, "Fashion Online: Retailers

Tackle the Gender Gap," *The Wall Street Journal*, March 13, 2008, pp. D1, D10). Suppose that the study was based on a sample of 600 men and 700 females and the standard deviation of the amount spent was $1,200 for men and $1,000 for women.

a. State the null and alternative hypothesis if you want to determine whether the mean amount spent is higher for men than for women.

b. In the context of this study, what is the meaning of the Type I error?

c. In the context of this study, what is the meaning of the Type II error?

d. At the 0.01 level of significance, is there evidence that the mean amount spent is higher for men than for women?

11.8 The American Society for Quality recently conducted a salary survey of its members. The following table includes summary statistics concerning annual salary for reliability/ safety engineers and software quality engineers for respondents working in the United States.

Title	*n*	Mean	Standard Deviation
Reliability/safety engineer	85	87,239	21,094
Software quality engineer	142	84,795	19,344

Source: *Data extracted from H. Lindborg, "Navigate Your Career Path with QP's Annual Salary Survey,"* Quality Progress, *December 2007, pp. 21–50.*

a. Assuming that the population variances are equal and $\alpha = 0.05$, can you prove that the mean salary of reliability/safety engineers differs from the mean salary of software quality engineers?

b. Assuming that the population variances are equal, construct a 95% confidence interval on the difference between the mean salary of reliability/safety engineers and the mean salary of software quality engineers.

c. Compare the results of (a) and (b) and discuss.

11.9 A problem with a telephone line that prevents a customer from receiving or making calls is disconcerting to both the customer and the telephone company. The data in the file **PHONE** represent samples of 20 problems reported to two different offices of a telephone company and the time to clear these problems (in minutes) from the customers' lines:

Central Office I Time to Clear Problems (minutes)

1.48 1.75 0.78 2.85 0.52 1.60 4.15 3.97 1.48 3.10
1.02 0.53 0.93 1.60 0.80 1.05 6.32 3.93 5.45 0.97

Central Office II Time to Clear Problems (minutes)

7.55 3.75 0.10 1.10 0.60 0.52 3.30 2.10 0.58 4.02
3.75 0.65 1.92 0.60 1.53 4.23 0.08 1.48 1.65 0.72

a. Assuming that the population variances from both offices are equal, is there evidence of a difference in the mean waiting time between the two offices? (Use $\alpha = 0.05$.)

b. Find the *p*-value in (a) and interpret its meaning.

c. What other assumption is necessary in (a)?

d. Assuming that the population variances from both offices are equal, construct and interpret a 95% confidence interval estimate of the difference between the population means in the two offices.

SELF Test **11.10** The Computer Anxiety Rating Scale (CARS) measures an individual's level of computer anxiety, on a scale from 20 (no anxiety) to 100 (highest level of anxiety). Researchers at Miami University administered CARS to 172 business students. One of the objectives of the study was to determine whether there is a difference in the level of computer anxiety experienced by female and male business students. They found the following:

	Males	Females
$\overline{X}$	40.26	36.85
S	13.35	9.42
n	100	72

Source: *Data extracted from T. Broome and D. Havelka, "Determinants of Computer Anxiety in Business Students,"* The Review of Business Information Systems, *Spring 2002, 6(2), pp. 9–16.*

a. At the 0.05 level of significance, is there evidence of a difference in the mean computer anxiety experienced by female and male business students?

b. Determine the *p*-value and interpret its meaning.

c. What assumptions do you have to make about the two populations in order to justify the use of the *t* test?

11.11 Digital cameras have taken over the majority of the point-and-shoot camera market. One of the important features of a camera is the battery life as measured by the number of shots taken until the battery needs to be recharged. The data in the file **Digitalcameras** contain the battery life of 31 subcompact cameras and 15 compact cameras (data extracted from "Cameras," *Consumer Reports*, November 2006, pp. 20–21).

a. Assuming that the population variances from both types of digital cameras are equal, is there evidence of a difference in the mean battery life between the two types of digital cameras ($\alpha = 0.05$)?

b. Determine the *p*-value in (a) and interpret its meaning.

c. Assuming that the population variances from both types of digital cameras are equal, construct and interpret a 95% confidence interval estimate of the difference between the population mean battery life of the two types of digital cameras.

11.12 A bank with a branch located in a commercial district of a city has developed an improved process for serving customers during the noon-to-1 P.M. lunch period. The waiting time (operationally defined as the time elapsed from when the customer enters the line until he or she reaches the teller window) needs to be shortened to increase customer satisfaction. A random sample of 15 customers is selected (and stored in the file Bank1), and the results (in minutes) are as follows:

4.21   5.55   3.02   5.13   4.77   2.34   3.54   3.20
4.50   6.10   0.38   5.12   6.46   6.19   3.79

Suppose that another branch, located in a residential area, is also concerned with the noon-to-1 P.M. lunch period. A random sample of 15 customers is selected (and stored in the file Bank2), and the results are as follows:

9.66   5.90   8.02   5.79   8.73   3.82   8.01   8.35
10.49   6.68   5.64   4.08   6.17   9.91   5.47

a. Assuming that the population variances from both banks are equal, is there evidence of a difference in the mean waiting time between the two branches? (Use $\alpha = 0.05$.)
b. Determine the p-value in (a) and interpret its meaning.
c. In addition to equal variances, what other assumption is necessary in (a)?
d. Construct and interpret a 95% confidence interval estimate of the difference between the population means in the two branches.

11.13 Repeat Problem 11.12(a), assuming that the population variances in the two branches are not equal. Compare the results with those of Problem 11.12(a).

11.14 In intaglio printing, a design or figure is carved beneath the surface of hard metal or stone. Suppose that an experiment is designed to compare differences in mean surface hardness of steel plates used in intaglio printing (measured in indentation numbers), based on two different surface conditions—untreated and treated by lightly polishing with emery paper. In the experiment, 40 steel plates are randomly assigned—20 that are untreated, and 20 that are treated. The data are shown here and stored in the file Intaglio :

Untreated		Treated	
164.368	177.135	158.239	150.226
159.018	163.903	138.216	155.620
153.871	167.802	168.006	151.233
165.096	160.818	149.654	158.653
157.184	167.433	145.456	151.204
154.496	163.538	168.178	150.869
160.920	164.525	154.321	161.657
164.917	171.230	162.763	157.016
169.091	174.964	161.020	156.670
175.276	166.311	167.706	147.920

a. Assuming that the population variances from both conditions are equal, is there evidence of a difference in the mean surface hardness between untreated and treated steel plates? (Use $\alpha = 0.05$.)
b. Determine the p-value in (a) and interpret its meaning.
c. In addition to equal variances, what other assumption is necessary in (a)?
d. Construct and interpret a 95% confidence interval estimate of the difference between the population means from treated and untreated steel plates.

11.15 Repeat Problem 11.14(a), assuming that the population variances from untreated and treated steel plates are not equal. Compare the results with those of Problem 11.14(a).

11.16 The director of training for an electronic equipment manufacturer is interested in determining whether different training methods have an effect on the productivity of assembly-line employees. She randomly assigns 42 recently hired employees into two groups of 21. The first group receives a computer-assisted, individual-based training program, and the other receives a team-based training program. Upon completion of the training, the employees are evaluated on the time (in seconds) it takes to assemble a part. The results are in the data file Training .
a. Assuming that the variances in the populations of training methods are equal, is there evidence of a difference between the mean assembly times (in seconds) of employees trained in a computer-assisted, individual-based program and those trained in a team-based program? (Use a 0.05 level of significance.)
b. In addition to equal variances, what other assumption is necessary in (a)?
c. Repeat (a), assuming that the population variances are not equal.
d. Compare the results of (a) and (c).
e. Assuming normality and equal variances, construct and interpret a 95% confidence interval estimate of the difference between the population means of the two training methods.

11.17 Nondestructive evaluation is a method that is used to describe the properties of components or materials without causing any permanent physical change to the units. It includes the determination of properties of materials and the classification of flaws by size, shape, type, and location. This method is most effective for detecting surface flaws and characterizing surface properties of electrically conductive materials. Recently, data were collected that classified each component as having a flaw or not based on manual inspection and operator judgment and also reported the size of the crack in the material. Do the components classified as unflawed have a smaller mean crack size than components classified as flawed? The results in terms of crack size (in inches) are in the data file Crack (data extracted from B. D. Olin and

W. Q. Meeker, "Applications of Statistical Methods to Nondestructive Evaluation," *Technometrics*, 38, 1996, p. 101).

a. Assuming that the population variances are equal, is there evidence that the mean crack size is smaller for the unflawed specimens than for the flawed specimens? (Use $\alpha = 0.05$.)

b. Repeat (a), assuming that the population variances are not equal.

c. Compare the results of (a) and (b).

11.2 Comparing the Means of Two Related Populations

The hypothesis-testing procedures examined in Section 11.1 enable you to make comparisons and examine differences in the means of two *independent* populations. In this section, you will learn about a procedure for analyzing the difference between the means of two populations when you collect sample data from populations that are related—that is, when results of the first population are *not* independent of the results of the second population.

There are two situations that involve related data between populations. Either you take repeated measurements from the same set of items or individuals or you match items or individuals according to some characteristic. In either situation, you are interested in the *difference between the two related values* rather than the *individual values* themselves.

When you take **repeated measurements** on the same items or individuals, you assume that the same items or individuals will behave alike if treated alike. Your objective is to show that any differences between two measurements of the same items or individuals are due to different treatment conditions. For example, when performing a taste-testing experiment comparing two beverages, you can use each person in the sample as his or her own control so that you can have *repeated measurements* on the same individual.

The second situation that involves related data between populations is when you have **matched samples**. Here items or individuals are paired together according to some characteristic of interest. For example, in test marketing a product under two different advertising campaigns, a sample of test markets can be *matched* on the basis of the test market population size and/or demographic variables. By accounting for the differences in test market population size and/or demographic variables, you are better able to measure the effects of the two different advertising campaigns.

Regardless of whether you have matched samples or repeated measurements, the objective is to study the difference between two measurements by reducing the effect of the variability that is due to the items or individuals themselves. Table 11.3 shows the differences in the individual values for two related populations. To read this table, let $X_{11}, X_{12}, \ldots, X_{1n}$ represent the n values from a sample. And let $X_{21}, X_{22}, \ldots, X_{2n}$ represent either the corresponding n matched values from a second sample or the corresponding n repeated measurements from the initial sample. Then, $D_1, D_2, \ldots, D_n$ will represent the corresponding set of n difference *scores* such that

$$D_1 = X_{11} - X_{21}, D_2 = X_{12} - X_{22}, \ldots, \text{and } D_n = X_{1n} - X_{2n}.$$

To test for the mean difference between two related populations, you treat the difference scores, each D_i, as values from a single sample.

TABLE 11.3

Determining the Difference Between Two Related Samples

Value	Sample 1	Sample 2	Difference
1	X_{11}	X_{21}	$D_1 = X_{11} - X_{21}$
2	X_{12}	X_{22}	$D_2 = X_{12} - X_{22}$
.	.	.	.
.	.	.	.
.	.	.	.
i	X_{1i}	X_{2i}	$D_i = X_{1i} - X_{2i}$
.	.	.	.
.	.	.	.
.	.	.	.
n	X_{1n}	X_{2n}	$D_n = X_{1n} - X_{2n}$

Paired *t* Test

If you assume that the difference scores are randomly and independently selected from a population that is normally distributed, you can use the **paired *t* test for the mean difference** in related populations to determine whether there is a significant population mean difference. Like the one-sample *t* test developed in Section 10.2 [see Equation (10.2)], the *t*-test statistic developed here follows the *t* distribution, with $n - 1$ degrees of freedom. Although you must assume that the population is normally distributed, as long as the sample size is not very small and the population is not highly skewed, you can use the paired *t* test.

To test the null hypothesis that there is no difference in the means of two related populations:

$$H_0: \mu_D = 0 \ (\text{where } \mu_D = \mu_1 - \mu_2)$$

against the alternative that the means are not the same:

$$H_1: \mu_D \neq 0$$

you compute the t_{STAT} test statistic using Equation (11.3).

PAIRED *t* TEST FOR THE MEAN DIFFERENCE

$$t_{STAT} = \frac{\overline{D} - \mu_D}{\dfrac{S_D}{\sqrt{n}}}$$

(11.3)

where

$$\mu_D = \text{hypothesized mean difference}$$

$$\overline{D} = \frac{\displaystyle\sum_{i=1}^{n} D_i}{n}$$

$$S_D = \sqrt{\frac{\displaystyle\sum_{i=1}^{n} (D_i - \overline{D})^2}{n - 1}}$$

The t_{STAT} test statistic follows a *t* distribution with $n - 1$ degrees of freedom.

For a two-tail test with a given level of significance, α, you reject the null hypothesis if the computed t_{STAT} test statistic is greater than the upper-tail critical value $t_{\alpha/2}$ from the *t* distribution, or if the computed t_{STAT} test statistic is less than the lower-tail critical value $-t_{\alpha/2}$ from the *t* distribution. The decision rule is

$$\text{Reject } H_0 \text{ if } t_{STAT} > t_{\alpha/2}$$

$$\text{or if } t_{STAT} < -t_{\alpha/2};$$

$$\text{otherwise, do not reject } H_0.$$

The following example illustrates the use of the *t* test for the mean difference. The Automobile Association of America (AAA) conducted a mileage test to compare the gasoline mileage from real-life driving done by AAA members and results of driving done according to government standards (J. Healey, "Fuel Economy Calculations to Be Altered," *USA Today*, January 11, 2006, p. 1B).

What is the best way to design an experiment to compare the gasoline mileage from real-life driving done by AAA members and results of driving done according to government standards? One approach is to take two independent samples and then use the hypothesis tests discussed in Section 11.1. In this approach, you would use one set of automobiles to test the real-life driving done by AAA members. Then you would use a second set of different automobiles to test the results of driving done according to government standards.

However, because the first set of automobiles to test the real-life driving done by AAA members may get lower or higher gasoline mileage than the second set of automobiles, this is not a good approach. A better approach is to use a repeated-measurements experiment. In this experiment, you use one set of automobiles. For each automobile, you conduct a test of real-life driving done by an AAA member and a test of driving done according to government standards. Measuring the two gasoline mileages for the same automobiles serves to reduce the variability in the gasoline mileages compared with what would occur if you used two independent sets of automobiles. This approach focuses on the differences between the real-life driving done by an AAA member and the driving done according to government standards.

Table 11.4 displays results (stored in the file **AAAMileage**) from a sample of $n = 9$ automobiles from such an experiment.

You want to determine whether there is any difference in the mean gasoline mileage between the real-life driving done by an AAA member and the driving done according to government standards. In other words, is there evidence that the mean gasoline mileage is different between the two types of driving? Thus, the null and alternative hypotheses are

H_0: $\mu_D = 0$ (There is no difference in mean gasoline mileage between the real-life driving done by an AAA member and the driving done according to government standards.)

H_1: $\mu_D \neq 0$ (There is a difference in mean gasoline mileage between the real-life driving done by an AAA member and the driving done according to government standards.)

Choosing the level of significance of $\alpha = 0.05$ and assuming that the differences are normally distributed, you use the paired t test [Equation (11.3)]. For a sample of $n = 9$ automobiles, there are $n - 1 = 8$ degrees of freedom. Using Table E.3, the decision rule is

$$\text{Reject } H_0 \text{ if } t_{STAT} > t_{0.025} = 2.3060$$

$$\text{or if } t_{STAT} < -t_{0.025} = -2.3060;$$

$$\text{otherwise, do not reject } H_0.$$

For the $n = 9$ differences (see Table 11.4), the sample mean difference is

and

$$\overline{D} = \frac{\sum_{i=1}^{n} D_i}{n} = \frac{-21.1}{9} = -2.3444$$

$$S_D = \sqrt{\frac{\sum_{i=1}^{n} (D_i - \overline{D})^2}{n - 1}} = 2.893575$$

TABLE 11.4	Model	Members	Government	Difference (D_i)
Repeated Measurements of Gasoline Mileage for Real-Life Driving by AAA Members and Driving Done According to Government Standards	2005 Ford F-150	14.3	16.8	−2.5
	2005 Chevrolet Silverado	15.0	17.8	−2.8
	2002 Honda Accord LX	27.8	26.2	+1.6
	2002 Honda Civic	27.9	33.2	−5.3
	2004 Honda Civic Hybrid	48.8	47.6	+1.2
	2002 Ford Explorer	16.8	18.3	−1.5
	2005 Toyota Camry	23.7	28.5	−4.8
	2003 Toyota Corolla	32.8	33.1	−0.3
	2005 Toyota Prius	37.3	44.0	−6.7

From Equation (11.3) on page 473,

$$t_{STAT} = \frac{\overline{D} - \mu_D}{\frac{S_D}{\sqrt{n}}} = \frac{-2.3444 - 0}{\frac{2.893575}{\sqrt{9}}} = -2.4307$$

Because $t_{STAT} = -2.431$ is less than -2.3060, you reject the null hypothesis, H_0 (see Figure 11.7). There is evidence of a difference in mean gasoline mileage between the real-life driving done by an AAA member and the driving done according to government standards. Real-life driving results in a lower mean gasoline mileage.

FIGURE 11.7

Two-tail paired *t* test at the 0.05 level of significance with 8 degrees of freedom

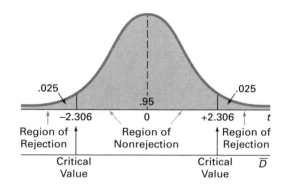

You can compute this test statistic along with the *p*-value by using SPSS (see Figure 11.8). Because the *p*-value = 0.041 < α = 0.05, you reject H_0. The *p*-value indicates that if the two types of driving have the same population mean gasoline mileage, the probability that one type of driving would have a sample mean that was 2.3444 miles per gallon less than the other type is 0.041. Because this probability is less than α = 0.05, you conclude that the alternative hypothesis is true.

FIGURE 11.8

SPSS results of paired *t* test for the car mileage data

Paired Samples Statistics

		Mean	N	Std. Deviation	Std. Error Mean
Pair 1	Members	27.156	9	11.3821	3.7940
	Government	29.500	9	11.1805	3.7268

Paired Samples Correlations

		N	Correlation	Sig.
Pair 1	Members & Goverment	9	.967	.000

Paired Samples Test

		Paired Differences							
					95% Confidence Interval of the Difference				
		Mean	Std. Deviation	Std. Error Mean	Lower	Upper	t	df	Sig. (2-tailed)
Pair 1	Members— Government	−2.3444	2.8936	.9645	−4.5686	−.1202	−2.431	8	.041

From Figure 11.9, observe that the boxplot shows approximate symmetry. Thus, the data do not greatly contradict the underlying assumption of normality. If a boxplot, histogram, or normal probability plot reveals that the assumption of underlying normality in the population is severely violated, then the *t* test is inappropriate. If this occurs, you can use either a *nonparametric* procedure that does not make the assumption of underlying normality (see references 1 and 2) or make a data transformation, and then recheck the assumptions to determine whether you should use the *t* test.

FIGURE 11.9

Minitab results of boxplot for the car mileage data

See Section M3.2 to create this. (Microsoft Excel users, see Section E3.3.)

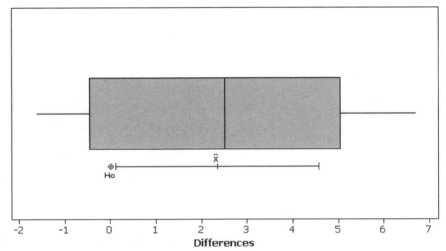

Boxplot of Differences
(with Ho and 95% t-confidence interval for the mean)

EXAMPLE 11.8

Paired *t* Test of Pizza Delivery Times

Recall from Example 11.1 that a local pizza restaurant situated across the street from a college campus advertises that it delivers to the dormitories faster than the local branch of a national pizza chain. In order to determine whether this advertisement is valid, you and some friends have decided to order 10 pizzas from the local pizza restaurant and 10 pizzas from the national chain. In fact, each time you ordered a pizza from the local pizza restaurant, your friends ordered a pizza from the national pizza chain. Thus, you have matched samples. For each of the ten times that pizzas were ordered, you have one measurement from the local pizza restaurant and one from the national chain. At the 0.05 level of significance, is the mean delivery time for the local pizza restaurant less than the mean delivery time for the national pizza chain?

SOLUTION Use the paired *t* test to analyze the data in Table 11.5 (see the file Pizzatime). Figure 11.10 illustrates SPSS paired *t*-test results for the pizza delivery data.

TABLE 11.5

Delivery Times for Local Pizza Restaurant and National Pizza Chain

Time	Local	Chain	Difference
1	16.8	22.0	−5.2
2	11.7	15.2	−3.5
3	15.6	18.7	−3.1
4	16.7	15.6	1.1
5	17.5	20.8	−3.3
6	18.1	19.5	−1.4
7	14.1	17.0	−2.9
8	21.8	19.5	2.3
9	13.9	16.5	−2.6
10	20.8	24.0	−3.2
			−21.8

Paired Samples Statistics

		Mean	N	Std. Deviation	Std. Error Mean
Pair 1	Local	16.700	10	3.0955	.9789
	Chain	18.880	10	2.8662	.9064

Paired Samples Correlations

		N	Correlation	Sig.
Pair 1	Local & Chain	10	.714	.020

Paired Samples Test

		Paired Differences		95% Confidence Interval of the Difference				
		Mean	Std. Deviation	Std. Error Mean	Lower	Upper	t	df	Sig. (2-tailed)
Pair 1	Local—Chain	−2.1800	2.2641	.7160	−3.7997	−.5603	−3.045	9	.014

The null and alternative hypotheses are

H_0: $\mu_D \geq 0$ (Mean delivery time for the local pizza restaurant is greater than or equal to the mean delivery time for the national pizza chain.)

H_1: $\mu_D < 0$ (Mean delivery time for the local pizza restaurant is less than the mean delivery time for the national pizza chain.)

Choosing the level of significance $\alpha = 0.05$ and assuming that the differences are normally distributed, you use the paired t test [Equation (11.3) on page 473]. For a sample of $n = 10$ delivery times, there are $n - 1 = 9$ degrees of freedom. Using Table E.3, the decision rule is

$$\text{Reject } H_0 \text{ if } t_{STAT} < -t_{0.05} = -1.8331;$$

$$\text{otherwise, do not reject } H_0.$$

For $n = 10$ differences (see Table 11.5), the sample mean difference is

$$D = \frac{\sum\limits_{i=1}^{n} D_i}{n} = \frac{-21.8}{10} = -2.18$$

and the sample standard deviation of the difference is

$$S_D = \sqrt{\frac{\sum\limits_{i=1}^{n}(D_i - \overline{D})^2}{n - 1}} = 2.2641$$

From Equation (11.3) on page 473,

$$t_{STAT} = \frac{\overline{D} - \mu_D}{\dfrac{S_D}{\sqrt{n}}} = \frac{-2.18 - 0}{\dfrac{2.2641}{\sqrt{10}}} = -3.045$$

Because $t_{STAT} = -3.045$ is less than -1.8331, you reject the null hypothesis H_0 (the p-value is $0.007 < 0.05$). There is evidence that the mean delivery time is lower for the local pizza restaurant than for the national pizza chain.

This conclusion is different from the one you reached in Example 11.1 when you used the pooled-variance t test for these data. By pairing the delivery times, you are able to focus on the differences between the two pizza delivery services and not the variability created by ordering pizzas at different times of day. The paired t test is a more powerful statistical procedure that is better able to detect the difference between the two pizza delivery services.

Thus, with 95% confidence, the mean difference in gasoline mileage between the real-life driving done by an AAA member and the driving done according to government standards is between -4.5686 and -0.1202 miles per gallon. Because the interval estimate contains only values less than zero, you can conclude that there is a difference in the population means. The mean miles per gallon for the real-life driving done by an AAA member is less than the mean miles per gallon for the driving done according to government standards.

SPSS—VERSION 16—Paired Samples T-Test

We will use the data depicted in Table 1 to demonstrate how to perform paired T test using SPSS. The data consists of the processing time for the financial applications projects that use the current market leader and new software package.

The results are for a sample of 10 financial applications projects as shown below:

Table 1	PROCESSING TIMES (IN SECONDS)	
Applications Project	By current market leader	By new software package
1	9.98	9.88
2	9.88	9.86
3	9.84	9.75
4	9.99	9.80
5	9.94	9.87
6	9.84	9.84
7	9.86	9.87
8	10.12	9.86
9	9.90	9.83
10	9.91	9.86

At the 0.05 level of significance, is there evidence that the mean processing time is greater when the financial applications projects use the current market leader rather than the new software package?

Solution:

Performing a Paired-Samples T Test on SPSS—Version 16

Step 1: Open the SPSS Data Editor.

Click **"cancel"** to cancel the SPSS opening window.

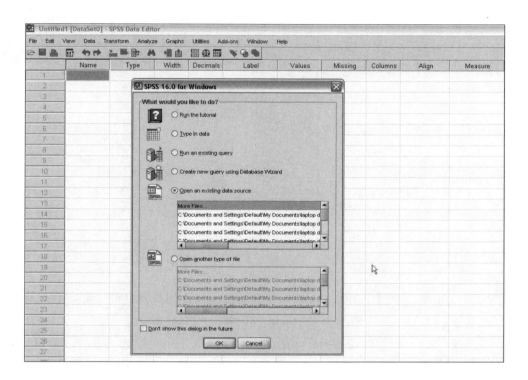

Step 2: Define the variables and give the variables a label.

Click **"Variable View"** (at the bottom of the window) to go to the **variable view** window in order to define the variables and fix the data at zero or one decimal places.

- Enter the first variable name -"current" and give the variable a label **'By current market leader'.**

- Enter the second variable name – "new" and label it as **"By new software package".**

See the Variable View window show below.

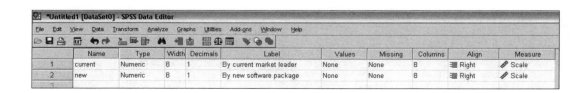

Step 3: Create a SPSS data file.

Click **"Data View"** to return to the data view window. Now, enter the raw data (in Table 1) into the respective column of variables.

After you have entered all the data, save it as "pairedTtest.sav" (or any filename).

Step 3: Perform Paired-samples t-test.

Make the following menu selections:

Analyze → Compare Means → Paired-Samples T test

At this point, the **Independent Samples T Test** dialog box will appear. Make these entries in the **Paired-Samples T Test** dialog box:

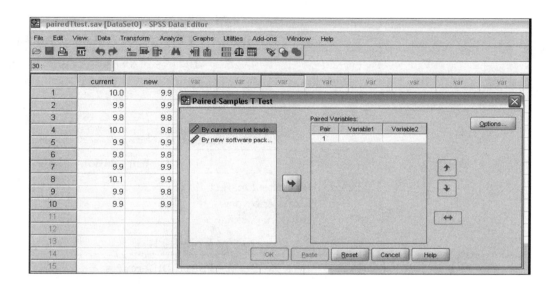

- Highlight on the **"By current market leader"** variable and click on the arrow key (→). The variable will automatically fall into the **Pair 1—Variable 1** cell.

- Highlight on the **"By new software package"** variable and click on the arrow key (→). The variable will automatically fall into the **Pair 1—Variable 2** cell.

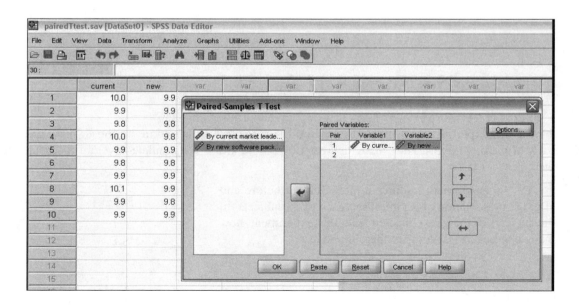

- Click on the **Ok** button to obtain the SPSS results.

Step 3: Go to **SPSS Viewer** to obtain your SPSS results.

SPSS output:

T-Test

Paired Samples Statistics

		Mean	N	Std. Deviation	Std. Error Mean
Pair 1	By current market leader	9.926	10	.0863	.0273
	By new software package	9.842	10	.0399	.0126

Paired Samples Correlations

		N	Correlation	Sig.
Pair 1	By current market leader & by new software package	10	.280	.434

Paired Samples Test

		Paired Differences							
					95% Confidence Interval of the Difference				
		Mean	Std. Deviation	Std. Error Mean	Lower	Upper	t	df	Sig. (2-tailed)
Pair 1	By current—market leader—by new software package	.0840	.0844	.0267	.0237	.1443	3.149	9	.012

Problems for Section 11.2

LEARNING THE BASICS

11.18 An experimental design for a paired t test has 20 pairs of identical twins. How many degrees of freedom are there in this t test?

11.19 An experiment requires a measurement before and after the presentation of a stimulus to each of 15 subjects. In the analysis of the data collected from this experiment, how many degrees of freedom are there in the test?

APPLYING THE CONCEPTS

✓ SELF Test **11.20** Nine experts rated two brands of Colombian coffee in a taste-testing experiment. A rating on a 7-point scale (1 = extremely unpleasing, 7 = extremely pleasing) is given for each of four characteristics: taste, aroma, richness, and acidity. The following data

(stored in the file **Coffee**) displays the summated ratings—accumulated over all four characteristics.

EXPERT	BRAND	
	A	B
C.C.	24	26
S.E.	27	27
E.G.	19	22
B.L.	24	27
C.M.	22	25
C.N.	26	27
G.N.	27	26
R.M.	25	27
P.V.	22	23

a. At the 0.05 level of significance, is there evidence of a difference in the mean summated ratings between the two brands?

b. What assumption is necessary about the population distribution in order to perform this test?

c. Determine the *p*-value in (a) and interpret its meaning.

d. Construct and interpret a 95% confidence interval estimate of the difference in the mean summated ratings between the two brands.

11.21 In industrial settings, alternative methods often exist for measuring variables of interest. The data in the file Measurement (coded to maintain confidentiality) represent measurements in-line that were collected from an analyzer during the production process and from an analytical lab (extracted from M. Leitnaker, "Comparing Measurement Processes: In-line Versus Analytical Measurements," *Quality Engineering*, 13, 2000–2001, pp. 293–298).

a. At the 0.05 level of significance, is there evidence of a difference in the mean measurements in-line and from an analytical lab?

b. What assumption is necessary about the population distribution in order to perform this test?

c. Use a graphical method to evaluate the validity of the assumption in (a).

d. Construct and interpret a 95% confidence interval estimate of the difference in the mean measurements in-line and from an analytical lab.

11.22 Can students save money by comparison shopping for textbooks at Amazon.com? To investigate this possibility, a random sample of 15 textbooks used during the Spring 2007 semester at Miami University was selected. The prices for these textbooks at both a local bookstore and through Amazon.com were recorded. The prices for the textbooks are stored in the file Textbook:

a. At the 0.01 level of significance, is there evidence of a difference between the mean price of textbooks at the local bookstore and Amazon.com?

b. What assumption is necessary about the population distribution in order to perform this test?

c. Construct a 99% confidence interval estimate of the mean difference in price. Interpret the interval.

d. Compare the results of (a) and (c).

11.23 A newspaper article discussed the opening of a Whole Foods Market in the Time-Warner building in New York City. The following data (stored in the file Wholefoods1) compared the prices of some kitchen staples at the new Whole Foods Market and at the Fairway supermarket located about 15 blocks from the Time-Warner building:

Source: *Data extracted from W. Grimes, "A Pleasure Palace Without the Guilt," The New York Times, February 18, 2004, pp. F1, F5.*

a. At the 0.01 level of significance, is there evidence that the mean price is higher at Whole Foods Market than at the Fairway supermarket?

b. Interpret the meaning of the *p*-value in (a).

c. What assumption is necessary about the population distribution in order to perform the test in (a)?

11.24 Multiple myeloma, or blood plasma cancer, is characterized by increased blood vessel formulation (angiogenesis) in the bone marrow that is a predictive factor in survival. One treatment approach used for multiple myeloma is stem cell transplantation with the patient's own stem cells. The following data (stored in the file Myeloma) represent the bone marrow microvessel density for patients who had a complete response to the stem cell transplant (as measured by blood and urine tests). The measurements were taken immediately prior to the stem cell transplant and at the time the complete response was determined:

Patient	Before	After
1	158	284
2	189	214
3	202	101
4	353	227
5	416	290
6	426	176
7	441	290

Source: *Data extracted from S. V. Rajkumar, R. Fonseca, T. E. Witzig, M. A. Gertz, and P. R. Greipp, "Bone Marrow Angiogenesis in Patients Achieving Complete Response After Stem Cell Transplantation for Multiple Myeloma," Leukemia, 1999, 13, pp. 469–472.*

a. At the 0.05 level of significance, is there evidence that the mean bone marrow microvessel density is higher before the stem cell transplant than after the stem cell transplant?

b. Interpret the meaning of the *p*-value in (a).

c. Construct and interpret a 95% confidence interval estimate of the mean difference in bone marrow microvessel density before and after the stem cell transplant.

d. What assumption is necessary about the population distribution in order to perform the test in (a)?

11.25 Over the past year, the vice president for human resources at a large medical center has run a series of three-month workshops aimed at increasing worker motivation and performance. To check the effectiveness of the workshops, she selected a random sample of 35 employees from the personnel files and recorded their most recent annual performance ratings, along with their ratings prior to attending the workshops. The data are stored in the file Perform. The Microsoft Excel results are shown below. State your findings and conclusions in a report to the vice president for human resources.

Paired Samples Statistics

		Mean	N	Std. Deviation	Std. Error Mean
Pair 1	before	74.54	35	8.995	1.520
	after	79.80	35	6.096	1.030

Paired Samples Correlations

		N	Correlation	Sig.
Pair 1	before & after	35	−.134	.442

Paired Samples Test

Paired Differences

		Mean	Std. Deviation	Std. Error Mean	95% Confidence Interval of the Difference Lower	95% Confidence Interval of the Difference Upper	t	df	Sig. (2-tailed)
Pair 1	before—after	−5.257 5.257	11.523	1.948	−9.216	−1.299	−2.699	34	.011

11.26 The data in the file `Concrete1` represent the compressive strength, in thousands of pounds per square inch (psi), of 40 samples of concrete taken two and seven days after pouring.

Source: *Data extracted from O. Carrillo-Gamboa and R. F. Gunst, "Measurement-Error-Model Collinearities," Technometrics, 34, 1992, pp. 454–464.*

a. At the 0.01 level of significance, is there evidence that the mean strength is lower at two days than at seven days?
b. What assumption is necessary about the population distribution in order to perform this test?
c. Find the p-value in (a) and interpret its meaning.

11.3 Comparing the Proportions of Two Independent Populations

Often, you need to make comparisons and analyze differences between two population proportions. You can perform a test for the difference between two proportions selected from independent populations by using two different methods. This section presents a procedure whose test statistic, Z_{STAT}, is approximated by a standardized normal distribution. In Section 12.1, a procedure is developed whose test statistic, χ^2_{STAT}, is approximated by a chi-square distribution. As you will see, the results from these two tests are equivalent.

Z Test for the Difference Between Two Proportions

In evaluating differences between two population proportions, you can use a **Z test for the difference between two proportions**. The Z_{STAT} test statistic is based on the difference between two sample proportions $(p_1 - p_2)$. This test statistic, given in Equation (11.5), approximately follows a standardized normal distribution for large enough sample sizes.

Z TEST FOR THE DIFFERENCE BETWEEN TWO PROPORTIONS

$$Z_{STAT} = \frac{(p_1 - p_2) - (\pi_1 - \pi_2)}{\sqrt{\bar{p}(1 - \bar{p})\left(\dfrac{1}{n_1} + \dfrac{1}{n_2}\right)}}$$

(11.5)

with

$$\bar{p} = \frac{X_1 + X_2}{n_1 + n_2} \quad p_1 = \frac{X_1}{n_1} \quad p_2 = \frac{X_2}{n_2}$$

where

p_1 = proportion of items of interest in sample 1

X_1 = number of items of interest in sample 1

n_1 = sample size of sample 1

π_1 = proportion of items of interest in population 1

p_2 = proportion of items of interest in sample 2

X_2 = number of items of interest in sample 2

n_2 = sample size of sample 2

π_2 = proportion of items of interest in population 2

$\bar{p}$ = pooled estimate of the population proportion of items of interest

The Z_{STAT} test statistic approximately follows a standardized normal distribution.

Under the null hypothesis, you assume that the two population proportions are equal $(\pi_1 = \pi_2)$. Because the pooled estimate for the population proportion is based on the null hypothesis, you combine, or pool, the two sample proportions to compute $\bar{p}$, an overall estimate of the common population proportion. This estimate is equal to the number of items of interest in the two samples combined $(X_1 + X_2)$ divided by the total sample size from the two samples combined $(n_1 + n_2)$.

As shown in the following table, you can use this Z test for the difference between population proportions to determine whether there is a difference in the proportion of items of interest in the two populations (two-tail test) or whether one population has a higher proportion of items of interest than the other population (one-tail test):

Two-Tail Test	**One-Tail Test**	**One-Tail Test**
$H_0: \pi_1 = \pi_2$	$H_0: \pi_1 \geq \pi_2$	$H_0: \pi_1 \leq \pi_2$
$H_0: \pi_1 \neq \pi_2$	$H_0: \pi_1 < \pi_2$	$H_0: \pi_1 > \pi_2$

where

π_1 = proportion of items of interest in population 1

π_2 = proportion of items of interest in population 2

To test the null hypothesis that there is no difference between the proportions of two independent populations:

$$H_0: \pi_1 = \pi_2$$

against the alternative that the two population proportions are not the same:

$$H_1: \pi_1 \neq \pi_2$$

use the Z_{STAT} test statistic, given by Equation (11.5). For a given level of significance α, reject the null hypothesis if the computed Z_{STAT} test statistic is greater than the upper-tail critical value from the standardized normal distribution, or if the computed Z_{STAT} test statistic is less than the lower-tail critical value from the standardized normal distribution.

To illustrate the use of the Z test for the equality of two proportions, suppose that you are the manager of T.C. Resort Properties, a collection of five upscale resort hotels located on two tropical islands. On one of the islands, T.C. Resort Properties has two hotels, the Beachcomber and the Windsurfer. In tabulating the responses to the single question, "Are you likely to choose this hotel again?" 163 of 227 guests at the Beachcomber responded yes, and 154 of 262 guests at the Windsurfer responded yes. At the 0.05 level of significance, is there evidence of a significant difference in guest satisfaction (as measured by the likelihood to return to the hotel) between the two hotels?

The null and alternative hypotheses are

$$H_0: \pi_1 = \pi_2 \quad \text{or} \quad \pi_1 - \pi_2 \neq 0$$

$$H_1: \pi_1 \neq \pi_2 \quad \text{or} \quad \pi_1 - \pi_2 \neq 0$$

Using the 0.05 level of significance, the critical values are -1.96 and $+1.96$ (see Figure 11.11), and the decision rule is

Reject H_0 if $Z_{STAT} < -1.96$

or if $Z_{STAT} > +1.96$;

otherwise, do not reject H_0.

FIGURE 11.11
Regions of rejection and nonrejection when testing a hypothesis for the difference between two proportions at the 0.05 level of significance

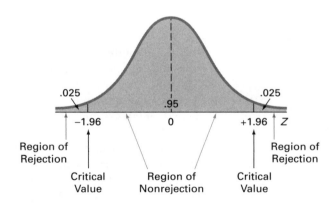

Using Equation (11.5) on page 478,

$$Z_{STAT} = \frac{(p_1 - p_2) - (\pi_1 - \pi_2)}{\sqrt{\bar{p}(1 - \bar{p})\left(\dfrac{1}{n_1} + \dfrac{1}{n_2}\right)}}$$

where

$$p_1 = \frac{X_1}{n_1} = \frac{163}{227} = 0.7181 \quad p_2 = \frac{X_2}{n_2} = \frac{154}{262} = 0.5878$$

and

$$\bar{p} = \frac{X_1 + X_2}{n_1 + n_2} = \frac{163 + 154}{227 + 262} = \frac{317}{489} = 0.6483$$

so that

$$Z_{STAT} = \frac{(0.7181 - 0.5878) - (0)}{\sqrt{0.6483(1 - 0.6483)\left(\frac{1}{227} + \frac{1}{262}\right)}}$$

$$= \frac{0.1303}{\sqrt{(0.228)(0.0082)}}$$

$$= \frac{0.1303}{\sqrt{0.00187}}$$

$$= \frac{0.1303}{0.0432} = +3.0087$$

Using the 0.05 level of significance, reject the null hypothesis because $Z_{STAT} = +3.0087 > +1.96$. The p-value is 0.0026 (calculated from Casio calculator results of Figure 11.12). For this two-tail test, the p-value is 0.0026. Because $0.0026 < \alpha = 0.05$, you reject the null hypothesis. There is evidence to conclude that the two hotels are significantly different with respect to guest satisfaction; a greater proportion of guests are willing to return to the Beachcomber than to the Windsurfer.

FIGURE 11.12

Casio calculator results for the Z test for the difference between two proportions for the hotel guest satisfaction problem

Solution: From the **Main Menu** select:

STAT **F3**(test) **F1**(Z) **F4**(2-P)   then enter the following items:

2-Prop ZTest

p1	: **F1**($\neq$p2) ▼	
x1	: **163**	**EXE**
n1	: **227**	**EXE**
x2	: **154**	**EXE**
n2	: **262**	**EXE**

Now key **EXE** or **F1** (Calc)

The calculator will now show the results:

2-Prop ZTest

p1	$\neq$p2
z	=3.0087
p	=2.6232E-03 (=0.0026232)
$\hat{p}1$	=0.71806
$\hat{p}2$	=0.58778
$\hat{p}3$	=0.64826
n1	=227
n2	=262

EXAMPLE 11.9

Testing for the Difference in Two Proportions

Technology has led to the rise of extreme workers who are on the job 60 hours a week or more. One of the reasons cited by employees about why they worked long hours was that they loved their job because it is stimulating/challenging/provides an adrenaline rush (data extracted from S. Armour, "Hi, I'm Joan and I'm a Workaholic," *USA Today*, May 23, 2007, pp. 1B, 2B). Suppose that the survey of 1,564 workaholics included 786 men and 778 women, and that 707 men and 638 women loved their job because it is stimulating/challenging/provides an adrenaline rush. At the 0.05 level of significance, you would like to determine whether the proportion of workaholic men who love their job because it is stimulating/challenging/provides an adrenaline rush is greater than the proportion of women.

SOLUTION Because you want to know whether there is evidence that the proportion of workaholic men who love their job because it is stimulating/challenging/provides an adrenaline rush is *greater* than the proportion of women, you have a one-tail test. The null and alternative hypotheses are

$H_0: \pi_1 \leq \pi_2$ (Proportion of workaholic men who love their job because it is stimulating/challenging/provides an adrenaline rush is less than or equal to the proportion of women.)

$H_1: \pi_1 > \pi_2$ (Proportion of workaholic men who love their job because it is stimulating/challenging/provides an adrenaline rush is greater than the proportion of women.)

Using the 0.05 level of significance, for the one-tail test in the upper tail, the critical value is $+1.645$. The decision rule is

$$\text{Reject } H_0 \text{ if } Z_{STAT} > +1.645;$$

$$\text{otherwise, do not reject } H_0.$$

Using Equation (11.5) on page 485,

$$Z_{STAT} = \frac{(p_1 - p_2) - (\pi_1 - \pi_2)}{\sqrt{\bar{p}(1 - \bar{p})\left(\frac{1}{n_1} + \frac{1}{n_2}\right)}}$$

where

$$p_1 = \frac{X_1}{n_1} = \frac{707}{786} = 0.8995 \quad p_2 = \frac{X_2}{n_2} = \frac{638}{778} = 0.8201$$

and

$$\bar{p} = \frac{X_1 + X_2}{n_1 + n_2} = \frac{707 + 638}{786 + 778} = \frac{1,345}{1,564} = 0.8600$$

so that

$$Z_{STAT} = \frac{(0.8995 - 0.8201) - (0)}{\sqrt{0.86(1 - 0.86)\left(\frac{1}{786} + \frac{1}{778}\right)}}$$

$$= \frac{0.0794}{\sqrt{(0.1204)(0.0025575)}}$$

$$= \frac{0.0794}{\sqrt{0.0003079}}$$

$$= \frac{0.0794}{0.017547} = +4.5266$$

Using the 0.05 level of significance, you reject the null hypothesis because $Z_{STAT} = +4.5266 > +1.645$. The p-value is approximately 0.0000. Therefore, if the null hypothesis is true, the probability that a Z_{STAT} test statistic is greater than $+4.5266$ is approximately 0.0000 (which is less than $\alpha = 0.05$). You conclude that there is evidence that the proportion of workaholic men who love their job because it is stimulating/challenging/provides an adrenaline rush is greater than the proportion of women.

CALCULATOR LESSON 12A

CFX-9850GB CALCULATOR

Lesson 12A—Z-Test of Two Proportions

EXAMPLE 11.10

A political candidate thinks that his level of support is different among male and female voters and would like to address this issue if it is true. Random samples of 200 male voters and 100 female voters in his riding revealed that 85 of the men would vote for the candidate but only 35 of the women would. At the 10% level of significance, what conclusion should the candidate make regarding the level of support?

Solution:

Let π_1 = the proportion of male voters that will vote for the candidate

π_2 = the proportion of female voters that will vote for the candidate

From the **Main Menu** select:

STAT   F3(test)   **F1**(Z)   **F4**(2-P)   then enter the following items:

2-Prop ZTest

p1	: **F1**($\neq$p2) ▼	
x1	: **85**	**EXE**
n1	: **200**	**EXE**
x2	: **35**	**EXE**
n2	: **100**	**EXE**

Now key **EXE** or **F1**(Calc)

The calculator will now show the results:

2-Prop ZTest

p1	$\neq$p2
z	=1.25
p	=0.21129
$\hat{p}1$	=0.425
$\hat{p}2$	=0.35
$\hat{p}$	=0.4
n1	=200
n2	=100

Since the p-value > 0.10, the conclusion is to *not reject* the null hypothesis. In other words the evidence indicates that the level of support for the candidate is the almost the same for both male and female voters.

CALCULATOR LESSON 12B

CASIO FX-9750GII CALCULATOR

Lesson 12B—Z-Test of Two Proportions

EXAMPLE 11.11

A political candidate thinks that his level of support is different among male and female voters and would like to address this issue if it is true. Random samples of 200 male voters and 100 female voters in his riding revealed that 85 of the men would vote for the candidate but only 35 of the women would. At the 10% level of significance, what conclusion should the candidate make regarding the level of support?

Solution:

Let π_1 = the proportion of male voters that will vote for the candidate

π_2 = the proportion of female voters that will vote for the candidate

From the **Main Menu** select:

STAT   F3(test)   **F1**(Z)   **F4**(2-P)   then enter the following items:

2-Prop ZTest

p1	: **F1**($\neq$p2)	▼
x1	: **85**	**EXE**
n1	: **200**	**EXE**
x2	: **35**	**EXE**
n2	: **100**	**EXE**
Save Res	: None	

Now key **EXE** or **F1**(Calc) or **F6**(DRAW)

If you select **F6**(DRAW), you will see a normal distribution.

If you select either **EXE** or **F1**(Calc), the calculator will now show the results:

2-Prop ZTest

p1	$\neq$p2
z	=1.25
p	=0.21129
$\hat{p}1$	=0.425
$\hat{p}2$	=0.35
$\hat{p}$	=0.4
n1	=200
n2	=100

Since the p-value > 0.10, the conclusion is to *not reject* the null hypothesis. In other words the evidence indicates that the level of support for the candidate is almost the same for both male and female voters.

Problems for Section 11.3

LEARNING THE BASICS

11.27 Let $n_1 = 100, X_1 = 50, n_2 = 100$, and $X_2 = 30$.
a. At the 0.05 level of significance, is there evidence of a significant difference between the two population proportions?
b. Construct a 95% confidence interval estimate of the difference between the two population proportions.

11.28 Let $n_1 = 100, X_1 = 45, n_2 = 50$, and $X_2 = 25$.
a. At the 0.01 level of significance, is there evidence of a significant difference between the two population proportions?
b. Construct a 99% confidence interval estimate of the difference between the two population proportions.

APPLYING THE CONCEPTS

11.29 A sample of 500 shoppers was selected in a large metropolitan area to determine various information concerning consumer behavior. Among the questions asked was, "Do you enjoy shopping for clothing?" Of 240 males, 136 answered yes. Of 260 females, 224 answered yes.

a. Is there evidence of a significant difference between males and females in the proportion that enjoy shopping for clothing at the 0.01 level of significance?

b. Find the p-value in (a) and interpret its meaning.

c. Construct and interpret a 99% confidence interval estimate of the difference between the proportion of males and females who enjoy shopping for clothing.

d. What are your answers to (a) through (c) if 206 males enjoyed shopping for clothing?

11.30 A study funded by the Massachusetts Institute of Technology tested the notion that even when it comes to sugar pills, some people think a costly one works better than a cheap one. Researchers randomly divided 82 healthy paid volunteers into two groups. All the volunteers thought they would be testing a new pain reliever. One group was told the pain reliever they would be using cost $2.50 a pill, and the other group was told it cost only 10 cents a pill. In reality, the pills they were all about to take were simply sugar pills. The volunteers were given a light electric shock on the wrist. Then the volunteers were given a sugar pill, and a short time later shocked again. Of the volunteers who took the expensive pill, 35 of the 41 said they felt less pain afterward. Of the volunteers who took the cheap pill, 25 of the 41 said they felt less pain afterward (R. Rubin, "Placebo Study Tests 'Costlier is Better' Notion," *usatoday.com*, March 5, 2008).

a. Set up the null and alternative hypotheses to try to prove that people think an expensive pill works better than a cheap pill.

b. Conduct the hypotheses defined in (a), using the 0.05 level of significance.

c. Does the result of your test in (b) make it appropriate to claim that people think an expensive pill works better than a cheap pill?

11.31 The results of a study conducted as part of a yield-improvement effort at a semiconductor manufacturing facility provided defect data for a sample of 450 wafers. The following contingency table presents a summary of the

PARTICLES	QUALITY OF WAFER		
	Good	Bad	Totals
Yes	14	36	50
No	320	80	400
Totals	334	116	450

Source: *Data extracted from S.W. Hall, "Analysis of Defectivity of Semiconductor Wafers by Contingency Table,"* Proceedings Institute of Environmental Sciences, Vol. 1, *1994, pp. 177–183*.

responses to two questions: "Was a particle found on the die that produced the wafer?" and "Is the wafer good or bad?"

a. At the 0.05 level of significance, is there evidence of a significant difference between the proportion of good and bad wafers that have particles?

b. Determine the p-value in (a) and interpret its meaning.

c. Construct and interpret a 95% confidence interval estimate of the difference between the population proportion of good and bad wafers that contain particles.

d. What conclusions can you reach from this analysis?

✓SELF Test **11.32** According to an Ipsos poll, the perception of unfairness in the U.S. tax code is spread fairly evenly across income groups, age groups, and education levels. In an April 2006 survey of 1,005 adults, Ipsos reported that almost 60% of all people said the code is unfair, whereas slightly more that 60% of those making more than $50,000 viewed the code as unfair (data extracted from "People Cry Unfairness," *The Cincinnati Enquirer*, April 16, 2006, p. A8). Suppose that the following contingency table represents the specific breakdown of responses:

U.S. TAX CODE	INCOME LEVEL		
	Less Than $50,000	More Than $50,000	Total
Fair	225	180	405
Unfair	280	320	600
Total	505	500	1,005

a. At the 0.05 level of significance, is there evidence of a difference in the proportion of adults who think the U.S. tax code is unfair between the two income groups?

b. Find the p-value in (a) and interpret its meaning.

11.33 Are women more risk averse in the stock market? A sample of men and women were asked the following question: "If both the stock market and a stock you owned dropped 25% in three months, would you buy more shares while the price is low?" (data extracted from "Snapshots: Women Are More Risk Averse in the Stock Market," *USA Today*, September 25, 2006, p. 1C). Of 965 women, 338 said yes. Of 1,066 men, 554 said yes.

a. At the 0.05 level of significance, is there evidence that the proportion of women who would buy more shares while the price is low is less than the proportion of men?

b. Find the p-value in (a) and interpret its meaning.

11.34 An experiment was conducted to study the choices made in mutual fund selection. Undergraduate and MBA students were presented with different S&P 500 index funds that were identical except for fees. Suppose 100 undergraduate students and 100 MBA students were selected. Partial results are shown in the following table:

	STUDENT GROUP	
FUND	**Undergraduate**	**MBA**
Highest-cost fund	27	18
Not-highest-cost fund	73	82

Source: *Data extracted from J. Choi, D. Laibson, and B. Madrian, "Why Does the Law of One Practice Fail? An Experiment on Mutual Funds,"* **www.som.yale.edu/faculty/jjc83/fees.pdf**.

a. At the 0.05 level of significance, is there evidence of a difference between undergraduate and MBA students in the proportion who selected the highest-cost fund?

b. Find the *p*-value in (a) and interpret its meaning.

11.35 Where people turn for news is different for various age groups (data extracted from P. Johnson, "Young People Turn to the Web for News," *USA Today*, March 23, 2006, p.

9D). Suppose that a study conducted on this issue was based on 200 respondents who were between the ages of 36 and 50, and 200 respondents who were above age 50. Of the 200 respondents who were between the ages of 36 and 50, 82 got their news primarily from newspapers. Of the 200 respondents who were above age 50, 104 got their news primarily from newspapers.

a. Is there evidence of a significant difference in the proportion that get their news primarily from newspapers between those respondents 36 to 50 years old and those above 50 years old? (Use $\alpha = 0.05$.)

b. Determine the *p*-value in (a) and interpret its meaning.

c. Construct and interpret a 95% confidence interval estimate of the difference between the population proportion of respondents who get their news primarily from newspapers between those respondents 36 to 50 years old and those above 50 years old.

11.4 *F* Test for the Difference Between Two Variances

Often you need to determine whether two independent populations have the same amount of variability. By testing variances, you can detect differences in the amount of variability. One important reason to test for the difference between the variances of two populations is to determine whether to use the pooled-variance *t* test (which assumes equal variances) or the separate-variance *t* test (which does not assume equal variances) while comparing two means.

The test for the difference between the variances of two independent populations is based on the ratio of the two sample variances. If you assume that each population is normally distributed, then the ratio S_1^2/S_2^2 follows the *F* distribution. The critical values of the **F distribution** in Table E.5 depend on the degrees of freedom in the two samples. The degrees of freedom in the numerator of the ratio are for the first sample, and the degrees of freedom in the denominator are for the second sample. The first sample taken from the first population is defined as the sample that has the *larger* sample variance. The second sample taken from the second population is the sample with the *smaller* sample variance. Equation (11.7) defines the **F test for the equality of two variances**.

F-TEST STATISTIC FOR TESTING THE EQUALITY OF TWO VARIANCES

The F_{STAT} test statistic is equal to the variance of sample 1 (the larger sample variance) divided by the variance of sample 2 (the smaller sample variance).

$$F_{STAT} = \frac{S_1^2}{S_2^2}$$ (11.7)

where

S_1^2 = variance of sample 1 (the larger sample variance)

S_2^2 = variance of sample 2 (the smaller sample variance)

n_1 = size of sample 1

n_2 = size of sample 2

$n_1 - 1$ = degrees of freedom from sample 1 (i.e., the numerator degrees of freedom)

$n_2 - 1$ = degrees of freedom from sample 2 (i.e., the denominator degrees of freedom)

The F_{STAT} test statistic follows an *F* distribution with $n_1 - 1$ and $n_2 - 1$ degrees of freedom.

For a given level of significance, α, to test the null hypothesis of equality of population variances:

$$H_0: \sigma_1^2 = \sigma_2^2$$

against the alternative hypothesis that the two population variances are not equal:

$$H_1: \sigma_1^2 \neq \sigma_2^2$$

you reject the null hypothesis if the computed F_{STAT} test statistic is greater than the upper-tail critical value, $F_{\alpha/2}$, from the F distribution with $n_1 - 1$ degrees of freedom in the numerator and $n_2 - 1$ degrees of freedom in the denominator. Thus, the decision rule is

$$\text{Reject } H_0 \text{ if } F_{STAT} > F_{\alpha/2};$$

otherwise, do not reject H_0.

To illustrate how to use the F test to determine whether the two variances are equal, return to the Using Statistics scenario from earlier concerning the sales of BLK Cola in two different aisle locations. To determine whether to use the pooled-variance t test or the separate-variance t test in Section 11.1, you can test the equality of the two population variances. The null and alternative hypotheses are

$$H_0: \sigma_1^2 = \sigma_2^2$$
$$H_1: \sigma_1^2 \neq \sigma_2^2$$

Because you are defining sample 1 as having the larger sample variance, the rejection region in the upper tail of the F distribution contains $\alpha/2$. Using the level of significance $\alpha = 0.05$, the rejection region in the upper tail contains 0.025 of the distribution.

Because there are samples of 10 stores for each of the two display locations, there are $10 - 1 = 9$ degrees of freedom in the numerator (the sample with the larger variance) and also in the denominator (the sample with the smaller variance). $F_{\alpha/2}$, the upper-tail critical value of the F distribution, is found directly from Table E.5, a portion of which is presented in Table 11.6. Because there are 9 degrees of freedom in the numerator and 9 degrees of freedom in the denominator, you find the upper-tail critical value, $F_{\alpha/2}$, by looking in the column labeled 9 and the row labeled 9. Thus, the upper-tail critical value of this F distribution is 4.03. Therefore the decision rule is

$$\text{Reject } H_0 \text{ if } F_{STAT} > F_{0.025} = 4.03;$$

otherwise, do not reject H_0.

TABLE 11.6

Finding the Upper-Tail Critical Value of *F* with 9 and 9 Degrees of Freedom for Upper-Tail Area of 0.025

	Cumulative Probabilities = 0.975 Upper-Tail Area = 0.025 Numerator df_1						
Denominator df_2	**1**	**2**	**3**	**...**	**7**	**8**	**9**
1	647.80	799.50	864.20	...	948.20	956.70	963.30
2	38.51	39.00	39.17	...	39.36	39.37	39.39
3	17.44	16.04	15.44	...	14.62	14.54	14.47
.	.	.	.	.	.	.	.
.	.	.	.	.	.	.	.
7	8.07	6.54	5.89	...	4.99	4.90	4.82
8	7.57	6.06	5.42	...	4.53	4.43	4.36
9	7.21	5.71	5.08	...	4.20	4.10	4.03

Source: *Extracted from Table E.5.*

Using Equation (11.7) on page 492 and the cola sales data (see Table 11.1 on page 454),

$$F_{STAT} = \frac{S_1^2}{S_2^2}$$

$$= \frac{350.6778}{157.3333} = 2.2288$$

Because $F_{STAT} = 2.2288 < 4.03$, you do not reject H_0. The p-value is 0.2482 for a two-tail test (shown in the Casio calculator results in Figure 11.13). Because $0.2482 > 0.05$, you conclude that there is no significant difference in the variability of the sales of cola for the two display locations.

FIGURE 11.13

Casio calculator F test results for the BLK Cola sales data

Solution: From the **Main Menu** select:

STAT   **F3**(test)   **F4**(F)   then enter the following items:

2-Sample FTest
Data	: **F2**(Var)	▼
$\sigma 1$	: **F1**($\neq \sigma 2$)	▼
x1σn-1	: **18.72639314**	**EXE**
n1	: **10**	**EXE**
x2σn-1	: **12.54325835**	**EXE**
n2	: **10**	**EXE**

Now key **EXE** or **F1** (Calc)

The calculator will now show the results:

2-Sample FTest
$\sigma 1$	$\neq \sigma 2$
F	=2.2288
p	=0.2482
x1σn-1	=18.726
x2σn-1	=12.543
n1	=10
n2	=10

In testing for a difference between two variances using the F test described in this section, you assume that each of the two populations is normally distributed. The F test is very sensitive to the normality assumption. If boxplots or normal probability plots suggest even a mild departure from normality for either of the two populations, you should not use the F test. If this happens, you should use the Levene test (see Section 11.5) or a nonparametric approach.

In testing for the equality of variances as part of assessing the validity of the pooled-variance t test procedure, the F test is a two-tail test with $\alpha/2$ in the upper tail. However, when you are interested in examining the variability in situations other than the pooled-variance t test, the F test is often a one-tail test. Example 11.8 illustrates a one-tail test.

EXAMPLE 11.12

A One-Tail Test for the Difference Between Two Variances

Shipments of meat, meat by-products, and other ingredients are mixed together in several filling lines at a pet food canning factory. Operations managers suspect that, although the mean amount filled per can of pet food is usually the same, the variability of the cans filled in line A is greater than that of line B. The following data from a sample of eight-ounce cans is as follows:

	Line A	Line B
$\overline{X}$	8.005	7.997
S	0.012	0.005
n	11	16

At the 0.05 level of significance, is there evidence that the variance in line A is greater than the variance in line B? Assume that the population amounts filled are normally distributed.

SOLUTION The null and alternative hypotheses are

$$H_0: \sigma_A^2 \leq \sigma_B^2$$
$$H_1: \sigma_A^2 > \sigma_B^2$$

The F_{STAT} test statistic is given by Equation (11.7):

$$F_{STAT} = \frac{S_1^2}{S_2^2}$$

You use Table E.5 to find the upper critical value of the F distribution. With $n_1 - 1 = 11 - 1 = 10$ degrees of freedom in the numerator, $n_2 - 1 = 16 - 1 = 15$ degrees of freedom in the denominator, and $\alpha = 0.05$, the upper critical value, $F_{0.05}$, is 2.54.

The decision rule is

Reject H_0 if $F_{STAT} > 2.54$;

otherwise, do not reject H_0.

From Equation (11.7),

$$F_{STAT} = \frac{S_1^2}{S_2^2}$$
$$= \frac{(0.012)^2}{(0.005)^2} = 5.76$$

Because $F_{STAT} = 5.76 > 2.54$, you reject H_0. Using a 0.05 level of significance, you conclude that there is evidence that the variance of line A is greater than the variance of line B. In other words, the amount of pet food in the cans filled by line A is more variable than the amount of pet food in cans filled by line B.

CALCULATOR LESSON 13A

CFX-9850GB CALCULATOR

EXAMPLE 11.13

Lesson 13A—F-test of two Variances

Recall the following example from Calculator Lesson 10.

A work team has developed a new process to assemble a certain component. They would like to know if this new process has significantly reduced the time to assemble the component. They have taken samples of 50 components produced by the existing process and 40 components produced by the new process. The mean and standard deviation of the assembly times for the existing process were 73.2 minutes and 3.6 minutes, respectively. The mean time was 71.4 minutes with a standard deviation of 3.2 minutes for the components assembled by the new process. Assume that the times for both processes are normally distributed with the same variance.

Suppose that instead of assuming that the variances of the assembly times for the two processes are equal, we do an F test to see if there is evidence to support such an assumption. Test at the 5% level of significance.

Solution: Let sample 1 be the existing process sample, and sample 2 the new process. From the **Main Menu** select:

STAT   F3(test)   **F4**(F)   then enter the following items:

2-Sample FTest

Data	: **F2**(Var)	▼
$\sigma 1$	: **F1**($\neq \sigma 2$)	▼
x1σn-1	: **3.6**	**EXE**
n1	: **50**	**EXE**
x2σn-1	: **3.2**	**EXE**
n2	: **40**	**EXE**

Now key **EXE** or **F1**(Calc)   The calculator will now show the results:

2-Sample FTest

$\sigma 1$	$\neq \sigma 2$
F	=1.2656
p	=0.44965
x1σn-1	=3.6
x2σn-1	=3.2
n1	=50
n2	=40

Since the p-value > 0.05, the conclusion is to *not reject* the null hypothesis. In other words the evidence does not indicate that the variances of the assembly times for the two processes are different, i.e. the variances are approximately the same.

EXAMPLE 11.14   Recall the following example from lesson 10.

We wish to determine if there is a difference in the braking distances for two types of tires. Use the 5% level of significance and assume that the braking distances for each type of tire are normally distributed with the same variance. Based on the data …

Braking distance (metres)

Tire A	Tire B
83	75
79	84
82	76
84	83
80	85
81	78
	83

Suppose we test to see if the assumption about equal variances seems reasonable at the 5% level.

Solution: Enter the data for Tire A in List 1 and the data for Tire B in List 2. From the **Main Menu** select:

STAT   F3(test)   **F4**(F)   then enter the following items:

2-Sample FTest

Data	: **F1**(List)	▼
σ1	: **F1**($\neq$σ2)	▼
List1	: **F1**(List1)	▼
List2	: **F2**(List2)	▼
Freq	: **1**	▼
Freq	: **1**	**EXE**

The calculator will now show the results:

σ1	$\neq$σ2
F	$=0.20646$
p	$=0.10432$
x1σn-1	$=1.8708$
x2σn-1	$=4.1173$
$\bar{x}1$	$=81.5$
$\bar{x}2$	$=80.571$
n1	$=6$
n2	$=7$

Since the *p*-value > 0.05, the conclusion is to *not reject* the null hypothesis. In other words the evidence does not indicate that the variances of the stopping distances for the two types of tires are different, i.e. the variances are approximately the same.

CALCULATOR LESSON 13B

CASIO FX-9750GII CALCULATOR

Lesson 13B—F-test of two variances

EXAMPLE 11.15

Recall the following example from Calculator Lesson 11.

A work team has developed a new process to assemble a certain component. They would like to know if this new process has significantly reduced the time to assemble the component. They have taken samples of 50 components produced by the existing process and 40 components produced by the new process. The mean and standard deviation of the assembly times for the existing process were 73.2 minutes and 3.6 minutes, respectively. The mean time was 71.4 minutes with a standard deviation of 3.2 minutes for the components assembled by the new process. Assume that the times for both processes are normally distributed with the same variance.

Suppose that instead of assuming that the variances of the assembly times for the two processes are equal, we do an F test to see if there is evidence to support such an assumption. Test at the 5% level of significance.

Solution: Let sample 1 be the existing process sample, and sample 2 the new process. From the **Main Menu** select:

STAT   F3(test)   **F4**(F)   then enter the following items:

2-Sample FTest

Data	: **F2**(Var)	▼
σ1	: **F1**($\neq$σ2)	▼
sx1	: **3.6**	**EXE**
n1	: **50**	**EXE**
sx2	: **3.2**	**EXE**
n2	: **40**	**EXE**
Save Res	: None	

Now key **EXE** or **F1**(Calc) or **F6**(DRAW)

If you select **F6**(DRAW), you will see a normal distribution.

If you select either **EXE** or **F1**(Calc), the calculator will now show the results:

2-Sample FTest

σ1	$\neq$σ2
F	=1.2656
p	=0.44965
sx1	=3.6
sx2	=3.2
n1	=50
n2	=40

Since the p-value > 0.05, the conclusion is to *not reject* the null hypothesis. In other words the evidence does not indicate that the variances of the assembly times for the two processes are different, i.e. the variances are approximately the same.

EXAMPLE 11.16   Recall the following example from lesson 11.

We wish to determine if there is a difference in the braking distances for two types of tires. Use the 5% level of significance and assume that the braking distances for each type of tire are normally distributed with the same variance. Based on the data …

Braking distance (metres)	
Tire A	Tire B
83	75
79	84
82	76
84	83
80	85
81	78
	83

Suppose we test to see if the assumption about equal variances seems reasonable at the 5% level.

Solution: Enter the data for Tire A in List 1 and the data for Tire B in List 2. From the **Main Menu** select:

STAT   F3(test) **F4**(F)   then enter the following items:

2-Sample FTest

Data	: **F1**(List)	▼
σ1	: **F1**($\neq$σ2)	▼
List1	: **F1**(List1)	▼
List2	: **F2**(List2)	▼
Freq	: **1**	▼
Freq	: **1**	**EXE**
Save Res	: None	

Now key **EXE** or **F1**(Calc) or **F6**(DRAW)

If you select **F6**(DRAW), you will see a normal distribution.

If you select either **EXE** or **F1**(Calc), the calculator will now show the results:

2-Sample FTest

σ1	$\neq$σ2
F	=0.20646
p	=0.10432
$\bar{x}1$	=81.5
$\bar{x}2$	=80.571
sx1	=1.8708
sx2	=4.1173
n1	=6
n2	=7

Since the p-value > 0.05, the conclusion is to *not reject* the null hypothesis. In other words the evidence does not indicate that the variances of the stopping distances for the two types of tires are different, i.e. the variances are approximately the same.

Problems for Section 11.4

LEARNING THE BASICS

11.36 Determine the upper-tail critical values of F, in each of the following two-tail tests:
a. $\alpha = 0.10, n_1 = 16, n_2 = 21$
b. $\alpha = 0.05, n_1 = 16, n_2 = 21$
c. $\alpha = 0.01, n_1 = 16, n_2 = 21$

11.37 Determine the upper-tail critical value of F in each of the following one-tail tests:
a. $\alpha = 0.05, n_1 = 16, n_2 = 21$
b. $\alpha = 0.01, n_1 = 16, n_2 = 21$

11.38 The following information is available for two samples drawn from independent normally distributed populations:

$$\text{Population A:} \quad n = 25 \quad S^2 = 16$$
$$\text{Population B:} \quad n = 25 \quad S^2 = 25$$

a. Which sample variance do you place in the numerator of F_{STAT}?
b. What is the value of F_{STAT}?

11.39 The following information is available for two samples drawn from independent normally distributed populations:

$$\text{Population A:} \quad n = 25 \quad S^2 = 161.9$$
$$\text{Population B:} \quad n = 25 \quad S^2 = 133.7$$

What is the value of F_{STAT} if you are testing the null hypothesis $H_0: \sigma_1^2 = \sigma_2^2$?

11.40 In Problem 11.39, how many degrees of freedom are there in the numerator and denominator of the F test?

11.41 In Problems 11.39 and 11.40, what is the upper critical value for F if the level of significance, α, is 0.05 and the alternative hypothesis is $H_1: \sigma_1^2 \neq \sigma_2^2$?

11.42 In Problems 11.39 through 11.40, what is your statistical decision?

11.43 The following information is available for two samples selected from independent but very right-skewed populations:

$$\text{Population A:} \quad n = 16 \quad S^2 = 47.3$$
$$\text{Population B:} \quad n = 13 \quad S^2 = 36.4$$

Should you use the F test to test the null hypothesis of equality of variances? Discuss.

11.44 In Problem 11.43, assume that two samples are selected from independent normally distributed populations.
a. At the 0.05 level of significance, is there evidence of a difference between σ_1^2 and σ_2^2?
b. Suppose that you want to perform a one-tail test. At the 0.05 level of significance, what is the upper-tail critical value of F to determine whether there is evidence that $\sigma_1^2 > \sigma_2^2$? What is your statistical decision?

APPLYING THE CONCEPTS

11.45 A professor in the accounting department of a business school claims that there is much more variability in the final exam scores of students taking the introductory accounting course who are not majoring in accounting than for students taking the course who are majoring in accounting. Random samples of 13 non-accounting majors and 10 accounting majors are taken from the professor's class roster in his large lecture, and the following results are computed based on the final exam scores:

$$\text{Non-Accounting:} \quad n = 13 \quad S^2 = 210.2$$
$$\text{Accounting:} \quad n = 10 \quad S^2 = 36.5$$

a. At the 0.05 level of significance, is there evidence to support the professor's claim?
b. Interpret the p-value.
c. What assumption do you need to make in (a) about the two populations in order to justify your use of the F test?

SELF Test **11.46** The Computer Anxiety Rating Scale (CARS) measures an individual's level of computer anxiety, on a scale from 20 (no anxiety) to 100 (highest level of anxiety). Researchers at Miami University administered CARS to 172 business students. One of the objectives of the study was to determine whether there is a difference between the level of computer anxiety experienced by female students and male students. They found the following:

	Males	**Females**
$\overline{X}$	40.26	36.85
S	13.35	9.42
n	100	72

Source: *Data extracted from T. Broome and D. Havelka, "Determinants of Computer Anxiety in Business Students,"* The Review of Business Information Systems, *Spring 2002, 6(2), pp. 9–16.*

a. At the 0.05 level of significance, is there evidence of a difference in the variability of the computer anxiety experienced by males and females?
b. Interpret the p-value.
c. What assumption do you need to make about the two populations in order to justify the use of the F test?
d. Based on (a) and (b), which t test defined in Section 11.1 should you use to test whether there is a significant difference in mean computer anxiety for female and male students?

11.47 A bank with a branch located in a commercial district of a city has developed an improved process for serving customers during the noon-to-1 P.M. lunch period. The waiting time (defined as the time elapsed from when the customer enters the line until he or she reaches the teller window) needs to be shortened to increase customer satisfaction. A random sample of 15 customers is selected (and stored in the file Bank1), and the results (in minutes) are as follows:

4.21	5.55	3.02	5.13	4.77	2.34	3.54	3.20
4.50	6.10	0.38	5.12	6.46	6.19	3.79	

Suppose that another branch, located in a residential area, is also concerned with the noon-to-1 P.M. lunch period. A random sample of 15 customers is selected (and stored in the file Bank2), and the results (in minutes) are as follows:

9.66	5.90	8.02	5.79	8.73	3.82	8.01	8.35
10.49	6.68	5.64	4.08	6.17	9.91	5.47	

a. Is there evidence of a difference in the variability of the waiting time between the two branches? (Use $\alpha = 0.05$.)
b. Determine the p-value in (a) and interpret its meaning.
c. What assumption about the population distribution of the two banks is necessary in (a)? Is the assumption valid for these data?
d. Based on the results of (a), is it appropriate to use the pooled-variance t test to compare the means of the two branches?

11.48 Digital cameras have taken over the majority of the point-and-shoot camera market. One of the important features of a camera is the battery life as measured by the number of shots taken until the battery needs to be recharged. The data in the file Digitalcameras contains the battery life of 31 subcompact cameras and 15 compact cameras (data extracted from "Cameras," *Consumer Reports*, November 2006, pp. 20–21).
a. Is there evidence of a difference in the variability of the battery life between the two types of digital cameras? (Use $\alpha = 0.05$.)
b. Determine the p-value in (a) and interpret its meaning.
c. What assumption about the population distribution of the two types of cameras is necessary in (a)? Is the assumption valid for these data?

d. Based on the results of (a), which t test defined in Section 11.1 should you use to compare the mean battery life of the two types of cameras?

11.49 The director of training for a company that manufactures electronic equipment is interested in determining whether different training methods have an effect on the productivity of assembly-line employees. She randomly assigns 21 of the 42 recently hired employees to a computer-assisted, individual-based training program. The other 21 are assigned to a team-based training program. Upon completion of the training, the employees are evaluated on the time (in seconds) it takes to assemble a part. The results are in the data file Training.
a. Using a 0.05 level of significance, is there evidence of a difference between the variances in assembly times (in seconds) of employees trained in a computer-assisted, individual-based program and those trained in a team-based program?
b. On the basis of the results in (a), which t test defined in Section 11.1 should you use to compare the means of the two training programs? Discuss.

11.50 Is there a difference in the variation of the yield of different types of investment between banks? The following data, from the file Bankyield, represent the yields for a sample of money market accounts and five-year CDs as of March 31, 2008:

Money Market Accounts	**Five-Year CD**
3.94 3.75 3.74 3.68 3.68	4.21 4.07 4.02 3.93 3.92

Source: *Data extracted from Bankrate.com, March 31, 2008.*

At the 0.05 level of significance, is there evidence of a difference in the variance of the yield between money market accounts and five-year CDs? Assume that the population yields are normally distributed.

11.5 One-Way Analysis of Variance

In Sections 11.1 through 11.4, you used hypothesis testing to reach conclusions about possible differences between two populations. In many situations you need to examine differences among *more than two* populations. In theses situations, populations are referred to as *groups*. The groups involved can be classified according to **levels** of a **factor** of interest. For example, a factor such as baking temperature may have several groups defined by *numerical levels* such as 300°, 350°, 400°, 450°, and a factor such as preferred supplier for a parachute manufacturer may have several groups defined by *categorical levels* such as Supplier 1, Supplier 2, Supplier 3, and Supplier 4.

F Test for Differences Among More Than Two Means

When you are analyzing a numerical variable and certain assumptions are met, you use the **analysis of variance (ANOVA)** to compare the means of the groups. The ANOVA procedure used when there is one factor of interest is referred to as the **one-way ANOVA**, and it is an extension of the *t* test for the difference between two means discussed in Section 11.1. Although ANOVA is an acronym for *analysis of variance*, the term is misleading because the objective is to analyze differences among the group means, *not* the variances. However, by analyzing the variation among and within the groups, you can reach conclusions about possible differences in group means. In ANOVA, the total variation is subdivided into variation that is due to differences *among* the groups and variation that is due to differences *within* the groups (see Figure 11.14). **Within-group variation** measures random variation. **Among-group variation** is due to differences from group to group. The symbol *c* is used to indicate the number of groups.

FIGURE 11.14

Partitioning the total variation in a completely randomized design

Partitioning the Total Variation
SST = SSA + SSW

Assuming that the *c* groups represent samples whose values are randomly and independently selected, from normal populations that have equal variances, the null hypothesis of no differences in the population means:

$$H_0: \mu_1 = \mu_2 = \cdots = \mu_c$$

is tested against the alternative that not all the *c* population means are equal:

$$H_1: \text{Not all } \mu_j \text{ are equal (where } j = 1, 2, \ldots, c).$$

To perform an ANOVA test of equality of population means, you subdivide the total variation in the values into two parts—that which is due to variation among the groups and that which is due to variation within the groups. The **total variation** is represented by the **sum of squares total (*SST*)**. Because the population means of the *c* groups are assumed to be equal under the null hypothesis, you compute the total variation among all the values by summing the squared differences between each individual value and the **grand mean**, $\overline{\overline{X}}$. The grand mean is the mean of all the values in all the groups combined. Equation (11.8) shows the computation of the total variation.

TOTAL VARIATION IN ONE-WAY ANOVA

$$SST = \sum_{j=1}^{c} \sum_{i=1}^{n_j} (X_{ij} - \overline{\overline{X}})^2 \tag{11.8}$$

where

$$\overline{\overline{X}} = \frac{\sum_{j=1}^{c} \sum_{i=1}^{n_j} X_{ij}}{n} = \text{Grand mean}$$

$X_{ij} = i\text{th value in group } j$

$n_j = \text{number of values in group } j$

$n = \text{total number of values in all groups combined (that is, } n = n_1 + n_2 + \cdots + n_c)$

$c = \text{number of groups}$

You compute the among-group variation, usually called the **sum of squares among groups** (**SSA**), by summing the squared differences between the sample mean of each group, $\overline{X}_j$, and the grand mean, $\overline{\overline{X}}$, weighted by the sample size, n_j, in each group. Equation (11.9) shows the computation of the among-group variation.

AMONG-GROUP VARIATION IN ONE-WAY ANOVA

$$SSA = \sum_{j=1}^{c} n_j(\overline{X}_j - \overline{\overline{X}})^2 \qquad (11.9)$$

where

$$c = \text{number of groups}$$
$$n_j = \text{number of values in group } j$$
$$\overline{X}_j = \text{sample mean of group } j$$
$$\overline{\overline{X}} = \text{grand mean}$$

The within-group variation, usually called the **sum of squares within groups** (**SSW**), measures the difference between each value and the mean of its own group and sums the squares of these differences over all groups. Equation (11.10) shows the computation of the within-group variation.

WITHIN-GROUP VARIATION IN ONE-WAY ANOVA

$$SSW = \sum_{j=1}^{c} \sum_{i=1}^{n_j} (X_{ij} - \overline{X}_j)^2 \qquad (11.10)$$

where

$$X_{ij} = i\text{th value in group } j$$
$$\overline{X}_j = \text{sample mean of group } j$$

Because you are comparing c groups, there are $c - 1$ degrees of freedom associated with the sum of squares among groups. Because each of the c groups contributes $n_j - 1$ degrees of freedom, there are $n - c$ degrees of freedom associated with the sum of squares within groups. In addition, there are $n - 1$ degrees of freedom associated with the sum of squares total because you are comparing each value, X_{ij}, to the grand mean, $\overline{\overline{X}}$, based on all n values.

If you divide each of these sums of squares by its associated degrees of freedom, you have three variances or **mean square** terms—*MSA* (mean square among), *MSW* (mean square within), and *MST* (mean square total).

MEAN SQUARES IN ONE-WAY ANOVA

$$MSA = \frac{SSA}{c - 1} \qquad (11.11a)$$

$$MSW = \frac{SSW}{n - c} \qquad (11.11b)$$

$$MST = \frac{SST}{n - 1} \qquad (11.11c)$$

Although you want to compare the means of the c groups to determine whether a difference exists among them, the name ANOVA comes from the fact that you are comparing variances. If the null hypothesis is true and there are no differences in the c group means, all three mean squares (or *variances*)—*MSA, MSW*, and *MST*—provide estimates of the overall variance in the data. Thus, to test the null hypothesis:

$$H_0: \mu_1 = \mu_2 = \cdots = \mu_c$$

against the alternative:

$$H_1: \text{Not all } \mu_j \text{ are equal (where } j = 1, 2, \ldots, c)$$

you compute the one-way ANOVA F_{STAT} test statistic as the ratio of *MSA* to *MSW*, as in Equation (11.12).

ONE-WAY ANOVA F_{STAT} TEST STATISTIC

$$F_{STAT} = \frac{MSA}{MSW} \qquad \textbf{(11.12)}$$

The F_{STAT} test statistic follows an F distribution, with $c - 1$ degrees of freedom in the numerator and $n - c$ degrees of freedom in the denominator. For a given level of significance, α, you reject the null hypothesis if the F_{STAT} test statistic computed in Equation (11.12), is greater than the upper-tail critical value, F_α, from the F distribution having $c - 1$ degrees of freedom in the numerator and $n - c$ in the denominator (see Table E.5). Thus, as shown in Figure 11.15, the decision rule is

$$\text{Reject } H_0 \text{ if } F_{STAT} > F_\alpha;$$

otherwise, do not reject H_0.

FIGURE 11.15

Regions of rejection and nonrejection when using ANOVA

If the null hypothesis is true, the computed F_{STAT} test statistic is expected to be approximately equal to 1 because both the numerator and denominator mean square terms are estimating the overall variance in the data. If H_0 is false (and there are differences in the group means), the computed F_{STAT} test statistic is expected to be larger than 1 because the numerator, *MSA*, is estimating the differences among groups in addition to the overall variability in the values, whereas the denominator, *MSW*, is measuring only the overall variability. Thus, the ANOVA procedure provides an F test in which you reject the null hypothesis at a selected level of significance, α, only if the computed F_{STAT} test statistic is greater than F_α, the upper-tail critical value of the F distribution having $c - 1$ and $n - c$ degrees of freedom, as illustrated in Figure 11.15.

The results of an analysis of variance are usually displayed in an **ANOVA summary table**, as shown in Table 11.7. The entries in this table include the sources of variation (i.e., among-

TABLE 11.7

Analysis-of-Variance Summary Table

Source	Degrees of Freedom	Sum of Squares	Mean Square (Variance)	F
Among groups	$c - 1$	SSA	$MSA = \dfrac{SSA}{c - 1}$	$F_{STAT} = \dfrac{MSA}{MSW}$
Within groups	$n - c$	SSW	$MSW = \dfrac{SSW}{n - c}$	
Total	$n - 1$	SST		

groups, within-groups, and total), the degrees of freedom, the sums of squares, the mean squares (i.e., the variances), and the computed F_{STAT} test statistic. In addition, Microsoft Excel and Minitab include the p-value (i.e., the probability of having an F_{STAT} as large as or larger than the one computed, given that the null hypothesis is true) in the ANOVA summary table. The p-value allows you to make direct conclusions about the null hypothesis without referring to a table of critical values of the F distribution. If the p-value is less than the chosen level of significance, α, you reject the null hypothesis.

To illustrate the one-way ANOVA F test, you can consider a company that weaves parachutes using synthetic fibers purchased from one of four different suppliers. The strength of the fibers is an important characteristic and you need to decide whether the synthetic fibers from each of the four suppliers result in parachutes of equal strength. The results of an experiment (in terms of tensile strength) are contained in the `Parachute` file and are displayed in Figure 11.16a, along with the sample mean and the sample standard deviation for each group.

FIGURE 11.16a

Microsoft Excel worksheet of the tensile strength for parachutes woven with synthetic fibers from four different suppliers along with the sample mean and sample standard deviation

	A	B	C	D	E
1		Supplier 1	Supplier 2	Supplier 3	Supplier 4
2		18.5	26.3	20.6	25.4
3		24.0	25.3	25.2	19.9
4		17.2	24.0	20.8	22.6
5		19.9	21.2	24.7	17.5
6		18.0	24.5	22.9	20.4
7					
8	Sample Mean	19.52	24.26	22.84	21.16
9	Sample Standard Deviation	2.69	1.92	2.13	2.98

FIGURE 11.16b

SPSS datasheet of the tensile strength for parachutes woven with synthetic fibers from four different suppliers

In Figure 11.16a, observe that there are differences in the sample means for the four suppliers. For Supplier 1, the mean tensile strength is 19.52. For Supplier 2, the mean tensile strength is 24.26. For Supplier 3, the mean tensile strength is 22.84, and for Supplier 4, the mean tensile strength is 21.16. What you need to determine is whether these sample results are sufficiently different to conclude that the *population* means are not all equal.

In the scatter plot shown in Figure 11.17, you can visually inspect the data and see how the measurements of tensile strength distribute. You can also observe differences among the groups as well as within groups. If the sample sizes in each group were larger, you could develop stem-and-leaf displays, boxplots, and normal probability plots to evaluate the assumption of normality in each group.

FIGURE 11.17

Microsoft Excel scatter plot of tensile strengths for four different suppliers

See Section E2.12 to create this.

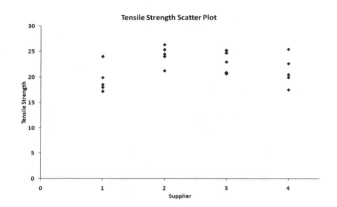

The null hypothesis states that there is no difference in mean tensile strength among the four suppliers:

$$H_0: \mu_1 = \mu_2 = \mu_3 = \mu_4$$

The alternative hypothesis states that at least one of the suppliers differs with respect to the mean tensile strength:

$$H_1: \text{Not all the means are equal.}$$

To construct the ANOVA summary table, you first compute the sample means in each group (see Figure 11.16a). Then you compute the grand mean by summing all 20 values and dividing by the total number of values:

$$\overline{\overline{X}} = \frac{\displaystyle\sum_{j=1}^{c}\sum_{i=1}^{n_j} X_{ij}}{n} = \frac{438.9}{20} = 21.945$$

Then, using Equations (11.8) through (11.10), you compute the sum of squares:

$$SSA = \sum_{j=1}^{c} n_j(\overline{X}_j - \overline{\overline{X}})^2 = (5)(19.52 - 21.945)^2 + (5)(24.26 - 21.945)^2$$
$$+ (5)(22.84 - 21.945)^2 + (5)(21.16 - 21.945)^2$$
$$= 63.2855$$

$$SSW = \sum_{j=1}^{c}\sum_{i=1}^{n_j} (X_{ij} - \overline{X}_j)^2$$
$$= (18.5 - 1+9.52)^2 + \cdots + (18 - 19.52)^2 + (26.3 - 24.26)^2 + \cdots + (24.5 - 24.26)^2$$
$$+ (20.6 - 22.84)^2 + \cdots + (22.9 - 22.84)^2 + (25.4 - 21.16)^2 + \cdots + (20.4 - 21.16)^2$$
$$= 97.5040$$

$$SST = \sum_{j=1}^{c}\sum_{i=1}^{n_j} (X_{ij} - \overline{\overline{X}})^2$$
$$= (18.5 - 21.945)^2 + (24 - 21.945)^2 + \cdots + (20.4 - 21.945)^2$$
$$= 160.7895$$

You compute the mean square terms by dividing the sum of squares by the corresponding degrees of freedom [see Equation (11.11) on page 493]. Because $c = 4$ and $n = 20$,

$$MSA = \frac{SSA}{c - 1} = \frac{63.2855}{4 - 1} = 21.0952$$

$$MSW = \frac{SSW}{n - c} = \frac{97.5040}{20 - 4} = 6.0940$$

so that using Equation (11.12) on page 504,

$$F_{STAT} = \frac{MSA}{MSW} = \frac{21.0952}{6.0940} = 3.4616$$

For a selected level of significance, α, you find the upper-tail critical value, F_{α}, from the F distribution using Table E.5. A portion of Table E.5 is presented in Table 11.8. In the parachute supplier example, there are 3 degrees of freedom in the numerator and 16 degrees of freedom in the denominator. F_{α}, the upper-tail critical value at the 0.05 level of significance, is 3.24.

TABLE 11.8

Finding the Critical Value of F with 3 and 16 Degrees of Freedom at the 0.05 Level of Significance

				Cumulative Probabilities = 0.95 Upper-Tail Area = 0.05 Numerator df_1						
Denominator df_2	1	2	3	4	5	6	7	8	9
.	.				.	.	.	.	.	.
.	.	.	.		.	.	.	.	.	.
.	.	.	.	.	.	.	.	.	.	.
11	4.84	3.98	3.59	3.36	3.20	3.09	3.01	2.95	2.90
12	4.75	3.89	3.49	3.26	3.11	3.00	2.91	2.85	2.80
13	4.67	3.81	3.41	3.18	3.03	2.92	2.83	2.77	2.71
14	4.60	3.74	3.34	3.11	2.96	2.85	2.76	2.70	2.65
15	4.54	3.68	3.29	3.06	2.90	2.79	2.71	2.64	2.59
16	4.49	3.63	3.24	3.01	2.85	2.74	2.66	2.59	2.54

Source: *Extracted from Table E.5.*

Because $F_{STAT} = 3.4616$ is greater than $F_{\alpha} = 3.24$, you reject the null hypothesis (see Figure 11.18). You conclude that there is a significant difference in the mean tensile strength among the four suppliers.

FIGURE 11.18

Regions of rejection and nonrejection for the one-way ANOVA at the 0.05 level of significance, with 3 and 16 degrees of freedom

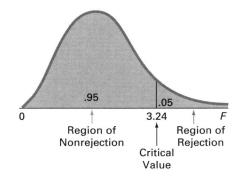

Figure 11.19 shows the SPSS ANOVA summary table and p-value.

FIGURE 11.19

SPSS ANOVA results for the parachute example

ANOVA

tensile-strength scale

	Sum of Squares	df	Mean Square	F	Sig.
Between Groups	63.285	3	21.095	3.462	.041
Within Groups	97.504	16	6.094		
Total	160.789	19			

The *p*-value, or probability of getting a computed F_{STAT} statistic of 3.462 or larger when the null hypothesis is true, is 0.041. Because this *p*-value is less than the specified α of 0.05, you reject the null hypothesis. The *p*-value of 0.041 indicates that there is a 4.1% chance of observing differences this large or larger if the population means for the four suppliers are all equal.

After performing the one-way ANOVA and finding a significant difference among the suppliers, you still do not know *which* suppliers differ. All that you know is that there is sufficient evidence to state that the population means are not all the same. In other words, at least one or more population means are significantly different.

Multiple Comparisons: The Tukey-Kramer Procedure (Using SPSS)

In the parachute company example, you used the one-way ANOVA F test to determine that there was a difference among the suppliers. The next step is to construct **multiple comparisons** to determine which suppliers are different, using SPSS.

FIGURE 11.20

SPSS Tukey-Kramer procedure worksheet for the parachute example

Post Hoc Tests

Multiple Comparisons

tensile-strength scale
Tukey HSD

(I) suppliers	(J) suppliers	Mean Difference (I-J)	Std. Error	Sig.	95% Confidence Interval Lower Bound	95% Confidence Interval Upper Bound
Supplier 1	Supplier 2	−4.74000*	1.56128	.036	−9.2069	−.2731
	Supplier 3	−3.32000	1.56128	.187	−7.7869	1.1469
	Supplier 4	−1.64000	1.56128	.723	−6.1069	2.8269
Supplier 2	Supplier 1	4.74000*	1.56128	.036	.2731	9.2069
	Supplier 3	1.42000	1.56128	.800	−3.0469	5.8869
	Supplier 4	3.10000	1.56128	.234	−1.3669	7.5669
Supplier 3	Supplier 1	3.32000	1.56128	.187	−1.1469	7.7869
	Supplier 2	−1.42000	1.56128	.800	−5.8869	3.0469
	Supplier 4	1.68000	1.56128	.708	−2.7869	6.1469
Supplier 4	Supplier 1	1.64000	1.56128	.723	−2.8269	6.1069
	Supplier 2	−3.10000	1.56128	.234	−7.5669	1.3669
	Supplier 3	−1.68000	1.56128	.708	−6.1469	2.7869

* The mean difference is significant at the 0.05 level.

Results:

1. Since the *p*-value = 0.036 < 0.05, the conclusion is to reject the null hypothesis and there is evidence to indicate that the means tensile strength for suppliers 1 and 2 are different.
2. Since the *p*-value = 0.187 > 0.05, the conclusion is to not to reject the null hypothesis and there is **no** evidence to indicate that the means tensile strength for suppliers 1 and 3 are different.
3. Since the *p*-value = 0.723 > 0.05, the conclusion is to not to reject null hypothesis and there is **no** evidence to indicate that the means tensile strength for suppliers 1 and 4 are different.
4. Since the *p*-value = 0.800 > 0.05, do not reject the null hypothesis; there is **no** evidence to indicate that the means tensile strength for suppliers 2 and 3 are different.

5. Since the p-value $= 0.234 > 0.05$, do not reject the null hypothesis; there is **no** evidence to indicate that the means tensile strength for suppliers 2 and 4 are different.
6. Since the p-value $= 0.708 > 0.05$, do not reject the null hypothesis; there is **no** evidence to indicate that the means tensile strength for suppliers 3 and 4 are different.

ANOVA Assumptions

In Chapter 10 and Sections 11.1–11.4, you learned about the assumptions required in order to use each hypothesis-testing procedure and the consequences of departures from these assumptions. To use the one-way ANOVA F test, you must also make certain assumptions about the populations. These assumptions are

- Randomness and independence
- Normality
- Homogeneity of variance

The first assumption, **randomness and independence**, is critically important. The validity of any experiment depends on random sampling and/or a randomization process. To avoid biases in the outcomes, you need to select random samples from the c groups or randomly assign the items to the c levels of the factor. Selecting a random sample, or randomly assigning the levels, ensures that a value from one group is independent of any other value in the experiment. Departures from this assumption can seriously affect inferences from the ANOVA.

The second assumption, **normality**, states that the sample values in each group are from a normally distributed population. Just as in the case of the t test, the one-way ANOVA F test is fairly robust against departures from the normal distribution. As long as the distributions are not extremely different from a normal distribution, the level of significance of the ANOVA F test is usually not greatly affected, particularly for large samples. You can assess the normality of each of the c samples by constructing a normal probability plot or a boxplot.

The third assumption, **homogeneity of variance**, states that the variances of the c groups are equal (that is, $\sigma_1^2 = \sigma_2^2 = \cdots = \sigma_c^2$). If you have equal sample sizes in each group, inferences based on the F distribution are not seriously affected by unequal variances. However, if you have unequal sample sizes, unequal variances can have a serious effect on inferences developed from the ANOVA procedure. Thus, when possible, you should have equal sample sizes in all groups. The modified Levene test for homogeneity of variance presented below is one method used to test whether the variances of the c groups are equal.

When only the normality assumption is violated, the Kruskal-Wallis rank test, a nonparametric procedure, is appropriate. When only the homogeneity-of-variance assumption is violated, procedures similar to those used in the separate-variance t test of Section 11.1 are available. When both the normality and homogeneity-of-variance assumptions have been violated, you need to use an appropriate data transformation that both normalizes the data and reduces the differences in variances or use a more general nonparametric procedure.

Levene Test for Homogeneity of Variance (Using SPSS)

Although the one-way ANOVA F test is relatively robust with respect to the assumption of equal group variances, large differences in the group variances can seriously affect the level of significance and the power of the F test. One procedure for testing the equality of the variances with high statistical power is the modified **Levene test**. To test for the homogeneity of variance, you use the following null hypothesis:

$$H_0: \sigma_1^2 = \sigma_2^2 = \cdots = \sigma_c^2$$

against the alternative hypothesis:

$$H_1: \text{Not all } \sigma_j^2 \text{ are equal } (j = 1, 2, 3, \ldots, c).$$

To test the null hypothesis of equal variances, perform a one-way ANOVA using SPSS by selecting 'option' button and select Homogeneity of Variance test in the "one-way ANOVA: OPTIONS" window. Most statisticians suggest using a level of significance of $\alpha = 0.05$ when performing the ANOVA. To illustrate the Levene test, return to the example concerning the tensile strength of parachutes.

FIGURE 11.21

SPSS ANOVA Levene test and ANOVA results

See Section E11.11 to create this.

Test of Homogeneity of Variances

tensile-strength scale

Levene Statistic	df1	df2	Sig.
.430	3	16	.734

ANOVA

tensile-strength scale

	Sum of Squares	df	Mean Square	F	Sig.
Between Groups	63.285	3	21.095	3.462	.041
Within Groups	97.504	16	6.094		
Total	160.789	19			

From Figure 11.21, observe that the p-value $= 0.734 > 0.05$, you do not reject H_0. There is no evidence of a significant difference among the four variances. In other words, it is reasonable to assume that the materials from the four suppliers produce parachutes with an equal amount of variability. Therefore, the homogeneity-of-variance assumption for the ANOVA procedure is justified.

EXAMPLE 11.17

ANOVA of the Speed of Drive-Through Service at Fast-Food Chains

For fast-food restaurants, the drive-through window is an increasing source of revenue. The chain that offers the fastest service is likely to attract additional customers. Each month QSR Magazine, **www.qsrmagazine.com**, publishes its results of drive-through service times (from menu board to departure) at fast-food chains. In a recent month, the mean time was 135.1 seconds for Wendy's, 156.2 seconds for Taco Bell, 163.9 seconds for McDonald's, 166 seconds for Burger King, and 173.2 seconds for KFC. Suppose the study was based on 20 customers for each fast-food chain and the ANOVA table given in Table 11.9 was developed.

TABLE 11.9

ANOVA Summary Table of Drive-Through Service Times at Fast-Food Chains

Source	Degrees of Freedom	Sum of Squares	Mean Squares	F	p-Value
Among chains	4	17,072.56	4,268.14	32.68	0.0000
Within chains	95	12,407.00	130.60		

At the 0.05 level of significance, is there evidence of a difference in the mean drive-through service times of the five chains?

SOLUTION

H_0: $\mu_1 = \mu_2 = \mu_3 = \mu_4 = \mu_5$ where 1 = Wendy's, 2 = Taco Bell, 3 = McDonald's, 4 = Burger King, 5 = KFC

H_1: Not all μ_j are equal where j = 1, 2, 3, 4, 5

Decision rule: If p-value < 0.05, reject H_0. Because the p-value is virtually 0, which is less than $\alpha = 0.05$, reject H_0. You have sufficient evidence to conclude that the mean drive-through times of the five chains are not all equal.

CALCULATOR LESSON 14A

CFX-9850GB CALCULATOR

EXAMPLE: The Perfect Parachute Company

TABLE 10.10

Summarizes the results of the 4 suppliers.

Lesson 14A—One-Way ANOVA

We will use the scenario, "The Perfect Parachute Company", to demonstrate how to perform one-way ANOVA on the calculator.

A research was conducted to determine if any significant differences exist in the strength of parachutes woven from synthetic fibers from the four suppliers. Five parachutes were woven for each group – Supplier 1, Supplier 2, Supplier 3 and Supplier 4. The amount of force required to tear the parachute is measured on a tensile-strength scale where the larger the value the stronger the parachute. The data is shown below:

Supplier 1	Supplier 2	Supplier 3	Supplier 4
18.5	26.3	20.6	25.4
24.0	25.3	25.2	19.9
17.2	24.0	20.8	22.6
19.9	21.2	24.7	17.5
18.0	24.5	22.9	20.4

Solution: First enter data into **List 1** (corresponding to Supplier 1), **List 2** (corresponding to Supplier 2), **List 3** (corresponding to Supplier 3), **List 4** (corresponding to Supplier 4)

Now, from the **Main Menu** select

STAT   TEST (F3)   ANOV (F5)   then enter the following items:

ANOVA
How many   : 4 (press **F3**)
List 1   : List 1 (F1)
List 2   : List 2 (F2)
List 3   : List 3 (F3)
List 4   : List 4 (F4)
Execute

Now press **EXE** or **F1** (Calc)

The calculator will now show the results:

ANOVA
  F   =3.4616
  p   =0.041365
  xpσn-1   =2.4686
    Fdf   =3
    SS   =63.285
    MS   =21.095
    Edf   =16
    SSe   =97.504
    MSe   =6.094

Since the *p*-value < 0.05, the conclusion is to reject the null hypothesis. In other words there is a significant difference in the mean tensile strength among the four suppliers. However, we do not know which suppliers differ. To answer this question, we perform the Tukey procedure using SPSS (see Figure 10.20).

CALCULATOR LESSON 14B

FX-9850GII CALCULATOR

EXAMPLE: The Perfect Parachute Company

Lesson 14B—One-Way ANOVA

We will use the scenario, "The Perfect Parachute Company", to demonstrate how to perform one-way ANOVA on the calculator.

A research was conducted to determine if any significant differences exist in the strength of parachutes woven from synthetic fibers from the four suppliers. Five parachutes were woven for each group – Supplier 1, Supplier 2, Supplier 3 and Supplier 4. The amount of force required to tear the parachute is measured on a tensile-strength scale where the larger the value the stronger the parachute. The data is shown below:

TABLE 11.10

Summarizes the results of the 4 suppliers.

Supplier 1	Supplier 2	Supplier 3	Supplier 4
18.5	26.3	20.6	25.4
24.0	25.3	25.2	19.9
17.2	24.0	20.8	22.6
19.9	21.2	24.7	17.5
18.0	24.5	22.9	20.4

Solution:

A. First enter data in **List 1** and **List 2** as followed:

Factor A	Dependent
List 1	List 2
1	18.5
1	24.0
1	17.2
1	19.9
1	18.0
2	26.3
2	25.3
2	24.0
2	21.2
2	24.5
3	20.6
3	25.2
3	20.8
3	24.7
3	22.9
4	25.4
4	19.9
4	22.6
4	17.5
4	20.4

B. Perform the ANOVA procedure

From the **Main Menu** select

STAT   TEST(F3) ANOV(F5)   then enter the following items:

ANOVA
How many   : 1 (press **F1**)
Factor A   : List 1 (F1)
Dependnt   : List 2 (F1)
Save Res   : None
Execute

Now press **EXE** or **F1**(Calc)
The calculator will now show the results:

ANOVA

	df	SS	mS	F	p
A	3	63.285	21.0952	3.46162	0.04137
ERR	16	97.504	6.094		

Since the p-value < 0.05, the conclusion is to reject the null hypothesis. In other words there is a significant difference in the mean tensile strength among the four suppliers. However, we do not know which suppliers differ. To answer this question, we perform the Tukey procedure using SPSS.

SPSS—VERSION 16—ANOVA

We will use the scenario, "The Perfect Parachute Company", to demonstrate how to perform one-way ANOVA using SPSS.

A research was conducted to determine if any significant differences exist in the strength of parachutes woven from synthetic fibers from the four suppliers. Five parachutes were woven for each group – Supplier 1, Supplier 2, Supplier 3 and Supplier 4. The amount of force required to tear the parachute is measured on a tensile-strength scale where the larger the value the stronger the parachute. The data is shown below:

Supplier 1	Supplier 2	Supplier 3	Supplier 4
18.5	26.3	20.6	25.4
24.0	25.3	25.2	19.9
17.2	24.0	20.8	22.6
19.9	21.2	24.7	17.5
18.0	24.5	22.9	20.4

Solution:

Performing a one-way ANOVA on SPSS – Version 16

Step 1: Open the SPSS Data Editor.

Click **"cancel"** to cancel the SPSS opening window.

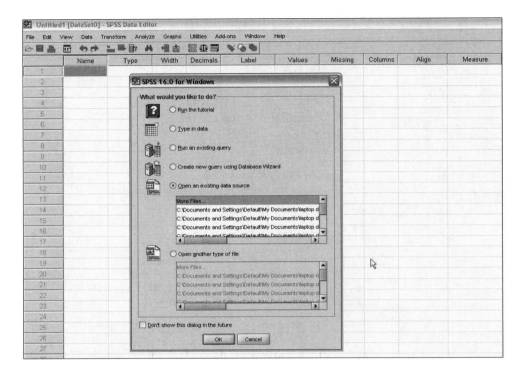

Step 2: Define the variables and give the variables a label.

Click **"Variable View"** (at the bottom of the window) to go to the variable view window to define the variables and fix the data at zero or one decimal places.

- Enter the first variable name -"suppliers" and then click **values.** Key "1" in the value box and key **"Supplier 1"** in the Label box, and then click **Add.** Similarly enter for the other three suppliers.

- Enter the second variable name – "Strength" and label it as "Tensile-Strength Scale".

Step 3: Create a SPSS data file.

Click **"Data View"** to return to the data view window. Now, enter the raw data into the respective column of variables.

After you have entered all the data, save it as "Anova.sav" (or any filename).

Step 3: Perform ANOVA.

Make the following menu selections:

Analyze → Compare Means → One-Way Anova

At this point, the **One-Way Anova** dialog box will appear. Make these entries in the **One-Way Anova** dialog box:

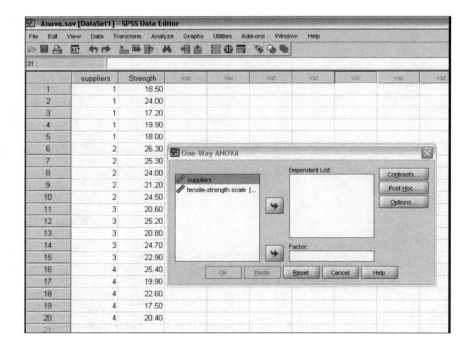

- Highlight on the **"tensile-strength scale"** variable and click on the arrow key (→). The variable will automatically fall into the **Dependent List** box.

- Highlight on the **"Suppliers"** variable and click on the arrow key (→). The variable will automatically fall into the **Factor** box.

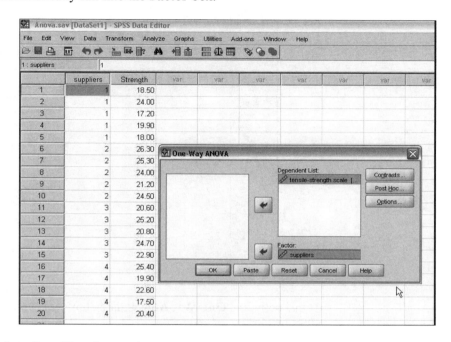

To Perform Post-Hoc Comparison Procedure

- Click on the **Post-Hoc** button. In the "One-Way Anova: Post Hoc Multiple Comparisons" window, select **Tukey** as the comparison method. Then click on **continue** button to return to the "One-Way Anova" window.

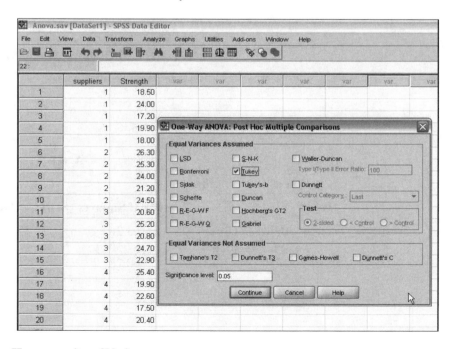

Test for Homogeneity of Variance

- Click on the **Options** button. In the "One-Way Anova: Options" window, select **Homogeneity of variance test** to test for the equality of variances. Then click on **continue** button to return to the "One-Way Anova" window.

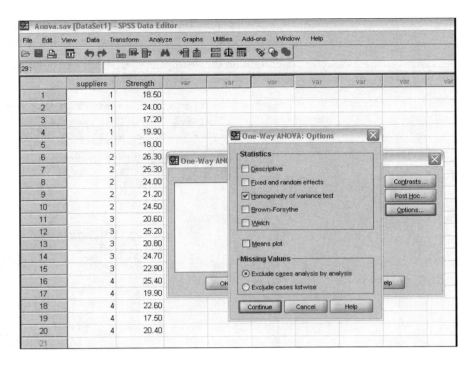

At this point, the **One-Way Anova** dialog box will appear. Click on the **Ok** button to obtain the SPSS results.

Step 3: Go to **SPSS Viewer** to obtain your SPSS results.

SPSS output:

Oneway

Test of Homogeneity of Variances

tensile-strength scale

Levene Statistic	df1	df2	Sig.
.430	3	16	.734

ANOVA

tensile-strength scale

	Sum of Squares	df	Mean Square	F	Sig.
Between Groups	63.285	3	21.095	3.462	.041
Within Groups	97.504	16	6.094		
Total	160.789	19			

Post Hoc Tests

Multiple Comparisons

tensile-strength scale
Tukey HSD

(I) suppliers	(J) suppliers	Mean Difference (I-J)	Std. Error	Sig.	95% Confidence Interval	
					Lower Bound	Upper Bound
Supplier 1	Supplier 2	−4.74000*	1.56128	.036	−9.2069	−.2731
	Supplier 3	−3.32000	1.56128	.187	−7.7869	1.1469
	Supplier 4	−1.64000	1.56128	.723	−6.1069	2.8269
Supplier 2	Supplier 1	4.74000*	1.56128	.036	.2731	9.2069
	Supplier 3	1.42000	1.56128	.800	−3.0469	5.8869
	Supplier 4	3.10000	1.56128	.234	−1.3669	7.5669
Supplier 3	Supplier 1	3.32000	1.56128	.187	−1.1469	7.7869
	Supplier 2	−1.42000	1.56128	.800	−5.8869	3.0469
	Supplier 4	1.68000	1.56128	.708	−2.7869	6.1469
Supplier 4	Supplier 1	1.64000	1.56128	.723	−2.8269	6.1069
	Supplier 2	−3.10000	1.56128	.234	−7.5669	1.3669
	Supplier 3	−1.68000	1.56128	.708	−6.1469	2.7869

* The mean difference is significant at the 0.05 level.

Homogeneous Subsets

tensile-strength scale

Tukey HSD

Suppliers	N	Subset for alpha = 0.05	
		1	2
Supplier 1	5	19.5200	
Supplier 4	5	21.1600	21.1600
Supplier 3	5	22.8400	22.8400
Supplier 2	5		24.2600
Sig.		.187	.234

Means for groups in homogeneous subsets are displayed.

Problems for Section 11.5

LEARNING THE BASICS

11.51 An experiment has five groups and seven values in each group.

a. How many degrees of freedom are there in determining the among-group variation?

b. How many degrees of freedom are there in determining the within-group variation?

c. How many degrees of freedom are there in determining the total variation?

11.52 You are working with the same experiment as in Problem 11.51.

a. If $SSA = 60$ and $SST = 210$, what is SSW?

b. What is MSA?

c. What is MSW?

d. What is the value of F_{STAT}?

11.53 You are working with the same experiment as in Problems 11.51 and 11.52.

a. Construct the ANOVA summary table and fill in all values in the table.

b. At the 0.05 level of significance, what is the upper-tail critical value from the F distribution?

c. State the decision rule for testing the null hypothesis that all five groups have equal population means.

d. What is your statistical decision?

11.54 Consider an experiment with three groups, with seven values in each.

a. How many degrees of freedom are there in determining the among-group variation?

b. How many degrees of freedom are there in determining the within-group variation?

c. How many degrees of freedom are there in determining the total variation?

11.55 Consider an experiment with four groups, with eight values in each. For the ANOVA summary table below, fill in all the missing results:

Source	Degrees of Freedom	Sum of Squares	Mean Square (Variance)	F
Among groups	$c - 1 = ?$	$SSA = ?$	$MSA = 80$	$F_{STAT} = ?$
Within groups	$n - c = ?$	$SSW = 560$	$MSW = ?$	
Total	$n - 1 = ?$	$SST = ?$		

11.56 You are working with the same experiment as in Problem 11.55.

a. At the 0.05 level of significance, state the decision rule for testing the null hypothesis that all four groups have equal population means.

b. What is your statistical decision?

c. At the 0.05 level of significance, what is the upper-tail critical value from the Studentized range distribution?

d. To perform the Tukey-Kramer procedure, what is the critical range?

APPLYING THE CONCEPTS

11.57 The Computer Anxiety Rating Scale (CARS) measures an individual's level of computer anxiety, on a scale from 20 (no anxiety) to 100 (highest level of anxiety). Researchers at Miami University administered CARS to 172 business students. One of the objectives of the study was to determine whether there are differences in the amount of computer anxiety experienced by students with different majors. They found the following:

Source	Degrees of Freedom	Sum of Squares	Mean Squares	F
Among majors	5	3,172		
Within majors	166	21,246		
Total	171	24,418		

Major	n	Mean
Marketing	19	44.37
Management	11	43.18
Other	14	42.21
Finance	45	41.80
Accountancy	36	37.56
MIS	47	32.21

Source: *Data extracted from T. Broome and D. Havelka, "Determinants of Computer Anxiety in Business Students,"* The Review of Business Information Systems, *Spring 2002, 6(2), pp. 9–16.*

a. Complete the ANOVA summary table.

b. At the 0.05 level of significance, is there evidence of a difference in the mean computer anxiety experienced by different majors?

c. If the results in (b) indicate that it is appropriate, use the Tukey-Kramer procedure to determine which majors differ in mean computer anxiety. Discuss your findings.

SELF Test **11.58** Students in a business statistics course performed an experiment to test the strength of four brands of trash bags. One-pound weights were placed into a bag, one at a time, until the bag broke. A total of 40 bags, 10 for each brand, were used. The data in the file **Trashbags** give the weight (in pounds) required to break the trash bags.

a. At the 0.05 level of significance, is there evidence of a difference in the mean strength of the four brands of trash bags?

b. If appropriate, determine which brands differ in mean strength.

c. At the 0.05 level of significance, is there evidence of a difference in the variation in strength among the four brands of trash bags?

d. Which brand(s) should you buy and which brand(s) should you avoid? Explain.

11.59 A hospital conducted a study of the waiting time in its emergency room. The hospital has a main campus and three satellite locations. Management had a business objective of reducing waiting time for emergency room cases that did not require immediate attention. To study this, a random sample of 15 emergency room cases at each location were selected on a particular day, and the waiting time (measured from check-in to when the patient was called into the clinic area) was measured. The results are stored in the file ERwaiting .

a. At the 0.05 level of significance, is there evidence of a difference in the mean waiting times in the four locations?

b. If appropriate, determine which locations differ in mean waiting time.

c. At the 0.05 level of significance, is there evidence of a difference in the variation in waiting time among the four locations?

11.60 An advertising agency has been hired by a manufacturer of pens to develop an advertising campaign for the upcoming holiday season. To prepare for this project, the research director decides to initiate a study of the effect of advertising on product perception. An experiment is designed to compare five different advertisements. Advertisement A greatly undersells the pen's characteristics. Advertisement B slightly undersells the pen's characteristics. Advertisement C slightly oversells the pen's characteristics. Advertisement D greatly oversells the pen's characteristics. Advertisement E attempts to correctly state the pen's characteristics. A sample of 30 adult respondents, taken from a larger focus group, is randomly assigned to the five advertisements (so that there are six respondents to each). After reading the advertisement and developing a sense of "product expectation," all respondents unknowingly receive the same pen to evaluate. The respondents are permitted to test the pen and the plausibility of the advertising copy. The respondents are then asked to rate the pen from 1 to 7 (lowest to highest) on the product characteristic scales of appearance, durability, and writing performance. The *combined* scores of three ratings (appearance, durability, and writing performance) for the 30 respondents (stored in the file Pen) are as follows:

A	B	C	D	E
15	16	8	5	12
18	17	7	6	19
17	21	10	13	18
19	16	15	11	12
19	19	14	9	17
20	17	14	10	14

a. At the 0.05 level of significance, is there evidence of a difference in the mean rating of the five advertisements?

b. If appropriate, determine which advertisements differ in mean ratings.

c. At the 0.05 level of significance, is there evidence of a difference in the variation in ratings among the five advertisements?

d. Which advertisement(s) should you use and which advertisement(s) should you avoid? Explain.

11.61 The following data (stored in the file CDyield) represent the nationwide highest yield of different types of accounts (extracted from **Bankrate.com**, March 31, 2008):

Money Market	Six-Month CD	One-Year CD	2.5-Year CD	Five-Year CD
4.00	3.85	4.05	3.80	4.30
3.82	3.60	3.61	3.70	4.15
3.80	3.60	3.60	3.51	4.10
3.75	3.45	3.60	3.35	4.00
3.75	3.43	3.50	3.35	4.00

a. At the 0.05 level of significance, is there evidence of a difference in the mean yields of the different accounts?

b. If appropriate, determine which accounts differ in mean yields.

c. At the 0.05 level of significance, is there evidence of a difference in the variation in yields among the different accounts?

d. What effect does your result in (c) have on the validity of the results in (a) and (b)?

11.62 A sporting goods manufacturing company wanted to compare the distance traveled by golf balls produced using each of four different designs. Ten balls were manufactured with each design and were brought to the local golf course for the club professional to test. The order in which the balls were hit with the same club from the first tee was randomized so that the pro did not know which type of ball was being hit. All 40 balls were hit in a short period of time, during which the environmental conditions were essentially the same. The results (distance traveled in yards) for the four designs were as follows (and are stored in the file Golfball):

	Design		
1	**2**	**3**	**4**
206.32	217.08	226.77	230.55
207.94	221.43	224.79	227.95
206.19	218.04	229.75	231.84
204.45	224.13	228.51	224.87
209.65	211.82	221.44	229.49
203.81	213.90	223.85	231.10
206.75	221.28	223.97	221.53
205.68	229.43	234.30	235.45
204.49	213.54	219.50	228.35
210.86	214.51	233.00	225.09

a. At the 0.05 level of significance, is there evidence of a difference in the mean distances traveled by the golf balls with different designs?

b. If the results in (a) indicate that it is appropriate, use the Tukey-Kramer procedure to determine which designs differ in mean distances.

c. What assumptions are necessary in (a)?

d. At the 0.05 level of significance, is there evidence of a difference in the variation of the distances traveled by the golf balls with different designs?

e. What golf ball design should the manufacturing manager choose? Explain.

USING STATISTICS   @ BLK Foods Revisited

In the Using Statistics scenario, you were the regional sales manager for BLK Foods. You compared the sales volume of the BLK cola when the product is placed in the normal shelf location to the sales volume when the product is featured in a special end-aisle display. An experiment was performed where 10 stores used the normal shelf location and 10 stores used the end-aisle displays. Using a *t* test for the difference between two means, you were able to conclude that the mean sales using end-aisle location are higher than the mean sales for the normal shelf location. A confidence interval allowed you to infer with 95% confidence that the end-aisle location sells, on average, 6.73 to 36.67 cases more than the normal shelf location. You also performed the *F* test for the difference between two variances to see if the store-to-store variability in sales in stores using the end-aisle location differed from the store-to-store variability in sales in stores using the normal shelf location. You concluded that there was no significant difference in the variability of the sales of cola for the two display locations. As regional sales manager, your next step in increasing sales is to convince more stores to use the special end-aisle display.

SUMMARY

In this chapter, you were introduced to a variety of tests for two or more samples. For situations in which the samples are independent, you learned statistical test procedures for analyzing possible differences between means, variances, and proportions. In addition, you learned a test procedure that is frequently used when analyzing differences between the means of two related samples. Remember that you need to select the test that is most appropriate for a given set of conditions and to critically investigate the validity of the assumptions underlying each of the hypothesis-testing procedures.

The roadmap in Figure 11.22 illustrates the steps needed in determining which test of hypothesis to use. The following are the questions you need to consider.

1. What type of data do you have? If you are dealing with categorical variables, use the *Z* test for the difference between two proportions. (This test assumes independent samples.)

2. If you have a numerical variable, determine whether you have independent samples or related samples. If you have related samples, use the paired *t* test.

3. If you have independent samples, is your focus on variability or central tendency? If the focus is variability, use the *F* test.

4. If your focus is central tendency, determine whether you can assume that the variances of the two populations are equal. (This assumption can be tested using the *F* test.)

5. If you can assume that the two populations have equal variances, use the pooled-variance *t* test. If you cannot assume that the two populations have equal variances, use the separate-variance *t* test.

6. If you have more than two independent samples, you can use the one-way ANOVA.

Table 11.11 provides a list of topics covered in this chapter.

FIGURE 11.22

Roadmap for selecting a test of hypothesis for two or more samples

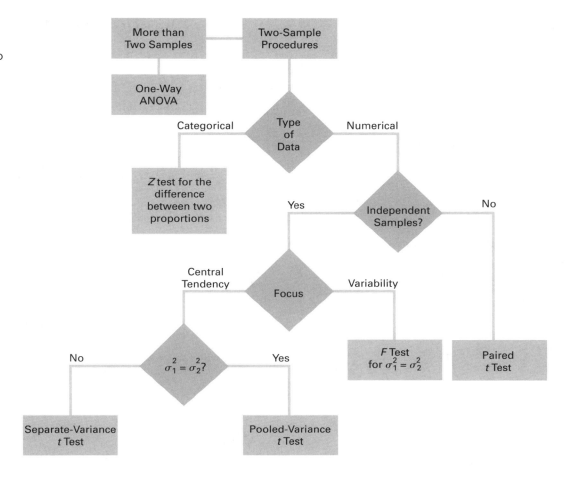

TABLE 11.11

Summary of Topics in Chapter 11

Type of Analysis	Types of Data	
	Numerical	**Categorical**
Comparing two populations	t tests for the difference in the means of two independent populations (Section 11.1)	Z test for the difference between two proportions (Section 11.3)
	Paired t test (Section 11.2)	
	F test for the difference between two variances (Section 11.4)	
Comparing more than two populations	One-way ANOVA (Section 11.5)	

KEY EQUATIONS

Pooled-Variance t Test for the Difference Between Two Means

$$t_{STAT} = \frac{(\bar{X}_1 - \bar{X}_2) - (\mu_1 - \mu_2)}{\sqrt{S_p^2\left(\dfrac{1}{n_1} + \dfrac{1}{n_2}\right)}} \qquad \textbf{(11.1)}$$

Confidence Interval Estimate of the Difference in the Means of Two Independent Populations

$$(\bar{X}_1 - \bar{X}_2) \pm t_{\alpha/2}\sqrt{S_p^2\left(\frac{1}{n_1} + \frac{1}{n_2}\right)} \qquad \textbf{(11.2)}$$

or

$$(\overline{X}_1 - \overline{X}_2) - t_{\alpha/2}\sqrt{S_p^2\left(\frac{1}{n_1} + \frac{1}{n_2}\right)} \le \mu_1 - \mu_2$$

$$\le (\overline{X}_1 - \overline{X}_2) + t_{\alpha/2}\sqrt{S_p^2\left(\frac{1}{n_1} + \frac{1}{n_2}\right)}$$

Paired t Test for the Mean Difference

$$t_{STAT} = \frac{\overline{D} - \mu_D}{\frac{S_D}{\sqrt{n}}} \tag{11.3}$$

Confidence Interval Estimate for the Mean Difference

$$\overline{D} \pm t_{\alpha/2}\frac{S_D}{\sqrt{n}} \tag{11.4}$$

or

$$\overline{D} - t_{\alpha/2}\frac{S_D}{\sqrt{n}} \le \mu_D \le \overline{D} + t_{\alpha/2}\frac{S_D}{\sqrt{n}}$$

Z Test for the Difference Between Two Proportions

$$Z_{STAT} = \frac{(p_1 - p_2) - (\pi_1 - \pi_2)}{\sqrt{\overline{p}(1 - \overline{p})\left(\frac{1}{n_1} + \frac{1}{n_2}\right)}} \tag{11.5}$$

Confidence Interval Estimate for the Difference Between Two Proportions

$$(p_1 - p_2) \pm Z_{\alpha/2}\sqrt{\left(\frac{p_1(1 - p_1)}{n_1} + \frac{p_2(1 - p_2)}{n_2}\right)} \tag{11.6}$$

or

$$(p_1 - p_2) - Z_{\alpha/2}\sqrt{\frac{p_1(1 - p_1)}{n_1} + \frac{p_2(1 - p_2)}{n_1}} \le (\pi_1 - \pi_2)$$

$$\le (p_1 - p_2) + Z_{\alpha/2}\sqrt{\frac{p_1(1 - p_1)}{n_1} + \frac{p_2(1 - p_2)}{n_1}}$$

F Test for the Equality of Two Variances

$$F_{STAT} = \frac{S_1^2}{S_2^2} \tag{11.7}$$

Total Variation in One-Way ANOVA

$$SST = \sum_{j=1}^{c}\sum_{i=1}^{n_j}(X_{ij} - \overline{\overline{X}})^2 \tag{11.8}$$

Among-Group Variation in One-Way ANOVA

$$SSA = \sum_{j=1}^{c}n_j(X_j - \overline{\overline{X}})^2 \tag{11.9}$$

Within-Group Variation in One-Way ANOVA

$$SSW = \sum_{j=1}^{c}\sum_{i=1}^{n_j}(X_{ij} - \overline{X}_j)^2 \tag{11.10}$$

Mean Squares in One-Way ANOVA

$$MSA = \frac{SSA}{c - 1} \tag{11.11a}$$

$$MSW = \frac{SSW}{n - c} \tag{11.11b}$$

$$MST = \frac{SST}{n - 1} \tag{11.11c}$$

One-Way ANOVA F_{STAT} Test Statistic

$$F_{STAT} = \frac{MSA}{MSW} \tag{11.12}$$

Critical Range for the Tukey-Kramer Procedure

$$\text{Critical range} = Q_\alpha\sqrt{\frac{MSW}{2}\left(\frac{1}{n_j} + \frac{1}{n_{j'}}\right)} \tag{11.13}$$

KEY TERMS

ANOVA summary table   504
analysis of variance (ANOVA)   502
among-group variation   502
factor   501
F distribution   492

F test for the equality of two variances   492
grand mean, $\overline{\overline{X}}$ 502
homogeneity of variance   509
levels   501

Levene test   509
matched samples   472
mean square   503
multiple comparisons   508
normality   509

CHAPTER REVIEW PROBLEMS

CHECKING YOUR UNDERSTANDING

11.63 What are some of the criteria used in the selection of a particular hypothesis-testing procedure?

11.64 Under what conditions should you use the pooled-variance *t* test to examine possible differences in the means of two independent populations?

11.65 Under what conditions should you use the *F* test to examine possible differences in the variances of two independent populations?

11.66 What is the distinction between two independent populations and two related populations?

11.67 What is the distinction between repeated measurements and matched items?

11.68 When you have two independent populations, explain the similarities and differences between the test of hypothesis for the difference between the means and the confidence interval estimate of the difference between the means.

11.69 What are the assumptions of ANOVA?

11.70 Under what conditions should you select the one-way ANOVA *F* test to examine possible differences among the means of *c* independent populations?

11.71 When and how should you use multiple comparison procedures for evaluating pairwise combinations of the group means?

APPLYING THE CONCEPTS

11.72 A study compared music compact disc prices for Internet-based retailers and traditional brick-and-mortar retailers [extracted from L. Zoonky and S. Gosain, "A Longitudinal Price Comparison for Music CDs in Electronic and Brick-and-Mortar Markets: Pricing Strategies in Emergent Electronic Commerce," *Journal of Business Strategies*, Spring 2002, 19(1), pp. 55–72]. Before collecting the data, the researchers carefully defined several research hypotheses, including:

1. The price dispersion on the Internet is lower than the price dispersion in the brick-and-mortar market.

2. Prices in electronic markets are lower than prices in physical markets.
   a. Consider research hypothesis 1. Write the null and alternative hypotheses in terms of population parameters. Carefully define the population parameters used.
   b. Define a Type I and Type II error for the hypotheses in (a).
   c. What type of statistical test should you use?
   d. What assumptions are needed to perform the test you selected?
   e. Repeat (a) through (d) for research hypothesis 2.

11.73 The pet-drug market is growing very rapidly. Before new pet drugs can be introduced into the marketplace, they must be approved by the U.S. Food and Drug Administration (FDA). In 1999, the Novartis company was trying to get Anafranil, a drug to reduce dog anxiety, approved. According to an article (E. Tanouye, "The Ow in Bowwow: With Growing Market in Pet Drugs, Makers Revamp Clinical Trials," *The Wall Street Journal*, April 13, 1999), Novartis had to find a way to translate a dog's anxiety symptoms into numbers that could be used to prove to the FDA that the drug had a statistically significant effect on the condition.
a. What is meant by the phrase *statistically significant effect*?
b. Consider an experiment in which dogs suffering from anxiety are divided into two groups. One group will be given Anafranil, and the other will be given a placebo (i.e., a drug without active ingredients). How can you translate a dog's anxiety symptoms into numbers? In other words, define a continuous variable, X_1, that measures the effectiveness of the drug Anafranil, and X_2, that measures the effectiveness of the placebo.
c. Building on your answer to part (b), define the null and alternative hypotheses for this study.

11.74 In response to lawsuits filed against the tobacco industry, many companies, such as Philip Morris, are running television advertisements that are supposed to educate teenagers about the dangers of smoking. Are these tobacco industry antismoking campaigns successful? Are state-sponsored antismoking commercials more effective? An article (G. Fairclough, "Philip Morris's Antismoking Campaign Draws Fire," *The Wall Street Journal*, April 6, 1999, p. B1) discussed a study in California that compared commercials made by the state of California and commercials produced by Philip Morris. Researchers showed the state ads and the Philip Morris ads to a group of California teenagers and measured the effectiveness of both. The researchers concluded that the state ads were more effective in relaying the dangers of smoking than the Philip Morris ads. The article suggests, however, that the study is not *statistically reliable* because the sample size was too small and because the study specifically selected participants who are considered more likely to start smoking than others.

a. How do you think the researchers measured effectiveness?

b. Define the null and alternative hypotheses for this study.

c. Explain the risks associated with Type I and Type II errors in this study.

d. What type of test is most appropriate in this situation?

e. What do you think is meant by the phrase *statistically reliable*?

11.75 Do male and female students study the same amount per week? In 2007, 58 sophomore business students were surveyed at a large university, which has over 1,000 sophomore business students each year. The file Studytime contains the gender and the number of hours spent studying in a typical week for the sampled students.

a. At the 0.05 level of significance, is there a difference in the variance of the study time for male students and female students?

b. Using the results of (a), which *t* test is appropriate to compare the mean study time for male and female students?

c. At the 0.05 level of significance, conduct the test selected in (b).

d. Write a short summary of your findings.

11.76 Two professors wanted to study how students from their two universities compared in their capabilities of using Excel spreadsheets in undergraduate information systems courses (data extracted from H. Howe and M. G. Simkin, "Factors Affecting the Ability to Detect Spreadsheet Errors," *Decision Sciences Journal of Innovative Education*, January 2006, pp. 101–122). A comparison of the student demographics was also performed. One school is a state university in the Western United States, and the other school is a state university in the Eastern United States. The following table contains information regarding the ages of the students:

School	Sample Size	Mean Age	Standard Deviation
Western	93	23.28	6.29
Eastern	135	21.16	1.32

a. Using a 0.01 level of significance, is there evidence of a difference between the variances in age of students at the Western school and at the Eastern school?

b. Discuss the practical implications of the test performed in (a). Address, specifically, the impact equal (or unequal) variances in age has on teaching an undergraduate information systems course.

c. To test for a difference in the mean age of students, is it most appropriate to use the pooled-variance *t* test or the separate-variance *t* test?

The following table contains information regarding the years of spreadsheet usage of the students:

School	Sample Size	Mean Years	Standard Deviation
Western	93	2.6	2.4
Eastern	135	4.0	2.1

d. Using a 0.01 level of significance, is there evidence of a difference between the variances in years of spreadsheet usage of students at the Western school and at the Eastern school?

e. Based on the results of (d), use the most appropriate test to determine, at the 0.01 level of significance, whether there is evidence of a difference in the mean years of spreadsheet usage of students at the Western school and at the Eastern school.

11.77 The data file Restaurants contains the ratings for food, decor, service, and the price per person for a sample of 50 restaurants located in an urban area and 50 restaurants located in a suburban area. Completely analyze the differences between urban and suburban restaurants for the variables food rating, decor rating, service rating, and price per person, using $\alpha = 0.05$.

Source: *Data extracted from* Zagat Survey 2006: New York City Restaurants *and* Zagat Survey 2005–2006: Long Island Restaurants.

11.78 A computer information systems professor is interested in studying the amount of time it takes students enrolled in the introduction to computers course to write and run a program in Visual Basic. The professor hires you to analyze the following results (in minutes) from a random sample of nine students (the data are stored in the VB file):

$$10 \quad 13 \quad 9 \quad 15 \quad 12 \quad 13 \quad 11 \quad 13 \quad 12$$

a. At the 0.05 level of significance, is there evidence that the population mean amount is greater than 10 minutes? What will you tell the professor?

b. Suppose the computer professor, when checking her results, realizes that the fourth student needed 51 minutes rather than the recorded 15 minutes to write and run the Visual Basic program. At the 0.05 level of significance, reanalyze the question posed in (a), using the revised data. What will you tell the professor now?

c. The professor is perplexed by these paradoxical results and requests an explanation from you regarding the justification for the difference in your findings in (a) and (b). Discuss.

d. A few days later, the professor calls to tell you that the dilemma is completely resolved. The original number 15 (the fourth data value) was correct, and therefore your findings in (a) are being used in the article she is writing for a computer journal. Now she wants to hire you to compare the results from that group of introduction to computers students against those from a sample of 11 computer majors in order to determine whether there is evidence that computer majors can write a Visual Basic program in less time than introductory students. For the computer majors, the sample mean is 8.5 minutes, and the sample standard deviation is 2.0 minutes. At the 0.05 level of significance, completely analyze these data. What will you tell the professor?

e. A few days later, the professor calls again to tell you that a reviewer of her article wants her to include the *p*-value for the "correct" result in (a). In addition, the professor inquires about an unequal-variances problem, which the reviewer wants her to discuss in her article. In your own words, discuss the concept of *p*-value and also describe the unequal-variances problem. Then, determine the *p*-value in (a) and discuss whether the unequal-variances problem had any meaning in the professor's study.

11.79 An article in *The New York Times* (A. Jennings, "What's Good for a Business Can be Hard on Friends," *The New York Times*, August 4, 2007, pp. C1–C2) reported that according to a poll, the mean number of cellphone calls per month was 290 for 18- to 24-year-olds and 194 for 45- to 54-year-olds, whereas the mean number of text messages per month was 290 for 18- to 24-year-olds and 57 for 45- to 54-year-olds. Suppose that the poll was based on a sample of 100 18- to 24-year-olds and 100 45- to 54-year-olds, and that the standard deviation of the number of cellphone calls per month was 100 for 18- to 24-year-olds and 90 for 45- to 54-year-olds, whereas the standard deviation of the number of text messages per month was 90 for 18- to 24-year-olds and 77 for 45- to 54-year-olds.

Use a level of significance of 0.05.

a. Is there evidence of a difference in the variances of the number of cellphone calls per month for 18- to 24-year-olds and 45- to 54-year-olds?

b. Is there evidence of a difference in the mean number of cellphone calls per month for 18- to 24-year-olds and 45- to 54-year-olds?

c. Construct and interpret a 95% confidence interval estimate of the difference in the mean number of cellphone calls per month for 18- to 24-year-olds and 45- to 54-year-olds.

d. Is there evidence of a difference in the variances of the number of text messages per month for 18- to 24-year-olds and 45- to 54-year-olds?

e. Is there evidence of a difference in the mean number of text messages per month for 18- to 24-year-olds and 45- to 54-year-olds?

f. Construct and interpret a 95% confidence interval estimate of the difference in the mean number of text messages per month for 18- to 24-year-olds and 45- to 54-year-olds.

g. Based on the results of (a) through (f), what conclusions can you make concerning cellphone and text message usage between 18- to 24-year-olds and 45- to 54-year-olds?

11.80 The lengths of life (in hours) of a sample of 40 100-watt lightbulbs produced by manufacturer A and a sample of 40 100-watt lightbulbs produced by manufacturer B are in the file **Bulbs**. Completely analyze the differences between the lengths of life of the bulbs produced by the two manufacturers (use $\alpha = 0.05$).

11.81 A hotel manager is concerned with increasing the return rate for hotel guests. One aspect of first impressions by guests relates to the time it takes to deliver the guest's luggage to the room after check-in to the hotel. A random sample of 20 deliveries on a particular day were selected in Wing A of the hotel, and a random sample of 20 deliveries were selected in Wing B. The results are stored in the file **Luggage**. Analyze the data and determine whether there is a difference in the mean delivery time in the two wings of the hotel. (Use $\alpha = 0.05$.)

11.82 Many companies are finding that customers are using various types of online content before purchasing products (data extracted from K. Spors, "How Are We Doing?" *The Wall Street Journal*, November 13, 2006, p. R9). The following results are the percentages of adults and youths who use various sources of online content. Suppose the survey was based on 100 adults and 100 youths.

TYPE OF ONLINE CONTENT	USE ONLINE CONTENT	
	Adult	Youth
Customer product ratings/reviews	71	81
For sale listings with seller ratings	69	77
For sale listings without seller ratings	58	65
Online classified ads	57	66
Message-board posts	57	71
Web blogs	55	67
Dating site profiles/personals	49	59
Peer-generated and peer-reference information	49	68
Peer-posted event listings	46	71

For *each type of online content*, determine whether there is a difference between adults and youths in the proportion who use the type of online content at the 0.05 level of significance.

11.83 The manufacturer of Boston and Vermont asphalt shingles knows that product weight is a major factor in the customer's perception of quality. Moreover, the weight represents the amount of raw materials being used and is therefore very important to the company from a cost standpoint. The last stage of the assembly line packages the shingles before they are placed on wooden pallets. Once a pallet is full (a pallet for most brands holds 16 squares of shingles), it is weighed, and the measurement is recorded. The data file Pallet contains the weight (in pounds) from a sample of 368 pallets of Boston shingles and 330 pallets of Vermont shingles. Completely analyze the differences in the weights of the Boston and Vermont shingles, using $\alpha = 0.05$.

11.84 The manufacturer of Boston and Vermont asphalt shingles provides its customers with a 20-year warranty on most of its products. To determine whether a shingle will last as long as the warranty period, accelerated-life testing is conducted at the manufacturing plant. Accelerated-life testing exposes the shingle to the stresses it would be subject to in a lifetime of normal use in a laboratory setting via an experiment that takes only a few minutes to conduct. In this test, a shingle is repeatedly scraped with a brush for a short period of time, and the shingle granules removed by the brushing are weighed (in grams). Shingles that experience low amounts of granule loss are expected to last longer in normal use than shingles that experience high amounts of granule loss. In this situation, a shingle should experience no more than 0.8 grams of granule loss if it is expected to last the length of the warranty period. The data file Granule contains a sample of 170 measurements made on the company's Boston shingles and 140 measurements made on Vermont shingles. Completely analyze the differences in the granule loss of the Boston and Vermont shingles, using $\alpha = 0.05$.

11.85 The quality control director for a clothing manufacturer wants to study the effect of machines on the breaking strength (in pounds) of wool serge material. A batch of the material is cut into square-yard pieces, and these are randomly assigned, 12 each, to the three machines chosen specifically for the experiment. The results (stored in the file Breakstw) are shown at the top of the next column:

At the 0.05 level of significance,
a. is there an effect due to machine?
b. Plot the mean breaking strength for each machine.
c. If appropriate, use the Tukey-Kramer procedure to examine differences among machines.
d. What can you conclude about the effects of machines on breaking strength? Explain.

MACHINE		
I	II	III
115	111	109
115	108	110
119	114	107
117	105	110
114	102	113
114	106	114
109	100	103
110	103	102
106	101	105
112	105	108
115	107	111
111	107	110

11.86 An operations manager wants to examine the effect of air-jet pressure (in psi) on the breaking strength of yarn. Three different levels of air-jet pressure are to be considered: 30 psi, 40 psi, and 50 psi. A random sample of 18 homogeneous filling yarns are selected from the same batch, and the yarns are randomly assigned, 6 each, to the 3 levels of air-jet pressure. The breaking strength scores are in the file Yarn .
a. Is there evidence of a significant difference in the variances of the breaking strengths for the three air-jet pressures? (Use $\alpha = 0.05$).
b. At the 0.05 level of significance, is there evidence of a difference among mean breaking strengths for the three air-jet pressures?
c. If appropriate, use the Tukey-Kramer procedure to determine which air-jet pressures significantly differ with respect to mean breaking strength. (Use $\alpha = 0.05$.)
d. What should the operations manager conclude?

REPORT WRITING EXERCISE

11.87 Referring to the results of Problems 11.83 and 11.84 concerning the weight and granule loss of Boston and Vermont shingles, write a report that summarizes your conclusions.

TEAM PROJECT

The data file Mutual Funds contains information regarding nine variables from a sample of 868 mutual funds. The variables are
   Category—Type of stocks comprising the mutual fund (small cap, mid cap, or large cap)
   Objective—Objective of stocks comprising the mutual fund (growth or value)
   Assets—In millions of dollars
   Fees—Sales charges (no or yes)
   Expense ratio—Ratio of expenses to net assets, in percentage

Return 2006—Twelve-month return in 2006

Three-year return—Annualized return, 2004–2006

Five-year return—Annualized return, 2002–2006

Risk—Risk-of-loss factor of the mutual fund (low, average, or high)

11.88 Completely analyze the difference between mutual funds without fees and mutual funds with fees in terms of 2006 return, three-year return, five-year return, and expense ratio. Write a report summarizing your findings.

11.89 Completely analyze the difference between mutual funds that have a growth objective and mutual funds that have a value objective in terms of 2006 return, three-year return, five-year return, and expense ratio. Write a report summarizing your findings.

11.90 Completely analyze the difference between small cap, mid cap, and large cap mutual funds in terms of 2006 return, three-year return, five-year return, and expense ratio. Write a report summarizing your findings.

11.91 Completely analyze the difference between low-risk, average-risk, and high-risk mutual funds in terms of 2006 return, three-year return, five-year return, and expense ratio. Write a report summarizing your findings.

STUDENT SURVEY DATA BASE

11.92 Problem 1.28 describes a survey of 50 undergraduate students (see the file Undergradsurvey). For these data,
a. at the 0.05 level of significance, is there evidence of a difference between males and females in grade point average, expected starting salary, salary expected in five years, age, and spending on textbooks and supplies?
b. at the 0.05 level of significance, is there evidence of a difference between those students who plan to go to graduate school and those who do not plan to go to graduate school in grade point average, expected starting salary, salary expected in five years, age, and spending on textbooks and supplies?

11.93 Problem 1.28 describes a survey of 50 undergraduate students (see the file Undergradsurvey).
a. Select a sample of 50 undergraduate students at your school and conduct a similar survey for them.
b. For the data collected in (a), repeat (a) and (b) of Problem 11.92.
c. Compare the results of (b) to those of Problem 11.92.

11.94 Problem 1.29 describes a survey of 40 MBA students (see the file Gradsurvey). For these data, at the 0.05 level of significance, is there evidence of a difference between males and females in age, undergraduate grade point average, graduate grade point average, GMAT score, expected salary upon graduation, salary expected in five years, and spending on textbooks and supplies?

11.95 Problem 1.29 describes a survey of 40 MBA students (see the file Gradsurvey).
a. Select a sample of 40 graduate students in your MBA program and conduct a similar survey for those students.
b. For the data collected in (a), repeat Problem 11.94.
c. Compare the results of (b) to those of Problem 11.94.

11.96 Problem 1.28 describes a survey of 50 undergraduate students (see the file). For these data,
a. at the 0.05 level of significance, is there evidence of a difference based on academic major in grade point average, expected starting salary, salary expected in five years, age, and spending on textbooks and supplies?
b. at the 0.05 level of significance, is there evidence of a difference based on graduate school intention in grade point average, expected starting salary, salary expected in five years, age, and spending on textbooks and supplies?
c. at the 0.05 level of significance, is there evidence of a difference based on employment status in grade point average, expected starting salary, salary expected in five years, age, and spending on textbooks and supplies?

11.97 Problem 1.28 describes a survey of 50 undergraduate students (see the file Undergradsurvey).
a. Select a sample of 50 undergraduate students at your school and conduct a similar survey for those students.
b. For the data collected in (a), repeat (a) through (c) of Problem 11.96.
c. Compare the results of (b) to those of Problem 11.96.

11.98 Problem 1.29 describes a survey of 40 MBA students (see the file Gradsurvey). For these data, at the 0.05 level of significance,
a. is there evidence of a difference, based on undergraduate major, in age, undergraduate grade point average, graduate grade point average, GMAT score, expected salary upon graduation, salary expected in five years, and spending on textbooks and supplies?
b. is there evidence of a difference, based on graduate major, in age, undergraduate grade point average, graduate grade point average, GMAT score, expected salary upon graduation, salary expected in five years, and spending on textbooks and supplies?
c. is there evidence of a difference, based on employment status, in age, undergraduate grade point average, graduate grade point average, GMAT score, expected salary upon graduation, salary expected in five years, and spending on textbooks and supplies?

11.99 Problem 1.29 describes a survey of 40 MBA students (see the file Gradsurvey).
a. Select a sample of 40 graduate students in your MBA program and conduct a similar survey for those students.
b. For the data collected in (a), repeat (a) through (c) of Problem 11.98.
c. Compare the results of (b) to those of Problem 11.98.

MANAGING THE *SPRINGVILLE HERALD*

Phase 1

A marketing department team is charged with improving the telemarketing process in order to increase the number of home-delivery subscriptions sold. After several brainstorming sessions, it was clear that the longer a caller speaks to a respondent, the greater the chance that the caller will sell a home-delivery subscription. Therefore, the team decided to find ways to increase the length of the phone calls.

Initially, the team investigated the impact that the time of a call might have on the length of the call. Under current arrangements, calls were made in the evening hours, between 5:00 P.M. and 9:00 P.M., Monday through Friday. The team wanted to compare the length of calls made early in the evening (before 7:00 P.M.) with those made later in the evening (after 7:00 P.M.) to determine whether one of these time periods leads to longer calls and, correspondingly, to increased subscription sales. The team selected a sample of 30 female callers who staff the telephone bank on Wednesday evenings and randomly assigned 15 of them to the "early" time period and 15 to the "later" time period. The callers knew that the team was observing their efforts that evening but didn't know which calls were monitored. The callers had been trained to make their telephone presentations in a structured manner. They were to read from a script, and their greeting was personal but informal ("Hi, this is Leigh Richardson from the *Springville Herald*. May I speak to Stuart Knoll?").

Measurements were taken on the length of the call (defined as the difference, in seconds, between the time the person answered the phone and the time he or she hung up). The results (stored in the file **SH11-1**) are presented in Table SH11.1.

TABLE SH11.1

Length of Calls, in Seconds, Based on Time of Call— Early Versus Late in the Evening

Time of Call		Time of Call	
Early	**Late**	**Early**	**Late**
41.3	37.1	40.6	40.7
37.5	38.9	33.3	38.0
39.3	42.2	39.6	43.6
37.4	45.7	35.7	43.8
33.6	42.4	31.3	34.9
38.5	39.0	36.8	35.7
32.6	40.9	36.3	47.4
37.3	40.5		

EXERCISES

SH11.1 Analyze the data in Table SH11.1 and write a report to the marketing department team that indicates your findings. Include an attached appendix in which you discuss the reason you selected a partic-

ular statistical test to compare the two independent groups of callers.

SH11.2 Suppose that instead of the research design described here, there were only 15 callers sampled, and each caller was to be monitored twice in the evening— once in the early time period and once in the later time period. Thus, in Table SH11.1, each pair of values represents a particular caller's two measurements. Reanalyze these data and write a report for presentation to the team that indicates your findings.

SH11.3 What other variables should be investigated next? Why?

DO NOT CONTINUE UNTIL THE PHASE 1 EXERCISES HAVE BEEN COMPLETED

Phase 2

In studying the home delivery solicitation process, the marketing department team determined that the so-called "later" calls made between 7:00 P.M. and 9:00 P.M. led to significantly longer calls than those made earlier in the evening (between 5:00 P.M. and 7:00 P.M.).

Knowing that the 7:00 P.M. to 9:00 P.M. time period is superior, the team sought to investigate the effect of the type of presentation on the length of the call. A group of 24 female callers was randomly assigned, 8 each, to one of three presentation plans—structured, semistructured, and unstructured and trained to make the telephone presentation. All calls were made between 7:00 P.M. and 9:00 P.M., the later time period, and the callers were to provide an introductory greeting that was personal but informal ("Hi, this is Leigh Richardson from the *Springville Herald*. May I speak to Stuart Knoll?"). The callers knew that the team was observing their efforts that evening but didn't know which particular calls were monitored. Measurements were taken on the length of call (defined as the difference, in seconds, between the time the person answers the phone and the time he or she hangs up). Table SH11.2 presents the results (which are stored in the file **SH11-2**).

TABLE SH11.2

Length of Calls (in Seconds) Based on Presentation Plan

PRESENTATION PLAN		
Structured	**Semistructured**	**Unstructured**
38.8	41.8	32.9
42.1	36.4	36.1
45.2	39.1	39.2
34.8	28.7	29.3
48.3	36.4	41.9
37.8	36.1	31.7
41.1	35.8	35.2
43.6	33.7	38.1

EXERCISE

SH11.4 Analyze the data in Table SH11.2 and write a report to the team that indicates your findings. Be sure to include your recommendations based on your findings.

WEB CASE

Apply your knowledge about hypothesis testing and ANOVA in this Web Case, which continues the cereal-fill packaging dispute Web Case from Chapters 7 and 10.

Even after the recent public experiment about cereal box weights, the Consumers Concerned About Cereal Cheaters (CCACC) remains convinced that Oxford Cereals has misled the public. The group has created and posted a document in which it claims that cereal boxes produced at Plant Number 2 in Springville weigh less than the claimed mean of 368 grams. Visit the CCACC More Cheating page at **www.prenhall.com/Springville/MoreCheating.htm** (or open this Web page file from the Student CD-ROM Web Case folder) and then answer the following:

1. Do the CCACC's results prove that there is a statistically significant difference in the mean weights of cereal boxes produced at Plant Numbers 1 and 2?

2. Perform the appropriate analysis to test the CCACC's hypothesis. What conclusions can you reach based on the data?

After reviewing CCACC's latest posting, Oxford Cereals is complaining that CCACC is guilty of using selective data. Visit Oxford Cereals' response page at **www.prenhall. com/Springville/OC_DataSelective.htm**, or open the OC_DataSelective.htm file from the Student CD-ROM Web Case folder and then answer the following:

3. Does Oxford Cereals have a legitimate argument? Why or why not?

4. Assuming that the samples Oxford Cereals has posted were randomly selected, perform the appropriate analysis to resolve the ongoing weight dispute.

5. What conclusions can you reach from your results? If you were called as an expert witness, would you support the claims of the CCACC or the claims of Oxford Cereals? Explain.

REFERENCES

1. Conover, W. J., *Practical Nonparametric Statistics*, 3rd ed. (New York: Wiley, 2000).
2. Daniel, W., *Applied Nonparametric Statistics*, 2nd ed. (Boston: Houghton Mifflin, 1990).
3. *Microsoft Excel 2007* (Redmond, WA: Microsoft Corp., 2007).
4. *Minitab for Windows Version 15* (State College, PA: Minitab, Inc., 2006).
5. Hicks, C. R., and K. V. Turner, *Fundamental Concepts in the Design of Experiments*, 5th ed. (New York: Oxford University Press, 1999).
6. Montgomery, D. M., *Design and Analysis of Experiments*, 6th ed. (New York: Wiley, 2005).
7. Neter, J., M. H. Kutner, C. Nachtsheim, and W. Wasserman, *Applied Linear Statistical Models*, 5th ed. (New York: McGraw-Hill-Irwin, 2005).
8. Satterthwaite, F. E., "An Approximate Distribution of Estimates of Variance Components," *Biometrics Bulletin*, 2(1946): 110–114.
9. Snedecor, G. W., and W. G. Cochran, *Statistical Methods*, 8th ed. (Ames, IA: Iowa State University Press, 1989).
10. Winer, B. J., D. R. Brown, and K. M. Michels, *Statistical Principles in Experimental Design*, 3rd ed. (New York: McGraw-Hill, 1989).

APPENDIX E11

Using Microsoft Excel for Two-Sample Tests and One-Way ANOVA

E11.1 Stacking and Unstacking Data

Unsummarized data for two (or more) samples can be entered as **stacked** or **unstacked** worksheet data. In a stacked arrangement, all the variable values appear in a single column next to a column that identifies the sample to which individual values belong. In an unstacked arrangement, the values for each sample appear in separate columns.

Specific ToolPak procedures or Excel worksheets for analyses involving two or more samples will require that your data be arranged either as stacked or unstacked data. If you need to change stacked data into its unstacked equivalent, you can sort your data by sample and then cut and paste the data of the second sample (now in contiguous rows) to a new column. (Use row 1 in that column to identify the second sample.) Likewise, to stack unstacked data, you can copy the data of the second sample to below the first sample and then add a column that identifies the sample. The `StackedAndUnstacked.xls` workbook illustrates both the stacked and unstacked arrangement of the BLK Cola weekly sales data of Table 11.1.

E11.2 Using the Pooled-Variance t test (unsummarized data)

For unsummarized data, you perform the pooled-variance t test by using the ToolPak t-Test: Two-Sample Assuming Equal Variances procedure.

Open to the worksheet containing the unsummarized data for the two samples. Select **Tools → Data Analysis** (Excel 97–2003) or **Data → Data Analysis** (Excel 2007). Then select **t-Test: Two-Sample Assuming Equal Variances** from the **Analysis Tools** list and then click **OK**. In the procedure's dialog box (shown at the top of the next column), enter the cell range of one sample as the **Variable 1 Range** and the cell range of the other sample as the **Variable 2 Range**. Enter the **Hypothesized Mean Difference**, click **Labels**, and click **OK**. Results appear on a new worksheet. Figure 11.3 shows the results for the Table 11.1 BLK Cola sales data.

E11.3 Using the Pooled-Variance t test (summarized data)

For summarized data, you perform the pooled-variance t test by making entries in the **PVt** worksheet of the `Pooled-Variance T.xls` workbook. This worksheet (see Figure E11.1 and E11.2) uses the **TINV(1-*confidence level, degrees***

	A	B	
1	Pooled-Variance t Test for Differences in Two Means		
2	(assumes equal population variances)		
3	Data		
4	Hypothesized Difference	0	
5	Level of Significance	0.05	
6	Population 1 Sample		
7	Sample Size	10	
8	Sample Mean	50.3	
9	Sample Standard Deviation	18.7	
10	Population 2 Sample		
11	Sample Size	10	
12	Sample Mean	72	
13	Sample Standard Deviation	12.5	
14			
15	Intermediate Calculations		
16	Population 1 Sample Degrees of Freedom	9	=B7 - 1
17	Population 2 Sample Degrees of Freedom	9	=B11 -1
18	Total Degrees of Freedom	18	=B16 + B17
19	Pooled Variance	252.97	=((B16 * B9^2) + (B17 * B13^2))/B18
20	Difference in Sample Means	-21.7	=B8 - B12
21	t Test Statistic	-3.0508	=(B20 - B4)/SQRT(B19 * (1/B7 + 1/B11))
22			
23	Two-Tail Test		
24	Lower Critical Value	-2.1009	=-(TINV(B5, B18))
25	Upper Critical Value	2.1009	=TINV(B5, B18)
26	p-Value	0.0069	=TDIST(ABS(B21), B18, 2)
27	Reject the null hypothesis		=IF(B26 < B5, "Reject the null hypothesis",
28			"Do not reject the null hypothesis")
29	Lower-Tail Test		
30	Lower Critical Value	-1.7341	=-TINV(2 * B5, B18)
31	p-Value	0.0034	=IF(B21 < 0, E32, E33)
32	Reject the null hypothesis		=IF(B31 < B5, "Reject the null hypothesis",
33			"Do not reject the null hypothesis")
34	Upper-Tail Test		
35	Upper Critical Value	1.7341	=(TINV(2 * B5 ,B18))
36	p-Value	0.9966	=IF(B21 < 0, E33, E32)
37	Do not reject the null hypothesis		=IF(B36 < B5, "Reject the null hypothesis",
			"Do not reject the null hypothesis")

Not shown
Cell E32: =TDIST(ABS(B21), B18, 1)
Cell E33: =1 - E32

FIGURE E11.1 PVt worksheet

532

	D	E	
1			
2			
3	**Confidence Interval Estimate**		
4	**of the Difference Between Two Means**		
5			
6	**Data**		
7	**Confidence Level**	95%	
8			
9	Intermediate Calculations		
10	Degrees of Freedom	18	=B16 + B17
11	*t* Value	2.1009	=TINV(1 - E7, E10)
12	Interval Half Width	14.9437	=(E11 * SQRT(B19 * (1/B7 + 1/B11)))
13			
14	**Confidence Interval**		
15	**Interval Lower Limit**	-36.6437	=B20 - E12
16	**Interval Upper Limit**	-6.7563	=B20 + E12

FIGURE E11.2 Confidence interval estimate area of PVt worksheet

of freedom) function to determine the lower and upper critical values. The worksheet also uses the **TDIST(ABS(*t*), degrees of freedom, tails)** function, in which **ABS(*t*)** is the absolute value of the *t*-test statistic, and *tails* is either 1, for a one-tail test, or 2, for a two-tail test, to help compute the *p*-values. IF functions in cells B31 and B36 select which one of two values computed in a calculations area (not shown in Figure E11.3) to use. IF functions in cells A27, A32, and A37 determine which one of two phrases will be displayed in those cells.

The worksheet contains entries based on the Table 11.1 BLK Cola weekly sales data. To adapt this worksheet to other problems, change, as is necessary, the hypothesized difference, level of significance, and the sample statistics of the two samples in cells B4, B5, B7:B9, and B11:B13. If you do not want to include a confidence interval estimate in your worksheet (see Figure E11.2), select and delete the cell range D3:E16.

E11.4 Using the Separate-Variance *t* test (unsummarized data)

For unsummarized data, you perform the separate-variance *t* test by using the ToolPak *t*-Test: Two-Sample Assuming Unequal Variances procedure. (There is no equivalent procedure for summarized data in Microsoft Excel.)

Open to the worksheet containing the unsummarized data for the two samples. Select **Tools → Data Analysis** (Excel 97–2003) or **Data → Data Analysis** (Excel 2007). Then select **t-Test: Two-Sample Assuming Unequal Variances** from the **Data Analysis** list and click **OK**. In the procedure's dialog box (shown at the top of the next column), enter the cell range of one sample as the **Variable 1 Range** and the cell range of the other sample as the **Variable 2 Range**. Enter the **Hypothesized Mean Difference**, click **Labels**, and click **OK**. Figure 11.7 shows the results of applying this procedure to the Table 11.1 BLK Cola weekly sales data.

E11.5 Using the Separate-Variance *t* test (summarized data)

For summarized data, you perform the separate-variance *t* test by making entries in the SVt worksheet of the **Separate-Variance T.xls** workbook. This worksheet (see Figure E11.3) uses the TINV and TDIST functions in ways similar to their use in the pooled-variance worksheet (see Section E11.3). IF functions in cells B32 and B37 select which one of two values computed in a calculations area (not shown in Figure E11.3) to use. IF functions in cells A28, A33, and A38 determine which one of two phrases will be displayed in those cells.

	A	B	
1	**Separate-Variances *t* Test**		
2	(assumes unequal population variances)		
3	**Data**		
4	**Hypothesized Difference**	0	
5	**Level of Significance**	0.05	
6	**Population 1 Sample**		
7	**Sample Size**	10	
8	**Sample Mean**	50.3	
9	**Sample Standard Deviation**	18.7264	
10	**Population 2 Sample**		
11	**Sample Size**	10	
12	**Sample Mean**	72	
13	**Sample Standard Deviation**	12.5433	
14			
15	Intermediate Calculations		
16	Numerator of Degrees of Freedom	2580.7663	=(E18 + E19)^2
17	Denominator of Degrees of Freedom	164.1436	=(E18^2)/(B7 - 1) + (E19^2)/(B11 - 1)
18	Total Degrees of Freedom	15.7226	=B16/B17
19	Degrees of Freedom	15	=INT(B18)
20	Separate Variance Denominator	7.1275	=SQRT(E18 + E19)
21	Difference in Sample Means	-21.7	=B8 - B12
22	**Separate-Variance *t* Test Statistic**	3.04455	=B21/B20
23			
24	**Two-Tail Test**		
25	**Lower Critical Value**	-2.1314	=-(TINV(B5, B19))
26	**Upper Critical Value**	2.1314	=TINV(B5, B19)
27	**p-Value**	0.0082	=TDIST(ABS(B22), B19, 2)
28	**Reject the null hypothesis**		=IF(B27 < B5,"Reject the null hypothesis", "Do not reject the null hypothesis")
29			
30	**Lower-Tail Test**		
31	**Lower Critical Value**	-1.7531	=-(TINV(2 * B5, B19))
32	**p-Value**	0.0041	=IF(B22 < 0, E21, E22)
33	**Reject the null hypothesis**		=IF(B32 < B5, "Reject the null hypothesis", "Do not reject the null hypothesis")
34			
35	**Upper-Tail Test**		
36	**Upper Critical Value**	1.7531	=(TINV(2 * B5, B19))
37	**p-Value**	0.9959	=IF(B22 < 0, E22, E21)
38	**Do not reject the null hypothesis**		=IF(B37 < B5, "Reject the null hypothesis", "Do not reject the null hypothesis")

Not shown
Cell E16: =B9^2
Cell E17: =B13^2
Cell E18: =E16/B7
Cell E19: =E17/B11
Cell E21: =TDIST(ABS(B22), B19, 1)
Cell E22: =1 - E21

FIGURE E11.3 Separate-variance (SVt) worksheet

The worksheet contains entries based on the Table 11.1 BLK Cola weekly sales data. To adapt this worksheet to other problems, change, as is necessary, the hypothesized difference, level of significance, and the sample statistics of the two samples in cells B4, B5, B7:B9, and B11:B13.

E11.6 Using the Paired t Test (unsummarized data)

For unsummarized data, you perform the paired t test by using the ToolPak t-Test: Paired Two Sample for Mean procedure. (There is no equivalent procedure for summarized data in Microsoft Excel.)

Open to the worksheet containing the unsummarized data for the two samples. Select **Tools → Data Analysis** (Excel 97–2003) or **Data → Data Analysis** (Excel 2007). Then select **t-Test: Paired Two Sample for Means** from the **Data Analysis** list and click **OK**. In the procedure's dialog box (shown below), enter the cell range of one sample as the **Variable 1 Range** and the cell range of the other sample as the **Variable 2 Range**. Enter the **Hypothesized Mean Difference**, click **Labels**, and click **OK**. Figure 11.8 on page 475 shows the results for the Table 11.4 car mileage data.

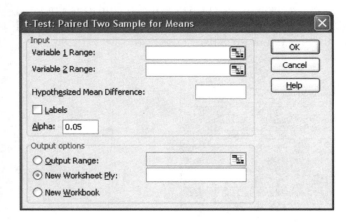

E11.7 Using the Z Test for the Difference Between Two Proportions

For summarized data, you perform the Z test for the difference between two proportions by making entries in either the **ZTP_TT** or **ZTP_All** worksheets of the `Z Two Proportions.xls` workbook. These worksheets use the **NORMSINV($P<X$)** function to determine the lower and upper critical values and use the **NORMSDIST(Z value)**

function to compute the p-values from the Z value calculated in cell B12. IF functions in cell A24 and in A29 and A34 determine which one of two phrases will be displayed in those cells.

The **ZTP_TT** worksheet (see Figure 11.12) applies the two-tail Z test to the Section 11.3 guest satisfaction example. The **ZTP_All** worksheet includes the two-tail test, the upper one-tail test, and the lower one-tail test on one worksheet and contains a confidence interval estimate of the difference between the two proportions. To adapt these worksheets to other problems, enter the hypothesized difference, level of significance, and the number of items of interest and sample size for each sample in cells B4, B5, B7, B8, B10, and B11, as is necessary.

E11.8 Using the F Test for the Difference Between Two Variances (unsummarized data)

For unsummarized data, you use the F test for the difference between two variances by using the ToolPak F Test Two-Sample for Variances procedure.

Open to the worksheet containing the unsummarized data for the two samples. Select **Tools → Data Analysis** (Excel 97–2003) or **Data → Data Analysis** (Excel 2007). Then select **F Test Two-Sample for Variances** from the **Data Analysis** list and click **OK**. In the procedure's dialog box, enter the cell range of one sample as the **Variable 1 Range** and the cell range of the other sample as the **Variable 2 Range**. Click **Labels** and click **OK**. Results appear on a new worksheet. Figure 11.13 shows results for the Table 11.1 BLK Cola weekly sales data.

E11.9 Using the *F* Test for the Difference Between Two Variances (summarized data)

For summarized data, you perform the *F* test for the difference between two variances by making entries in the **F Two Variances** worksheet of the F Two Variances.xls workbook.

The worksheet uses the **FINV(*upper-tailed* p-*value*, *numerator degrees of freedom, denominator degrees of freedom*)** function, in which ***upper-tailed* p-*value*** is the probability that *F* will be greater than the value, to compute the upper and lower critical values and **FDIST(F-*test statistic, numerator degrees of freedom, denominator degrees of freedom*)** function to compute the *p*-values.

The worksheet (shown in Figure E11.4) applies the *F* test to the Section 11.4 BLK Cola weekly sales example. Because sample 1 has been defined as the sample with the larger variance, a lower-tail test section is unnecessary in this worksheet.

To adapt this worksheet to other problems, change the level of significance and the sample statistics for the two population samples in the tinted cells B4, B6, B7, B9, and B10. Should you inadvertently enter the data of the sample with the largest standard deviation as the "smaller-variance sample," IF functions in cells A28 and A29 (not shown in Figure E11.4) will display messages asking you to review your entries.

E11.10 Using One-Way ANOVA with Multiple Comparisons

You perform a one-way ANOVA with multiple comparisons by first using the ToolPak Anova: Single Factor procedure and then making entries in a worksheet in the Tukey-Kramer.xls workbook.

Open to the worksheet containing unstacked data for the three or more independent groups. Select **Tools → Data Analysis** (Excel 97–2003) or **Data → Data Analysis** (Excel 2007). Then select **Anova: Single Factor** from the **Data Analysis** list and click **OK**. In the procedure's dialog box (shown at the top of the next column), enter the cell range of the data as the **Input Range**, click **Columns** (if necessary), click **Labels in first row**, and click **OK**. Results appear on a new worksheet. Record the sample size and sample mean of each group (found in the Count and Average columns, respectively). Also record the *MSW* value, found in the cell that is the intersection of the **MS** column and **Within Groups** row, and the denominator degrees of freedom, found in the cell that is the intersection of the **df** column and **Within Groups** row.

Next, open the **Tukey-Kramer.xls** workbook and select the worksheet for your number of groups. If you have three groups, select the **TukeyKramer3** worksheet. If you have four groups, select the **TukeyKramer4** worksheet. (There are also worksheets for five, six, and seven groups.) Enter the sample size, sample mean, *MSW* value, and the denominator degrees of freedom you recorded earlier. Then look up the Studentized Range *Q* statistic from Table E.8 on page

	A	B	
1	F Test for Differences in Two Variances		
2			
3	**Data**		
4	Level of Significance	0.05	
5	**Larger-Variance Sample**		
6	Sample Size	10	
7	Sample Standard Deviation	18.7264	
8	**Smaller-Variance Sample**		
9	Sample Size	10	
10	Sample Standard Deviation	12.543	
11			
12	**Intermediate Calculations**		
13	F Test Statistic	2.2290	=B7^2/B10^2
14	Population 1 Sample Degrees of Freedom	9	=B6 - 1
15	Population 2 Sample Degrees of Freedom	9	=B9 - 1
16			
17	**Two-Tail Test**		
18	Upper Critical Value	4.0260	=FINV(B4/2, B14, B15)
19	p-Value	0.2482	=2 * E17
20	Do not reject the null hypothesis		=IF(B20 < B4, "Reject the null hypothesis", "Do not reject the null hypothesis")
21			
22	**Upper-Tail Test**		
23	Upper Critical Value	3.1789	=FINV(B4, B14, B15)
24	p-Value	0.1241	=E17
25	Do not reject the null hypothesis		=IF(B24 < B4, "Reject the null hypothesis", "Do not reject the null hypothesis")

Not shown
Cell E17: =FDIST(B13, B14, B15)

FIGURE E11.4   *F* Two Variances worksheet

697 for the level of significance of 0.05 and the numerator and denominator degrees of freedom values displayed in the worksheet.

To learn about the formulas used in the worksheets, open to the **TukeyKramer4Formulas** worksheet that displays the formulas that are used to compute the results shown in Figure 11.20.

E11.11 Using the Levene Test

You perform the Levene test by using the instructions of Section E11.10 with data from an Excel worksheet. Open to the worksheet that contains your unstacked multiple group data. The procedure must contain groups with equal sample sizes.

Add a row of formulas that use the **MEDIAN(*cell range*)** function to compute the median for each group. Then add a new set of columns that compute the absolute differences of each measurement and its corresponding median. Use the worksheets of the **Absolute Differences.xls** workbook as guides for creating these formulas. Once you create your new columns, follow the instructions of Section E11.10, using the cell range of the set of new absolute difference columns as the **Input Range** cell range. For example, if you were using the **Model** worksheet of the Absolute Differences workbook, you would enter **F1:I6** as the **Input Range**.

12

Chi-Square Tests

Learning Objective

In this chapter, you learn:

• How and when to use the chi-square test for contingency tables

@ T.C. Resort Properties

You are the manager of T.C. Resort Properties, a collection of five upscale hotels located on two tropical islands. Guests who are satisfied with the quality of services during their stay are more likely to return on a future vacation and to recommend the hotel to friends and relatives. To assess the quality of services being provided by your hotels, guests are encouraged to complete a satisfaction survey when they check out. You need to analyze the data from these surveys to determine the overall satisfaction with the services provided, the likelihood that the guests will return to the hotel, and the reasons some guests indicate that they will not return. For example, on one island, T.C. Resort Properties operates the Beachcomber and Windsurfer hotels. Is the perceived quality at the Beachcomber Hotel the same as at the Windsurfer Hotel? If a difference is present, how can you use this information to improve the overall quality of service at T.C. Resort Properties? Furthermore, if guests indicate that they are not planning to return, what are the most common reasons given for this decision? Are the reasons given unique to a certain hotel or common to all hotels operated by T.C. Resort Properties?

I n the preceding two chapters, you used hypothesis-testing procedures to analyze both numerical and categorical data. Chapter 10 presented some one-sample tests, and Chapter 11 developed several two-sample tests and the one-way analysis of variance (ANOVA). This chapter extends hypothesis testing to analyze differences between population proportions based on two or more samples, as well as the hypothesis of *independence* in the joint responses to two categorical variables.

12.1 Chi-Square Test for the Difference Between Two Proportions

In Section 11.3, you studied the Z test for the difference between two proportions. In this section, the data are examined from a different perspective. The hypothesis-testing procedure uses a test statistic that is approximated by a chi-square (χ^2) distribution. The results of this χ^2 test are equivalent to those of the Z test described in Section 11.3.

If you are interested in comparing the counts of categorical responses between two independent groups, you can develop a two-way **contingency table** (see Section 2.4) to display the frequency of occurrence of items of interest and items not of interest for each group. In Chapter 4, contingency tables were used to define and study probability.

To illustrate the contingency table, return to the Using Statistics scenario concerning T.C. Resort Properties. On one of the islands, T.C. Resort Properties has two hotels (the Beachcomber and the Windsurfer). In tabulating the responses to the single question "Are you likely to choose this hotel again?" 163 of 227 guests at the Beachcomber responded yes, and 154 of 262 guests at the Windsurfer responded yes. At the 0.05 level of significance, is there evidence of a significant difference in guest satisfaction (as measured by likelihood to return to the hotel) between the two hotels?

The contingency table displayed in Table 12.1 has two rows and two columns and is called a **2 × 2 contingency table**. The cells in the table indicate the frequency for each row and column combination.

TABLE 12.1

Layout of a 2 × 2 Contingency Table

	COLUMN VARIABLE (GROUP)		
ROW VARIABLE	**1**	**2**	**Totals**
Items of interest	X_1	X_2	X
Items not of interest	$n_1 - X_1$	$n_2 - X_2$	$n - X$
Totals	n_1	n_2	n

where

$$X_1 = \text{number of items of interest in group 1}$$
$$X_2 = \text{number of items of interest in group 2}$$
$$n_1 - X_1 = \text{number of items that are not of interest in group 1}$$
$$n_2 - X_2 = \text{number of items that are not of interest in group 2}$$
$$X = X_1 + X_2, \text{the total number of items of interest}$$
$$n - X = (n_1 - X_1) + (n_2 - X_2), \text{the total number of items that are not of interest}$$
$$n_1 = \text{sample size in group 1}$$
$$n_2 = \text{sample size in group 2}$$
$$n = n_1 + n_2 = \text{total sample size}$$

Table 12.2 contains the contingency table for the hotel guest satisfaction study. The contingency table has two rows, indicating whether the guests would return to the hotel or would not return to the hotel, and two columns, one for each hotel. The cells in the table indicate the frequency of each row and column combination. The row totals indicate the number of guests who would return to the hotel and those who would not return to the hotel. The column totals are the sample sizes for each hotel location.

TABLE 12.2

2 × 2 Contingency Table for the Hotel Guest Satisfaction Survey

	HOTEL		
CHOOSE HOTEL AGAIN?	**Beachcomber**	**Windsurfer**	**Total**
Yes	163	154	317
No	64	108	172
Total	227	262	489

To test whether the population proportion of guests who would return to the Beachcomber, π_1, is equal to the population proportion of guests who would return to the Windsurfer, π_2, you can use the χ^2 **test for the difference between two proportions**. To test the null hypothesis that there is no difference between the two population proportions:

$$H_0: \pi_1 = \pi_2$$

against the alternative that the two population proportions are not the same:

$$H_1: \pi_1 \neq \pi_2$$

you use the χ^2_{STAT} test statistic, shown in Equation (12.1).

χ^2 TEST FOR THE DIFFERENCE BETWEEN TWO PROPORTIONS

The χ^2_{STAT} test statistic is equal to the squared difference between the observed and expected frequencies, divided by the expected frequency in each cell of the table, summed over all cells of the table.

$$\chi^2_{STAT} = \sum_{all\ cells} \frac{(f_o - f_e)^2}{f_e} \qquad (12.1)$$

where

f_o = **observed frequency** in a particular cell of a contingency table

f_e = **expected frequency** in a particular cell if the null hypothesis is true

The χ^2_{STAT} test statistic approximately follows a chi-square distribution with 1 degree of freedom.[1]

[1]In general, the degrees of freedom in a contingency table are equal to the (number of rows − 1) multiplied by the (number of columns − 1).

To compute the expected frequency, f_e, in any cell, you need to understand that if the null hypothesis is true, the proportion of items of interest in the two populations will be equal. Then the sample proportions you compute from each of the two groups would differ from each other only by chance. Each would provide an estimate of the common population parameter, π. A statistic that combines these two separate estimates together into one overall estimate of the population parameter provides more information than either of the two separate estimates could provide by itself. This statistic, given by the symbol $\bar{p}$, represents the estimated overall proportion of items of interest for the two groups combined (i.e., the total number of items of interest divided by the total sample size). The complement of $\bar{p}$, $1 - \bar{p}$, represents the estimated overall proportion of items that are not of interest in the two groups. Using the notation presented in Table 12.1, Equation (12.2) defines $\bar{p}$.

COMPUTING THE ESTIMATED OVERALL PROPORTION FOR 2 GROUPS

$$\bar{p} = \frac{X_1 + X_2}{n_1 + n_2} = \frac{X}{n} \qquad (12.2)$$

To compute the expected frequency, f_e, for each cell pertaining to items of interest (i.e., the cells in the first row in the contingency table), you multiply the sample size (or column total) for a group by $\bar{p}$. To compute the expected frequency, f_e, for each cell pertaining to items that are not of interest (i.e., the cells in the second row in the contingency table), you multiply the sample size (or column total) for a group by $1 - \bar{p}$.

The χ^2_{STAT} test statistic shown in Equation (12.1) approximately follows a **chi-square** (χ^2) **distribution** (see Table E.4) with 1 degree of freedom. Using a level of significance α, you reject the null hypothesis if the computed χ^2_{STAT} test statistic is greater than χ^2_α, the upper-tail critical value from the χ^2 distribution having 1 degree of freedom. Thus, the decision rule is

$$\text{Reject } H_0 \text{ if } \chi^2_{STAT} > \chi^2_\alpha;$$

$$\text{otherwise do not reject } H_0.$$

Figure 12.1 illustrates the decision rule.

FIGURE 12.1

Regions of rejection and nonrejection when using the chi-square test for the difference between two proportions, with level of significance α

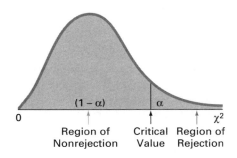

If the null hypothesis is true, the computed χ^2_{STAT} test statistic should be close to zero because the squared difference between what is actually observed in each cell, f_o, and what is theoretically expected, f_e, should be very small. If H_0 is false, then there are differences in the population proportions and the computed χ^2_{STAT} test statistic is expected to be large. However, what is a large difference in a cell is relative. The same actual difference between f_o and f_e from a cell with a small number of expected frequencies contributes more to the χ^2_{STAT} test statistic than a cell with a large number of expected frequencies.

To illustrate the use of the chi-square test for the difference between two proportions, return to the Using Statistics scenario concerning T.C. Resort Properties and the corresponding contingency table displayed in Table 12.2. The null hypothesis $(H_0: \pi_1 = \pi_2)$ states that there is no difference between the proportion of guests who are likely to choose either of these hotels again. To begin,

$$\bar{p} = \frac{X_1 + X_2}{n_1 + n_2} = \frac{163 + 154}{227 + 262} = \frac{317}{489} = 0.6483$$

$\bar{p}$ is the estimate of the common parameter π, the population proportion of guests who are likely to choose either of these hotels again if the null hypothesis is true. The estimated proportion of guests who are *not* likely to choose these hotels again is the complement of $\bar{p}$, $1 - 0.6483 = 0.3517$. Multiplying these two proportions by the sample size for the Beachcomber Hotel gives the number of guests expected to choose the Beachcomber again and the number not expected to choose this hotel again. In a similar manner, multiplying the two proportions by the Windsurfer Hotel's sample size yields the corresponding expected frequencies for that group.

EXAMPLE 12.1

Computing the Expected Frequencies

Compute the expected frequencies for each of the four cells of Table 12.2.

SOLUTION

Yes—Beachcomber: $\bar{p} = 0.6483$ and $n_1 = 227$, so $f_e = 147.16$

Yes—Windsurfer: $\bar{p} = 0.6483$ and $n_2 = 262$, so $f_e = 169.84$

No—Beachcomber: $1 - \bar{p} = 0.3517$ and $n_1 = 227$, so $f_e = 79.84$

No—Windsurfer: $1 - \bar{p} = 0.3517$ and $n_2 = 262$, so $f_e = 92.16$

Table 12.3 presents these expected frequencies next to the corresponding observed frequencies.

TABLE 12.3

Comparing the Observed (f_o) and Expected (f_e) Frequencies

	HOTEL				
	BEACHCOMBER		**WINDSURFER**		
CHOOSE HOTEL AGAIN?	**Observed**	**Expected**	**Observed**	**Expected**	**Total**
Yes	163	147.16	154	169.84	317
No	64	79.84	108	92.16	172
Total	227	227.00	262	262.00	489

To test the null hypothesis that the population proportions are equal:

$$H_0: \pi_1 = \pi_2$$

against the alternative that the population proportions are not equal:

$$H_1: \pi_1 \neq \pi_2$$

you use the observed and expected frequencies from Table 12.3 to compute the χ^2_{STAT} test statistic given by Equation (12.1). Table 12.4 presents the calculations.

TABLE 12.4

Computing the χ^2_{STAT} Test Statistic for the Hotel Guest Satisfaction Survey

f_o	f_e	$(f_o - f_e)$	$(f_o - f_e)^2$	$(f_o - f_e)^2 / f_e$
163	147.16	15.84	250.91	1.71
154	169.84	-15.84	250.91	1.48
64	79.84	-15.84	250.91	3.14
108	92.16	15.84	250.91	2.72
				9.05

The chi-square (χ^2) distribution is a right-skewed distribution whose shape depends solely on the number of degrees of freedom. You find the critical value for the χ^2 test from Table E.4, a portion of which is presented as Table 12.5.

TABLE 12.5

Finding the Critical Value from the Chi-Square Distribution with 1 Degree of Freedom, Using the 0.05 Level of Significance

	Cumulative Probabilities						
	.005	**.01**	**...**	**.95**	**.975**	**.99**	**.995**
	Upper-Tail Area						
Degrees of Freedom	**.995**	**.99**	**...**	**.05**	**.025**	**.01**	**.005**
1			...	3.841	5.024	6.635	7.879
2	0.010	0.020	...	5.991	7.378	9.210	10.597
3	0.072	0.115	...	7.815	9.348	11.345	12.838
4	0.207	0.297	...	9.488	11.143	13.277	14.860
5	0.412	0.554	...	11.071	12.833	15.086	16.750

The values in Table 12.5 refer to selected upper-tail areas of the χ^2 distribution. A 2×2 contingency table has $(2 - 1)(2 - 1) = 1$ degree of freedom. Using $\alpha = 0.05$, with 1 degree of freedom, the critical value of χ^2 from Table 12.5 is 3.841. You reject H_0 if the computed χ^2_{STAT} test statistic is greater than 3.841 (see Figure 12.2). Because $\chi^2_{STAT} = 9.05 > 3.841$, you reject H_0. You conclude that the proportion of guests who would return to the Beachcomber is different from the proportion of guests who would return to the Windsurfer.

FIGURE 12.2

Regions of rejection and nonrejection when finding the χ^2 critical value with 1 degree of freedom, at the 0.05 level of significance

Figure 12.3 represents a Casio calculator worksheet for the guest satisfaction contingency table (Table 12.2).

These results include the expected frequencies, χ^2_{STAT}, degrees of freedom, and p-value. The computed χ^2_{STAT} test statistic is 9.0525, which is greater than the critical value of 3.8415 (or the p-value $= 0.0026 < 0.05$), so you reject the null hypothesis that there is no difference in guest satisfaction between the two hotels. The p-value of 0.0026 is the probability of observing sample proportions as different as or more different than the actual difference $(0.718 - 0.588 = 0.13)$ observed in the sample data, if the population proportions for the Beachcomber and Windsurfer hotels are equal. Thus, there is strong evidence to conclude that the two hotels are significantly different with respect to guest satisfaction, as measured by whether a guest is likely to return to the hotel again. An examination of Table 12.3 on page 543 indicates that a greater proportion of guests are likely to return to the Beachcomber than to the Windsurfer.

For the χ^2 test to give accurate results for a 2×2 table, you must assume that each expected frequency is at least 5. If this assumption is not satisfied, you can use alternative procedures such as Fisher's exact test (see references 1, 2, and 4).

In the hotel guest satisfaction survey, both the Z test based on the standardized normal distribution (see Section 11.3) and the χ^2 test based on the chi-square distribution provide the same conclusion. You can explain this result by the interrelationship between the standardized normal distribution and a chi-square distribution with 1 degree of freedom. For such situations, the χ^2_{STAT} test statistic is the square of the Z_{STAT} test statistic. For instance, in the guest satisfaction study, the computed Z_{STAT} test statistic is $+3.0088$ and the computed χ^2_{STAT} test statistic is 9.0526. Except for rounding error, this latter value is the square of $+3.0088$ [i.e., $(+3.0088)^2 \cong 9.0526$]. Also, if you compare the critical values of the test statistics from the two distributions, at the 0.05 level of significance, the χ^2 value of 3.841 with one degree of freedom is the square of the Z value of ± 1.96. Furthermore, the p-values for both tests are equal. Therefore, when testing the null hypothesis of equality of proportions:

$$H_0: \pi_1 = \pi_2$$

against the alternative that the population proportions are not equal:

$$H_1: \pi_1 \neq \pi_2$$

FIGURE 12.3

Casio calculator FX 9750GII result for the hotel guest satisfaction data

Solution: Using Casio calculator FX 9750GII

Press **MENU** and select **STAT TEST** (F3) **CHI** (F3)
Under option **CHI**, select **2WAY** (F2)

You will see the following on the screen:

χ^2 Test

| Observed | : Mat A |

Expected : Mat B
Save Res : none
Execute

The cursor highlights on "Observed : Mat A"
There are two options:
1. **Mat (F1)** to select Matrix name A to Z
2. **▶Mat (F2)** to define matrix dimension and enter data.

To define dimension and enter data, select ▶Mat (F2) and you will see the following on the screen:

Matrx
Mat A : 2 × 2   **Press DIM(F3) to define or**
Mat B : None   **change dimension.**
Mat C : None
Mat D : None
Mar E : None
Mat F : None

Dimension : m × n
m: 2   EXE
n: 2   EXE

After you have entered the dimension for **Mat A**, you will see the **2 × 2 matrix A** appears on the screen. Use this screen to input your data.

A	1	2
1	163 EXE	154 EXE
2	64 EXE	108 EXE

After you have entered your data in Matrix A, now press **EXIT** two times until you see the following on the screen:

χ^2 Test

Observed : Mat A

| Expected | : Mat B |

Save Res : none
Execute

Highlight on "Expected : Mat B"
Select ▶Mat (F2) to define matrix dimension.
The **Expected Matrix** should have the same dimensions as the **Observed matrix**.

To define dimension, select ▶Mat (F2) and you will see the following on the screen:

Matrix
Mat A : 2 × 2
Mat B : 2 × 2   **Press DIM (F3) to define or**
Mat C : None   **change dimension.**
Mat D : None
Mar E : None
Mat F : None

Dimension : m × n
m: 2   EXE
n: 2   EXE

You will see a **2 by 2 matrix B**. You are not required to enter any values. The calculator will give you the expected values.

Now press **EXIT** two times until you see the following on the screen:

χ^2 Test
Observed : Mat A
Expected : Mat B
Save Res : none
Execute

At this point, press either **EXE** or **F1** (Calc)
The calculator will now show the results:

χ^2 Test

$\chi^2 = 9.0525978$
$p = 2.6232E\text{-}03 \ (0.0026232)$
$df = 1$

To obtain the expected value matrix select ▶**Mat** (F6), and then highlight on **MAT B** and press **EXE**. You will see the expected value matrix displayed on the screen as follows:

Ans	1	2
1	147.1554	169.8445
2	79.8446	92.1554

the Z test and the χ^2 test are equivalent. If you are interested in determining whether there is evidence of a *directional* difference, such as $\pi_1 > \pi_2$, then you must use the Z test, with the entire rejection region located in one tail of the standardized normal distribution. In Section 12.2, the χ^2 test is extended to make comparisons and evaluate differences between the proportions among more than two groups. However, you cannot use the Z test if there are more than two groups.

Problems for Section 12.1

LEARNING THE BASICS

12.1 Determine the critical value of χ^2 with 1 degree of freedom in each of the following circumstances:
a. $\alpha = 0.01$
b. $\alpha = 0.005$
c. $\alpha = 0.10$

12.2 Determine the critical value of χ^2 with 1 degree of freedom in each of the following circumstances:
a. $\alpha = 0.05$
b. $\alpha = 0.025$
c. $\alpha = 0.01$

12.3 Use the following contingency table:

	A	B	Total
1	20	30	50
2	30	45	75
Total	50	75	125

a. Find the expected frequency for each cell.
b. Compare the observed and expected frequencies for each cell.
c. Compute χ^2_{STAT}. Is it significant at $\alpha = 0.05$?

12.4 Use the following contingency table:

	A	B	Total
1	20	30	50
2	30	20	50
Total	50	50	100

a. Find the expected frequency for each cell.
b. Compute χ^2_{STAT}. Is it significant at $\alpha = 0.05$?

APPLYING THE CONCEPTS

12.5 A sample of 500 shoppers was selected in a large metropolitan area to determine various information concerning consumer behavior. Among the questions asked was, "Do you enjoy shopping for clothing?" The results are summarized in the following contingency table:

| ENJOY SHOPPING | GENDER | | |
FOR CLOTHING	Male	Female	Total
Yes	136	224	360
No	104	36	140
Total	240	260	500

a. Is there evidence of a significant difference between the proportion of males and females who enjoy shopping for clothing at the 0.01 level of significance?

b. Determine the *p*-value in (a) and interpret its meaning.

c. What are your answers to (a) and (b) if 206 males enjoyed shopping for clothing and 34 did not?

d. Compare the results of (a) through (c) to those of Problem 10.29(a), (b), and (d).

12.6 A study funded by the Massachusetts Institute of Technology tested the notion that even when it comes to sugar pills, some people think a costly one works better than a cheap one. Researchers randomly divided 82 healthy paid volunteers into two groups. All the volunteers thought they would be testing a new pain reliever. One group was told the pain reliever they would be using cost $2.50 a pill, and the other group was told it cost only 10 cents a pill. In reality, the pills they were all about to take were simply sugar pills. The volunteers were given a light electric shock on the wrist. Then the volunteers were given a sugar pill, and a short time later shocked again. Of the volunteers who took the expensive pill, 35 of the 41 said they felt less pain afterward. Of the volunteers who took the cheap pill, 25 of the 41 said they felt less pain afterward (R. Rubin, "Placebo Study Tests 'Costlier is Better' Notion," ***usatoday.com***, March 5, 2008).

a. Is there evidence of a difference in the proportion of people who think an expensive pill works to reduce pain and the proportion of people who think a cheap pill works to reduce pain at the 0.05 level of significance?

b. Determine the *p*-value in (a) and interpret its meaning.

c. Why shouldn't you compare the results in (a) to those of Problem 11.30 (b)?

12.7 Some people enjoy the *anticipation* of an upcoming product or event and prefer to pay in advance and delay the actual consumption/delivery date. In other cases, people do not want a delay. An article in the *Journal of Marketing Research* reported on an experiment where 50 individuals were told that they had just purchased a ticket to a concert and 50 were told that they had just purchased a personal digital assistant (PDA). The participants were then asked to indicate their preferences for attending the concert or receiving the PDA. Did they prefer tonight or tomorrow, or would they prefer to wait two to four weeks? The individuals were told to ignore their schedule constraints in order to better measure

their willingness to delay the consumption/delivery of their purchase. The following table gives partial results of the study.

	Concert	PDA
Tonight or Tomorrow	28	47
Two to Four Weeks	22	3
Total	50	50

Source: *Data adapted from O. Amir and D. Ariely, "Decisions by Rules: The Case of Unwillingness to Pay for Beneficial Delays,"* Journal of Marketing Research, *February 2007, Vol. XLIV, pp. 142–152.*

a. What proportion of the participants would prefer delaying the date of the concert?

b. What proportion of the participants would prefer delaying receipt of a new PDA?

c. Using the 0.05 level of significance, is there evidence of a significance difference in the proportion willing to delay the date of the concert and the proportion willing to delay receipt of a new PDA?

✓ SELF Test **12.8** According to an Ipsos poll, the perception of unfairness in the U.S. tax code is spread fairly evenly across income groups, age groups, and education levels. In an April 2006 survey of 1,005 adults, Ipsos reported that almost 60% of all people said the code is unfair, whereas slightly more than 60% of those making more than $50,000 viewed the code as unfair (data extracted from "People Cry Unfairness," *The Cincinnati Enquirer*, April 16, 2006, p. A8). Suppose that the following contingency table represents the specific breakdown of responses:

| U.S. TAX | INCOME LEVEL | | |
CODE	Less Than $50,000	More Than $50,000	Total
Fair	225	180	405
Unfair	280	320	600
Total	505	500	1,005

a. At the 0.05 level of significance, is there evidence of a difference in the proportion of adults who think the U.S. tax code is unfair between the two income groups?

b. Determine the *p*-value in (a) and interpret its meaning.

c. Compare the results of (a) and (b) to those of Problem 11.32.

12.9 Where people turn to for news is different for various age groups. Suppose that a study conducted on this issue (data extracted from P. Johnson, "Young People Turn to the Web for News," *USA Today*, March 23, 2006, p. 9D) was based on 200 respondents who were between the ages of 36 and 50 and 200 respondents who were above age 50. Of the 200 respondents who were between the ages of 36 and 50, 82 got their news primarily from newspapers. Of the 200 respondents who were above age 50, 104 got their news primarily from newspapers.

a. Construct a 2 × 2 contingency table.
b. Is there evidence of a significant difference in the proportion who get their news primarily from newspapers between those 36 to 50 years old and those above 50 years old? (Use $\alpha = 0.05$.)
c. Determine the p-value in (b) and interpret its meaning.
d. Compare the results of (b) and (c) to those of Problem 11.35(a) and (b).

12.10 An experiment was conducted to study the choices made in mutual fund selection. Undergraduate and MBA students were presented with different S&P 500 index funds that were identical except for fees. Suppose 100 undergraduate students and 100 MBA students were selected. Partial results are shown as follows:

	STUDENT GROUP	
FUND	**Undergraduate**	**MBA**
Highest-cost fund	27	18
Not highest-cost fund	73	82

Source: *Data extracted from J. Choi, D. Laibson, and B. Madrian, "Why Does the Law of One Practice Fail? An Experiment on Mutual Funds,"* **www.som.yale.edu/faculty/jjc83/fees.pdf**.

a. At the 0.05 level of significance, is there evidence of a difference between undergraduate and MBA students in the proportion who selected the highest-cost fund?
b. Determine the p-value in (a) and interpret its meaning.
c. Compare the results of (a) and (b) to those of Problem 11.34.

12.2 Chi-Square Test for Differences Among More Than Two Proportions

In this section, the χ^2 test is extended to compare more than two independent populations. The letter c is used to represent the number of independent populations under consideration. Thus, the contingency table now has two rows and c columns. To test the null hypothesis that there are no differences among the c population proportions:

$$H_0: \pi_1 = \pi_2 = \cdots = \pi_c$$

against the alternative that not all the c population proportions are equal:

$$H_1: \text{Not all } \pi_j \text{ are equal (where } j = 1, 2, \ldots, c)$$

you use Equation (12.1):

$$\chi^2_{STAT} = \sum_{all \text{ cells}} \frac{(f_o - f_e)^2}{f_e}$$

where

f_o = observed frequency in a particular cell of a 2 × c contingency table
f_e = expected frequency in a particular cell if the null hypothesis is true

If the null hypothesis is true and the proportions are equal across all c populations, the c sample proportions should differ only by chance. In such a situation, a statistic that combines these c separate estimates into one overall estimate of the population proportion, π, provides more information than any one of the c separate estimates alone. To expand on Equation (12.2), the statistic $\bar{p}$ in Equation (12.3) represents the estimated overall proportion for all c groups combined.

COMPUTING THE ESTIMATED OVERALL PROPORTION FOR c GROUPS

$$\bar{p} = \frac{X_1 + X_2 + \cdots + X_c}{n_1 + n_2 + \cdots + n_c} = \frac{X}{n} \tag{12.3}$$

To compute the expected frequency,   , for each cell in the first row in the contingency table, multiply each sample size (or column total) by $\bar{p}$. To compute the expected frequency, f_e, for each cell in the second row in the contingency table, multiply each sample size (or column total) by $(1 - \bar{p})$. The test statistic shown in Equation (12.1) approximately follows a chi-square distribution, with degrees of freedom equal to the number of rows in the contingency table minus 1, times the number of columns in the table minus 1. For a **2 × c contingency table**, there are $c - 1$ degrees of freedom:

$$\text{Degrees of freedom} = (2 - 1)(c - 1) = c - 1$$

Using the level of significance α, you reject the null hypothesis if the computed χ^2_{STAT} test statistic is greater than χ^2_α, the upper-tail critical value from a chi-square distribution with $c - 1$ degrees of freedom. Therefore, the decision rule is

$$\text{Reject } H_0 \text{ if } \chi^2_{STAT} > \chi^2_\alpha;$$

otherwise do not reject H_0.

Figure 12.4 illustrates the decision rule.

FIGURE 12.4

Regions of rejection and nonrejection when testing for differences among c proportions using the χ^2 test

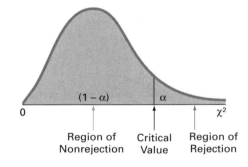

To illustrate the χ^2 test for equality of proportions when there are more than two groups, return to the Using Statistics scenario concerning T.C. Resort Properties. A similar survey was recently conducted on a different island on which T.C. Resort Properties has three different hotels. Table 12.6 presents the responses to a question concerning whether guests would be likely to choose this hotel again.

TABLE 12.6

2 × 3 Contingency Table for Guest Satisfaction Survey

	HOTEL			
CHOOSE HOTEL AGAIN?	**Golden Plam**	**Palm Royale**	**Palm Princess**	**Total**
Yes	128	199	186	513
No	88	33	66	187
Total	216	232	252	700

Because the null hypothesis states that there are no differences among the three hotels in the proportion of guests who would likely return again, you use Equation (12.3) to calculate an estimate of π, the population proportion of guests who would likely return again:

$$\bar{p} = \frac{X_1 + X_2 + \cdots + X_c}{n_1 + n_2 + \cdots + n_c} = \frac{X}{n}$$

$$= \frac{(128 + 199 + 186)}{(216 + 232 + 252)} = \frac{513}{700}$$

$$= 0.733$$

The estimated overall proportion of guests who would *not* be likely to return again is the complement, $(1 - \bar{p})$, or 0.267. Multiplying these two proportions by the sample size taken at each hotel yields the expected number of guests who would and would not likely return.

EXAMPLE 12.2

Computing the Expected Frequencies

Compute the expected frequencies for each of the six cells in Table 12.6.

SOLUTION

Yes—Golden Palm: $\bar{p} = 0.733$ and $n_1 = 216$, so $f_e = 158.30$

Yes—Palm Royale: $\bar{p} = 0.733$ and $n_2 = 232$, so $f_e = 170.02$

Yes—Palm Princess: $\bar{p} = 0.733$ and $n_3 = 252$, so $f_e = 184.68$

No—Golden Palm: $1 - \bar{p} = 0.267$ and $n_1 = 216$, so $f_e = 57.70$

No—Palm Royale: $1 - \bar{p} = 0.267$ and $n_2 = 232$, so $f_e = 61.98$

No—Palm Princess: $1 - \bar{p} = 0.267$ and $n_3 = 252$, so $f_e = 67.32$

Table 12.7 presents these expected frequencies.

TABLE 12.7

Contingency Table of Expected Frequencies from a Guest Satisfaction Survey of Three Hotels

	HOTEL			
CHOOSE HOTEL AGAIN?	**Golden Palm**	**Palm Royale**	**Palm Princess**	**Total**
Yes	158.30	170.02	184.68	513
No	57.70	61.98	67.32	187
Total	216.00	232.00	252.00	700

To test the null hypothesis that the proportions are equal:

$$H_0: \pi_1 = \pi_2 = \pi_3$$

against the alternative that not all three proportions are equal:

$$H_1: \text{Not all } \pi_j \text{ are equal (where } j = 1, 2, 3)$$

you use the observed frequencies from Table 12.6 above and the expected frequencies from Table 12.7 to compute the χ^2_{STAT} test statistic [given by Equation (12.1)]. Table 12.8 presents the calculations.

TABLE 12.8

Computing the χ^2_{STAT} Test Statistic for the Guest Satisfaction Survey of Three Hotels

f_o	f_e	$(f_o - f_e)$	$(f_o - f_e)^2$	$(f_o - f_e)^2/f_e$
128	158.30	−30.30	918.09	5.80
199	170.02	28.98	839.84	4.94
186	184.68	1.32	1.74	0.01
88	57.70	30.30	918.09	15.91
33	61.98	−28.98	839.84	13.55
66	67.32	−1.32	1.74	0.02
				40.23

You use Table E.4 to find the critical value of the χ^2 test statistic. In the guest satisfaction survey, because three hotels are evaluated, there are $(2 - 1)(3 - 1) = 2$ degrees of freedom. Using $\alpha = 0.05$, the χ^2 critical value with 2 degrees of freedom is 5.991. Because the computed χ^2_{STAT} test statistic is 40.23 which is greater than this critical value, you reject the null hypothesis (see Figure 12.5). Casio calculator (see Figure 12.6 on page 551) also report the p-value. Likewise, because the p-value is approximately 0.0000, which is less than $\alpha = 0.05$, you reject the null hypothesis. Further, this p-value indicates that there is virtually no chance to see differences this large or larger among the three sample proportions, if the population proportions for the three hotels are equal. Thus, there is sufficient evidence to conclude that the hotel properties are different with respect to the proportion of guests who are likely to return.

FIGURE 12.5

Regions of rejection and nonrejection when testing for differences in three proportions at the 0.05 level of significance, with 2 degrees of freedom

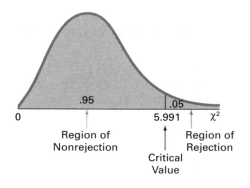

FIGURE 12.6

Casio calculator result for the guest satisfaction data of Table 12.6

Solution: Using Casio calculator FX 9750GII

Press **MENU** and select **STAT TEST** (F3) **CHI** (F3)
Under option **CHI**, select **2WAY** (F2)

You will see the following on the screen:

χ^2 Test

The cursor highlights on "Observed : Mat A"
There are two options:
1. **Mat (F1)** to select Matrix name A to Z
2. **▶Mat (F2)** to define matrix dimension and enter data.

To define dimension and enter data, select ▶Mat (F2) and you will see the following on the screen:

Matrx
Mat A   : 2 × 3   **Press DIM(F3) to define or**
Mat B   : None   **change dimension.**
Mat C   : None
Mat D   : None
Mar E   : None
Mat F   : None

Dimension : m × n
m: 2   EXE
n: 3   EXE

After you have entered the dimension for **Mat A**, you will see the **2 × 2 matrix A** appears on the screen. Use this screen to input your data.

A	1	2	3
1	128 EXE	199 EXE	186 EXE
2	88 EXE	33 EXE	66 EXE

After you have entered your data in Matrix A, now press **EXIT** two times until you see the following on the screen:

χ^2 Test

Highlight on "Expected : Mat B"
Select ▶Mat (F2) to define matrix dimension.
The **Expected Matrix** should have the same dimensions as the **Observed matrix**.

To define dimension, select ▶Mat (F2) and you will see the following on the screen:

Matrix

Mat A	: 2 × 3
Mat B	: 2 × 3
Mat C	: None
Mat D	: None
Mar E	: None
Mat F	: None

Press DIM (F3) to define or change dimension. →

Dimension : m × n
m: 2   EXE
n: 3   EXE

You will see a **2 by 3 matrix B**. You are not required to enter any values. The calculator will give you the expected values.

Now press **EXIT** two times until you see the following on the screen:

χ^2 Test

Observed	: Mat A
Expected	: Mat B
Save Res	: none
Execute	

At this point, press either **EXE** or **F1** (Calc)
The calculator will now show the results:

χ^2 Test

$\chi^2 = 40.2283986$
$p = 1.8387E-09 \ (0.0000000018387)$
$df = 2$

To obtain the expected value matrix select **▶Mat** (F6), and then highlight on **MAT B** and press **EXE**. You will see the expected value matrix displayed on the screen as follows:

Ans	1	2	3
1	158.2971	170.0229	184.68
2	57.7029	61.9771	67.32

For the χ^2 test to give accurate results when dealing with $2 \times c$ contingency tables, all expected frequencies must be large. There is much debate among statisticians about the definition of *large*. Some statisticians (see reference 5) have found that the test gives accurate results as long as all expected frequencies are at least 0.5. Other statisticians, more conservative in their approach, require that no more than 20% of the cells contain expected frequencies less than 5 and no cells have expected frequencies less than 1 (see reference 3). A reasonable compromise between these points of view is to make sure that each expected frequency is at least 1. To ensure that the expected frequencies are sufficiently large to conduct the χ^2 test accurately, you may need to collapse two or more low-expected-frequency categories into one category in the contingency table before performing the test. If combining categories is undesirable, alternative procedures are available (see references 1, 2, and 7).

CALCULATOR LESSON 15A

CFX-9850GB CALCULATOR

Lesson 15A – Chi-Square Test for Differences among more than two Proportions (section 11.2)

EXAMPLE 12.3

(A) Lesson 15A – Chi-Square Test for Differences among more than two Proportions Example.

Five printers of different brands are tested using the same paper and graphic output. The results are judged as conforming or nonconforming. At 5% level of significance, test for a difference in proportion of nonconforming pages. The results are as followed.

TABLE 12.9

	Number of Pages Printed				
	Brand of the printer				
Classification	A	B	C	D	E
Nonconforming	13	10	16	9	12
Conforming	187	190	184	191	188

Solution: From the **Main Menu** select:

MAT   EXE

Enter the following in response to the screen prompts.

Matrix

Mat A	**:**	**2 EXE**	**4EXE**
Mat B	:	None	
Mat C	:	None	
Mat D	:	None	
Mat E	:	None	
Mat F	:	None	

You will see the part of the matrix appears on the screen. Use this screen to input your data.

A	1	2	3	4 →
1	0	0	0	0
2	0	0	0	0

Enter the data values into the appropriate cells. To begin entering your data, use the Arrow key to highlight the cell 1,1 (top left corner of the cell). Type 13 and press **EXE.** The cursor will automatically scrolls to the next cell.

A	1	2	3	4	5
1	13 EXE	10 EXE	16 EXE	9 EXE	12 EXE
2	187 EXE	190 EXE	184 EXE	191 EXE	188 EXE

After you have enter your data in Matrix A, now press **MENU** and select

STAT EXE

TEST (F3) **CHI** (F3)   then enter the following items:

χ^2 Test
Observed: Mat A (F1)
Execute
Now Press **EXE**

The calculator will now show the results:

χ^2 Test
$\quad \chi^2 = 2.6595$
$\quad$ p = 0.6163
$\quad$ df = 2
Expected = Mat Ans

We may obtain the expected value matrix by making the following selection:

MENU   MAT EXE

Use the cursor ▼ arrow to scroll down to the bottom of the matrix list until the cursor is on;

Mat Ans   : 2 x 5
EXE

You will see the expected value matrix displayed on the screen as follows:

Ans	1	2	3	4	5
1	12	12	12	12	12
2	188	188	188	188	188

Conclusion:

Since p-value = 0.6163 is greater than α, we do not reject H_o.

The statistical evidence does not indicate that we may conclude that there is a difference in the proportion of nonconforming pages produced by the printers.

CALCULATOR LESSON 15B

FX-9850GII CALCULATOR

Lesson 15B – Chi-Square Test for Differences among more than two Proportions (section 12.2 of page 548)

EXAMPLE 12.4

(A) Lesson 15B: Chi-Square Test for Differences among more than two Proportions Example.

Five printers of different brands are tested using the same paper and graphic output. The results are judged as conforming or nonconforming. At 5% level of significance, test for a difference in proportion of nonconforming pages. The results are as followed.

TABLE 12.10

	Number of Pages Printed				
	Brand of the printer				
Classification	A	B	C	D	E
Nonconforming	13	10	16	9	12
Conforming	187	190	184	191	188

Solution:

Press **MENU** and select **STAT TEST** (F3)   **CHI** (F3)
Under option **CHI**, select **2WAY** (F2)

You will see the following on the screen:

χ^2 Test

Observed	**: Mat A**

Expected   : Mat B
Save Res   : none
Execute

The cursor highlights on "Observed : Mat A"
There are two options:
1. **Mat (F1)** to select Matrix name A to Z
2. ▶**Mat (F2)** to define matrix dimension and enter data.

To define dimension and enter data, select ▶Mat (F2) and you will see the following on the screen:

Matrx
Mat A   : 2 × 5   **Press DIM(F3) to define or**
Mat B   : None   **change dimension.**
Mat C   : None
Mat D   : None
Mar E   : None
Mat F   : None

Dimension : m × n
m: 2   EXE
n: 5   EXE

After you have entered the dimension for **Mat A**, you will see the **2 × 5 matrix A** appears on the screen. Use this screen to input your data. Enter the data values into the appropriate cells. To begin entering your data, use the Arrow key to highlight the cell 1,1 (top left corner of the cell). Type 13 and press **EXE**. The cursor will automatically scrolls to the next cell.

A	1	2	3	4⟶	5
1	13 EXE	10 EXE	16 EXE	9 EXE	12 EXE
2	187 EXE	190 EXE	184 EXE	191 EXE	188 EXE

After you have entered your data in Matrix A, now press **EXIT** two times until you see the following on the screen:

χ^2 Test

Observed   : Mat A

Expected   : Mat B

Highlight on "Expected : Mat B"
Select ▶Mat (F2) to define matrix dimension.
The **Expected Matrix** should have the same dimensions as the **Observed matrix**.

Save Res   : none
Execute

To define dimension, select ▶Mat (F2) and you will see the following on the screen:

Matrix
Mat A   : 2 × 5
Mat B   : 2 × 5   **Press DIM (F3) to define or**
Mat C   : None   **change dimension.**
Mat D   : None
Mar E   : None
Mat F   : None

Dimension : m × n
m: 2   EXE
n: 5   EXE

You will see a **2 by 5 matrix B**. You are not required to enter any values. The calculator will give you the expected values.

Now press **EXIT** two times until you see the following on the screen:

χ^2 Test
Observed   : Mat A
Expected   : Mat B
Save Res   : none
Execute

At this point, press either **EXE** or **F1** (Calc)
The calculator will now show the results:

χ^2 Test

$\chi^2 = 2.6595$
$p = 0.6163$
$df = 4$

To obtain the expected value matrix select ▶**Mat** (F6), and then highlight on **MAT B** and press **EXE**. You will see the expected value matrix displayed on the screen as follows:

Ans	1	2	3	4	5
1	12	12	12	12	12
2	188	188	188	188	188

Conclusion:
Since p-value $= 0.6163$ is greater than α, we do not reject H_o.
The statistical evidence does not indicate that we may conclude that there is a difference in the proportion of nonconforming pages produced by the printers.

Problems for Section 12.2

LEARNING THE BASICS

12.11 Consider a contingency table with two rows and five columns.
a. Find the degrees of freedom.
b. Find the critical value for $\alpha = 0.05$.
c. Find the critical value for $\alpha = 0.01$.

12.12 Use the following contingency table:

	A	B	C	Total
1	10	30	50	90
2	40	45	50	135
Total	50	75	100	225

a. Compute the expected frequencies for each cell.
b. Compute χ^2_{STAT}. Is it significant at $\alpha = 0.05$?

12.13 Use the following contingency table:
a. Compute the expected frequencies for each cell.
b. Compute χ^2_{STAT}. Is it significant at $\alpha = 0.05$?

	A	B	C	Total
1	20	30	25	75
2	30	20	25	75
Total	50	50	50	150

APPLYING THE CONCEPTS

12.14 A survey was conducted in five countries. The percentages of respondents who said that they eat out once a week or more are as follows:

Germany	10%
France	12%
United Kindom	28%
Greece	39%
United States	57%

Source: *Data adapted from M. Kissel, "Americans Are Keen on Cocooning," The Wall Street Journal, July 22, 2003, p. D3.*

Suppose that the survey was based on 1,000 respondents in each country.
a. At the 0.05 level of significance, determine whether there is a significant difference in the proportion of people who eat out at least once a week in the various countries.
b. Find the p-value in (a) and interpret its meaning.

12.15 The health-care industry and consumer advocacy groups are at odds over the sharing of a patient's medical records without the patient's consent. The health-care industry believes that no consent should be necessary to openly share data among doctors, hospitals, pharmacies, and insurance companies.

Suppose a study is conducted in which 600 patients are randomly assigned, 200 each, to three "organizational groupings"—insurance companies, pharmacies, and medical researchers. Each patient is given material to read about the advantages and disadvantages concerning the sharing of medical records within the assigned "organizational grouping." Each patient is then asked "would you object to the sharing of your medical records with . . ." and the results are recorded in the cross-classification table below.

OBJECT TO SHARING INFORMATION	ORGANIZATIONAL GROUPING		
	Insurance	**Pharmacies**	**Research**
Yes	40	80	90
No	160	120	110

a. Is there evidence of a difference in objection to sharing information among the organizational groupings? (Use $\alpha = 0.05$.)
b. Compute the p-value and interpret its meaning.

✓SELF Test **12.16** More shoppers do the majority of their grocery shopping on Saturday than any other day of the week. However, is there a difference in the various age groups in the proportion of people who do the majority of their grocery shopping on Saturday? A study showed the results for the different age groups (data extracted from "Major Shopping by Day," *Progressive Grocer Annual Report*, April 30, 2002). The data were reported as percentages, and no sample sizes were given:

MAJOR SHOPPING DAY	AGE		
	Under 35	**35–54**	**Over 54**
Saturday	24%	28%	12%
A day other than Saturday	76%	72%	88%

Assume that 200 shoppers for each age category were surveyed.
a. Is there evidence of a significant difference among the age groups with respect to major grocery shopping day? (Use $\alpha = 0.05$.)
b. Determine the p-value in (a) and interpret its meaning.
c. Discuss the managerial implications of (a) and (b). How can grocery stores use this information to improve marketing and sales? Be specific.

12.17 Repeat (a) through (b) of Problem 12.16, assuming that only 50 shoppers for each age category were surveyed. Discuss the implications of sample size on the χ^2 test for differences among more than two populations.

12.18 More and more people are finding that they need to delay retirement for financial reasons (data extracted from T. Luhby, "When Retirement Is a Luxury You Can't Afford," *Newsday*, September 30, 2006, pp. B4, B5, B8). A study reported that 52% of men age 62–64 were still working, 41% of women age 62–64 were still working, 31% men age 65–69 were still working, and 23% of women age 65–69 were still working. Suppose that the study was based on a sample size of 100 in each group.

a. Is there evidence of a significant difference among the groups with respect to the proportion who are still working? (Use $\alpha = 0.05$.)

b. Determine the *p*-value in (a) and interpret its meaning.

12.19 More and more people are paying with plastic (extracted from *USA Today Snapshots*, March 6, 2007, p. 1B). A study taken in 1995 reported that 18% of the respondents paid for a specific type of purchase with plastic, whereas a similar study in 2005 indicated that 25% paid for a specific type of purchase with plastic. (No sample sizes were reported for either study.) Suppose that a new survey taken in 2007 indicated that 31% paid for a specific type of purchase with plastic. Suppose that all three studies used a sample size of 500.

a. Is there evidence of a significant difference among the three years in the proportion of respondents who paid for a specific type of purchase with plastic? (Use $\alpha = 0.05$.)

b. Determine the *p*-value in (a) and interpret its meaning.

12.3 Chi-Square Test of Independence

In Sections 12.1 and 12.2, you used the χ^2 test to evaluate potential differences among population proportions. For a contingency table that has r rows and c columns, you can generalize the χ^2 test as a *test of independence* for two categorical variables.

For a test of independence, the null and alternative hypotheses follow:

H_0: The two categorical variables are independent (i.e., there is no relationship between them).

H_1: The two categorical variables are dependent (i.e., there is a relationship between them).

Once again, you use Equation (12.1) to compute the test statistic:

$$\chi^2_{STAT} = \sum_{all\ cells} \frac{(f_o - f_e)^2}{f_e}$$

You reject the null hypothesis at the α level of significance if the computed value of the χ^2_{STAT} test statistic is greater than χ^2_α, the upper-tail critical value from a chi-square distribution with $(r-1)(c-1)$ degrees of freedom (see Figure 12.7). Thus, the decision rule is

Reject H_0 if $\chi^2_{STAT} > \chi^2_\alpha$;

otherwise do not reject H_0.

FIGURE 12.7

Regions of rejection and nonrejection when testing for independence in an $r \times c$ contingency table, using the χ^2 test

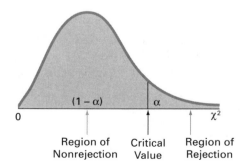

The χ^2 **test of independence** is similar to the χ^2 test for equality of proportions. The test statistics and the decision rules are the same, but the stated hypotheses and conclusions are different. For example, in the guest satisfaction survey of Sections 12.1 and 12.2, there is evidence of a significant difference between the hotels with respect to the proportion of guests who would return. From a different viewpoint, you could conclude that there is a significant relationship between the hotels and the likelihood that a guest would return. Nevertheless, there is a fundamental difference between the two types of tests. The major difference is in how the samples are selected.

In a test for equality of proportions, there is one factor of interest, with two or more levels. These levels represent samples drawn from independent populations. The categorical responses in each sample group or level are classified into two categories, such as *item of interest* and *not an item of interest*. The objective is to make comparisons and evaluate differences between the proportions of *the items of interest* among the various levels. However, in a test for independence, there are two factors of interest, each of which has two or more levels. You select one sample and tally the joint responses to the two categorical variables into the cells of a contingency table.

To illustrate the χ^2 test for independence, suppose that, in the survey on hotel guest satisfaction, a second question was asked of all respondents who indicated that they were not likely to return. These guests were asked to indicate the primary reason for their response. Table 12.11 presents the resulting 4×3 contingency table.

In Table 12.11, observe that of the primary reasons for not planning to return to the hotel, 67 were due to price, 60 were due to location, 31 were due to room accommodation, and 29 were due to other reasons. As in Table 12.6, there were 88 guests in the Golden Palm, 33 guests in the Palm Royale, and 66 guests in the Palm Princess who were not planning to return. The observed frequencies in the cells of the 4×3 contingency table represent the joint tallies of the sampled guests with respect to primary reason for not returning and the hotel.

TABLE 12.11

Contingency Table of Primary Reason for Not Returning and Hotel

PRIMARY REASON FOR NOT RETURNING	HOTEL			
	Golden Palm	Palm Royale	Palm Princess	Total
Price	23	7	37	67
Location	39	13	8	60
Room accommodation	13	5	13	31
Other	13	8	8	29
Total	88	33	66	187

The null and alternative hypotheses are:

H_0: There is no relationship between the primary reason for not returning and the hotel.

H_1: There is a relationship between the primary reason for not returning and the hotel.

To test this null hypothesis of independence against the alternative that there is a relationship between the two categorical variables, you use Equation (12.1) to compute the test statistic:

$$\chi^2_{STAT} = \sum_{all\ cells} \frac{(f_o - f_e)^2}{f_e}$$

where

f_o = observed frequency in a particular cell of the $r \times c$ contingency table

f_e = expected frequency in a particular cell if the null hypothesis of independence were true

To compute the expected frequency, f_e, in any cell, you use the multiplication rule for independent events discussed in Chapter Four [see Equation (4.7)]. For example, under the null hypothesis of independence, the probability of responses expected in the upper-left-corner cell representing primary reason of price for the Golden Palm is the product of the two separate probabilities: $P(\text{Price})$ and $P(\text{Golden Palm})$. Here, the proportion of reasons that are due to price, $P(\text{Price})$, is $67/187 = 0.3583$, and the proportion of all responses from the Golden Palm, $P(\text{Golden Palm})$, is $88/187 = 0.4706$. If the null hypothesis is true, then the primary reason for not returning and the hotel are independent:

$$P(\text{Price }and\text{ Golden Palm}) = P(\text{Price}) \times P(\text{Golden Palm})$$
$$= (0.3583) \times (0.4706)$$
$$= 0.1686$$

The expected frequency is the product of the overall sample size, n, and this probability, $187 \times 0.1686 = 31.53$. The f_e values for the remaining cells are calculated in a similar manner (see Table 12.13).

Equation (12.4) presents a simpler way to compute the expected frequency.

COMPUTING THE EXPECTED FREQUENCY

The expected frequency in a cell is the product of its Row total and Column total, divided by the overall sample size.

$$f_e = \frac{\text{Row total} \times \text{Column total}}{n} \qquad\qquad \textbf{(12.4)}$$

where

$$\text{row total} = \text{sum of all the frequencies in the row}$$

$$\text{column total} = \text{sum of all the frequencies in the column}$$

$$n = \text{overall sample size}$$

For example, using Equation (12.4) for the upper-left-corner cell (price for the Golden Palm),

$$f_e = \frac{\text{Row total} \times \text{Column total}}{n} = \frac{(67)(88)}{187} = 31.53$$

and for the lower-right-corner cell (other reason for the Palm Princess),

$$f_e = \frac{\text{Row total} \times \text{Column total}}{n} = \frac{(29)(66)}{187} = 10.24$$

Table 12.12 lists the entire set of f_e values.

TABLE 12.12

Contingency Table of Expected Frequencies of Primary Reason for Not Returning with Hotel

PRIMARY REASON FOR NOT RETURNING	HOTEL			
	Golden Palm	**Palm Royale**	**Palm Princess**	**Total**
Price	31.53	11.82	23.65	67
Location	28.24	10.59	21.18	60
Room accommodation	14.59	5.47	10.94	31
Other	13.65	5.12	10.24	29
Total	88.00	33.00	66.00	187

To perform the test of independence, you use the χ^2_{STAT} test statistic shown in Equation (12.1). The χ^2_{STAT} test statistic approximately follows a chi-square distribution, with degrees of freedom equal to the number of rows in the contingency table minus 1, times the number of columns in the table minus 1:

$$\text{Degrees of freedom} = (r - 1)(c - 1)$$
$$= (4 - 1)(3 - 1) = 6$$

Table 12.13 illustrates the computations for the χ^2_{STAT} test statistic.

TABLE 12.13

Computing the χ^2_{STAT} Test Statistic for the Test of Independence

Cell	f_o	f_e	$(f_o - f_e)$	$(f_o - f_e)^2$	$(f_o - f_e)^2/f_e$
Price/Golden Palm	23	31.53	−8.53	72.76	2.31
Price/Palm Royale	7	11.82	−4.82	23.23	1.97
Price/Palm Princess	37	23.65	13.35	178.22	7.54
Location/Golden Palm	39	28.24	10.76	115.78	4.10
Location/Palm Royale	13	10.59	2.41	5.81	0.55
Location/Palm Princess	8	21.18	−13.18	173.71	8.20
Room/Golden Palm	13	14.59	−1.59	2.53	0.17
Room/Palm Royale	5	5.47	−0.47	0.22	0.04
Room/Palm Princess	13	10.94	2.06	4.24	0.39
Other/Golden Palm	13	13.65	−0.65	0.42	0.03
Other/Palm Royale	8	5.12	2.88	8.29	1.62
Other/Palm Princess	8	10.24	−2.24	5.02	0.49
					27.41

Using the level of significance $\alpha = 0.05$, the upper-tail critical value from the chi-square distribution with 6 degrees of freedom is 12.592 (see Table E.4). Because $\chi^2_{STAT} = 27.41 > 12.592$, you reject the null hypothesis of independence (see Figure 12.8).

FIGURE 12.8

Regions of rejection and nonrejection when testing for independence in the hotel guest satisfaction survey example at the 0.05 level of significance, with 6 degrees of freedom

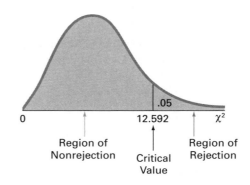

You can use the Casio calculator in Figure 12.9 to conduct the test of independence using the *p*-value approach. Because the *p*-value $= 0.0001 < 0.05$, you reject the null hypothesis of independence. The *p*-value indicates that there is virtually no chance of having a relationship this strong or stronger between hotels and primary reasons for not returning in a sample, if the primary reasons for not returning are independent of the specific hotels in the entire population. Thus, there is strong evidence of a relationship between primary reason for not returning and the hotel.

Examination of the observed and expected frequencies (see Table 12.12) reveals that price is underrepresented as a reason for not returning to the Golden Palm (i.e., $f_o = 23$ and $f_e = 31.53$) but is overrepresented at the Palm Princess. Guests are more satisfied with the price at the Golden Palm compared to the Palm Princess. Location is overrepresented as a reason for not returning to the Golden Palm but greatly underrepresented at the Palm Princess. Thus, guests are much more satisfied with the location of the Palm Princess than that of the Golden Palm.

To ensure accurate results, all expected frequencies need to be large in order to use the χ^2 test when dealing with $r \times c$ contingency tables. As in the case of $2 \times c$ contingency tables in Section 12.2, all expected frequencies should be at least 1. For cases in which one or more expected frequencies are less than 1, you can use the test after collapsing two or more low-frequency rows into one row (or collapsing two or more low-frequency columns into one column). Merging of rows or columns usually results in expected frequencies sufficiently large to conduct the χ^2 test accurately.

FIGURE 12.9

Casio calculator FX-9750GII result for the 4 × 3 contingency table for primary reason for not returning and hotel

Solution: Using Casio calculator FX 9750GII

Press **MENU** and select **STAT TEST** (F3)   **CHI** (F3)
Under option **CHI**, select **2WAY** (F2)

You will see the following on the screen:

χ^2 Test

| Observed | : Mat A |

Expected   : Mat B
Save Res   : none
Execute

The cursor highlights on "Observed : Mat A"
There are two options:
1. **Mat (F1)** to select Matrix name A to Z
2. **▶Mat (F2)** to define matrix dimension and enter data.

To define dimension and enter data, select ▶Mat (F2) and you will see the following on the screen:

Matrx
Mat A   : 4 × 3   **Press DIM(F3) to define or**
Mat B   : None   **change dimension.**
Mat C   : None
Mat D   : None
Mar E   : None
Mat F   : None

Dimension : m × n
m: 4   EXE
n: 3   EXE

After you have entered the dimension for **Mat A**, you will see the **4 × 3 matrix A** appears on the screen. Use this screen to input your data.

A	1	2	3
1	23	7	37
2	39	13	8
3	13	5	13
4	13	8	8

After you have entered your data in Matrix A, now press **EXIT** two times until you see the following on the screen:

χ^2 Test

Observed   : Mat A

| Expected | : Mat B |

Save Res   : none
Execute

Highlight on "Expected : Mat B"
Select ▶Mat (F2) to define matrix dimension.
The **Expected Matrix** should have the same dimensions as the **Observed matrix**.

To define dimension, select ▶Mat (F2) and you will see the following on the screen:

Matrix
Mat A   : 4 × 3
Mat B   : 4 × 3   **Press DIM (F3) to define or**
Mat C   : None   **change dimension.**
Mat D   : None
Mar E   : None
Mat F   : None

Dimension : m × n
m: 4   EXE
n: 3   EXE

You will see a **4 by 3 matrix B**. You are not required to enter any values. The calculator will give you the expected values.

Now press **EXIT** two times until you see the following on the screen:

χ^2 Test
Observed   : Mat A
Expected   : Mat B
Save Res   : none
Execute

At this point, press either **EXE** or **F1** (Calc)
The calculator will now show the results:

χ^2 Test

$\chi^2 = 27.41$
   $p = 1.2128\text{E-}04$
   $df = 6$

To obtain the expected value matrix select ▶**Mat** (F6), and then highlight on **MAT B** and press **EXE**. You will see the expected value matrix displayed on the screen as follows:

Ans	1	2	3
1	31.529	11.823	23.647
2	28.235	10.588	21.176
3	14.588	5.4705	10.9411
4	13.647	5.1176	10.235

CALCULATOR LESSON 16A

CFX-9850GB CALCULATOR

Lesson 16A – Chi-Square Test for Independence (Section 11.3)

EXAMPLE 12.5

Lesson 16A – Chi-Square Test for Independence

Example.

A Copier service has two laser printers used to produce colour transparencies. The thickness of a transparency can create printing problems. Four common problems are; smearing, streaking, skipping and fogging. A random sample reveals the following information. We wish to test whether the problems depend on the printer used. We will use a significance level of 0.05.

TABLE 12.14

	Problems			
Printer	**Smearing**	**Streaking**	**Skipping**	**Fogging**
A	20	32	44	10
B	10	48	21	15

Solution: From the **Main Menu** select:

MAT   EXE

Enter the following in response to the screen prompts.

Matrix

Mat A	:	2 EXE	4EXE
Mat B	:	None	
Mat C	:	None	
Mat D	:	None	
Mat E	:	None	
Mat F	:	None	

You will see the part of the matrix appears on the screen. Use this screen to input your data.

A	1	2	3	4 →
1	0	0	0	0
2	0	0	0	0

Enter the data values into the appropriate cells. To begin entering your data, use the Arrow key to highlight the cell 1,1 (top left corner of the cell). Type 20 and press **EXE.** The cursor will automatically scrolls to the next cell.

A	1	2	3	4 →
1	20 EXE	32 EXE	44 EXE	10 EXE
2	10 EXE	48 EXE	21 EXE	15 EXE

After you have enter your data in Matrix A, now press **MENU** and select

STAT EXE

TEST (F3) **CHI** (F3)   then enter the following items:

χ^2 Test
Observed: Mat A (F1)
Execute
Now Press **EXE**

The calculator will now show the results:

χ^2 Test
    χ^2 = 15.005
    p = 1.8116E-03   (= 0.0018116)
    df = 3
Expected = Mat Ans

We may obtain the expected value matrix by making the following selection:

MENU MAT EXE

Use the cursor ▼ arrow to scroll down to the bottom of the matrix list until the cursor is on;

Mat Ans   : 2 x 4
EXE

You will see the expected value matrix displayed on the screen as follows:

Ans	1	2	3	4 →
1	15.9	42.4	34.45	13.25
2	14.1	37.6	30.55	11.75

Conclusion:

Since p-value = 0.0018 is smaller than α, we reject H_o.

The statistical evidence indicate that we may conclude that there is a difference in the proportion of nonconforming pages produced by the printers.

CALCULATOR LESSON 16B

**FX-9850GII
CALCULATOR**

EXAMPLE 12.6

Lesson 16B – Chi-Square Test for Independence (Section 12.3)

Lesson 16B – Chi-Square Test for Independence

Example.

A Copier service has two laser printers used to produce colour transparencies. The thickness of a transparency can create printing problems. Four common problems are; smearing, streaking, skipping and fogging. A random sample reveals the following information. We wish to test whether the problems depend on the printer used. We will use a significance level of 0.05.

TABLE 12.15

	Problems			
Printer	Smearing	Streaking	Skipping	Fogging
A	20	32	44	10
B	10	48	21	15

Solution:

Press **MENU** and select **STAT TEST** (F3)   **CHI** (F3)
Under option **CHI**, select **2WAY** (F2)

You will see the following on the screen:

χ^2 Test

Observed : Mat A	→	The cursor highlights on "Observed : Mat A" There are two options: 1. **Mat (F1)** to select Matrix name A to Z 2. **▶Mat (F2)** to define matrix dimension and enter data.

Expected : Mat B
Save Res   : none
Execute

To define dimension and enter data, select ▶Mat (F2) and you will see the following on the screen:

Matrx
Mat A   : 2 × 4   **Press DIM(F3) to define or** | Dimension : m × n |
Mat B   : None   **change dimension.**   → | m: 2   EXE |
Mat C   : None | n: 4   EXE |
Mat D   : None
Mar E   : None
Mat F   : None

After you have entered the dimension for **Mat A**, you will see the **2 × 4 matrix A** appears on the screen. Use this screen to input your data.

A	1	2	3	4 →
1	0	0	0	0
2	0	0	0	0

Enter the data values into the appropriate cells. To begin entering your data, use the Arrow key to highlight the cell 1,1 (top left corner of the cell). Type 13 and press **EXE**. The cursor will automatically scrolls to the next cell.

A	1	2	3	4
1	20 EXE	32 EXE	44 EXE	10 EXE
2	10 EXE	48 EXE	21 EXE	15 EXE

After you have entered your data in Matrix A, now press **EXIT** two times until you see the following on the screen:

χ^2 Test

Observed : Mat A

Expected : Mat B → Highlight on "Expected : Mat B"
Select ▶Mat (F2) to define matrix dimension.
The **Expected Matrix** should have the same
dimensions as the **Observed matrix**.

Save Res   : none
Execute

To define dimension, select ▶Mat (F2) and you will see the following on the screen:

Matrix
Mat A   : 2 × 4
Mat B   : 2 × 4   **Press DIM (F3) to define or**   Dimension : m × n
Mat C   : None   **change dimension.**   →   m: 2   EXE
Mat D   : None   n: 4   EXE
Mar E   : None
Mat F   : None

You will see a **2 by 4 matrix B**. You are not required to enter any values. The calculator will give you the expected values.

Now press **EXIT** two times until you see the following on the screen:

χ^2 Test
Observed : Mat A
Expected : Mat B
Save Res   : none
Execute

At this point, press either **EXE** or **F1** (Calc)
The calculator will now show the results:

χ^2 Test

$\chi^2 = 15.005$
$p = 1.8116\text{E-}03 \ (0.0018116)$
$df = 3$

To obtain the expected value matrix select **▶Mat** (F6), and then highlight on **MAT B** and press **EXE**. You will see the expected value matrix displayed on the screen as follows:

Ans	1	2	3	4 →
1	15.9	42.4	34.45	13.25
2	14.1	37.6	30.55	11.75

Conclusion:
Since p-value = 0.0018 is greater than α, we do not reject H_o.
The statistical evidence does not indicate that we may conclude that there is a difference in the proportion of nonconforming pages produced by the printers.

Problems for Section 12.3

LEARNING THE BASICS

12.20 If a contingency table has three rows and four columns, how many degrees of freedom are there for the χ^2 test for independence?

12.21 When performing a χ^2 test for independence in a contingency table with r rows and c columns, determine the upper-tail critical value of the test statistic in each of the following circumstances:
a. $\alpha = 0.05$, $r = 4$ rows, $c = 5$ columns
b. $\alpha = 0.01$, $r = 4$ rows, $c = 5$ columns
c. $\alpha = 0.01$, $r = 4$ rows, $c = 6$ columns
d. $\alpha = 0.01$, $r = 3$ rows, $c = 6$ columns
e. $\alpha = 0.01$, $r = 6$ rows, $c = 3$ columns

APPLYING THE CONCEPTS

12.22 The Committee of 200 is an international not-for-profit association comprised of preeminent business-women who collectively control over $100 billion annually in revenue. According to the association's Web site, **www.c200.org**, the purpose of the Committee of 200 "is to meet the needs of our membership in areas of business synergies, leadership advancement, education, mentoring, and recognition. Additionally, as an agent of change, we want to improve opportunities for women business leaders, be a source for governmental representation, and a source for research on issues relevant to women in business." The association sponsored a survey where MBAs from top business schools were asked if executives were paid too much. The responses (in percentages, but without sample sizes) are in the following table and were published in "Snapshots: Are Execs Paid Too Much?" *USA Today*, **www.usatoday.com**, January 15, 2007.

	Yes	No	Neutral
Women	61%	11%	28%
Men	49%	27%	24%

a. Do you think executives are paid too much?
b. Suppose that the survey was based on 100 males and 100 females. Using the 0.01 level of significance, perform a hypothesis test to see if you can prove that men and women feel differently about executive pay.
c. Suppose that the survey was based on 200 males and 200 females. Using the 0.01 level of significance, perform a hypothesis test to see if you can prove that men and women feel differently about executive pay.
d. Discuss the importance of sample size on reporting survey results.

12.23 *USA Today* reported on preferred types of office communication by different age groups ("Talking Face to Face vs. Group Meetings," *USA Today*, October 13, 2003, p. A1). Suppose the results were based on a survey of 500 respondents in each age group. The results are cross-classified in the following table:

	TYPE OF COMMUNICATION PREFERRED				
AGE GROUP	Group Meetings	Face-to-Face Meetings with Individuals	E-mails	Other	Total
Generation Y	180	260	50	10	500
Generation X	210	190	65	35	500
Boomer	205	195	65	35	500
Mature	200	195	50	55	500
Total	795	840	230	135	2,000

Source: *Data extracted from "Talking Face to Face vs. Group Meetings,"* USA Today, *October 13, 2003, p. A1.*

At the 0.05 level of significance, is there evidence of a relationship between age group and type of communication preferred?

✓ SELF Test **12.24** A large corporation is interested in determining whether a relationship exists between the commuting time of its employees and the level of stress-related problems observed on the job. A study of 116 assembly-line workers reveals the following:

	STRESS LEVEL			
COMMUTING TIME	High	Moderate	Low	Total
Under 15 min.	9	5	18	32
15–45 min.	17	8	28	53
Over 45 min.	18	6	7	31
Total	44	19	53	116

a. At the 0.01 level of significance, is there evidence of a significant relationship between commuting time and stress level?
b. What is your answer to (a) if you use the 0.05 level of significance?

12.25 Where people turn to for news is different for various age groups. A study indicated where different age groups primarily get their news:

MEDIA	AGE GROUP		
	Under 36	36–50	50 +
Local TV	107	119	133
National TV	73	102	127
Radio	75	97	109
Local newspaper	52	79	107
Internet	95	83	76

At the 0.05 level of significance, is there evidence of a significant relationship between the age group and where people primarily get their news? If so, explain the relationship.

12.26 *USA Today* reported on when the decision of what to have for dinner is made. Suppose the results were based on a survey of 1,000 respondents and considered whether the household included any children under 18 years old. The results were cross-classified in the following table:

WHEN DECISION MADE	TYPE OF HOUSEHOLD		
	One Adult/ No Children	Two or More Adults/ Children	Two or More Adults/ No Children
Just before eating	162	54	154
In the afternoon	73	38	69
In the morning	59	58	53
A few days before	21	64	45
The night before	15	50	45
Always eat the same thing on this night	2	16	2
Not sure	7	6	7

Source: *Data extracted from "What's for Dinner,"* USA Today, *January 10, 2000.*

At the 0.05 level of significance, is there evidence of a significant relationship between when the decision is made of what to have for dinner and the type of household?

USING STATISTICS @ T.C. Resort Properties Revisited

In the Using Statistics scenario, you were the manager of T.C. Resort Properties, a collection of five upscale hotels located on two tropical islands. To assess the quality of services being provided by your hotels, guests are encouraged to complete a satisfaction survey when they check out. You analyzed the data from these surveys to determine the overall satisfaction with the services provided, the likelihood that the guests will return to the hotel, and the reasons given by some guests for not wanting to return.

On one island, T.C. Resort Properties operates the Beachcomber and Windsurfer hotels. You performed a chi-square test for the difference in two proportions and concluded that a greater proportion of guests are willing to return to the Beachcomber Hotel than to the Windsurfer. On the other island, T.C. Resort Properties operates the Golden Palm, Palm Royale, and Palm Princess hotels. To see if guest satisfaction was the same among the three hotels, you performed a chi-square test for the differences among more than two proportions. The test confirmed that the three proportions are not equal, and guests are most likely to return to the Palm Royale, and least likely to return to the Golden Palm.

In addition, you investigated whether the reasons given for not returning to the Golden Palm, Palm Royale, and Palm Princess were unique to a certain hotel or common to all three hotels. By performing a chi-square test of independence, you determined that the reasons given for wanting to return or not depended on which hotel they had been staying in. By examining the observed and expected frequencies, you concluded that guests are more satisfied with the price at the Golden Palm, and were much more satisfied with the location of the Palm Princess. Guest satisfaction with room accommodations was not significantly different among the three hotels.

SUMMARY

Figure 12.10 presents a roadmap for this chapter. For analyzing categorical response data from two samples, a chi-square test was presented. This chi-square test is equivalent to the Z test based on the standardized normal distribution in Section 11.3. Then, the chi-square test was generalized for use in analyzing categorical response data from three or more samples. In addition, the rules of probability from Section 4.2 were extended to the hypothesis of independence in the joint responses to two categorical variables.

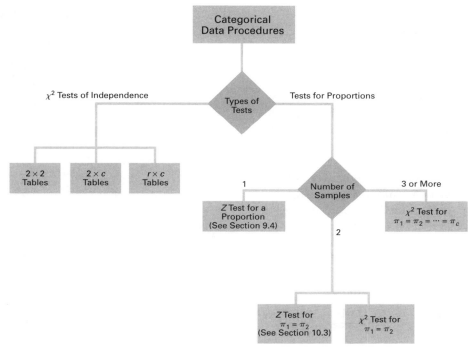

FIGURE 12.10   Roadmap of Chapter 12

KEY EQUATIONS

χ^2 Test for the Difference Between Two Proportions

$$\chi^2_{STAT} = \sum_{all\ cells} \frac{(f_0 - f_e)^2}{f_e} \tag{12.1}$$

Computing the Estimated Overall Proportion for 2 Groups

$$\bar{p} = \frac{X_1 + X_2}{n_1 + n_2} = \frac{X}{n} \tag{12.2}$$

Computing the Estimated Overall Proportion for c Groups

$$\bar{p} = \frac{X_1 + X_2 + \cdots + X_c}{n_1 + n_2 + \cdots + n_c} = \frac{X}{n} \tag{12.3}$$

Computing the Expected Frequencies

$$f_e = \frac{\text{Row total} \times \text{Column total}}{n} \tag{12.4}$$

KEY TERMS

chi-square (χ^2) distribution   542
chi-square (χ^2) test of independence 558
chi-square (χ^2) test for the difference between two proportions   541

contingency table   540
expected frequency (f_e) 541
observed frequency (f_o) 541

$2 \times c$ contingency table   549
2×2 contingency table   540

CHAPTER REVIEW PROBLEMS

CHECKING YOUR UNDERSTANDING

12.27 Under what conditions should you use the χ^2 test to determine whether there is a difference between the proportions of two independent populations?

12.28 Under what conditions should you use the χ^2 test to determine whether there is a difference between the proportions of more than two independent populations?

12.29 Under what conditions should you use the χ^2 test of independence?

APPLYING THE CONCEPTS

12.30 Undergraduate students at Miami University in Oxford, Ohio, were surveyed in order to evaluate the effect of gender and price on purchasing a pizza from Pizza Hut. Students were told to suppose that they were planning on having a large two-topping pizza delivered to their residence that evening. The students had to decide between ordering from Pizza Hut at a reduced price of $8.49 (the regular price for a large two-topping pizza from the Oxford Pizza Hut at this time was $11.49) and ordering a pizza from a different pizzeria. The results from this question are summarized in the following contingency table:

| | PIZZERIA | | |
GENDER	Pizza Hut	Other	Total
Female	4	13	17
Male	6	12	18
Total	10	25	35

The survey also evaluated purchase decisions at other prices. These results are summarized in the following contingency table:

| | PRICE | | | |
PIZZERIA	$8.49	$11.49	$14.49	Total
Pizza Hut	10	5	2	17
Other	25	23	27	75
Total	35	28	29	92

a. Using a 0.05 level of significance and using the data in the first contingency table, is there evidence of a significant relationship between a student's gender and his or her pizzeria selection?
b. What is your answer to (a) if nine of the male students selected Pizza Hut and nine selected other?
c. Using a 0.05 level of significance and using the data in the second contingency table, is there evidence of a difference in pizzeria selection based on price?
d. Determine the p-value in (c) and interpret its meaning.

12.31 Many companies are finding that customers are using various types of online content before purchasing products (data extracted from K. Spors, "How Are We Doing?" *The Wall Street Journal*, November 13, 2006, p. R9). The following results are the percentages of older adults (over age 45), younger adults (21–45), and youths (below 21) who use various sources of online content. Suppose the survey was based on 100 older adults, 100 younger adults, and 100 youths.

| | USE ONLINE CONTENT | | |
TYPE OF ONLINE CONTENT	Older Adults	Younger Adults	Youth
Customer product ratings/ reviews	71	78	81
For sale listings with seller ratings	69	72	77
For sale listings without seller ratings	58	60	65
Online classified ads	57	59	66
Message-board posts	57	65	71
Webblogs	55	61	67
Dating site profiles/personals	49	52	59
Peer-generated and peer-reference information	49	55	68
Peer-posted event listings	46	53	71

For *each type of online content*, is there a significant difference among the age groups in the proportion who use the type of online content? (Use $\alpha = 0.05$.)

12.32 A company is considering an organizational change by adopting the use of self-managed work teams. To assess the attitudes of employees of the company toward this change, a sample of 400 employees is selected and asked whether they favor the institution of self-managed work teams in the organization. Three responses are permitted: favor, neutral, or oppose. The results of the survey, cross-classified by type of job and attitude toward self-managed work teams, are summarized as follows:

| | SELF-MANAGED WORK TEAMS | | | |
TYPE OF JOB	Favor	Neutral	Oppose	Total
Hourly worker	108	46	71	225
Supervisor	18	12	30	60
Middle management	35	14	26	75
Upper management	24	7	9	40
Total	185	79	136	400

a. At the 0.05 level of significance, is there evidence of a relationship between attitude toward self-managed work teams and type of job?

The survey also asked respondents about their attitudes toward instituting a policy whereby an employee could take one additional vacation day per month without pay. The results, cross-classified by type of job, are as follows:

TYPE OF JOB	VACATION TIME WITHOUT PAY			
	Favor	Neutral	Oppose	Total
Hourly worker	135	23	67	225
Supervisor	39	7	14	60
Middle management	47	6	22	75
Upper management	26	6	8	40
Total	247	42	111	400

b. At the 0.05 level of significance, is there evidence of a relationship between attitude toward vacation time without pay and type of job?

12.33 A company that produces and markets recorded DVDs continuing education programs for the financial industry has traditionally mailed sample DVDs that contain previews of the programs to prospective customers. Customers then agree to purchase the DVDs or return the sample DVDs. A group of sales representatives studied how to increase sales and found that many prospective customers believed it was difficult to tell from a sample DVD alone whether the educational programs would meet their needs. The sales representatives performed an experiment to test whether sending the complete DVDs for review by customers would increase sales. They selected 80 customers from the mailing list and randomly assigned 40 to receive the sample DVDs and 40 to receive the full-program DVDs for review. They then determined the number of DVDs that were purchased and returned in each group. The results of the experiment are as follows:

ACTION	TYPE OF DVD RECEIVED		
	Sample	Full	Total
Purchased	6	14	20
Returned	34	26	60
Total	40	40	80

a. At the 0.05 level of significance, is there evidence of a difference in the proportion of DVDs purchased on the basis of the type of DVD sent to the customer?

b. On the basis of the results of (a), which type do you think a representative should send in the future? Explain the rationale for your decision.

The sales representatives also wanted to determine which of three initial sales approaches result in the most sales: (1) a sales-information DVD mailed to prospective customers, (2) a personal sales call to prospective customers, and (3) a telephone call to prospective customers. A random sample of 300 prospective customers was selected, and 100 were randomly assigned to each of the three sales approaches. The results, in terms of purchases of the full-program DVD, are as follows:

ACTION	SALES APPROACH			
	DVD	Personal Sales Call	Telephone	Total
Purchase	19	27	14	60
Don't purchase	81	73	86	240
Total	100	100	100	300

c. At the 0.05 level of significance, is there evidence of a difference in the proportion of DVDs purchased on the basis of the sales strategy used?

d. On the basis of the results of (c), which sales approach do you think a representative should use in the future? Explain the rationale for your decision.

12.34 Researchers studied the goals and outcomes of 349 work teams from various manufacturing companies in Ohio. In the first table, teams are categorized as to whether they had specified environmental improvements as a goal and also according to one of four types of manufacturing processes that best described their workplace. The following three tables indicate different outcomes the teams accomplished, based on whether the team had specified cost cutting as one of the team goals.

TYPE OF MANUFACTURING PROCESS	ENVIRONMENTAL GOAL		
	Yes	No	Total
Job shop or batch	2	42	44
Repetitive batch	4	57	61
Discrete process	15	147	162
Continuous process	17	65	82
Total	38	311	349

OUTCOME	COST-CUTTING GOAL		
	Yes	No	Total
Improved environmental performance	77	52	129
Environmental performance not improved	91	129	220
Total	168	181	349

OUTCOME	COST-CUTTING GOAL		
	Yes	**No**	**Total**
Improved profitability	70	68	138
Profitability not improved	98	113	211
Total	168	181	349

OUTCOME	COST-CUTTING GOAL		
	Yes	**No**	**Total**
Improved morale	67	55	122
Morale not improved	101	126	227
Total	168	181	349

Source: *Data extracted from M. Hanna, W. Newman, and P. Johnson,* "*Linking Operational and Environmental Improvement Thru Employee Involvement,*" International Journal of Operations and Production Management, *2000, 20, pp. 148–165.*

a. At the 0.05 level of significance, determine whether there is evidence of a significant relationship between the presence of environmental goals and the type of manufacturing process.

b. Determine the *p*-value in (a) and interpret its meaning.

c. At the 0.05 level of significance, is there evidence of a difference in improved environmental performance for teams with and without a specified goal of cutting costs?

d. Determine the *p*-value in (c) and interpret its meaning.

e. At the 0.05 level of significance, is there evidence of a difference in improved profitability for teams with a specified goal of cutting costs?

f. Determine the *p*-value in (e) and interpret its meaning.

g. At the 0.05 level of significance, is there evidence of a difference in improved morale for teams with and without a specified goal of cutting costs?

h. Determine the *p*-value in (g) and interpret its meaning.

TEAM PROJECT

The data file **Mutual Funds** contains information regarding nine variables from a sample of 868 mutual funds. The variables are:

Category—Type of stocks comprising the mutual fund (small cap, mid cap, or large cap)

Objective—Objective of stocks comprising the mutual fund (growth or value)

Assets—In millions of dollars

Fees—Sales charges (no or yes)

Expense ratio—Ratio of expenses to net assets in percentage

Return 2006—Twelve-month return in 2006

Three-year return—Annualized return, 2004–2006

Five-year return—Annualized return, 2002–2006

Risk—Risk-of-loss factor of the mutual fund (low, average, or high)

12.35 a. Construct a 2×2 contingency table, using fees as the row variable and objective as the column variable.

b. At the 0.05 level of significance, is there evidence of a significant relationship between the objective of a mutual fund and whether there is a fee?

12.36 a. Construct a 2×3 contingency table, using fees as the row variable and risk as the column variable.

b. At the 0.05 level of significance, is there evidence of a significant relationship between the perceived risk of a mutual fund and whether there is a fee?

12.37 a. Construct a 3×2 contingency table, using risk as the row variable and objective as the column variable.

b. At the 0.05 level of significance, is there evidence of a significant relationship between the objective of a mutual fund and its perceived risk?

12.38 a. Construct a 3×3 contingency table, using risk as the row variable and category as the column variable.

b. At the 0.05 level of significance, is there evidence of a significant relationship between the category of a mutual fund and its perceived risk?

STUDENT SURVEY DATA BASE

12.39 Problem 1.28 describes a survey of 50 undergraduate students (see the file **Undergradsurvey**). For these data, construct contingency tables, using gender, major, plans to go to graduate school, and employment status. (You need to construct six tables, taking two variables at a time.) Analyze the data at the 0.05 level of significance to determine whether any significant relationships exist among these variables.

12.40 Problem 1.28 describes a survey of 50 undergraduate students (see the file **Undergradsurvey**).

a. Select a sample of 50 undergraduate students at your school and conduct a similar survey for those students.

b. For the data collected in (a), repeat Problem 12.39.

c. Compare the results of (b) to those of Problem 12.39.

12.41 Problem 1.29 describes a survey of 40 MBA students (see the file **Gradsurvey**). For these data, construct contingency tables, using gender, undergraduate major, graduate major, and employment status. (You need to construct six tables, taking two variables at a time.) Analyze the data at the 0.05 level of significance to determine whether any significant relationships exist among these variables.

12.42 Problem 1.29 describes a survey of 40 MBA students (see the file **Gradsurvey**).

a. Select a sample of 40 graduate students in your MBA program and conduct a similar survey for those students.

b. For the data collected in (a), repeat Problem 12.41.

c. Compare the results of (b) to those of Problem 12.41.

MANAGING THE *SPRINGVILLE HERALD*

PHASE 1

Reviewing the results of its research, the marketing department team concluded that a segment of Springville households might be interested in a discounted trial home subscription to the *Herald*. The team decided to test various discounts before determining the type of discount to offer during the trial period. It decided to conduct an experiment using three types of discounts plus a plan that offered no discount during the trial period:

1. No discount for the newspaper. Subscribers would pay $4.50 per week for the newspaper during the 90-day trial period.

2. Moderate discount for the newspaper. Subscribers would pay $4.00 per week for the newspaper during the 90-day trial period.

3. Substantial discount for the newspaper. Subscribers would pay $3.00 per week for the newspaper during the 90-day trial period.

4. Discount restaurant card. Subscribers would be given a card providing a discount of 15% at selected restaurants in Springville during the trial period.

Each participant in the experiment was randomly assigned to a discount plan. A random sample of 100 subscribers to each plan during the trial period was tracked to determine how many would continue to subscribe to the *Herald* after the trial period. Table SH12.1 summarizes the results.

TABLE SH12.1

Number of Subscribers Who Continue Subscriptions After Trial Period with Four Discount Plans

CONTINUE SUBSCRIPTIONS AFTER TRIAL PERIOD	DISCOUNT PLANS				
	No Discount	Moderate Discount	Substantial Discount	Restaurant Card	Total
Yes	34	37	38	61	170
No	66	63	62	39	230
Total	100	100	100	100	400

EXERCISE

SH12.1 Analyze the results of the experiment. Write a report to the team that includes your recommendation for which discount plan to use. Be prepared to discuss the limitations and assumptions of the experiment.

DO NOT CONTINUE UNTIL THE PHASE 1 EXERCISE HAS BEEN COMPLETED.

PHASE 2

The marketing department team discussed the results of the survey presented in Chapter 8. The team realized that the evaluation of individual questions was providing only limited information. In order to further understand the market for home-delivery subscriptions, the data were organized in the following contingency tables:

HOME DELIVERY	READ OTHER NEWSPAPER		
	Yes	No	Total
Yes	61	75	136
No	77	139	216
Total	138	214	352

HOME DELIVERY	RESTAURANT CARD		
	Yes	No	Total
Yes	26	110	136
No	40	176	216
Total	66	286	352

INTEREST IN TRIAL SUBSCRIPTION	MONDAY–SATURDAY PURCHASE BEHAVIOR			
	Every Day	Most Days	Occasionally or Never	Total
Yes	29	14	3	46
No	49	81	40	170
Total	78	95	43	216

INTEREST IN TRIAL SUBSCRIPTION	SUNDAY PURCHASE BEHAVIOR			
	Every Sunday	2–3 Times a Month	No More Than Once a Month	Total
Yes	35	10	1	46
No	103	44	23	170
Total	138	54	24	216

WHERE PURCHASED	INTEREST IN TRIAL SUBSCRIPTION		
	Yes	No	Total
Convenience store	12	62	74
Newsstand/candy store	15	80	95
Vending machine	10	11	21
Supermarket	5	8	13
Other locations	4	9	13
Total	46	170	216

| SUNDAY PURCHASE BEHAVIOR | MONDAY–SATURDAY PURCHASE BEHAVIOR | | | |
	Every Day	Most Days	Occasionally or Never	Total
Every Sunday	55	65	18	138
2–3 times/month	19	23	12	54
Once/month	4	7	13	24
Total	78	95	43	216

EXERCISE

SH12.2 Analyze the results of the contingency tables. Write a report for the marketing department team and discuss the marketing implications of the results for the *Springville Herald*.

WEB CASE

Apply your knowledge of testing for the difference between two proportions in this Web Case, which extends the T.C. Resort Properties Using Statistics scenario of this chapter.

As T.C. Resort Properties seeks to improve its customer service, the company faces new competition from SunLow Resorts. SunLow has recently opened resort hotels on the islands where T.C. Resort Properties has its five hotels. SunLow is currently advertising that a random survey of 300 customers revealed that about 60% percent of the customers preferred its "Concierge Class" travel reward program over the T.C. Resorts "TCPass Plus" program. Visit the SunLow Web site, **www.prenhall.com/Springville/**

SunLowHome.htm (or open the SunLowHome.htm file in the Student CD-ROM Web Case folder), and examine the survey data. Then answer the following:

1. Are the claims made by SunLow valid?
2. What analyses of the survey data would lead to a more favorable impression about T.C. Resort Properties?
3. Perform one of the analyses identified in your answer to step 2.
4. Review the data about the T.C. Resorts Properties customers presented in this chapter. Are there any other questions that you might include in a future survey of travel reward programs? Explain.

REFERENCES

1. Conover, W. J., *Practical Nonparametric Statistics*, 3rd ed. (New York: Wiley, 2000).
2. Daniel, W. W., *Applied Nonparametric Statistics*, 2nd ed. (Boston: PWS Kent, 1990).
3. Dixon, W. J., and F. J. Massey, Jr., *Introduction to Statistical Analysis*, 4th ed. (New York: McGraw-Hill, 1983).
4. Hollander, M., and D. A. Wolfe, *Nonparametric Statistical Methods*, 2nd ed. (New York: Wiley, 1999).
5. Lewontin, R. C., and J. Felsenstein, "Robustness of Homogeneity Tests in 2 * n Tables," *Biometrics* 21 (March 1965): pp. 19–33.
6. Marascuilo, L. A., "Large-Sample Multiple Comparisons," *Psychological Bulletin* 65 (1966): pp. 280–290.
7. Marascuilo, L. A., and M. McSweeney, *Nonparametric and Distribution-Free Methods for the Social Sciences* (Monterey, CA: Brooks/Cole, 1977).
8. *Microsoft Excel 2007* (Redmond, WA: Microsoft Corp., 2007).
9. *Minitab for Windows Version 15* (State College, PA: Minitab, Inc., 2006).

APPENDIX E12

Using Microsoft Excel for Chi-Square Tests

E12.1 Using the Chi-Square Test for the Difference Between Two Proportions

You perform the chi-square test for the difference between two proportions by making entries in the **ChiSquare2P** worksheet of the `Chi-Square.xls` workbook. This worksheet (see Figure 12.3) uses the **CHIINV(*level of significance, degrees of freedom*)** and **CHIDIST(χ^2 *test statistic, degrees of freedom*)** functions to compute the critical value and *p*-value, respectively, for the Section 12.1 guest satisfaction example. To adapt this worksheet to other problems, enter the problem's contingency table data into the rows 4 through 7 Observed Frequencies area, the level of significance in cell B18, and enter a new title in cell A1. To examine all formulas in this worksheet, including the ones not shown in Figure 12.3, open to the **ChiSquare2PFormulas** worksheet in the same workbook.

E12.2 Using the Chi-Square Test for the Difference Among More Than Two Proportions

You perform the chi-square test for the difference among more than two proportions by making entries in one of the worksheets in the `Chi-Square Worksheets.xls` workbook.

Open the workbook to the worksheet that contains the appropriate $2 \times c$ observed frequency table for your problem. For example, for the Section 12.2 guest satisfaction example that requires a 2×3 table, open to the **ChiSquare2×3** worksheet. Worksheets with empty observed frequencies table will display the message #DIV/0! in many cells. This is not an error and these messages will disappear once you enter your contingency table data.

All $2 \times c$ worksheets contain formulas similar to those in the ChiSquare2P worksheet discussed in Section E12.1. To examine all formulas in the ChiSquare2×3 worksheet, including those not shown in Figure 12.6, open to the **ChiSquare2x3Formulas** worksheet.

E12.3 Using the Chi-Square Test of Independence

You perform the chi-square test of independence by making entries in one of the worksheets in the `Chi-Square Worksheets.xls` workbook. The workbook contains worksheets for 3×4, 4×3, 7×3, and 8×3 tables, in addition to the $2 \times c$ worksheets discussed in Section E12.2. Figure 12.9 uses the ChiSquare4×3 worksheet.

13 Simple Linear Regression

Learning Objectives

In this chapter, you learn:

- To use regression analysis to predict the value of a dependent variable based on an independent variable
- The meaning of the regression coefficients b_0 and b_1
- To evaluate the assumptions of regression analysis and know what to do if the assumptions are violated
- To make inferences about the slope and correlation coefficient
- To estimate mean values and predict individual values

@ Sunflowers Apparel

The sales for Sunflowers Apparel, a chain of upscale clothing stores for women, have increased during the past 12 years as the chain has expanded the number of stores. Until now, Sunflowers managers selected sites based on subjective factors, such as the availability of a good lease or the perception that a location seemed ideal for an apparel store. As the new director of planning, you need to develop a systematic approach that will lead to making better decisions during the site selection process. As a starting point, you believe that the size of the store significantly contributes to store sales, and you want to use this relationship in the decision-making process. How can you use statistics so that you can forecast the annual sales of a proposed store based on the size of that store?

I n this chapter and the next chapter, you learn how **regression analysis** enables you to develop a model to predict the values of a numerical variable, based on the value of other variables. In regression analysis, the variable you wish to predict is called the **dependent variable**. The variables used to make the prediction are called **independent variables**. In addition to predicting values of the dependent variable, regression analysis also allows you to identify the type of mathematical relationship that exists between a dependent and an independent variable, to quantify the effect that changes in the independent variable have on the dependent variable, and to identify unusual observations. For example, as the director of planning, you may wish to predict sales for a Sunflowers store, based on the size of the store. Other examples include predicting the monthly rent of an apartment, based on its size, and predicting the monthly sales of a product in a supermarket, based on the amount of shelf space devoted to the product.

This chapter discusses **simple linear regression**, in which a *single* numerical independent variable, X, is used to predict the numerical dependent variable Y, such as using the size of a store to predict the annual sales of the store. Chapter 14 discusses *multiple regression models*, which use *several* independent variables to predict a numerical dependent variable, Y. For example, you could use the amount of advertising expenditures, price, and the amount of shelf space devoted to a product to predict its monthly sales.

13.1 Types of Regression Models

In Section 2.5, you used a **scatter plot** (also known as a **scatter diagram**) to examine the relationship between an X variable on the horizontal axis and a Y variable on the vertical axis. The nature of the relationship between two variables can take many forms, ranging from simple to extremely complicated mathematical functions. The simplest relationship consists of a straight-line or **linear relationship**. Figure 13.1 illustrates a straight-line relationship.

FIGURE 13.1

A straight-line relationship

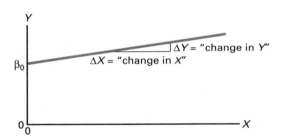

Equation (13.1) represents the straight-line (linear) model.

SIMPLE LINEAR REGRESSION MODEL

$$Y_i = \beta_0 + \beta_1 X_i + \varepsilon_i \qquad (13.1)$$

where

$\beta_0 = Y$ intercept for the population

$\beta_1 = $ slope for the population

$\varepsilon_i = $ random error in Y for observation i

$Y_i = $ dependent variable (sometimes referred to as the **response variable**) for observation i

$X_i = $ independent variable (sometimes referred to as the **explanatory variable**) for observation i

---

The portion $Y_i = \beta_0 + \beta_1 X_i$ of the simple linear regression model expressed in Equation (13.1) is a straight line. The **slope** of the line, β_1, represents the expected change in Y per unit change in X. It represents the mean amount that Y changes (either positively or negatively) for a one-unit change in X. The **Y intercept**, β_0, represents the mean value of Y when X equals 0. The last component of the model, ε_i, represents the random error in Y for each observation, i. In other words, ε_i is the vertical distance of the actual value of Y_i above or below the expected value of Y_i on the line.

The selection of the proper mathematical model depends on the distribution of the X and Y values on the scatter plot. In Panel A of Figure 13.2, the values of Y are generally increasing linearly as X increases. This panel is similar to Figure 13.3, which illustrates the positive relationship between the square footage of the store and the annual sales at branches of the Sunflowers Apparel women's clothing store chain.

FIGURE 13.2

Six types of relationships found in scatter plots

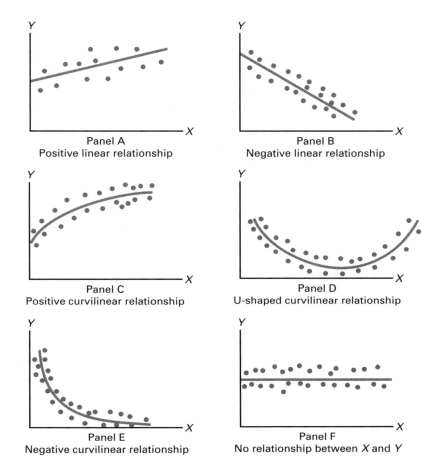

change in X. It represents the mean amount that Y changes (either positively or negatively) for

Panel A
Positive linear relationship

Panel B
Negative linear relationship

Panel C
Positive curvilinear relationship

Panel D
U-shaped curvilinear relationship

Panel E
Negative curvilinear relationship

Panel F
No relationship between X and Y

Panel B is an example of a negative linear relationship. As X increases, the values of Y are generally decreasing. An example of this type of relationship might be the price of a particular product and the amount of sales.

The data in Panel C show a positive curvilinear relationship between X and Y. The values of Y increase as X increases, but this increase tapers off beyond certain values of X. An example of a positive curvilinear relationship might be the age and maintenance cost of a machine. As a machine gets older, the maintenance cost may rise rapidly at first, but then level off beyond a certain number of years.

Panel D shows a U-shaped relationship between X and Y. As X increases, at first Y generally decreases; but as X continues to increase, Y not only stops decreasing but actually increases above its minimum value. An example of this type of relationship might be the number of errors per hour at a task and the number of hours worked. The number of errors per hour decreases as the individual becomes more proficient at the task, but then it increases beyond a certain point because of factors such as fatigue and boredom.

Panel E indicates an exponential relationship between X and Y. In this case, Y decreases very rapidly as X first increases, but then it decreases much less rapidly as X increases further.

An example of an exponential relationship could be the resale value of an automobile and its age. The resale value drops drastically from its original price in the first year, but decreases much less rapidly in subsequent years.

Finally, Panel F shows a set of data in which there is very little or no relationship between X and Y. High and low values of Y appear at each value of X.

In this section, a variety of different models that represent the relationship between two variables were briefly examined. Although scatter plots are useful in visually displaying the mathematical form of a relationship, more sophisticated statistical procedures are available to determine the most appropriate model for a set of variables. The rest of this chapter discusses the model used when there is a *linear* relationship between variables.

13.2 Determining the Simple Linear Regression Equation

In the Using Statistics scenario at the beginning of this chapter, the stated goal is to forecast annual sales for all new stores, based on store size. To examine the relationship between the store size in square feet and its annual sales, a sample of 14 stores was selected. Table 13.1 summarizes the results for these 14 stores, which are stored in the file **Site**.

TABLE 13.1

Square Footage (in Thousands of Square Feet) and Annual Sales (in Millions of Dollars) for a Sample of 14 Branches of Sunflowers Apparel

Store	Square Feet (Thousands)	Annual Sales (in Millions of Dollars)	Store	Square Feet (Thousands)	Annual Sales (in Millions of Dollars)
1	1.7	3.7	8	1.1	2.7
2	1.6	3.9	9	3.2	5.5
3	2.8	6.7	10	1.5	2.9
4	5.6	9.5	11	5.2	10.7
5	1.3	3.4	12	4.6	7.6
6	2.2	5.6	13	5.8	11.8
7	1.3	3.7	14	3.0	4.1

Figure 13.3 displays the scatter plot for the data in Table 13.1. Observe the increasing relationship between square feet (X) and annual sales (Y). As the size of the store increases, annual sales increase approximately as a straight line. Thus, you can assume that a straight line provides a useful mathematical model of this relationship. Now you need to determine the specific straight line that is the *best* fit to these data.

FIGURE 13.3

Microsoft Excel scatter plot for the Sunflowers Apparel data

See Section E2.13 to create this.

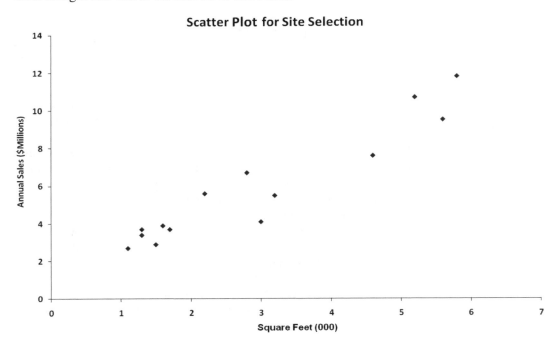

The Least-Squares Method

In the preceding section, a statistical model is hypothesized to represent the relationship between two variables, square footage and sales, in the entire population of Sunflowers Apparel stores. However, as shown in Table 13.1, the data are from only a random sample of stores. If certain assumptions are valid (see Section 13.4), you can use the sample Y intercept, b_0, and the sample slope, b_1, as estimates of the respective population parameters, β_0 and β_1. Equation (13.2) uses these estimates to form the **simple linear regression equation**. This straight line is often referred to as the **prediction line**.

SIMPLE LINEAR REGRESSION EQUATION: THE PREDICTION LINE

The predicted value of Y equals the Y intercept plus the slope multiplied by the value of X.

$$\hat{Y}_i = b_0 + b_1 X_i \tag{13.2}$$

where

$$\hat{Y}_i = \text{predicted value of } Y \text{ for observation } i$$

$$X_i = \text{value of } X \text{ for observation } i$$

$$b_0 = \text{sample } Y \text{ intercept}$$

$$b_1 = \text{sample slope}$$

Equation (13.2) requires the determination of two **regression coefficients**—b_0 (the sample Y intercept) and b_1 (the sample slope). The most common approach to finding b_0 and b_1 is the method of least squares. This method minimizes the sum of the squared differences between the actual values (Y_i) and the predicted values ($\hat{Y}_i$) using the simple linear regression equation [i.e., the prediction line; see Equation (13.2)]. This sum of squared differences is equal to

$$\sum_{i=1}^{n} (Y_i - \hat{Y}_i)^2$$

Because $\hat{Y}_i = b_0 + b_1 X_i$,

$$\sum_{i=1}^{n} (Y_i - \hat{Y}_i)^2 = \sum_{i=1}^{n} [Y_i - (b_0 + b_1 X_i)]^2$$

Because this equation has two unknowns, b_0 and b_1, the sum of squared differences depends on the sample Y intercept, b_0, and the sample slope, b_1. The **least-squares method** determines the values of b_0 and b_1 that minimize the sum of squared differences around the prediction line. Any values for b_0 and b_1 other than those determined by the least-squares method result in a greater sum of squared differences between the actual values (Y_i) and the predicted values ($\hat{Y}_i$). In this book, Casio calculator and SPSS are used to perform the computations involved in the least-squares method. For the data of Table 13.1, Figure 13.4 presents results from SPSS and Figure 13.5 shows Excel results.

To understand how the results are computed, many of the computations involved are illustrated in Examples 13.3 and 13.4. In Figure 13.4 or 13.5, observe that $b_0 = 0.964$ and $b_1 = 1.670$. Thus, the prediction line [see Equation (13.2) above] for these data is

$$\hat{Y}_i = 0.964 + 1.670 X_i$$

FIGURE 13.4

SPSS results worksheet
for the Sunflowers
Apparel data

Model Summary

Model	R	R Square	Adjusted R Square	Std. Error of the Estimate
1	.951[a]	.904	.896	.9664

a. Predictors: (Constant), square feet (thousands)

ANOVA[b]

Model	Sum of Squares	df	Mean Square	F	Sig.
1 Regression	105.748	1	105.748	113.234	.000[a]
Residual	11.207	12	.934		
Total	116.954	13			

a. Predictors: (Constant), square feet (thousands)
b. Dependent Variable: Annual Sales (in Millions of Dollars)

Coefficients[a]

Model	Unstandardized Coefficients		Standardized Coefficients	t	Sig.
	B	Std. Error	Beta		
1 (Constant)	.964	.526		1.833	.092
square feet (thousands)	1.670	.157	.951	10.641	.000

a. Dependent Variable: Annual Sales (in Millions of Dollars)

The slope, b_1, is $+1.67$. This means that for each increase of 1 unit in X, the mean value of Y is estimated to increase by 1.670 units. In other words, for each increase of 1.0 thousand square feet in the size of the store, the mean annual sales are estimated to increase by 1.670 millions of dollars. Thus, the slope represents the portion of the annual sales that are estimated to vary according to the size of the store.

The Y intercept, b_0, is $+0.964$. The Y intercept represents the mean value of Y when X equals 0. Because the square footage of the store cannot be 0, this Y intercept has little or no practical interpretation. Also, the Y intercept for this example is outside the range of the observed values of the X variable, and therefore interpretations of the value of b_0 should be made cautiously. Figure 13.5 displays the actual observations and the prediction line. To

FIGURE 13.5

Microsoft Excel scatter
plot and prediction line
for Sunflowers Apparel
data

*See Section E13.2 to create
this.*

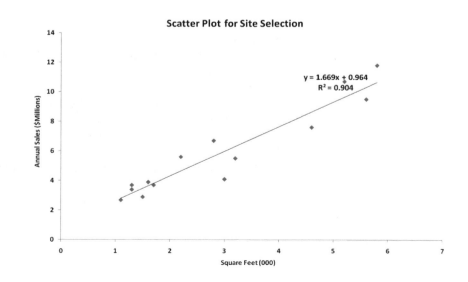

illustrate a situation in which there is a direct interpretation for the Y intercept, b_0, see Example 13.1.

EXAMPLE 13.1

Interpreting the Y Intercept, b_0, and the Slope, b_1

A statistics professor wants to use the number of hours a student studies for a statistics final exam (X) to predict the final exam score (Y). A regression model was fit based on data collected for a class during the previous semester, with the following results:

$$\hat{Y}_i = 35.0 + 3X_i$$

What is the interpretation of the Y intercept, b_0, and the slope, b_1?

SOLUTION The Y intercept $b_0 = 35.0$ indicates that when the student does not study for the final exam, the predicted final exam score is 35.0. The slope $b_1 = 3$ indicates that for each increase of one hour in studying time, the mean change in the final exam score is predicted to be $+3.0$. In other words, the final exam score is predicted to increase by 3 points for each one-hour increase in studying time.

Return to the Using Statistics scenario concerning the Sunflowers Apparel stores. Example 13.2 illustrates how you use the prediction equation to predict the mean annual sales.

EXAMPLE 13.2

Predicting Annual Sales, Based on Square Footage

Use the prediction line to predict the annual sales for a store with 4,000 square feet.

SOLUTION You can determine the predicted value by substituting $X = 4$ (thousands of square feet) into the simple linear regression equation:

$$\hat{Y}_i = 0.964 + 1.670X_i$$

$$\hat{Y}_i = 0.964 + 1.670(4) = 7.644 \text{ or } \$7,644,000$$

Thus, the predicted annual sales of a store with 4,000 square feet is $7,644,000.

Predictions in Regression Analysis: Interpolation versus Extrapolation

When using a regression model for prediction purposes, you need to consider only the **relevant range** of the independent variable in making predictions. This relevant range includes all values from the smallest to the largest X used in developing the regression model. Hence, when predicting Y for a given value of X, you can interpolate within this relevant range of the X values, but you should not extrapolate beyond the range of X values. When you use the square footage to predict annual sales, the square footage (in thousands of square feet) varies from 1.1 to 5.8 (see Table 13.1). Therefore, you should predict annual sales *only* for stores whose size is between 1.1 and 5.8 thousands of square feet. Any prediction of annual sales for stores outside this range assumes that the observed relationship between sales and store size for store sizes from 1.1 to 5.8 thousand square feet is the same as for stores outside this range. For example, you cannot extrapolate the linear relationship beyond 5,800 square feet in Example 13.2. It would be improper to use the prediction line to forecast the sales for a new store containing 8,000 square feet because it is quite possible that store size has a point of diminishing returns. If that is true, as square footage increases beyond 5,800 square feet, the effect on sales becomes smaller and smaller.

Computing the Y Intercept, b_0, and the Slope, b_1

For small data sets, you can use a hand calculator to compute the least-squares regression coefficients. Equations (13.3) and (13.4) give the values of b_0 and b_1, which minimize

$$\sum_{i=1}^{n}(Y_i - \hat{Y}_i)^2 = \sum_{i=1}^{n}[Y_i - (b_0 + b_1 X_i)]^2$$

COMPUTATIONAL FORMULA FOR THE SLOPE, b_1

$$b_1 = \frac{SSXY}{SSX} \tag{13.3}$$

where

$$SSXY = \sum_{i=1}^{n}(X_i - \overline{X})(Y_i - \overline{Y}) = \sum_{i=1}^{n}X_i Y_i - \frac{\left(\sum_{i=1}^{n}X_i\right)\left(\sum_{i=1}^{n}Y_i\right)}{n}$$

$$SSX = \sum_{i=1}^{n}(X_i - \overline{X})^2 = \sum_{i=1}^{n}X_i^2 - \frac{\left(\sum_{i=1}^{n}X_i\right)^2}{n}$$

COMPUTATIONAL FORMULA FOR THE Y INTERCEPT, b_0

$$b_0 = \overline{Y} - b_1\overline{X} \tag{13.4}$$

where

$$\overline{Y} = \frac{\sum_{i=1}^{n}Y_i}{n}$$

$$\overline{X} = \frac{\sum_{i=1}^{n}X_i}{n}$$

EXAMPLE 13.3

Computing the Y Intercept, b_0, and the Slope, b_1

Compute the Y intercept, b_0, and the slope, b_1, for the Sunflowers Apparel data.

SOLUTION Examining Equations (13.3) and (13.4), you see that five quantities are needed to determine b_1 and b_0. These are n, the sample size; $\sum_{i=1}^{n}X_i$, the sum of the X values; $\sum_{i=1}^{n}Y_i$, the sum of the Y values; $\sum_{i=1}^{n}X_i^2$, the sum of the squared X values; and $\sum_{i=1}^{n}X_i Y_i$, the sum of the product of X and Y. For the Sunflowers Apparel data, the number of square feet is used to predict the annual sales in a store. Table 13.2 presents the computations of the various sums needed for the site selection problem. The table also includes $\sum_{i=1}^{n} Y_i^2$, the sum of the squared Y values that will be used to compute SST in Section 13.3.

TABLE 13.2

Computations for the Sunflowers Apparel Data

Store	Square Feet (X)	Annual Sales (Y)	X^2	Y^2	XY
1	1.7	3.7	2.89	13.69	6.29
2	1.6	3.9	2.56	15.21	6.24
3	2.8	6.7	7.84	44.89	18.76
4	5.6	9.5	31.36	90.25	53.20
5	1.3	3.4	1.69	11.56	4.42
6	2.2	5.6	4.84	31.36	12.32
7	1.3	3.7	1.69	13.69	4.81
8	1.1	2.7	1.21	7.29	2.97
9	3.2	5.5	10.24	30.25	17.60
10	1.5	2.9	2.25	8.41	4.35
11	5.2	10.7	27.04	114.49	55.64
12	4.6	7.6	21.16	57.76	34.96
13	5.8	11.8	33.64	139.24	68.44
14	3.0	4.1	9.00	16.81	12.30
Totals	40.9	81.8	157.41	594.90	302.30

Using Equations (13.3) and (13.4), you can compute the values of b_0 and b_1:

$$SSXY = \sum_{i=1}^{n}(X_i - \overline{X})(Y_i - \overline{Y}) = \sum_{i=1}^{n} X_i Y_i - \frac{\left(\sum_{i=1}^{n} X_i\right)\left(\sum_{i=1}^{n} Y_i\right)}{n}$$

$$SSXY = 302.3 - \frac{(40.9)(81.8)}{14}$$

$$= 302.3 - 238.97285$$

$$= 63.32715$$

$$SSX = \sum_{i=1}^{n}(X_i - \overline{X})^2 = \sum_{i=1}^{n} X_i^2 - \frac{\left(\sum_{i=1}^{n} X_i\right)^2}{n}$$

$$= 157.41 - \frac{(40.9)^2}{14}$$

$$= 157.41 - 119.48642$$

$$= 37.92358$$

Therefore,

$$b_1 = \frac{SSXY}{SSX}$$

$$= \frac{63.32715}{37.92358}$$

$$= 1.67$$

And,

$$\bar{Y} = \frac{\sum_{i=1}^{n} Y_i}{n} = \frac{81.8}{14} = 5.842857$$

$$\bar{X} = \frac{\sum_{i=1}^{n} X_i}{n} = \frac{40.9}{14} = 2.92143$$

Therefore,

$$b_0 = \bar{Y} - b_1\bar{X}$$
$$= 5.842857 - (1.6699)(2.92143)$$
$$= 0.9645$$

VISUAL EXPLORATIONS   Exploring Simple Linear Regression Coefficients

Use the Visual Explorations Simple Linear Regression procedure to create a prediction line that is as close as possible to the prediction line defined by the least-squares solution. Open the `Visual Explorations.xla` add-in workbook and select **VisualExplorations → Simple Linear Regression** (Excel 97–2003) or **Add-ins → VisualExplorations → Simple Linear Regression** (Excel 2007).

The procedure displays a scatter plot of the Sunflowers Apparel data of Table 13.1, along with an initial prediction line (see illustration on following page). In the Simple Linear Regression dialog box, click the spinner buttons to change the values for b_1, the slope of the prediction line, and b_0, the Y intercept of the prediction line to change the prediction line.

Using the chart display as visual feedback, try to create a prediction line that is as close as possible to the prediction line defined by the least-squares estimates and thus make the Difference from Target SSE value as small as possible. At any time, click **Reset** to reset the b_1 and b_0 values or **Solution** to reveal the prediction line defined by the least-squares method. Click **Finish** when you are finished with this exercise.

Using Your Own Regression Data

To use Visual Explorations to find a prediction line for your own data, select **VisualExplorations → Simple** **Linear Regression with your worksheet data** (Excel 97–2003) or **Add-ins → VisualExplorations → Simple Linear Regression with your worksheet data** (Excel 2007). In the procedure's dialog box (shown below), enter your Y variable cell range as the **Y Variable Cell Range** and your X variable cell range as the **X Variable Cell Range**. Click **First cells in both ranges contain a label**, enter a title as the **Title**, and click **OK**. When the scatter plot with an initial prediction line appears, use the instructions in the first part of this section to try to produce the prediction line defined by the least-squares plot.

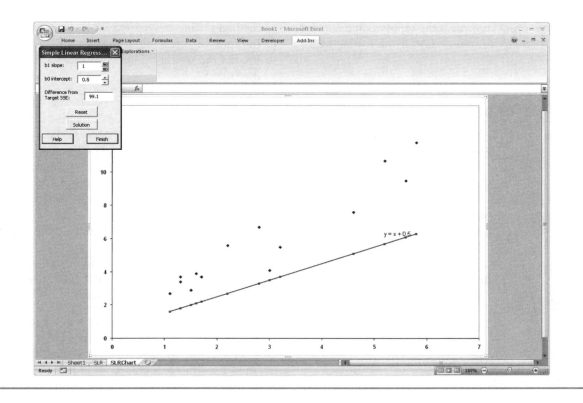

Problems for Section 13.2

LEARNING THE BASICS

13.1 Fitting a straight line to a set of data yields the following prediction line:

$$\hat{Y}_i = 2 + 5X_i$$

a. Interpret the meaning of the Y intercept, b_0.
b. Interpret the meaning of the slope, b_1.
c. Predict the value of Y for $X = 3$.

13.2 If the values of X in Problem 13.1 range from 2 to 25, should you use this model to predict the mean value of Y when X equals
a. 3?
b. −3?
c. 0?
d. 24?

13.3 Fitting a straight line to a set of data yields the following prediction line:

$$\hat{Y}_i = 16 - 0.5X_i$$

a. Interpret the meaning of the Y intercept, b_0.
b. Interpret the meaning of the slope, b_1.
c. Predict the value of Y for $X = 6$.

APPLYING THE CONCEPTS

✓ SELF | Test **13.4** The marketing manager of a large supermarket chain would like to use shelf space to predict the sales of pet food. A random sample of 12 equal-sized stores is selected, with the following results (stored in the file **Petfood**):

Store	Shelf Space (X) (Feet)	Weekly Sales (Y) ($)
1	5	160
2	5	220
3	5	140
4	10	190
5	10	240
6	10	260
7	15	230
8	15	270
9	15	280
10	20	260
11	20	290
12	20	310

a. Construct a scatter plot.
For these data, $b_0 = 145$ and $b_1 = 7.4$.
b. Interpret the meaning of the slope, b_1, in this problem.
c. Predict the weekly sales of pet food for stores with 8 feet of shelf space for pet food.

13.5 Circulation is the lifeblood of the publishing business. The larger the sales of a magazine, the more it can charge advertisers. Recently, a circulation gap has appeared between the publishers' reports of magazines' newsstand sales and subsequent audits by the Audit Bureau of Circulations. The data in the file Circulation represent the reported and audited newsstand yearly sales (in thousands) for the following 10 magazines:

Magazine	Reported (X)	Audited (Y)
YM	621.0	299.6
CosmoGirl	359.7	207.7
Rosie	530.0	325.0
Playboy	492.1	336.3
Esquire	70.5	48.6
TeenPeople	567.0	400.3
More	125.5	91.2
Spin	50.6	39.1
Vogue	353.3	268.6
Elle	263.6	214.3

Source: *Data extracted from M. Rose, "In Fight for Ads, Publishers Often Overstate Their Sales,"* The Wall Street Journal, *August 6, 2003, pp. A1, A10.*

a. Construct a scatter plot.
For these data, $b_0 = 26.724$ and $b_1 = 0.5719$.
b. Interpret the meaning of the slope, b_1, in this problem.
c. Predict the audited newsstand sales for a magazine that reports newsstand sales of 400,000.

13.6 The owner of a moving company typically has his most experienced manager predict the total number of labor hours that will be required to complete an upcoming move. This approach has proved useful in the past, but he would like to be able to develop a more accurate method of predicting labor hours by using the number of cubic feet moved. In a preliminary effort to provide a more accurate method, he has collected data for 36 moves in which the origin and destination were within the borough of Manhattan in New York City and in which the travel time was an insignificant portion of the hours worked. The data are stored in the file Moving.
a. Construct a scatter plot.
b. Assuming a linear relationship, use the least-squares method to find the regression coefficients b_0 and b_1.
c. Interpret the meaning of the slope, b_1, in this problem.
d. Predict the labor hours for moving 500 cubic feet.

13.7 A critically important aspect of customer service in a supermarket is the waiting time at the checkout (defined as the time the customer enters the line until he or she is served). Data were collected during time periods where there were a constant number of checkout counters open. The total number of customers in the store and the waiting times (in minutes) were recorded. The results are stored in the Supermarket file.
a. Construct a scatter plot.

b. Assuming a linear relationship, use the least-squares method to find the regression coefficients b_0 and b_1.
c. Interpret the meaning of the slope, b_1, in this problem.
d. Predict the waiting time when there are 20 customers in the store.

13.8 The value of a sports franchise is directly related to the amount of revenue that a franchise can generate. The data in the file BBrevenue represent the value in 2005 (in millions of dollars) and the annual revenue (in millions of dollars) for 30 baseball franchises. Suppose you want to develop a simple linear regression model to predict franchise value based on annual revenue generated.
a. Construct a scatter plot.
b. Use the least-squares method to find the regression coefficients b_0 and b_1.
c. Interpret the meaning of b_0 and b_1 in this problem.
d. Predict the value of a baseball franchise that generates $150 million of annual revenue.

13.9 An agent for a residential real estate company in a large city would like to be able to predict the monthly rental cost for apartments, based on the size of the apartment, as defined by square footage. A sample of 25 apartments (stored in the file Rent) in a particular residential neighborhood was selected, and the information gathered revealed the following:
a. Construct a scatter plot.
b. Use the least-squares method to find the regression coefficients b_0 and b_1.
c. Interpret the meaning of b_0 and b_1 in this problem.
d. Predict the monthly rent for an apartment that has 1,000 square feet.
e. Why would it not be appropriate to use the model to predict the monthly rent for apartments that have 500 square feet?
f. Your friends Jim and Jennifer are considering signing a lease for an apartment in this residential neighborhood. They are trying to decide between two apartments, one with 1,000 square feet for a monthly rent of $1,275 and the other with 1,200 square feet for a monthly rent of $1,425. Based on (a) through (d), which apartment do you think is a better deal?

13.10 A company that holds the DVD distribution rights to movies previously released only in theaters wants to estimate sales of DVDs based on box office success. Data are available in the file Movie that indicate the box office gross (in $millions) for each of 30 movies and the number of DVDs sold (in thousands). For these data:
a. Construct a scatter plot.
b. Assuming a linear relationship, use the least-squares method to find the regression coefficients b_0 and b_1.
c. Interpret the meaning of the slope, b_1, in this problem.
d. Predict the sales for a movie that had a box office gross of $75 million.

13.3 Measures of Variation

When using the least-squares method to determine the regression coefficients for a set of data, you need to compute three important measures of variation. The first measure, the **total sum of squares (SST)**, is a measure of variation of the Y_i values around their mean, $\overline{Y}$. The **total variation** or total sum of squares is subdivided into **explained variation** and **unexplained variation**. The explained variation or **regression sum of squares (SSR)** is due to the relationship between X and Y, and the unexplained variation, or **error sum of squares (SSE)**, is due to factors other than the relationship between X and Y. Figure 13.6 shows these different measures of variation.

FIGURE 13.6
Measures of variation

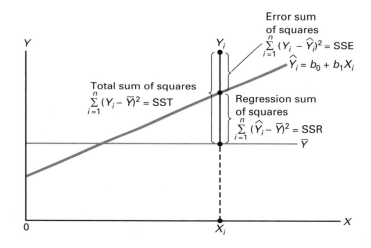

Computing the Sum of Squares

The regression sum of squares (SSR) is based on the difference between $\hat{Y}_i$ (the predicted value of Y from the prediction line) and $\overline{Y}$ (the mean value of Y). The error sum of squares (SSE) represents the part of the variation in Y that is not explained by the regression. It is based on the difference between Y_i and $\hat{Y}_i$. Equations (13.5), (13.6), (13.7), and (13.8) define these measures of variation.

MEASURES OF VARIATION IN REGRESSION

The total sum of squares is equal to the regression sum of squares plus the error sum of squares.

$$SST = SSR + SSE \tag{13.5}$$

TOTAL SUM OF SQUARES (SST)

The total sum of squares (SST) is equal to the sum of the squared differences between each observed value of Y and the mean value of Y.

$$SST = \text{Total sum of squares}$$

$$= \sum_{i=1}^{n}(Y_i - \overline{Y})^2 \tag{13.6}$$

REGRESSION SUM OF SQUARES (*SSR*)

The regression sum of squares (*SSR*) is equal to the sum of the squared differences between each predicted value of *Y* and the mean value of *Y*.

$$SSR = \text{Explained variation or regression sum of squares}$$

$$= \sum_{i=1}^{n} (\hat{Y}_i - \overline{Y})^2 \tag{13.7}$$

ERROR SUM OF SQUARES (*SSE*)

The error sum of squares (*SSE*) is equal to the sum of the squared differences between each observed value of *Y* and the predicted value of *Y*.

$$SSE = \text{Unexplained variation or error sum of squares}$$

$$= \sum_{i=1}^{n} (Y_i - \hat{Y}_i)^2 \tag{13.8}$$

Figure 13.7 shows the sum of squares portion of the worksheet containing the SPSS results for the Sunflowers Apparel data. The total variation, *SST*, is equal to 116.954. This amount is subdivided into the sum of squares explained by the regression (*SSR*), equal to 105.748, and the sum of squares unexplained by the regression (*SSE*), equal to 11.207. From Equation (13.5):

$$SST = SSR + SSE$$

$$116.954 = 105.748 + 11.207$$

FIGURE 13.7

SPSS sum of squares for the Sunflowers Apparel data

ANOVA[b]					
Model	**Sum of Squares**	**df**	**Mean Square**	**F**	**Sig.**
1 Regression	105.748	1	105.748	113.234	.000[a]
Residual	11.207	12	.934		
Total	116.954	13			

a. *Predictors: (Constant), square feet (thousands)*
b. *Dependent Variable: Annual Sales (in Millions of Dollars)*

Coefficients[a]					
	Unstandardized Coefficients		**Standardized Coefficients**		
Model	**B**	**Std. Error**	**Beta**	**t**	**Sig.**
1 (Constant)	.964	.526		1.833	.092
square feet (thousands)	1.670	.157	.951	10.641	.000

a. *Dependent Variable: Annual Sales (in Millions of Dollars)*

In a data set that has a large number of significant digits, the results of a regression analysis are sometimes displayed using a numerical format known as *scientific notation*. This type of format is used to display very small or very large values. The number after the letter E represents the number of digits that the decimal point needs to be moved to the left (for a negative number) or to the right (for a positive number). For example, the number 3.7431E+02 means that the decimal point should be moved two places to the right, producing the number 374.31. The number 3.7431E−02 means that the decimal point should be moved two places to the left, producing the number 0.037431. When scientific notation is used, fewer significant digits are usually displayed, and the numbers may appear to be rounded.

The Coefficient of Determination

By themselves, *SSR, SSE*, and *SST* provide little information. However, the ratio of the regression sum of squares (*SSR*) to the total sum of squares (*SST*) measures the proportion of variation in *Y* that is explained by the independent variable *X* in the regression model. This ratio is called the coefficient of determination, r^2, and is defined in Equation (13.9).

COEFFICIENT OF DETERMINATION

The coefficient of determination is equal to the regression sum of squares (i.e., explained variation) divided by the total sum of squares (i.e., total variation).

$$r^2 = \frac{\text{Regression sum of squares}}{\text{Total sum of squares}} = \frac{SSR}{SST} \quad \text{(13.9)}$$

The **coefficient of determination** measures the proportion of variation in *Y* that is explained by the independent variable *X* in the regression model.

For the Sunflowers Apparel data, with $SSR = 105.748$, $SSE = 11.207$, and $SST = 116.954$,

$$r^2 = \frac{105.748}{116.954} = 0.904$$

Therefore, 90.4% of the variation in annual sales is explained by the variability in the size of the store as measured by the square footage. This large r^2 indicates a strong linear relationship between these two variables because the use of a regression model has reduced the variability in predicting annual sales by 90.4%. Only 9.6% of the sample variability in annual sales is due to factors other than what is accounted for by the linear regression model that uses square footage.

Figure 13.8 presents the coefficient of determination portion of the SPSS results for the Sunflowers Apparel data.

FIGURE 13.8

Partial SPSS regression results for the Sunflowers Apparel data

Model Summary				
Model	**R**	**R Square**	**Adjusted R Square**	**Std. Error of the Estimate**
1	.951[a]	.904	.896	.9664

a. *Predictors: (Constant), square feet (thousands)*

EXAMPLE 13.4

Computing the Coefficient of Determination

Compute the coefficient of determination, r^2, for the Sunflowers Apparel data.

SOLUTION You can compute SST, SSR, and SSE, that are defined in Equations (13.6), (13.7), and (13.8), by using Equations (13.10), (13.11), and (13.12).

COMPUTATIONAL FORMULA FOR SST

$$SST = \sum_{i=1}^{n}(Y_i - \overline{Y})^2 = \sum_{i=1}^{n} Y_i^2 - \frac{\left(\sum_{i=1}^{n} Y_i\right)^2}{n} \tag{13.10}$$

COMPUTATIONAL FORMULA FOR SSR

$$SSR = \sum_{i=1}^{n}(\hat{Y}_i - \overline{Y})^2$$

$$= b_0 \sum_{i=1}^{n} Y_i + b_1 \sum_{i=1}^{n} X_i Y_i - \frac{\left(\sum_{i=1}^{n} Y_i\right)^2}{n} \tag{13.11}$$

COMPUTATIONAL FORMULA FOR SSE

$$SSE = \sum_{i=1}^{n}(Y_i - \hat{Y}_i)^2 = \sum_{i=1}^{n} Y_i^2 - b_0 \sum_{i=1}^{n} Y_i - b_1 \sum_{i=1}^{n} X_i Y_i \tag{13.12}$$

Using the summary results from Table 13.2 on page 585,

$$SST = \sum_{i=1}^{n}(Y_i - \overline{Y})^2 = \sum_{i=1}^{n} Y_i^2 - \frac{\left(\sum_{i=1}^{n} Y_i\right)^2}{n}$$

$$= 594.9 - \frac{(81.8)^2}{14}$$

$$= 594.9 - 477.94571$$

$$= 116.95429$$

$$SSR = \sum_{i=1}^{n}(\hat{Y}_i - \overline{Y})^2$$

$$= b_0 \sum_{i=1}^{n} Y_i + b_1 \sum_{i=1}^{n} X_i Y_i - \frac{\left(\sum_{i=1}^{n} Y_i\right)^2}{n}$$

$$= (0.9645)(81.8) + (1.6699)(302.3) - \frac{(81.8)^2}{14}$$

$$= 105.74726$$

$$SSE = \sum_{i=1}^{n}(Y_i - \hat{Y}_i)^2$$

$$= \sum_{i=1}^{n} Y_i^2 - b_0 \sum_{i=1}^{n} Y_i - b_1 \sum_{i=1}^{n} X_i Y_i$$

$$= 594.9 - (0.9645)(81.8) - (1.6699)(302.3)$$

$$= 11.2067$$

Therefore,

$$r^2 = \frac{105.74726}{116.95429} = 0.9042$$

Standard Error of the Estimate

Although the least-squares method results in the line that fits the data with the minimum amount of error, unless all the observed data points fall on a straight line, the prediction line is not a perfect predictor. Just as all data values cannot be expected to be exactly equal to their mean, neither can all the values in a regression analysis be expected to fall exactly on the prediction line. Figure 13.5 illustrates the variability around the prediction line for the Sunflowers Apparel data. Observe that, although many of the actual values of Y fall near the prediction line, none of the values are exactly on the line.

The **standard error of the estimate** measures the variability of the actual Y values from the predicted Y values in the same way that the standard deviation in Chapter 3 measures the variability of each value around the sample mean. In other words, the standard error of the estimate is the standard deviation *around* the prediction line, whereas the standard deviation in Chapter 3 is the standard deviation *around* the sample mean. Equation (13.13) defines the standard error of the estimate, represented by the symbol S_{YX}.

STANDARD ERROR OF THE ESTIMATE

$$S_{YX} = \sqrt{\frac{SSE}{n-2}} = \sqrt{\frac{\sum_{i=1}^{n}(Y_i - \hat{Y}_i)^2}{n-2}} \qquad \textbf{(13.13)}$$

where

$$Y_i = \text{actual value of } Y \text{ for a given } X_i$$

$$\hat{Y}_i = \text{predicted value of } Y \text{ for a given } X_i$$

$$SSE = \text{error sum of squares}$$

From Equation (13.8) and Figure 13.8 on pages 590–591, $SSE = 11.207$. Thus,

$$S_{YX} = \sqrt{\frac{11.2067}{14-2}} = 0.9664$$

This standard error of the estimate, equal to 0.9664 millions of dollars (i.e., \$966,400), is labeled Standard Error in the SPSS results shown in Figure 13.8. The standard error of the estimate represents a measure of the variation around the prediction line. It is measured in the same units as the dependent variable Y. The interpretation of the standard error of the estimate is similar to that of the standard deviation. Just as the standard deviation measures variability around the mean, the standard error of the estimate measures variability around the prediction line. For Sunflowers Apparel, the typical difference between actual annual sales at a store and the predicted annual sales using the regression equation is approximately \$966,400.

Problems for Section 13.3

LEARNING THE BASICS

13.11 How do you interpret a coefficient of determination, r^2, equal to 0.80?

13.12 If $SSR = 36$ and $SSE = 4$, determine SST and then compute the coefficient of determination, r^2, and interpret its meaning.

13.13 If $SSR = 66$ and $SST = 88$, compute the coefficient of determination, r^2, and interpret its meaning.

13.14 If $SSE = 10$ and $SSR = 30$, compute the coefficient of determination, r^2, and interpret its meaning.

13.15 If $SSR = 120$, why is it impossible for SST to equal 110?

APPLYING THE CONCEPTS

13.16 In Problem 13.4, the marketing manager used shelf space for pet food to predict weekly sales (stored in the file Petfood). For that data, $SSR = 20,535$ and $SST = 30,025$.
a. Determine the coefficient of determination, r^2, and interpret its meaning.
b. Determine the standard error of the estimate.
c. How useful do you think this regression model is for predicting sales?

13.17 In Problem 13.5, you used reported magazine newsstand sales to predict audited sales (stored in the file Circulation). For that data, $SSR = 130,301.41$ and $SST = 144,538.64$.
a. Determine the coefficient of determination, r^2, and interpret its meaning.
b. Determine the standard error of the estimate.
c. How useful do you think this regression model is for predicting audited sales?

13.18 In Problem 13.6, an owner of a moving company wanted to predict labor hours, based on the cubic feet moved (stored in the file Moving). Using the results of that problem,
a. determine the coefficient of determination, r^2, and interpret its meaning.
b. determine the standard error of the estimate.
c. How useful do you think this regression model is for predicting labor hours?

13.19 In Problem 13.7, you used the number of customers to predict the waiting time at the checkout line in a supermarket (stored in the file Supermarket). Using the results of that problem,
a. determine the coefficient of determination, r^2, and interpret its meaning.
b. determine the standard error of the estimate.
c. How useful do you think this regression model is for predicting the waiting time at the checkout line in a supermarket?

13.20 In Problem 13.8, you used annual revenues to predict the value of a baseball franchise (stored in the file BBrevenue). Using the results of that problem,
a. determine the coefficient of determination, r^2, and interpret its meaning.
b. determine the standard error of the estimate.
c. How useful do you think this regression model is for predicting the value of a baseball franchise?

13.21 In Problem 13.9, an agent for a real estate company wanted to predict the monthly rent for apartments, based on the size of the apartment (stored in the file Rent). Using the results of that problem,
a. determine the coefficient of determination, r^2, and interpret its meaning.
b. determine the standard error of the estimate, and interpret its meaning.
c. How useful do you think this regression model is for predicting the monthly rent?
d. Can you think of other variables that might explain the variation in monthly rent?

13.22 In Problem 13.10, you used box office gross to predict sales of DVDs (stored in the file Movie). Using the results of that problem,
a. determine the coefficient of determination, r^2, and interpret its meaning.
b. determine the standard error of the estimate, and interpret its meaning.
c. How useful do you think this regression model is for predicting sales of DVDs?
d. Can you think of other variables that might explain the variation in DVD sales?

13.4 Assumptions

The discussion of hypothesis testing and the analysis of variance emphasized the importance of the assumptions to the validity of any conclusions reached. The assumptions necessary for regression are similar to those of the analysis of variance because both topics fall in the general category of *linear models* (reference 4).

The four **assumptions of regression** (known by the acronym LINE) are as follows:

- Linearity
- Independence of errors
- Normality of error
- Equal variance

The first assumption, **linearity**, states that the relationship between variables is linear. Relationships between variables that are not linear are discussed in Reference 4.

The second assumption, **independence of errors**, requires that the errors (ε_i) are independent of one another. This assumption is particularly important when data are collected over a period of time. In such situations, the errors for a specific time period are sometimes correlated with those of the previous time period.

The third assumption, **normality**, requires that the errors (ε_i) are normally distributed at each value of X. Like the t test and the ANOVA F test, regression analysis is fairly robust against departures from the normality assumption. As long as the distribution of the errors at each level of X is not extremely different from a normal distribution, inferences about β_0 and β_1 are not seriously affected.

The fourth assumption, **equal variance** or **homoscedasticity**, requires that the variance of the errors (ε_i) are constant for all values of X. In other words, the variability of Y values is the same when X is a low value as when X is a high value. The equal variance assumption is important when making inferences about β_0 and β_1. If there are serious departures from this assumption, you can use either data transformations or weighted least-squares methods (see reference 4).

13.5 Residual Analysis

In Section 13.1, regression analysis was introduced. In Sections 13.2 and 13.3, a regression model was developed using the least-squares approach for the Sunflowers Apparel data. Is this the correct model for these data? Are the assumptions introduced in Section 13.4 valid? In this section, a graphical approach called **residual analysis** is used to evaluate the assumptions and determine whether the regression model selected is an appropriate model.

The **residual** or estimated error value, e_i, is the difference between the observed (Y_i) and predicted $(\hat{Y}_i)$ values of the dependent variable for a given value of X_i. Graphically, a residual appears on a scatter plot as the vertical distance between an observed value of Y and the prediction line. Equation (13.14) defines the residual.

> RESIDUAL
>
> The residual is equal to the difference between the observed value of Y and the predicted value of Y.
>
> $$e_i = Y_i - \hat{Y}_i \tag{13.14}$$

Evaluating the Assumptions

Recall from Section 13.4 that the four assumptions of regression (known by the acronym LINE) are linearity, independence, normality, and equal variance.

Linearity To evaluate linearity, you plot the residuals on the vertical axis against the corresponding X_i values of the independent variable on the horizontal axis. If the linear model is appropriate for the data, there is no apparent pattern in this plot. However, if the linear model is not appropriate, there is a relationship between the X_i values and the residuals, e_i. You can see such a pattern in Figure 13.9. Panel A shows a situation in which, although there is an increasing trend in Y as X increases, the relationship seems curvilinear because the upward trend decreases for increasing values of X. This quadratic effect is highlighted in Panel B, where there is a clear relationship between X_i and e_i. By plotting the residuals, the linear trend of X with Y has been removed, thereby exposing the lack of fit in the simple linear model. Thus, a quadratic model is a better fit and should be used in place of the simple linear model.

FIGURE 13.9

Studying the appropriateness of the simple linear regression model

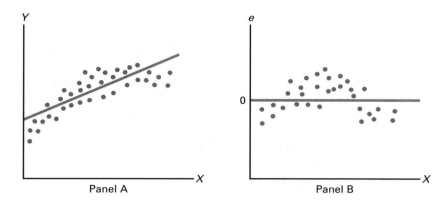

To determine whether the simple linear regression model is appropriate, return to the evaluation of the Sunflowers Apparel data. Figure 13.10 provides the predicted values and residuals computed by Microsoft Excel. To assess linearity, the residuals are plotted against the independent variable (store size, in thousands of square feet) in Figure 13.11. Although there is widespread scatter in the residual plot, there is no apparent pattern or relationship between the residuals and X_i. The residuals appear to be evenly spread above and below 0 for the differing values of X. You can conclude that the linear model is appropriate for the Sunflowers Apparel data.

FIGURE 13.10

Microsoft Excel residual output area for the Sunflowers Apparel data

See Sections E13.3 to create the worksheet that contains this.)

	A	B	C
22	**RESIDUAL OUTPUT**		
23			
24	*Observation*	*Predicted Annual Sales*	*Residuals*
25	1	3.803239598	-0.103239598
26	2	3.636253367	0.263746633
27	3	5.640088147	1.059911853
28	4	10.31570263	-0.815702635
29	5	3.135294672	0.264705328
30	6	4.638170757	0.961829243
31	7	3.135294672	0.564705328
32	8	2.801322208	-0.101322208
33	9	6.308033074	-0.808033074
34	10	3.469267135	-0.569267135
35	11	9.647757708	1.052242292
36	12	8.645840318	-1.045840318
37	13	10.6496751	1.150324902
38	14	5.974060611	-1.874060611

FIGURE 13.11

Microsoft Excel plot of residuals against the square footage of a store for the Sunflowers Apparel data

See Sections E2.13 and E13.1 to create this.

Independence You can evaluate the assumption of independence of the errors by plotting the residuals in the order or sequence in which the data were collected. If the values of Y are part of a time series (see Section 2.5), a value of Y is sometimes related to the previous value of Y, and thus there is a relationship between consecutive residuals. If this relationship exists (which violates the assumption of independence), there is a cyclical pattern in the plot of the residuals versus the time in which the data were collected. Because the Sunflowers Apparel data were collected during the same time period, you do not need to evaluate the independence assumption.

Normality You can evaluate the assumption of normality in the errors by tallying the residuals into a frequency distribution and displaying the results in a histogram (see Section 2.3). For the Sunflowers Apparel data, the residuals have been tallied into a frequency distribution in Table 13.3. (There is an insufficient number of values, however, to construct a histogram.) You can also evaluate the normality assumption by comparing the actual versus theoretical values of the residuals or by constructing a boxplot (see Section 3.4) or normal probability plot (see Section 6.3) of the residuals. Figure 13.12 is a normal probability plot of the residuals for the Sunflower Apparel data.

TABLE 13.3

Frequency Distribution of 14 Residual Values for the Sunflowers Apparel Data

Residuals	Frequency
-2.25 but less than -1.75	1
-1.75 but less than -1.25	0
-1.25 but less than -0.75	3
-0.75 but less than -0.25	1
-0.25 but less than $+0.25$	2
$+0.25$ but less than $+0.75$	3
$+0.75$ but less than $+1.25$	4
	14

FIGURE 13.12

Microsoft Excel normal probability plot of the residuals for the Sunflowers Apparel data

See Section E6.2 to create this.

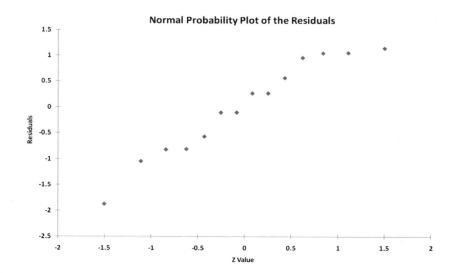

It is difficult to evaluate the normality assumption for a sample of only 14 values, regardless of whether you use a histogram, stem-and-leaf display, boxplot, or normal probability plot. You can see from Figure 13.12 that the data do not appear to depart substantially from a normal distribution. The robustness of regression analysis with modest departures from normality enables you to conclude that you should not be overly concerned about departures from this normality assumption in the Sunflowers Apparel data.

Equal Variance You can evaluate the assumption of equal variance from a plot of the residuals with X_i. For the Sunflowers Apparel data of Figure 13.11, there do not appear to be major differences in the variability of the residuals for different X_i values. Thus, you can conclude that there is no apparent violation in the assumption of equal variance at each level of X.

To examine a case in which the equal variance assumption is violated, observe Figure 13.13, which is a plot of the residuals with X_i for a hypothetical set of data. In this plot, the variability of the residuals increases dramatically as X increases, demonstrating the lack of homogeneity in the variances of Y_i at each level of X. For these data, the equal variance assumption is invalid.

FIGURE 13.13

Violation of equal variance

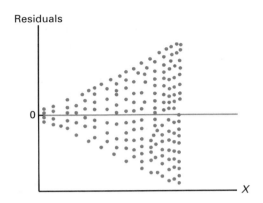

Problems for Section 13.5

LEARNING THE BASICS

13.23 The results below provide the X values, residuals, and a residual plot from a regression analysis:

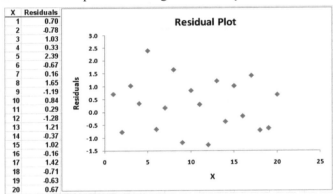

Is there any evidence of a pattern in the residuals? Explain.

13.24 The results below show the X values, residuals, and a residual plot from a regression analysis:

Is there any evidence of a pattern in the residuals? Explain.

APPLYING THE CONCEPTS

13.25 In Problem 13.5, you used reported magazine newsstand sales to predict audited sales. The data are stored in the file **Circulation**. Perform a residual analysis for these data. Evaluate whether the assumptions of regression have been seriously violated.

✓SELF **13.26** In Problem 13.4, the marketing manager
Test used shelf space for pet food to predict weekly sales. The data are stored in the file **Petfood**. Perform a residual analysis for these data. Evaluate whether the assumptions of regression have been seriously violated.

13.27 In Problem 13.7, you used the number of customers to predict the waiting time at a supermarket checkout. The data are stored in the file **Supermarket**. Perform a residual analysis for these data. Based on these results, evaluate whether the assumptions of regression have been seriously violated.

13.28 In Problem 13.6, the owner of a moving company wanted to predict labor hours based on the cubic feet moved. The data are stored in the file **Moving**. Perform a residual analysis for these data. Based on these results, evaluate whether the assumptions of regression have been seriously violated.

13.29 In Problem 13.9, an agent for a real estate company wanted to predict the monthly rent for apartments, based on the size of the apartments. The data are stored in the file **Rent**. Perform a residual analysis for these data. Based on these results, evaluate whether the assumptions of regression have been seriously violated.

13.30 In Problem 13.8, you used annual revenues to predict the value of a baseball franchise. The data are stored in the file BBrevenue. Perform a residual analysis for these data. Based on these results, evaluate whether the assumptions of regression have been seriously violated.

13.31 In Problem 13.10, you used box office gross to predict the sales of DVDs. The data are stored in the file Movie. Perform a residual analysis for these data. Based on these results, evaluate whether the assumptions of regression have been seriously violated.

13.6 Inferences About the Slope and Correlation Coefficient

In Sections 13.1 through 13.3, regression was used solely for descriptive purposes. You learned how the least-squares method determines the regression coefficients and how to predict Y for a given value of X. In addition, you learned how to compute and interpret the standard error of the estimate and the coefficient of determination.

When residual analysis, as discussed in Section 13.5, indicates that the assumptions of a least-squares regression model are not seriously violated and that the straight-line model is appropriate, you can make inferences about the linear relationship between the variables in the population.

t Test for the Slope

To determine the existence of a significant linear relationship between the X and Y variables, you test whether β_1 (the population slope) is equal to 0. The null and alternative hypotheses are as follows:

H_0: $\beta_1 = 0$ [There is no linear relationship (the slope is zero).]
H_1: $\beta_1 \neq 0$ [There is a linear relationship (the slope is not zero).]

If you reject the null hypothesis, you conclude that there is evidence of a linear relationship. Equation (13.15) defines the test statistic.

TESTING A HYPOTHESIS FOR A POPULATION SLOPE, β_1, USING THE t TEST

The t_{STAT} test statistic equals the difference between the sample slope and hypothesized value of the population slope divided by the standard error of the slope.

$$t_{STAT} = \frac{b_1 - \beta_1}{S_{b_1}}$$ **(13.15)**

where

$$S_{b_1} = \frac{S_{YX}}{\sqrt{SSX}}$$

$$SSX = \sum_{i=1}^{n}(X_i - \bar{X})^2$$

The t_{STAT} test statistic follows a t distribution with $n - 2$ degrees of freedom.

Return to the Using Statistics scenario from the beginning of this chapter concerning Sunflowers Apparel. To test whether there is a significant linear relationship between the size of the store and the annual sales at the 0.05 level of significance, refer to the SPSS output for the t test results presented in Figure 13.14.

FIGURE 13.14
SPSS *t*-test results of the slope for the Sunflowers Apparel data

Coefficients[a]					
	Unstandardized Coefficients		Standardized Coefficients		
Model	B	Std. Error	Beta	t	Sig.
1 (Constant)	.964	.526		1.833	.092
square feet (thousands)	1.670	.157	.951	10.641	.000

a. *Dependent Variable: Annual Sales (in Millions of Dollars)*

From Figure 13.14,

$$b_1 = +1.670 \quad n = 14 \quad S_{b_1} = 0.157$$

and

$$t_{STAT} = \frac{b_1 - \beta_1}{S_{b_1}}$$

$$= \frac{1.670 - 0}{0.157} = 10.641$$

SPSS labels this t_{STAT} test statistic *t* Stat (see Figure 13.14). Using the 0.05 level of significance, the critical value of *t* with $n - 2 = 12$ degrees of freedom is 2.1788. Because $t_{STAT} = 10.641 > 2.1788$, you reject H_0 (see Figure 13.15). Using the *p*-value, you reject H_0 because the *p*-value is approximately 0, which is less than $\alpha = 0.05$. Hence, you can conclude that there is a significant linear relationship between mean annual sales and the size of the store.

FIGURE 13.15
Testing a hypothesis about the population slope at the 0.05 level of significance, with 12 degrees of freedom

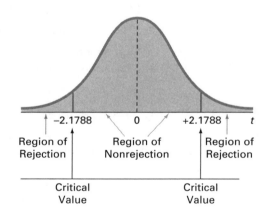

F Test for the Slope

As an alternative to the *t* test, you can use an *F* test to determine whether the slope in simple linear regression is statistically significant. In Section 10.4, you used the *F* distribution to test the ratio of two variances. Equation (13.16) defines the *F* test for the slope as the ratio of the variance that is due to the regression (*MSR*) divided by the error variance ($MSE = S_{YX}^2$).

TESTING A HYPOTHESIS FOR A POPULATION SLOPE, β_1, USING THE *F* TEST

The F_{STAT} test statistic is equal to the regression mean square (*MSR*) divided by the error mean square (*MSE*).

$$F_{STAT} = \frac{MSR}{MSE} \tag{13.16}$$

where

$$MSR = \frac{SSR}{1} = SSR$$

$$MSE = \frac{SSE}{n - 2}$$

The F_{STAT} test statistic follows an F distribution with 1 and $n - 2$ degrees of freedom.

Using a level of significance α, the decision rule is

$$\text{Reject } H_0 \text{ if } F_{STAT} > F_\alpha;$$

$$\text{otherwise, do not reject } H_0.$$

Table 13.4 organizes the complete set of results into an Analysis of Variance (ANOVA) table.

TABLE 13.4

ANOVA Table for Testing the Significance of a Regression Coefficient

Source	df	Sum of Squares	Mean Square (Variance)	F
Regression	1	SSR	$MSR = \dfrac{SSR}{1} = SSR$	$F_{STAT} = \dfrac{MSR}{MSE}$
Error	$n - 2$	SSE	$MSE = \dfrac{SSE}{n - 2}$	
Total	$n - 1$	SST		

The completed ANOVA table is also part of the SPSS results shown in Figure 13.16. These results show that the computed F_{STAT} test statistic is 113.234 and the p-value is approximately 0.

FIGURE 13.16

SPSS *F*-test results for the Sunflowers Apparel data

See Section E13.1 to create the worksheet that contains this.

ANOVA[b]					
Model	Sum of Squares	df	Mean Square	F	Sig.
1 Regression	105.748	1	105.748	113.234	.000[a]
Residual	11.207	12	.934		
Total	116.954	13			

a. *Predictors: (Constant), square feet (thousands)*
b. *Dependent Variable: Annual Sales (in Millions of Dollars)*

Coefficients[a]					
	Unstandardized Coefficients		Standardized Coefficients		
Model	B	Std. Error	Beta	t	Sig.
1 (Constant)	.964	.526		1.833	.092
square feet (thousands)	1.670	.157	.951	10.641	.000

a. *Dependent Variable: Annual Sales (in Millions of Dollars)*

Using a level of significance of 0.05, from Table E.5, the critical value of the F distribution, with 1 and 12 degrees of freedom, is 4.75 (see Figure 13.17). Because $F_{STAT} = 113.234 > 4.75$ or because the p-value $= 0.000 < 0.05$, you reject H_0 and conclude that the size of the store is significantly related to annual sales. Because the F test in Equation (13.16) is equivalent to the t test in Equation (13.15), you reach the same conclusion.

FIGURE 13.17

Regions of rejection and nonrejection when testing for the significance of the slope at the 0.05 level of significance, with 1 and 12 degrees of freedom

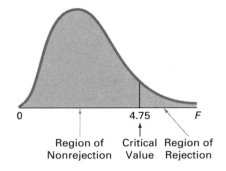

Region of   Critical   Region of
Nonrejection   Value   Rejection

Confidence Interval Estimate for the Slope

In testing for the existence of a linear relationship between the variables, you can construct a confidence interval estimate of β_1 using Equation (13.17).

> **CONFIDENCE INTERVAL ESTIMATE OF THE SLOPE, β_1**
>
> The confidence interval estimate for the population slope can be constructed by taking the sample slope, b_1, and adding and subtracting the critical t value multiplied by the standard error of the slope.
>
> $$b_1 \pm t_{\alpha/2} S_{b_1} \qquad (13.17)$$
>
> where $t_{\alpha/2}$ is the critical value corresponding to an upper-tail probability of $\alpha/2$ from the t distribution with $n - 2$ degrees of freedom (i.e., a cumulative area of $1 - \alpha/2$).

From the SPSS results of Figure 13.14,

$$b_1 = 1.670 \quad n = 14 \quad S_{b_1} = 0.157$$

To construct a 95% confidence interval estimate, $\alpha/2 = 0.025$, and from Table E.3, $t_{\alpha/2} = 2.1788$. Thus,

$$b_1 \pm t_{\alpha/2} S_{b_1} = 1.670 \pm (2.1788)(0.157)$$

$$= 1.670 \pm 0.3419$$

$$1.3280 \le \beta_1 \le 2.0118$$

Therefore, you estimate with 95% confidence that the population slope is between 1.3280 and 2.0118. Because these values are both above 0, you conclude that there is a significant linear relationship between annual sales and the size of the store. Had the interval included 0, you would have concluded that no significant relationship exists between the variables. The confidence interval indicates that for each increase of 1,000 square feet, mean annual sales are estimated to increase by at least \$1,328,000 but no more than \$2,011,800.

t Test for the Correlation Coefficient

In Section 3.5, the strength of the relationship between two numerical variables was measured, using the **correlation coefficient**, r. The values of the coefficient of correlation range from -1 for a perfect negative correlation to $+1$ for a perfect positive correlation. You can use the correlation coefficient to determine whether there is a statistically significant linear relationship between X and Y. To do so, you hypothesize that the population correlation coefficient, ρ, is 0. Thus, the null and alternative hypotheses are

$$H_0: \rho = 0 \text{ (no correlation)}$$

$$H_1: \rho \neq 0 \text{ (correlation)}$$

Equation (13.18) defines the test statistic for determining the existence of a significant correlation.

TESTING FOR THE EXISTENCE OF CORRELATION

$$t_{STAT} = \frac{r - \rho}{\sqrt{\dfrac{1 - r^2}{n - 2}}} \tag{13.18a}$$

where

$$r = +\sqrt{r^2} \text{ if } b_1 > 0$$
$$r = -\sqrt{r^2} \text{ if } b_1 < 0$$

The t_{STAT} test statistic follows a t distribution with $n - 2$ degrees of freedom.

An alternative method to calculate r is as follows:

$$r = \frac{\text{cov}(X,Y)}{S_X S_Y} \tag{13.18b}$$

where

$$\text{cov}(X,Y) = \frac{\sum_{i=1}^{n}(X_i - \overline{X})(Y_i - \overline{Y})}{n - 1}$$

$$S_X = \sqrt{\frac{\sum_{i=1}^{n}(X_i - \overline{X})^2}{n - 1}}$$

$$S_Y = \sqrt{\frac{\sum_{i=1}^{n}(Y_i - \overline{Y})^2}{n - 1}}$$

In the Sunflowers Apparel problem, $r^2 = 0.904$ (see Figure 13.8) and $b_1 = +1.670$ (see Figure 13.4). Because $b_1 > 0$, the correlation coefficient for annual sales and store size is the positive square root of r^2, that is, $r = +\sqrt{0.9042} = +0.951$ (see Figure 13.8). Using Equation (13.18a) to test the null hypothesis that there is no correlation between these two variables results in the following observed t statistic:

$$t_{STAT} = \frac{r - 0}{\sqrt{\dfrac{1 - r^2}{n - 2}}}$$

$$= \frac{0.9509 - 0}{\sqrt{\dfrac{1 - (0.9509)^2}{14 - 2}}} = 10.6411$$

Using the 0.05 level of significance, because $t_{STAT} = 10.6411 > 2.1788$, you reject the null hypothesis. You conclude that there is a significant association between annual sales and store size. This t_{STAT} test statistic is equivalent to the t_{STAT} test statistic found when testing whether the population slope, β_1, is equal to zero.

Problems for Section 13.6

LEARNING THE BASICS

13.32 You are testing the null hypothesis that there is no linear relationship between two variables, X and Y. From your sample of $n = 18$, you determine that $b_1 = +4.5$ and $S_{b_1} = 1.5$.
a. What is the value of t_{STAT}?
b. At the $\alpha = 0.05$ level of significance, what are the critical values?
c. Based on your answers to (a) and (b), what statistical decision should you make?
d. Construct a 95% confidence interval estimate of the population slope, β_1.

13.33 You are testing the null hypothesis that there is no linear relationship between two variables, X and Y. From your sample of $n = 20$, you determine that $SSR = 60$ and $SSE = 40$.
a. What is the value of F_{STAT}?
b. At the $\alpha = 0.05$ level of significance, what is the critical value?
c. Based on your answers to (a) and (b), what statistical decision should you make?
d. Compute the correlation coefficient by first computing r^2 and assuming that b_1 is negative.
e. At the 0.05 level of significance, is there a significant correlation between X and Y?

APPLYING THE CONCEPTS

✓ SELF Test **13.34** In Problem 13.4, the marketing manager used shelf space for pet food to predict weekly sales. The data are stored in the file **Petfood**. From the results of that problem, $b_1 = 7.4$ and $S_{b_1} = 1.59$.
a. At the 0.05 level of significance, is there evidence of a linear relationship between shelf space and sales?
b. Construct a 95% confidence interval estimate of the population slope, β_1.

13.35 In Problem 13.5, you used reported magazine newsstand sales to predict audited sales. The data are stored in the file **Circulation**. Using the results of that problem, $b_1 = 0.5719$ and $S_{b_1} = 0.0668$.
a. At the 0.05 level of significance, is there evidence of a linear relationship between reported sales and audited sales?
b. Construct a 95% confidence interval estimate of the population slope, β_1.

13.36 In Problem 13.6, the owner of a moving company wanted to predict labor hours, based on the number of cubic feet moved. The data are stored in the file **Moving**. Using the results of that problem,
a. at the 0.05 level of significance, is there evidence of a linear relationship between the number of cubic feet moved and labor hours?
b. construct a 95% confidence interval estimate of the population slope, β_1.

13.37 In Problem 13.7, you used the number of customers to predict the waiting time on the checkout line. The data are stored in the file **Supermarket**. Using the results of that problem,
a. at the 0.05 level of significance, is there evidence of a linear relationship between the number of customers and the waiting time on the checkout line?
b. construct a 95% confidence interval estimate of the population slope, β_1.

13.38 In Problem 13.8, you used annual revenues to predict the value of a baseball franchise. The data are stored in the file **BBrevenue**. Using the results of that problem,
a. at the 0.05 level of significance, is there evidence of a linear relationship between annual revenue and franchise value?
b. construct a 95% confidence interval estimate of the population slope, β_1.

13.39 In Problem 13.9, an agent for a real estate company wanted to predict the monthly rent for apartments, based on the size of the apartment. The data are stored in the file **Rent**. Using the results of that problem,
a. at the 0.05 level of significance, is there evidence of a linear relationship between the size of the apartment and the monthly rent?
b. construct a 95% confidence interval estimate of the population slope, β_1.

13.40 In Problem 13.10, you used box office gross to predict the sales of DVDs. The data are stored in the file **Movie**. Using the results of that problem,
a. at the 0.05 level of significance, is there evidence of a linear relationship between box office gross and sales of DVDs?
b. construct a 95% confidence interval estimate of the population slope, β_1.

13.41 The volatility of a stock is often measured by its beta value. You can estimate the beta value of a stock by developing a simple linear regression model, using the percentage weekly change in the stock as the dependent variable and the percentage weekly change in a market index as the independent variable. The S&P 500 Index is a common index to use. For example, if you wanted to estimate the beta for Disney, you could use the following model, which is sometimes referred to as a *market model*:

(% weekly change in Disney) $= \beta_0$
$+ \beta_1(\%$ weekly change in S&P 500 index$) + \varepsilon$

The least-squares regression estimate of the slope b_1 is the estimate of the beta value for Disney. A stock with a beta value of 1.0 tends to move the same as the overall market. A stock with a beta value of 1.5 tends to move 50% more than the overall market, and a stock with a beta value of 0.6 tends to move only 60% as much as the overall market.

Stocks with negative beta values tend to move in a direction opposite that of the overall market. The following table gives some beta values for some widely held stocks:

Company	Ticker Symbol	Beta
AT&T	T	1.07
Disney Company	DIS	0.64
Alcoa	AA	1.26
LSI Logic	LSI	1.81
Wave Systems	WAVX	2.72

Source: *Data extracted from* **finance.yahoo.com**, *April 29, 2008.*

a. For each of the five companies, interpret the beta value.
b. How can investors use the beta value as a guide for investing?

13.42 Index funds are mutual funds that try to mimic the movement of leading indexes, such as the S&P 500 Index, the NASDAQ 100 Index, or the Russell 2000 Index. The beta values (as described in Problem 13.41) for these funds are therefore approximately 1.0. The estimated market models for these funds are approximately

(% weekly change in index fund) = 0.0
+ 1.0(% weekly change in the index)

Leveraged index funds are designed to magnify the movement of major indexes. An article in *Mutual Funds* (L. O'Shaughnessy, "Reach for Higher Returns," *Mutual Funds*, July 1999, pp. 44–49) described some of the risks and rewards associated with these funds and gave details on some of the most popular leveraged funds, including those in the following table:

Name (Ticker Symbol)	Fund Description
Potomac Small Cap Plus (POSCX)	125% of Russell 2000 Index
Rydex "Inv" Nova (RYNVX)	150% of the S&P 500 Index
ProFund UltraOTC "Inv" (UOPIX)	Double (200%) the NASDAQ 100 Index

The estimated market models for these funds are approximately

(% weekly change in POSCX) = 0.0
+ 1.25 (% weekly change in the Russell 2000 Index)
(% weekly change in RYNVX) = 0.0
+ 1.50 (% weekly change in the S&P 500 Index)
(% weekly change in UOPIX fund) = 0.0
+ 2.0 (% weekly change in the NASDAQ 100 Index)

Thus, if the Russell 2000 Index gains 10% over a period of time, the leveraged mutual fund POSCX gains approximately 12.5%. On the downside, if the same index loses 20%, POSCX loses approximately 25%.

a. Consider the leveraged mutual fund ProFund UltraOTC "Inv" (UOPIX), whose description is 200% of the performance of the NASDAQ 100 Index. What is its approximate market model?
b. If the NASDAQ gains 30% in a year, what return do you expect UOPIX to have?
c. If the NASDAQ loses 35% in a year, what return do you expect UOPIX to have?
d. What type of investors should be attracted to leveraged funds? What type of investors should stay away from these funds?

13.43 The data in the file `Coffeedrink` represent the calories and fat (in grams) of 16-ounce iced coffee drinks at Dunkin' Donuts and Starbucks:

Product	Calories	Fat
Dunkin' Donuts Iced Mocha Swirl latte (whole milk)	240	8.0
Starbucks Coffee Frappuccino blended coffee	260	3.5
Dunkin' Donuts Coffee Coolatta (cream)	350	22.0
Starbucks Iced Coffee Mocha Espresso (whole milk and whipped cream)	350	20.0
Starbucks Mocha Frappuccino blended coffee (whipped cream)	420	16.0
Starbucks Chocolate Brownie Frappuccino blended coffee (whipped cream)	510	22.0
Starbucks Chocolate Frappuccino Blended Crème (whipped cream)	530	19.0

Source: *Data extracted from "Coffee as Candy at Dunkin' Donuts and Starbucks,"* Consumer Reports, *June 2004, p. 9.*

a. Compute and interpret the coefficient of correlation, *r*.
b. At the 0.05 level of significance, is there a significant linear relationship between calories and fat?

13.44 There are several methods for calculating fuel economy. The following table (contained in the file `Mileage`) indicates the mileage as calculated by owners and by current government standards:

Vehicle	Owner	Government Standards
2005 Ford F-150	14.3	16.8
2005 Chevrolet Silverado	15.0	17.8
2002 Honda Accord LX	27.8	26.2
2002 Honda Civic	27.9	34.2
2004 Honda Civic Hybrid	48.8	47.6
2002 Ford Explorer	16.8	18.3
2005 Toyota Camry	23.7	28.5
2003 Toyota Corolla	32.8	33.1
2005 Toyota Prius	37.3	56.0

a. Compute and interpret the coefficient of correlation, r.

b. At the 0.05 level of significance, is there a significant linear relationship between the mileage as calculated by owners and by current government standards?

13.45 College basketball is big business, with coaches' salaries, revenues, and expenses in millions of dollars. The data in the file Colleges-basketball represent the coaches' salaries and revenues for college basketball at selected schools in a recent year (data extracted from R. Adams, "Pay for Playoffs," *The Wall Street Journal*, March 11–12, 2006, pp. P1, P8).

a. Compute and interpret the coefficient of correlation, r.

b. At the 0.05 level of significance, is there a significant linear relationship between a coach's salary and revenue?

13.46 College football players trying out for the NFL are given the Wonderlic standardized intelligence test. The data

in the file Wonderlic represent the average Wonderlic scores of football players trying out for the NFL and the graduation rates for football players at the schools they attended (data extracted from S. Walker, "The NFL's Smartest Team," *The Wall Street Journal*, September 30, 2005, pp. W1, W10).

a. Compute and interpret the coefficient of correlation, r.

b. At the 0.05 level of significance, is there a significant linear relationship between the average Wonderlic score of football players trying out for the NFL and the graduation rates for football players at selected schools?

c. What conclusions can you reach about the relationship between the average Wonderlic score of football players trying out for the NFL and the graduation rates for football players at selected schools?

13.7 Estimation of Mean Values and Prediction of Individual Values

This section presents methods of making inferences about the mean of Y and predicting individual values of Y.

The Confidence Interval Estimate

In Example 13.2, you used the prediction line to predict the value of Y for a given X. The mean annual sales for stores with 4,000 square feet was predicted to be 7.644 millions of dollars ($7,644,000). This estimate, however, is a *point estimate* of the population mean. In Chapter 8, you studied the concept of the confidence interval estimate of the population mean. In a similar fashion, Equation (13.19) defines the **confidence interval estimate for the mean response** for a given X.

CONFIDENCE INTERVAL ESTIMATE FOR THE MEAN OF Y

$$\hat{Y}_i \pm t_{\alpha/2} S_{YX} \sqrt{h_i}$$

$$\hat{Y}_i - t_{\alpha/2} S_{YX} \sqrt{h_i} \leq \mu_{Y|X=X_i} \leq \hat{Y}_i + t_{\alpha/2} S_{YX} \sqrt{h_i} \qquad (13.19)$$

where

$$h_i = \frac{1}{n} + \frac{(X_i - \bar{X})^2}{SSX}$$

$\hat{Y}_i$ = predicted value of Y; $\hat{Y}_i = b_0 + b_1 X_i$

S_{YX} = standard error of the estimate

n = sample size

X_i = given value of X

$$\mu_{Y|X=X_i} = \text{mean value of } Y \text{ when } X = X_i$$

$$SSX = \sum_{i=1}^{n} (X_i - \overline{X})^2$$

$t_{\alpha/2}$ is the critical value corresponding to an upper-tail probability of $\alpha/2$ from the t distribution with $n - 2$ degrees of freedom (i.e., a cumulative area of $1 - \alpha/2$).

The width of the confidence interval in Equation (13.19) depends on several factors. Increased variation around the prediction line, as measured by the standard error of the estimate, results in a wider interval. However, as you would expect, increased sample size reduces the width of the interval. In addition, the width of the interval also varies at different values of X. When you predict Y for values of X close to $\overline{X}$, the interval is narrower than for predictions for X values more distant from $\overline{X}$.

In the Sunflowers Apparel example, suppose you want to construct a 95% confidence interval estimate of the mean annual sales for the entire population of stores that contain 4,000 square feet ($X = 4$). Using the simple linear regression equation,

$$\hat{Y}_i = 0.9645 + 1.6699X_i$$

$$= 0.9645 + 1.6699(4) = 7.6439 \text{ (millions of dollars)}$$

Also, given the following:

$$\overline{X} = 2.9214 \quad S_{YX} = 0.9664$$

$$SSX = \sum_{i=1}^{n} (X_i - \overline{X})^2 = 37.9236$$

From Table E.3, $t_{\alpha/2} = 2.1788$. Thus,

$$\hat{Y}_i \pm t_{\alpha/2}S_{YX}\sqrt{h_i}$$

where

$$h_i = \frac{1}{n} + \frac{(X_i - \overline{X})^2}{SSX}$$

so that

$$\hat{Y}_i \pm t_{\alpha/2}S_{YX}\sqrt{\frac{1}{n} + \frac{(X_i - \overline{X})^2}{SSX}}$$

$$= 7.6439 \pm (2.1788)(0.9664)\sqrt{\frac{1}{14} + \frac{(4 - 2.9214)^2}{37.9236}}$$

$$= 7.6439 \pm 0.6728$$

so

$$6.9711 \leq \mu_{Y|X=4} \leq 8.3167$$

Therefore, the 95% confidence interval estimate is that the mean annual sales are between $6,971,100 and $8,316,700 for the population of stores with 4,000 square feet.

The Prediction Interval

Often, it is important to predict the response for an individual value. In addition to calculating the predicted value $\hat{Y}$, you can construct a prediction interval. Although the form of the prediction interval is similar to that of the confidence interval estimate of Equation (13.19), the prediction interval is predicting an individual value, not estimating a parameter. Equation

(13.20) defines the **prediction interval for an individual response, *Y***, at a particular value, X_i, denoted by $Y_{X=X_i}$.

PREDICTION INTERVAL FOR AN INDIVIDUAL RESPONSE, *Y*

$$\hat{Y}_i \pm t_{\alpha/2}S_{YX}\sqrt{1 + h_i} \tag{13.20}$$

$$\hat{Y}_i - t_{\alpha/2}S_{YX}\sqrt{1 + h_i} \leq Y_{X=X_i} \leq \hat{Y}_i + t_{\alpha/2}S_{YX}\sqrt{1 + h_i}$$

where h_i, $\hat{Y}_i$, S_{YX}, n, and X_i are defined as in Equation (13.19) on page 590 and $Y_{X=X_i}$ is a future value of *Y* when $X = X_i$.

$t_{\alpha/2}$ is the critical value corresponding to an upper-tail probability of $\alpha/2$ from the *t* distribution with $n - 2$ degrees of freedom (i.e., a cumulative area of $1 - \alpha/2$).

To construct a 95% prediction interval of the annual sales for an individual store that contains 4,000 square feet $(X = 4)$, you first compute $\hat{Y}_i$. Using the prediction line:

$$\hat{Y}_i = 0.9645 + 1.6699X_i$$

$$= 0.9645 + 1.6699(4)$$

$$= 7.6439 \,(\text{millions of dollars})$$

Also, given the following:

$$\overline{X} = 2.9214 \quad S_{YX} = 0.9664$$

$$SSX = \sum_{i=1}^{n}(X_i - \overline{X})^2 = 37.9236$$

From Table E.3, $t_{\alpha/2} = 2.1788$. Thus,

$$\hat{Y}_i \pm t_{\alpha/2}S_{YX}\sqrt{1 + h_i}$$

where

$$h_i = \frac{1}{n} + \frac{(X_i - \overline{X})^2}{\sum_{i=1}^{n}(X_i - \overline{X})^2}$$

so that

$$\hat{Y}_i \pm t_{\alpha/2}S_{YX}\sqrt{1 + \frac{1}{n} + \frac{(X_i - \overline{X})^2}{SSX}}$$

$$= 7.6439 \pm (2.1788)(0.9664)\sqrt{1 + \frac{1}{14} + \frac{(4 - 2.9214)^2}{37.9236}}$$

$$= 7.6439 \pm 2.2104$$

so

$$5.4335 \leq Y_{X=4} \leq 9.8543$$

Therefore, with 95% confidence, you predict that the annual sales for an individual store with 4,000 square feet is between $5,433,500 and $9,854,300.

Figure 13.18 is a SPSS worksheet that illustrates the confidence interval estimate and the prediction interval for the Sunflowers Apparel problem. If you compare the results of the confidence interval estimate and the prediction interval, you see that the width of the prediction interval for an individual store is much wider than the confidence interval estimate for the mean. Remember that there is much more variation in predicting an individual value than in estimating a mean value.

SPSS confidence interval estimate and prediction interval worksheet for the Sunflowers Apparel data

	size	sales	PRE_1	RES_1	LMCI_1	UMCI_1	LICI_1	UICI_1
1	1.7	3.7	3.80324	-0.10324	3.10247	4.50401	1.58413	6.02235
2	1.6	3.9	3.63625	0.26375	2.91459	4.35792	1.41045	5.86205
3	2.8	6.7	5.64009	1.05991	5.07582	6.20435	3.46023	7.81995
4	5.6	9.5	10.31570	-0.81570	9.24080	11.39061	7.95164	12.67977
5	1.3	3.4	3.13529	0.26471	2.34535	3.92524	0.88643	5.38416
6	2.2	5.6	4.63817	0.96183	4.02375	5.25259	2.44479	6.83155
7	1.3	3.7	3.13529	0.56471	2.34535	3.92524	0.88643	5.38416
8	1.1	2.7	2.80132	-0.10132	1.96197	3.64067	0.53463	5.06801
9	3.2	5.5	6.30803	-0.80803	5.73729	6.87877	4.12649	8.48958
10	1.5	2.9	3.46927	-0.56927	2.72572	4.21282	1.23628	5.70226
11	5.2	10.7	9.64776	1.05224	8.68671	10.60881	7.33324	11.96228
12	4.6	7.6	8.64584	-1.04584	7.84206	9.44962	6.39208	10.89960
13	5.8	11.8	10.64968	1.15032	9.51594	11.78341	8.25829	13.04106
14	3.0	4.1	5.97406	-1.87406	5.41069	6.53744	3.79443	8.15369
15								

Problems for Section 13.7

LEARNING THE BASICS

13.47 Based on a sample of $n = 20$, the least-squares method was used to develop the following prediction line: $\hat{Y}_i = 5 + 3X_i$. In addition,

$$S_{YX} = 1.0 \quad \overline{X} = 2 \quad \sum_{i=1}^{n} (X_i - \overline{X})^2 = 20$$

a. Construct a 95% confidence interval estimate of the population mean response for $X = 2$.

b. Construct a 95% prediction interval of an individual response for $X = 2$.

13.48 Based on a sample of $n = 20$, the least-squares method was used to develop the following prediction line: $\hat{Y}_i = 5 + 3X_i$. In addition,

$$S_{YX} = 1.0 \quad \overline{X} = 2 \quad \sum_{i=1}^{n} (X_i - \overline{X})^2 = 20$$

a. Construct a 95% confidence interval estimate of the population mean response for $X = 4$.

b. Construct a 95% prediction interval of an individual response for $X = 4$.

c. Compare the results of (a) and (b) with those of Problem 13.47(a) and (b). Which interval is wider? Why?

APPLYING THE CONCEPTS

13.49 In Problem 13.5, you used reported sales to predict audited sales of magazines. The data are stored in the file

Circulation . For these data $S_{YX} = 42.186$ and $h_i = 0.108$ when $X = 400$.

a. Construct a 95% confidence interval estimate of the mean audited sales for magazines that report newsstand sales of 400,000.

b. Construct a 95% prediction interval of the audited sales for an individual magazine that reports newsstand sales of 400,000.

c. Explain the difference in the results in (a) and (b).

✓ SELF Test **13.50** In Problem 13.4, the marketing manager used shelf space for pet food to predict weekly sales. The data are stored in the file Petfood . For these data $S_{YX} = 30.81$ and $h_i = 0.1373$ when $X = 8$.

a. Construct a 95% confidence interval estimate of the mean weekly sales for all stores that have 8 feet of shelf space for pet food.

b. Construct a 95% prediction interval of the weekly sales of an individual store that has 8 feet of shelf space for pet food.

c. Explain the difference in the results in (a) and (b).

13.51 In Problem 13.7, you used the total number of customers in the store to predict the waiting time at the checkout counter. The data are stored in the file Supermarket .

a. Construct a 95% confidence interval estimate of the mean waiting time for all customers when there are 20 customers in the store.

b. Construct a 95% prediction interval of the waiting time for an individual customer when there are 20 customers in the store.

c. Why is the interval in (a) narrower than the interval in (b)?

13.52 In Problem 13.6, the owner of a moving company wanted to predict labor hours based on the number of cubic feet moved. The data are stored in the file Moving.

a. Construct a 95% confidence interval estimate of the mean labor hours for all moves of 500 cubic feet.

b. Construct a 95% prediction interval of the labor hours of an individual move that has 500 cubic feet.

c. Why is the interval in (a) narrower than the interval in (b)?

13.53 In Problem 13.9, an agent for a real estate company wanted to predict the monthly rent for apartments, based on the size of the apartment. The data are stored in the file Rent.

a. Construct a 95% confidence interval estimate of the mean monthly rental for all apartments that are 1,000 square feet in size.

b. Construct a 95% prediction interval of the monthly rental of an individual apartment that is 1,000 square feet in size.

c. Explain the difference in the results in (a) and (b).

13.54 In Problem 13.8, you predicted the value of a baseball franchise, based on current revenue. The data are stored in the file BBrevenue.

a. Construct a 95% confidence interval estimate of the mean value of all baseball franchises that generate $150 million of annual revenue.

b. Construct a 95% prediction interval of the value of an individual baseball franchise that generates $150 million of annual revenue.

c. Explain the difference in the results in (a) and (b).

13.55 In Problem 13.10, you used box office gross to predict the number of DVDs sold. The data are stored in the file Movie. The company is about to release a movie on DVD that had a box office gross of $30 million.

a. What is the predicted number of DVDs that the company will sell?

b. Which interval is more useful here, the confidence interval estimate of the mean or the predicted interval for an individual response? Explain.

c. Construct and interpret the interval you selected in (b).

13.8 Pitfalls in Regression

Some of the pitfalls involved in using regression analysis are as follows:

- Lacking an awareness of the assumptions of least-squares regression
- Not knowing how to evaluate the assumptions of least-squares regression
- Not knowing what the alternatives are to least-squares regression if a particular assumption is violated
- Using a regression model without knowledge of the subject matter
- Extrapolating outside the relevant range
- Concluding that a significant relationship identified in an observational study is due to a cause-and-effect relationship

TABLE 13.5

Four Sets of Artificial Data

	Data Set A		Data Set B		Data Set C		Data Set D	
X_i	Y_i	X_i	Y_i	X_i	Y_i	X_i	Y_i	
10	8.04	10	9.14	10	7.46	8	6.58
14	9.96	14	8.10	14	8.84	8	5.76
5	5.68	5	4.74	5	5.73	8	7.71
8	6.95	8	8.14	8	6.77	8	8.84
9	8.81	9	8.77	9	7.11	8	8.47
12	10.84	12	9.13	12	8.15	8	7.04
4	4.26	4	3.10	4	5.39	8	5.25
7	4.82	7	7.26	7	6.42	19	12.50
11	8.33	11	9.26	11	7.81	8	5.56
13	7.58	13	8.74	13	12.74	8	7.91
6	7.24	6	6.13	6	6.08	8	6.89

Source: *Data extracted from F. J. Anscombe, "Graphs in Statistical Analysis,"* American Statistician, *vol. 27 (1973), pp. 17–21.*

The widespread availability of spreadsheet and statistical software has made regression analysis much more feasible. However, for many users, this enhanced availability of software has not been accompanied by an understanding of how to use regression analysis properly. Someone who is not familiar with either the assumptions of regression or how to evaluate the assumptions cannot be expected to know what the alternatives to least-squares regression are if a particular assumption is violated.

The data in Table 13.5 (stored in the file **Anscombe**) illustrate the importance of using scatter plots and residual analysis to go beyond the basic number crunching of computing the Y intercept, the slope, and r^2.

Anscombe (reference 1) showed that all four data sets given in Table 13.5 have the following identical results:

$$\hat{Y}_i = 3.0 + 0.5X_i$$

$$S_{YX} = 1.237$$

$$S_{b_1} = 0.118$$

$$r^2 = 0.667$$

$$SSR = \text{Explained variation} = \sum_{i=1}^{n}(\hat{Y}_i - \overline{Y})^2 = 27.51$$

$$SSE = \text{unexplained variation} = \sum_{i=1}^{n}(Y_i - \hat{Y}_i)^2 = 13.76$$

$$SST = \text{Total variation} = \sum_{i=1}^{n}(Y_i - \overline{Y})^2 = 41.27$$

Thus, with respect to these statistics associated with a simple linear regression analysis, the four data sets are identical. Were you to stop the analysis at this point, you would fail to observe the important differences among the four data sets.

From the scatter plots of Figure 13.19 and the residual plots of Figure 13.20, you see how different the data sets are. Each has a different relationship between X and Y. The only data set that seems to approximately follow a straight line is data set A. The residual plot for data set A does not show any obvious patterns or outlying residuals. This is certainly not true for data sets B, C, and D. The scatter plot for data set B shows that a curvilinear regression model is more appropriate. This conclusion is reinforced by the residual plot for data set B. The scatter plot

FIGURE 13.19

Scatter plots for four data sets

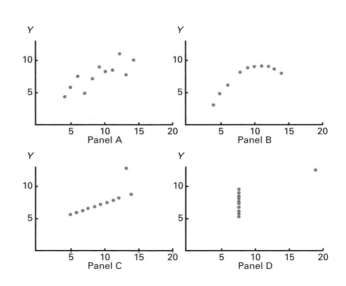

FIGURE 13.20

Residual plots for four data sets

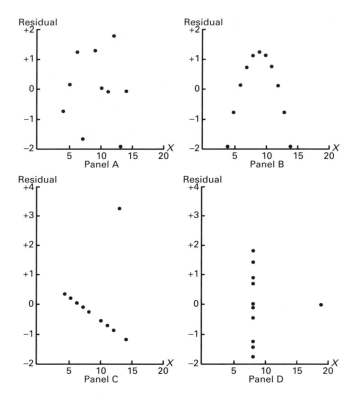

and the residual plot for data set C clearly show an outlying observation. If this is the case, you may want to remove the outlier and reestimate the regression model (see reference 4). Similarly, the scatter plot for data set D represents the situation in which the model is heavily dependent on the outcome of a single response ($X_8 = 19$ and $Y_8 = 12.50$). You would have to cautiously evaluate any regression model because its regression coefficients are heavily dependent on a single observation.

In summary, scatter plots and residual plots are of vital importance to a complete regression analysis. The information they provide is so basic to a credible analysis that you should always include these graphical methods as part of a regression analysis. Thus, a strategy that you can use to help avoid the pitfalls of regression is as follows:

1. Start with a scatter plot to observe the possible relationship between X and Y.
2. Check the assumptions of regression (**L**inearity, **I**ndependence, **N**ormality, **E**qual variance) by performing a residual analysis that includes:
    a. Plotting the residuals versus the independent variable to determine whether the linear model is appropriate and to check for equal variance.
    b. Constructing a histogram, stem-and-leaf display, boxplot, or normal probability plot of the residuals to check for normality.
    c. Plotting the residuals versus time to check for independence (this step is necessary only if the data are collected over time).
3. If there are violations of the assumptions, use alternative methods to least-squares regression or alternative least-squares models.
4. If there are no violations of the assumptions, carry out tests for the significance of the regression coefficients and develop confidence and prediction intervals.
5. Avoid making predictions and forecasts outside the relevant range of the independent variable.
6. Keep in mind that the relationships identified in observational studies may or may not be due to cause-and-effect relationships. Remember that, although causation implies correlation, correlation does not imply causation.

THINK ABOUT THIS | America's Top Models

Perhaps you are familiar with the TV competition produced by Tyra Banks to find "America's top model." You may be less familiar with another set of top models that are emerging from the business world.

In a *Business Week* article from its January 23, 2006, edition (S. Baker, "Why Math Will Rock Your World: More Math Geeks Are Calling the Shots in Business. Is Your Industry Next?" *Business Week*, pp. 54–62), Stephen Baker talks about how "quants" turned finance upside down and are moving on to other business fields. The name *quants* derives from the "quantitative methods" that "math geeks" use to develop models and forecasts. These methods are built on the principles of regression analysis discussed in this chapter, although the actual models are much more complicated than the simple linear models discussed in this chapter.

Regression-based models have become the top models for many types of business analyses. Some examples include:

- **Advertising and marketing** Managers use econometric models (in other words, regression models) to determine the effect of an advertisement on sales, based on a set of factors. Also, managers use data mining to predict patterns of behavior of what customers will buy in the future, based on historic information about the consumer.

- **Finance** Any time you read about a financial "model," you should understand that some type of regression model is being used. For example, a *New York Times* article on June 18, 2006, titled "An Old Formula That Points to New Worry" by Mark Hulbert (p. BU8) discusses a market timing model that predicts the return of stocks in the next three to five years, based on the dividend yield of the stock market and the interest rate of 90-day Treasury bills.

- **Food and beverage** Believe it or not, Enologix, a California consulting company, has developed a "formula" (a regression model) that predicts a wine's quality index, based on a set of chemical compounds found in the wine (see D. Darlington, "The Chemistry of a 90+ Wine," *The New York Times Magazine*, August 7, 2005, pp. 36–39).

- **Publishing** A study of the effect of price changes on sales at Amazon.com and BN.com (again, regression analysis) found that a 1% price increase at BN.com pushed sales down 4%, but the same price increase at Amazon.com pushed sales down only 0.5%.

- **Transportation** Farecast.com uses data mining and predictive technologies to objectively predict airfare pricing (see D. Darlin, "Airfares Made Easy (Or Easier)," *The New York Times*, July 1, 2006, pp. C1, C6).

- **Real estate** Zillow.com uses information about the features contained in a home and its location to develop estimates about the market value of the home, using a "formula" built with a proprietary model.

In the *Business Week* article, Baker stated that statistics and probability will become core skills for businesspeople and consumers. Those who are successful will know how to use statistics, whether they are building financial models or making marketing plans. He also strongly endorsed the need for people in business to know how to use Microsoft Excel to perform statistical analysis and create reports.

USING STATISTICS | @ Sunflowers Apparel Revisited

I n the Using Statistics scenario, you were the director of planning for Sunflowers Apparel, a chain of upscale clothing stores for women. Until now, Sunflowers managers selected sites based on factors such as the availability of a good lease or a subjective opinion that a location seemed like a good place for a store. To make more objective decisions, you developed a regression model to analyze the relationship between the size of a store and its annual sales. The model indicated that about 90.4% of the variation in sales was explained by the size of the store. Furthermore, for each increase of one thousand square feet, mean annual sales were estimated to increase by $1.67 million. You can now use your model to help make better decisions when selecting new sites for stores as well as to forecast sales for existing stores.

SUMMARY

As you can see from the chapter roadmap in Figure 13.21, this chapter develops the simple linear regression model and discusses the assumptions and how to evaluate them. Once you are assured that the model is appropriate, you can predict values by using the prediction line and test for the significance of the slope. In Chapter 14, regression analysis is extended to situations in which more than one independent variable is used to predict the value of a dependent variable.

FIGURE 13.21
Roadmap for simple
linear regression

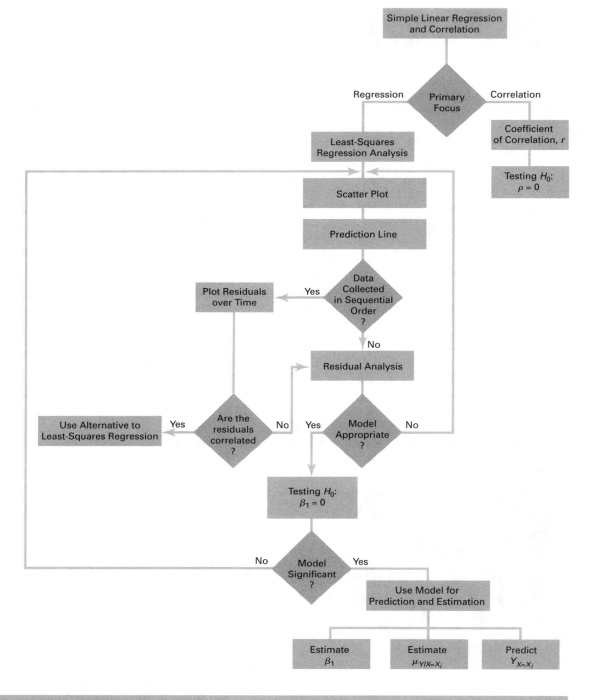

KEY EQUATIONS

Simple Linear Regression Model

$$Y_i = \beta_0 + \beta_1 X_i + \varepsilon_i \qquad (13.1)$$

Simple Linear Regression Equation: The Prediction Line

$$\hat{Y}_i = b_0 + b_1 X_i \qquad (13.2)$$

Computational Formula for the Slope, b_1

$$b_1 = \frac{SSXY}{SSX} \qquad (13.3)$$

Computational Formula for the Y Intercept, b_0

$$b_0 = \overline{Y} - b_1 \overline{X} \qquad (13.4)$$

Measures of Variation in Regression

$$SST = SSR + SSE \qquad (13.5)$$

Total Sum of Squares (SST)

$$SST = \text{Total sum of squares} = \sum_{i=1}^{n}(Y_i - \overline{Y})^2 \qquad (13.6)$$

Regression Sum of Squares (*SSR*)

SSR = Explained variation or regression sum of squares

$$= \sum_{i=1}^{n}(\hat{Y}_i - \overline{Y})^2 \qquad (13.7)$$

Error Sum of Squares (*SSE*)

SSE = Unexplained variation or error sum of squares

$$= \sum_{i=1}^{n}(Y_i - \hat{Y}_i)^2 \qquad (13.8)$$

Coefficient of Determination

$$r^2 = \frac{\text{Regression sum of squares}}{\text{Total sum of squares}} = \frac{SSR}{SST} \qquad (13.9)$$

Computational Formula for *SST*

$$SST = \sum_{i=1}^{n}(Y_i - \overline{Y})^2 = \sum_{i=1}^{n}Y_i^2 - \frac{\left(\sum_{i=1}^{n}Y_i\right)^2}{n} \qquad (13.10)$$

Computational Formula for *SSR*

$$SSR = \sum_{i=1}^{n}(\hat{Y}_i - \overline{Y})^2$$

$$= b_0\sum_{i=1}^{n}Y_i + b_1\sum_{i=1}^{n}X_iY_i - \frac{\left(\sum_{i=1}^{n}Y_i\right)^2}{n} \qquad (13.11)$$

Computational Formula for *SSE*

$$SSE = \sum_{i=1}^{n}(Y_i - \hat{Y}_i)^2 = \sum_{i=1}^{n}Y_i^2 - b_0\sum_{i=1}^{n}Y_i - b_1\sum_{i=1}^{n}X_iY_i \qquad (13.12)$$

Standard Error of the Estimate

$$S_{YX} = \sqrt{\frac{SSE}{n-2}} = \sqrt{\frac{\sum_{i=1}^{n}(Y_i - \hat{Y}_i)^2}{n-2}} \qquad (13.13)$$

Residual

$$e_i = Y_i - \hat{Y}_i \qquad (13.14)$$

Testing a Hypothesis for a Population Slope β_1, Using the *t* Test

$$t_{STAT} = \frac{b_1 - \beta_1}{S_{b_1}} \qquad (13.15)$$

Testing a Hypothesis for a Population Slope, β_1, Using the *F* Test

$$F_{STAT} = \frac{MSR}{MSE} \qquad (13.16)$$

Confidence Interval Estimate of the Slope, β_1

$$b_1 \pm t_{\alpha/2}S_{b_1}$$

$$b_1 - t_{\alpha/2}S_{b_1} \le \beta_1 \le b_1 + t_{\alpha/2}S_{b_1} \qquad (13.17)$$

Testing for the Existence of Correlation

$$t_{STAT} = \frac{r - \rho}{\sqrt{\dfrac{1 - r^2}{n - 2}}} \qquad (13.18a)$$

$$r = \frac{cov(X,Y)}{S_X S_Y} \qquad (13.18b)$$

Confidence Interval Estimate for the Mean of *Y*

$$\hat{Y}_i \pm t_{\alpha/2}S_{YX}\sqrt{h_i}$$

$$\hat{Y}_i - t_{\alpha/2}S_{YX}\sqrt{h_i} \le \mu_{Y|X=X_i} \le \hat{Y}_i + t_{\alpha/2}S_{YX}\sqrt{h_i} \qquad (13.19)$$

Prediction Interval for an Individual Response, *Y*

$$\hat{Y}_i \pm t_{\alpha/2}S_{YX}\sqrt{1 + h_i}$$

$$\hat{Y}_i - t_{\alpha/2}S_{YX}\sqrt{1 + h_i} \le Y_{X=X_i} \le \hat{Y}_i + t_{\alpha/2}S_{YX}\sqrt{1 + h_i} \qquad (13.20)$$

KEY TERMS

assumptions of regression   595
coefficient of determination   591
confidence interval estimate for the mean response   606
correlation coefficient   602
dependent variable   578
equal variance   595
error sum of squares (*SSE*)   589
explained variation   589
explanatory variable   578
homoscedasticity   595
independence of errors   595
independent variables   578

least-squares method   581
linearity   595
linear relationship   578
normality   595
prediction interval for an individual response, *Y*   608
prediction line   581
regression analysis   578
regression coefficient   581
regression sum of squares (*SSR*)   589
relevant range   583
residual   595
residual analysis   595

response variable   578
scatter diagram   578
scatter plot   578
simple linear regression   578
simple linear regression equation   581
slope   578
standard error of the estimate   593
total sum of squares (*SST*)   589
total variation   589
unexplained variation   589
Y intercept   579

CALCULATOR LESSON 17A

CFX-9850GB CALCULATOR

EXAMPLE 13.5

Lesson 17A – Simple Linear Regression

We will use the scenario, "Forecasting Sales for a Clothing Store," to demonstrate how to perform simple linear regression on the calculator.

The sales for Sunflowers, a chain of apparel stores for women, have increased during the past 12 years as the chain expanded the number of stores open. Until now, Sunflowers senior managers selected sites based on subjective factors such as the availability of a good lease or the perception that a location seemed ideal for an apparel store. As the new director of planning, you need to develop a systematic approach to selecting new sites that will allow Sunflowers to make better-informed decisions for opening additional stores. This plan must be able to forecast annual sales for all potential stores under consideration. You believe that the size of the store significantly contributes to the success of a store and you want to use this relationship in the decision-making process. You wish to predict annual sales based on the size of the store in square feet.

Table 13.6 summarizes the results of the 14 stores.

TABLE 13.6

Store	Square Feet (000)	Annual Sales (in millions of dollars)	Store	Square Feet (000)	Annual Sales (in millions of dollars)
1	1.7	3.7	8	1.1	2.7
2	1.6	3.9	9	3.2	5.5
3	2.8	6.7	10	1.5	2.9
4	5.6	9.5	11	5.2	10.7
5	1.3	3.4	12	4.6	7.6
6	2.2	5.6	13	5.8	11.8
7	1.3	3.7	14	3.0	4.1

The dependent variable, y, is the annual sales (in millions of dollars) and the independent variable, x, is the size of the store (in square feet)

1. Compute the regression coefficients – b_0 (intercept) and b_1 (slope)
To obtain the regression coefficients, use the calculator and follow these steps.

a) From the **Main Menu** select **STAT** and press **EXE**.

b) You enter the x values (square feet) in List 1 and the y values (annual sales) in List 2.

c) Now press **F2 (CALC)** and then press **F6 (SET)**
   The first row will be highlighted. Use the Arrow key to highlight the third row (2 Var XList : List 1).

d) Now enter the following in response to the screen prompts.

   2 Var XList   :   List 1 (F1)   *Note: You entered the x values in List 1*

   2 Var YLIst   :   List 2 (F2)   *Note: You entered the y values in List 2*

   2 Var Freq   :   1

e) Now press **EXIT** to return to the display of the data.

f) Now press **F3 (REG)** and then press **F1 (X).**
   The calculator will now show the results:

   Linear-Reg
   a = 1.66986231
   b = 0.96447365
   r = 0.95088327
   r^2 = 0.904179
   y = ax + b

The values are put together to obtain the simple linear regression equation (the prediction line):

$$\hat{y} = 0.96447365 + 1.66986231x$$

The coefficient of determination, r^2 is 0.904179.

2. Hypothesis Tests for the Slope and Correlation Coefficient

At the 0.05 level of significance, is there evidence of a linear relationship between the size of the store and annual sales?

Solution:

We test for a linear relationship between the variables x and y by testing whether the population regression coefficient (slope), B, is different from zero.

H_0: $\beta_1 = 0$ (There is *no* a linear relationship)

H_a: $\beta_1 \neq 0$ (There is a linear relationship)

Note: Use the same data in which you enter the x values (square feet) in List 1 and the y values (annual sales) in List 2.

From the **Main Menu** select:

STAT F3(TEST) F1(t) F3(REG)   then enter the following items:

(Note: Only use the **EXE** key after a new data entry. Otherwise, use the cursor ▼ arrow. If you accidentally hit the wrong key, use **AC/ON** or **EXIT** to go back.)

1-Sample ZInterval

β & ρ	: $\neq$(F1)0	▼
XList	: .List1 (F1)	**EXE**
YList	: .List2 (F2)	**EXE**
Freq	: 1 (F1)	**EXE**
Execute		

Now press key **EXE** or **F1**(Calc)

The calculator will now show the results:

LinearReg tTest

$\beta \neq 0$ & $\rho \neq 0$

    t   = 10.641
    p   = 1.8226E-07
    df = 12
    a   = 0.96447
    b   = 1.6698
    y   = a + bx

Use the cursor ▼ arrow to scroll down for more results.

    df = 12
    a   = 0.96447
    b   = 1.6698
    s   = 0.96637
    r   = 0.95088
    r^2 = 0.90417
    y   = a + bx

Conclusion:

p-value = 0.00000018226 < 0.05 = α , hence we reject H$_o$.

There is sufficient evidence to conclude that there is a linear relationship between size of the store and annual sales.

3. Compute the Prediction value

What is the average annual sales if the size of the store is 1.8 (000) square feet?

Note: You have to make sure that the information of this example (in **#1**) is still recorded in the calculator and the regression calculations have been performed before you can compute the prediction value).

From the **Main Menu** select:

MENU   RUN   EXE   then enter   **1.8   OPTN**

Use the following options on the bottom of the display.

Select   **STAT (F5)** $\bar{y}$**(F2)**   **EXE**

The calculator will now show the result:

    3.97022583

We interpret the value as follows:

$$\hat{y} = 0.96447365 + 1.66986231 \, (1.8) = 3.97022583$$

We predict that the annual sales will be $3.97022583 (in millions of dollars) if the size of the store is 1.8 (000) square feet.

4. Compute the Residuals

After obtaining the regression results, you can find the residuals by following these steps.

From the **Main Menu** select:

MENU   STAT   EXE

SHIFT   SET UP

You should see the following display on the screen: *(Note: if you do not see this on the screen, repeat #1c to #1f steps. And try again and press* **SHIFT   SET UP**

Stat Wind	: Auto
Graph Func	: On
Background	: None
Plot/Line	: Blue
Angle	: Rad
Coord	: On
Grid	: Off

Use the cursor ▼ arrow to scroll down to the bottom of the screen.

Axes	: On
Label	: Off
Display	: Norml
Resid List	**: None**

Scroll to the bottom of the screen prompts until you reach Resid List and it is highlighted. (DO NOT press **EXE** at this point)

Use the following options on the bottom of the display.

Select **LIST (F2)**	**LIST3* (F3)**	**EXE**	
Select **CALC (F2)**	**REG (F3)**	**X (F1)**	**EXE**

The residuals appear in List 3* as specified above. Press **EXIT** and you will see the residuals appear in List 3.

CALCULATOR LESSON 17B

FX-9850GII CALCULATOR

EXAMPLE 13.6

Lesson 17B – Simple Linear Regression

We will use the scenario, "Forecasting Sales for a Clothing Store," to demonstrate how to perform simple linear regression on the calculator.

The sales for Sunflowers, a chain of apparel stores for women, have increased during the past 12 years as the chain expanded the number of stores open. Until now, Sunflowers senior managers selected sites based on subjective factors such as the availability of a good lease or the perception that a location seemed ideal for an apparel store. As the new director of planning, you need to develop a systematic approach to selecting new sites that will allow Sunflowers to make better-informed decisions for opening additional stores. This plan must be able to forecast annual sales for all potential stores under consideration. You believe that the size of the store significantly contributes to the success of a store and you want to use this relationship in the decision-making process. You wish to predict annual sales based on the size of the store in square feet.

Table 13.7 summarizes the results of the 14 stores.

TABLE 13.7

Store	Square Feet (000)	Annual Sales (in millions of dollars)	Store	Square Feet (000)	Annual Sales (in millions of dollars)
1	1.7	3.7	8	1.1	2.7
2	1.6	3.9	9	3.2	5.5
3	2.8	6.7	10	1.5	2.9
4	5.6	9.5	11	5.2	10.7
5	1.3	3.4	12	4.6	7.6
6	2.2	5.6	13	5.8	11.8
7	1.3	3.7	14	3.0	4.1

The dependent variable, y, is the annual sales (in millions of dollars) and the independent variable, x, is the size of the store (in square feet)

1. Compute the regression coefficients – b_0 (intercept) and b_1 (slope)
To obtain the regression coefficients, use the calculator and follow these steps.

a) From the **Main Menu** select **STAT** and press **EXE.**

b) You enter the x values (square feet) in List 1 and the y values (annual sales) in List 2.

c) Now press **F2 (CALC)** and then press **F6 (SET)**
The first row will be highlighted. Use the Arrow key to highlight the third row (2 Var XList : List 1).

d) Now enter the following in response to the screen prompts.

   2 Var XList   :   List 1 (F1)   *Note: You entered the x values in List 1*

   2 Var YLIst   :   List 2 (F2)   *Note: You entered the y values in List 2*

   2 Var Freq   :   1

e) Now press **EXIT** to return to the display of the data.

f) Now press **F3 (REG)** and then press **F1 (X).**

g) At this point you have two options:
   1. ax + b (corresponds to function key **F1**)
   2. a + bx (corresponds to function key **F2**)
   Select either one and the linear regression equation should be the format you selected above.
   Suppose you select **F1 (ax + b)**.
   The calculator will now show the results:

   Linear-Reg
   a = 1.66986231
   b = 0.96447365
   r = 0.95088327
   r^2 = 0.904179
   y = ax + b

The values are put together to obtain the simple linear regression equation (the prediction line):

$$\hat{y} = 0.96447365 + 1.66986231x$$

The coefficient of determination, r^2 is 0.904179.

2. Hypothesis Tests for the Slope and Correlation Coefficient

At the 0.05 level of significance, is there evidence of a linear relationship between the size of the store and annual sales?

Solution:

We test for a linear relationship between the variables x and y by testing whether the population regression coefficient (slope), B, is different from zero.

H_0: $\beta_1 = 0$ (There is *not* a linear relationship)

H_a: $\beta_1 \neq 0$ (There is a linear relationship)

Note: Use the same data in which you enter the x values (square feet) in List 1 and the y values (annual sales) in List 2.

From the **Main Menu** select:

STAT   F3(TEST)   F1(t)   F3(REG)   then enter the following items:

(Note: Only use the **EXE** key after a new data entry. Otherwise, use the cursor ▼ arrow. If you accidentally hit the wrong key, use **AC/ON** or **EXIT** to go back.)

   1-Sample ZInterval
   $\beta \& \rho$: ≠(F1)0   ▼
   XList   : .List1 (F1)   **EXE**
   YList   : .List2 (F2)   **EXE**
   Freq   : 1 (F1)   **EXE**
   Save Res   : None
   Execute

Now press key **EXE** or **F1**(Calc)

The calculator will now show the results:

LinearReg tTest
$\beta \neq 0$ & $\rho \neq 0$
t = 10.641
p = 1.8226E-07
df = 12
a = 0.96447
b = 1.6698

Use the cursor ▼ arrow to scroll down for more results.
df = 12
a = 0.96447
b = 1.6698
se = 0.96637
r = 0.95088
r^2 = 0.90417

Conclusion:

p-value = 0.00000018226 < 0.05 = α , hence we reject H_o.

There is sufficient evidence to conclude that there is a linear relationship between size of the store and annual sales.

3. Compute the Prediction value

What is the average annual sales if the size of the store is 1.8 (000) square feet?

Note: You have to make sure that the information of this example (in **#1**) is still recorded in the calculator and the regression calculations have been performed before you can compute the prediction value).

From the **Main Menu** select:

MENU   RUN-MAT   EXE   then enter **1.8   OPTN**   (a black key just under function key F2)

Use the following options at the bottom of the display.

Select   **STAT (F5)** $\bar{y}$**(F2)**   **EXE**

The calculator will now show the result:

3.97022583

We interpret the value as follows:

$\hat{y}$ = 0.96447365 + 1.66986231 (1.8) = 3.97022583

We predict that the annual sales will be $3.97022583 (in millions of dollars) if the size of the store is 1.8 (000) square feet.

4. Compute the Residuals

You can find the residuals by following these steps.

From the **Main Menu** select:

MENU   STAT   EXE   TEST(F3)   **t**(F2)   **REG**(F3)

You should see the following display on the screen:

1-Sample tInterval

$\beta \& \rho$	: ≠(F1)0 ▼	
XList	: .List1 (F1)	**EXE**
YList	: .List2 (F2)	**EXE**
Freq	: 1 (F1)	**EXE**
Save Res	: List3	
Execute		

Scroll to the bottom of the screen prompts until you reach **'Save Res'** and it is highlighted. (DO NOT press **EXE** at this point)
Use the following options on the bottom of the display.
Select   **LIST (F2)**   and a pop up screen will prompt you to enter List No.

At this point enter "3" since lists 1 and 2 contain the data.

The residuals appear in List 3* as specified above. Press **EXIT** and you will see the residuals appear in List 3.

SPSS—Version 16—Simple Linear Regression

We will use the scenario, "Forecasting Sales for a Clothing Store", to demonstrate how to perform simple linear regression using SPSS.

The dependent variable, y, is the annual sales (in millions of dollars) and the independent variable, x, is the size of the store (in square feet). You wish to predict annual sales based on the size of the store in square feet.

A random sample of 14 stores was selected with the results shown in Table 13.8.

Table 13.8 summarizes the results of the 14 stores.

T A B L E   1 3 . 8

Store	Square Feet (000)	Annual Sales (in millions of dollars)	Store	Square Feet (000)	Annual Sales (in millions of dollars)
1	1.7	3.7	8	1.1	2.7
2	1.6	3.9	9	3.2	5.5
3	2.8	6.7	10	1.5	2.9
4	5.6	9.5	11	5.2	10.7
5	1.3	3.4	12	4.6	7.6
6	2.2	5.6	13	5.8	11.8
7	1.3	3.7	14	3.0	4.1

Performing a simple linear regression on SPSS—Version 16

Step 1: Open the SPSS Data Editor.

Click **"cancel"** to cancel the SPSS opening window.

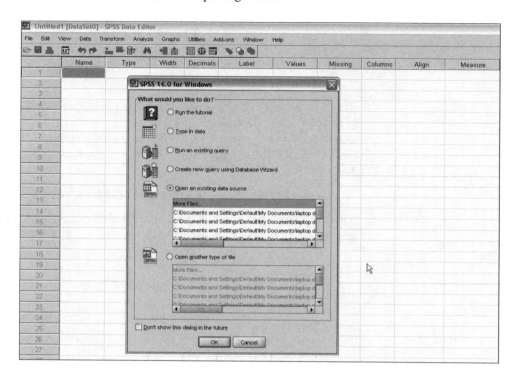

Step 2: Define the variables and give the variables a label.

Click **"Variable View"** (at the bottom of the window) to go to the variable view window to define the variables and fix the data at zero or one decimal places.

- Give variable name – "size" and label it as "Square feet (thousands)"
- Give variable name – "sales" and label it as "Annual sales (millions of dollars)".

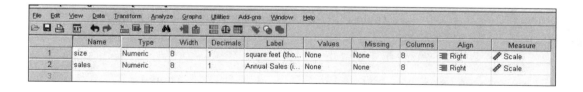

Step 3: Create a SPSS data file.

Click **"Data View"** to return to the data view window. Now, enter the raw data (in Table 13.8) into the respective column of variable.

	size	sales	var
1	1.7	3.7	
2	1.6	3.9	
3	2.8	6.7	
4	5.6	9.5	
5	1.3	3.4	
6	2.2	5.6	
7	1.3	3.7	
8	1.1	2.7	
9	3.2	5.5	
10	1.5	2.9	
11	5.2	10.7	
12	4.6	7.6	
13	5.8	11.8	
14	3.0	4.1	
15			
16			
17			

After you have entered all the data, save it as "sales.sav" (or any filename).

Step 3: Perform Regression Analysis.

Make the following menu selections:

Analyze → Regression → Linear

At this point, the **Linear Regression** dialog box will appear. Make these entries in the **Linear Regression** dialog box:

- Highlight on the **"Annual sales (or sales)"** variable and click on the arrow key (→). The variable will automatically fall into the **Dependent** box.

- Highlight on **"square feet (or size)"** variable and click on the arrow key (→). The variable will fall into the **Independent(s)** box.

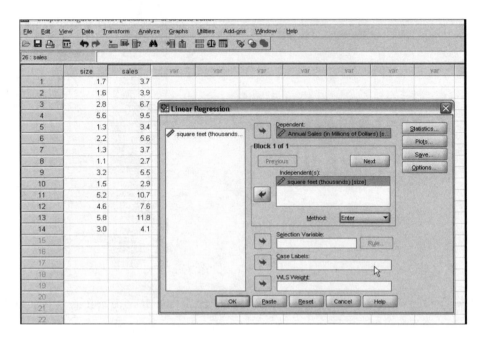

- ***Obtaining Predictions and Residuals***   Click on save button (Note that the **Save** is a button on the pop-up menu and not the usual File save option) and the **save** dialog box will pop-up. In the **save** dialog box, click on **Unstandardized** in the the **Predicted Values** box. Click on **Unstandardized** in the **Residuals** box. Click on **Mean** and **Individual** in the **Prediction Intervals** box. Click on **Continue** to return to the **Linear Regression** dialog box. Then click **Ok.**

Step 3: Go to **SPSS Viewer** to obtain your SPSS results.

SPSS output:
Regression

Variables Entered/Removed[b]			
Model	**Variables Entered**	**Variables Removed**	**Method**
1	square feet (thousands)[a]		Enter

a. *Predictors: (Constant), square feet (thousands)*
b. *Dependent Variable: Annual Sales (in Millions of Dollars)*

Model Summary				
Model	**R**	**R Square**	**Adjusted R Square**	**Std. Error of the Estimate**
1	.951[a]	.904	.896	.9664

a. *Predictors: (Constant), square feet (thousands)*
b. *Dependent Variable: Annual Sales (in Millions of Dollars)*

ANOVA[b]					
Model	Sum of Squares	df	Mean Square	F	Sig.
1 Regression	105.748	1	105.748	113.234	.000[a]
Residual	11.207	12	.934		
Total	116.954	13			

a. *Predictors: (Constant), square feet (thousands)*
b. *Dependent Variable: Annual Sales (in Millions of Dollars)*

Coefficients[a]					
	Unstandardized Coefficients		Standardized Coefficients		
Model	B	Std. Error	Beta	t	Sig.
1 (Constant)	.964	.526		1.833	.092
square feet (thousands)	1.670	.157	.951	10.641	.000

a. *Dependent Variable: Annual Sales (in Millions of Dollars)*

Residuals Statistics[a]					
	Minimum	Maximum	Mean	Std. Deviation	N
Predicted Value	2.801	10.650	5.843	2.8521	14
Std. Predicted Value	−1.066	1.685	.000	1.000	14
Standard Error of Predicted Value	.259	.520	.356	.083	14
Adjusted Predicted Value	2.820	10.603	5.821	2.8263	14
Residual	−1.8741	1.1503	.0000	.9285	14
Std. Residual	−1.939	1.190	.000	.961	14
Stud. Residual	−2.013	1.413	.010	1.038	14
Deleted Residual	−2.0186	1.6200	.0215	1.0888	14
Stud. Deleted Residual	−2.368	1.481	−.009	1.104	14
Mahal. Distance	.002	2.840	.929	.886	14
Cook's Distance	.001	.407	.090	.113	14
Centered Leverage Value	.000	.218	.071	.068	14

a. *Dependent Variable: Annual Sales (in Millions of Dollars)*

Obtaining Predictions and Residuals

The confidence interval values and prediction interval values are displayed on the **SPSS Data Editor** under the variables PRE_1, RES_1, LMCI_1, UMCI_1, LICI_1 and UICI_1.

Notation:

PRE_1—Unstandardized Predicted (for Model 1)

RES_1—Unstandardized Residual (for Model 1)

LMCI_1—95% Lower Confidence Interval for y mean (for Model 1)

UMCI_1—95% Upper Confidence Interval for y mean (for Model 1)

LICI_1—95% Lower Confidence Interval for y individual (for Model 1)

UICI_1—5% Upper Confidence Interval for y individual (for Model 1)

	size	sales	PRE_1	RES_1	LMCI_1	UMCI_1	LICI_1	UICI_1
1	1.7	3.7	3.80324	-0.10324	3.10247	4.50401	1.58413	6.02235
2	1.6	3.9	3.63625	0.26375	2.91459	4.35792	1.41045	5.86205
3	2.8	6.7	5.64009	1.05991	5.07582	6.20435	3.46023	7.81995
4	5.6	9.5	10.31570	-0.81570	9.24080	11.39061	7.95164	12.67977
5	1.3	3.4	3.13529	0.26471	2.34535	3.92524	0.88643	5.38416
6	2.2	5.6	4.63817	0.96183	4.02375	5.25259	2.44479	6.83155
7	1.3	3.7	3.13529	0.56471	2.34535	3.92524	0.88643	5.38416
8	1.1	2.7	2.80132	-0.10132	1.96197	3.64067	0.53463	5.06801
9	3.2	5.5	6.30803	-0.80803	5.73729	6.87877	4.12649	8.48958
10	1.5	2.9	3.46927	-0.56927	2.72572	4.21282	1.23628	5.70226
11	5.2	10.7	9.64776	1.05224	8.68671	10.60881	7.33324	11.96228
12	4.6	7.6	8.64584	-1.04584	7.84206	9.44962	6.39208	10.89960
13	5.8	11.8	10.64968	1.15032	9.51594	11.78341	8.25829	13.04106
14	3.0	4.1	5.97406	-1.87406	5.41069	6.53744	3.79443	8.15369
15								

CHAPTER REVIEW PROBLEMS

CHECKING YOUR UNDERSTANDING

13.56 What is the interpretation of the Y intercept and the slope in the simple linear regression equation?

13.57 What is the interpretation of the coefficient of determination?

13.58 When is the unexplained variation (i.e., error sum of squares) equal to 0?

13.59 When is the explained variation (i.e., regression sum of squares) equal to 0?

13.60 Why should you always carry out a residual analysis as part of a regression model?

13.61 What are the assumptions of regression analysis and how do you evaluate them?

13.62 What is the difference between a confidence interval estimate of the mean response, $\mu_{Y|X=X_i}$, and a prediction interval of $Y_{X=X_i}$?

APPLYING THE CONCEPTS

13.63 Researchers from the Lubin School of Business at Pace University in New York City conducted a study on Internet-supported courses. In one part of the study, four numerical variables were collected on 108 students in an introductory management course that met once a week for an entire semester. One variable collected was *hit consistency*. To measure hit consistency, the researchers did the following: If a student did not visit the Internet site between classes, the student was given a 0 for that time period. If a student visited the Internet site one or more times between classes, the student was given a 1 for that time period. Because there were 13 time periods, a student's score on hit consistency could range from 0 to 13.

The other three variables included the student's course average, the student's cumulative grade point average (GPA), and the total number of hits the student had on the Internet site supporting the course. The following table gives the correlation coefficient for all pairs of variables. Note that correlations marked with an * are statistically significant, using $\alpha = 0.001$:

Variable	Correlation
Course Average, Cumulative GPA	0.72*
Course Average, Total Hits	0.08
Course Average, Hit Consistency	0.37*
Cumulative GPA, Total Hits	0.12
Cumulative GPA, Hit Consistency	0.32*
Total Hits, Hit Consistency	0.64*

Source: *Data extracted from D. Baugher, A. Varanelli, and E. Weisbord, "Student Hits in an Internet-Supported Course: How Can Instructors Use Them and What Do They Mean?" Decision Sciences Journal of Innovative Education, Fall 2003, 1(2), pp. 159–179.*

a. What conclusions can you reach from this correlation analysis?
b. Are you surprised by the results, or are they consistent with your own observations and experiences?

13.64 Management of a soft-drink bottling company wants to develop a method for allocating delivery costs to customers. Although one cost clearly relates to travel time within a particular route, another variable cost reflects the time required to unload the cases of soft drink at the delivery point. A sample of 20 deliveries within a territory was selected. The delivery times and the number of cases delivered were recorded in the **Delivery** file:

Customer	Number of Cases	Delivery Time (Minutes)	Customer	Number of Cases	Delivery Time (Minutes)
1	52	32.1	11	161	43.0
2	64	34.8	12	184	49.4
3	73	36.2	13	202	57.2
4	85	37.8	14	218	56.8
5	95	37.8	15	243	60.6
6	103	39.7	16	254	61.2
7	116	38.5	17	267	58.2
8	121	41.9	18	275	63.1
9	143	44.2	19	287	65.6
10	157	47.1	20	298	67.3

Develop a regression model to predict delivery time, based on the number of cases delivered.

a. Use the least-squares method to compute the regression coefficients b_0 and b_1.
b. Interpret the meaning of b_0 and b_1 in this problem.
c. Predict the delivery time for 150 cases of soft drink.
d. Should you use the model to predict the delivery time for a customer who is receiving 500 cases of soft drink? Why or why not?
e. Determine the coefficient of determination, r^2, and explain its meaning in this problem.
f. Perform a residual analysis. Is there any evidence of a pattern in the residuals? Explain.
g. At the 0.05 level of significance, is there evidence of a linear relationship between delivery time and the number of cases delivered?
h. Construct a 95% confidence interval estimate of the mean delivery time for 150 cases of soft drink and a 95% prediction interval of the delivery time for a single delivery of 150 cases of soft drink.

13.65 Mixed costs are very common in business and consist of a fixed cost element and a variable cost element. Fixed costs are a recurring, constant cost that does not vary when business activity varies. Variable costs are added costs associated with each unit of business activity the organization experiences. The relationship can be characterized by the following equation:

Total costs = Fixed cost + (Cost per unit)

$\times$ (Number of units of business activity)

In a leading managerial accounting textbook, the authors discuss a hospital's total maintenance costs, and use regression analysis to estimate the fixed cost element of maintenance and the variable cost associated with the number of patient-days. The hospital's total maintenance costs and number of patient-days for seven months are listed in the following table and stored in the file MixedCosts .

Total Maintenance Costs	Patient-Days
$7,900	5,600
$8,500	7,100
$7,400	5,000
$8,200	6,500
$9,100	7,300
$9,800	8,000
$7,800	6,200

Source: *Data extracted from P. C. Brewer, R. H. Garrison, and E. W. Noreen, Introduction to Managerial Accounting, 4e* (Boston: McGraw-Hill Irwin, 2008).

a. Using total maintenance costs as the dependent variable and patient-days as the independent variable, use the least-squares method to find the regression coefficients b_0 and b_1.
b. Which regression coefficient represents fixed cost?
c. Which regression coefficient represents the variable cost per each patient-day?
d. Predict total maintenance costs for a month with 7,500 patient-days.

13.66 You want to develop a model to predict the selling price of homes based on assessed value. A sample of 30 recently sold single-family houses in a small city is selected to study the relationship between selling price (in thousands of dollars) and assessed value (in thousands of dollars). The houses in the city had been reassessed at full value one year prior to the study. The results are in the file House1 .

(*Hint:* First, determine which are the independent and dependent variables.)

a. Construct a scatter plot and, assuming a linear relationship, use the least-squares method to compute the regression coefficients b_0 and b_1.
b. Interpret the meaning of the Y intercept, b_0, and the slope, b_1, in this problem.
c. Use the prediction line developed in (a) to predict the selling price for a house whose assessed value is $170,000.
d. Determine the coefficient of determination, r^2, and interpret its meaning in this problem.
e. Perform a residual analysis on your results and evaluate the regression assumptions.

f. At the 0.05 level of significance, is there evidence of a linear relationship between selling price and assessed value?
g. Construct a 95% confidence interval estimate of the population slope.

13.67 You want to develop a model to predict the assessed value of houses, based on heating area. A sample of 15 single-family houses is selected in a city. The assessed value (in thousands of dollars) and the heating area of the houses (in thousands of square feet) are recorded, with the results stored in the file House2 .

(*Hint:* First, determine which are the independent and dependent variables.)

a. Construct a scatter plot and, assuming a linear relationship, use the least-squares method to compute the regression coefficients b_0 and b_1.
b. Interpret the meaning of the Y intercept, b_0, and the slope, b_1, in this problem.
c. Use the prediction line developed in (a) to predict the assessed value for a house whose heating area is 1,750 square feet.
d. Determine the coefficient of determination, r^2, and interpret its meaning in this problem.
e. Perform a residual analysis on your results and evaluate the regression assumptions.
f. At the 0.05 level of significance, is there evidence of a linear relationship between assessed value and heating area?

13.68 The director of graduate studies at a large college of business would like to predict the grade point average (GPA) of students in an MBA program based on the Graduate Management Admission Test (GMAT) score. A sample of 20 students who had completed 2 years in the program is selected. The results are stored in the file GPIGMAT.

(*Hint:* First, determine which are the independent and dependent variables.)

a. Construct a scatter plot and, assuming a linear relationship, use the least-squares method to compute the regression coefficients b_0 and b_1.
b. Interpret the meaning of the Y intercept, b_0, and the slope, b_1, in this problem.
c. Use the prediction line developed in (a) to predict the GPA for a student with a GMAT score of 600.
d. Determine the coefficient of determination, r^2, and interpret its meaning in this problem.
e. Perform a residual analysis on your results and evaluate the regression assumptions.
f. At the 0.05 level of significance, is there evidence of a linear relationship between GMAT score and GPA?
g. Construct a 95% confidence interval estimate of the mean GPA of students with a GMAT score of 600 and a 95% prediction interval of the GPA for a particular student with a GMAT score of 600.
h. Construct a 95% confidence interval estimate of the population slope.

13.69 An accountant for a large department store would like to develop a model to predict the amount of time it takes to process invoices. Data are collected from the last 32 working days, and the number of invoices processed and completion time (in hours) is stored in the file Invoice.

(*Hint:* First, determine which are the independent and dependent variables.)

a. Assuming a linear relationship, use the least-squares method to compute the regression coefficients b_0 and b_1.

b. Interpret the meaning of the Y intercept, b_0, and the slope, b_1, in this problem.

c. Use the prediction line developed in (a) to predict the amount of time it would take to process 150 invoices.

d. Determine the coefficient of determination, r^2, and interpret its meaning.

e. Plot the residuals against the number of invoices processed and also against time.

f. Based on the plots in (e), does the model seem appropriate?

g. Based on the results of (e) and (f) what conclusions can you make about the validity of the prediction made in (c)?

13.70 On January 28, 1986, the space shuttle *Challenger* exploded, and seven astronauts were killed. Prior to the launch, the predicted atmospheric temperature was for freezing weather at the launch site. Engineers for Morton Thiokol (the manufacturer of the rocket motor) prepared charts to make the case that the launch should not take place due to the cold weather. These arguments were rejected, and the launch tragically took place. Upon investigation after the tragedy, experts agreed that the disaster occurred because of leaky rubber O-rings that did not seal properly due to the cold temperature. Data indicating the atmospheric temperature at the time of 23 previous launches and the O-ring damage index are stored in the file O-ring).

Note: Data from flight 4 is omitted due to unknown O-ring condition.

Source: *Data extracted from Report of the Presidential Commission on the Space Shuttle Challenger Accident,* Washington, DC, 1986, Vol. II (H1-H3) and Vol. IV (664), and *Post Challenger Evaluation of Space Shuttle Risk Assessment and Management,* Washington, DC, 1988, pp. 135–136.

a. Construct a scatter plot for the seven flights in which there was O-ring damage (O-ring damage index $\neq$ 0). What conclusions, if any, can you draw about the relationship between atmospheric temperature and O-ring damage?

b. Construct a scatter plot for all 23 flights.

c. Explain any differences in the interpretation of the relationship between atmospheric temperature and O-ring damage in (a) and (b).

d. Based on the scatter plot in (b), provide reasons why a prediction should not be made for an atmospheric temperature of 31°F, the temperature on the morning of the launch of the *Challenger*.

e. Although the assumption of a linear relationship may not be valid for the set of 23 flights, fit a simple linear regression model to predict O-ring damage, based on atmospheric temperature.

f. Include the prediction line found in (e) on the scatter plot developed in (b).

g. Based on the results of (f), do you think a linear model is appropriate for these data? Explain.

h. Perform a residual analysis. What conclusions do you reach?

13.71 Crazy Dave, a well-known baseball analyst, would like to study various team statistics for the 2007 baseball season to determine which variables might be useful in predicting the number of wins achieved by teams during the season. He has decided to begin by using a team's earned run average (ERA), a measure of pitching performance, to predict the number of wins. The data for the 30 Major League Baseball teams are in the file BB2007.

(*Hint:* First, determine which are the independent and dependent variables.)

a. Assuming a linear relationship, use the least-squares method to compute the regression coefficients b_0 and b_1.

b. Interpret the meaning of the Y intercept, b_0, and the slope, b_1, in this problem.

c. Use the prediction line developed in (a) to predict the number of wins for a team with an ERA of 4.50.

d. Compute the coefficient of determination, r^2, and interpret its meaning.

e. Perform a residual analysis on your results and determine the adequacy of the fit of the model.

f. At the 0.05 level of significance, is there evidence of a linear relationship between the number of wins and the ERA?

g. Construct a 95% confidence interval estimate of the mean number of wins expected for teams with an ERA of 4.50.

h. Construct a 95% prediction interval of the number of wins for an individual team that has an ERA of 4.50.

i. Construct a 95% confidence interval estimate of the population slope.

j. The 30 teams constitute a population. In order to use statistical inference, as in (f) through (i), the data must be assumed to represent a random sample. What "population" would this sample be drawing conclusions about?

k. What other independent variables might you consider for inclusion in the model?

13.72 College football players trying out for the NFL are given the Wonderlic standardized intelligence test. The data in the file Wonderlic contains the average Wonderlic scores of football players trying out for the NFL and the graduation rates for football players at selected schools (data extracted from S. Walker, "The NFL's Smartest Team," *The Wall Street Journal*, September 30, 2005, pp. W1, W10). You plan to develop a regression model to predict the Wonderlic scores for football players trying out for the NFL, based on the graduation rate of the school they attended.

a. Assuming a linear relationship, use the least-squares method to compute the regression coefficients b_0 and b_1.

b. Interpret the meaning of the Y intercept, b_0, and the slope, b_1, in this problem.

c. Use the prediction line developed in (a) to predict the Wonderlic score for football players trying out for the NFL from a school that has a graduation rate of 50%.

d. Compute the coefficient of determination, r^2, and interpret its meaning.

e. Perform a residual analysis on your results and evaluate the regression assumptions.

f. At the 0.05 level of significance, is there evidence of a linear relationship between the Wonderlic score for a football player trying out for the NFL from a school and the school's graduation rate?

g. Construct a 95% confidence interval estimate of the mean Wonderlic score for football players trying out for the NFL from a school that has a graduation rate of 50%.

h. Construct a 95% prediction interval of the Wonderlic score for a football player trying out for the NFL from a school that has a graduation rate of 50%.

13.73 College basketball is big business, with coaches' salaries, revenues, and expenses in millions of dollars. The data in the file **Colleges-basketball** contains the coaches' salaries and revenues for college basketball at selected schools in a recent year (data extracted from R. Adams, "Pay for Playoffs," *The Wall Street Journal*, March 11–12, 2006, pp. P1, P8). You plan to develop a regression model to predict a coach's salary based on revenue.

a. Assuming a linear relationship, use the least-squares method to compute the regression coefficients b_0 and b_1.

b. Interpret the meaning of the Y intercept, b_0, and the slope, b_1, in this problem.

c. Use the prediction line developed in (a) to predict the coach's salary for a school that has revenue of $7 million.

d. Compute the coefficient of determination, r^2, and interpret its meaning.

e. Perform a residual analysis on your results and evaluate the regression assumptions.

f. At the 0.05 level of significance, is there evidence of a linear relationship between the coach's salary and revenue?

g. Construct a 95% confidence interval estimate of the population slope.

13.74 During the fall harvest season in the United States, pumpkins are sold in large quantities at farm stands. Often, instead of weighing the pumpkins prior to sale, the farm stand operator will just place the pumpkin in the appropriate circular cutout on the counter. When asked why this was done, one farmer replied, "I can tell the weight of the pumpkin from its circumference." To determine whether this was really true, a sample of 23 pumpkins were measured for circumference and weighed, with the results stored in the file **Pumpkin**.

a. Assuming a linear relationship, use the least-squares method to compute the regression coefficients b_0 and b_1.

b. Interpret the meaning of the slope, b_1, in this problem.

c. Predict the weight for a pumpkin that is 60 centimeters in circumference.

d. Do you think it is a good idea for the farmer to sell pumpkins by circumference instead of weight? Explain.

e. Determine the coefficient of determination, r^2, and interpret its meaning.

f. Perform a residual analysis for these data and evaluate the regression assumptions.

g. At the 0.05 level of significance, is there evidence of a linear relationship between the circumference and the weight of a pumpkin?

h. Construct a 95% confidence interval estimate of the population slope, β_1.

13.75 Can demographic information be helpful in predicting sales at sporting goods stores? The data stored in the file **Sporting** are the monthly sales totals from a random sample of 38 stores in a large chain of nationwide sporting goods stores. All stores in the franchise, and thus within the sample, are approximately the same size and carry the same merchandise. The county or, in some cases, counties in which the store draws the majority of its customers is referred to here as the customer base. For each of the 38 stores, demographic information about the customer base is provided. The data are real, but the name of the franchise is not used at the request of the company. The variables in the data set are:

  Sales—Latest one-month sales total (dollars)
  Age—Median age of customer base (years)
  HS—Percentage of customer base with a high school diploma
  College—Percentage of customer base with a college diploma
  Growth—Annual population growth rate of customer base over the past 10 years
  Income—Median family income of customer base (dollars)

a. Construct a scatter plot, using sales as the dependent variable and median family income as the independent variable. Discuss the scatter plot.

b. Assuming a linear relationship, use the least-squares method to compute the regression coefficients b_0 and b_1.

c. Interpret the meaning of the Y intercept, b_0, and the slope, b_1, in this problem.

d. Compute the coefficient of determination, r^2, and interpret its meaning.

e. Perform a residual analysis on your results and determine the adequacy of the fit of the model.

f. At the 0.05 level of significance, is there evidence of a linear relationship between the independent variable and the dependent variable?

g. Construct a 95% confidence interval estimate of the population slope and interpret its meaning.

13.76 For the data of Problem 13.75, repeat (a) through (g), using median age as the independent variable.

13.77 For the data of Problem 13.75, repeat (a) through (g), using high school graduation rate as the independent variable.

13.78 For the data of Problem 13.75, repeat (a) through (g), using college graduation rate as the independent variable.

13.79 For the data of Problem 13.75, repeat (a) through (g), using population growth as the independent variable.

13.80 Zagat's publishes restaurant ratings for various locations in the United States. The data file `Restaurants` contains the Zagat rating for food, decor, service, and the price per person for a sample of 100 restaurants located in New York City and in a suburb of New York City. Develop a regression model to predict the price per person, based on a variable that represents the sum of the ratings for food, decor, and service.

Source: *Extracted from Zagat Survey 2006 New York City Restaurants and Zagat Survey 2005–2006, Long Island Restaurants.*

a. Assuming a linear relationship, use the least-squares method to compute the regression coefficients b_0 and b_1.
b. Interpret the meaning of the Y intercept, b_0, and the slope, b_1, in this problem.
c. Use the prediction line developed in (a) to predict the price per person for a restaurant with a summated rating of 50.
d. Compute the coefficient of determination, r^2, and interpret its meaning.
e. Perform a residual analysis on your results and evaluate the regression assumptions.
f. At the 0.05 level of significance, is there evidence of a linear relationship between the price per person and the summated rating?
g. How useful do you think the summated rating is as a predictor of price? Explain.

13.81 Refer to the discussion of beta values and market models in Problem 13.41. The S&P 500 Index tracks the overall movement of the stock market by considering the stock prices of 500 large corporations. The data file `Stocks2008` contains weekly data for this index as well as the weekly closing stock price for three companies during 2008. The variables included are:

WEEK—Week ending on date given
S&P—Weekly closing value for the S&P 500 Index
GE—Weekly closing stock price for General Electric
IBM—Weekly closing stock price for IBM
APPL—Weekly closing stock price for Apple

Source: *Data extracted from finance.yahoo.com,* May 2, 2008.

a. Estimate the market model for GE. (*Hint:* Use the percentage change in the S&P 500 Index as the independent variable and the percentage change in GE's stock price as the dependent variable.)
b. Interpret the beta value for GE.
c. Repeat (a) and (b) for IBM.
d. Repeat (a) and (b) for Apple.
e. Write a brief summary of your findings.

13.82 The data file `Stocks2008` contains the stock prices of three companies, collected weekly in 2008. The variables are:

WEEK—Week ending on date given
GE—Weekly closing stock price for General Electric
IBM—Weekly closing stock price for IBM
APPL—Weekly closing stock price for Apple

Source: *Data Extracted from finance.yahoo.com,* May 2, 2008.

a. Calculate the correlation coefficient, r, for each pair of stocks. (There are three of them.)
b. Interpret the meaning of r for each pair.
c. Is it a good idea to have all the stocks in an individual's portfolio be strongly positively correlated among each other? Explain.

13.83 The first quarter of 2008 saw an increased volatility in the precious metals market and the price of gold reached an all-time high of over $1,000 an ounce (P. Lesova, "Gold Price volatility surges in first quarter: WGC," **MarketWatch.com**, April 22, 2008). The file `FirstQuarter` contains the daily closing price of Gold, Silver, the S&P 500, and the Nasdaq for each trading day in the first quarter of 2008.

a. Compute the coefficients of correlations among the four different investments. (There are 6 of them).
b. At the 0.05 level of significance, are any of the correlations of the different investments statistically significant?

REPORT WRITING EXERCISES

13.84 In Problems 13.75–13.79, you developed regression models to predict monthly sales at a sporting goods store. Now, write a report based on the models you developed. Append to your report all appropriate charts and statistical information.

MANAGING THE *SPRINGVILLE HERALD*

To ensure that as many trial subscriptions as possible are converted to regular subscriptions, the *Herald* marketing department works closely with the distribution department to accomplish a smooth initial delivery process for the trial subscription customers. To assist in this effort, the marketing department needs to accurately forecast the number of new regular subscriptions for the coming months.

A team consisting of managers from the marketing and distribution departments was convened to develop a better method of forecasting new subscriptions. Previously, after examining new subscription data for the prior three months, a group of three managers would develop a subjective forecast of the number of new subscriptions. Lauren Hall, who was recently hired by the company to provide expertise in quantitative forecasting methods, suggested that the department look for factors that might help in predicting new subscriptions.

Members of the team found that the forecasts in the past year had been particularly inaccurate because in some months, much more time was spent on telemarketing than in other months. In particular, in the past month, only 1,055 hours were completed because callers were busy during the first week of the month attending training sessions on the personal but formal greeting style and a new standard presentation guide (see "Managing the *Springville Herald*" in Chapter 11). Lauren collected data (stored in the file **SH13**) for the number of new subscriptions and hours spent on telemarketing for each month for the past two years.

EXERCISES

SH13.1 What criticism can you make concerning the method of forecasting that involved taking the new subscriptions data for the prior three months as the basis for future projections?

SH13.2 What factors other than number of telemarketing hours spent might be useful in predicting the number of new subscriptions? Explain.

SH13.3 a. Analyze the data and develop a regression model to predict the number of new subscriptions for a month, based on the number of hours spent on telemarketing for new subscriptions.

b. If you expect to spend 1,200 hours on telemarketing per month, estimate the mean number of new subscriptions for the month. Indicate the assumptions on which this prediction is based. Do you think these assumptions are valid? Explain.

c. What would be the danger of predicting the number of new subscriptions for a month in which 2,000 hours were spent on telemarketing?

WEB CASE

Apply your knowledge of simple linear regression in this Web Case, which extends the Sunflowers Apparel Using Statistics scenario from this chapter.

Leasing agents from the Triangle Mall Management Corporation have suggested that Sunflowers consider several locations in some of Triangle's newly renovated lifestyle malls that cater to shoppers with higher-than-mean disposable income. Although the locations are smaller than the typical Sunflowers location, the leasing agents argue that higher-than-mean disposable income in the surrounding community is a better predictor of higher sales than store size. The leasing agents maintain that sample data from 14 Sunflowers stores prove that this is true.

Review the leasing agents' proposal and supporting documents that describe the data at the company's Web site,

www.prenhall.com/Springville/Triangle_Sunflower. htm (or open the Triangle_Sunflowr.htm file from the Student CD-ROM's Web Case folder), and then answers the following:

1. Should mean disposable income be used to predict sales based on the sample of 14 Sunflowers stores?

2. Should the management of Sunflowers accept the claims of Triangle's leasing agents? Why or why not?

3. Is it possible that the mean disposable income of the surrounding area is not an important factor in leasing new locations? Explain.

4. Are there any other factors not mentioned by the leasing agents that might be relevant to the store leasing decision?

REFERENCES

1. Anscombe, F. J., "Graphs in Statistical Analysis," *The American Statistician*, 27 (1973): 17–21.

2. Hoaglin, D. C., and R. Welsch, "The Hat Matrix in Regression and ANOVA," *The American Statistician* 32 (1978): 17–22.

3. Hocking, R. R., "Developments in Linear Regression Methodology: 1959–1982," *Technometrics* 25 (1983): 219–250.

4. Kutner, M. H., C. J. Nachtsheim, J. Neter, and W. Li, *Applied Linear Statistical Models*, 5th ed. (New York: McGraw-Hill/Irwin, 2005).

5. *Microsoft Excel 2007* (Redmond, WA: Microsoft Corp., 2007).

6. *Minitab for Windows Version 15* (State College, PA: Minitab, Inc., 2006).

Using Microsoft Excel for Simple Linear Regression

E13.1 Performing Simple Linear Regression Analyses

You perform simple linear regression analyses by using the ToolPak Regression procedure.

Open to the worksheet containing the data for the regression analysis. Select **Tools → Data Analysis** (Excel 97–2003) or **Data → Data Analysis** (Excel 2007). Then select **Regression** from the Data Analysis list and click **OK**. In the procedure's dialog box below, enter the cell range of the *Y* variable data as the **Input Y Range** and enter the cell range of the *X* variable data as the **Input X Range**. Click **Labels**, click **Confidence Level** and enter a value in its box, and then click **OK**. Results similar to Figure 13.4 appear on a new worksheet.

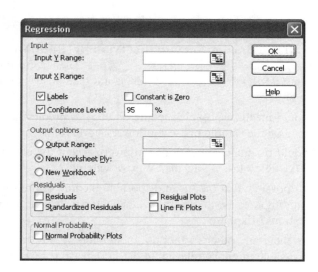

E13.2 Creating a Prediction Line on Scatter Plots: Overview

You create a prediction line on a scatter plot by first using Excel charting features to create a scatter plot and then using the **Trendline** charting option to add a prediction line.

E13.2A Creating a Prediction Line on Scatter Plots (Excel 97–2003)

Open to the scatter plot or use the instructions of Section E2.12 to first create a scatter plot. With your workbook open to the plot, select **Chart → Add Trendline**. In the Add Trendline dialog box (see Figure E13.1), click the **Type** tab

and then click **Linear**. Click the **Options** tab and select the **Automatic** option. Click **Display equation on chart** and **Display R-squared value on chart** and then click **OK**. If your data range contains a label, that label and not the label **Series1** shown in Figure E13.1 will appear in the Options tab.

FIGURE E13.1 Add Trendline dialog box (Excel 97–2003)

If there are *Y* axis values that are less than zero, the *X* axis will most likely not be placed at the bottom of the plot. To relocate the *X* axis to this position, right-click the **Y-axis**, and click **Format Axis** from the shortcut menu. In the Format Axis dialog box that appears, click the **Scale** tab and enter the value found in the **Minimum** box as the **Value (X) axis Crosses at** value. Then click **OK**.

E13.2B Creating a Prediction Line on Scatter Plots (Excel 2007)

Open to the scatter plot or use the instructions of Section E2.12 to first create a scatter plot. With your workbook open to the plot, select **Layout → Trendline** and in the Trendline gallery (not shown), select **More Trendline Options**. In the

Format Trendline dialog box that appears (shown in Figure E13.2), click **Trendline Options** in the left panel. In the right panel, click **Linear, Display equation on chart** and **Display R-squared value on chart**, and then click **Close**.

FIGURE E13.2 Format Trendline dialog box (Excel 2007)

If there are *Y* axis values that are less than zero, the *X* axis will most likely not be placed at the bottom of the plot. To relocate the *X* axis to this position, right-click the **Y axis**, and click **Format Axis** from the shortcut menu. In the Format Axis dialog box that appears, click **Axis Options** in the left panel. In the right panel, click **Axis value** and in its box enter the value shown in the dimmed **Minimum** box at the top of the panel. Then click **Close**.

E13.3 Performing Residual Analyses

You perform residual analysis by modifying the instructions of Section E13.1 to click **Residuals** and **Residual Plots** in the Regression dialog box before your click **OK**.

E13.4 Estimating Mean Values and Predicting Individual Values

You estimate the mean of *Y* and predict individual values of *Y* by making entries in the `CIEandPIforSLR.xls` workbook. Open to the **CIEandPI** worksheet and, in cell B13, enter the standard error of the estimate. This value always appears labeled as the **Standard Error** in cell B7 of a regression results worksheet such as the one shown in Figure 13.4.

With the standard error value entered, open to the **DataCopy** worksheet. This worksheet contains the *Y* and *X* values in column A and B and formulas in column C and F. Noteworthy is the cell F5 formula that uses the **TREND(Y *variable cell range*, X *variable cell range*, X *value*)** function to calculate the predicted *Y* value.

Initially, the DataCopy worksheet contains the data for the Section 13.8 Sunflowers Apparel example. To change this worksheet for other problems, follow the instructions in the worksheet for adding or deleting rows of data. (Following those instructions will ensure that the formulas in column F of the DataCopy worksheet are properly updated.)

When you are finished updating the DataCopy worksheet, return to the CIEandPI worksheet and note the results. To predict an individual *Y* value, enter a *X* value in cell B4.

14

Multiple Regression

Learning Objectives

In this chapter, you learn:

- How to develip a multiple regression model
- How to interpret the regression coefficients
- How to determine which independent variables to include in the regression model
- How to use categorical independent variables in a regression model

USING STATISTICS

@ OmniFoods

You are the marketing manager for OmniFoods, a large food products company. The company is planning a nationwide introduction of OmniPower, a new high-energy bar. Although originally marketed to runners, mountain climbers, and other athletes, high-energy bars are now popular with the general public. OmniFoods is anxious to capture a share of this thriving market.

Because the marketplace already contains several successful energy bars, you need to develop an effective marketing strategy. In particular, you need to determine the effect that price and in-store promotions will have on the sales of OmniPower. Before marketing the bar nationwide, you plan to conduct a test-market study of OmniPower sales using a sample of 34 stores in a supermarket chain. How can you extend the linear regression methods discussed in Chapter 13 to incorporate the effects of price *and* promotion into the same model? How can you use this model to improve the success of the nationwide introduction of OmniPower?

C hapter 13 focused on simple linear regression models that use *one* numerical independent variable, X, to predict the value of a numerical dependent variable, Y. Often you can make better predictions by using *more than one* independent variable. This chapter introduces you to **multiple regression models** that use two or more independent variables to predict the value of a dependent variable.

14.1 Developing a Multiple Regression Model

A sample of 34 stores in a supermarket chain is selected for a test-market study of OmniPower. All the stores selected have approximately the same monthly sales volume. Two independent variables are considered here—the price of an OmniPower bar, as measured in cents (X_1), and the monthly budget for in-store promotional expenditures, measured in dollars (X_2). In-store promotional expenditures typically include signs and displays, in-store coupons, and free samples. The dependent variable Y is the number of OmniPower bars sold in a month. Table 14.1 presents the results (stored in the file **OmniPower**) of the test-market study.

TABLE 14.1

Monthly OmniPower Sales, Price, and Promotional Expenditures

Store	Sales	Price	Promotion	Store	Sales	Price	Promotion
1	4,141	59	200	18	2,730	79	400
2	3,842	59	200	19	2,618	79	400
3	3,056	59	200	20	4,421	79	400
4	3,519	59	200	21	4,113	79	600
5	4,226	59	400	22	3,746	79	600
6	4,630	59	400	23	3,532	79	600
7	3,507	59	400	24	3,825	79	600
8	3,754	59	400	25	1,096	99	200
9	5,000	59	600	26	761	99	200
10	5,120	59	600	27	2,088	99	200
11	4,011	59	600	28	820	99	200
12	5,015	59	600	29	2,114	99	400
13	1,916	79	200	30	1,882	99	400
14	675	79	200	31	2,159	99	400
15	3,636	79	200	32	1,602	99	400
16	3,224	79	200	33	3,354	99	600
17	2,295	79	400	34	2,927	99	600

With two independent variables and a dependent variable, the data are in three dimensions. Figure 14.1 presents a three-dimensional plot constructed by Minitab.

FIGURE 14.1

Minitab three-dimensional plot of monthly OmniPower sales, price, and promotional expenditures

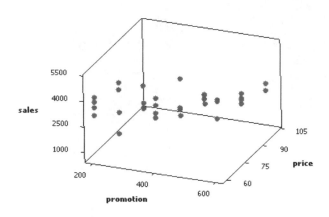

3D Scatterplot of sales vs price and promotion

Interpreting the Regression Coefficients

When there are several independent variables, you can extend the simple linear regression model of Equation (13.1) by assuming a linear relationship between each independent variable and the dependent variable. For example, with k independent variables, the multiple regression model is expressed in Equation (14.1).

MULTIPLE REGRESSION MODEL WITH k INDEPENDENT VARIABLES

$$Y_i = \beta_0 + \beta_1 X_{1i} + \beta_2 X_{2i} + \beta_3 X_{3i} + \cdots + \beta_k X_{ki} + \varepsilon_i \qquad (14.1)$$

where

$\beta_0 = Y$ intercept

$\beta_1 =$ slope of Y with variable X_1, holding variables $X_2, X_3, \ldots, X_k$ constant

$\beta_2 =$ slope of Y with variable X_2, holding variables $X_1, X_3, \ldots, X_k$ constant

$\beta_3 =$ slope of Y with variable X_3, holding variables $X_1, X_2, X_4, \ldots, X_k$ constant

.

.

.

$\beta_k =$ slope of Y with variable X_k, holding variables $X_1, X_2, X_3, \ldots, X_{k-1}$ constant

$\varepsilon_i =$ random error in Y for observation i

Equation (14.2) defines the multiple regression model with two independent variables.

MULTIPLE REGRESSION MODEL WITH TWO INDEPENDENT VARIABLES

$$Y_i = \beta_0 + \beta_1 X_{1i} + \beta_2 X_{2i} + \varepsilon_i \qquad (14.2)$$

where

$\beta_0 = Y$ intercept

$\beta_1 =$ slope of Y with variable X_1, holding variable X_2 constant

$\beta_2 =$ slope of Y with variable X_2, holding variable X_1 constant

$\varepsilon_i =$ random error in Y for observation i

Compare the multiple regression model to the simple linear regression model [Equation (13.1)]:

$$Y_i = \beta_0 + \beta_1 X_i + \varepsilon_i$$

In the simple linear regression model, the slope, β_1, represents the change in the mean of Y per unit change in X and does not take into account any other variables. In the multiple regression model with two independent variables [Equation (14.2)], the slope, β_1, represents the change in the mean of Y per unit change in X_1, taking into account the effect of X_2.

As in the case of simple linear regression, you use the sample regression coefficients (b_0, b_1, and b_2) as estimates of the population parameters (β_0, β_1, and β_2). Equation (14.3) defines the regression equation for a multiple regression model with two independent variables.

MULTIPLE REGRESSION EQUATION WITH TWO INDEPENDENT VARIABLES

$$\hat{Y}_i = b_0 + b_1 X_{1i} + b_2 X_{2i} \qquad (14.3)$$

You can use Microsoft Excel or Minitab to compute the values of the three regression coefficients for the OmniPower sales data (see Figures 14.2 or 14.3).

	A	B	C	D	E	F	G
1	OmniPower Sales Analysis						
2							
3	Regression Statistics						
4	Multiple R	0.8705					
5	R Square	0.7577					
6	Adjusted R Square	0.7421					
7	Standard Error	638.0653					
8	Observations	34					
9							
10	ANOVA						
11		df	SS	MS	F	Significance F	
12	Regression	2	39472730.77	19736365.387	48.4771	2.86258E-10	
13	Residual	31	12620946.67	407127.312			
14	Total	33	52093677.44				
15							
16		Coefficients	Standard Error	t Stat	P-value	Lower 95%	Upper 95%
17	Intercept	5837.5208	628.1502	9.2932	1.791E-10	4556.3992	7118.6423
18	Price	-53.2173	6.8522	-7.7664	9.200E-09	-67.1925	-39.2421
19	Promotion	3.6131	0.6852	5.2728	9.822E-06	2.2155	5.0106

From Figure 14.2 or 14.3, the computed values of the regression coefficients are

$$b_0 = 5837.521 \quad b_1 = -53.217 \quad b_2 = 3.613$$

Therefore, the multiple regression equation is

$$\hat{Y}_i = 5{,}837.521 - 53.217X_{1i} + 3.613X_{2i}$$

where

$\hat{Y}_i =$ predicted monthly sales of OmniPower bars for store i

$X_{1i} =$ price of OmniPower bar (in cents) for store i

$X_{2i} =$ monthly in-store promotional expenditures (in dollars) for store i

The sample Y intercept ($b_0 = 5{,}837.521$) estimates the number of OmniPower bars sold in a month if the price is \$0.00 and the total amount spent on promotional expenditures is also \$0.00. Because these values of price and promotion are outside the range of price and promotion used in the test-market study, and are nonsensical, the value of b_0 has little or no practical interpretation.

The slope of price with OmniPower sales ($b_1 = -53.217$) indicates that, for a given amount of monthly promotional expenditures, the mean sales of OmniPower are estimated to decrease by 53.217 bars per month for each 1-cent increase in the price. The slope of monthly promotional expenditures with OmniPower sales ($b_2 = 3.613$) indicates that, for a given price, the mean sales of OmniPower are estimated to increase by 3.613 bars for each additional \$1 spent on promotions. These estimates allow you to better understand the likely effect that price and promotion decisions will have in the marketplace. For example, a 10-cent decrease in price is estimated to increase mean sales by 532.17 bars, with a fixed amount of monthly promotional expenditures. A \$100 increase in promotional expenditures is estimated to increase mean sales by 361.31 bars, for a given price.

Regression coefficients in multiple regression are called **net regression coefficients**; they estimate the mean change in Y per unit change in a particular X, *holding constant the effect of the other X variables*. For example, in the study of OmniPower bar sales, for a store with a given amount of promotional expenditures, the mean sales are estimated to decrease by 53.217 bars per month for each 1-cent increase in the price of an OmniPower bar. Another way to interpret this "net effect" is to think of two stores with an equal amount of promotional expenditures. If the first store charges 1 cent more than the other store, the net effect of this difference is that the first store is predicted to sell 53.217 fewer bars per month than the sec-

FIGURE 14.3   SPSS results

Variables Entered/Removed[b]

Model	Variables Entered	Variables Removed	Method
1	Price, Promotion[a]		Enter

a. All requested variables entered.
b. Dependent Variable: Sales

Model Summary

Model	R	R Square	Adjusted R Square	Std. Error of the Estimate
1	.870[a]	.758	.742	638.065

a. Predictors: (Constant), Price, Promotion

ANOVA[b]

Model		Sum of Squares	df	Mean Square	F	Sig.
1	Regression	3.947E7	2	1.974E7	48.477	.000[a]
	Residual	1.262E7	31	407127.312		
	Total	5,209E7	33			

a. Predictors: (Constant), Price, Promotion
b. Dependent Variable: Sales

Coefficients[a]

Model		Unstandardized Coefficients B	Std. Error	Standardized Coefficients Beta	t	Sig.
1	(Constant)	5837.521	628.150		9.293	.000
	Promotion	−3.613	.685	.468	5.273	.000
	Price	−53.2117	6.852	−.690	−7.766	.000

a. Dependent Variable: Assessed value

ond store. To interpret the net effect of promotional expenditures, you can consider two stores that are charging the same price. If the first store spends $1 more on promotional expenditures, the net effect of this difference is that the first store is predicted to sell 3.613 more bars per month than the second store.

Predicting the Dependent Variable Y

You can use the multiple regression equation computed by Microsoft Excel or SPSS to predict values of the dependent variable. For example, what are the predicted sales for a store charging 79 cents during a month in which promotional expenditures are $400? Using the multiple regression equation,

$$\hat{Y}_i = 5{,}837.521 - 53.217X_{1i} + 3.613X_{2i}$$

with $X_{1i} = 79$ and $X_{2i} = 400$,

$$\hat{Y}_i = 5{,}837.521 - 53.217(79) + 3.613(400)$$
$$= 3{,}078.57$$

Thus, your sales prediction for stores charging 79 cents and spending $400 in promotional expenditures is 3,078.57 OmniPower bars per month.

After you have developed the regression equation, done a residual analysis (see Section 14.3), and determined the significance of the overall fitted model (see Section 14.2), the next step often involves a confidence interval estimate of the mean value and a prediction interval for an individual value. The computation of these intervals is too complex to do by hand, and you should use Microsoft Excel or Minitab to perform the calculations. Figure 14.4 below illustrates Microsoft Excel results.

The 95% confidence interval estimate of the mean OmniPower sales for all stores charging 79 cents and spending $400 in promotional expenditures is 2,854.07 to 3,303.08 bars. The prediction interval for an individual store is 1,758.01 to 4,399.14 bars.

FIGURE 14.4

Microsoft Excel confidence interval estimate and prediction interval worksheet for the OmniPower sales data

See Section E14.3 to create this.

	A	B	C	D
1	Confidence Interval Estimate and Prediction Interval			
2				
3	Data			
4	Confidence Level	95%		
5		1		
6	Price given value	79		
7	Promotion given value	400		
8				
9	X'X	34	2646	13200
10		2646	214674	1018800
11		13200	1018800	6000000
12				
13	Inverse of X'X	0.969163	-0.00941	-0.00053
14		-0.009408	0.000115	1.12E-06
15		-0.000535	1.12E-06	1.15E-06
16				
17	X'G times Inverse of X'X	0.012054	0.000149	1.49E-05
18				
19	[X'G times Inverse of X'X] times XG	0.029762	=MMULT(B17:D17, B5:B7)	
20	t Statistic	2.0395	=TINV(1 - B4, MR!B13)	
21	Predicted Y (YHat)	3078.57	{=MMULT(TRANSPOSE(B5:B7), MR!B17:B19)}	
22				
23	For Average Predicted Y (YHat)			
24	Interval Half Width	224.50	=B20 * SQRT(B19) * MR!B7	
25	Confidence Interval Lower Limit	2854.07	=B21 - B24	
26	Confidence Interval Upper Limit	3303.08	=B21 + B24	
27				
28	For Individual Response Y			
29	Interval Half Width	1320.57	=B20 * SQRT(1 + B19) * MR!B7	
30	Prediction Interval Lower Limit	1758.01	=B21 - B29	
31	Prediction Interval Upper Limit	4399.14	=B21 + B29	

Problems for Section 14.1

LEARNING THE BASICS

14.1 For this problem, use the following multiple regression equation:

$$\hat{Y}_i = 10 + 5X_{1i} + 3X_{2i}$$

a. Interpret the meaning of the slopes.
b. Interpret the meaning of the Y intercept.

14.2 For this problem, use the following multiple regression equation:

$$\hat{Y}_i = 50 - 2X_{1i} + 7X_{2i}$$

a. Interpret the meaning of the slopes.
b. Interpret the meaning of the Y intercept.

APPLYING THE CONCEPTS

14.3 A marketing analyst for a shoe manufacturer is considering the development of a new brand of running shoes. The marketing analyst wants to determine which variables to use in predicting durability (i.e., the effect of long-term impact). Two independent variables under consideration are X_1 (FOREIMP), a measurement of the forefoot shock-absorbing capability, and X_2 (MIDSOLE), a measurement of the change in impact properties over time. The dependent variable Y is LTIMP, a measure of the shoe's durability after a repeated impact test. A random sample of 15 types of currently manufactured running shoes was selected for testing, with the following results:

Variable	Coefficients	Standard Error	t Statistic	p-Value
INTERCEPT	−0.02686	0.06905	−0.39	0.7034
FOREIMP	0.79116	0.06295	12.57	0.0000
MIDSOLE	0.60484	0.07174	8.43	0.0000

a. State the multiple regression equation.
b. Interpret the meaning of the slopes, b_1 and b_2, in this problem.

✓SELF Test **14.4** A mail-order catalog business selling personal computer supplies, software, and hardware maintains a centralized warehouse. Management is currently examining the process of distribution from the warehouse and wants to study the factors that affect warehouse distribution costs. Currently, a small handling fee is added to each order, regardless of the amount of the order. Data collected over the past 24 months (stored in the file Warecost) indicate the warehouse distribution costs (in thousands of dollars), the sales (in thousands of dollars), and the number of orders received.
a. State the multiple regression equation.
b. Interpret the meaning of the slopes, b_1 and b_2, in this problem.
c. Explain why the regression coefficient, b_0, has no practical meaning in the context of this problem.
d. Predict the monthly warehouse distribution cost when sales are $400,000 and the number of orders is 4,500.
e. Construct a 95% confidence interval estimate for the mean monthly warehouse distribution cost when sales are $400,000 and the number of orders is 4,500.
f. Construct a 95% prediction interval for the monthly warehouse distribution cost for a particular month when sales are $400,000 and the number of orders is 4,500.
g. Explain why the interval in (e) is narrower than the interval in (f).

14.5 A consumer organization wants to develop a regression model to predict gasoline mileage (as measured by miles per gallon) based on the horsepower of the car's engine and the weight of the car (in pounds). A sample of 50 recent car models was selected, with the results recorded in the file Auto.
a. State the multiple regression equation.
b. Interpret the meaning of the slopes, b_1 and b_2, in this problem.
c. Explain why the regression coefficient, b_0, has no practical meaning in the context of this problem.
d. Predict the miles per gallon for a car that has 60 horsepower and weigh 2,000 pounds.
e. Construct a 95% confidence interval estimate for the mean miles per gallon for cars that have 60 horsepower and weigh 2,000 pounds.
f. Construct a 95% prediction interval for the miles per gallon for an individual car that has 60 horsepower and weighs 2,000 pounds.

14.6 A consumer products company wants to measure the effectiveness of different types of advertising media in the promotion of its products. Specifically, the company is interested in the effectiveness of radio advertising and newspaper advertising (including the cost of discount coupons). A sample of 22 cities with approximately equal populations is selected for study during a test period of one month. Each city is allocated a specific expenditure level both for radio advertising and for newspaper advertising. The sales of the product (in thousands of dollars) and also the levels of media expenditure (in thousands of dollars) during the test month are recorded, with the results stored in the file Advertise:
a. State the multiple regression equation.
b. Interpret the meaning of the slopes, b_1 and b_2, in this problem.
c. Interpret the meaning of the regression coefficient, b_0.
d. Which type of advertising is more effective? Explain.

14.7 The director of broadcasting operations for a television station wants to study the issue of standby hours (i.e., hours in which unionized graphic artists at the station are paid but are not actually involved in any activity). The variables in the study include:

Standby hours (Y)—Total number of standby hours in a week
Total staff present (X_1)—Weekly total of people-days
Remote hours (X_2)—Total number of hours worked by employees at locations away from the central plant

The results for a period of 26 weeks are in the data file Standby.
a. State the multiple regression equation.
b. Interpret the meaning of the slopes, b_1 and b_2, in this problem.
c. Explain why the regression coefficient, b_0, has no practical meaning in the context of this problem.
d. Predict the standby hours for a week in which the total staff present have 310 people-days and the remote hours are 400.
e. Construct a 95% confidence interval estimate for the mean standby hours for weeks in which the total staff present have 310 people-days and the remote hours are 400.
f. Construct a 95% prediction interval for the standby hours for a single week in which the total staff present have 310 people-days and the remote hours are 400.

14.8 Nassau County is located approximately 25 miles east of New York City. Data in the file GlenCove include the appraised value, land area of the property in acres, and age, in years, for a sample of 30 single-family homes located in Glen Cove, a small city in Nassau County. Develop a multiple linear regression model to predict appraised value based on land area of the property and age, in years.
a. State the multiple regression equation.

b. Interpret the meaning of the slopes, b_1 and b_2, in this problem.

c. Explain why the regression coefficient, b_0, has no practical meaning in the context of this problem.

d. Predict the appraised value for a house that has a land area of 0.25 acres and is 45 years old.

e. Construct a 95% confidence interval estimate for the mean appraised value for houses that have a land area of 0.25 acres and are 45 years old.

f. Construct a 95% prediction interval for the appraised value for an individual house that has a land area of 0.25 acres and is 45 years old.

14.2 r^2, Adjusted r^2, and the Overall F Test

This section discusses three methods you can use to evaluate the overall multiple regression model: the coefficient of multiple determination r^2, the adjusted r^2, and the overall F test.

Coefficient of Multiple Determination

Recall from Section 13.3 that the coefficient of determination, r^2, measures the proportion of the variation in Y that is explained by the independent variable X in the simple linear regression model. In multiple regression, the **coefficient of multiple determination** represents the proportion of the variation in Y that is explained by the set of independent variables. Equation (14.4) defines the coefficient of multiple determination for a multiple regression model with two or more independent variables.

COEFFICIENT OF MULTIPLE DETERMINATION

The coefficient of multiple determination is equal to the regression sum of squares (SSR) divided by the total sum of squares (SST).

$$r^2 = \frac{\text{Regression sum of squares}}{\text{Total sum of squares}} = \frac{SSR}{SST} \qquad (14.4)$$

where

$$SSR = \text{Regression sum of squares}$$

$$SST = \text{Total sum of squares}$$

In the OmniPower example, from Figure 14.2 or 14.3 on pages 642–643, $SSR = 39{,}472{,}730.77$ and $SST = 52{,}093{,}677.44$. Thus,

$$r^2 = \frac{SSR}{SST} = \frac{39{,}472{,}730.77}{52{,}093{,}677.44} = 0.7577$$

The coefficient of multiple determination ($r^2 = 0.7577$) indicates that 75.77% of the variation in sales is explained by the variation in the price and in the promotional expenditures. You can also find the coefficient of multiple determination directly from the Microsoft Excel results in Figure 14.2, labeled "R Square"; or from the Minitab results in Figure 14.3, labeled "R-Sq."

Adjusted r^2

When considering multiple regression models, some statisticians suggest that you should use the **adjusted r^2** to reflect both the number of independent variables in the model and the sample size. Reporting the adjusted r^2 is extremely important when you are comparing two or more regression models that predict the same dependent variable but have a different number of independent variables. Equation (14.5) defines the adjusted r^2.

ADJUSTED r^2

$$r_{adj}^2 = 1 - \left[(1 - r^2) \frac{n-1}{n-k-1} \right] \qquad (14.5)$$

where k is the number of independent variables in the regression equation.

Thus, for the OmniPower data, because $r^2 = 0.7577$, $n = 34$, and $k = 2$,

$$r_{adj}^2 = 1 - \left[(1 - 0.7577) \frac{34-1}{34-2-1} \right]$$

$$= 1 - \left[(0.2423) \frac{33}{31} \right]$$

$$= 1 - 0.2579$$

$$= 0.7421$$

Hence, 74.21% of the variation in sales is explained by the multiple regression model after adjusting for the number of independent variables and the sample size. You can also find the adjusted r^2 directly from the Microsoft Excel results in Figure 14.2, labeled "Adjusted R Square"; or from the Minitab results in Figure 14.3, labeled "R-Sq(adj)."

Test for the Significance of the Overall Multiple Regression Model

You use the **overall F test** to test whether there is a significant relationship between the dependent variable and the entire set of independent variables (the overall multiple regression model). Because there is more than one independent variable, you use the following null and alternative hypotheses:

H_0: $\beta_1 = \beta_2 = \cdots = \beta_k = 0$ (There is no linear relationship between the dependent variable and the independent variables.)

H_1: At least one $\beta_j \neq 0$, $j = 1, 2, \ldots, k$ (There is a linear relationship between the dependent variable and at least one of the independent variables.)

Equation (14.6) defines the statistic for the overall F test. Table 14.2 presents the associated ANOVA summary table.

OVERALL F TEST

The F_{STAT} test statistic is equal to the regression mean square (MSR) divided by the mean square error (MSE).

$$F_{STAT} = \frac{MSR}{MSE} \qquad (14.6)$$

where

F_{STAT} = test statistic from an F distribution with k and $n - k - 1$ degrees of freedom

k = number of independent variables in the regression model

The decision rule is

Reject H_0 at the α level of significance if $F_{STAT} > F_\alpha$;

otherwise, do not reject H_0.

TABLE 14.2

ANOVA Summary Table for the Overall *F* Test

Source	Degrees of Freedom	Sum of Squares	Mean Square (Variance)	F
Regression	k	SSR	$MSR = \dfrac{SSR}{k}$	$F_{STAT} = \dfrac{MSR}{MSE}$
Error	$n - k - 1$	SSE	$MSE = \dfrac{SSE}{n - k - 1}$	
Total	$n - 1$	SST		

Using a 0.05 level of significance, the critical value of the *F* distribution with 2 and 31 degrees of freedom found from Table E.5 is approximately 3.32 (see Figure 14.5 below). From Figure 14.2 or 14.3, the F_{STAT} test statistic given in the ANOVA summary table is 48.4771. Because 48.4771 > 3.32, or because the *p*-value = 0.000 < 0.05, you reject H_0 and conclude that at least one of the independent variables (price and/or promotional expenditures) is related to sales.

FIGURE 14.5

Testing for the significance of a set of regression coefficients at the 0.05 level of significance, with 2 and 31 degrees of freedom

Problems for Section 14.2

LEARNING THE BASICS

14.9 The following ANOVA summary table is for a multiple regression model with two independent variables:

Source	Degrees of Freedom	Sum of Squares	Mean Squares	F
Regression	2	60		
Error	18	120		
Total	20	180		

a. Determine the regression mean square (*MSR*) and the mean square error (*MSE*).
b. Compute the overall F_{STAT} test statistic.
c. Determine whether there is a significant relationship between *Y* and the two independent variables at the 0.05 level of significance.
d. Compute the coefficient of multiple determination, r^2, and interpret its meaning.
e. Compute the adjusted r^2.

14.10 The following ANOVA summary table is for a multiple regression model with two independent variables:

Source	Degrees of Freedom	Sum of Squares	Mean Squares	F
Regression	2	30		
Error	10	120		
Total	12	150		

a. Determine the regression mean square (*MSR*) and the mean square error (*MSE*).
b. Compute the overall F_{STAT} test statistic.
c. Determine whether there is a significant relationship between *Y* and the two independent variables at the 0.05 level of significance.
d. Compute the coefficient of multiple determination, r^2, and interpret its meaning.
e. Compute the adjusted r^2.

APPLYING THE CONCEPTS

14.11 Eileen M. Van Aken and Brian M. Kleiner, professors at Virginia Polytechnic Institute and State University, investigated the factors that contribute to the effectiveness of teams (data extracted from "Determinants of Effectiveness for Cross-Functional Organizational Design Teams," *Quality Management Journal*, 1997, 4, pp. 51–79). The researchers studied 34 independent variables, such as team skills, diversity, meeting frequency, and clarity in expectations. For each of the teams studied, each of the variables was given a value of 1 through 100, based on the results of interviews and survey data, where 100 represents the highest rating. The dependent variable, team performance, was also given a value of 1 through 100, with 100 representing the highest rating. Many different regression models were explored, including the following:

Model 1

$$\text{Team performance} = \beta_0 + \beta_1(\text{Team skill}) + \varepsilon,$$

$$r^2_{\text{adj}} = 0.68$$

Model 2

$$\text{Team performance} = \beta_0 + \beta_1(\text{Clarity in expectations}) + \varepsilon,$$

$$r^2_{\text{adj}} = 0.78$$

Model 3

$$\text{Team performance} = \beta_0 + \beta_1(\text{Team skills}) +$$
$$\beta_2(\text{Clarity in expectations}) + \varepsilon$$
$$r^2_{\text{adj}} = 0.97$$

a. Interpret the adjusted r^2 for each of the three models.
b. Which of these three models do you think is the best predictor of team performance?

14.12 In Problem 14.3, you predicted the durability of a brand of running shoe, based on the forefoot shock-absorbing capability and the change in impact properties over time. The regression analysis resulted in the following ANOVA summary table:

Source	Degrees of Freedom	Sum of Squares	Mean Squares	F	p-value
Regression	2	12.61020	6.30510	97.69	0.0001
Error	12	0.77453	0.06454		
Total	14	13.38473			

a. Determine whether there is a significant relationship between durability and the two independent variables at the 0.05 level of significance.
b. Interpret the meaning of the *p*-value.
c. Compute the coefficient of multiple determination, r^2, and interpret its meaning.
d. Compute the adjusted r^2.

14.13 In Problem 14.5, you used horsepower and weight to predict gasoline mileage (see the Auto file). Using the results from that problem,
a. determine whether there is a significant relationship between gasoline mileage and the two independent

variables (horsepower and weight) at the 0.05 level of significance.
b. interpret the meaning of the *p*-value.
c. compute the coefficient of multiple determination, r^2, and interpret its meaning.
d. compute the adjusted r^2.

14.14 In Problem 14.4, you used sales and number of orders to predict distribution costs at a mail-order catalog business (see the Warecost file). Using the results from that problem,
a. determine whether there is a significant relationship between distribution costs and the two independent variables (sales and number of orders) at the 0.05 level of significance.
b. interpret the meaning of the *p*-value.
c. compute the coefficient of multiple determination, r^2, and interpret its meaning.
d. compute the adjusted r^2.

14.15 In Problem 14.7, you used the total staff present and remote hours to predict standby hours (see the file Standby). Using the results from that problem,
a. determine whether there is a significant relationship between standby hours and the two independent variables (total staff present and remote hours) at the 0.05 level of significance.
b. interpret the meaning of the *p*-value.
c. compute the coefficient of multiple determination, r^2, and interpret its meaning.
d. compute the adjusted r^2.

14.16 In Problem 14.6, you used radio advertising and newspaper advertising to predict sales (see the Advertise file). Using the results from that problem,
a. determine whether there is a significant relationship between sales and the two independent variables (radio advertising and newspaper advertising) at the 0.05 level of significance.
b. interpret the meaning of the *p*-value.
c. compute the coefficient of multiple determination, r^2, and interpret its meaning.
d. compute the adjusted r^2.

14.17 In Problem 14.8, you used the land area of a property and the age of a house to predict appraised value (see the GlenCove file). Using the results from that problem,
a. determine whether there is a significant relationship between appraised value and the two independent variables (land area of a property and age of a house) at the 0.05 level of significance.
b. interpret the meaning of the *p*-value.
c. compute the coefficient of multiple determination, r^2, and interpret its meaning.
d. compute the adjusted r^2.

14.3 Residual Analysis for the Multiple Regression Model

In Section 13.5, you used residual analysis to evaluate the adequacy of the simple linear regression model. For the multiple regression model with two independent variables, you need to construct and analyze the following residual plots:

1. Residuals versus $\hat{Y}_i$
2. Residuals versus X_{1i}
3. Residuals versus X_{2i}
4. Residuals versus time

The first residual plot examines the pattern of residuals versus the predicted values of Y. If the residuals show a pattern for different predicted values of Y, then there is a curvilinear effect in at least one independent variable, a possible violation of the assumption of equal variance (see Figure 13.13), and/or the need to transform the Y variable.

The second and third residual plots involve the independent variables. Patterns in the plot of the residuals versus an independent variable may indicate the existence of a curvilinear effect and, therefore, the need to add a curvilinear independent variable to the multiple regression model. The fourth plot is used to investigate patterns in the residuals in order to validate the independence assumption when the data are collected in time order. A cyclical pattern with this residual plot indicates that the residuals are correlated, not independent.

Figure 14.6 illustrates the Microsoft Excel residual plots for the OmniPower sales example. There is very little or no pattern in the relationship between the residuals and the predicted value of Y, the value of X_1 (price), or the value of X_2 (promotional expenditures). Thus, you can conclude that the multiple regression model is appropriate for predicting sales. There is no need to plot the residuals versus time since the data were not collected in time order.

Problems for Section 14.3

APPLYING THE CONCEPTS

14.18 In Problem 14.4, you used sales and number of orders to predict distribution costs at a mail-order catalog business (see the `Warecost` file).
a. Plot the residuals versus $\hat{Y}_i$
b. Plot the residuals versus X_{1i}.
c. Plot the residuals versus X_{2i}.
d. Plot the residuals versus time.
e. In the residuals plots created in (a) through (d), is there any evidence of a violation to the regression assumptions? Explain.

14.19 In Problem 14.5, you used horsepower and weight to predict gasoline mileage (see the `Auto` file).
a. Plot the residuals versus $\hat{Y}_i$.
b. Plot the residuals versus X_{1i}.
c. Plot the residuals versus X_{2i}.
d. In the residuals plots created in (a) through (c), is there any evidence of a violation to the regression assumptions? Explain.

14.20 In Problem 14.6, you used radio advertising and newspaper advertising to predict sales (see the `Advertise` file).
a. Perform a residual analysis on your results.
b. Are the regression assumptions valid for these data?

14.21 In Problem 14.7, you used the total staff present and remote hours to predict standby hours (see the `Standby` file).
a. Perform a residual analysis on your results.
b. Are the regression assumptions valid for these data?

14.22 In Problem 14.8, you used the land area of a property and the age of a house to predict appraised value (see the `GlenCove` file).
a. Perform a residual analysis on your results.
b. Are the regression assumptions valid for these data?

FIGURE 14.6

Microsoft Excel residual plots for the OmniPower sales data: Panel *A*, residuals versus predicted *Y*; Panel *B*, residuals versus price; Panel *C*, residuals versus promotional expenditures

See Section E14.2 to create this.

Panel A

Panel B

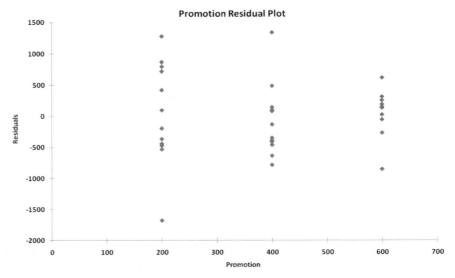

Panel C

14.4 Inferences Concerning the Population Regression Coefficients

In Section 13.6, you tested the slope in a simple linear regression model to determine the significance of the relationship between X and Y. In addition, you constructed a confidence interval estimate of the population slope. This section extends those procedures to multiple regression.

Tests of Hypothesis

In a simple linear regression model, to test a hypothesis concerning the population slope, β_1, you used Equation (13.15):

$$t_{STAT} = \frac{b_1 - \beta_1}{S_{b_1}}$$

Equation (14.7) generalizes this equation for multiple regression.

TESTING FOR THE SLOPE IN MULTIPLE REGRESSION

$$t_{STAT} = \frac{b_j - \beta_j}{S_{b_j}} \tag{14.7}$$

where

b_j = slope of variable j with Y, holding constant the effects of all other independent variables

S_{b_j} = standard error of the regression coefficient b_j

t_{STAT} = test statistic for a t distribution with $n - k - 1$ degrees of freedom

k = number of independent variables in the regression equation

β_j = hypothesized value of the population slope for variable j, holding constant the effects of all other independent variables

To determine whether variable X_2 (amount of promotional expenditures) has a significant effect on sales, taking into account the price of OmniPower bars, the null and alternative hypotheses are

$$H_0: \beta_2 = 0$$
$$H_1: \beta_2 \neq 0$$

From Equation (14.7) and Figures 14.2 or 14.3.

$$t_{STAT} = \frac{b_2 - \beta_2}{S_{b_2}}$$

$$= \frac{3.6131 - 0}{0.6852} = 5.2728$$

If you select a level of significance of 0.05, the critical values of t for 31 degrees of freedom from Table E.3 are -2.0395 and $+2.0395$ (see Figure 14.7).

From Figure 14.2 or 14.3, observe that the computed t_{STAT} test statistic is 5.2728. Because $t_{STAT} = 5.2728 > 2.0395$, you reject H_0 and conclude that there is a significant relationship between the variable X_2 (promotional expenditures) and sales, taking into account the price,

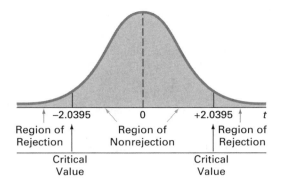

X_1. Using the *p*-value approach, note that the *p*-value is approximately zero. This extremely small *p*-value allows you to strongly reject the null hypothesis that there is no linear relationship between sales and promotional expenditures. Example 14.1 presents the test for the significance of β_1, the slope of sales with price.

EXAMPLE 14.1

Testing for the
Significance of the
Slope of Sales with
Price

At the 0.05 level of significance, is there evidence that the slope of sales with price is different from zero?

SOLUTION From Figure 14.2 or 14.3, $t_{STAT} = -7.766 < -2.0395$ (the critical value for $\alpha = 0.05$) or the *p*-value $= 0.0000 < 0.05$. Thus, there is a significant relationship between price, X_1, and sales, taking into account the promotional expenditures, X_2.

As seen with each of the two X variables, the test of significance for a specific regression coefficient is actually a test for the significance of adding that variable into a regression model, given that the other variable is included. Therefore, the t test for the regression coefficient is equivalent to testing for the contribution of each independent variable.

Confidence Interval Estimation

Instead of testing the significance of a population slope, you may want to estimate the value of a population slope. Equation (14.8) defines the confidence interval estimate for a population slope in multiple regression.

CONFIDENCE INTERVAL ESTIMATE FOR THE SLOPE

$$b_j \pm t_{\alpha/2}S_{b_j} \qquad (14.8)$$

where $t_{\alpha/2}$ is the critical value corresponding to an upper-tail probability of $\alpha/2$ from the t distribution with $n - k - 1$ degrees of freedom (i.e., a cumulative area of $1 - \alpha/2$), and k is the number of independent variables.

To construct a 95% confidence interval estimate of the population slope, β_1 (the effect of price, X_1, on sales, Y, holding constant the effect of promotional expenditures, X_2), the critical value of t at the 95% confidence level with 31 degrees of freedom is 2.0395 (see Table E.3). Then, using Equation (14.8) and Figure 14.2 or 14.3,

$$b_1 \pm t_{\alpha/2}S_{b_1}$$

$$-53.217 \pm (2.0395)(6.852)$$

$$-53.217 \pm 13.9752$$

$$-67.1925 \le \beta_1 \le -39.2421$$

Taking into account the effect of promotional expenditures, the estimated effect of a 1-cent increase in price is to reduce mean sales by approximately 39.2 to 67.2 bars. You have 95% confidence that this interval correctly estimates the relationship between these variables. From a hypothesis-testing viewpoint, because this confidence interval does not include 0, you conclude that the regression coefficient, β_1, has a significant effect.

Example 14.2 constructs and interprets a confidence interval estimate for the slope of sales with promotional expenditures.

EXAMPLE 14.2

Constructing a Confidence Interval Estimate for the Slope of Sales with Promotional Expenditures

Construct a 95% confidence interval estimate of the population slope of sales with promotional expenditures.

SOLUTION The critical value of t at the 95% confidence level, with 31 degrees of freedom, is 2.0395 (see Table E.3). Using Equation (14.8) and Figure 14.2 or 14.3,

$$b_2 \pm t_{\alpha/2}S_{b_2}$$

$$3.613 \pm (2.0395)(0.685)$$

$$3.613 \pm 1.3975$$

$$2.2156 \le \beta_2 \le 5.0106$$

Thus, taking into account the effect of price, the estimated effect of each additional dollar of promotional expenditures is to increase mean sales by approximately 2.2 to 5.0 bars. You have 95% confidence that this interval correctly estimates the relationship between these variables. From a hypothesis-testing viewpoint, because this confidence interval does not include 0, you can conclude that the regression coefficient, β_2, has a significant effect.

Problems for Section 14.4

LEARNING THE BASICS

14.23 Given the following information from a multiple regression analysis:

$$n = 25 \quad b_1 = 5 \quad b_2 = 10 \quad S_{b_1} = 2 \quad S_{b_2} = 8$$

a. Which variable has the largest slope, in units of a t statistic?
b. Construct a 95% confidence interval estimate of the population slope, β_1.
c. At the 0.05 level of significance, determine whether each independent variable makes a significant contribution to the regression model. On the basis of these results, indicate the independent variables to include in this model.

14.24 Given the following information from a multiple regression analysis:

$$n = 20 \quad b_1 = 4 \quad b_2 = 3 \quad S_{b_1} = 1.2 \quad S_{b_2} = 0.8$$

a. Which variable has the largest slope, in units of a t statistic?
b. Construct a 95% confidence interval estimate of the population slope, β_1.
c. At the 0.05 level of significance, determine whether each independent variable makes a significant contribution to the regression model. On the basis of these results, indicate the independent variables to include in this model.

APPLYING THE CONCEPTS

14.25 In Problem 14.3, you predicted the durability of a brand of running shoe, based on the forefoot shock-absorbing capability (FOREIMP) and the change in impact properties over time (MIDSOLE) for a sample of 15 pairs of shoes. Use the following results:

Variable	Coefficient	Standard Error	t Statistic	p-Value
INTERCEPT	-0.02686	0.06905	-0.39	0.7034
FOREIMP	0.79116	0.06295	12.57	0.0000
MIDSOLE	0.60484	0.07174	8.43	0.0000

a. Construct a 95% confidence interval estimate of the population slope between durability and forefoot shock-absorbing capability.
b. At the 0.05 level of significance, determine whether each independent variable makes a significant contribution to the regression model. On the basis of these results, indicate the independent variables to include in this model.

✓ SELF Test **14.26** In Problem 14.4, you used sales and number of orders to predict distribution costs at a mail-order catalog business (see the **Warecost** file). Using the results from that problem,

a. construct a 95% confidence interval estimate of the population slope between distribution cost and sales.

b. at the 0.05 level of significance, determine whether each independent variable makes a significant contribution to the regression model. On the basis of these results, indicate the independent variables to include in this model.

14.27 In Problem 14.5, you used horsepower and weight to predict gasoline mileage (see the Auto file). Using the results from that problem,

a. construct a 95% confidence interval estimate of the population slope between gasoline mileage and horsepower.

b. at the 0.05 level of significance, determine whether each independent variable makes a significant contribution to the regression model. On the basis of these results, indicate the independent variables to include in this model.

14.28 In Problem 14.6, you used radio advertising and newspaper advertising to predict sales (see the Advertise file). Using the results from that problem,

a. construct a 95% confidence interval estimate of the population slope between sales and radio advertising.

b. at the 0.05 level of significance, determine whether each independent variable makes a significant contribution to

the regression model. On the basis of these results, indicate the independent variables to include in this model.

14.29 In Problem 14.7, you used the total number of staff present and remote hours to predict standby hours (see the Standby file). Using the results from that problem,

a. construct a 95% confidence interval estimate of the population slope between standby hours and total number of staff present.

b. at the 0.05 level of significance, determine whether each independent variable makes a significant contribution to the regression model. On the basis of these results, indicate the independent variables to include in this model.

14.30 In Problem 14.8, you used land area of a property and age of a house to predict appraised value (see the GlenCove file). Using the results from that problem,

a. construct a 95% confidence interval estimate of the population slope between appraised value and land area of a property.

b. at the 0.05 level of significance, determine whether each independent variable makes a significant contribution to the regression model. On the basis of these results, indicate the independent variables to include in this model.

14.5 Using Dummy Variables and Interaction Terms in Regression Models

The multiple regression models discussed in Sections 14.1 through 14.4 assumed that each independent variable is numerical. However, in some situations, you might need to include categorical independent variables in the regression model. For example, in Section 14.1, you used price and promotional expenditures to predict the monthly sales of OmniPower high-energy bars. In addition to these numerical independent variables, you may need to include the effect of the shelf location in the store (e.g., end-aisle display or no end-aisle display) when developing a model to predict OmniPower sales.

The use of **dummy variables** allows you to include categorical independent variables in the regression model. If a given categorical independent variable has two categories, then you need only one dummy variable to represent the two categories. A dummy variable, X_d, is defined as

$$X_d = 0 \text{ if the observation is in category 1}$$

$$X_d = 1 \text{ if the observation is in category 2}$$

To illustrate the application of dummy variables in regression, consider a model for predicting the assessed value from a sample of 15 houses, based on the size of the house (in thousands of square feet) and whether the house has a fireplace. To include the categorical variable concerning the presence of a fireplace, the dummy variable X_2 is defined as

$$X_2 = 0 \text{ if the house does not have a fireplace}$$

$$X_2 = 1 \text{ if the house has a fireplace}$$

Table 14.3 presents the data, which are also stored in the file House3. In the last column of Table 14.3, you can see how the categorical variable is converted to a dummy variable with numerical values.

TABLE 14.3

Predicting Assessed Value, Based on Size of the House and Presence of a Fireplace

Assessed Value	Size	Fireplace	Fireplace Coded
234.4	2.00	Yes	1
227.4	1.71	No	0
225.7	1.45	No	0
235.9	1.76	Yes	1
229.1	1.93	No	0
220.4	1.20	Yes	1
225.8	1.55	Yes	1
235.9	1.93	Yes	1
228.5	1.59	Yes	1
229.2	1.50	Yes	1
236.7	1.90	Yes	1
229.3	1.39	Yes	1
224.5	1.54	No	0
233.8	1.89	Yes	1
226.8	1.59	No	0

Assuming that the slope of assessed value with the size of the house is the same for houses that have and do not have a fireplace, the multiple regression model is

$$Y_i = \beta_0 + \beta_1 X_{1i} + \beta_2 X_{2i} + \varepsilon_i$$

where

Y_i = assessed value in thousands of dollars for house i

β_0 = Y intercept

X_{1i} = size of the house, in thousands of square feet, for house i

β_1 = slope of assessed value with size of the house, holding constant the presence or absence of a fireplace

X_{2i} = dummy variable representing the presence or absence of a fireplace for house i

β_2 = net effect of the presence of a fireplace on assessed value, holding constant the size of the house

ε_i = random error in Y for house i

Figure 14.8 illustrates the SPSS results for this model.

From Figure 14.8, the regression equation is

$$\hat{Y}_i = 200.090 + 16.186 X_{1i} + 3.853 X_{2i}$$

For houses without a fireplace, you substitute $X_2 = 0$ into the regression equation:

$$\hat{Y}_i = 200.090 + 16.186 X_{1i} + 3.853 X_{2i}$$

$$= 200.090 + 16.186 X_{1i} + 3.853(0)$$

$$= 200.090 + 16.186 X_{1i}$$

For houses with a fireplace, you substitute $X_2 = 1$ into the regression equation:

$$\hat{Y}_i = 200.090 + 16.186 X_{1i} + 3.853 X_{2i}$$

$$= 200.090 + 16.186 X_{1i} + 3.853(1)$$

$$= 203.943 + 16.186 X_{1i}$$

In this model, the regression coefficients are interpreted as follows:

1. Holding constant whether a house has a fireplace, for each increase of 1.0 thousand square feet in the size of the house, the mean assessed value is estimated to increase by 16.186 thousand dollars (i.e., $16,186.00).

FIGURE 14.8

SPSS regression results worksheet for the regression model that includes size of the house and presence of fireplace

Variables Entered/Removed[b]

Model	Variables Entered	Variables Removed	Method
1	Square feet (thousands)[a]		Enter

a. *All requested variables entered.*
b. *Dependent Variable: Annual Sales (in Millions of Dollars)*

Model Summary[b]

Variables Entered/Removed[b]

Model	Variables Entered	Variables Removed	Method
1	size, Fireplace[a]		Enter

a. *All requested variables entered.*
b. *Dependent Variable: Assessed value*

Model Summary

Model	R	R Square	Adjusted R Square	Std. Error of the Estimate
1	.901[a]	.811	.780	2.2626

a. *Predictors: (Constant), size, Fireplace*

ANOVA[b]

Model		Sum of Squares	df	Mean Square	F	Sig.
1	Regression	263.704	2	131.852	25.756	.000[a]
	Residual	61.432	12	5.119		
	Total	325.136	14			

a. *Predictors: (Constant), size, Fireplace*
b. *Dependent Variable: Assessed value*

Coefficients[a]

Model		Unstandardized Coefficients		Standardized Coefficients	t	Sig.
		B	Std. Error	Beta		
1	(Constant)	200.090	4.352		45.980	.000
	Fireplace	3.853	1.241	.390	3.104	.009
	size	16.186	2.574	.790	6.287	.000

2. Holding constant the size of the house, the presence of a fireplace is estimated to increase the mean assessed value of the house by 3.853 thousand dollars (i.e. $3,853).

In Figure 14.8, the t_{STAT} test statistic for the slope of the size of the house with assessed value is 6.287, and the p-value is approximately 0.000; the t_{STAT} test statistic for presence of a fireplace is 3.104, and the p-value is 0.009. Thus, each of the two variables makes a significant contribution to the model at a level of significance of 0.01. In addition, the coefficient of multiple determination indicates that 81.11% of the variation in assessed value is explained by variation in the size of the house and whether the house has a fireplace.

Interactions

In all the regression models discussed so far, the *effect* an independent variable has on the dependent variable was assumed to be statistically independent of the other independent variables in the model. An **interaction** occurs if the effect of an independent variable on the dependent variable is affected by the *value* of a second independent variable. For example, it is possible for advertising to have a large effect on the sales of a product when the price of a product is low. However, if the price of the product is too high, increases in advertising will not dramatically change sales. In this case, price and advertising are said to interact. In other words, you cannot make general statements about the effect of advertising on sales. The effect that advertising has on sales is *dependent* on the price. You use an **interaction term** (sometimes referred to as a **cross-product term**) to model an interaction effect in a regression model.

FIGURE 14.9

SPSS regression results worksheet for a regression model that includes size, presence of fireplace, and interaction of size and fireplace

Variables Entered/Removed[b]

Model	Variables Entered	Variables Removed	Method
1	Interaction, size, Fireplace[a]		Enter

a. *All requested variables entered.*
b. *Dependent Variable: Assessed value*

Model Summary

Model	R	R Square	Adjusted R Square	Std. Error of the Estimate
1	.918[a]	.843	.800	2.1573

a. *Predictors: (Constant), Interaction, size, Fireplace*

ANOVA[b]

Model		Sum of Squares	df	Mean Square	F	Sig.
1	Regression	273.944	3	91.315	19.621	.000[a]
	Residual	51.192	11	4.654		
	Total	325.136	14			

a. *Predictors: (Constant), Interaction, size, Fireplace*
b. *Dependent Variable: Assessed value*

Coefficients[a]

Model		Unstandardized Coefficients		Standardized Coefficients		
		B	Std. Error	Beta	t	Sig.
1	(Constant)	212.952	9.612		22.154	.000
	Fireplace	−11.840	10.646	−1.199	−1.112	.290
	size	8.362	5.817	.408	1.438	.178
	Interaction	9.518	6.416	1.664	1.483	.166

a. *Dependent Variable: Assessed value*

To illustrate the concept of interaction and use of an interaction term, return to the example concerning the assessed values of homes. In the regression model, you assumed that the effect the size of the house has on the assessed value is independent of whether the house has a fireplace. In other words, you assumed that the slope of assessed value with size is the same for houses with fireplaces as it is for houses without fireplaces. If these two slopes are different, then an interaction exists between the size of the house and the presence of a fireplace.

To evaluate the possibility of an interaction, you first define an interaction term that equals the product of the independent variable X_1 (size of house) and the dummy variable X_2 (fireplace). You then test whether this interaction variable makes a significant contribution to the regression model. If the interaction is significant, you cannot use the original model for prediction. For the data of Table 14.3, let

$$X_3 = X_1 \times X_2$$

Figure 14.9 illustrates SPSS results for this regression model, which includes the size of the house, X_1, the presence of a fireplace, X_2, and the interaction of X_1 and X_2 (which is defined as X_3).

To test for the existence of an interaction, you use the null hypothesis

$$H_0: \beta_3 = 0$$

versus the alternative hypothesis

$$H_1: \beta_3 \neq 0.$$

In Figure 14.9, the t_{STAT} test statistic for the interaction of size and fireplace is 1.483. Because $t_{STAT} = 1.483 < 2.201$ or the p-value $= 0.1661 > 0.05$, you do not reject the null hypothesis. Therefore, the interaction does not make a significant contribution to the model, given that size and presence of a fireplace are already included. You can conclude that the slope of assessed value with size is the same for houses with fireplaces and without fireplaces.

Problems for Section 14.5

LEARNING THE BASICS

14.31 Suppose X_1 is a numerical variable and X_2 is a dummy variable and the regression equation for a sample of $n = 20$ is

$$\hat{Y}_i = 6 + 4X_{1i} + 2X_{2i}$$

a. Interpret the regression coefficient associated with variable X_1.
b. Interpret the regression coefficient associated with variable X_2.

14.32 Suppose that in Problem 14.31, the t_{STAT} test statistic for testing the contribution of variable X_2 is 3.27. At the 0.05 level of significance, is there evidence that variable X_2 makes a significant contribution to the model?

APPLYING THE CONCEPTS

14.33 The chair of the accounting department wants to develop a regression model to predict the grade point average in accounting for graduating accounting majors, based on the student's SAT score and whether the student received a grade of B or higher in the introductory statistics course (0 = no and 1 = yes).

a. Explain the steps involved in developing a regression model for these data. Be sure to indicate the particular models you need to evaluate and compare.
b. Suppose the regression coefficient for the variable of whether the student received a grade of B or higher in the introductory statistics course is +0.30. How do you interpret this result?

14.34 A real estate association in a suburban community would like to study the relationship between the size of a single-family house (as measured by the number of rooms) and the selling price of the house (in thousands of dollars). Two different neighborhoods are included in the study, one on the east side of the community (=0) and the other on the west side (=1). A random sample of 20 houses was selected, with the results given in the file **Neighbor**. For (a) through (j) do not include an interaction term.

a. State the multiple regression equation that predicts the selling price based on the number of rooms and the neighborhood.
b. Interpret the regression coefficients in (a).
c. Predict the selling price for a house with nine rooms that is located in an east-side neighborhood. Construct a 95% confidence interval estimate and a 95% prediction interval.

d. Perform a residual analysis on the results and determine if the regression assumptions are valid.

e. Is there a significant relationship between selling price and the two independent variables (rooms and neighborhood) at the 0.05 level of significance?

f. At the 0.05 level of significance, determine whether each independent variable makes a contribution to the regression model. Indicate the most appropriate regression model for this set of data.

g. Construct and interpret a 95% confidence interval estimate for the relationship between selling price and number of rooms.

h. Construct and interpret a 95% confidence interval estimate for the relationship between selling price and neighborhood.

i. Compute and interpret the adjusted r^2.

j. What assumption do you need to make about the slope of selling price with number of rooms?

k. Add an interaction term to the model and, at the 0.05 level of significance, determine whether it makes a significant contribution to the model.

l. On the basis of the results of (f) and (k), which model is most appropriate? Explain.

14.35 The marketing manager of a large supermarket chain would like to determine the effect of shelf space and whether the product was placed at the front (=1) or back (=0) of the aisle on the sales of pet food. A random sample of 12 equal-sized stores is selected, with the results stored in the file **Petfood**.

For (a) through (l), do not include an interaction term.

a. State the multiple regression equation that predicts sales based on shelf space and location.

b. Interpret the regression coefficients in (a).

c. Predict the weekly sales of pet food for a store with 8 feet of shelf space situated at the back of the aisle. Construct a 95% confidence interval estimate and a 95% prediction interval.

d. Perform a residual analysis on the results and determine if the regression assumptions are valid.

e. Is there a significant relationship between sales and the two independent variables (shelf space and aisle position) at the 0.05 level of significance?

f. At the 0.05 level of significance, determine whether each independent variable makes a contribution to the regression model. Indicate the most appropriate regression model for this set of data.

g. Construct and interpret a 95% confidence interval estimates for the relationship between sales and shelf space and between sales and aisle location.

h. Compare the slope in (b) with the slope for the simple linear regression model of Problem 13.4. Explain the difference in the results.

i. Computer and interpret the meaning of the coefficient of multiple determination, r^2.

j. Compute and interpret the adjusted r^2.

k. Compare r^2 with the r^2 value computed in Problem 13.16(a).

l. What assumption about the slope of shelf space with sales do you need to make in this problem?

m. Add an interaction term to the model and, at the 0.05 level of significance, determine whether it makes a significant contribution to the model.

n. On the basis of the results of (f) and (m), which model is most appropriate? Explain.

14.36 In mining engineering, holes are often drilled through rock, using drill bits. As the drill hole gets deeper, additional rods are added to the drill bit to enable additional drilling to take place. It is expected that drilling time increases with depth. This increased drilling time could be caused by several factors, including the mass of the drill rods that are strung together. A key question relates to whether drilling is faster using dry drilling holes or wet drilling holes. Using dry drilling holes involves forcing compressed air down the drill rods to flush the cuttings and drive the hammer. Using wet drilling holes involves forcing water rather than air down the hole. The data file **Drill** contains measurements for a sample of 50 drill holes of the time to drill each additional 5 feet (in minutes), the depth (in feet), and whether the hole was a dry drilling hole or a wet drilling hole. Develop a model to predict additional drilling time, based on depth and type of drilling hole (dry or wet). For (a) through (j) do not include an interaction term.

Source: *Data extracted from R. Penner and D. G. Watts, "Mining Information," The American Statistician, 45, 1991, pp. 4–9.*

a. State the multiple regression equation.

b. Interpret the regression coefficients in (a).

c. Predict the additional drilling time for a dry drilling hole at a depth of 100 feet. Construct a 95% confidence interval estimate and a 95% prediction interval.

d. Perform a residual analysis on the results and determine if the regression assumptions are valid.

e. Is there a significant relationship between additional drilling time and the two independent variables (depth and type of drilling hole) at the 0.05 level of significance?

f. At the 0.05 level of significance, determine whether each independent variable makes a contribution to the regression model. Indicate the most appropriate regression model for this set of data.

g. Construct a 95% confidence interval estimate for the relationship between additional drilling time and depth.

h. Construct a 95% confidence interval estimate for the relationship between additional drilling time and the type of hole drilled.

i. Compute and interpret the adjusted r^2.

j. What assumption do you need to make about the slope of additional drilling time with depth?

k. Add an interaction term to the model and, at the 0.05 level of significance, determine whether it makes a significant contribution to the model.

l. On the basis of the results of (f) and (k), which model is most appropriate? Explain.

14.37 The owner of a moving company typically has his most experienced manager predict the total number of labor hours that will be required to complete an upcoming move. This approach has proved useful in the past, but the owner would like to be able to develop a more accurate method of predicting the labor hours by using the number of cubic feet moved and whether there is an elevator in the apartment building. In a preliminary effort to provide a more accurate method, he has collected data for 36 moves in which the origin and destination were within the borough of Manhattan in New York City and the travel time was an insignificant portion of the hours worked. The data are stored in the file **Moving**. For (a) through (j) do not include an interaction term.

a. State the multiple regression equation for predicting labor hours using the number of cubic feet moved and whether there is an elevator.
b. Interpret the regression coefficients in (a).
c. Predict the labor hours for moving 500 cubic feet in an apartment building that has an elevator, and construct a 95% confidence interval estimate and a 95% prediction interval.
d. Perform a residual analysis on the results and determine if the regression assumptions are valid.
e. Is there a significant relationship between labor hours and the two independent variables (cubic feet moved and whether there is an elevator in the apartment building) at the 0.05 level of significance?
f. At the 0.05 level of significance, determine whether each independent variable makes a contribution to the regression model. Indicate the most appropriate regression model for this set of data.
g. Construct a 95% confidence interval estimate for the relationship between labor hours and cubic feet moved.
h. Construct a 95% confidence interval estimate for the relationship between labor hours and the presence of an elevator.
i. Compute and interpret the adjusted r^2.
j. What assumption about the slope of labor hours with cubic feet moved do you need to make?
k. Add an interaction term to the model and, at the 0.05 level of significance, determine whether it makes a significant contribution to the model.
l. On the basis of the results of (f) and (k), which model is most appropriate? Explain.

14.38 In Problem 14.4, you used sales and orders to predict distribution cost (see the file **Warecost**). Develop a regression model to predict distribution cost that includes the sales, orders, and the interaction of sales and orders.
a. At the 0.05 level of significance, is there evidence that the interaction term makes a significant contribution to the model?

b. Which regression model is more appropriate, the one used in (a) or the one used in Problem 14.4? Explain.

14.39 Zagat's publishes restaurant ratings for various locations in the United States. The data file **Restaurants** contains the Zagat rating for food, décor, service, and the price per person for a sample of 50 restaurants located in an urban area and 50 restaurants located in a suburban area. Develop a regression model to predict the price per person based on a variable that represents the sum of the ratings for food, décor, and service and a dummy variable concerning location (urban versus suburban). For (a) through (l) do not include an interaction term.

Source: *Data extracted from* Zagat Survey 2006 New York City Restaurants *and* Zagat Survey 2005–2006 Long Island Restaurants.

a. State the multiple regression equation.
b. Interpret the regression coefficients in (a).
c. Predict the price for a restaurant with a summated rating of 60 that is located in an urban area and construct a 95% confidence interval estimate and a 95% prediction interval.
d. Perform a residual analysis on the results and determine if the regression assumptions are satisfied.
e. Is there a significant relationship between price and the two independent variables (summated rating and location) at the 0.05 level of significance?
f. At the 0.05 level of significance, determine whether each independent variable makes a contribution to the regression model. Indicate the most appropriate regression model for this set of data.
g. Construct a 95% confidence interval estimate for the relationship between price and summated rating.
h. Compare the slope in (b) with the slope for the simple linear regression model of Problem 12.80. Explain the difference in the results.
i. Compute and interpret the meaning of the coefficient of multiple determination.
j. Compute and interpret the adjusted r^2.
k. Compare r^2 with the r^2 value computed in Problem 12.80(d).
l. What assumption about the slope of price with summated rating do you need to make in this problem?
m. Add an interaction term to the model and, at the 0.05 level of significance, determine whether it makes a significant contribution to the model.
n. On the basis of the results of (f) and (m), which model is most appropriate? Explain.

14.40 In Problem 14.6, you used radio advertising and newspaper advertising to predict sales (see the file **Advertise**). Develop a regression model to predict sales that includes radio advertising, newspaper advertising, and the interaction of radio advertising and newspaper advertising.
a. At the 0.05 level of significance, is there evidence that the interaction term makes a significant contribution to the model?

b. Which regression model is more appropriate, the one used in this problem or the one used in Problem 14.6? Explain.

14.41 In Problem 14.5, horsepower and weight were used to predict miles per gallon (see the file Auto). Develop a regression model that includes horsepower, weight, and the interaction of horsepower and weight to predict miles per gallon.

a. At the 0.05 level of significance, is there evidence that the interaction term makes a significant contribution to the model?

b. Which regression model is more appropriate, the one used in this problem or the one used in Problem 14.5? Explain.

14.42 In Problem 14.7, you used total staff present and remote hours to predict standby hours (see the file Standby). Develop a regression model to predict standby hours that includes total staff present, remote hours, and the interaction of total staff present and remote hours.

a. At the 0.05 level of significance, is there evidence that the interaction term makes a significant contribution to the model?

b. Which regression model is more appropriate, the one used in this problem or the one used in Problem 14.7? Explain.

USING STATISTICS   @ OmniFoods Revisited

In the Using Statistics scenario, you were the marketing manager for OmniFoods, a large food products company planning a nationwide introduction of a new high-energy bar, OmniPower. You needed to determine the effect that price and in-store promotions would have on the sales of OmniPower in order to develop an effective marketing strategy. A sample of 34 stores in a supermarket chain was selected for a test-market study. The stores charged between 59 and 99 cents per bar, and were given an in-store promotion budget between $200 and $600.

At the end of the one month test-market study, you performed a multiple regression analysis on the data. Two independent variables were considered, the price of an OmniPower bar and the monthly budget for in-store promotional expenditures. The dependent variable was the number of OmniPower bars sold in a month. The coefficient of determination indicated that 75.8% of the variation in sales was explained by knowing the price charged and the amount spent on in-store promotions. The model indicated that the mean sales of OmniPower are estimated to decrease by 532 bars per month for each 10-cent increase in the price, and estimated to increase by 361 bars for each additional $100 spent on promotions.

After studying the relative effects of price and promotion, OmniFoods needs to set price and promotion standards for a nationwide introduction (obviously lower prices and higher promotion budgets lead to more sales, but do so at a lower profit margin). You determined that if stores spend $400 a month in in-store promotions and charge 79 cents, the 95% confidence interval estimate of the mean monthly sales was 2,854 to 3,303 bars. OmniFoods can multiply the lower and upper bounds of this confidence interval by the number of stores included in the nationwide introduction to estimate total monthly sales. For example, if 1,000 stores are in the nationwide introduction, then total monthly sales should be between 2.854 million and 3.308 million bars.

SUMMARY

In this chapter, you learned how multiple regression models allow you to use two or more independent variables to predict the value of a dependent variable. You also learned how to include categorical independent variables and interaction terms in regression models. Figure 14.10 presents a road map of the chapter.

FIGURE 14.10
Roadmap for multiple regression

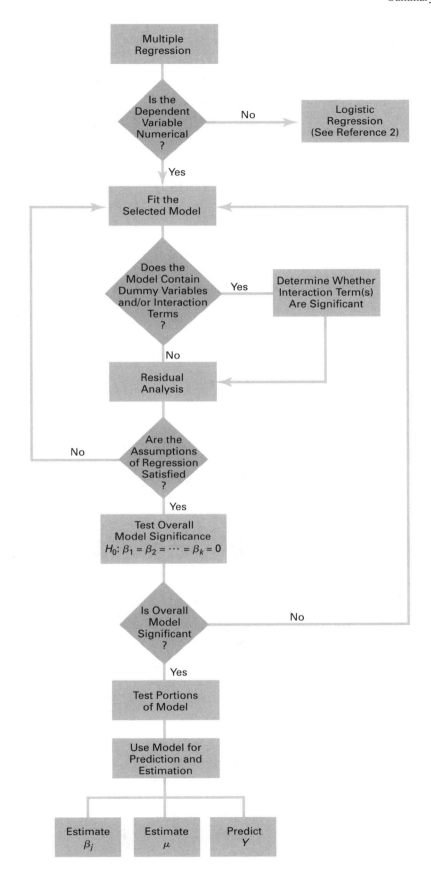

KEY EQUATIONS

Multiple Regression Model with k Independent Variables

$$Y_i = \beta_0 + \beta_1 X_{1i} + \beta_2 X_{2i} + \beta_3 X_{3i} + \cdots + \beta_k X_{ki} + \varepsilon_i$$

(14.1)

Multiple Regression Model with Two Independent Variables

$$Y_i = \beta_0 + \beta_1 X_{1i} + \beta_2 X_{2i} + \varepsilon_i \quad \textbf{(14.2)}$$

Multiple Regression Equation with Two Independent Variables

$$\hat{Y}_i = b_0 + b_1 X_{1i} + b_2 X_{2i} \quad \textbf{(14.3)}$$

Coefficient of Multiple Determination

$$r^2 = \frac{\text{Regression sum of squares}}{\text{Total sum of squares}} = \frac{SSR}{SST} \quad \textbf{(14.4)}$$

Adjusted r^2

$$r_{\text{adj}}^2 = 1 - \left[(1 - r^2) \frac{n-1}{n-k-1} \right] \quad \textbf{(14.5)}$$

Overall F Test

$$F_{STAT} = \frac{MSR}{MSE} \quad \textbf{(14.6)}$$

Testing for the Slope in Multiple Regression

$$t_{STAT} = \frac{b_j - \beta_j}{S_{b_j}} \quad \textbf{(14.7)}$$

Confidence Interval Estimate for the Slope

$$b_j \pm t_{\alpha/2} S_{b_j} \quad \textbf{(14.8)}$$

KEY TERMS

adjusted r^2 646
coefficient of multiple determination   646
cross-product term   658

dummy variables   655
interaction   658
interaction term   658
multiple regression model   640

net regression coefficients   642
overall F test   647

CHAPTER REVIEW PROBLEMS

CHECKING YOUR UNDERSTANDING

14.43 What is the difference between r^2 and the adjusted r^2?

14.44 How does the interpretation of the regression coefficients differ in multiple regression and simple linear regression?

14.45 How does testing the significance of the entire multiple regression model differ from testing the contribution of each independent variable?

14.46 Why and how do you use dummy variables?

14.47 How can you evaluate whether the slope of the dependent variable with an independent variable is the same for each level of the dummy variable?

14.48 Under what circumstances do you include an interaction term in a regression model?

APPLYING THE CONCEPTS

14.49 Increasing customer satisfaction typically results in increased purchase behavior. For many products, there is more than one measure of customer satisfaction. In many of these instances, purchase behavior can increase dramatically with an increase in any one of the customer satisfaction measures, not necessarily all of them at the same time. Gunst and Barry ("One Way to Moderate Ceiling Effects," *Quality Progress*, October 2003, pp. 83–85) consider a product with two satisfaction measures, X_1 and X_2, that range from the lowest level of satisfaction, 1, to the highest level of satisfaction, 7. The dependent variable, Y, is a measure of purchase behavior, with the highest value generating the most sales. The following regression equation is presented:

$$\hat{Y}_i = -3.888 + 1.449 X_{1i} + 1.462 X_{2i} - 0.190 X_{1i} X_{2i}$$

Suppose that X_1 is the perceived quality of the product and X_2 is the perceived value of the product. (*Note:* If the product is overpriced in the view of the customer, he or she perceives it to be of low value and vice versa.)

a. What is the predicted purchase behavior when $X_1 = 2$ and $X_2 = 2$?

b. What is the predicted purchase behavior when $X_1 = 2$ and $X_2 = 7$?

c. What is the predicted purchase behavior when $X_1 = 7$ and $X_2 = 2$?

d. What is the predicted purchase behavior when $X_1 = 7$ and $X_2 = 7$?

e. What is the regression equation when $X_2 = 2$? What is the slope for X_1 now?

f. What is the regression equation when $X_2 = 7$? What is the slope for X_1 now?

g. What is the regression equation when $X_1 = 2$? What is the slope for X_2 now?

h. What is the regression equation when $X_1 = 7$? What is the slope for X_2 now?

i. Discuss the implications of (a) through (h) within the context of increasing sales for this product with two customer satisfaction measures.

14.50 The owner of a moving company typically has his most experienced manager predict the total number of labor hours that will be required to complete an upcoming move. This approach has proved useful in the past, but the owner would like to be able to develop a more accurate method of predicting the labor hours by using the number of cubic feet moved and the number of pieces of large furniture. In a preliminary effort to provide a more accurate method, he has collected data for 36 moves in which the origin and destination were within the borough of Manhattan in New York City and the travel time was an insignificant portion of the hours worked. The data are stored in the file Moving .

a. State the multiple regression equation.

b. Interpret the meaning of the slopes in this equation.

c. Predict the labor hours for moving 500 cubic feet with two large pieces of furniture.

d. Perform a residual analysis on your results and determine if the regression assumptions are valid.

e. Determine whether there is a significant relationship between labor hours and the two independent variables (the amount of cubic feet moved and the number of pieces of large furniture) at the 0.05 level of significance.

f. Determine the p-value in (e) and interpret its meaning.

g. Interpret the meaning of the coefficient of multiple determination in this problem.

h. Determine the adjusted r^2.

i. At the 0.05 level of significance, determine whether each independent variable makes a significant contribution to the regression model. Indicate the most appropriate regression model for this set of data.

j. Determine the p-values in (i) and interpret their meaning.

k. Construct a 95% confidence interval estimate of the population slope between labor hours and the number of cubic feet moved. How does the interpretation of the slope here differ from that in Problem 13.36?

14.51 Professional basketball has truly become a sport that generates interest among fans around the world. More and more players come from outside the United States to play in the National Basketball Association (NBA). You want to develop a regression model to predict the number of wins achieved by each NBA team, based on field goal (shots made) percentage for the team and for the opponent. The data are stored in the file NBA2008 .

a. State the multiple regression equation.

b. Interpret the meaning of the slopes in this equation.

c. Predict the number of wins for a team that has a field goal percentage of 45% and an opponent field goal percentage of 44%.

d. Perform a residual analysis on your results and determine if the regression assumptions are valid.

e. Is there a significant relationship between number of wins and the two independent variables (field goal percentage for the team and for the opponent) at the 0.05 level of significance?

f. Determine the p-value in (e) and interpret its meaning.

g. Interpret the meaning of the coefficient of multiple determination in this problem.

h. Determine the adjusted r^2.

i. At the 0.05 level of significance, determine whether each independent variable makes a significant contribution to the regression model. Indicate the most appropriate regression model for this set of data.

j. Determine the p-values in (i) and interpret their meaning.

14.52 A sample of 30 recently sold single-family houses in a small city is selected. Develop a model to predict the selling price (in thousands of dollars), using the assessed value (in thousands of dollars) as well as time period when sold (in months since reassessment). The houses in the city had been reassessed at full value one year prior to the study. The results are contained in the file House1 .

a. State the multiple regression equation.

b. Interpret the meaning of the slopes in this equation.

c. Predict the selling price for a house that has an assessed value of $170,000 and was sold in time period 12.

d. Perform a residual analysis on your results and determine if the regression assumptions are valid.

e. Determine whether there is a significant relationship between selling price and the two independent variables (assessed value and time period) at the 0.05 level of significance.

f. Determine the p-value in (e) and interpret its meaning.

g. Interpret the meaning of the coefficient of multiple determination in this problem.

h. Determine the adjusted r^2.

i. At the 0.05 level of significance, determine whether each independent variable makes a significant contribution to the regression model. Indicate the most appropriate regression model for this set of data.

j. Determine the p-values in (i) and interpret their meaning.

k. Construct a 95% confidence interval estimate of the population slope between selling price and assessed value. How does the interpretation of the slope here differ from that in Problem 13.66?

14.53 Measuring the height of a California redwood tree is very difficult because these trees grow to heights of over

300 feet. People familiar with these trees understand that the height of a California redwood tree is related to other characteristics of the tree, including the diameter of the tree at the breast height of a person and the thickness of the bark of the tree. The data in the file **Redwood** represent the height, diameter at breast height of a person, and bark thickness for a sample of 21 California redwood trees.

a. State the multiple regression equation that predicts the height of a tree based on the tree's diameter at breast height and the thickness of the bark.

b. Interpret the meaning of the slopes in this equation.

c. Predict the height for a tree that has a breast height diameter of 25 inches and a bark thickness of 2 inches.

d. Interpret the meaning of the coefficient of multiple determination in this problem.

e. Perform a residual analysis on the results and determine if the regression assumptions are valid.

f. Determine whether there is a significant relationship between the height of redwood trees and the two independent variables (breast-height diameter and the bark thickness) at the 0.05 level of significance.

g. Construct a 95% confidence interval estimate of the population slope between the height of redwood trees and breast-height diameter and between the height of redwood trees and the bark thickness.

h. At the 0.05 level of significance, determine whether each independent variable makes a significant contribution to the regression model. Indicate the independent variables to include in this model.

i. Construct a 95% confidence interval estimate of the mean height for trees that have a breast-height diameter of 25 inches and a bark thickness of 2 inches along with a prediction interval for an individual tree.

14.54 Develop a model to predict the assessed value (in thousands of dollars), using the size of the houses (in thousands of square feet) and the age of the houses (in years) from the data stored in the file **House2**.

a. State the multiple regression equation.

b. Interpret the meaning of the slopes in this equation.

c. Predict the assessed value for a house that has a size of 1,750 square feet and is 10 years old.

d. Perform a residual analysis on the results and determine if the regression assumptions are valid.

e. Determine whether there is a significant relationship between assessed value and the two independent variables (size and age) at the 0.05 level of significance.

f. Determine the p-value in (e) and interpret its meaning.

g. Interpret the meaning of the coefficient of multiple determination in this problem.

h. Determine the adjusted r^2.

i. At the 0.05 level of significance, determine whether each independent variable makes a significant contribution to the regression model. Indicate the most appropriate regression model for this set of data.

j. Determine the p-values in (i) and interpret their meaning.

k. Construct a 95% confidence interval estimate of the population slope between assessed value and size. How does the interpretation of the slope here differ from that of Problem 13.67?

l. The real estate assessor's office has been publicly quoted as saying that the age of a house has no bearing on its assessed value. Based on your answers to (a) through (k), do you agree with this statement? Explain.

14.55 Crazy Dave, a well-known baseball analyst, wants to determine which variables are important in predicting a team's wins in a given season. He has collected data related to wins, earned run average (ERA), and runs scored for the 2007 season (stored in the file **BB2007**). Develop a model to predict the number of wins based on ERA and runs scored.

a. State the multiple regression equation.

b. Interpret the meaning of the slopes in this equation.

c. Predict the number of wins for a team that has an ERA of 4.50 and has scored 750 runs.

d. Perform a residual analysis on the results and determine if the regression assumptions are valid.

e. Is there a significant relationship between number of wins and the two independent variables (ERA and runs scored) at the 0.05 level of significance?

f. Determine the p-value in (e) and interpret its meaning.

g. Interpret the meaning of the coefficient of multiple determination in this problem.

h. Determine the adjusted r^2.

i. At the 0.05 level of significance, determine whether each independent variable makes a significant contribution to the regression model. Indicate the most appropriate regression model for this set of data.

j. Determine the p-values in (i) and interpret their meaning.

k. Which is more important in predicting wins—pitching, as measured by ERA, or offense, as measured by runs scored? Explain.

14.56 Referring to Problem 14.55, suppose that in addition to using ERA to predict the number of wins, Crazy Dave wants to include the league (American vs. National) as an independent variable. Develop a model to predict wins based on ERA and league. For (a)–(h), do not include an interaction term.

a. State the multiple regression equation.

b. Interpret the regression coefficients in (a).

c. Predict the number of wins for a team with an ERA of 4.50 in the American League. Construct a 95% confidence interval estimate for all teams and a 95% prediction interval for an individual team.

d. Perform a residual analysis on the results and determine if the regression assumptions are valid.

e. Is there a significant relationship between wins and the two independent variables (ERA and league) at the 0.05 level of significance?

f. At the 0.05 level of significance, determine whether each independent variable makes a contribution to the regression model. Indicate the most appropriate regression model for this set of data.

g. Compute and interpret the adjusted r^2.

h. What assumption do you have to make about the slope of wins with ERA?

i. Add an interaction term to the model and, at the 0.05 level of significance, determine whether it makes a significant contribution to the model.

j. On the basis of the results of (f) and (i), which model is most appropriate? Explain.

14.57 You are a real estate broker who wants to compare property values in Glen Cove and Roslyn (which are located approximately 8 miles apart). In order to do so, you will analyze the data in the GCRoslyn file that includes samples of houses from Glen Cove and Roslyn. Making sure to include the dummy variable for location (Glen Cove or Roslyn), develop a regression model to predict appraised value, based on the land area of a property, the age of a house, and location. Be sure to determine whether any interaction terms need to be included in the model.

14.58 Many factors determine the attendance at Major League Baseball games. These factors can include when the game is played, the weather, the opponent, and whether the team is having a good season. In an effort to increase ticket sales, ball clubs run promotions such as free concerts after the game, or giveaways of team hats or bobbleheads of star players (T. C. Boyd and T. C. Krehbiel, "An Analysis of the Effects of Specific Promotion Types on Attendance at Major League Baseball Games," *American Journal of Business*, 2006, 21, pp. 21–32). The data file Phillies includes the following variables for a recent season:

> Attendance—Paid attendance for each Philadelphia Phillies home game
> Temp—High temperature for the day
> Win—Team's winning percentage at the time of the game
> OpWin—Opponent team's winning percentage at the time of the game
> Weekend—Dummy variable, 1 if game played on Friday, Saturday, or Sunday; 0 otherwise
> Promotion—Dummy variable, 1 if a promotion was held; 0 if no promotion was held

a. Perform a regression analysis using attendance as the dependent variable and the other five variables as independent variables.

b. Interpret the coefficient of determination.

c. Determine which factors significantly influenced attendance (use $\alpha = 0.05$).

d. Interpret the regression coefficient associated with the variable Promotion. Do you think the promotions run by the Phillies were effective? Explain.

MANAGING THE *SPRINGVILLE HERALD*

In its continuing study of the home-delivery subscription solicitation process, a marketing department team wants to test the effects of two types of structured sales presentations (personal formal and personal informal) and the number of hours spent on telemarketing on the number of new subscriptions. The staff has recorded these data in the file SH14 for the past 24 weeks. You can find this data set at **www.prenhall.com/HeraldCase/EffectsData.htm** and in the EffectsData.htm file in the **Herald Case** folder on the Student CD-ROM that accompanies this book.

Analyze these data and develop a multiple regression model to predict the number of new subscriptions for a week, based on the number of hours spent on telemarketing and the sales presentation type. Write a report, giving detailed findings concerning the regression model used.

WEB CASE

Apply your knowledge of multiple regression models in this Web Case, which extends the Using Statistics OmniFoods scenario from this chapter.

To ensure a successful test marketing of its OmniPower energy bars, the OmniFoods marketing department has contracted with In-Store Placements Group (ISPG), a merchandising consultancy. ISPG will work with the grocery store chain that is conducting the test-market study. Using the same 34-store sample used in the test-market study, ISPG claims that the choice of shelf location and the presence of in-store OmniPower coupon dispensers each increase sale of the energy bars.

Review the ISPG claims and supporting data at the OmniFoods internal Web page, **www.prenhall. com/Springville/Omni_ISPGMemo.htm** (or open the Omni_ISPGMemo.htm file from the Student CD-ROM Web Case folder) and then answer the following:

1. Are the supporting data consistent with ISPG's claims? Perform an appropriate statistical analysis to confirm (or discredit) the stated relationship between sales and the two independent variables of product shelf location and the presence of in-store OmniPower coupon dispensers.

2. If you were advising OmniFoods, would you recommend using a specific shelf location and in-store coupon dispensers to sell OmniPower bars?

3. What additional data would you advise collecting in order to determine the effectiveness of the sales promotion techniques used by ISPG?

REFERENCES

1. Davenport, T., and J. Harris, *Competing on Analytics: The New Science of Winning* (Boston, MA: Harvard Business School Press, 2007).
2. Hosmer, D. W., and S. Lemeshow, *Applied Logistic Regression*, 2nd ed. (New York: Wiley, 2001).
3. Kutner, M., C. Nachtsheim, J. Neter, and W. Li, *Applied Linear Statistical Models*, 5th ed. (New York: McGraw-Hill/Irwin, 2005).
4. *Microsoft Excel 2007* (Redmond, WA: Microsoft Corp., 2007).
5. *Minitab for Windows Version 15* (State College, PA: Minitab, Inc., 2006).

APPENDIX A14a

SPSS—Version 16—Multiple Regression

Suppose the professor wanted to develop a model to predict the students' marks at the end of the QMS 202 course as measured in percentage based on how frequent they missed class, number of problems solved, total hours spend studying and how frequent they seek help from the teaching assistant.

The dependent variable, Y, is the final QMS 202 marks (in percentage). Three independent variables are:

- Number of lectures missed during the semester (X_1)
- Total number of problems solved (X_2)
- Total hours spent per week studying for QMS 202 (X_3)
- Total number of times the student seek the teaching assistant's help (X_4)

A random sample of 35 students who enrolled in QMS 202 course was selected with the results shown in Table 14.4.

TABLE 14.4

Data for Multiple Regression Model to Predict QMS202 Marks

Student	y = QMS 202 Marks	X1 = Number of lectures missed during the semester	X2 = Total number of problems solved	X3 = Total hours spent studying for QMS 202	X4 = Total number of times the student seeks the teaching assistant's help
1	90	0	100	24.2	11
2	60	5	20	5.3	2
3	45	9	5	1.2	0
4	85	1	50	11.5	5
5	72	3	45	8.6	6
6	96	1	110	22.3	12
7	50	6	10	3.5	4
8	65	3	34	7.8	5
9	87	2	78	10.4	11
10	88	1	77	11.6	10
11	78	2	50	9.2	8
12	73	3	49	10.3	10
13	59	5	22	6.4	4
14	49	7	6	2.6	0
15	94	0	110	25.4	12
16	55	4	21	4.5	5
17	52	5	20	5.8	3
18	63	3	40	8.9	4
19	51	6	20	4.0	3
20	93	1	107	19.1	12
21	50	7	15	3.3	5
22	65	4	30	6.4	4
23	87	1	80	11.6	12
24	88	0	87	12.2	11
25	78	1	55	10.1	9
26	73	4	51	14.2	11
27	56	6	30	5.5	3
28	44	9	3	1.6	0
29	95	0	115	23.8	12
30	56	7	27	3.9	4
31	52	6	24	3.4	5
32	63	5	46	5.5	2
33	56	8	23	3.7	1
34	98	0	150	23.8	12
35	71	1	48	3.9	6

Performing a multiple regression on SPSS—Version 16

Step 1: Open the SPSS Data Editor.

Click **"cancel"** to cancel the SPSS opening window.

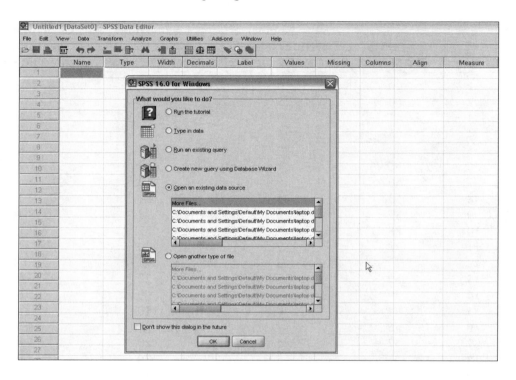

Step 2: Define the variables and give the variables a label.

Click **"Variable View"** (at the bottom of the window) to go to the variable view window to define the variables and fix the data at zero or one decimal places.

- Give variable name—"student" to trace the respondent's responses if there is a data entry error.

- Give variable name—"y" and label it as "QMS 202 Marks".

- Give variable name—"x1" and label it as "Number of lectures missed during the semester".

- Give variable name—"x2" and label it as "Total number of problems solved".

- Give variable name—"x3" and label it as "Total hours spent studying for QMS 202".

- Give variable name—"x4" and label it as "Total number of times the student seeks the teaching assistant's help".

	Name	Type	Width	Decimals	Label	Values	Missing	Columns	Align	Measure
1	student	Numeric	8	0		None	None	8	Right	Scale
2	y	Numeric	8	0	QMS 202 Marks	None	None	8	Right	Scale
3	x1	Numeric	8	0	Number of lectures missed during the semester	None	None	8	Right	Scale
4	x2	Numeric	8	0	Total number of problems solved	None	None	8	Right	Scale
5	x3	Numeric	8	1	Total hours spent studying for QMS 202	None	None	8	Right	Scale
6	x4	Numeric	8	0	Total number of times the student seek the teaching assistant's help	None	None	8	Right	Scale

Step 3: Create a SPSS data file.

Click **"Data View"** to return to the data view window. Now, enter the raw data (in Table 14.4) into the respective column of variable.

	student	y	x1	x2	x3	x4
1	1	90	0	100	24.2	11
2	2	60	5	20	5.3	2
3	3	45	9	5	1.2	0
4	4	85	1	50	11.5	5
5	5	72	3	45	8.6	6
6	6	96	1	110	22.3	12
7	7	50	6	10	3.5	4
8	8	65	3	34	7.8	5
9	9	87	2	78	10.4	11
10	10	88	1	77	11.6	10
11	11	78	2	50	9.2	8
12	12	73	3	49	10.3	10
13	13	59	5	22	6.4	4
14	14	49	7	6	2.6	0
15	15	94	0	110	25.4	12
16	16	55	4	21	4.5	5
17	17	52	5	20	5.8	3
18	18	63	3	40	8.9	4
19	19	51	6	20	4.0	3
20	20	93	1	107	19.1	12
21	21	50	7	15	3.3	5
22	22	65	4	30	6.4	4
23	23	87	1	80	11.6	12
24	24	88	0	87	12.2	11
25	25	78	1	55	10.1	9
26	26	73	4	51	14.2	11
27	27	56	6	30	5.5	3
28	28	44	9	3	1.6	0
29	29	95	0	115	23.8	12
30	30	56	7	27	3.9	4
31	31	52	6	24	3.4	5

After you have entered all the data, save it as "qms202mark.sav" (or any filename).

Step 3: Perform Regression Analysis.

Make the following menu selections:

Analyze → Regression → Linear

At this point, the **Linear Regression** dialog box will appear. Make these entries in the **Linear Regression** dialog box:

- Highlight on the **"QMS 202 Marks"** variable and click on the arrow key ($\rightarrow$). The variable will automatically fall into the **Dependent** box.

- Highlight on each x_1, x_2, x_3, and x_4 variable and click on the arrow key ($\rightarrow$). The variable will fall into the **Independent(s)** box.

- Click on the **Enter** button next to the **Method.** Select **stepwise** as the method to develop several multiple regression models.

Note: The **Stepwise** method uses a step-by-step algorithm that starts building a regression model with one independent variable. At each step the algorithm checks to see if any of the variables (already included in the model) can be removed and adds a variable (not yet included in the model) by examining the fit of the model. The algorithm stops when there are no more significant independent variables to be considered.

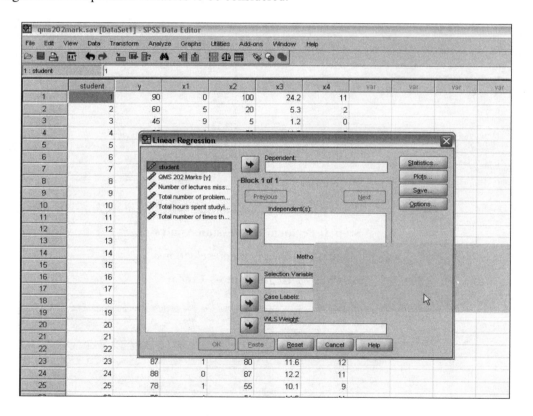

- *Obtaining Predictions and Residuals*   Click on save button (Note that the **Save** is a button on the pop-up menu and not the usual File save option) and the **save** dialog box will pop-up. In the **save** dialog box, click on **Unstandardized** in the the **Predicted Values** box. Click on **Unstandardized** in the **Residuals** box. Click on **Mean** and **Individual** in the **Prediction Intervals** box. Click on **Continue** to return to the **Linear Regression** dialog box. Then click **Ok.**

Step 3: Go to **SPSS Viewer** to obtain your SPSS results.

SPSS output:
Regression

Model Summary[c]

Model	R	R Square	Adjusted R Square	Std. Error of the Estimate
1	.948[a]	.898	.895	5.541
2	.975[b]	.952	.949	3.874

a. *Predictors: (Constant), Total number of problems solved*
b. *Predictors: (Constant), Total number of problems solved, Number of lectures missed during the semester*
c. *Dependent Variable: QMS 202 Marks*

ANOVA[c]

	Model	Sum of Squares	df	Mean Square	F	Sig.
1	Regression	8906.850	1	8906.850	290.062	.000[a]
	Residual	1013.322	33	30.707		
	Total	9920.171	34			
2	Regression	9439.916	2	4719.958	314.497	.000[b]
	Residual	480.255	32	15.008		
	Total	9920.171	34			

a. *Predictors: (Constant), Total number of problems solved*
b. *Predictors: (Constant), Total number of problems solved, Number of lectures missed during the semester*
c. *Dependent Variable: QMS 202 Marks*

Coefficients[a]

	Model	Unstandardized Coefficients		Standardized Coefficients		
		B	Std. Error	Beta	t	Sig.
1	(Constant)	47.864	1.584		30.208	.000
	Total number of problems solved	.433	.025	.948	17.031	.000
2	(Constant)	66.176	3.266		20.261	.000
	Total number of problems solved	.262	.034	.574	7.781	.000
	Number of lectures missed during the semester	−2.703	.454	−.440	−5.960	.000

a. *Dependent Variable: QMS 202 Marks*

Obtaining Predictions and Residuals

The confidence interval values and prediction interval values are displayed on the **SPSS Data Editor** under the variables PRE_1, RES_1, LMCI_1, UMCI_1, LICI_1 and UICI_1.

Notation:

PRE_1—Unstandardized Predicted (for Model 1)

RES_1—Unstandardized Residual (for Model 1)

LMCI_1—95% Lower Confidence Interval for y mean (for Model 1)

UMCI_1—95% Upper Confidence Interval for y mean (for Model 1)

LICI_1—95% Lower Confidence Interval for y individual (for Model 1)

UICI_1—5% Upper Confidence Interval for y individual (for Model 1)

*qms202mark.sav [DataSet1] - SPSS Data Editor

File Edit View Data Transform Analyze Graphs Utilities Add-ons Window Help

1 : student   1   Visible

	student	y	x1	x2	x3	x4	PRE_1	RES_1	LMCI_1	UMCI_1	LICI_1	UICI_1
1	1	90	0	100	24.2	11	92.42439	-2.42439	90.14242	94.70635	84.20995	100.63882
2	2	60	5	20	5.3	2	57.90953	2.09047	56.12041	59.69865	49.81814	66.00091
3	3	45	9	5	1.2	0	43.15942	1.84058	40.00047	46.31836	34.65951	51.65933
4	4	85	1	50	11.5	5	76.59692	8.40308	73.83760	79.35623	68.23729	84.95654
5	5	72	3	45	8.6	6	69.87807	2.12193	68.27996	71.47619	61.82677	77.92938
6	6	96	1	110	22.3	12	92.34603	3.65397	89.57978	95.11228	83.98411	100.70795
7	7	50	6	10	3.5	4	52.58147	-2.58147	50.60136	54.56157	44.44572	60.71721
8	8	65	3	34	7.8	5	66.99074	-1.99074	64.89777	69.08370	58.82679	75.15468
9	9	87	2	78	10.4	11	81.24329	5.75671	79.58637	82.92022	73.17598	89.31061
10	10	88	1	77	11.6	10	83.68402	4.31598	81.83363	85.53440	75.57887	91.78917
11	11	78	2	50	9.2	8	73.89371	4.10629	71.89270	75.89472	65.75285	82.03457
12	12	73	3	49	10.3	10	70.92801	2.07199	69.45388	72.40215	62.90040	78.95563
13	13	59	5	22	6.4	4	58.43450	0.56550	56.71665	60.15234	50.35857	66.51042
14	14	49	7	6	2.6	0	48.82832	0.17168	46.66977	50.98687	40.64731	57.00933
15	15	94	0	110	25.4	12	95.04924	-1.04924	92.50056	97.59792	86.75675	103.34172
16	16	55	4	21	4.5	5	60.87522	-5.87522	58.70999	63.04045	52.69245	69.05799
17	17	52	5	20	5.8	3	57.90953	-5.90953	56.12041	59.69865	49.81814	66.00091
18	18	63	3	40	8.9	4	68.56565	-5.56565	66.76493	70.36636	60.47169	76.65960
19	19	51	6	20	4.0	3	55.20632	-4.20632	53.42214	56.99050	47.11603	63.29661
20	20	93	1	107	19.1	12	91.55857	1.44143	88.94270	94.17445	83.24519	99.87196
21	21	50	7	15	3.3	5	51.19068	-1.19068	49.04963	53.33174	43.01428	59.36709
22	22	65	4	30	6.4	4	63.23759	1.76241	61.51281	64.96237	55.16019	71.31499
23	23	87	1	80	11.6	12	84.47147	2.52853	82.63208	86.31086	76.36882	92.57412
24	24	88	0	87	12.2	11	89.01208	-1.01208	86.78851	91.23565	80.81367	97.21048
25	25	78	1	55	10.1	9	77.90934	0.09066	75.39568	80.42301	69.62755	86.19113
26	26	73	4	51	14.2	11	68.74978	4.25022	67.35271	70.14685	60.73595	76.76360
27	27	56	6	30	5.5	3	57.83117	-1.83117	55.98994	59.67241	49.72810	65.93424
28	28	44	9	3	1.6	0	42.63445	1.36555	39.52208	45.74682	34.15173	51.11716
29	29	95	0	115	23.8	12	96.36166	-1.36166	93.62413	99.09920	88.00920	104.71413
30	30	56	7	27	3.9	4	54.34051	1.65949	51.95856	56.72246	46.09774	62.58328
31	31	52	6	24	3.4	5	56.25626	-4.25626	54.48067	58.03185	48.16786	64.34466

Data View   Variable View

APPENDIX E14

Using Microsoft Excel for Multiple Regression Models

E14.1 Performing Multiple Regression Analyses

You perform a multiple regression analysis by using the ToolPak Regression procedure.

Open to the worksheet that contains data for the Y variable and the X variables. Data for the X variables must be placed in contiguous columns. (Use cut-and-paste to rearrange the data, if necessary.) Select **Tools → Data Analysis** (Excel 97–2003) or **Data → Data Analysis** (Excel 2007). Then select **Regression** from the Data Analysis list, and click **OK**. In the procedure's dialog box (see below), enter the cell range of the Y variable data as the **Input Y Range**, the cell range of the X variables data as the **Input X Range**, and click **Labels**. Click **Confidence Level**, enter a value in its box, and then click **OK**. Results appear on a new worksheet similar to Figure 14.2.

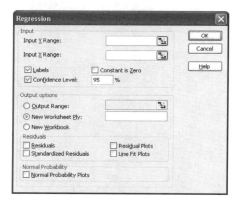

E14.2 Performing Multiple Regression Residual Analysis

You perform multiple regression residual analysis using a two-step process. You first modify the instructions of Section E14.1, clicking **Residuals** in the Regression dialog box before you click **OK**. This option adds a residual table. You then use Excel charting features to do a residual analysis of a multiple regression model. (Although the Regression dialog box contains a **Residuals Plots** option, this option will create only the residual plots for each independent variable.)

The residuals table allows you to create the residual plot of the residuals versus $\hat{Y}_i$, the predicted values of Y. Apply the instructions of Section E2.12 to create this residual plot, using the cell range of the residuals as the Y variable and the cell range of the predicted Y as the X variable.

Residual plots of residuals versus X_{1i}, X_{2i}, or *Observation* require more work as initially data for these plots will not be in proper order (X variable first, then Y variable) or will not appear together on one worksheet, as required when creating scatter plots.

For these plots, first copy the Residuals cell range column to column A of a new worksheet and then copy the $X_{1i} X_{2i}$ or *Observation* values to column B. The X_{1i} and X_{2i} values appear on your original data worksheet and the *Observation* values appear on the regression results worksheet. Then apply the instructions of Section E2.12 to create a residual plot, using the column A (residuals) cell range as the Y variable and the column B cell range as the X variable.

E14.3 Computing the Confidence Interval Estimate of the Mean Response and the Prediction Interval

You compute the confidence interval estimate of the mean response and the prediction interval using Excel techniques that are beyond the scope of this book. If you are an advanced Excel user, you can use the **CIEandPI** worksheet of the **CIEandPIforMR.xls** workbook (shown in Figure 14.4) as a model for your own solutions. This worksheet uses the **TINV(1-*confidence level, degrees of freedom*)** function to compute the t statistic in cell B20 and uses the **TRANSPOSE(*cell range*)**, **MMULT(*cell range 1, cell range 2*)**, and **MINVERSE(*cell range*)** array functions to perform advanced matrix mathematics. Some worksheet formulas reference a regression results worksheet named **MR**, whereas others, not shown in Figure 14.4, refer to a **DC** worksheet that contains a copy of the regression data and a column of all 1's. (Review the **CIEandPIFormulas** worksheet to see all of the formulas in the **CIEandPI** worksheet.)

E14.4 Creating Dummy Variables

You create dummy variables by using the Excel find-and-replace command to "find" each categorical value and "replace" it with a number.

Open the worksheet that contains your data. Copy all of the values of the categorical variable for which you are creating a dummy variable and paste the values into the first empty column of your worksheet.

Select all of the newly pasted values and press **Crtl+H**, the keyboard shortcut that displays the Find and Replace dialog box (shown below). For each unique categorical value in the column:

1. Enter the categorical value in the **Find what** box.
2. Enter the number that will represent that categorical value in the **Replace with** box.
3. Click **Replace All**. If a message box to confirm the replacement appears, click **OK** to continue.

Click **Close** when you are finished making all replacements. If you inadvertently click the worksheet while using this dialog box, reselect all of the newly pasted values before continuing to replace. When you finish, verify your work by comparing the original column of categorical values to your new column of numeric values.

E14.5 Defining Interaction Terms

You define the interaction term of an independent variable X_1 and a second independent variable X_2 by creating a column of formulas that multiply the X_1 variable by the X_2 variable. For example, if the first independent variable appeared in column B and the second independent variable appeared in column C, you would enter the formula **=B2*C2** in the row 2 cell of an empty column and then copy the formula down through all rows of data.

Appendices

E   Tables

TABLE E.1
Table of Random Numbers

	Column							
Row	**00000** **12345**	**00001** **67890**	**11111** **12345**	**11112** **67890**	**22222** **12345**	**22223** **67890**	**33333** **12345**	**33334** **67890**
01	49280	88924	35779	00283	81163	07275	89863	02348
02	61870	41657	07468	08612	98083	97349	20775	45091
03	43898	65923	25078	86129	78496	97653	91550	08078
04	62993	93912	30454	84598	56095	20664	12872	64647
05	33850	58555	51438	85507	71865	79488	76783	31708
06	97340	03364	88472	04334	63919	36394	11095	92470
07	70543	29776	10087	10072	55980	64688	68239	20461
08	89382	93809	00796	95945	34101	81277	66090	88872
09	37818	72142	67140	50785	22380	16703	53362	44940
10	60430	22834	14130	96593	23298	56203	92671	15925
11	82975	66158	84731	19436	55790	69229	28661	13675
12	30987	71938	40355	54324	08401	26299	49420	59208
13	55700	24586	93247	32596	11865	63397	44251	43189
14	14756	23997	78643	75912	83832	32768	18928	57070
15	32166	53251	70654	92827	63491	04233	33825	69662
16	23236	73751	31888	81718	06546	83246	47651	04877
17	45794	26926	15130	82455	78305	55058	52551	47182
18	09893	20505	14225	68514	47427	56788	96297	78822
19	54382	74598	91499	14523	68479	27686	46162	83554
20	94750	89923	37089	20048	80336	94598	26940	36858
21	70297	34135	53140	33340	42050	82341	44104	82949
22	85157	47954	32979	26575	57600	40881	12250	73742
23	11100	02340	12860	74697	96644	89439	28707	25815
24	36871	50775	30592	57143	17381	68856	25853	35041
25	23913	48357	63308	16090	51690	54607	72407	55538
26	79348	36085	27973	65157	07456	22255	25626	57054
27	92074	54641	53673	54421	18130	60103	69593	49464
28	06873	21440	75593	41373	49502	17972	82578	16364
29	12478	37622	99659	31065	83613	69889	58869	29571
30	57175	55564	65411	42547	70457	03426	72937	83792
31	91616	11075	80103	07831	59309	13276	26710	73000
32	78025	73539	14621	39044	47450	03197	12787	47709
33	27587	67228	80145	10175	12822	86687	65530	49325
34	16690	20427	04251	64477	73709	73945	92396	68263
35	70183	58065	65489	31833	82093	16747	10386	59293
36	90730	35385	15679	99742	50866	78028	75573	67257
37	10934	93242	13431	24590	02770	48582	00906	58595
38	82462	30166	79613	47416	13389	80268	05085	96666
39	27463	10433	07606	16285	93699	60912	94532	95632
40	02979	52997	09079	92709	90110	47506	53693	49892
41	46888	69929	75233	52507	32097	37594	10067	67327
42	53638	83161	08289	12639	08141	12640	28437	09268
43	82433	61427	17239	89160	19666	08814	37841	12847
44	35766	31672	50082	22795	66948	65581	84393	15890
45	10853	42581	08792	13257	61973	24450	52351	16602
46	20341	27398	72906	63955	17276	10646	74692	48438
47	54458	90542	77563	51839	52901	53355	83281	19177
48	26337	66530	16687	35179	46560	00123	44546	79896
49	34314	23729	85264	05575	96855	23820	11091	79821
50	28603	10708	68933	34189	92166	15181	66628	58599
51	66194	28926	99547	16625	45515	67953	12108	57846
52	78240	43195	24837	32511	70880	22070	52622	61881
53	00833	88000	67299	68215	11274	55624	32991	17436
54	12111	86683	61270	58036	64192	90611	15145	01748
55	47189	99951	05755	03834	43782	90599	40282	51417
56	76396	72486	62423	27618	84184	78922	73561	52818
57	46409	17469	32483	09083	76175	19985	26309	91536

TABLE E.1

Table of Random
Numbers (*Continued*)

Row	00000 12345	00001 67890	11111 12345	11112 67890	22222 12345	22223 67890	33333 12345	33334 67890
				Column				
58	74626	22111	87286	46772	42243	68046	44250	42439
59	34450	81974	93723	49023	58432	67083	36876	93391
60	36327	72135	33005	28701	34710	49359	50693	89311
61	74185	77536	84825	09934	99103	09325	67389	45869
62	12296	41623	62873	37943	25584	09609	63360	47270
63	90822	60280	88925	99610	42772	60561	76873	04117
64	72121	79152	96591	90305	10189	79778	68016	13747
65	95268	41377	25684	08151	61816	58555	54305	86189
66	92603	09091	75884	93424	72586	88903	30061	14457
67	18813	90291	05275	01223	79607	95426	34900	09778
68	38840	26903	28624	67157	51986	42865	14508	49315
69	05959	33836	53758	16562	41081	38012	41230	20528
70	85141	21155	99212	32685	51403	31926	69813	58781
71	75047	59643	31074	38172	03718	32119	69506	67143
72	30752	95260	68032	62871	58781	34143	68790	69766
73	22986	82575	42187	62295	84295	30634	66562	31442
74	99439	86692	90348	66036	48399	73451	26698	39437
75	20389	93029	11881	71685	65452	89047	63669	02656
76	39249	05173	68256	36359	20250	68686	05947	09335
77	96777	33605	29481	20063	09398	01843	35139	61344
78	04860	32918	10798	50492	52655	33359	94713	28393
79	41613	42375	00403	03656	77580	87772	86877	57085
80	17930	00794	53836	53692	67135	98102	61912	11246
81	24649	31845	25736	75231	83808	98917	93829	99430
82	79899	34061	54308	59358	56462	58166	97302	86828
83	76801	49594	81002	30397	52728	15101	72070	33706
84	36239	63636	38140	65731	39788	06872	38971	53363
85	07392	64449	17886	63632	53995	17574	22247	62607
86	67133	04181	33874	98835	67453	59734	76381	63455
87	77759	31504	32832	70861	15152	29733	75371	39174
88	85992	72268	42920	20810	29361	51423	90306	73574
89	79553	75952	54116	65553	47139	60579	09165	85490
90	41101	17336	48951	53674	17880	45260	08575	49321
91	36191	17095	32123	91576	84221	78902	82010	30847
92	62329	63898	23268	74283	26091	68409	69704	82267
93	14751	13151	93115	01437	56945	89661	67680	79790
94	48462	59278	44185	29616	76537	19589	83139	28454
95	29435	88105	59651	44391	74588	55114	80834	85686
96	28340	29285	12965	14821	80425	16602	44653	70467
97	02167	58940	27149	80242	10587	79786	34959	75339
98	17864	00991	39557	54981	23588	81914	37609	13128
99	79675	80605	60059	35862	00254	36546	21545	78179
00	72335	82037	92003	34100	29879	46613	89720	13274

Source: *Data partially extracted from the Rand Corporation,* A Million Random Digits with 100,000 Normal
Deviates *(Glencoe, IL, The Free Press, 1955).*

TABLE E.2

The Cumulative Standardized Normal Distribution

Entry represents area under the cumulative standardized
normal distribution from $-\infty$ to Z

				Cumulative Probabilities						
Z	0.00	0.01	0.02	0.03	0.04	0.05	0.06	0.07	0.08	0.09
−6.0	0.000000001									
−5.5	0.000000019									
−5.0	0.000000287									
−4.5	0.000003398									
−4.0	0.000031671									
−3.9	0.00005	0.00005	0.00004	0.00004	0.00004	0.00004	0.00004	0.00004	0.00003	0.00003
−3.8	0.00007	0.00007	0.00007	0.00006	0.00006	0.00006	0.00006	0.00005	0.00005	0.00005
−3.7	0.00011	0.00010	0.00010	0.00010	0.00009	0.00009	0.00008	0.00008	0.00008	0.00008
−3.6	0.00016	0.00015	0.00015	0.00014	0.00014	0.00013	0.00013	0.00012	0.00012	0.00011
−3.5	0.00023	0.00022	0.00022	0.00021	0.00020	0.00019	0.00019	0.00018	0.00017	0.00017
−3.4	0.00034	0.00032	0.00031	0.00030	0.00029	0.00028	0.00027	0.00026	0.00025	0.00024
−3.3	0.00048	0.00047	0.00045	0.00043	0.00042	0.00040	0.00039	0.00038	0.00036	0.00035
−3.2	0.00069	0.00066	0.00064	0.00062	0.00060	0.00058	0.00056	0.00054	0.00052	0.00050
−3.1	0.00097	0.00094	0.00090	0.00087	0.00084	0.00082	0.00079	0.00076	0.00074	0.00071
−3.0	0.00135	0.00131	0.00126	0.00122	0.00118	0.00114	0.00111	0.00107	0.00103	0.00100
−2.9	0.0019	0.0018	0.0018	0.0017	0.0016	0.0016	0.0015	0.0015	0.0014	0.0014
−2.8	0.0026	0.0025	0.0024	0.0023	0.0023	0.0022	0.0021	0.0021	0.0020	0.0019
−2.7	0.0035	0.0034	0.0033	0.0032	0.0031	0.0030	0.0029	0.0028	0.0027	0.0026
−2.6	0.0047	0.0045	0.0044	0.0043	0.0041	0.0040	0.0039	0.0038	0.0037	0.0036
−2.5	0.0062	0.0060	0.0059	0.0057	0.0055	0.0054	0.0052	0.0051	0.0049	0.0048
−2.4	0.0082	0.0080	0.0078	0.0075	0.0073	0.0071	0.0069	0.0068	0.0066	0.0064
−2.3	0.0107	0.0104	0.0102	0.0099	0.0096	0.0094	0.0091	0.0089	0.0087	0.0084
−2.2	0.0139	0.0136	0.0132	0.0129	0.0125	0.0122	0.0119	0.0116	0.0113	0.0110
−2.1	0.0179	0.0174	0.0170	0.0166	0.0162	0.0158	0.0154	0.0150	0.0146	0.0143
−2.0	0.0228	0.0222	0.0217	0.0212	0.0207	0.0202	0.0197	0.0192	0.0188	0.0183
−1.9	0.0287	0.0281	0.0274	0.0268	0.0262	0.0256	0.0250	0.0244	0.0239	0.0233
−1.8	0.0359	0.0351	0.0344	0.0336	0.0329	0.0322	0.0314	0.0307	0.0301	0.0294
−1.7	0.0446	0.0436	0.0427	0.0418	0.0409	0.0401	0.0392	0.0384	0.0375	0.0367
−1.6	0.0548	0.0537	0.0526	0.0516	0.0505	0.0495	0.0485	0.0475	0.0465	0.0455
−1.5	0.0668	0.0655	0.0643	0.0630	0.0618	0.0606	0.0594	0.0582	0.0571	0.0559
−1.4	0.0808	0.0793	0.0778	0.0764	0.0749	0.0735	0.0721	0.0708	0.0694	0.0681
−1.3	0.0968	0.0951	0.0934	0.0918	0.0901	0.0885	0.0869	0.0853	0.0838	0.0823
−1.2	0.1151	0.1131	0.1112	0.1093	0.1075	0.1056	0.1038	0.1020	0.1003	0.0985
−1.1	0.1357	0.1335	0.1314	0.1292	0.1271	0.1251	0.1230	0.1210	0.1190	0.1170
−1.0	0.1587	0.1562	0.1539	0.1515	0.1492	0.1469	0.1446	0.1423	0.1401	0.1379
−0.9	0.1841	0.1814	0.1788	0.1762	0.1736	0.1711	0.1685	0.1660	0.1635	0.1611
−0.8	0.2119	0.2090	0.2061	0.2033	0.2005	0.1977	0.1949	0.1922	0.1894	0.1867
−0.7	0.2420	0.2388	0.2358	0.2327	0.2296	0.2266	0.2236	0.2206	0.2177	0.2148
−0.6	0.2743	0.2709	0.2676	0.2643	0.2611	0.2578	0.2546	0.2514	0.2482	0.2451
−0.5	0.3085	0.3050	0.3015	0.2981	0.2946	0.2912	0.2877	0.2843	0.2810	0.2776
−0.4	0.3446	0.3409	0.3372	0.3336	0.3300	0.3264	0.3228	0.3192	0.3156	0.3121
−0.3	0.3821	0.3783	0.3745	0.3707	0.3669	0.3632	0.3594	0.3557	0.3520	0.3483
−0.2	0.4207	0.4168	0.4129	0.4090	0.4052	0.4013	0.3974	0.3936	0.3897	0.3859
−0.1	0.4602	0.4562	0.4522	0.4483	0.4443	0.4404	0.4364	0.4325	0.4286	0.4247
−0.0	0.5000	0.4960	0.4920	0.4880	0.4840	0.4801	0.4761	0.4721	0.4681	0.4641

TABLE E.2

The Cumulative Standardized Normal Distribution (*Continued*)

Entry represents area under the cumulative standardized
normal distribution from $-\infty$ to Z

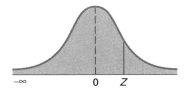

	Cumulative Probabilities									
Z	0.00	0.01	0.02	0.03	0.04	0.05	0.06	0.07	0.08	0.09
0.0	0.5000	0.5040	0.5080	0.5120	0.5160	0.5199	0.5239	0.5279	0.5319	0.5359
0.1	0.5398	0.5438	0.5478	0.5517	0.5557	0.5596	0.5636	0.5675	0.5714	0.5753
0.2	0.5793	0.5832	0.5871	0.5910	0.5948	0.5987	0.6026	0.6064	0.6103	0.6141
0.3	0.6179	0.6217	0.6255	0.6293	0.6331	0.6368	0.6406	0.6443	0.6480	0.6517
0.4	0.6554	0.6591	0.6628	0.6664	0.6700	0.6736	0.6772	0.6808	0.6844	0.6879
0.5	0.6915	0.6950	0.6985	0.7019	0.7054	0.7088	0.7123	0.7157	0.7190	0.7224
0.6	0.7257	0.7291	0.7324	0.7357	0.7389	0.7422	0.7454	0.7486	0.7518	0.7549
0.7	0.7580	0.7612	0.7642	0.7673	0.7704	0.7734	0.7764	0.7794	0.7823	0.7852
0.8	0.7881	0.7910	0.7939	0.7967	0.7995	0.8023	0.8051	0.8078	0.8106	0.8133
0.9	0.8159	0.8186	0.8212	0.8238	0.8264	0.8289	0.8315	0.8340	0.8365	0.8389
1.0	0.8413	0.8438	0.8461	0.8485	0.8508	0.8531	0.8554	0.8577	0.8599	0.8621
1.1	0.8643	0.8665	0.8686	0.8708	0.8729	0.8749	0.8770	0.8790	0.8810	0.8830
1.2	0.8849	0.8869	0.8888	0.8907	0.8925	0.8944	0.8962	0.8980	0.8997	0.9015
1.3	0.9032	0.9049	0.9066	0.9082	0.9099	0.9115	0.9131	0.9147	0.9162	0.9177
1.4	0.9192	0.9207	0.9222	0.9236	0.9251	0.9265	0.9279	0.9292	0.9306	0.9319
1.5	0.9332	0.9345	0.9357	0.9370	0.9382	0.9394	0.9406	0.9418	0.9429	0.9441
1.6	0.9452	0.9463	0.9474	0.9484	0.9495	0.9505	0.9515	0.9525	0.9535	0.9545
1.7	0.9554	0.9564	0.9573	0.9582	0.9591	0.9599	0.9608	0.9616	0.9625	0.9633
1.8	0.9641	0.9649	0.9656	0.9664	0.9671	0.9678	0.9686	0.9693	0.9699	0.9706
1.9	0.9713	0.9719	0.9726	0.9732	0.9738	0.9744	0.9750	0.9756	0.9761	0.9767
2.0	0.9772	0.9778	0.9783	0.9788	0.9793	0.9798	0.9803	0.9808	0.9812	0.9817
2.1	0.9821	0.9826	0.9830	0.9834	0.9838	0.9842	0.9846	0.9850	0.9854	0.9857
2.2	0.9861	0.9864	0.9868	0.9871	0.9875	0.9878	0.9881	0.9884	0.9887	0.9890
2.3	0.9893	0.9896	0.9898	0.9901	0.9904	0.9906	0.9909	0.9911	0.9913	0.9916
2.4	0.9918	0.9920	0.9922	0.9925	0.9927	0.9929	0.9931	0.9932	0.9934	0.9936
2.5	0.9938	0.9940	0.9941	0.9943	0.9945	0.9946	0.9948	0.9949	0.9951	0.9952
2.6	0.9953	0.9955	0.9956	0.9957	0.9959	0.9960	0.9961	0.9962	0.9963	0.9964
2.7	0.9965	0.9966	0.9967	0.9968	0.9969	0.9970	0.9971	0.9972	0.9973	0.9974
2.8	0.9974	0.9975	0.9976	0.9977	0.9977	0.9978	0.9979	0.9979	0.9980	0.9981
2.9	0.9981	0.9982	0.9982	0.9983	0.9984	0.9984	0.9985	0.9985	0.9986	0.9986
3.0	0.99865	0.99869	0.99874	0.99878	0.99882	0.99886	0.99889	0.99893	0.99897	0.99900
3.1	0.99903	0.99906	0.99910	0.99913	0.99916	0.99918	0.99921	0.99924	0.99926	0.99929
3.2	0.99931	0.99934	0.99936	0.99938	0.99940	0.99942	0.99944	0.99946	0.99948	0.99950
3.3	0.99952	0.99953	0.99955	0.99957	0.99958	0.99960	0.99961	0.99962	0.99964	0.99965
3.4	0.99966	0.99968	0.99969	0.99970	0.99971	0.99972	0.99973	0.99974	0.99975	0.99976
3.5	0.99977	0.99978	0.99978	0.99979	0.99980	0.99981	0.99981	0.99982	0.99983	0.99983
3.6	0.99984	0.99985	0.99985	0.99986	0.99986	0.99987	0.99987	0.99988	0.99988	0.99989
3.7	0.99989	0.99990	0.99990	0.99990	0.99991	0.99991	0.99992	0.99992	0.99992	0.99992
3.8	0.99993	0.99993	0.99993	0.99994	0.99994	0.99994	0.99994	0.99995	0.99995	0.99995
3.9	0.99995	0.99995	0.99996	0.99996	0.99996	0.99996	0.99996	0.99996	0.99997	0.99997
4.0	0.999968329									
4.5	0.999996602									
5.0	0.999999713									
5.5	0.999999981									
6.0	0.999999999									

For a particular number of degrees of freedom, entry represents the critical value of t corresponding to the cumulative probability $(1 - \alpha)$ and a specified upper-tail area (α).

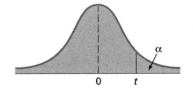

Degrees of Freedom	Cumulative Probabilities					
	0.75	0.90	0.95	0.975	0.99	0.995
	Upper-Tail Areas					
	0.25	0.10	0.05	0.025	0.01	0.005
1	1.0000	3.0777	6.3138	12.7062	31.8207	63.6574
2	0.8165	1.8856	2.9200	4.3027	6.9646	9.9248
3	0.7649	1.6377	2.3534	3.1824	4.5407	5.8409
4	0.7407	1.5332	2.1318	2.7764	3.7469	4.6041
5	0.7267	1.4759	2.0150	2.5706	3.3649	4.0322
6	0.7176	1.4398	1.9432	2.4469	3.1427	3.7074
7	0.7111	1.4149	1.8946	2.3646	2.9980	3.4995
8	0.7064	1.3968	1.8595	2.3060	2.8965	3.3554
9	0.7027	1.3830	1.8331	2.2622	2.8214	3.2498
10	0.6998	1.3722	1.8125	2.2281	2.7638	3.1693
11	0.6974	1.3634	1.7959	2.2010	2.7181	3.1058
12	0.6955	1.3562	1.7823	2.1788	2.6810	3.0545
13	0.6938	1.3502	1.7709	2.1604	2.6503	3.0123
14	0.6924	1.3450	1.7613	2.1448	2.6245	2.9768
15	0.6912	1.3406	1.7531	2.1315	2.6025	2.9467
16	0.6901	1.3368	1.7459	2.1199	2.5835	2.9208
17	0.6892	1.3334	1.7396	2.1098	2.5669	2.8982
18	0.6884	1.3304	1.7341	2.1009	2.5524	2.8784
19	0.6876	1.3277	1.7291	2.0930	2.5395	2.8609
20	0.6870	1.3253	1.7247	2.0860	2.5280	2.8453
21	0.6864	1.3232	1.7207	2.0796	2.5177	2.8314
22	0.6858	1.3212	1.7171	2.0739	2.5083	2.8188
23	0.6853	1.3195	1.7139	2.0687	2.4999	2.8073
24	0.6848	1.3178	1.7109	2.0639	2.4922	2.7969
25	0.6844	1.3163	1.7081	2.0595	2.4851	2.7874
26	0.6840	1.3150	1.7056	2.0555	2.4786	2.7787
27	0.6837	1.3137	1.7033	2.0518	2.4727	2.7707
28	0.6834	1.3125	1.7011	2.0484	2.4671	2.7633
29	0.6830	1.3114	1.6991	2.0452	2.4620	2.7564
30	0.6828	1.3104	1.6973	2.0423	2.4573	2.7500
31	0.6825	1.3095	1.6955	2.0395	2.4528	2.7440
32	0.6822	1.3086	1.6939	2.0369	2.4487	2.7385
33	0.6820	1.3077	1.6924	2.0345	2.4448	2.7333
34	0.6818	1.3070	1.6909	2.0322	2.4411	2.7284
35	0.6816	1.3062	1.6896	2.0301	2.4377	2.7238
36	0.6814	1.3055	1.6883	2.0281	2.4345	2.7195
37	0.6812	1.3049	1.6871	2.0262	2.4314	2.7154
38	0.6810	1.3042	1.6860	2.0244	2.4286	2.7116
39	0.6808	1.3036	1.6849	2.0227	2.4258	2.7079
40	0.6807	1.3031	1.6839	2.0211	2.4233	2.7045
41	0.6805	1.3025	1.6829	2.0195	2.4208	2.7012
42	0.6804	1.3020	1.6820	2.0181	2.4185	2.6981
43	0.6802	1.3016	1.6811	2.0167	2.4163	2.6951
44	0.6801	1.3011	1.6802	2.0154	2.4141	2.6923
45	0.6800	1.3006	1.6794	2.0141	2.4121	2.6896
46	0.6799	1.3002	1.6787	2.0129	2.4102	2.6870
47	0.6797	1.2998	1.6779	2.0117	2.4083	2.6846
48	0.6796	1.2994	1.6772	2.0106	2.4066	2.6822

Degrees of Freedom	Cumulative Probabilities					
	0.75	0.90	0.95	0.975	0.99	0.995
	Upper-Tail Areas					
	0.25	0.10	0.05	0.025	0.01	0.005
49	0.6795	1.2991	1.6766	2.0096	2.4049	2.6800
50	0.6794	1.2987	1.6759	2.0086	2.4033	2.6778
51	0.6793	1.2984	1.6753	2.0076	2.4017	2.6757
52	0.6792	1.2980	1.6747	2.0066	2.4002	2.6737
53	0.6791	1.2977	1.6741	2.0057	2.3988	2.6718
54	0.6791	1.2974	1.6736	2.0049	2.3974	2.6700
55	0.6790	1.2971	1.6730	2.0040	2.3961	2.6682
56	0.6789	1.2969	1.6725	2.0032	2.3948	2.6665
57	0.6788	1.2966	1.6720	2.0025	2.3936	2.6649
58	0.6787	1.2963	1.6716	2.0017	2.3924	2.6633
59	0.6787	1.2961	1.6711	2.0010	2.3912	2.6618
60	0.6786	1.2958	1.6706	2.0003	2.3901	2.6603
61	0.6785	1.2956	1.6702	1.9996	2.3890	2.6589
62	0.6785	1.2954	1.6698	1.9990	2.3880	2.6575
63	0.6784	1.2951	1.6694	1.9983	2.3870	2.6561
64	0.6783	1.2949	1.6690	1.9977	2.3860	2.6549
65	0.6783	1.2947	1.6686	1.9971	2.3851	2.6536
66	0.6782	1.2945	1.6683	1.9966	2.3842	2.6524
67	0.6782	1.2943	1.6679	1.9960	2.3833	2.6512
68	0.6781	1.2941	1.6676	1.9955	2.3824	2.6501
69	0.6781	1.2939	1.6672	1.9949	2.3816	2.6490
70	0.6780	1.2938	1.6669	1.9944	2.3808	2.6479
71	0.6780	1.2936	1.6666	1.9939	2.3800	2.6469
72	0.6779	1.2934	1.6663	1.9935	2.3793	2.6459
73	0.6779	1.2933	1.6660	1.9930	2.3785	2.6449
74	0.6778	1.2931	1.6657	1.9925	2.3778	2.6439
75	0.6778	1.2929	1.6654	1.9921	2.3771	2.6430
76	0.6777	1.2928	1.6652	1.9917	2.3764	2.6421
77	0.6777	1.2926	1.6649	1.9913	2.3758	2.6412
78	0.6776	1.2925	1.6646	1.9908	2.3751	2.6403
79	0.6776	1.2924	1.6644	1.9905	2.3745	2.6395
80	0.6776	1.2922	1.6641	1.9901	2.3739	2.6387
81	0.6775	1.2921	1.6639	1.9897	2.3733	2.6379
82	0.6775	1.2920	1.6636	1.9893	2.3727	2.6371
83	0.6775	1.2918	1.6634	1.9890	2.3721	2.6364
84	0.6774	1.2917	1.6632	1.9886	2.3716	2.6356
85	0.6774	1.2916	1.6630	1.9883	2.3710	2.6349
86	0.6774	1.2915	1.6628	1.9879	2.3705	2.6342
87	0.6773	1.2914	1.6626	1.9876	2.3700	2.6335
88	0.6773	1.2912	1.6624	1.9873	2.3695	2.6329
89	0.6773	1.2911	1.6622	1.9870	2.3690	2.6322
90	0.6772	1.2910	1.6620	1.9867	2.3685	2.6316
91	0.6772	1.2909	1.6618	1.9864	2.3680	2.6309
92	0.6772	1.2908	1.6616	1.9861	2.3676	2.6303
93	0.6771	1.2907	1.6614	1.9858	2.3671	2.6297
94	0.6771	1.2906	1.6612	1.9855	2.3667	2.6291
95	0.6771	1.2905	1.6611	1.9853	2.3662	2.6286
96	0.6771	1.2904	1.6609	1.9850	2.3658	2.6280
97	0.6770	1.2903	1.6607	1.9847	2.3654	2.6275
98	0.6770	1.2902	1.6606	1.9845	2.3650	2.6269
99	0.6770	1.2902	1.6604	1.9842	2.3646	2.6264
100	0.6770	1.2901	1.6602	1.9840	2.3642	2.6259
110	0.6767	1.2893	1.6588	1.9818	2.3607	2.6213
120	0.6765	1.2886	1.6577	1.9799	2.3578	2.6174
∞	0.6745	1.2816	1.6449	1.9600	2.3263	2.5758

TABLE E.4

Critical Values of χ^2

For a particular number of degrees of freedom, entry represents the critical value of χ^2 corresponding to the cumulative probability $(1 - \alpha)$ and a specified upper-tail area (α).

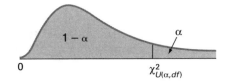

	Cumulative Probabilities											
	0.005	0.01	0.025	0.05	0.10	0.25	0.75	0.90	0.95	0.975	0.99	0.995
	Upper-Tail Areas (α)											
Degrees of Freedom	0.995	0.99	0.975	0.95	0.90	0.75	0.25	0.10	0.05	0.025	0.01	0.005
1			0.001	0.004	0.016	0.102	1.323	2.706	3.841	5.024	6.635	7.879
2	0.010	0.020	0.051	0.103	0.211	0.575	2.773	4.605	5.991	7.378	9.210	10.597
3	0.072	0.115	0.216	0.352	0.584	1.213	4.108	6.251	7.815	9.348	11.345	12.838
4	0.207	0.297	0.484	0.711	1.064	1.923	5.385	7.779	9.488	11.143	13.277	14.860
5	0.412	0.554	0.831	1.145	1.610	2.675	6.626	9.236	11.071	12.833	15.086	16.750
6	0.676	0.872	1.237	1.635	2.204	3.455	7.841	10.645	12.592	14.449	16.812	18.458
7	0.989	1.239	1.690	2.167	2.833	4.255	9.037	12.017	14.067	6.013	18.475	20.278
8	1.344	1.646	2.180	2.733	3.490	5.071	10.219	13.362	15.507	17.535	20.090	21.955
9	1.735	2.088	2.700	3.325	4.168	5.899	11.389	14.684	16.919	19.023	21.666	23.589
10	2.156	2.558	3.247	3.940	4.865	6.737	12.549	15.987	18.307	20.483	23.209	25.188
11	2.603	3.053	3.816	4.575	5.578	7.584	13.701	17.275	19.675	21.920	24.725	26.757
12	3.074	3.571	4.404	5.226	6.304	8.438	14.845	18.549	21.026	23.337	26.217	28.299
13	3.565	4.107	5.009	5.892	7.042	9.299	15.984	19.812	22.362	24.736	27.688	29.819
14	4.075	4.660	5.629	6.571	7.790	10.165	17.117	21.064	23.685	26.119	29.141	31.319
15	4.601	5.229	6.262	7.261	8.547	11.037	18.245	22.307	24.996	27.488	30.578	32.801
16	5.142	5.812	6.908	7.962	9.312	11.912	19.369	23.542	26.296	28.845	32.000	34.267
17	5.697	6.408	7.564	8.672	10.085	12.792	20.489	24.769	27.587	30.191	33.409	35.718
18	6.265	7.015	8.231	9.390	10.865	13.675	21.605	25.989	28.869	31.526	34.805	37.156
19	6.844	7.633	8.907	10.117	11.651	14.562	22.718	27.204	30.144	32.852	36.191	38.582
20	7.434	8.260	9.591	10.851	12.443	15.452	23.828	28.412	31.410	34.170	37.566	39.997
21	8.034	8.897	10.283	11.591	13.240	16.344	24.935	29.615	32.671	35.479	38.932	41.401
22	8.643	9.542	10.982	12.338	14.042	17.240	26.039	30.813	33.924	36.781	40.289	42.796
23	9.260	10.196	11.689	13.091	14.848	18.137	27.141	32.007	35.172	38.076	41.638	44.181
24	9.886	10.856	12.401	13.848	15.659	19.037	28.241	33.196	36.415	39.364	42.980	45.559
25	10.520	11.524	13.120	14.611	16.473	19.939	29.339	34.382	37.652	40.646	44.314	46.928
26	11.160	12.198	13.844	15.379	17.292	20.843	30.435	35.563	38.885	41.923	45.642	48.290
27	11.808	12.879	14.573	16.151	18.114	21.749	31.528	36.741	40.113	43.194	46.963	49.645
28	12.461	13.565	15.308	16.928	18.939	22.657	32.620	37.916	41.337	44.461	48.278	50.993
29	13.121	14.257	16.047	17.708	19.768	23.567	33.711	39.087	42.557	45.722	49.588	52.336
30	13.787	14.954	16.791	18.493	20.599	24.478	34.800	40.256	43.773	46.979	50.892	53.672

For larger values of degrees of freedom (df) the expression $Z = \sqrt{2\chi^2} - \sqrt{2(df) - 1}$ may be used and the resulting upper-tail area can be found from the cumulative standardized normal distribution (Table E.2).

TABLE E.5

Critical Values of F

For a particular combination of numerator and denominator degrees of freedom, entry represents the critical values of F corresponding to the cumulative probability $(1 - \alpha)$ and a specified upper-tail area (α).

α = 0.05

Cumulative Probabilities = 0.95

Upper-Tail Areas = 0.05

Numerator, df_1

Denominator, df_2	1	2	3	4	5	6	7	8	9	10	12	15	20	24	30	40	60	120	∞
1	161.40	199.50	215.70	224.60	230.20	234.00	236.80	238.90	240.50	241.90	243.90	245.90	248.00	249.10	250.10	251.10	252.20	253.30	254.30
2	18.51	19.00	19.16	19.25	19.30	19.33	19.35	19.37	19.38	19.40	19.41	19.43	19.45	19.45	19.46	19.47	19.48	19.49	19.50
3	10.13	9.55	9.28	9.12	9.01	8.94	8.89	8.85	8.81	8.79	8.74	8.70	8.66	8.64	8.62	8.59	8.57	8.55	8.53
4	7.71	6.94	6.59	6.39	6.26	6.16	6.09	6.04	6.00	5.96	5.91	5.86	5.80	5.77	5.75	5.72	5.69	5.66	5.63
5	6.61	5.79	5.41	5.19	5.05	4.95	4.88	4.82	4.77	4.74	4.68	4.62	4.56	4.53	4.50	4.46	4.43	4.40	4.36
6	5.99	5.14	4.76	4.53	4.39	4.28	4.21	4.15	4.10	4.06	4.00	3.94	3.87	3.84	3.81	3.77	3.74	3.70	3.67
7	5.59	4.74	4.35	4.12	3.97	3.87	3.79	3.73	3.68	3.64	3.57	3.51	3.44	3.41	3.38	3.34	3.30	3.27	3.23
8	5.32	4.46	4.07	3.84	3.69	3.58	3.50	3.44	3.39	3.35	3.28	3.22	3.15	3.12	3.08	3.04	3.01	2.97	2.93
9	5.12	4.26	3.86	3.63	3.48	3.37	3.29	3.23	3.18	3.14	3.07	3.01	2.94	2.90	2.86	2.83	2.79	2.75	2.71
10	4.96	4.10	3.71	3.48	3.33	3.22	3.14	3.07	3.02	2.98	2.91	2.85	2.77	2.74	2.70	2.66	2.62	2.58	2.54
11	4.84	3.98	3.59	3.36	3.20	3.09	3.01	2.95	2.90	2.85	2.79	2.72	2.65	2.61	2.57	2.53	2.49	2.45	2.40
12	4.75	3.89	3.49	3.26	3.11	3.00	2.91	2.85	2.80	2.75	2.69	2.62	2.54	2.51	2.47	2.43	2.38	2.34	2.30
13	4.67	3.81	3.41	3.18	3.03	2.92	2.83	2.77	2.71	2.67	2.60	2.53	2.46	2.42	2.38	2.34	2.30	2.25	2.21
14	4.60	3.74	3.34	3.11	2.96	2.85	2.76	2.70	2.65	2.60	2.53	2.46	2.39	2.35	2.31	2.27	2.22	2.18	2.13
15	4.54	3.68	3.29	3.06	2.90	2.79	2.71	2.64	2.59	2.54	2.48	2.40	2.33	2.29	2.25	2.20	2.16	2.11	2.07
16	4.49	3.63	3.24	3.01	2.85	2.74	2.66	2.59	2.54	2.49	2.42	2.35	2.28	2.24	2.19	2.15	2.11	2.06	2.01
17	4.45	3.59	3.20	2.96	2.81	2.70	2.61	2.55	2.49	2.45	2.38	2.31	2.23	2.19	2.15	2.10	2.06	2.01	1.96
18	4.41	3.55	3.16	2.93	2.77	2.66	2.58	2.51	2.46	2.41	2.34	2.27	2.19	2.15	2.11	2.06	2.02	1.97	1.92
19	4.38	3.52	3.13	2.90	2.74	2.63	2.54	2.48	2.42	2.38	2.31	2.23	2.16	2.11	2.07	2.03	1.98	1.93	1.88
20	4.35	3.49	3.10	2.87	2.71	2.60	2.51	2.45	2.39	2.35	2.28	2.20	2.12	2.08	2.04	1.99	1.95	1.90	1.84
21	4.32	3.47	3.07	2.84	2.68	2.57	2.49	2.42	2.37	2.32	2.25	2.18	2.10	2.05	2.01	1.96	1.92	1.87	1.81
22	4.30	3.44	3.05	2.82	2.66	2.55	2.46	2.40	2.34	2.30	2.23	2.15	2.07	2.03	1.98	1.94	1.89	1.84	1.78
23	4.28	3.42	3.03	2.80	2.64	2.53	2.44	2.37	2.32	2.27	2.20	2.13	2.05	2.01	1.96	1.91	1.86	1.81	1.76
24	4.26	3.40	3.01	2.78	2.62	2.51	2.42	2.36	2.30	2.25	2.18	2.11	2.03	1.98	1.94	1.89	1.84	1.79	1.73
25	4.24	3.39	2.99	2.76	2.60	2.49	2.40	2.34	2.28	2.24	2.16	2.09	2.01	1.96	1.92	1.87	1.82	1.77	1.71
26	4.23	3.37	2.98	2.74	2.59	2.47	2.39	2.32	2.27	2.22	2.15	2.07	1.99	1.95	1.90	1.85	1.80	1.75	1.69
27	4.21	3.35	2.96	2.73	2.57	2.46	2.37	2.31	2.25	2.20	2.13	2.06	1.97	1.93	1.88	1.84	1.79	1.73	1.67
28	4.20	3.34	2.95	2.71	2.56	2.45	2.36	2.29	2.24	2.19	2.12	2.04	1.96	1.91	1.87	1.82	1.77	1.71	1.65
29	4.18	3.33	2.93	2.70	2.55	2.43	2.35	2.28	2.22	2.18	2.10	2.03	1.94	1.90	1.85	1.81	1.75	1.70	1.64
30	4.17	3.32	2.92	2.69	2.53	2.42	2.33	2.27	2.21	2.16	2.09	2.01	1.93	1.89	1.84	1.79	1.74	1.68	1.62
40	4.08	3.23	2.84	2.61	2.45	2.34	2.25	2.18	2.12	2.08	2.00	1.92	1.84	1.79	1.74	1.69	1.64	1.58	1.51
60	4.00	3.15	2.76	2.53	2.37	2.25	2.17	2.10	2.04	1.99	1.92	1.84	1.75	1.70	1.65	1.59	1.53	1.47	1.39
120	3.92	3.07	2.68	2.45	2.29	2.17	2.09	2.02	1.96	1.91	1.83	1.75	1.66	1.61	1.55	1.50	1.43	1.35	1.25
∞	3.84	3.00	2.60	2.37	2.21	2.10	2.01	1.94	1.88	1.83	1.75	1.67	1.57	1.52	1.46	1.39	1.32	1.22	1.00

continued

TABLE E.5

Critical Values of F (Continued)

α = 0.025

Cumulative Probabilities = 0.975

Upper-Tail Areas = 0.025

Numerator, df_1

Denominator, df_2	1	2	3	4	5	6	7	8	9	10	12	15	20	24	30	40	60	120	∞
1	647.80	799.50	864.20	899.60	921.80	937.10	948.20	956.70	963.30	968.60	976.70	984.90	993.10	997.20	1,001.00	1,006.00	1,010.00	1,014.00	1,018.00
2	38.51	39.00	39.17	39.25	39.30	39.33	39.36	39.39	39.39	39.40	39.41	39.43	39.45	39.46	39.46	39.47	39.48	39.49	39.50
3	17.44	16.04	15.44	15.10	14.88	14.73	14.62	14.54	14.47	14.42	14.34	14.25	14.17	14.12	14.08	14.04	13.99	13.95	13.90
4	12.22	10.65	9.98	9.60	9.36	9.20	9.07	8.98	8.90	8.84	8.75	8.66	8.56	8.51	8.46	8.41	8.36	8.31	8.26
5	10.01	8.43	7.76	7.39	7.15	6.98	6.85	6.76	6.68	6.62	6.52	6.43	6.33	6.28	6.23	6.18	6.12	6.07	6.02
6	8.81	7.26	6.60	6.23	5.99	5.82	5.70	5.60	5.52	5.46	5.37	5.27	5.17	5.12	5.07	5.01	4.96	4.90	4.85
7	8.07	6.54	5.89	5.52	5.29	5.12	4.99	4.90	4.82	4.76	4.67	4.57	4.47	4.42	4.36	4.31	4.25	4.20	4.14
8	7.57	6.06	5.42	5.05	4.82	4.65	4.53	4.43	4.36	4.30	4.20	4.10	4.00	3.95	3.89	3.84	3.78	3.73	3.67
9	7.21	5.71	5.08	4.72	4.48	4.32	4.20	4.10	4.03	3.96	3.87	3.77	3.67	3.61	3.56	3.51	3.45	3.39	3.33
10	6.94	5.46	4.83	4.47	4.24	4.07	3.95	3.85	3.78	3.72	3.62	3.52	3.42	3.37	3.31	3.26	3.20	3.14	3.08
11	6.72	5.26	4.63	4.28	4.04	3.88	3.76	3.66	3.59	3.53	3.43	3.33	3.23	3.17	3.12	3.06	3.00	2.94	2.88
12	6.55	5.10	4.47	4.12	3.89	3.73	3.61	3.51	3.44	3.37	3.28	3.18	3.07	3.02	2.96	2.91	2.85	2.79	2.72
13	6.41	4.97	4.35	4.00	3.77	3.60	3.48	3.39	3.31	3.25	3.15	3.05	2.95	2.89	2.84	2.78	2.72	2.66	2.60
14	6.30	4.86	4.24	3.89	3.66	3.50	3.38	3.29	3.21	3.15	3.05	2.95	2.84	2.79	2.73	2.67	2.61	2.55	2.49
15	6.20	4.77	4.15	3.80	3.58	3.41	3.29	3.20	3.12	3.06	2.96	2.86	2.76	2.70	2.64	2.59	2.52	2.46	2.40
16	6.12	4.69	4.08	3.73	3.50	3.34	3.22	3.12	3.05	2.99	2.89	2.79	2.68	2.63	2.57	2.51	2.45	2.38	2.32
17	6.04	4.62	4.01	3.66	3.44	3.28	3.16	3.06	2.98	2.92	2.82	2.72	2.62	2.56	2.50	2.44	2.38	2.32	2.25
18	5.98	4.56	3.95	3.61	3.38	3.22	3.10	3.01	2.93	2.87	2.77	2.67	2.56	2.50	2.44	2.38	2.32	2.26	2.19
19	5.92	4.51	3.90	3.56	3.33	3.17	3.05	2.96	2.88	2.82	2.72	2.62	2.51	2.45	2.39	2.33	2.27	2.20	2.13
20	5.87	4.46	3.86	3.51	3.29	3.13	3.01	2.91	2.84	2.77	2.68	2.57	2.46	2.41	2.35	2.29	2.22	2.16	2.09
21	5.83	4.42	3.82	3.48	3.25	3.09	2.97	2.87	2.80	2.73	2.64	2.53	2.42	2.37	2.31	2.25	2.18	2.11	2.04
22	5.79	4.38	3.78	3.44	3.22	3.05	2.93	2.84	2.76	2.70	2.60	2.50	2.39	2.33	2.27	2.21	2.14	2.08	2.00
23	5.75	4.35	3.75	3.41	3.18	3.02	2.90	2.81	2.73	2.67	2.57	2.47	2.36	2.30	2.24	2.18	2.11	2.04	1.97
24	5.72	4.32	3.72	3.38	3.15	2.99	2.87	2.78	2.70	2.64	2.54	2.44	2.33	2.27	2.21	2.15	2.08	2.01	1.94
25	5.69	4.29	3.69	3.35	3.13	2.97	2.85	2.75	2.68	2.61	2.51	2.41	2.30	2.24	2.18	2.12	2.05	1.98	1.91
26	5.66	4.27	3.67	3.33	3.10	2.94	2.82	2.73	2.65	2.59	2.49	2.39	2.28	2.22	2.16	2.09	2.03	1.95	1.88
27	5.63	4.24	3.65	3.31	3.08	2.92	2.80	2.71	2.63	2.57	2.47	2.36	2.25	2.19	2.13	2.07	2.00	1.93	1.85
28	5.61	4.22	3.63	3.29	3.06	2.90	2.78	2.69	2.61	2.55	2.45	2.34	2.23	2.17	2.11	2.05	1.98	1.91	1.83
29	5.59	4.20	3.61	3.27	3.04	2.88	2.76	2.67	2.59	2.53	2.43	2.32	2.21	2.15	2.09	2.03	1.96	1.89	1.81
30	5.57	4.18	3.59	3.25	3.03	2.87	2.75	2.65	2.57	2.51	2.41	2.31	2.20	2.14	2.07	2.01	1.94	1.87	1.79
40	5.42	4.05	3.46	3.13	2.90	2.74	2.62	2.53	2.45	2.39	2.29	2.18	2.07	2.01	1.94	1.88	1.80	1.72	1.64
60	5.29	3.93	3.34	3.01	2.79	2.63	2.51	2.41	2.33	2.27	2.17	2.06	1.94	1.88	1.82	1.74	1.67	1.58	1.48
120	5.15	3.80	3.23	2.89	2.67	2.52	2.39	2.30	2.22	2.16	2.05	1.94	1.82	1.76	1.69	1.61	1.53	1.43	1.31
∞	5.02	3.69	3.12	2.79	2.57	2.41	2.29	2.19	2.11	2.05	1.94	1.83	1.71	1.64	1.57	1.48	1.39	1.31	1.00

TABLE E.5

Critical Values of F (Continued)

α = 0.01

Cumulative Probabilities = 0.99

Upper-Tail Areas = 0.01

Numerator, df_1

continued

Denominator, df_2	1	2	3	4	5	6	7	8	9	10	12	15	20	24	30	40	60	120	∞
1	4,052.00	4,999.50	5,403.00	5,625.00	5,764.00	5,859.00	5,928.00	5,982.00	6,022.00	6,056.00	6,106.00	6,157.00	6,209.00	6,235.00	6,261.00	6,287.00	6,313.00	6,339.00	6,366.00
2	98.50	99.00	99.17	99.25	99.30	99.33	99.36	99.37	99.39	99.40	99.42	99.43	44.45	99.46	99.47	99.47	99.48	99.49	99.50
3	34.12	30.82	29.46	28.71	28.24	27.91	27.67	27.49	27.35	27.23	27.05	26.87	26.69	26.60	26.50	26.41	26.32	26.22	26.13
4	21.20	18.00	16.69	15.98	15.52	15.21	14.98	14.80	14.66	14.55	14.37	14.20	14.02	13.93	13.84	13.75	13.65	13.56	13.46
5	16.26	13.27	12.06	11.39	10.97	10.67	10.46	10.29	10.16	10.05	9.89	9.72	9.55	9.47	9.38	9.29	9.20	9.11	9.02
6	13.75	10.92	9.78	9.15	8.75	8.47	8.26	8.10	7.98	7.87	7.72	7.56	7.40	7.31	7.23	7.14	7.06	6.97	6.88
7	12.25	9.55	8.45	7.85	7.46	7.19	6.99	6.84	6.72	6.62	6.47	6.31	6.16	6.07	5.99	5.91	5.82	5.74	5.65
8	11.26	8.65	7.59	7.01	6.63	6.37	6.18	6.03	5.91	5.81	5.67	5.52	5.36	5.28	5.20	5.12	5.03	4.95	4.86
9	10.56	8.02	6.99	6.42	6.06	5.80	5.61	5.47	5.35	5.26	5.11	4.96	4.81	4.73	4.65	4.57	4.48	4.40	4.31
10	10.04	7.56	6.55	5.99	5.64	5.39	5.20	5.06	4.94	4.85	4.71	4.56	4.41	4.33	4.25	4.17	4.08	4.00	3.91
11	9.65	7.21	6.22	5.67	5.32	5.07	4.89	4.74	4.63	4.54	4.40	4.25	4.10	4.02	3.94	3.86	3.78	3.69	3.60
12	9.33	6.93	5.95	5.41	5.06	4.82	4.64	4.50	4.39	4.30	4.16	4.01	3.86	3.78	3.70	3.62	3.54	3.45	3.36
13	9.07	6.70	5.74	5.21	4.86	4.62	4.44	4.30	4.19	4.10	3.96	3.82	3.66	3.59	3.51	3.43	3.34	3.25	3.17
14	8.86	6.51	5.56	5.04	4.69	4.46	4.28	4.14	4.03	3.94	3.80	3.66	3.51	3.43	3.35	3.27	3.18	3.09	3.00
15	8.68	6.36	5.42	4.89	4.56	4.32	4.14	4.00	3.89	3.80	3.67	3.52	3.37	3.29	3.21	3.13	3.05	2.96	2.87
16	8.53	6.23	5.29	4.77	4.44	4.20	4.03	3.89	3.78	3.69	3.55	3.41	3.26	3.18	3.10	3.02	2.93	2.81	2.75
17	8.40	6.11	5.18	4.67	4.34	4.10	3.93	3.79	3.68	3.59	3.46	3.31	3.16	3.08	3.00	2.92	2.83	2.75	2.65
18	8.29	6.01	5.09	4.58	4.25	4.01	3.84	3.71	3.60	3.51	3.37	3.23	3.08	3.00	2.92	2.84	2.75	2.66	2.57
19	8.18	5.93	5.01	4.50	4.17	3.94	3.77	3.63	3.52	3.43	3.30	3.15	3.00	2.92	2.84	2.76	2.67	2.58	2.49
20	8.10	5.85	4.94	4.43	4.10	3.87	3.70	3.56	3.46	3.37	3.23	3.09	2.94	2.86	2.78	2.69	2.61	2.52	2.42
21	8.02	5.78	4.87	4.37	4.04	3.81	3.64	3.51	3.40	3.31	3.17	3.03	2.88	2.80	2.72	2.64	2.55	2.46	2.36
22	7.95	5.72	4.82	4.31	3.99	3.76	3.59	3.45	3.35	3.26	3.12	2.98	2.83	2.75	2.67	2.58	2.50	2.40	2.31
23	7.88	5.66	4.76	4.26	3.94	3.71	3.54	3.41	3.30	3.21	3.07	2.93	2.78	2.70	2.62	2.54	2.45	2.35	2.26
24	7.82	5.61	4.72	4.22	3.90	3.67	3.50	3.36	3.26	3.17	3.03	2.89	2.74	2.66	2.58	2.49	2.40	2.31	2.21
25	7.77	5.57	4.68	4.18	3.85	3.63	3.46	3.32	3.22	3.13	2.99	2.85	2.70	2.62	2.54	2.45	2.36	2.27	2.17
26	7.72	5.53	4.64	4.14	3.82	3.59	3.42	3.29	3.18	3.09	2.96	2.81	2.66	2.58	2.50	2.42	2.33	2.23	2.13
27	7.68	5.49	4.60	4.11	3.78	3.56	3.39	3.26	3.15	3.06	2.93	2.78	2.63	2.55	2.47	2.38	2.29	2.20	2.10
28	7.64	5.45	4.57	4.07	3.75	3.53	3.36	3.23	3.12	3.03	2.90	2.75	2.60	2.52	2.44	2.35	2.26	2.17	2.06
29	7.60	5.42	4.54	4.04	3.73	3.50	3.33	3.20	3.09	3.00	2.87	2.73	2.57	2.49	2.41	2.33	2.23	2.14	2.03
30	7.56	5.39	4.51	4.02	3.70	3.47	3.30	3.17	3.07	2.98	2.84	2.70	2.55	2.47	2.39	2.30	2.21	2.11	2.01
40	7.31	5.18	4.31	3.83	3.51	3.29	3.12	2.99	2.89	2.80	2.66	2.52	2.37	2.29	2.20	2.11	2.02	1.92	1.80
60	7.08	4.98	4.13	3.65	3.34	3.12	2.95	2.82	2.72	2.63	2.50	2.35	2.20	2.12	2.03	1.94	1.84	1.73	1.60
120	6.85	4.79	3.95	3.48	3.17	2.96	2.79	2.66	2.56	2.47	2.34	2.19	2.03	1.95	1.86	1.76	1.66	1.53	1.38
∞	6.63	4.61	3.78	3.32	3.02	2.80	2.64	2.51	2.41	2.32	2.18	2.04	1.88	1.79	1.70	1.59	1.47	1.32	1.00

TABLE E.5

Critical Values of F (Continued)

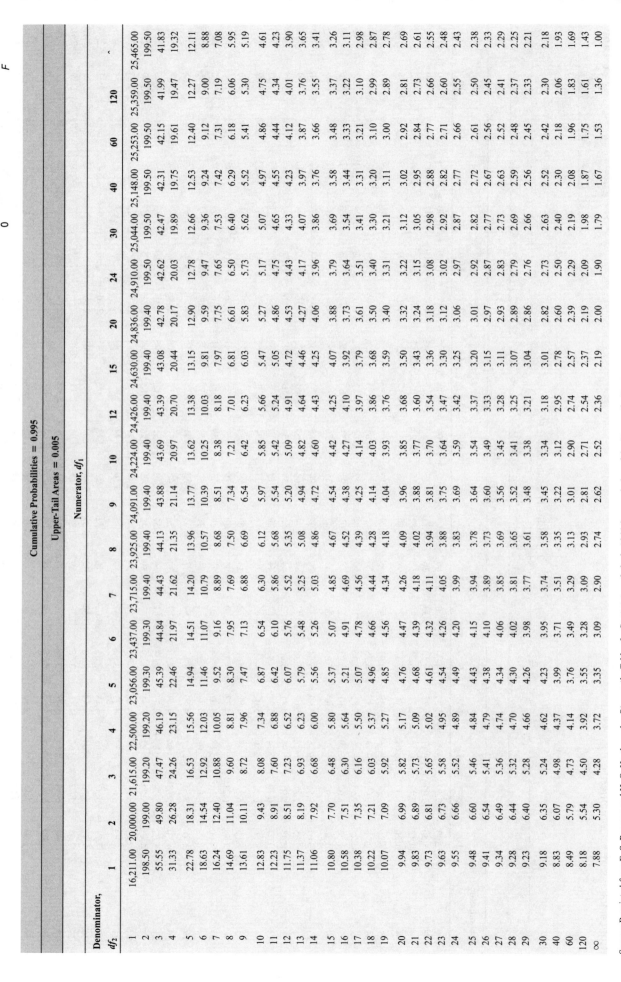

$\alpha = 0.005$

Cumulative Probabilities = 0.995

Upper-Tail Areas = 0.005

Numerator, df_1

Denominator, df_2	1	2	3	4	5	6	7	8	9	10	12	15	20	24	30	40	60	120	∞
1	16,211.00	20,000.00	21,615.00	22,500.00	23,056.00	23,437.00	23,715.00	23,925.00	24,091.00	24,224.00	24,426.00	24,630.00	24,836.00	24,910.00	25,044.00	25,148.00	25,253.00	25,359.00	25,465.00
2	198.50	199.00	199.20	199.20	199.30	199.30	199.40	199.40	199.40	199.40	199.40	199.40	199.40	199.50	199.50	199.50	199.50	199.50	199.50
3	55.55	49.80	47.47	46.19	45.39	44.84	44.43	44.13	43.88	43.69	43.39	43.08	42.78	42.62	42.47	42.31	42.15	41.99	41.83
4	31.33	26.28	24.26	23.15	22.46	21.97	21.62	21.35	21.14	20.97	20.70	20.44	20.17	20.03	19.89	19.75	19.61	19.47	19.32
5	22.78	18.31	16.53	15.56	14.94	14.51	14.20	13.96	13.77	13.62	13.38	13.15	12.90	12.78	12.66	12.53	12.40	12.27	12.11
6	18.63	14.54	12.92	12.03	11.46	11.07	10.79	10.57	10.39	10.25	10.03	9.81	9.59	9.47	9.36	9.24	9.12	9.00	8.88
7	16.24	12.40	10.88	10.05	9.52	9.16	8.89	8.68	8.51	8.38	8.18	7.97	7.75	7.65	7.53	7.42	7.31	7.19	7.08
8	14.69	11.04	9.60	8.81	8.30	7.95	7.69	7.50	7.34	7.21	7.01	6.81	6.61	6.50	6.40	6.29	6.18	6.06	5.95
9	13.61	10.11	8.72	7.96	7.47	7.13	6.88	6.69	6.54	6.42	6.23	6.03	5.83	5.73	5.62	5.52	5.41	5.30	5.19
10	12.83	9.43	8.08	7.34	6.87	6.54	6.30	6.12	5.97	5.85	5.66	5.47	5.27	5.17	5.07	4.97	4.86	4.75	4.61
11	12.23	8.91	7.60	6.88	6.42	6.10	5.86	5.68	5.54	5.42	5.24	5.05	4.86	4.75	4.65	4.55	4.44	4.34	4.23
12	11.75	8.51	7.23	6.52	6.07	5.76	5.52	5.35	5.20	5.09	4.91	4.72	4.53	4.43	4.33	4.23	4.12	4.01	3.90
13	11.37	8.19	6.93	6.23	5.79	5.48	5.25	5.08	4.94	4.82	4.64	4.46	4.27	4.17	4.07	3.97	3.87	3.76	3.65
14	11.06	7.92	6.68	6.00	5.56	5.26	5.03	4.86	4.72	4.60	4.43	4.25	4.06	3.96	3.86	3.76	3.66	3.55	3.41
15	10.80	7.70	6.48	5.80	5.37	5.07	4.85	4.67	4.54	4.42	4.25	4.07	3.88	3.79	3.69	3.58	3.48	3.37	3.26
16	10.58	7.51	6.30	5.64	5.21	4.91	4.69	4.52	4.38	4.27	4.10	3.92	3.73	3.64	3.54	3.44	3.33	3.22	3.11
17	10.38	7.35	6.16	5.50	5.07	4.78	4.56	4.39	4.25	4.14	3.97	3.79	3.61	3.51	3.41	3.31	3.21	3.10	2.98
18	10.22	7.21	6.03	5.37	4.96	4.66	4.44	4.28	4.14	4.03	3.86	3.68	3.50	3.40	3.30	3.20	3.10	2.99	2.87
19	10.07	7.09	5.92	5.27	4.85	4.56	4.34	4.18	4.04	3.93	3.76	3.59	3.40	3.31	3.21	3.11	3.00	2.89	2.78
20	9.94	6.99	5.82	5.17	4.76	4.47	4.26	4.09	3.96	3.85	3.68	3.50	3.32	3.22	3.12	3.02	2.92	2.81	2.69
21	9.83	6.89	5.73	5.09	4.68	4.39	4.18	4.02	3.88	3.77	3.60	3.43	3.24	3.15	3.05	2.95	2.84	2.73	2.61
22	9.73	6.81	5.65	5.02	4.61	4.32	4.11	3.94	3.81	3.70	3.54	3.36	3.18	3.08	2.98	2.88	2.77	2.66	2.55
23	9.63	6.73	5.58	4.95	4.54	4.26	4.05	3.88	3.75	3.64	3.47	3.30	3.12	3.02	2.92	2.82	2.71	2.60	2.48
24	9.55	6.66	5.52	4.89	4.49	4.20	3.99	3.83	3.69	3.59	3.42	3.25	3.06	2.97	2.87	2.77	2.66	2.55	2.43
25	9.48	6.60	5.46	4.84	4.43	4.15	3.94	3.78	3.64	3.54	3.37	3.20	3.01	2.92	2.82	2.72	2.61	2.50	2.38
26	9.41	6.54	5.41	4.79	4.38	4.10	3.89	3.73	3.60	3.49	3.33	3.15	2.97	2.87	2.77	2.67	2.56	2.45	2.33
27	9.34	6.49	5.36	4.74	4.34	4.06	3.85	3.69	3.56	3.45	3.28	3.11	2.93	2.83	2.73	2.63	2.52	2.41	2.29
28	9.28	6.44	5.32	4.70	4.30	4.02	3.81	3.65	3.52	3.41	3.25	3.07	2.89	2.79	2.69	2.59	2.48	2.37	2.25
29	9.23	6.40	5.28	4.66	4.26	3.98	3.77	3.61	3.48	3.38	3.21	3.04	2.86	2.76	2.66	2.56	2.45	2.33	2.21
30	9.18	6.35	5.24	4.62	4.23	3.95	3.74	3.58	3.45	3.34	3.18	3.01	2.82	2.73	2.63	2.52	2.42	2.30	2.18
40	8.83	6.07	4.98	4.37	3.99	3.71	3.51	3.35	3.22	3.12	2.95	2.78	2.60	2.50	2.40	2.30	2.18	2.06	1.93
60	8.49	5.79	4.73	4.14	3.76	3.49	3.29	3.13	3.01	2.90	2.74	2.57	2.39	2.29	2.19	2.08	1.96	1.83	1.69
120	8.18	5.54	4.50	3.92	3.55	3.28	3.09	2.93	2.81	2.71	2.54	2.37	2.19	2.09	1.98	1.87	1.75	1.61	1.43
∞	7.88	5.30	4.28	3.72	3.35	3.09	2.90	2.74	2.62	2.52	2.36	2.19	2.00	1.90	1.79	1.67	1.53	1.36	1.00

Source: Reprinted from E. S. Pearson and H. O. Hartley, eds., *Biometrika Tables for Statisticians*, 3rd ed., 1966, by permission of the *Biometrika* Trustees.

Table E.6

TABLE OF BINOMIAL PROBABILITIES
(BEGINS ON THE FOLLOWING PAGE)

TABLE E.6

Table of Binomial Probabilities

For a given combination of n and π, entry indicates the probability of obtaining a specified value of X. To locate entry, when $\pi \leq .50$ read π across the top heading and both n and X down the left margin; when $\pi \geq .50$ read π across the bottom heading and both n and X up the right margin.

n	X	0.01	0.02	0.03	0.04	0.05	0.06	0.07	0.08	0.09	0.10	0.15	0.20	0.25	0.30	0.35	0.40	0.45	0.50	X	n
2	0	0.9801	0.9604	0.9409	0.9216	0.9025	0.8836	0.8649	0.8464	0.8281	0.8100	0.7225	0.6400	0.5625	0.4900	0.4225	0.3600	0.3025	0.2500	2	
	1	0.0198	0.0392	0.0582	0.0768	0.0950	0.1128	0.1302	0.1472	0.1638	0.1800	0.2550	0.3200	0.3750	0.4200	0.4550	0.4800	0.4950	0.5000	1	
	2	0.0001	0.0004	0.0009	0.0016	0.0025	0.0036	0.0049	0.0064	0.0081	0.0100	0.0225	0.0400	0.0625	0.0900	0.1225	0.1600	0.2025	0.2500	0	2
3	0	0.9703	0.9412	0.9127	0.8847	0.8574	0.8306	0.8044	0.7787	0.7536	0.7290	0.6141	0.5120	0.4219	0.3430	0.2746	0.2160	0.1664	0.1250	3	
	1	0.0294	0.0576	0.0847	0.1106	0.1354	0.1590	0.1816	0.2031	0.2236	0.2430	0.3251	0.3840	0.4219	0.4410	0.4436	0.4320	0.4084	0.3750	2	
	2	0.0003	0.0012	0.0026	0.0046	0.0071	0.0102	0.0137	0.0177	0.0221	0.0270	0.0574	0.0960	0.1406	0.1890	0.2389	0.2880	0.3341	0.3750	1	
	3	0.0000	0.0000	0.0000	0.0001	0.0001	0.0002	0.0003	0.0005	0.0007	0.0010	0.0034	0.0080	0.0156	0.0270	0.0429	0.0640	0.0911	0.1250	0	3
4	0	0.9606	0.9224	0.8853	0.8493	0.8145	0.7807	0.7481	0.7164	0.6857	0.6561	0.5220	0.4096	0.3164	0.2401	0.1785	0.1296	0.0915	0.0625	4	
	1	0.0388	0.0753	0.1095	0.1416	0.1715	0.1993	0.2252	0.2492	0.2713	0.2916	0.3685	0.4096	0.4219	0.4116	0.3845	0.3456	0.2995	0.2500	3	
	2	0.0006	0.0023	0.0051	0.0088	0.0135	0.0191	0.0254	0.0325	0.0402	0.0486	0.0975	0.1536	0.2109	0.2646	0.3105	0.3456	0.3675	0.3750	2	
	3	0.0000	0.0000	0.0001	0.0002	0.0005	0.0008	0.0013	0.0019	0.0027	0.0036	0.0115	0.0256	0.0469	0.0756	0.1115	0.1536	0.2005	0.2500	1	
	4	—	0.0000	0.0000	0.0000	0.0000	0.0000	0.0000	0.0000	0.0001	0.0001	0.0005	0.0016	0.0039	0.0081	0.0150	0.0256	0.0410	0.0625	0	4
5	0	0.9510	0.9039	0.8587	0.8154	0.7738	0.7339	0.6957	0.6591	0.6240	0.5905	0.4437	0.3277	0.2373	0.1681	0.1160	0.0778	0.0503	0.0312	5	
	1	0.0480	0.0922	0.1328	0.1699	0.2036	0.2342	0.2618	0.2866	0.3086	0.3280	0.3915	0.4096	0.3955	0.3601	0.3124	0.2592	0.2059	0.1562	4	
	2	0.0010	0.0038	0.0082	0.0142	0.0214	0.0299	0.0394	0.0498	0.0610	0.0729	0.1382	0.2048	0.2637	0.3087	0.3364	0.3456	0.3369	0.3125	3	
	3	0.0000	0.0001	0.0003	0.0006	0.0011	0.0019	0.0030	0.0043	0.0060	0.0081	0.0244	0.0512	0.0879	0.1323	0.1811	0.2304	0.2757	0.3125	2	
	4	0.0000	0.0000	0.0000	0.0000	0.0000	0.0001	0.0001	0.0002	0.0003	0.0004	0.0022	0.0064	0.0146	0.0283	0.0488	0.0768	0.1128	0.1562	1	
	5	—	0.0000	0.0000	0.0000	0.0000	0.0000	0.0000	0.0000	0.0000	0.0000	0.0001	0.0003	0.0010	0.0024	0.0053	0.0102	0.0185	0.0312	0	5
6	0	0.9415	0.8858	0.8330	0.7828	0.7351	0.6899	0.6470	0.6064	0.5679	0.5314	0.3771	0.2621	0.1780	0.1176	0.0754	0.0467	0.0277	0.0156	6	
	1	0.0571	0.1085	0.1546	0.1957	0.2321	0.2642	0.2922	0.3164	0.3370	0.3543	0.3993	0.3932	0.3560	0.3025	0.2437	0.1866	0.1359	0.0937	5	
	2	0.0014	0.0055	0.0120	0.0204	0.0305	0.0422	0.0550	0.0688	0.0833	0.0984	0.1762	0.2458	0.2966	0.3241	0.3280	0.3110	0.2780	0.2344	4	
	3	0.0000	0.0002	0.0005	0.0011	0.0021	0.0036	0.0055	0.0080	0.0110	0.0146	0.0415	0.0819	0.1318	0.1852	0.2355	0.2765	0.3032	0.3125	3	
	4	—	0.0000	0.0000	0.0000	0.0001	0.0002	0.0003	0.0005	0.0008	0.0012	0.0055	0.0154	0.0330	0.0595	0.0951	0.1372	0.1861	0.2344	2	
	5	—	—	—	0.0000	0.0000	0.0000	0.0000	0.0000	0.0000	0.0001	0.0004	0.0015	0.0044	0.0102	0.0205	0.0369	0.0609	0.0937	1	
	6	—	—	—	0.0000	0.0000	0.0000	0.0000	0.0000	0.0000	0.0000	0.0000	0.0001	0.0002	0.0007	0.0018	0.0041	0.0083	0.0156	0	6

π

n	X	0.50	0.55	0.60	0.65	0.70	0.75	0.80	0.85	0.90	0.91	0.92	0.93	0.94	0.95	0.96	0.97	0.98	0.99
7	7	0.0078	0.0152	0.0280	0.0490	0.0824	0.1335	0.2097	0.3206	0.4783	0.5168	0.5578	0.6017	0.6485	0.6983	0.7514	0.8080	0.8681	0.9321
	6	0.0547	0.0872	0.1306	0.1848	0.2471	0.3115	0.3670	0.3960	0.3720	0.3578	0.3396	0.3170	0.2897	0.2573	0.2192	0.1749	0.1240	0.0659
	5	0.1641	0.2140	0.2613	0.2985	0.3177	0.3115	0.2753	0.2097	0.1240	0.1061	0.0886	0.0716	0.0555	0.0406	0.0274	0.0162	0.0076	0.0020
	4	0.2734	0.2918	0.2903	0.2679	0.2269	0.1730	0.1147	0.0617	0.0230	0.0175	0.0128	0.0090	0.0059	0.0036	0.0019	0.0008	0.0003	0.0000
	3	0.2734	0.2388	0.1935	0.1442	0.0972	0.0577	0.0287	0.0109	0.0026	0.0017	0.0011	0.0007	0.0004	0.0002	0.0001	0.0000	0.0000	—
	2	0.1641	0.1172	0.0774	0.0466	0.0250	0.0115	0.0043	0.0012	0.0002	0.0001	0.0001	0.0000	0.0000	0.0000	0.0000	—	—	—
	1	0.0547	0.0320	0.0172	0.0084	0.0036	0.0013	0.0004	0.0001	0.0000	0.0000	0.0000	—	—	—	—	—	—	—
	0	0.0078	0.0037	0.0016	0.0006	0.0002	0.0001	0.0000	0.0000	0.0000	0.0000	0.0000	—	—	—	—	—	—	—
8	8	0.0039	0.0084	0.0168	0.0319	0.0576	0.1001	0.1678	0.2725	0.4305	0.4703	0.5132	0.5596	0.6096	0.6634	0.7214	0.7837	0.8508	0.9227
	7	0.0312	0.0548	0.0896	0.1373	0.1977	0.2670	0.3355	0.3847	0.3826	0.3721	0.3570	0.3370	0.3113	0.2793	0.2405	0.1939	0.1389	0.0746
	6	0.1094	0.1569	0.2090	0.2587	0.2965	0.3115	0.2936	0.2376	0.1488	0.1288	0.1087	0.0888	0.0695	0.0515	0.0351	0.0210	0.0099	0.0026
	5	0.2187	0.2568	0.2787	0.2786	0.2541	0.2076	0.1468	0.0839	0.0331	0.0255	0.0189	0.0134	0.0089	0.0054	0.0029	0.0013	0.0004	0.0001
	4	0.2734	0.2627	0.2322	0.1875	0.1361	0.0865	0.0459	0.0185	0.0046	0.0031	0.0021	0.0013	0.0007	0.0004	0.0002	0.0001	0.0000	0.0000
	3	0.2187	0.1719	0.1239	0.0808	0.0467	0.0231	0.0092	0.0026	0.0004	0.0002	0.0001	0.0001	0.0000	0.0000	0.0000	0.0000	—	—
	2	0.1094	0.0703	0.0413	0.0217	0.0100	0.0038	0.0011	0.0002	0.0000	0.0000	0.0000	0.0000	—	—	—	—	—	—
	1	0.0312	0.0164	0.0079	0.0033	0.0012	0.0004	0.0001	0.0000	0.0000	—	—	—	—	—	—	—	—	—
	0	0.0039	0.0017	0.0007	0.0002	0.0001	0.0000	0.0000	—	—	—	—	—	—	—	—	—	—	—
9	9	0.0020	0.0046	0.0101	0.0207	0.0404	0.0751	0.1342	0.2316	0.3874	0.4279	0.4722	0.5204	0.5730	0.6302	0.6925	0.7602	0.8337	0.9135
	8	0.0176	0.0339	0.0605	0.1004	0.1556	0.2253	0.3020	0.3679	0.3874	0.3809	0.3695	0.3525	0.3292	0.2985	0.2597	0.2116	0.1531	0.0830
	7	0.0703	0.1110	0.1612	0.2162	0.2668	0.3003	0.3020	0.2597	0.1722	0.1507	0.1285	0.1061	0.0840	0.0629	0.0433	0.0262	0.0125	0.0034
	6	0.1641	0.2119	0.2508	0.2716	0.2668	0.2336	0.1762	0.1069	0.0446	0.0348	0.0261	0.0186	0.0125	0.0077	0.0042	0.0019	0.0006	0.0001
	5	0.2461	0.2600	0.2508	0.2194	0.1715	0.1168	0.0661	0.0283	0.0074	0.0052	0.0034	0.0021	0.0012	0.0006	0.0003	0.0001	0.0000	0.0000
	4	0.2461	0.2128	0.1672	0.1181	0.0735	0.0390	0.0165	0.0050	0.0008	0.0005	0.0003	0.0002	0.0001	0.0000	0.0000	0.0000	—	—
	3	0.1641	0.1160	0.0743	0.0424	0.0210	0.0087	0.0028	0.0006	0.0001	0.0000	0.0000	0.0000	0.0000	—	—	—	—	—
	2	0.0703	0.0407	0.0212	0.0098	0.0039	0.0012	0.0003	0.0000	0.0000	—	—	—	—	—	—	—	—	—
	1	0.0176	0.0083	0.0035	0.0013	0.0004	0.0001	0.0000	—	—	—	—	—	—	—	—	—	—	—
	0	0.0020	0.0008	0.0003	0.0001	0.0000	0.0000	0.0000	—	—	—	—	—	—	—	—	—	—	—
10	10	0.0010	0.0025	0.0060	0.0135	0.0282	0.0563	0.1074	0.1969	0.3487	0.3894	0.4344	0.4840	0.5386	0.5987	0.6648	0.7374	0.8171	0.9044
	9	0.0098	0.0207	0.0403	0.0725	0.1211	0.1877	0.2684	0.3474	0.3874	0.3851	0.3777	0.3643	0.3438	0.3151	0.2770	0.2281	0.1667	0.0914
	8	0.0439	0.0763	0.1209	0.1757	0.2335	0.2816	0.3020	0.2759	0.1937	0.1714	0.1478	0.1234	0.0988	0.0746	0.0519	0.0317	0.0153	0.0042
	7	0.1172	0.1665	0.2150	0.2522	0.2668	0.2503	0.2013	0.1298	0.0574	0.0452	0.0343	0.0248	0.0168	0.0105	0.0058	0.0026	0.0008	0.0001
	6	0.2051	0.2384	0.2508	0.2377	0.2001	0.1460	0.0881	0.0401	0.0112	0.0078	0.0052	0.0033	0.0019	0.0010	0.0004	0.0001	0.0000	0.0000
	5	0.2461	0.2340	0.2007	0.1536	0.1029	0.0584	0.0264	0.0085	0.0015	0.0009	0.0005	0.0003	0.0001	0.0001	0.0000	0.0000	—	—
	4	0.2051	0.1596	0.1115	0.0689	0.0368	0.0162	0.0055	0.0012	0.0001	0.0001	0.0000	0.0000	0.0000	0.0000	—	—	—	—
	3	0.1172	0.0746	0.0425	0.0212	0.0090	0.0031	0.0008	0.0001	0.0000	0.0000	—	—	—	—	—	—	—	—
	2	0.0439	0.0229	0.0106	0.0043	0.0014	0.0004	0.0001	0.0000	0.0000	—	—	—	—	—	—	—	—	—
	1	0.0098	0.0042	0.0016	0.0005	0.0001	0.0000	0.0000	—	—	—	—	—	—	—	—	—	—	—
	0	0.0010	0.0003	0.0001	0.0000	0.0000	0.0000	—	—	—	—	—	—	—	—	—	—	—	—

continued

TABLE E.6

Table of Binomial Probabilities (Continued)

π

n	X	0.01	0.02	0.03	0.04	0.05	0.06	0.07	0.08	0.09	0.10	0.15	0.20	0.25	0.30	0.35	0.40	0.45	0.50	X	n
20	0	0.8179	0.6676	0.5438	0.4420	0.3585	0.2901	0.2342	0.1887	0.1516	0.1216	0.0388	0.0115	0.0032	0.0008	0.0002	0.0000	0.0000	—	20	
	1	0.1652	0.2725	0.3364	0.3683	0.3774	0.3703	0.3526	0.3282	0.3000	0.2702	0.1368	0.0576	0.0211	0.0068	0.0020	0.0005	0.0001	0.0000	19	
	2	0.0159	0.0528	0.0988	0.1458	0.1887	0.2246	0.2521	0.2711	0.2818	0.2852	0.2293	0.1369	0.0699	0.0278	0.0100	0.0031	0.0008	0.0002	18	
	3	0.0010	0.0065	0.0183	0.0364	0.0596	0.0860	0.1139	0.1414	0.1672	0.1901	0.2428	0.2054	0.1339	0.0716	0.0323	0.0123	0.0040	0.0011	17	
	4	0.0000	0.0006	0.0024	0.0065	0.0133	0.0233	0.0364	0.0523	0.0703	0.0898	0.1821	0.2182	0.1897	0.1304	0.0738	0.0350	0.0139	0.0046	16	
	5	—	0.0000	0.0002	0.0009	0.0022	0.0048	0.0088	0.0145	0.0222	0.0319	0.1028	0.1746	0.2023	0.1789	0.1272	0.0746	0.0365	0.0148	15	
	6	—	—	0.0000	0.0001	0.0003	0.0008	0.0017	0.0032	0.0055	0.0089	0.0454	0.1091	0.1686	0.1916	0.1712	0.1244	0.0746	0.0370	14	
	7	—	—	—	0.0000	0.0000	0.0001	0.0002	0.0005	0.0011	0.0020	0.0160	0.0545	0.1124	0.1643	0.1844	0.1659	0.1221	0.0739	13	
	8	—	—	—	0.0000	0.0000	0.0000	0.0000	0.0001	0.0002	0.0004	0.0046	0.0222	0.0609	0.1144	0.1614	0.1797	0.1623	0.1201	12	
	9	—	—	—	—	—	—	0.0000	0.0000	0.0000	0.0001	0.0011	0.0074	0.0271	0.0654	0.1158	0.1597	0.1771	0.1602	11	
	10	—	—	—	—	—	—	—	0.0000	—	0.0000	0.0002	0.0020	0.0099	0.0308	0.0686	0.1171	0.1593	0.1762	10	
	11	—	—	—	—	—	—	—	—	—	—	0.0000	0.0005	0.0030	0.0120	0.0336	0.0710	0.1185	0.1602	9	
	12	—	—	—	—	—	—	—	—	—	—	0.0000	0.0001	0.0008	0.0039	0.0136	0.0355	0.0727	0.1201	8	
	13	—	—	—	—	—	—	—	—	—	—	—	0.0000	0.0002	0.0010	0.0045	0.0146	0.0366	0.0739	7	
	14	—	—	—	—	—	—	—	—	—	—	—	—	0.0000	0.0002	0.0012	0.0049	0.0150	0.0370	6	
	15	—	—	—	—	—	—	—	—	—	—	—	—	—	0.0000	0.0003	0.0013	0.0049	0.0148	5	
	16	—	—	—	—	—	—	—	—	—	—	—	—	—	—	0.0000	0.0003	0.0013	0.0046	4	
	17	—	—	—	—	—	—	—	—	—	—	—	—	—	—	—	0.0000	0.0002	0.0011	3	
	18	—	—	—	—	—	—	—	—	—	—	—	—	—	—	—	—	0.0000	0.0002	2	
	19	—	—	—	—	—	—	—	—	—	—	—	—	—	—	—	—	—	0.0000	1	
	20	—	—	—	—	—	—	—	—	—	—	—	—	—	—	—	—	—	—	0	20
n	X	0.99	0.98	0.97	0.96	0.95	0.94	0.93	0.92	0.91	0.90	0.85	0.80	0.75	0.70	0.65	0.60	0.55	0.50	X	n

TABLE E.7

Table of Poisson Probabilities

For a given value of λ, entry indicates the probability of a specified value of X.

					λ					
X	0.1	0.2	0.3	0.4	0.5	0.6	0.7	0.8	0.9	1.0
0	0.9048	0.8187	0.7408	0.6703	0.6065	0.5488	0.4966	0.4493	0.4066	0.3679
1	0.0905	0.1637	0.2222	0.2681	0.3033	0.3293	0.3476	0.3595	0.3659	0.3679
2	0.0045	0.0164	0.0333	0.0536	0.0758	0.0988	0.1217	0.1438	0.1647	0.1839
3	0.0002	0.0011	0.0033	0.0072	0.0126	0.0198	0.0284	0.0383	0.0494	0.0613
4	0.0000	0.0001	0.0003	0.0007	0.0016	0.0030	0.0050	0.0077	0.0111	0.0153
5	0.0000	0.0000	0.0000	0.0001	0.0002	0.0004	0.0007	0.0012	0.0020	0.0031
6	0.0000	0.0000	0.0000	0.0000	0.0000	0.0000	0.0001	0.0002	0.0003	0.0005
7	0.0000	0.0000	0.0000	0.0000	0.0000	0.0000	0.0000	0.0000	0.0000	0.0001

					λ					
X	1.1	1.2	1.3	1.4	1.5	1.6	1.7	1.8	1.9	2.0
0	0.3329	0.3012	0.2725	0.2466	0.2231	0.2019	0.1827	0.1653	0.1496	0.1353
1	0.3662	0.3614	0.3543	0.3452	0.3347	0.3230	0.3106	0.2975	0.2842	0.2707
2	0.2014	0.2169	0.2303	0.2417	0.2510	0.2584	0.2640	0.2678	0.2700	0.2707
3	0.0738	0.0867	0.0998	0.1128	0.1255	0.1378	0.1496	0.1607	0.1710	0.1804
4	0.0203	0.0260	0.0324	0.0395	0.0471	0.0551	0.0636	0.0723	0.0812	0.0902
5	0.0045	0.0062	0.0084	0.0111	0.0141	0.0176	0.0216	0.0260	0.0309	0.0361
6	0.0008	0.0012	0.0018	0.0026	0.0035	0.0047	0.0061	0.0078	0.0098	0.0120
7	0.0001	0.0002	0.0003	0.0005	0.0008	0.0011	0.0015	0.0020	0.0027	0.0034
8	0.0000	0.0000	0.0001	0.0001	0.0001	0.0002	0.0003	0.0005	0.0006	0.0009
9	0.0000	0.0000	0.0000	0.0000	0.0000	0.0000	0.0001	0.0001	0.0001	0.0002

					λ					
X	2.1	2.2	2.3	2.4	2.5	2.6	2.7	2.8	2.9	3.0
0	0.1225	0.1108	0.1003	0.0907	0.0821	0.0743	0.0672	0.0608	0.0550	0.0498
1	0.2572	0.2438	0.2306	0.2177	0.2052	0.1931	0.1815	0.1703	0.1596	0.1494
2	0.2700	0.2681	0.2652	0.2613	0.2565	0.2510	0.2450	0.2384	0.2314	0.2240
3	0.1890	0.1966	0.2033	0.2090	0.2138	0.2176	0.2205	0.2225	0.2237	0.2240
4	0.0992	0.1082	0.1169	0.1254	0.1336	0.1414	0.1488	0.1557	0.1622	0.1680
5	0.0417	0.0476	0.0538	0.0602	0.0668	0.0735	0.0804	0.0872	0.0940	0.1008
6	0.0146	0.0174	0.0206	0.0241	0.0278	0.0319	0.0362	0.0407	0.0455	0.0504
7	0.0044	0.0055	0.0068	0.0083	0.0099	0.0118	0.0139	0.0163	0.0188	0.0216
8	0.0011	0.0015	0.0019	0.0025	0.0031	0.0038	0.0047	0.0057	0.0068	0.0081
9	0.0003	0.0004	0.0005	0.0007	0.0009	0.0011	0.0014	0.0018	0.0022	0.0027
10	0.0001	0.0001	0.0001	0.0002	0.0002	0.0003	0.0004	0.0005	0.0006	0.0008
11	0.0000	0.0000	0.0000	0.0000	0.0000	0.0001	0.0001	0.0001	0.0002	0.0002
12	0.0000	0.0000	0.0000	0.0000	0.0000	0.0000	0.0000	0.0000	0.0000	0.0001

					λ					
X	3.1	3.2	3.3	3.4	3.5	3.6	3.7	3.8	3.9	4.0
0	0.0450	0.0408	0.0369	0.0334	0.0302	0.0273	0.0247	0.0224	0.0202	0.0183
1	0.1397	0.1340	0.1217	0.1135	0.1057	0.0984	0.0915	0.0850	0.0789	0.0733
2	0.2165	0.2087	0.2008	0.1929	0.1850	0.1771	0.1692	0.1615	0.1539	0.1465
3	0.2237	0.2226	0.2209	0.2186	0.2158	0.2125	0.2087	0.2046	0.2001	0.1954
4	0.1734	0.1781	0.1823	0.1858	0.1888	0.1912	0.1931	0.1944	0.1951	0.1954
5	0.1075	0.1140	0.1203	0.1264	0.1322	0.1377	0.1429	0.1477	0.1522	0.1563
6	0.0555	0.0608	0.0662	0.0716	0.0771	0.0826	0.0881	0.0936	0.0989	0.1042
7	0.0246	0.0278	0.0312	0.0348	0.0385	0.0425	0.0466	0.0508	0.0551	0.0595
8	0.0095	0.0111	0.0129	0.0148	0.0169	0.0191	0.0215	0.0241	0.0269	0.0298
9	0.0033	0.0040	0.0047	0.0056	0.0066	0.0076	0.0089	0.0102	0.0116	0.0132
10	0.0010	0.0013	0.0016	0.0019	0.0023	0.0028	0.0033	0.0039	0.0045	0.0053
11	0.0003	0.0004	0.0005	0.0006	0.0007	0.0009	0.0011	0.0013	0.0016	0.0019
12	0.0001	0.0001	0.0001	0.0002	0.0002	0.0003	0.0003	0.0004	0.0005	0.0006
13	0.0000	0.0000	0.0000	0.0000	0.0001	0.0001	0.0001	0.0001	0.0002	0.0002
14	0.0000	0.0000	0.0000	0.0000	0.0000	0.0000	0.0000	0.0000	0.0000	0.0001

continued

TABLE E.7

Table of Poisson Probabilities (*Continued*)

					λ					
X	4.1	4.2	4.3	4.4	4.5	4.6	4.7	4.8	4.9	5.0
0	0.0166	0.0150	0.0136	0.0123	0.0111	0.0101	0.0091	0.0082	0.0074	0.0067
1	0.0679	0.0630	0.0583	0.0540	0.0500	0.0462	0.0427	0.0395	0.0365	0.0337
2	0.1393	0.1323	0.1254	0.1188	0.1125	0.1063	0.1005	0.0948	0.0894	0.0842
3	0.1904	0.1852	0.1798	0.1743	0.1687	0.1631	0.1574	0.1517	0.1460	0.1404
4	0.1951	0.1944	0.1933	0.1917	0.1898	0.1875	0.1849	0.1820	0.1789	0.1755
5	0.1600	0.1633	0.1662	0.1687	0.1708	0.1725	0.1738	0.1747	0.1753	0.1755
6	0.1093	0.1143	0.1191	0.1237	0.1281	0.1323	0.1362	0.1398	0.1432	0.1462
7	0.0640	0.0686	0.0732	0.0778	0.0824	0.0869	0.0914	0.0959	0.1002	0.1044
8	0.0328	0.0360	0.0393	0.0428	0.0463	0.0500	0.0537	0.0575	0.0614	0.0653
9	0.0150	0.0168	0.0188	0.0209	0.0232	0.0255	0.0280	0.0307	0.0334	0.0363
10	0.0061	0.0071	0.0081	0.0092	0.0104	0.0118	0.0132	0.0147	0.0164	0.0181
11	0.0023	0.0027	0.0032	0.0037	0.0043	0.0049	0.0056	0.0064	0.0073	0.0082
12	0.0008	0.0009	0.0011	0.0014	0.0016	0.0019	0.0022	0.0026	0.0030	0.0034
13	0.0002	0.0003	0.0004	0.0005	0.0006	0.0007	0.0008	0.0009	0.0011	0.0013
14	0.0001	0.0001	0.0001	0.0001	0.0002	0.0002	0.0003	0.0003	0.0004	0.0005
15	0.0000	0.0000	0.0000	0.0000	0.0001	0.0001	0.0001	0.0001	0.0001	0.0002

					λ					
X	5.1	5.2	5.3	5.4	5.5	5.6	5.7	5.8	5.9	6.0
0	0.0061	0.0055	0.0050	0.0045	0.0041	0.0037	0.0033	0.0030	0.0027	0.0025
1	0.0311	0.0287	0.0265	0.0244	0.0225	0.0207	0.0191	0.0176	0.0162	0.0149
2	0.0793	0.0746	0.0701	0.0659	0.0618	0.0580	0.0544	0.0509	0.0477	0.0446
3	0.1348	0.1293	0.1239	0.1185	0.1133	0.1082	0.1033	0.0985	0.0938	0.0892
4	0.1719	0.1681	0.1641	0.1600	0.1558	0.1515	0.1472	0.1428	0.1383	0.1339
5	0.1753	0.1748	0.1740	0.1728	0.1714	0.1697	0.1678	0.1656	0.1632	0.1606
6	0.1490	0.1515	0.1537	0.1555	0.1571	0.1584	0.1594	0.1601	0.1605	0.1606
7	0.1086	0.1125	0.1163	0.1200	0.1234	0.1267	0.1298	0.1326	0.1353	0.1377
8	0.0692	0.0731	0.0771	0.0810	0.0849	0.0887	0.0925	0.0962	0.0998	0.1033
9	0.0392	0.0423	0.0454	0.0486	0.0519	0.0552	0.0586	0.0620	0.0654	0.0688
10	0.0200	0.0220	0.0241	0.0262	0.0285	0.0309	0.0334	0.0359	0.0386	0.0413
11	0.0093	0.0104	0.0116	0.0129	0.0143	0.0157	0.0173	0.0190	0.0207	0.0225
12	0.0039	0.0045	0.0051	0.0058	0.0065	0.0073	0.0082	0.0092	0.0102	0.0113
13	0.0015	0.0018	0.0021	0.0024	0.0028	0.0032	0.0036	0.0041	0.0046	0.0052
14	0.0006	0.0007	0.0008	0.0009	0.0011	0.0013	0.0015	0.0017	0.0019	0.0022
15	0.0002	0.0002	0.0003	0.0003	0.0004	0.0005	0.0006	0.0007	0.0008	0.0009
16	0.0001	0.0001	0.0001	0.0001	0.0001	0.0002	0.0002	0.0002	0.0003	0.0003
17	0.0000	0.0000	0.0000	0.0000	0.0000	0.0000	0.0001	0.0001	0.0001	0.0001

					λ					
X	6.1	6.2	6.3	6.4	6.5	6.6	6.7	6.8	6.9	7.0
0	0.0022	0.0020	0.0018	0.0017	0.0015	0.0014	0.0012	0.0011	0.0010	0.0009
1	0.0137	0.0126	0.0116	0.0106	0.0098	0.0090	0.0082	0.0076	0.0070	0.0064
2	0.0417	0.0390	0.0364	0.0340	0.0318	0.0296	0.0276	0.0258	0.0240	0.0223
3	0.0848	0.0806	0.0765	0.0726	0.0688	0.0652	0.0617	0.0584	0.0552	0.0521
4	0.1294	0.1249	0.1205	0.1162	0.1118	0.1076	0.1034	0.0992	0.0952	0.0912
5	0.1579	0.1549	0.1519	0.1487	0.1454	0.1420	0.1385	0.1349	0.1314	0.1277
6	0.1605	0.1601	0.1595	0.1586	0.1575	0.1562	0.1546	0.1529	0.1511	0.1490
7	0.1399	0.1418	0.1435	0.1450	0.1462	0.1472	0.1480	0.1486	0.1489	0.1490
8	0.1066	0.1099	0.1130	0.1160	0.1188	0.1215	0.1240	0.1263	0.1284	0.1304
9	0.0723	0.0757	0.0791	0.0825	0.0858	0.0891	0.0923	0.0954	0.0985	0.1014
10	0.0441	0.0469	0.0498	0.0528	0.0558	0.0588	0.0618	0.0649	0.0679	0.0710
11	0.0245	0.0265	0.0285	0.0307	0.0330	0.0353	0.0377	0.0401	0.0426	0.0452
12	0.0124	0.0137	0.0150	0.0164	0.0179	0.0194	0.0210	0.0277	0.0245	0.0264
13	0.0058	0.0065	0.0073	0.0081	0.0089	0.0098	0.0108	0.0119	0.0130	0.0142
14	0.0025	0.0029	0.0033	0.0037	0.0041	0.0046	0.0052	0.0058	0.0064	0.0071

TABLE E.7

Table of Poisson
Probabilities
(*Continued*)

					λ					
X	6.1	6.2	6.3	6.4	6.5	6.6	6.7	6.8	6.9	7.0
15	0.0010	0.0012	0.0014	0.0016	0.0018	0.0020	0.0023	0.0026	0.0029	0.0033
16	0.0004	0.0005	0.0005	0.0006	0.0007	0.0008	0.0010	0.0011	0.0013	0.0014
17	0.0001	0.0002	0.0002	0.0002	0.0003	0.0003	0.0004	0.0004	0.0005	0.0006
18	0.0000	0.0001	0.0001	0.0001	0.0001	0.0001	0.0001	0.0002	0.0002	0.0002
19	0.0000	0.0000	0.0000	0.0000	0.0000	0.0000	0.0000	0.0001	0.0001	0.0001

					λ					
X	7.1	7.2	7.3	7.4	7.5	7.6	7.7	7.8	7.9	8.0
0	0.0008	0.0007	0.0007	0.0006	0.0006	0.0005	0.0005	0.0004	0.0004	0.0003
1	0.0059	0.0054	0.0049	0.0045	0.0041	0.0038	0.0035	0.0032	0.0029	0.0027
2	0.0208	0.0194	0.0180	0.0167	0.0156	0.0145	0.0134	0.0125	0.0116	0.0107
3	0.0492	0.0464	0.0438	0.0413	0.0389	0.0366	0.0345	0.0324	0.0305	0.0286
4	0.0874	0.0836	0.0799	0.0764	0.0729	0.0696	0.0663	0.0632	0.0602	0.0573
5	0.1241	0.1204	0.1167	0.1130	0.1094	0.1057	0.1021	0.0986	0.0951	0.0916
6	0.1468	0.1445	0.1420	0.1394	0.1367	0.1339	0.1311	0.1282	0.1252	0.1221
7	0.1489	0.1486	0.1481	0.1474	0.1465	0.1454	0.1442	0.1428	0.1413	0.1396
8	0.1321	0.1337	0.1351	0.1363	0.1373	0.1382	0.1388	0.1392	0.1395	0.1396
9	0.1042	0.1070	0.1096	0.1121	0.1144	0.1167	0.1187	0.1207	0.1224	0.1241
10	0.0740	0.0770	0.0800	0.0829	0.0858	0.0887	0.0914	0.0941	0.0967	0.0993
11	0.0478	0.0504	0.0531	0.0558	0.0585	0.0613	0.0640	0.0667	0.0695	0.0722
12	0.0283	0.0303	0.0323	0.0344	0.0366	0.0388	0.0411	0.0434	0.0457	0.0481
13	0.0154	0.0168	0.0181	0.0196	0.0211	0.0227	0.0243	0.0260	0.0278	0.0296
14	0.0078	0.0086	0.0095	0.0104	0.0113	0.0123	0.0134	0.0145	0.0157	0.0169
15	0.0037	0.0041	0.0046	0.0051	0.0057	0.0062	0.0069	0.0075	0.0083	0.0090
16	0.0016	0.0019	0.0021	0.0024	0.0026	0.0030	0.0033	0.0037	0.0041	0.0045
17	0.0007	0.0008	0.0009	0.0010	0.0012	0.0013	0.0015	0.0017	0.0019	0.0021
18	0.0003	0.0003	0.0004	0.0004	0.0005	0.0006	0.0006	0.0007	0.0008	0.0009
19	0.0001	0.0001	0.0001	0.0002	0.0002	0.0002	0.0003	0.0003	0.0003	0.0004
20	0.0000	0.0000	0.0001	0.0001	0.0001	0.0001	0.0001	0.0001	0.0001	0.0002
21	0.0000	0.0000	0.0000	0.0000	0.0000	0.0000	0.0000	0.0000	0.0001	0.0001

					λ					
X	8.1	8.2	8.3	8.4	8.5	8.6	8.7	8.8	8.9	9.0
0	0.0003	0.0003	0.0002	0.0002	0.0002	0.0002	0.0002	0.0002	0.0001	0.0001
1	0.0025	0.0023	0.0021	0.0019	0.0017	0.0016	0.0014	0.0013	0.0012	0.0011
2	0.0100	0.0092	0.0086	0.0079	0.0074	0.0068	0.0063	0.0058	0.0054	0.0050
3	0.0269	0.0252	0.0237	0.0222	0.0208	0.0195	0.0183	0.0171	0.0160	0.0150
4	0.0544	0.0517	0.0491	0.0466	0.0443	0.0420	0.0398	0.0377	0.0357	0.0337
5	0.0882	0.0849	0.0816	0.0784	0.0752	0.0722	0.0692	0.0663	0.0635	0.0607
6	0.1191	0.1160	0.1128	0.1097	0.1066	0.1034	0.1003	0.0972	0.0941	0.0911
7	0.1378	0.1358	0.1338	0.1317	0.1294	0.1271	0.1247	0.1222	0.1197	0.1171
8	0.1395	0.1392	0.1388	0.1382	0.1375	0.1366	0.1356	0.1344	0.1332	0.1318
9	0.1256	0.1269	0.1280	0.1290	0.1299	0.1306	0.1311	0.1315	0.1317	0.1318
10	0.1017	0.1040	0.1063	0.1084	0.1104	0.1123	0.1140	0.1157	0.1172	0.1186
11	0.0749	0.0776	0.0802	0.0828	0.0853	0.0878	0.0902	0.0925	0.0948	0.0970
12	0.0505	0.0530	0.0555	0.0579	0.0604	0.0629	0.0654	0.0679	0.0703	0.0728
13	0.0315	0.0334	0.0354	0.0374	0.0395	0.0416	0.0438	0.0459	0.0481	0.0504
14	0.0182	0.0196	0.0210	0.0225	0.0240	0.0256	0.0272	0.0289	0.0306	0.0324
15	0.0098	0.0107	0.0116	0.0126	0.0136	0.0147	0.0158	0.0169	0.0182	0.0194
16	0.0050	0.0055	0.0060	0.0066	0.0072	0.0079	0.0086	0.0093	0.0101	0.0109
17	0.0024	0.0026	0.0029	0.0033	0.0036	0.0040	0.0044	0.0048	0.0053	0.0058
18	0.0011	0.0012	0.0014	0.0015	0.0017	0.0019	0.0021	0.0024	0.0026	0.0029
19	0.0005	0.0005	0.0006	0.0007	0.0008	0.0009	0.0010	0.0011	0.0012	0.0014
20	0.0002	0.0002	0.0002	0.0003	0.0003	0.0004	0.0004	0.0005	0.0005	0.0006
21	0.0001	0.0001	0.0001	0.0001	0.0001	0.0002	0.0002	0.0002	0.0002	0.0003
22	0.0000	0.0000	0.0000	0.0000	0.0001	0.0001	0.0001	0.0001	0.0001	0.0001

continued

TABLE E.7

Table of Poisson Probabilities (*Continued*)

					λ					
X	**9.1**	**9.2**	**9.3**	**9.4**	**9.5**	**9.6**	**9.7**	**9.8**	**9.9**	**10**
0	0.0001	0.0001	0.0001	0.0001	0.0001	0.0001	0.0001	0.0001	0.0001	0.0000
1	0.0010	0.0009	0.0009	0.0008	0.0007	0.0007	0.0006	0.0005	0.0005	0.0005
2	0.0046	0.0043	0.0040	0.0037	0.0034	0.0031	0.0029	0.0027	0.0025	0.0023
3	0.0140	0.0131	0.0123	0.0115	0.0107	0.0100	0.0093	0.0087	0.0081	0.0076
4	0.0319	0.0302	0.0285	0.0269	0.0254	0.0240	0.0226	0.0213	0.0201	0.0189
5	0.0581	0.0555	0.0530	0.0506	0.0483	0.0460	0.0439	0.0418	0.0398	0.0378
6	0.0881	0.0851	0.0822	0.0793	0.0764	0.0736	0.0709	0.0682	0.0656	0.0631
7	0.1145	0.1118	0.1091	0.1064	0.1037	0.1010	0.0982	0.0955	0.0928	0.0901
8	0.1302	0.1286	0.1269	0.1251	0.1232	0.1212	0.1191	0.1170	0.1148	0.1126
9	0.1317	0.1315	0.1311	0.1306	0.1300	0.1293	0.1284	0.1274	0.1263	0.1251
10	0.1198	0.1210	0.1219	0.1228	0.1235	0.1241	0.1245	0.1249	0.1250	0.1251
11	0.0991	0.1012	0.1031	0.1049	0.1067	0.1083	0.1098	0.1112	0.1125	0.1137
12	0.0752	0.0776	0.0799	0.0822	0.0844	0.0866	0.0888	0.0908	0.0928	0.0948
13	0.0526	0.0549	0.0572	0.0594	0.0617	0.0640	0.0662	0.0685	0.0707	0.0729
14	0.0342	0.0361	0.0380	0.0399	0.0419	0.0439	0.0459	0.0479	0.0500	0.0521
15	0.0208	0.0221	0.0235	0.0250	0.0265	0.0281	0.0297	0.0313	0.0330	0.0347
16	0.0118	0.0127	0.0137	0.0147	0.0157	0.0168	0.0180	0.0192	0.0204	0.0217
17	0.0063	0.0069	0.0075	0.0081	0.0088	0.0095	0.0103	0.0111	0.0119	0.0128
18	0.0032	0.0035	0.0039	0.0042	0.0046	0.0051	0.0055	0.0060	0.0065	0.0071
19	0.0015	0.0017	0.0019	0.0021	0.0023	0.0026	0.0028	0.0031	0.0034	0.0037
20	0.0007	0.0008	0.0009	0.0010	0.0011	0.0012	0.0014	0.0015	0.0017	0.0019
21	0.0003	0.0003	0.0004	0.0004	0.0005	0.0006	0.0006	0.0007	0.0008	0.0009
22	0.0001	0.0001	0.0002	0.0002	0.0002	0.0002	0.0003	0.0003	0.0004	0.0004
23	0.0000	0.0001	0.0001	0.0001	0.0001	0.0001	0.0001	0.0001	0.0002	0.0002
24	0.0000	0.0000	0.0000	0.0000	0.0000	0.0000	0.0000	0.0001	0.0001	0.0001

X	**λ = 20**	**X**	**λ = 20**	**X**	**λ = 20**	**X**	**λ = 20**
0	0.0000	10	0.0058	20	0.0888	30	0.0083
1	0.0000	11	0.0106	21	0.0846	31	0.0054
2	0.0000	12	0.0176	22	0.0769	32	0.0034
3	0.0000	13	0.0271	23	0.0669	33	0.0020
4	0.0000	14	0.0387	24	0.0557	34	0.0012
5	0.0001	15	0.0516	25	0.0446	35	0.0007
6	0.0002	16	0.0646	26	0.0343	36	0.0004
7	0.0005	17	0.0760	27	0.0254	37	0.0002
8	0.0013	18	0.0844	28	0.0181	38	0.0001
9	0.0029	19	0.0888	29	0.0125	39	0.0001

TABLE E.8

Critical Values of the Studentized Range, Q

Upper 5% Points ($\alpha = 0.05$)

Denominator, df	\multicolumn{19}{c}{Numerator, df}
	2	3	4	5	6	7	8	9	10	11	12	13	14	15	16	17	18	19	20
1	18.00	27.00	32.80	37.10	40.40	43.10	45.40	47.40	49.10	50.60	52.00	53.20	54.30	55.40	56.30	57.20	58.00	58.80	59.60
2	6.09	8.30	9.80	10.90	11.70	12.40	13.00	13.50	14.00	14.40	14.70	15.10	15.40	15.70	15.90	16.10	16.40	16.60	16.80
3	4.50	5.91	6.82	7.50	8.04	8.48	8.85	9.18	9.46	9.72	9.95	10.15	10.35	10.52	10.69	10.84	10.98	11.11	11.24
4	3.93	5.04	5.76	6.29	6.71	7.05	7.35	7.60	7.83	8.03	8.21	8.37	8.52	8.66	8.79	8.91	9.03	9.13	9.23
5	3.64	4.60	5.22	5.67	6.03	6.33	6.58	6.80	6.99	7.17	7.32	7.47	7.60	7.72	7.83	7.93	8.03	8.12	8.21
6	3.46	4.34	4.90	5.31	5.63	5.89	6.12	6.32	6.49	6.65	6.79	6.92	7.03	7.14	7.24	7.34	7.43	7.51	7.59
7	3.34	4.16	4.68	5.06	5.36	5.61	5.82	6.00	6.16	6.30	6.43	6.55	6.66	6.76	6.85	6.94	7.02	7.09	7.17
8	3.26	4.04	4.53	4.89	5.17	5.40	5.60	5.77	5.92	6.05	6.18	6.29	6.39	6.48	6.57	6.65	6.73	6.80	6.87
9	3.20	3.95	4.42	4.76	5.02	5.24	5.43	5.60	5.74	5.87	5.98	6.09	6.19	6.28	6.36	6.44	6.51	6.58	6.64
10	3.15	3.88	4.33	4.65	4.91	5.12	5.30	5.46	5.60	5.72	5.83	5.93	6.03	6.11	6.20	6.27	6.34	6.40	6.47
11	3.11	3.82	4.26	4.57	4.82	5.03	5.20	5.35	5.49	5.61	5.71	5.81	5.90	5.99	6.06	6.14	6.20	6.26	6.33
12	3.08	3.77	4.20	4.51	4.75	4.95	5.12	5.27	5.40	5.51	5.62	5.71	5.80	5.88	5.95	6.03	6.09	6.15	6.21
13	3.06	3.73	4.15	4.45	4.69	4.88	5.05	5.19	5.32	5.43	5.53	5.63	5.71	5.79	5.86	5.93	6.00	6.05	6.11
14	3.03	3.70	4.11	4.41	4.64	4.83	4.99	5.13	5.25	5.36	5.46	5.55	5.64	5.72	5.79	5.85	5.92	5.97	6.03
15	3.01	3.67	4.08	4.37	4.60	4.78	4.94	5.08	5.20	5.31	5.40	5.49	5.58	5.65	5.72	5.79	5.85	5.90	5.96
16	3.00	3.65	4.05	4.33	4.56	4.74	4.90	5.03	5.15	5.26	5.35	5.44	5.52	5.59	5.66	5.72	5.79	5.84	5.90
17	2.98	3.63	4.02	4.30	4.52	4.71	4.86	4.99	5.11	5.21	5.31	5.39	5.47	5.55	5.61	5.68	5.74	5.79	5.84
18	2.97	3.61	4.00	4.28	4.49	4.67	4.82	4.96	5.07	5.17	5.27	5.35	5.43	5.50	5.57	5.63	5.69	5.74	5.79
19	2.96	3.59	3.98	4.25	4.47	4.65	4.79	4.92	5.04	5.14	5.23	5.32	5.39	5.46	5.53	5.59	5.65	5.70	5.75
20	2.95	3.58	3.96	4.23	4.45	4.62	4.77	4.90	5.01	5.11	5.20	5.28	5.36	5.43	5.49	5.55	5.61	5.66	5.71
24	2.92	3.53	3.90	4.17	4.37	4.54	4.68	4.81	4.92	5.01	5.10	5.18	5.25	5.32	5.38	5.44	5.50	5.54	5.59
30	2.89	3.49	3.84	4.10	4.30	4.46	4.60	4.72	4.83	4.92	5.00	5.08	5.15	5.21	5.27	5.33	5.38	5.43	5.48
40	2.86	3.44	3.79	4.04	4.23	4.39	4.52	4.63	4.74	4.82	4.91	4.98	5.05	5.11	5.16	5.22	5.27	5.31	5.36
60	2.83	3.40	3.74	3.98	4.16	4.31	4.44	4.55	4.65	4.73	4.81	4.88	4.94	5.00	5.06	5.11	5.16	5.20	5.24
120	2.80	3.36	3.69	3.92	4.10	4.24	4.36	4.48	4.56	4.64	4.72	4.78	4.84	4.90	4.95	5.00	5.05	5.09	5.13
∞	2.77	3.31	3.63	3.86	4.03	4.17	4.29	4.39	4.47	4.55	4.62	4.68	4.74	4.80	4.85	4.89	4.93	4.97	5.01

continued

TABLE E.8
Critical Values of the Studentized Range, Q (Continued)

Upper 1% Points ($\alpha = 0.01$)

Denominator, df	Numerator, df																		
	2	3	4	5	6	7	8	9	10	11	12	13	14	15	16	17	18	19	20
1	90.00	135.00	164.00	186.00	202.00	216.00	227.00	237.00	246.00	253.00	260.00	266.00	272.00	277.00	282.00	286.00	290.00	294.00	298.00
2	14.00	19.00	22.30	24.70	26.60	28.20	29.50	30.70	31.70	32.60	33.40	34.10	34.80	35.40	36.00	36.50	37.00	37.50	37.90
3	8.26	10.60	12.20	13.30	14.20	15.00	15.60	16.20	16.70	17.10	17.50	17.90	18.20	18.50	18.80	19.10	19.30	19.50	19.80
4	6.51	8.12	9.17	9.96	10.60	11.10	11.50	11.90	12.30	12.60	12.80	13.10	13.30	13.50	13.70	13.90	14.10	14.20	14.40
5	5.70	6.97	7.80	8.42	8.91	9.32	9.67	9.97	10.24	10.48	10.70	10.89	11.08	11.24	11.40	11.55	11.68	11.81	11.93
6	5.24	6.33	7.03	7.56	7.97	8.32	8.61	8.87	9.10	9.30	9.49	9.65	9.81	9.95	10.08	10.21	10.32	10.43	10.54
7	4.95	5.92	6.54	7.01	7.37	7.68	7.94	8.17	8.37	8.55	8.71	8.86	9.00	9.12	9.24	9.35	9.46	9.55	9.65
8	4.74	5.63	6.20	6.63	6.96	7.24	7.47	7.68	7.87	8.03	8.18	8.31	8.44	8.55	8.66	8.76	8.85	8.94	9.03
9	4.60	5.43	5.96	6.35	6.66	6.91	7.13	7.32	7.49	7.65	7.78	7.91	8.03	8.13	8.23	8.32	8.41	8.49	8.57
10	4.48	5.27	5.77	6.14	6.43	6.67	6.87	7.05	7.21	7.36	7.48	7.60	7.71	7.81	7.91	7.99	8.07	8.15	8.22
11	4.39	5.14	5.62	5.97	6.26	6.48	6.67	6.84	6.99	7.13	7.25	7.36	7.46	7.56	7.65	7.73	7.81	7.88	7.95
12	4.32	5.04	5.50	5.84	6.10	6.32	6.51	6.67	6.81	6.94	7.06	7.17	7.26	7.36	7.44	7.52	7.59	7.66	7.73
13	4.26	4.96	5.40	5.73	5.98	6.19	6.37	6.53	6.67	6.79	6.90	7.01	7.10	7.19	7.27	7.34	7.42	7.48	7.55
14	4.21	4.89	5.32	5.63	5.88	6.08	6.26	6.41	6.54	6.66	6.77	6.87	6.96	7.05	7.12	7.20	7.27	7.33	7.39
15	4.17	4.83	5.25	5.56	5.80	5.99	6.16	6.31	6.44	6.55	6.66	6.76	6.84	6.93	7.00	7.07	7.14	7.20	7.26
16	4.13	4.78	5.19	5.49	5.72	5.92	6.08	6.22	6.35	6.46	6.56	6.66	6.74	6.82	6.90	6.97	7.03	7.09	7.15
17	4.10	4.74	5.14	5.43	5.66	5.85	6.01	6.15	6.27	6.38	6.48	6.57	6.66	6.73	6.80	6.87	6.94	7.00	7.05
18	4.07	4.70	5.09	5.38	5.60	5.79	5.94	6.08	6.20	6.31	6.41	6.50	6.58	6.65	6.72	6.79	6.85	6.91	6.96
19	4.05	4.67	5.05	5.33	5.55	5.73	5.89	6.02	6.14	6.25	6.34	6.43	6.51	6.58	6.65	6.72	6.78	6.84	6.89
20	4.02	4.64	5.02	5.29	5.51	5.69	5.84	5.97	6.09	6.19	6.29	6.37	6.45	6.52	6.59	6.65	6.71	6.76	6.82
24	3.96	4.54	4.91	5.17	5.37	5.54	5.69	5.81	5.92	6.02	6.11	6.19	6.26	6.33	6.39	6.45	6.51	6.56	6.61
30	3.89	4.45	4.80	5.05	5.24	5.40	5.54	5.65	5.76	5.85	5.93	6.01	6.08	6.14	6.20	6.26	6.31	6.36	6.41
40	3.82	4.37	4.70	4.93	5.11	5.27	5.39	5.50	5.60	5.69	5.77	5.84	5.90	5.96	6.02	6.07	6.12	6.17	6.21
60	3.76	4.28	4.60	4.82	4.99	5.13	5.25	5.36	5.45	5.53	5.60	5.67	5.73	5.79	5.84	5.89	5.93	5.98	6.02
120	3.70	4.20	4.50	4.71	4.87	5.01	5.12	5.21	5.30	5.38	5.44	5.51	5.56	5.61	5.66	5.71	5.75	5.79	5.83
∞	3.64	4.12	4.40	4.60	4.76	4.88	4.99	5.08	5.16	5.23	5.29	5.35	5.40	5.45	5.49	5.54	5.57	5.61	5.65

Source: Reprinted from E. S. Pearson and H. O. Hartley, eds., Table 29 of *Biometrika Tables for Statisticians, Vol. 1*, 3rd ed., 1966, by permission of the *Biometrika* Trustees, London.

TABLE E.9
Control Chart Factors

Number of Observations in Sample (n)	d_2	d_3	D_3	D_4	A_2
2	1.128	0.853	0	3.267	1.880
3	1.693	0.888	0	2.575	1.023
4	2.059	0.880	0	2.282	0.729
5	2.326	0.864	0	2.114	0.577
6	2.534	0.848	0	2.004	0.483
7	2.704	0.833	0.076	1.924	0.419
8	2.847	0.820	0.136	1.864	0.373
9	2.970	0.808	0.184	1.816	0.337
10	3.078	0.797	0.223	1.777	0.308
11	3.173	0.787	0.256	1.744	0.285
12	3.258	0.778	0.283	1.717	0.266
13	3.336	0.770	0.307	1.693	0.249
14	3.407	0.763	0.328	1.672	0.235
15	3.472	0.756	0.347	1.653	0.223
16	3.532	0.750	0.363	1.637	0.212
17	3.588	0.744	0.378	1.622	0.203
18	3.640	0.739	0.391	1.609	0.194
19	3.689	0.733	0.404	1.596	0.187
20	3.735	0.729	0.415	1.585	0.180
21	3.778	0.724	0.425	1.575	0.173
22	3.819	0.720	0.435	1.565	0.167
23	3.858	0.716	0.443	1.557	0.162
24	3.895	0.712	0.452	1.548	0.157
25	3.931	0.708	0.459	1.541	0.153

Source: *Reprinted from ASTM-STP 15D by kind permission of the American Society for Testing and Materials.*

TABLE E.10
The Standardized Normal Distribution

Entry represents area under the standardized normal
distribution from the mean to Z

Z	.00	.01	.02	.03	.04	.05	.06	.07	.08	.09
0.0	.0000	.0040	.0080	.0120	.0160	.0199	.0239	.0279	.0319	.0359
0.1	.0398	.0438	.0478	.0517	.0557	.0596	.0636	.0675	.0714	.0753
0.2	.0793	.0832	.0871	.0910	.0948	.0987	.1026	.1064	.1103	.1141
0.3	.1179	.1217	.1255	.1293	.1331	.1368	.1406	.1443	.1480	.1517
0.4	.1554	.1591	.1628	.1664	.1700	.1736	.1772	.1808	.1844	.1879
0.5	.1915	.1950	.1985	.2019	.2054	.2088	.2123	.2157	.2190	.2224
0.6	.2257	.2291	.2324	.2357	.2389	.2422	.2454	.2486	.2518	.2549
0.7	.2580	.2612	.2642	.2673	.2704	.2734	.2764	.2794	.2823	.2852
0.8	.2881	.2910	.2939	.2967	.2995	.3023	.3051	.3078	.3106	.3133
0.9	.3159	.3186	.3212	.3238	.3264	.3289	.3315	.3340	.3365	.3389
1.0	.3413	.3438	.3461	.3485	.3508	.3531	.3554	.3577	.3599	.3621
1.1	.3643	.3665	.3686	.3708	.3729	.3749	.3770	.3790	.3810	.3830
1.2	.3849	.3869	.3888	.3907	.3925	.3944	.3962	.3980	.3997	.4015
1.3	.4032	.4049	.4066	.4082	.4099	.4115	.4131	.4147	.4162	.4177
1.4	.4192	.4207	.4222	.4236	.4251	.4265	.4279	.4292	.4306	.4319
1.5	.4332	.4345	.4357	.4370	.4382	.4394	.4406	.4418	.4429	.4441
1.6	.4452	.4463	.4474	.4484	.4495	.4505	.4515	.4525	.4535	.4545
1.7	.4554	.4564	.4573	.4582	.4591	.4599	.4608	.4616	.4625	.4633
1.8	.4641	.4649	.4656	.4664	.4671	.4678	.4686	.4693	.4699	.4706
1.9	.4713	.4719	.4726	.4732	.4738	.4744	.4750	.4756	.4761	.4767
2.0	.4772	.4778	.4783	.4788	.4793	.4798	.4803	.4808	.4812	.4817
2.1	.4821	.4826	.4830	.4834	.4838	.4842	.4846	.4850	.4854	.4857
2.2	.4861	.4864	.4868	.4871	.4875	.4878	.4881	.4884	.4887	.4890
2.3	.4893	.4896	.4898	.4901	.4904	.4906	.4909	.4911	.4913	.4916
2.4	.4918	.4920	.4922	.4925	.4927	.4929	.4931	.4932	.4934	.4936
2.5	.4938	.4940	.4941	.4943	.4945	.4946	.4948	.4949	.4951	.4952
2.6	.4953	.4955	.4956	.4957	.4959	.4960	.4961	.4962	.4963	.4964
2.7	.4965	.4966	.4967	.4968	.4969	.4970	.4971	.4972	.4973	.4974
2.8	.4974	.4975	.4976	.4977	.4977	.4978	.4979	.4979	.4980	.4981
2.9	.4981	.4982	.4982	.4983	.4984	.4984	.4985	.4985	.4986	.4986
3.0	.49865	.49869	.49874	.49878	.49882	.49886	.49889	.49893	.49897	.49900
3.1	.49903	.49906	.49910	.49913	.49916	.49918	.49921	.49924	.49926	.49929
3.2	.49931	.49934	.49936	.49938	.49940	.49942	.49944	.49946	.49948	.49950
3.3	.49952	.49953	.49955	.49957	.49958	.49960	.49961	.49962	.49964	.49965
3.4	.49966	.49968	.49969	.49970	.49971	.49972	.49973	.49974	.49975	.49976
3.5	.49977	.49978	.49978	.49979	.49980	.49981	.49981	.49982	.49983	.49983
3.6	.49984	.49985	.49985	.49986	.49986	.49987	.49987	.49988	.49988	.49989
3.7	.49989	.49990	.49990	.49990	.49991	.49991	.49992	.49992	.49992	.49992
3.8	.49993	.49993	.49993	.49994	.49994	.49994	.49994	.49995	.49995	.49995
3.9	.49995	.49995	.49996	.49996	.49996	.49996	.49996	.49996	.49997	.49997

Use this appendix to find answers to the most frequently asked questions about using the resources on the Student CD-ROM and using Microsoft Excel and PHStat2.

F.1 About the Student CD-ROM

What does the Student CD-ROM contain?

The Student CD-ROM contains six categories of files that support this book:

1. **Data files.** These files contain the data used in chapter examples or named in problems. They exist as Excel workbook files (in the **.xls** format, compatible with all Excel versions), worksheet (**.mtw**) files and SPSS worksheet **.sav** files. See Appendix D.2 for a complete listing of data files included on the Student CD-ROM.
2. **Case files.** These files, a mix of data and document files as well as facsimiles of Web page files, support both the *Managing the Springville Herald* running case and the various Web Cases.
3. **Excel appendix workbooks.** These files are Microsoft Excel workbooks that contain model solutions for applying Microsoft Excel to various statistical analyses. Most are designed as fill-in-the-data templates that can be reused indefinitely.
4. **Visual Explorations files.** These files support Visual Explorations, the interactive Excel add-in that illustrates selected statistical concepts.
5. **Windows applications.** These files are specific to Microsoft Windows XP or Vista (any version) and include the PHStat2 setup program, and the Adobe Reader setup program, and the Student CD-ROM's own "start" program that simplifies access to the contents of the Student CD-ROM.

Can I use the Student CD-ROM with an Apple Mac running the Mac OS?

Although the Student CD-ROM is marked "For Windows," most Mac users will be able to retrieve and use the first four categories of files listed in the previous answer.

Does the Student CD-ROM contain Microsoft Excel or Minitab?

No, these programs must be acquired separately. Specially priced student-oriented versions of Microsoft Office (containing Excel) are available at many retailers and select retailers, including **mypearsonstore.com**, sell the student version of Minitab.

Can I copy the Excel workbook files to my local hard disk or other storage device?

Yes, you can, and you are encouraged to do so. Windows users can use the CD-ROM's own "start" program to facilitate this task. Some files that you copy may be reported as being a "read-only" file. If you make changes to such files, you will need to save the file under a different name.

Can I buy a replacement Student CD-ROM disk?

No, Student CD-ROM disks are not sold separately. However, a PHStat2 version either identical or similar to the one included on the Student CD-ROM is available for separate purchase.

F.2 About Microsoft Excel

Will I need access to my original Microsoft Office/Excel CDs or DVD?

Yes, if you are using PHStat2 you may need to use the original program disks if the Analysis ToolPak and Analysis ToolPak–VBA (referred to as the "ToolPak" in this book) has not been installed on your system.

What Microsoft Office security settings should I use? How do I change Office security settings?

See Section E1.8, "Using Add-ins" on page 19 for specific answers to these questions. If you plan to use the Prentice Hall PHStat2 Excel add-in, also read the PHStat2 readme file on the Student CD-ROM.

How can I check to see if the ToolPak has been installed in Excel 97–2003?

Open Excel and select **Tools → Add-Ins** and in the Add-Ins dialog box that appears, verify that **Analysis ToolPak** (and **Analysis ToolPak–VBA**, if using PHStat2) is checked in the **Add-Ins available** list. If **Analysis ToolPak** does not appear, you will need to install it separately.

How can I check to see if the ToolPak has been installed in Excel 2007?

Open Excel and click the **Office Button**. In the Office Button pane, click **Excel Options**. In the Excel options dialog box that appears, click **Add-Ins** in the left pane and look for **Analysis ToolPak** (and **Analysis ToolPak–VBA**, if using PHStat2) under **Active Application Add-Ins**. If they do not appear, click **Go** and continue with the instructions for using the Add-Ins dialog box presented in the answer for Excel 97–2003.

How can I install the ToolPak?

Close Microsoft Excel and rerun the Microsoft Office or Microsoft Excel setup program. When the setup program runs, choose the option that allows you to add components.

This option is variously described as the **modify**, **add**, or **custom** option. Then, select install **Analysis ToolPak** (and **Analysis ToolPak–VBA**, if using PHStat2). You may need access to the original Microsoft Office/Excel setup CD-ROMs or DVDs to complete this task.

Do I need to run a setup program to use the Visual Explorations add-in workbook (Visual Explorations.xla)?
No, you can copy the files and install the files from the Visual Exporations folder on the Student CD-ROM and use this add-in file as you would use any of the workbook data files. You will need to properly adjust your Microsoft Office security settings (see Section E1.8 on page 19) in order to use this add-in.

In Excel 97–2003, how can I specify the custom settings that you recommend?
First, select **Tools → Customize**. In the Customize dialog box, clear (uncheck) the **Menus show recently used commands first** check box if it is checked and click the **Close** button. Then select **Tools → Options**. In the Options dialog box, click the **Calculation** tab and verify that the **Automatic** option button of the Calculation group has been selected. Click the **Edit** tab and verify that all check boxes except the **Fixed decimal, Provide feedback with Animation**, and **Enable automatic percent entry** have been selected. (Excel 97 does not contain an Automatic percent entry check box.) Click the **General** tab and verify that the **R1C1 reference style** check box is cleared, and, if using Excel 97, check the **Macro virus protection** check box. Enter **3** as the number of **Sheets in new workbook**, select **Arial** from the **Standard font** list, and select **10** from the **Size** drop-down list. Then click **OK** to finish the customization.

In Excel 2007, how can I specify the custom settings that you recommend?
First, click the **Office Button** and then click **Excel Options**. In the Excel Options dialog box, click **Formulas** in the left panel. In the **Formulas** right pane, click **Automatic** under Workbook Calculation and verify that all check boxes are checked except **Enable iterative calculation, R1C1 reference style**, and **Formulas referring to empty cells**. For greater customization, click **Advanced** in the left panel and scroll through the **Advanced options for working with Excel** that appears in the right panel. Click **OK** when finished.

F.3 About PHStat2

What is PHStat2?

PHStat2 is software that makes operating Microsoft Excel as distraction free as possible. As a student studying statistics, you can focus mainly on learning statistics and not worry about having to fully master Excel first. When PHStat2 is combined with the ToolPak add-in supplied with Microsoft Excel, just about all statistical methods taught in an introductory statistics course can be illustrated using Microsoft Excel.

I do not want to use an add-in that will not be available in my business environment. Any comments?
Chapter 1 talks about these issues in detail. To summarize those pages, PHStat2 helps you learn Microsoft Excel, and using PHStat2 will not leave you any less equipped to work with Microsoft Excel in a setting where it is not available.

What do I need to do in order to begin using PHStat2?
You run the PHStat2 setup program (setup.exe) that is included on the Student CD-ROM. To use this program successfully, you must have logged in to Windows using an account that has administrator or software-installing privileges. (Student and faculty accounts to log in to networked computers in academic settings typically do not have this privilege. If you have such an account, ask your network or lab technician for assistance.) If you are using Windows Vista or certain firewall or security-suite programs, you may see messages asking you to permit or allow certain system operations as the PHStat2 setup runs. (If you decline permission, PHStat2 will not be successfully set up.)

What are the technical requirements for setting up and adding PHStat2 to my system?
If your system can run Microsoft Excel, it can also run PHStat2. You need approximately up to 10 MB hard disk free space during the setup process and up to 3 MB hard disk space after PHStat2 is installed. You must also ensure that the Microsoft Excel Analysis ToolPak and Analysis ToolPak–VBA add-ins have been installed. (See related question in Section F.2.)

Are updates to PHStat2 available?
Yes, free minor updates to resolve issues may be available for download from the PHStat2 Web site (**www.prenhall. com/phstat**). When you visit that Web site, note that the Student CD-ROM contains version 2.8 of PHStat2.

How can I identify which version of PHStat2 I have?
Open Microsoft Excel with PHStat2 and select **Help for PHStat** from the PHStat menu. A dialog box will display your current XLA and DLL version numbers. The XLA version number identifies the version of PHStat2 you have. Both of these numbers will initially be 2.8.0 after you set up PHStat2 from the Student CD-ROM.

Where can I get help setting up PHStat2?
First, carefully review the Student CD-ROM PHStat2 readme file. If your problem is unresolved, visit the PHStat2 Web site (**www.prenhall.com/phstat**) for further information. If your problem is still unresolved, contact Pearson Education technical support at **247pearsoned.custhelp.com**.

Where can I find tips for using PHStat2?
While your classmates and instructor can be the best source of tips, you can also visit the online PHStat2 community at **phstatcommunity.org**

F.4 About Minitab

Which versions of Minitab can I use with this book?

You should use Minitab 14 or Minitab 15 when following the instructions in the Minitab appendices. There is a student version of Minitab that can be bundled with the book.

F.5 Additional Information For New Microsoft Excel 2007 Users

I do not see the menu for an add-in workbook that I opened. Where is it?

Unlike earlier versions of Excel that allowed add-ins to add menus to the menu bar, Excel 2007 places all add-in menus under the Add-ins tab. If you click Add-ins, you find the menus of all properly loaded add-ins.

What does "Compatibility Mode" mean?

When you see "Compatibility Mode" in the title bar, Excel 2007 is telling you that you are using a workbook compatible with earlier Excel versions. When you save such a workbook, Excel 2007 will automatically use the .xls file format of earlier versions.

How can I update an older (.xls) workbook to the Excel 2007 .xlsx workbook format?

The simplest way is to open the workbook file and select **Office Button → Convert**. Then save your file (select **Office Button → Save**). You can also open the workbook file and select **Office Button → Save As** and in the Save As dialog box, select **Excel Workbook (*.xlsx)** from the **Save as type** list.

Self-Test Solutions and Answers to Selected Problems

The following represent worked-out solutions to Self-Test Problems and brief answers to most of the selected problems in the text. For more detailed solutions, including explanations, interpretations, and Excel and Minitab output, see the *Student Solutions Manual*.

CHAPTER 1

1.2 Small, medium, and large sizes represent different categories.

1.4 (a) The number of telephones is a numerical variable that is discrete because the outcome is a count. **(b)** The length of the longest long-distance call is a numerical variable that is continuous because any value within a range of values can occur. **(c)** Whether there is a cell phone in the household is a categorical variable because the answer can be only yes or no. **(d)** Same answer as in (c).

1.6 (a) Categorical. **(b)** Numerical, continuous. **(c)** Numerical, discrete. **(d)** Numerical, discrete.

1.8 (a) Numerical, continuous. **(b)** Numerical, discrete. **(c)** Numerical, continuous. **(d)** Categorical.

1.25 (a) All people living in the United States aged 18 and older. **(b)** A telephone interview of 1,102 respondents. **(c)** The population percentage of people living in the United States aged 18 and older who have made major changes in their shopping and living habits over the last five years to help protect the environment. **(d)** Twenty-eight percent of respondents have made major changes in their shopping and living habits over the last five years to help protect the environment.

1.27 (a) Cat owner households in the United States. **(b)** 1. Categorical. 2. Categorical. 3. Numerical, discrete. 4. Categorical.

1.29 (a) Gender, current major, undergraduate major, current employment status, satisfaction with advisement services. **(b)** Age, height, graduate cumulative grade point average, undergraduate cumulative grade point average, GMAT score, number of full-time jobs, starting salary, salary in five years, amount spent on textbooks and supplies. **(c)** Number of full-time jobs. (GMAT score could also be considered discrete.)

CHAPTER 2

2.4 (b) The Pareto chart is best for portraying these data because it not only sorts the frequencies in descending order, it also provides the cumulative polygon on the same scale. **(c)** You can conclude that friends/family account for the largest percentage of 45%. When other, news media, and online user reviews are added to friends/family, this accounts for 83%.

2.6 (b) 85%. **(d)** The Pareto chart allows you to see which sources account for most of the electricity.

2.8 (b) The bar chart is more suitable if the purpose is to compare the categories. The pie chart is more suitable if the main objective is to investigate the portion of the whole that is in a particular category.

2.21 (a) 10 but less than 20, 20 but less than 30, 30 but less than 40, 40 but less than 50, 50 but less than 60, 60 but less than 70, 70 but less than 80, 80 but less than 90, 90 but less than 100. **(b)** 10. **(c)** 15, 25, 35, 45, 55, 65, 75, 85, 95.

2.23 (a)

Electricity Costs	Frequency	Percentage
$80 and under $100	4	8%
$100 and under $120	7	14
$120 and under $140	9	18
$140 and under $160	13	26
$160 and under $180	9	18
$180 and under $200	5	10
$200 and under $220	3	6

(c)

Electricity Costs	Frequency	Percentage	Cumulative %
$99	4	8.00%	8.00%
$119	7	14.00	22.00
$139	9	18.00	40.00
$159	13	26.00	66.00
$179	9	18.00	84.00
$199	5	10.00	94.00
$219	3	6.00	100.00

(d) The majority of utility charges are clustered between $120 and $180.

2.25 The property taxes per capita appear to be right-skewed with approximately 90% falling between $399 and $1,700, and the remaining 10% falling between $1,700 and $2,100. The center is at about $1,000.

2.27 (a)

Width	Frequency	Percentage
8.310–8.329	3	6.12%
8.330–8.349	2	4.08
8.350–8.369	1	2.04
8.370–8.389	4	8.16
8.390–8.409	5	10.20
8.410–8.429	16	31.65
8.430–8.449	5	10.20
8.450–8.469	5	10.20
8.470–8.489	6	12.24
8.490–8.509	2	4.08

(d) All the troughs will meet the company's requirements of between 8.31 and 8.61 inches wide.

2.29 (a)

Bulb Life (hrs)	Percentage, Mfgr A	Percentage, Mfgr B
650–749	7.5%	0.0%
750–849	12.5	5.0
850–949	50.0	20.0
950–1,049	22.5	40.0
1,050–1,149	7.5	22.5
1,150–1,249	0.0	12.5

(c)

% Less Than	Percentage Less Than, Mfgr A	Percentage Less Than, Mfgr B
750	7.5%	0.0%
850	20.0	5.0
950	70.0	25.0
1,050	92.5	65.0
1,150	100.0	87.5
1,250	100.0	100.0

(d) Manufacturer B produces bulbs with longer lives than Manufacturer A. The cumulative percentage for Manufacturer B shows 65% of its bulbs lasted less than 1,050 hours, contrasted with 70% of Manufacturer A's bulbs, which lasted less than 950 hours. None of Manufacturer A's bulbs lasted more than 1,149 hours, but 12.5% of Manufacturer B's bulbs lasted between 1,150 and 1,249 hours. At the same time, 7.5% of Manufacturer A's bulbs lasted less than 750 hours, whereas all of Manufacturer B's bulbs lasted at least 750 hours.

2.39 (a) Table of frequencies for all student responses:

GENDER	STUDENT MAJOR CATEGORIES			
	A	C	M	Totals
Male	14	9	2	25
Female	6	6	3	15
Totals	20	15	5	40

(b) Table of percentages based on overall student responses:

GENDER	STUDENT MAJOR CATEGORIES			
	A	C	M	Totals
Male	35.0%	22.5%	5.0%	62.5%
Female	15.0	15.0	7.5	37.5
Totals	50.0	37.5	12.5	100.0

(c) Table based on row percentages:

GENDER	STUDENT MAJOR CATEGORIES			
	A	C	M	Totals
Male	56.0%	36.0%	8.0%	100.0%
Female	40.0	40.0	20.0	100.0
Totals	50.0	37.5	12.5	100.0

(d) Table based on column percentages:

GENDER	STUDENT MAJOR CATEGORIES			
	A	C	M	Totals
Male	70.0%	60.0%	40.0%	62.5%
Female	30.0	40.0	60.0	37.5
Totals	100.0	100.0	100.0	100.0

2.41 (a) Table of row percentages:

ENJOY SHOPPING FOR CLOTHING	GENDER		
	Male	Female	Total
Yes	38%	62%	100%
No	74	26	100
Total	48	52	100

Table of column percentages:

	GENDER		
	Male	Female	Total
Yes	57%	86%	72%
No	43	14	28
Total	100	100	100

Table of total percentages:

ENJOY SHOPPING FOR CLOTHING	GENDER		
	Male	Female	Total
Yes	27%	45%	72%
No	21	7	28
Total	48	52	100

(b) A higher percentage of females enjoy shopping for clothing.

2.43 (b) The number of MBA and undergraduate students who choose the lowest-cost fund and the second-lowest-cost fund is about the same. More MBA students chose the third-lowest cost fund whereas more undergraduate students chose the highest cost fund.

2.45 (b) Yes, there is a strong positive relationship between X and Y. As X increases, so does Y.

2.47 (b) There is a positive relationship between owner mileage and current government standard mileage.

2.49 (b) There appears to be a positive relationship between the coaches' salary and revenue. **(c)** Yes, this is borne out by the data.

2.51 (b) The unemployment rate was stable at around 4% from January 2000 to around January 2001. Then it trended upward and leveled off at around 6% by December 2001. Around October 2003, it started to trend downward and reached about 4.5% by December 2006 before staying between 4.5% and 5% in 2007.

2.53 (b) There is an obvious upward trend in the average number of TV channels that the U.S. home received from 1985 to 2005. **(c)** With extrapolation, you would predict the average number of TV channels that the U.S. home will receive in 2010 to be around 140.

2.71 (c) The publisher gets the largest portion (64.8%) of the revenue. About half (32.3%) of the revenue received by the publisher covers manufacturing costs. The publisher's marketing and promotion account for the next largest share of the revenue, at 15.4%. Author, bookstore employee salaries and benefits, and publisher administrative costs and taxes each account for around 10% of the revenue, whereas the publisher after-tax profit, bookstore operations, bookstore pretax profit, and freight constitute the "trivial few" allocations of the revenue. Yes, the bookstore gets twice the revenue of the authors.

2.73 (b) The Pareto plot is most appropriate because it not only sorts the frequencies in descending order, it also provides the cumulative polygon on the same scale. **(d)** The Pareto plot is most appropriate because it not only sorts the frequencies in descending order, it also provides the cumulative polygon on the same scale. **(e)** "Paid search" constitutes the largest category on U.S. online ad spending at 43%. Excluding the generic keyword "sneakers," searches using the keywords "sneaker pimps" and "Jordan sneaker" make up the majority of the searches for sneakers on specific brands.

2.75 (a)

DESSERT ORDERED	GENDER		
	Male	**Female**	**Total**
Yes	71%	29%	100%
No	48	52	100
Total	53	47	100

DESSERT ORDERED	GENDER		
	Male	**Female**	**Total**
Yes	30%	14%	23%
No	70	86	77
Total	100	100	100

DESSERT ORDERED	BEEF ENTRÉE		
	Yes	**No**	**Total**
Yes	52%	48%	100%
No	25	75	100
Total	31	69	100

DESSERT ORDERED	BEEF ENTRÉE		
	Yes	**No**	**Total**
Yes	38%	16%	23%
No	62	84	77
Total	100	100	100

DESSERT ORDERED	BEEF ENTRÉE		
	Yes	**No**	**Total**
Yes	12%	11%	23%
No	19	58	77
Total	31	69	100

(b) If the owner is interested in finding out the percentage of males and females who order dessert or the percentage of those who order a beef entrée and a dessert among all patrons, the table of total percentages is most informative. If the owner is interested in the effect of gender on ordering of dessert or the effect of ordering a beef entrée on the ordering of dessert, the table of column percentages will be most informative. Because dessert is usually ordered after the main entrée, and the owner has no direct control over the gender of patrons, the table of row percentages is not very useful here. **(c)** 30% of the men ordered desserts, compared to 14% of the women; men are more than twice as likely to order desserts as women. Almost 38% of the patrons ordering a beef entrée ordered dessert, compared to 16% of patrons ordering all other entrees. Patrons ordering beef are more than 2.3 times as likely to order dessert as patrons ordering any other entrée.

2.77 (a) 23575R15 accounts for over 80% of the warranty claims. **(b)** 91.82% of the warranty claims are from the ATX model. **(c)** Tread separation accounts for 73.23% of the warranty claims among the ATX model. **(d)** The number of claims is evenly distributed among the three incidents; other/unknown incidents account for almost 40% of the claims,

tread separation accounts for about 35% of the claims, and blowout accounts for about 25% of the claims.

2.79 (c) Majority (about 71%) of the beer have percentage alcohol between 4.1% and 5.1% with one beer (O'Doul's) containing only 0.4% alcohol. There are two clusters in the distribution of calories. About 60% of the beer have between 135 and 175 calories and another cluster of 25% has between 95 and 115 calories. The distribution of carbohydrates is slightly right-skewed with carbohydrates for Sam Adams Cream Stout having a value equal to 23.9. There appears to be a positive relationship between percentage alcohol in a beer and its calorie content. There is also an obvious positive relationship between calorie content and carbohydrate content. Percentage alcohol content and calorie content do not appear to be related.

2.81 (c) The distribution of the yields of the money market accounts is right skewed with almost 87% of them having a return of less than 1.2% whereas only about 3% of them have yields higher than 2.0%. The distribution of the yields of one-year CDs is more bell-shaped between 1.2% and 3.8% with only about 15% of them having a yield of less than 1.5%. Only 10% of the five-year CDs have yields that are lower than 2% and about 13% of them have yields higher than 3.5%. There appear to be positive relationships between all pairs of yields with one-year CDs and five-year CDs demonstrating the strongest positive relationship.

2.83 (a)

Frequencies (Boston)		
Weight (Boston)	**Frequency**	**Percentage**
3,015 and under 3,050	2	0.54%
3,050 and under 3,085	44	11.96
3,085 and under 3,120	122	33.15
3,120 and under 3,155	131	35.60
3,155 and under 3,190	58	15.76
3,190 and under 3,225	7	1.90
3,225 and under 3,260	3	0.82
3,260 and under 3,295	1	0.27

(b)

Frequencies (Vermont)		
Weight (Vermont)	**Frequency**	**Percentage**
3,550 and under 3,600	4	1.21%
3,600 and under 3,650	31	9.39
3,650 and under 3,700	115	34.85
3,700 and under 3,750	131	39.70
3,750 and under 3,800	36	10.91
3,800 and under 3,850	12	3.64
3,850 and under 3,900	1	0.30

(d) 0.54% of the Boston shingles pallets are underweight, whereas 0.27% are overweight. 1.21% of the Vermont shingles pallets are underweight, whereas 3.94% are overweight.

2.85 (a), (c)

Calories	Frequency	Percentage	Limit	Percentage Less Than
50 and under 100	3	12%	100	12%
100 and under 150	3	12	150	24
150 and under 200	9	36	200	60
200 and under 250	6	24	250	84
250 and under 300	3	12	300	96
300 and under 350	0	0	350	96
350 and under 400	1	4	400	100

Protein	Frequency	Percentage	Limit	Percentage Less Than
16 and under 20	1	4%	20	4%
20 and under 24	5	20	24	24
24 and under 28	8	32	28	56
28 and under 32	9	36	32	92
32 and under 36	2	8	36	100

< Calories from Fat	Frequency	Percentage	Limit	Percentage Less Than
0% and under 10%	3	12%	10	12%
10% and under 20%	4	16	20	28
20% and under 30%	2	8	30	36
30% and under 40%	5	20	40	56
40% and under 50%	3	12	50	68
50% and under 60%	5	20	60	88
60% and under 70%	2	8	70	96
70% and under 80%	1	4	80	100

Calories from Saturated Fat	Frequency	Percentage	Limit	Percentage Less Than
0% and under 5%	6	24%	5	24%
5% and under 10%	2	8	10	32
10% and under 15%	5	20	15	52
15% and under 20%	5	20	20	72
20% and under 25%	5	20	25	92
25% and under 30%	2	8	30	100

Cholesterol	Frequency	Percentage	Limit	Percentage Less Than
0 and under 50	2	8%	50	8%
50 and under 100	17	68	100	76
100 and under 150	4	16	150	92
150 and under 200	1	4	200	96
200 and under 250	0	0	250	96
250 and under 300	0	0	300	96
300 and under 350	0	0	350	96
350 and under 400	0	0	400	96
400 and under 450	0	0	450	96
450 and under 500	1	4	500	100

(d) The sampled fresh red meats, poultry, and fish vary from 98 to 397 calories per serving, with the highest concentration between 150 to 200 calories. One protein source, spareribs, with 397 calories, is more than 100 calories above the next highest caloric food. The protein content of the sampled foods varies from 16 to 33 grams, with 68% of the data values falling between 24 and 32 grams. Spareribs and fried liver are both very different from other foods sampled—the former on calories and the latter on cholesterol content.

2.87 (c) Total fat seems to be most closely related to calories because the points in the scatter plot are closer to the imaginary line that passes through the data points.

2.89 (b) There is a downward trend in the amount filled. **(c)** The amount filled in the next bottle will most likely be below 1.894 liter. **(d)** The scatter plot of the amount of soft drink filled against time reveals the trend of the data, whereas a histogram only provides information on the distribution of the data.

CHAPTER 3

3.35 (a) Population mean, $\mu = 6$. **(b)** Population standard deviation, $\sigma = 1.673$, population variance, $\sigma^2 = 2.8$.

3.37 (a) 68%. **(b)** 95%. **(c)** Not calculable, 75%, 88.89%. **(d)** $\mu - 4\sigma$ to $\mu + 4\sigma$ or -2.8 to 19.2.

3.39 (a) Mean = 12,999.2158, variance = 14,959,700.52, standard deviation = 3,867.7772. **(b)** 64.71%, 98.04%, and 100% of these states have a mean per-capita energy consumption within 1, 2, and 3 standard deviations of the mean, respectively. **(c)** This is consistent with 68%, 95%, and 99.7%, according to the empirical rule. **(d)(a)** Mean = 12,857.7402, variance = 14,238,110.67, standard deviation = 3,773.3421. **(b)** 66%, 98%, and 100% of these states have a mean per-capita energy consumption within 1, 2, and 3 standard deviations of the mean, respectively. **(c)** This is consistent with 68%, 95%, and 99.7% according to the empirical rule.

3.45 (a) 4, 9, 5. **(b)** 3, 4, 7, 9, 12. **(c)** The distances between the median and the extremes are close, 4 and 5, but the differences in the tails are different (1 on the left and 3 on the right), so this distribution is slightly right-skewed. **(d)** In 3.2 (d), because mean = median, the distribution is symmetric. The box part of the graph is symmetric, but the tails show right-skewness.

3.47 (a) -6.5, 8, 14.5. **(b)** -8, -6.5, 7, 8, 9. **(c)** The shape is left-skewed. **(d)** This is consistent with the answer in 3.4 (d).

3.49 (a) $Q_1 = \$0.68$ $Q_3 = \$1.14$ Interquartile range = \$0.46. **(b)** Five-number summary: 0.55 0.68 0.88 1.14 1.51. **(c)** The distribution is skewed to the right.

3.51 (a) First Quartile = 17, Third Quartile = 20, Interquartile Range = 3. **(b)** Five-number summary: 16 17 18 20 23. **(c)** The MPG of SUVs is right-skewed.

3.53 (a) Commercial district five-number summary: 0.38 3.2 4.5 5.55 6.46. Residential area five-number summary: 3.82 5.64 6.68 8.73 10.49. **(b)** Commercial district: The distribution is skewed to the left. Residential area: The distribution is skewed slightly to the right. **(c)** The central tendency of the waiting times for the bank branch located in the commercial district of a city is lower than that of the branch located in the residential area. There are a few long waiting times for the branch located in the residential area, whereas there are a few exceptionally short waiting times for the branch located in the commercial area.

3.55 U.S. stocks are highly correlated with the German stock market, somewhat correlated with the Brazilian stock market, and not very correlated with the Japanese stock market.

3.57 (a) $\text{cov}(X, Y) = 591.667$. **(b)** $r = 0.7196$. **(c)** The correlation coefficient is more valuable for expressing the relationship between calories and fat because it does not depend on the units used to measure calories and fat. **(d)** There is a strong positive linear relationship between calories and fat.

3.59 (a) $\text{cov}(X,Y) = 1.2132$. **(b)** $S_X^2 = 0.1944$, $S_Y^2 = 20.4054$

$$r = \frac{\text{cov}(X,Y)}{S_X S_Y} = \frac{1.2132}{(0.4409)(4.5172)} = 0.6092$$

(c) There is a moderate positive linear relationship between the coaches' salary and revenue.

3.88 (a) Mean $= 43.89$, median $= 45$, 1st quartile $= 18$, 3rd quartile $= 63$. **(b)** Range $= 76$, interquartile range $= 45$, variance $= 639.2564$, standard deviation $= 25.28$, $CV = 57.61\%$. **(c)** The distribution is skewed to the right because there are a few policies that require an exceptionally long period to be approved. **(d)** The mean approval process takes 43.89 days, with 50% of the policies being approved in less than 45 days. 50% of the applications are approved between 18 and 63 days. About 67% of the applications are approved between 18.6 and 69.2 days.

3.90 (a) Mean $= 8.421$, median $= 8.42$, range $= 0.186$, $S = 0.0461$. The mean and median width are both 8.42 inches. The range of the widths is 0.186 inch, and the average scatter around the mean is 0.0461 inch. **(b)** 8.312, 8.404, 8.42, 8.459, 8.498. **(c)** Even though mean $=$ median, the left tail is slightly longer so the distribution is slightly left-skewed. **(d)** All the troughs in this sample meet the specifications.

3.92 (a), (b)
Excel output:

	In-State Tuition/Fees	Out-of-State Tuition/Fees
Mean	6841.8155	17167.71
Median	6340	16340
Mode	7062	14901
Standard Deviation	2212.2215	4274.009
Sample Variance	4893924.034	18267150
Kurtosis	4.29574	-0.33509
Skewness	1.3504	0.5244
Range	14466	20007
Minimum	3094	8965
Maximum	17560	28972
Sum	704707	1768274
Count	103	103
First Quartile	5378	13928
Third Quartile	8143	20134
Interquartile Range	2765	6206
Coefficient of Variation	32.33%	24.90%

(c) Both in-state and out-of-state tuition and fees are right-skewed.

(d) $r = \dfrac{\text{cov}(X,Y)}{S_X S_Y} = 0.4911.$

(e) Both in-state and out-of-state tuition and fees are right-skewed due to the outliers in the right tails. There is a moderate positive linear relationship between in-state and out-of-state tuition and fees. Those schools with high in-state tuition and fees tend to also have high out-of-state tuition and fees.

3.94 (a) Boston: 0.04, 0.17, 0.23, 0.32, 0.98; Vermont: 0.02, 0.13, 0.20, 0.28, 0.83. **(b)** Both distributions are right-skewed. **(c)** Both sets of shingles did quite well in achieving a granule loss of 0.8 gram or less. The Boston shingles had only two data points greater than 0.8 gram. The next highest to these was 0.6 gram. These two data points can be considered outliers. Only 1.176% of the shingles failed the specification. In the Vermont shingles, only one data point was greater than 0.8 gram. The next highest was 0.58 gram. Thus, only 0.714% of the shingles failed to meet the specification.

3.96 (a) 0.80. **(b)** 0.53. **(c)** 0.92. **(d)** Total fat seems to be most closely related to calories because it has the highest correlation coefficient with calories.

3.98 (a) Mean $= 7.5273$, median $= 7.263$, first quartile $= 6.353$, third quartile $= 8.248$. **(b)** Range $= 7.416$, interquartile range $= 1.895$, variance $= 2.6609$, standard deviation $= 1.6312$, $CV = 21.67\%$. **(c)** The data are skewed to the right. **(d)** The per-capita spending by the 50 states is right-skewed because a few states spend a lot more than the rest.

CHAPTER 4

4.2 (a) Simple events include selecting a red ball. **(b)** Selecting a white ball.

4.4 (a) $60/100 = 3/5 = 0.6$. **(b)** $10/100 = 1/10 = 0.1$. **(c)** $35/100 = 7/20 = 0.35$. **(d)** $9/10 = 0.9$.

4.6 (a) Mutually exclusive, not collectively exhaustive. **(b)** Not mutually exclusive, not collectively exhaustive. **(c)** Mutually exclusive, not collectively exhaustive. **(d)** Mutually exclusive, collectively exhaustive.

4.8 (a) "Makes less than \$50,000." **(b)** "Makes less than \$50,000 and tax code is unfair." **(c)** The complement of "tax code is fair" is "tax code is unfair." **(d)** "Tax code is fair and makes less than \$50,000" is a joint event because it consists of two characteristics.

4.10 (a) "A wafer is good." **(b)** "A wafer is good and no particle was found on the die." **(c)** "Bad wafer." **(d)** A wafer that is a "good wafer" and was produced by a die "with particles" is a joint event because it consists of two characteristics.

4.12 (a) $P(\text{Selected the highest-cost fund}) = (27 + 18)/200 = 0.225$. **(b)** $P(\text{Selected the highest-cost fund and is an undergraduate}) = 27/200 = 0.135$. **(c)** $P(\text{Selected the highest-cost fund or is an undergraduate}) = (45 + 100 - 27)/200 = 0.59$. **(d)** The probability of "selected the highest-cost fund or is an undergraduate" includes the probability of "selected the highest-cost fund," plus the probability of "undergraduate minus the joint probability of highest-cost fund and undergraduate."

4.14 (a) $360/500 = 18/25 = 0.72$. **(b)** $224/500 = 56/125 = 0.448$. **(c)** $396/500 = 99/125 = 0.792$. **(d)** $500/500 = 1.00$.

4.16 (a) $10/30 = 1/3 = 0.33$. **(b)** $20/60 = 1/3 = 0.33$. **(c)** $40/60 = 2/3 = 0.67$. **(d)** Because $P(A/B) = P(A) = 1/3$, events A and B are independent.

4.18 $\frac{1}{2} = 0.5$.

4.20 Because $P(A \text{ and } B) = 0.20$ and $P(A)P(B) = 0.12$, events A and B are not independent.

4.22 (a) $36/116 = 0.3103$. **(b)** $14/334 = 0.0419$. **(c)** $320/334 = 0.9581$. $P(\text{No particles}) = 400/450 = 0.8889$. Because $P(\text{No particles}|\text{Good}) \neq P(\text{No particles})$, "a good wafer" and "a die with no particle" are not independent.

4.24 (a) $P(\text{Selected the highest-cost fund}|\text{Is an undergraduate}) = 27/100 = 0.27$. **(b)** $P(\text{Is an undergraduate}|\text{Selected the highest-cost fund}) = 27/(27 + 18) = 0.6$. **(c)** The conditional events are reversed. **(d)** Because $P(\text{Selected the highest-cost fund}|\text{Is an undergraduate}) = 0.27$ is not equal to $P(\text{Selected the highest-cost fund}) = 0.225$, the two events "student group" and "fund selected" are not independent.

4.26 (a) $0.025/0.6 = 0.0417$. **(b)** $0.015/0.4 = 0.0375$. **(c)** Because $P(\text{Needs warranty repair}|\text{Manufacturer based in U.S.}) = 0.0417$ and $P(\text{Needs warranty repair}) = 0.04$, the two events are not independent.

4.28 (a) 0.0045. **(b)** 0.012. **(c)** 0.0059. **(d)** 0.0483.

4.30 0.095.

4.32 (a) 0.736. **(b)** 0.997.

4.34 (a) $P(B'|O) = \dfrac{(0.5)(0.3)}{(0.5)(0.3) + (0.25)(0.7)} = 0.4615$. **(b)** $P(O) = 0.175 + 0.15 = 0.325$.

4.36 (a) $P(\text{Huge success}|\text{Favorable review}) = 0.099/0.459 = 0.2157$; $P(\text{Moderate success}|\text{Favorable review}) = 0.14/0.459 = 0.3050$; $P(\text{Break Break even}|\text{Favorable review}) = 0.16/0.459 = 0.3486$; $P(\text{Loser}|\text{Favorable review}) = 0.06/0.459 = 0.1307$. **(b)** $P(\text{Favorable review}) = 0.459$.

4.46 (a)

		Age		
		18–25	**26–40**	**Total**
Goals	Getting Rich	405	310	715
	Other	95	190	285
	Total	500	500	1000

(b) Simple event: "Has a goal of getting rich." Joint event: "Has a goal of getting rich and is between 18–25 years old." **(c)** 676 $P(\text{Has a goal of gettingrich}) = 715/1000 = 0.715$. **(d)** $P(\text{Has a goal of getting rich and is in the 26–40-year-old group}) = 310/1000 = 0.31$. **(e)** Not independent

4.48 (a) 0.0225. **(b)** 3,937.5 $\cong$ 3,938 can be expected to read the advertisement and place an order. **(c)** 0.03. **(d)** 5,250 can be expected to read the advertisement and place an order.

4.50 (a) 0.4712. **(b)** Because the probability that a fatality involved a rollover, given that the fatality involved an SUV, a van, or a pickup is 0.4712, which is almost twice the probability that a fatality involved a rollover with any vehicle type, at 0.24, SUVs, vans, and pickups are generally more prone to rollover accidents.

CHAPTER 5

5.2 (a) $\mu = 0(0.10) + 1(0.20) + 2(0.45) + 3(0.15) + 4(0.05) + 5(0.05) - 2.0$.

(b) $\sigma = \sqrt{\begin{array}{l}(0-2)^2(0.10) + (1-2)^2(0.20) + (2-2)^2(0.45) \\ + (3-2)^2(0.15) + (4-2)^2(0.05) + (5-2)^2(0.05)\end{array}}$
$= 1.183$.

5.4 (a)

X	P(X)
$ - 1	21/36
$ + 1	15/36

(b)

X	P(X)
$ - 1	21/36
$ + 1	15/36

(c)

X	P(X)
$ - 1	30/36
$ + 4	6/36

(d) -0.167 for each method of play.

5.6 (a) 2.105769. **(b)** 1.467063.

5.17 (a) 0.0778; **(b)** 0.6826; **(c)** 0.0870; **(d)(a)** $P(X = 5) = 0.3277$ **(b)** $P(X \geq 3) = 0.9421$; **(c)** $P(X < 2) = 0.0067$

5.20 (a) $P(X = 0) =$ approximately 0; **(b)** $P(X = 1) =$ approximately 0; **(c)** $P(X \leq 2) = 0.000000374$; **(d)** $P(X \geq 3) = 1.0$

5.22 (a) 0.000014; **(b)** 0.9721; **(c)** 0.000447

5.23 (a) 0.2770; **(b)** 0.0936; **(c)** 1.75 children

5.24 (a) 0.0601; **(b)** 0.9 def. chips; **(c)** 0.1920

5.25 (a) 0.9981; **(b)** 0.0135

5.26 0.1495

5.27 (a) 0.9254; **(b)** 0.5489

5.29 (a) 0.5997. **(b)** 0.0016. **(c)** 0.0439. **(d)** 0.4018.

5.31 (a) $P(X = 0) = 0.7351$. **(b)** If the probabilities of the six events are not all equal, then you would calculate the probability in (a) by multiplying together the probability of no failure in each of the six events.

5.33 Given $\pi = 0.861$ and $n = 3$,

(a) $P(X = 3) = \dfrac{n!}{X!(n-x)!}\pi^X(1-\pi)^{n-X} = \dfrac{3!}{3!0!}(0.861)^3(0.139)^0 = 0.6383$

(b) $P(X = 0) = \dfrac{n!}{X!(n-x)!}\pi^X(1-\pi)^{n-X} = \dfrac{3!}{0!0!}(0.861)^0(0.139)^3 = 0.0027$

(c) $P(X \geq 2) = P(X = 2) + P(X = 3)$

$= \dfrac{3!}{2!1!}(0.861)^2(0.139)^1 + \dfrac{3!}{3!0!}(0.861)^3(0.139)^0 = 0.9474$

(d) $E(X) = n\pi = 3(0.861) = 2.583$ $\sigma_X = \sqrt{n\pi(1-\pi)}$
$= \sqrt{3(0.861)(0.139)} = 0.5992$.

5.36 (a) $P(X < 5) = P(X = 0) + P(X = 1) + P(X = 2) + P(X = 3) + P(X = 4)$

$= \dfrac{e^{-6}(6)^0}{0!} + \dfrac{e^{-6}(6)^1}{1!} + \dfrac{e^{-6}(6)^2}{2!} + \dfrac{e^{-6}(6)^3}{3!} + \dfrac{e^{-6}(6)^4}{4!}$

$= 0.002479 + 0.014873 + 0.044618 + 0.089235 + 0.133853$
$= 0.2851$.

(b) $P(X = 5) = \dfrac{e^{-6}(6)^5}{5!} = 0.1606$.

(c) $P(X \geq 5) = 1 - P(X < 5) = 1 - 0.2851 = 0.7149$.

(d) $P(X = 4 \text{ or } X = 5) = P(X = 4) + P(X = 5) = \dfrac{e^{-6}(6)^4}{4!} + \dfrac{e^{-6}(6)^5}{5!}$
$= 0.2945$.

5.38 $\lambda = 7$. **(a)** $P(X = 0) = 0.0009$. **(b)** $P(X \geq 1) = 0.9991$. **(c)** $P(X \geq 2) = 0.9927$.

5.40 (a) 0.0176. **(b)** 0.9093. **(c)** 0.9220.

5.42 (a) 0.2441. **(b)** 0.8311. **(c)** Because Ford had a lower mean rate of problems per car in 2008 compared to Dodge, the probability of a randomly selected Ford having zero problems and the probability of no more than 2 problems are both higher than their values for Dodge.

5.44 (a) 0.2671. **(b)** 0.8525. **(c)** Because Dodge had a higher mean rate of problems per car in 2008 compared to 2007, the probability of a randomly selected Dodge having zero problems and the probability of no more than 2 problems are both lower in 2008 than their values in 2007.

5.46 (a) 0.0527

5.47 (a) 0.1353	(b) 0.3712
5.48 (a) 0.2231	**(b)** 0.3423
5.49 (a) 0.0174	**(b)** 0.9975
5.50 (a) 0.2707	**(b)** 0.2149
5.51 (a) 0.6310	**(b)** 0.8488

5.53 (a) 0.0062; **(b)** 0.1173; **(c)** Because Kia has a higher mean rate of problems per car, the probability that a randomly selected Kia will have no more than 2 problems is lower than that of a randomly chosen Lexus.

Likewise, the probability that a randomly selected Kia will have zero problems is lower than that of a randomly chosen Lexus.

5.55 (a) 0.2165; **(b)** 0.8013; **(c)** Because Kia has a lower mean rate of problems per car in 2004 compared to 2003, the probability that a randomly selected Kia has zero problems and the probability of no more than 2 problems are both higher than their values in 2003.

5.60 (a) 0.74. **(b)** 0.74. **(c)** 0.3898. **(d)** 0.0012. **(e)** The assumption of independence may not be true.

5.61 (a) If $\pi = 0.50$ and $n = 11, P(X \geq 9) = 0.0327$. **(b)** If $\pi = 0.74$ and $n = 11, P(X \geq 9) = 0.4247$.

5.64 (a) 0.1074. **(b)** 0.2684. **(c)** 0.6242. **(d)** Mean = 2.0, standard deviation = 1.2649.

5.66 (a) $\mu = n\pi = 2.6$. **(b)** $\sigma = \sqrt{n\pi(1-\pi)} = 1.5040$. **(c)** $P(X = 0) = 0.0617$. **(d)** $P(X \leq 2) = 0.5080$. **(e)** $P(X \geq 3) = 0.4920$.

5.68 (a) If $\pi = 0.50$ and $n = 38, P(X \geq 32) = 0.0001$. **(b)** If $\pi = 0.70$ and $n = 38, P(X \geq 32) = 0.03595$. **(c)** If $\pi = 0.90$ and $n = 38$, $P(X \geq 32) = 0.92005$. **(d)** Based on the results in (a)–(c), the probability that the Standard & Poor's 500 index will increase if there is an early gain in the first five trading days of the year is very likely to be close to 0.90 because that yields a probability of 92% that at least 32 of the 38 years the Standard & Poor's 500 index will increase the entire year.

5.70 (a) The assumptions needed are (i) the probability that a golfer loses a golf ball in a given interval is constant, (ii) the probability that a golfer loses more than one golf ball approaches 0 as the interval gets smaller, and (iii) the probability that a golfer loses a golf ball is independent from interval to interval. **(b)** 0.0111. **(c)** 0.70293. **(d)** 0.29707.

CHAPTER 6

6.1 (a) 0.1056, **(b)** 10.56%, **(c)** 75.995 km

6.2 (a) 0.9522, **(b)** 0.9902, **(c)** 0.3829, **(d)** $2.9 million

6.3 (a) 0.7430, **(b)** 92 papers

6.4 (a) 0.8944, **(b)** IQ = 74

6.5 (a) Stocks: P(lose) = 0.2736   Bonds: P(lose) = 0.2727

(b) Stocks: 0.4498   Bonds: 0.1272

(c) 29.7%

6.6 (a) 0.7340, **(b)** 2.42%, **(c)** GPA = 3.59

6.8 (a) 0.4082; **(b)** 0.2508; **(c)** 39.9 thousand miles;

(d)(a) 0.4452

  (b) 0.1815

  (c) 41.6 thousand miles

6.10 (a) 0.9878; **(b)** 0.8185; **(c)** 86.16%; **(d)** Option 1: Since your score of 81% on this exam represents a Z-score of 1.00, which is below the minimum Z-score of 1.28, you will not earn an "A" grade on the exam under this grading option. Option 2: Since your score of 68% on this exam represents a Z-score of 2.00, which is well above the minimum Z-score of 1.28, you will earn an "A" grade on the exam under this grading option. You should prefer Option 2.

6.13 (a) 0.9089. **(b)** 0.0911. **(c)** +1.96. **(d)** -1.00 and $+1.00$.

6.15 (a) 0.1401. **(b)** 0.4168. **(c)** 0.3918. **(d)** +1.00.

6.17 (a) 0.9599. **(b)** 0.0228. **(c)** 43.42. **(d)** 46.64 and 53.36.

6.19 (a) $P(34 < X < 50) = P(-1.33 < Z < 0) = 0.4082$. **(b)** $P(X < 30) + P(X > 60) = P(Z < -1.67) + P(Z > 0.83) = 0.0475 + (1.0 - 0.7967) = 0.2508$. **(c)** $P(Z < -0.84) \cong 0.20$, $Z = -0.84 = \dfrac{X - 50}{12}$. $X = 50 - 0.84(12) = 39.92$ thousand miles, or 39,920 miles. **(d)** The smaller standard deviation makes the Z values larger.

(a) $P(34 < X < 50) = P(-1.60 < Z < 0) = 0.4452$. **(b)** $P(X < 30) + P(X > 60) = P(Z < -2.00) + P(Z > 1.00) = 0.0228 + (1.0 - 0.8413) = 0.1815$. **(c)** $X = 50 - 0.84(10) = 41.6$ thousand miles, or 41,600 miles.

6.21 (a) 0.9878. **(b)** 0.8185. **(c)** 86.16%. **(d)** Option 1: Because your score of 81% on this exam represents a Z score of 1.00, which is below the minimum Z score of 1.28, you will not earn an A grade on the exam under this grading option. Option 2: Because your score of 68% on this exam represents a Z score of 2.00, which is well above the minimum Z score of 1.28, you will earn an A grade on the exam under this grading option. You should prefer Option 2.

6.23 (a) 0.1189. **(b)** 0.4135. **(c)** 0.0529.

6.25 With 39 values, the smallest of the standard normal quantile values covers an area under the normal curve of 0.025. The corresponding Z value is -1.96. The middle (20th) value has a cumulative area of 0.50 and a corresponding Z value of 0.0. The largest of the standard normal quantile values covers an area under the normal curve of 0.975, and its corresponding Z value is $+1.96$.

6.27 (a) Mean = 23.2, median = 23.5, range = 52, standard deviation = 12.3868, $6(S_X) = 6(12.3868) = 74.3205$, interquartile range = 14, $1.33(S_X) = 1.33(12.3868) = 16.4744$. The mean is almost equal to the median; the range is smaller than 6 times the standard deviation, and the interquartile range is slightly smaller than 1.33 times the standard deviation. The data appear to be approximately normally distributed but slightly skewed to the right. **(b)** The normal probability plot suggests that the data are skewed to the right.

6.29 (a) Mean = 1040.863, median = 981, range = 1732, $6(S_X) = 2571.2310$, interquartile range = 593, $1.33(S_X) = 569.9562$. There are 62.75%, 78.43%, and 94.12% of the observations that fall within 1, 1.28, and 2 standard deviations of the mean, respectively, as compared to the approximate theoretical 66.67%, 80%, and 95%. Because the mean is slightly larger than the median, the interquartile range is slightly larger than 1.33 times the standard deviation, and the range is much smaller than 6 times the standard deviation, the data appear to deviate slightly from the normal distribution. **(b)** The normal probability plot suggests that the data appear to be slightly right-skewed.

6.31 (a) Interquartile range = 0.0025, $S_X = 0.0017$, range = 0.008, $1.33(S_X) = 0.0023$, $6(S_X) = 0.0102$. Because the interquartile range is close to $1.33(S_X)$ and the range is also close to $6(S_X)$, the data appear to be approximately normally distributed. **(b)** The normal probability plot suggests that the data appear to be approximately normally distributed.

6.33 (a) Five-number summary: 82 127 148.5 168 213; mean = 147.06, mode = 130, range = 131, interquartile range = 41, standard deviation = 31.69. The mean is very close to the median. The five-number summary suggests that the distribution is approximately symmetrical around the median. The interquartile range is very close to 1.33 times the standard deviation. The range is about $50 below 6 times the standard deviation. In general, the distribution of the data appears to closely resemble a normal distribution. **(b)** The normal probability plot confirms that the data appear to be approximately normally distributed.

6.41 (a) 0.4772. **(b)** 0.9544. **(c)** 0.0456. **(d)** 1.8835. **(e)** 1.8710 and 2.1290.

6.43 (a) 0.2734. **(b)** 0.2038. **(c)** 4.404 ounces. **(d)** 4.188 ounces and 5.212 ounces.

6.45 (a) Waiting time will more closely resemble an exponential distribution. **(b)** Seating time will more closely resemble a normal distribution. **(c)** Both the histogram and normal probability plot suggest that waiting time more closely resembles an exponential distribution. **(d)** Both the histogram and normal probability plot suggest that seating time more closely resembles a normal distribution.

6.47 (a) 0.8413. **(b)** 0.9330. **(c)** 0.9332. **(d)** 0.3347. **(e)** 0.4080 and 1.1920.

6.49 (a) Mean $= 3,019.7255$, median $= 2,972$, range $= 1174, 6(S_X) = 1,393.4693$, interquartile range $= 284, 1.33(S_X) = 308.8857$. There are 70.59%, 86.27%, and 96.08% of the observations that fall within 1, 1.28, and 2 standard deviations of the mean, respectively, as compared to the approximate theoretical 66.67%, 80%, and 95%. Because the mean is slightly larger than the median, the interquartile range is slightly smaller than 1.33 times the standard deviation, and the range is much smaller than 6 times the standard deviation, the data appear to deviate slightly from the normal distribution. The normal probability plot suggests that the data appear to be slightly right-skewed. **(b)** The variable RANK 2006 has a uniform distribution between 1 and 52.

CHAPTER 7

7.2 Sample without replacement: Read from left to right in three-digit sequences and continue unfinished sequences from the end of the row to the beginning of the next row:

Row 05: 338 505 855 551 438 855 077 186 579 488 767 833 170
Rows 05–06: 897
Row 06: 340 033 648 847 204 334 639 193 639 411 095 924
Rows 06–07: 707
Row 07: 054 329 776 100 871 007 255 980 646 886 823 920 461
Row 08: 893 829 380 900 796 959 453 410 181 277 660 908 887
Rows 08–09: 237
Row 09: 818 721 426 714 050 785 223 801 670 353 362 449
Rows 09–10: 406

Note: All sequences above 902 and duplicates are discarded.

7.4 A simple random sample would be less practical for personal interviews because of travel costs (unless interviewees are paid to go to a central interviewing location).

7.6 Here all members of the population are equally likely to be selected, and the sample selection mechanism is based on chance. But selection of two elements is not independent; for example, if A is in the sample, we know that B is also and that C and D are not.

7.8 (a)

Row 16: 2323 6737 5131 8888 1718 0654 6832 4647 6510 4877
Row 17: 4579 4269 2615 1308 2455 7830 5550 5852 5514 7182
Row 18: 0989 3205 0514 2256 8514 4642 7567 8896 2977 8822
Row 19: 5438 2745 9891 4991 4523 6847 9276 8646 1628 3554
Row 20: 9475 0899 2337 0892 0048 8033 6945 9826 9403 6858
Row 21: 7029 7341 3553 1403 3340 4205 0823 4144 1048 2949
Row 22: 8515 7479 5432 9792 6575 5760 0408 8112 2507 3742
Row 23: 1110 0023 4012 8607 4697 9664 4894 3928 7072 5815
Row 24: 3687 1507 7530 5925 7143 1738 1688 5625 8533 5041
Row 25: 2391 3483 5763 3081 6090 5169 0546

Note: All sequences above 5,000 are discarded. There were no repeating sequences.

(b) 089 189 289 389 489 589 689 789 889 989
1089 1189 1289 1389 1489 1589 1689 1789 1889 1989
2089 2189 2289 2389 2489 2589 2689 2789 2889 2989
3089 3189 3289 3389 3489 3589 3689 3789 3889 3989
4089 4189 4289 4389 4489 4589 4689 4789 4889 4989

(c) With the single exception of invoice #0989, the invoices selected in the simple random sample are not the same as those selected in the systematic sample. It would be highly unlikely that a simple random sample would select the same units as a systematic sample.

7.10 Before accepting the results of a survey of college students, you might want to know, for example:

Who funded the survey? Why was it conducted? What was the population from which the sample was selected? What sampling design was used? What mode of response was used: a personal interview, a telephone interview, or a mail survey? Were interviewers trained? Were survey questions field-tested? What questions were asked? Were they clear, accurate, unbiased, and valid? What operational definition of "vast majority" was used? What was the response rate? What was the sample size?

7.12 (a) The four types of survey errors are: coverage error, nonresponse error, sampling error, and measurement error. **(b)** When people who answer the survey tell you what they think you want to hear, rather than what they really believe, it introduces the halo effect, which is a source of measurement error. Also, every survey will have sampling error that reflects the chance differences from sample to sample, based on the probability of particular individuals being selected in the particular sample.

7.14 Before accepting the results of the survey, you might want to know, for example:

Who funded the study? Why was it conducted? What was the population from which the sample was selected? What sampling design was used? What mode of response was used: a personal interview, a telephone interview, or a mail survey? Were interviewers trained? Were survey questions field-tested? What other questions were asked? Were they clear, accurate, unbiased, and valid? What was the response rate? What was the margin of error? What was the sample size? What was the frame being used?

7.16 (a) Virtually zero. **(b)** 0.1587. **(c)** 0.0139. **(d)** 50.195.

7.18 (a) Both means are equal to 6. This property is called unbiasedness. **(c)** The distribution for $n = 3$ has less variability. The larger sample size has resulted in sample means being closer to μ.

7.20 (a) When $n = 2$, the shape of the sampling distribution of $\overline{X}$ should closely resemble the shape of the distribution of the population from which the sample is selected. Because the mean is larger than the median, the distribution of the sales price of new houses is skewed to the right, and so is the sampling distribution of $\overline{X}$. **(b)** If you select samples of $n = 100$, the shape of the sampling distribution of the sample mean will be very close to a normal distribution with a mean of $296,400 and a standard deviation of $9,000. **(c)** 0.6554. **(d)** 0.2298.

7.22 (a) $P(\overline{X} > 3) = P(Z > -1.00) = 1.0 - 0.1587 = 0.8413$. **(b)** $P(Z < 1.04) = 0.85; \overline{X} = 3.10 + 1.04(0.1) = 3.204$. **(c)** To be able to use the standardized normal distribution as an approximation for the area under the curve, you must assume that the population is approximately symmetrical. **(d)** $P(Z < 1.04) = 0.85; \overline{X} = 3.10 + 1.04(0.05) = 3.152$.

7.23 (a) 0.8351, **(b)** 108.4 kw

7.24 0.2424

7.25 4 years

7.26 (a) 0.2195, **(b)** 0.0933, **(c)** 4.2 proposals

7.27 (a) 0.0008, **(b)** 0.1030

7.28 74.6%

7.29 (a) 451 manhours, **(b)** 0.3085

7.30 (a) 0.9608, b) 0.9802

7.31 (a) 50 managers, **(b)** $252,802

7.32 (a) 0.8571, **(b)** 0.2084

7.33 2.28%

7.34 (a) 0.2375, **(b)** 0.0766, **(c)** 0.000003, **(d)** 0.0032

7.35 399 bags

7.36 1072 days

7.37 (a) 0.0938, **(b)** 1692 drills

7.38 9.52%

7.39 0.0002

7.40 (a) 0.0004, **(b)** 40.8 minutes

7.41 (a) 0.2051, **(b)** $60,702

7.42 (a) 0.3366, **(b)** 21%

7.44 (a) 0.9128, **(b)** 0.0823, **(c)** 0.3186, **(d)** 31.6 to 63.0 minutes

7.45 (a) 9.62 minutes, **(b)** 0.1513, **(c)** 0.0669, **(d)** 0.1459

7.46 (a) 0.7058, **(b)** 0.0471, **(c)** 0.1796, **(d)** 5.06 minutes

7.47 (a) 0.9328, **(b)** 0.1999, **(c)** 0.6271, **(d)** 8.0 minutes

7.51 (a) 0.30. **(b)** 0.0693.

7.53 (a) $\pi = 0.501, \sigma_P = \sqrt{\dfrac{\pi(1-\pi)}{n}} = \sqrt{\dfrac{0.501(1-0.501)}{100}} = 0.05$
$P(p > 0.55) = P(Z > 0.98) = 1.0 - 0.8365 = 0.1635.$

(b) $\pi = 0.60, \sigma_P = \sqrt{\dfrac{\pi(1-\pi)}{n}} = \sqrt{\dfrac{0.6(1-0.6)}{100}} = 0.04899$
$P(p > 0.55) = P(Z > -1.021) = 1.0 - 0.1539 = 0.8461.$

(c) $\pi = 0.49, \sigma_P = \sqrt{\dfrac{\pi(1-\pi)}{n}} = \sqrt{\dfrac{0.49(1-0.49)}{100}} = 0.05$
$P(p > 0.55) = P(Z > 1.20) = 1.0 - 0.8849 = 0.1151.$
(d) Increasing the sample size by a factor of 4 decreases the standard error by a factor of 2.
(a) $P(p > 0.55) = P(Z > 1.96) = 1.0 - 0.9750 = 0.0250.$
(b) $P(p > 0.55) = P(Z > -2.04) = 1.0 - 0.0207 = 0.9793.$
(c) $P(p > 0.55) = P(Z > 2.40) = 1.0 - 0.9918 = 0.0082.$

7.55 (a) 0.9298. **(b)** 0.8596. **(c)** 0.9865. **(d) (a)** 0.7695. **(b)** 0.5390.
(c) 0.8656.

7.57 (a) Because $n = 200$, which is quite large, you use the sample proportion to approximate the population proportion and, hence, $\pi = 0.50.$

$$\mu_P = \pi = 0.5, \sigma_P = \sqrt{\dfrac{\pi(1-\pi)}{n}} = \sqrt{\dfrac{0.46(0.54)}{200}} = 0.0352$$

$P(0.45 < \pi < 0.55) = P(-0.2841 < Z < 2.5568) = 0.6065.$
(b) $P(A < \pi < B) = P(-1.6499 < Z < 1.6449) = 0.90. A = 0.46 - 1.6449(0.0352) = 0.4021. B = 0.46 + 1.6449(0.0352) = 0.5179.$

The probability is 90% that the sample percentage will be contained within 5.79% symmetrically around the population percentage.
(c) $P(A < \pi < B) = P(-1.96 < Z + 1.96) = 0.95. A = 0.46 - 1.96(0.0352) = 391. B = 0.50 + 1.96(0.0352) = 0.529.$ The probability is 95% that the sample percentage will be contained within 6.9% symmetrically around the population percentage.

7.59 (a) 0.1134. **(b)** 0.0034. **(c)** Increasing the sample size by a factor of 5 decreases the standard error by a factor of $\sqrt{5}$. The sampling distribution of the proportion becomes more concentrated around the true proportion of 0.56 and, hence, the probability in (b) becomes smaller than that in (a).

7.71 (a) 0.4999. **(b)** 0.00009. **(c)** 0. **(d)** 0. **(e)** 0.7518.

7.73 (a) 0.8944. **(b)** 4.617; 4.783. **(c)** 4.641.

7.75 (a) 0.0106. **(b)** 0.7941. **(c)** 0.7650.

7.77 Even though Internet polling is less expensive and faster and offers higher response rates than telephone surveys, it is a self-selection response method. Because respondents who choose to participate in the survey may not represent the view of the public, the data collected may not be appropriate for making inferences about the general population.

7.79 (a) Before accepting the results of this survey, you would like to know (i) how big is the sample size, (ii) what is the purpose of the survey, (iii) what sampling method is being used, (iv) what is the frame being used, (v) what is the response rate, and (vi) how the questions are being phrased. **(b)** The population will be all the AOL users. The frame can be compiled from the list of the AOL subscribers. Because there are two natural strata in the population, adults and teens, a stratified sampling method should be used to better represent the population.

CHAPTER 8

8.1 $UCL_R = 1.53$ $LCL_R = 0$ $UCL_{\bar{x}} = 75.936$ $LCL_{\bar{x}} = 74.960$

8.2 $UCL_R = 0.677$ $LCL_R = 0$ $UCL_{\bar{x}} = 35.562$ $LCL_{\bar{x}} = 35.236$

8.3 $UCL_R = 50.1$ $LCL_R = 0$ $UCL_{\bar{x}} = 117.7$ $LCL_{\bar{x}} = 90.3$

In samples 21 to 30, sample 24: $\bar{X} = 89$ and sample 28: R = 51 are O-O-C

8.4 $UCL_R = 57.7$ $LCL_R = 0$ $UCL_{\bar{x}} = 400.77$ $LCL_{\bar{x}} = 363.89$

8.5 $UCL_R = 5.73$ $LCL_R = 0$ $UCL_{\bar{x}} = 17.09$ $LCL_{\bar{x}} = 13.97$

8.6 $UCL_R = 2.73$ $LCL_R = 0$ $UCL_{\bar{x}} = 201.13$ $LCL_{\bar{x}} = 199.81$

8.8 (a) $\bar{R} = \dfrac{\sum_{i=1}^{k} R_i}{k} = 3.275, \bar{\bar{X}} = \dfrac{\sum_{i=1}^{k} \bar{X}_i}{k} = 5.9413.$

R chart: UCL $= D_4\bar{R} = 2.282(3.275) = 7.4736.$ LCL does not exist. $\bar{X}$ chart: UCL $= \bar{\bar{X}} + A_2\bar{R} = 5.9413 + 0.729(3.275) = 8.3287.$
LCL $= \bar{\bar{X}} - A_2\bar{R} = 5.9413 - 0.729(3.275) = 3.5538.$
(b) The process appears to be in control because there are no points outside the control limits and there is no evidence of a pattern in the range chart, and there are no points outside the control limits and there is no evidence of a pattern in the $\bar{X}$ chart.

8.10 (a) $\bar{R} = 0.8794,$ LCL does not exist, UCL $= 2.0068.$
(b) $\bar{\bar{X}} = 20.1065,$ LCL $= 19.4654,$ UCL $= 20.7475.$ **(c)** The process is in control.

8.12 (a) $\bar{R} = 8.145,$ LCL does not exist, UCL $= 18.5869;$
$\bar{\bar{X}} = 18.12,$ UCL $= 24.0577,$ LCL $= 12.1823.$ **(b)** There are no sample ranges outside the control limits and there does not appear to be a pattern in the range chart. The mean is above the UCL on Day 15 and below the LCL on Day 16. Therefore, the process is not in control.

8.14 (a) $\bar{R} = 0.3022$, LCL does not exist, UCL $= 0.6389$; $\bar{\bar{X}} = 90.1312$, UCL $= 90.3060$, LCL $= 89.9573$. **(b)** On Days 5 and 6, the sample ranges were above the UCL. The mean chart may be erroneous because the range is out of control. The process is out of control.

8.22 (a) The main reason that service quality is lower than product quality is because the former involves human interaction, which is prone to variation. Also, the most critical aspects of a service are often timeliness and professionalism, and customers can always perceive that the service could be done quicker and with greater professionalism. For products, customers often cannot perceive a better or more ideal product than the one they are getting. For example, a new laptop is better and contains more interesting features than any laptop the owner has ever imagined. **(b)** Both services and products are the results of processes. However, measuring services is often harder because of the dynamic variation due to the human interaction between the service provider and the customer. Product quality is often a straightforward measurement of a static physical characteristic like the amount of sugar in a can of soda. Categorical data are also more common in service quality. **(c)** Yes. **(d)** Yes.

8.24 (a) $\bar{p} = 0.2702$, LCL $= 0.1700$, UCL $= 0.3703$. **(b)** Yes, RudyBird's market share is in control before the in-store promotion. **(c)** All seven days of the in-store promotion are above the UCL. The promotion increased market share.

8.26 (a) $\bar{p} = 0.75175$, LCL $= 0.62215$, UCL $= 0.88135$. Although none of the points are outside the control limits, there is a clear pattern over time, with the last 13 points above the center line. Therefore, this process is not in control. **(b)** Because the increasing trend begins around Day 20, this change in method would be the assignable cause. **(c)** The control chart would have been developed using the first 20 days, and then a different control chart would be used for the final twenty points because they represent a different process.

8.28 (a) $\bar{p} = 0.1198$, LCL $= 0.0205$, UCL $= 0.2191$. **(b)** Day 24 is below the LCL; therefore, the process is out of control; using Minitab with the exact n_i, day 24 is not out-of-control. **(c)** Special causes of variation should be investigated to improve the process. Next, the process should be improved to decrease the proportion of undesirable trades.

CHAPTER 9

9.2 $114.68 \leq \mu \leq 135.32$.

9.4 (a) You would compute the mean first because you need the mean to compute the standard deviation. If you had a sample, you would compute the sample mean. If you had the population mean, you would compute the population standard deviation. **(b)** If you have a sample, you are computing the sample standard deviation, not the population standard deviation needed in Equation (9.1). If you have a population and have computed the population mean and population standard deviation, you don't need a confidence interval estimate of the population mean because you already know the mean.

9.6 Equation (9.1) assumes that you know the population standard deviation. Because you are selecting a sample of 100 from the population, you are computing a sample standard deviation, not the population standard deviation.

9.8 (a) 2.2622. **(b)** 3.2498. **(c)** 2.0395. **(d)** 1.9977. **(e)** 1.7531.

9.10 $-0.12 \leq \mu \leq 11.84$, $2.00 \leq \mu \leq 6.00$. The presence of the outlier increases the sample mean and greatly inflates the sample standard deviation.

9.12 (a) $32 \pm (2.0096)(9)/\sqrt{50}$; $29.44 \leq \mu \leq 34.56$ **(b)** The quality improvement team can be 95% confident that the population mean turnaround time is between 29.44 hours and 34.56 hours. **(c)** The project

was a success because the initial turnaround time of 68 hours does not fall into the interval.

9.14 (a) $31.9267 \leq \mu \leq 41.1399$. **(b)** You can be 95% confident that the population mean price for two tickets with online service charges, large popcorn, and two medium soft drinks is somewhere between \$31.93 and \$41.14.

9.16 (a) $17.876 \leq \mu \leq 19.669$. **(b)** You can be 95% confident that the population mean miles per gallon of 2008 SUVs priced under \$30,000 is somewhere between 17.876 and 19.669. **(c)** Because the 95% confidence interval for population mean miles per gallon of 2008 SUVs priced under \$30,000 does not overlap with that for the population mean miles per gallon of 2008 sedans priced under \$20,000, you are 95% confident that the population mean miles per gallon of 2008 SUVs is lower than that of 2008 sedans.

9.18 (a) $31.12 \leq \mu \leq 54.96$. **(b)** The number of days is approximately normally distributed. **(c)** No, the outliers skew the data. **(d)** Because the sample size is fairly large, at $n = 50$, the use of the t distribution is appropriate.

9.20 (a) $\$0.7367 \leq \mu \leq \$1.1147$. **(b)** The population distribution needs to be normally distributed. **(c)** Both the normal probability plot and the boxplot show that the distribution for the cost of dark chocolate bars is right skewed.

9.22 $0.19 \leq \pi \leq 0.31$.

9.24 (a) $p = \dfrac{X}{n} = \dfrac{135}{500} = 0.27$

$$p \pm Z\sqrt{\frac{p(1-p)}{n}} = 0.27 \pm 2.58\sqrt{\frac{0.27(0.73)}{500}} \quad 0.2189 \leq \pi \leq 0.3211.$$

(b) The manager in charge of promotional programs concerning residential customers can infer that the proportion of households that would purchase an additional telephone line if it were made available at a substantially reduced installation cost is somewhere between 0.22 and 0.32, with 99% confidence.

9.26 (a) $0.2311 \leq \pi \leq 0.3089$. **(b)** $0.2425 \leq \pi \leq 0.2975$. **(c)** The larger the sample size, the narrower the confidence interval, holding everything else constant.

9.28 (a) $0.5638 \leq \pi \leq 0.6362$. **(b)** $0.2272 \leq \pi \leq 0.2920$.

9.30 $n = 35$.

9.32 $n = 1{,}041$.

9.34 (a) $n = \dfrac{Z^2\sigma^2}{e^2} = \dfrac{(1.96)^2(400)^2}{50^2} = 245.86$

Use $n = 246$.

(b) $n = \dfrac{Z^2\sigma^2}{e^2} = \dfrac{(1.96)^2(400)^2}{25^2} = 983.41$

Use $n = 984$.

9.36 $n = 97$.

9.38 (a) $n = 167$. **(b)** $n = 97$.

9.40 (a) $n = 246$. **(b)** $n = 385$. **(c)** $n = 554$. **(d)** When there is more variability in the population, a larger sample is needed to accurately estimate the mean.

9.42 (a) $p = 0.5498$; $0.5226 \leq \pi \leq 0.5770$. **(b)** $p = 0.4697$; $0.4424 \leq \pi \leq 0.4970$. **(c)** $p = 0.2799$; $0.2544 \leq \pi \leq 0.3045$. **(d) (a)** $n = 2{,}378$. **(b)** $= 2{,}393$. **(c)** $= 1{,}936$.

9.44 (a) If you conduct a follow-up study to estimate the population proportion of individuals who view oil companies favorably, you would use $\pi = 0.15$ in the sample size formula because it provides the most conservative value based on past information on the proportion. **(b)** $n = 545$.

9.50 $940.50 \leq \mu \leq 1007.50$. Based on the evidence gathered from the sample of 34 stores, the 95% confidence interval for the mean per-store count in all of the franchise's stores is from 940.50 to 1,007.50. With a 95% level of confidence, the franchise can conclude that the mean per-store count in all its stores is somewhere between 940.50 and 1,007.50, which is larger than the original average of 900 mean per-store count before the price reduction. Hence, reducing coffee prices is a good strategy to increase the mean customer count.

9.52 (a) $14.085 \leq \mu \leq 16.515$. **(b)** $0.530 \leq \pi \leq 0.820$. **(c)** $n = 25$. **(d)** $n = 784$. **(e)** If a single sample were to be selected for both purposes, the larger of the two sample sizes ($n = 784$) should be used.

9.54 (a) $8.049 \leq \mu \leq 11.351$. **(b)** $0.284 \leq \pi \leq 0.676$. **(c)** $n = 35$. **(d)** $n = 121$. **(e)** If a single sample were to be selected for both purposes, the larger of the two sample sizes ($n = 121$) should be used.

9.56 (a) $\$36.66 \leq \mu \leq \$40.42$. **(b)** $0.2027 \leq \pi \leq 0.3973$. **(c)** $n = 110$. **(d)** $n = 423$. **(e)** If a single sample were to be selected for both purposes, the larger of the two sample sizes ($n = 423$) should be used.

9.58 (a) $8.41 \leq \mu \leq 8.43$. **(b)** With 95% confidence, the population mean width of troughs is somewhere between 8.41 and 8.43 inches. **(c)** The assumption is valid as the width of the troughs is approximately normally distributed.

9.60 (a) $0.2425 \leq \mu \leq 0.2856$. **(b)** $0.1975 \leq \mu \leq 0.2385$. **(c)** The amounts of granule loss for both brands are skewed to the right, but the sample sizes are large enough. **(d)** Because the two confidence intervals do not overlap, you can conclude that the mean granule loss of Boston shingles is higher than that of Vermont shingles.

CHAPTER 10

10.2 Because $Z_{STAT} = +2.21 > 1.96$, reject H_0.

10.4 Reject H_0 if $Z_{STAT} < -2.58$ or if $Z_{STAT} > 2.58$.

10.6 p-value $= 0.0456$.

10.8 p-value $= 0.1676$.

10.10 H_0: Defendant is guilty; H_1: Defendant is innocent. A Type I error would be not convicting a guilty person. A Type II error would be convicting an innocent person.

10.12 H_0: $\mu = 20$ minutes. 20 minutes is adequate travel time between classes. H_1: $\mu \neq 20$ minutes. 20 minutes is not adequate travel time between classes.

10.14 H_0: $\mu = 1.00$. The mean amount of paint per one-gallon can is one gallon. H_1: $\mu \neq 1.00$. The mean amount of paint per one-gallon can differs from one gallon.

10.16 $t_{STAT} = 2.00$

10.18 (a) ± 2.1315.

10.20 No, you should not use a t test because the original population is left-skewed and the sample size is not large enough for the t test to be valid.

10.22 (a) $t_{STAT} = (3.57 - 3.70)/0.8/\sqrt{64} = -1.30$; Because $-1.9983 < t_{STAT} = -1.30 < 1.9983$ and the p-value of $0.1984 > 0.05$

There is no evidence that the population mean waiting time is different from 3.7 minutes. **(b)** Since $n = 64$, the central limit theorem should ensure that the sampling distribution of the mean is approximately normal. In general, the t test is appropriate for this sample size except for the case where the population is extremely skewed or bimodal.

10.24 (a) Because $-2.5706 < t_{STAT} = 0.8556 < 2.5706$, do not reject H_0. There is not enough evidence to conclude that the mean price for two tickets, with online service charges, large popcorn, and two medium soft drinks, is different from $35. **(b)** The p-value is 0.4313. If the population mean is $35, the probability of observing a sample of six theater chains that will result in a sample mean farther away from the hypothesized value than this sample is 0.4313. **(c)** That the distribution of prices is normally distributed. **(d)** With a small sample size, it is difficult to evaluate the assumption of normality. However, the distribution may be symmetric because the mean and the median are close in value.

10.26 (a) Because $-2.0096 < t_{STAT} = 0.114 < 2.0096$, do not reject H_0. There is no evidence that the mean amount is different from two liters. **(b)** p-value $= 0.9095$. **(c) and (d)** Yes, the data appear to have met the normality assumption. **(e)** The amount of fill is decreasing over time. Therefore, the t test is invalid.

10.28 (a) Because $t_{STAT} = -5.9355 < -2.0106$, reject H_0. There is enough evidence to conclude that mean widths of the troughs is different from 8.46 inches. **(b)** That the population distribution is normal. **(c)** Although the distribution of the widths is left-skewed, the large sample size means that the validity of the t test is not seriously affected.

10.30 (a) Because $-2.68 < t_{STAT} = 0.094 < 2.68$, do not reject H_0. **(b)** $5.462 \leq \mu \leq 5.542$. **(c)** The conclusions are the same.

10.32 p-value $= 0.0228$.

10.34 p-value $= 0.0838$.

10.36 p-value $= 0.9162$.

10.38 $t_{STAT} = 2.7638$.

10.40 $t_{STAT} = -2.5280$.

10.42 (a) $t_{STAT} = (2.73 - 2.80)/0.2/\sqrt{25} = -1.75$; Because $t_{STAT} = -1.75 < -1.7109$, reject H_0. **(b)** p-value $= 0.0464 < 0.05$, reject H_0. **(c)** The probability of getting a sample mean of 2.73 feet or less if the population mean is 2.8 feet is 0.0464. **(d)** They are the same.

10.44 (a) H_0: $\mu \leq 5$; H_1: $\mu > 5$. **(b)** A Type I error occurs when you conclude that children take a mean of more than five trips a week to the store when in fact they take a mean of no more than five trips a week to the store. A Type II error occurs when you conclude that children take a mean of no more than five trips a week to the store when in fact they take a mean of more than five trips a week to the store. **(c)** Because $t_{STAT} = 2.9375 > 2.3263$ or the p-value of 0.0021 is less than 0.01, reject H_0. There is enough evidence to conclude the population mean number of trips to the store is greater than five per week. **(d)** The probability that the sample mean is 5.47 trips or more when the null hypothesis is true is 0.0021.

10.46 $p = 0.22$.

10.48 Do not reject H_0.

10.50 (a) $Z_{STAT} = 9.61$, p-value $= 0.0000$. Because $Z_{STAT} = 9.61 > 1.645$ or $0.0000 > 0.05$, reject H_0. There is evidence to show that more than half of readers of online magazines have linked to an advertiser's Web site. **(b)** $Z_{STAT} = 1.20$ p-value $= 0.115$. Because $Z_{STAT} = 1.20 < 1.645$ do not reject H_0. There is insufficient evidence to show that more than half of the readers of online magazines have linked to an advertiser's Web site. **(c)** The sample size had a major effect on being able to reject the null hypothesis. **(d)** You would be very unlikely to reject the null hypothesis with a sample of 20.

10.52 (a) H_0: $\pi = 0.6$; H_1: $\pi \neq 0.6$. Decision rule: If $Z_{STAT} > 1.96$ or $Z_{STAT} < -1.96$, reject H_0.

$$p = \frac{650}{1{,}000} = 0.65$$

Test statistic:

$$Z_{STAT} = \frac{p - \pi}{\sqrt{\frac{\pi(1-\pi)}{n}}} = \frac{0.65 - 0.60}{\sqrt{\frac{0.6(1-0.6)}{1{,}000}}} = 3.2275$$

Because $Z_{STAT} = 3.2275 > 1.96$ or p-value $= 0.0012 < 0.05$, reject H_0 and conclude that there is evidence that the percentage of young job seekers who prefer to look for a job in a place they want to reside is different from 60%.

10.54 (a) H_0: $\pi \leq 0.08$. No more than 8% of students at your school are Omnivores. H_1: $\pi > 0.08$. More than 8% of students at your school are Omnivores. **(b)** $Z_{STAT} = 3.6490$, p-value $= 0.0001316$. Because $Z_{STAT} = 3.6490 > 1.96$ or p-value $= 0.0001316 < 0.05$, reject H_0. There is enough evidence to show that the percentage of Omnivores at your school is greater than 8%.

10.64 (a) Buying a site that is not profitable. **(b)** Not buying a profitable site. **(c)** Type I. **(d)** If the executives adopt a less stringent rejection criterion by buying sites for which the computer model predicts moderate or large profit, the probability of committing a Type I error will increase. Many more of the sites the computer model predicts that will generate moderate profit may end up not being profitable at all. On the other hand, the less stringent rejection criterion will lower the probability of committing a Type II error since more potentially profitable sites will be purchased.

10.66 (a) Because $t_{STAT} = 3.248 > 2.0010$, reject H_0. **(b)** p-value $= 0.0019$. **(c)** Because $Z_{STAT} = -0.32 > -1.645$, do not reject H_0. **(d)** Because $-2.0010 < t_{STAT} = 0.75 < 2.0010$, do not reject H_0. **(e)** Because $t_{STAT} = -1.61 > -1.645$, do not reject H_0.

10.68 (a) Because $t_{STAT} = -1.69 > -1.7613$, do not reject H_0. **(b)** The data are from a population that is normally distributed. **(c)** and **(d)** With the exception of one extreme point, the data are approximately normally distributed. **(e)** There is insufficient evidence to state that the waiting time is less than five minutes.

10.70 (a) Because $t_{STAT} = -1.47 > -1.6896$, do not reject H_0. **(b)** p-value $= 0.0748$. If the null hypothesis is true, the probability of obtaining a t_{STAT} of -1.47 or more extreme is 0.0748. **(c)** Because $t_{STAT} = -3.10 < -1.6973$, reject H_0. **(d)** p-value $= 0.0021$. If the null hypothesis is true, the probability of obtaining a t_{STAT} of -3.10 or more extreme is 0.0021. **(e)** The data in the population are assumed to be normally distributed. **(f)** Both boxplots suggest that the data are skewed slightly to the right, more so for the Boston shingles. However, the very large sample sizes mean that the results of the t test are relatively insensitive to the departure from normality.

10.72 (a) $t_{STAT} = -21.61$, reject H_0. **(b)** p-value $= 0.0000$. **(c)** $t_{STAT} = -27.19$, reject H_0. **(d)** p-value $= 0.0000$. **(e)** Because of the large sample sizes, you do not need to be concerned with the normality assumption.

CHAPTER 11

11.2 (a) $t = 3.8959$. **(b)** $df = 21$. **(c)** 2.5177. **(d)** Because $t_{STAT} = 3.8959 > 2.5177$, reject H_0.

11.4 $3.73 \leq \mu_1 - \mu_2 \leq 12.27$.

11.6 Because $t_{STAT} = 2.6762 < 2.9979$ or p-value $= 0.0158 > 0.01$, do not reject H_0. There is evidence of a difference in the means of the two populations.

11.8 (a) Because $-1.9706 < t_{STAT} = 0.8904 < 1.9706$ or p-value $= 0.3742 > 0.05$, do not reject H_0. There is insufficient evidence to conclude that the mean salary of reliability/safety engineers is different from the mean salary of software quality engineers. $-\$2{,}964.92 \leq \mu_1 - \mu_2 \leq \$7{,}852.92$. **(c)** The results are the same since the interval includes 0.

11.10 (a) H_0: $\mu_1 = \mu_2$, where Populations: 1 = Males, 2 = Females.
H_1: $\mu_1 \neq \mu_2$
Decision rule: $df = 170$. If $t_{STAT} < -1.974$ or $t_{STAT} > 1.974$, reject H_0.
Test statistic:

$$S_p^2 = \frac{(n_1-1)(S_1^2) + (n_2-1)(S_2^2)}{(n_1-1) + (n_2-1)}$$

$$= \frac{(99)(13.35^2) + (71)(9.42^2)}{99 + 71} = 140.8489$$

$$t_{STAT} = \frac{(\bar{X}_1 - \bar{X}_2) - (\mu_1 - \mu_2)}{\sqrt{S_p^2\left(\frac{1}{n_1} + \frac{1}{n_2}\right)}}$$

$$= \frac{(40.26 - 36.85) - 0}{\sqrt{140.8489\left(\frac{1}{100} + \frac{1}{72}\right)}} = 1.859$$

Decision: Because $-1.974 < t_{STAT} = 1.859 < 1.974$, do not reject H_0. There is not enough evidence to conclude that the mean computer anxiety experienced by males and females is different. **(b)** p-value $= 0.0648$. **(c)** In order to use the pooled-variance t test, you need to assume that the populations are normally distributed with equal variances.

11.12 (a) Because $t_{STAT} = -4.1343 < -2.0484$, reject H_0. **(b)** p-value $= 0.0003$. **(c)** The original populations of waiting times are approximately normally distributed. **(d)** $-4.2292 \leq \mu_1 - \mu_2 \leq -1.4268$.

11.14 (a) Because $t_{STAT} = 4.10 > 2.024$, reject H_0. There is evidence of a difference in the mean surface hardness between untreated and treated steel plates. **(b)** p-value $= 0.0002$. The probability that two samples have a mean difference of 10.3634 or more is 0.02% if there is no difference in the mean surface hardness between untreated and treated steel plates. **(c)** You need to assume that the population distribution of hardness of both untreated and treated steel plates is normally distributed. **(d)** $4.7447 \leq \mu_1 - \mu_2 \leq 13.9821$.

11.16 (a) Because $t_{STAT} = -2.1522 < -2.0211$, reject H_0. There is enough evidence to conclude that the mean assembly times, in seconds, are different between employees trained in a computer-assisted, individual-based program and those trained in a team-based program. **(b)** You must assume that each of the two independent populations is normally distributed. **(c)** Because $t_{STAT} = -2.152 < -2.052$ or p-value $= 0.041 < 0.05$, reject H_0. **(d)** The results in (a) and (c) are the same. **(e)** $-4.52 \leq \mu_1 - \mu_2 \leq -0.14$. You are 95% confident that the difference between the population means of the two training methods is between -4.52 and -0.14.

11.18 $df = 19$.

11.20 (a) $t_{STAT} = (-1.5566)/(1.424)/\sqrt{9} = -3.2772$; Because $t_{STAT} = -3.2772 < -2.306$ or p-value $= 0.0112 < 0.05$, reject H_0. There is enough evidence of a difference in the mean summated ratings between the two brands. **(b)** You must assume that the distribution of the differences between the two ratings is approximately normal. **(c)** p-value is 0.0112. The probability of obtaining a mean difference in ratings that gives rise to a test statistic that deviates from 0 by 3.2772 or more in either direction is 0.0112 if there is no difference in the mean summated ratings between the two brands. **(d)** $-2.6501 \leq \mu_D \leq -0.4610$. You are

95% confident that the mean difference in summated ratings between brand A and brand B is somewhere between -2.6501 and -0.4610.

11.22 (a) Because $t_{STAT} = 6.7876 > 2.9768$ or p-value $= 0.0000 < 0.01$, reject H_0. There is evidence to conclude that there is a difference between the mean price of textbooks at the local bookstore and Amazon.com. **(b)** You must assume that the distribution of the differences between the measurements is approximately normal. **(c)** $\$9.27 \le \mu_D \le \$23.25$. You are 99% confident that the mean difference between the price of textbooks at the local bookstore and Amazon.com is somewhere between $10.27 and $23.25. **(d)** The results in (a) and (c) are the same. The hypothesized value of 0 for the difference in the price of textbooks between the local bookstore and Amazon.com is outside the 99% confidence interval.

11.24 (a) Because $t_{STAT} = 1.8425 < 1.943$, do not reject H_0. There is not enough evidence to conclude that the mean bone marrow microvessel density is higher before the stem cell transplant than after the stem cell transplant. **(b)** p-value $= 0.0575$. The probability that the t statistic for the mean difference in density is 1.8425 or more is 5.75% if the mean density is not higher before the stem cell transplant than after the stem cell transplant. **(c)** $-28.26 \le \mu_D \le 200.55$. You are 95% confident that the mean difference in bone marrow microvessel density before and after the stem cell transplant is somewhere between -28.26 and 200.55.

11.26 (a) Because $t_{STAT} = -9.3721 < -2.4258$, reject H_0. **(b)** The population of differences in strength is approximately normally distributed. **(c)** $p = 0.000$.

11.28 (a) Because $-2.58 \le Z_{STAT} = -0.58 \le 2.58$, do not reject H_0. **(b)** $-0.273 \le \pi_1 - \pi_2 \le 0.173$.

11.30 (a) $H_0: \pi_1 \le \pi_2. H_1: \pi_1 > \pi_2$. Populations: 1 = expensive pill, 2 = cheap pill. **(b)** Because $Z_{STAT} = 2.4924 > 1.6449$, or p-value $= 0.0064 < 0.05$ reject H_0. There is sufficient evidence to conclude that the population proportion of people who think the expensive pill works greater than the population proportion of people who think the cheap pill works. **(c)** Yes, the result in (b) makes it appropriate to claim that people think the expensive pill works better.

11.32 (a) $H_0: \pi_1 = \pi_2. H_1: \pi_1 \ne \pi_2$. Decision rule: If $|Z_{STAT}| > 1.96$, reject H_0.
Test statistic:

$$\bar{p} = \frac{X_1 + X_2}{n_1 + n_2} = \frac{280 + 320}{505 + 500} = 0.5970$$

$$Z_{STAT} = \frac{(p_1 - p_2) - (\pi_2 - \pi_2)}{\sqrt{\bar{p}(1 - \bar{p})\left(\frac{1}{n_1} + \frac{1}{n_2}\right)}} = \frac{(0.5545 - 0.64) - 0}{\sqrt{0.5970(1 - 0.5970)\left(\frac{1}{505} + \frac{1}{500}\right)}}$$

$$= -2.7644.$$

Decision: Because $Z_{STAT} = -2.7644 < -1.96$, reject H_0. There is sufficient evidence to conclude that there is a difference in the proportion of adults who think the U.S. tax code is unfair between the two income groups. **(b)** p-value $= 0.0057$. The probability of obtaining a difference in proportions that gives rise to a test statistic that deviates from 0 by 2.7644 or more in either direction is 0.0057 if there is no difference in the proportion of adults who think the U.S. tax code is unfair between the two income groups.

11.34 (a) Because $-1.96 < Z_{STAT} = 1.5240 < 1.96$, do not reject H_0. There is insufficient evidence of a difference between undergraduate and MBA students in the proportion who selected the highest-cost fund. **(b)** p-value $= 0.1275$. The probability of obtaining a difference in proportions that gives rise to a test statistic that deviates from 0 by 1.5240 or more in either direction is 0.1275 if there is no difference between

undergraduate and MBA students in the proportion who selected the highest-cost fund.

11.36 (a) 2.20. **(b)** 2.57. **(c)** 3.50.

11.38 (a) Population B. $S^2 = 25$. **(b)** 1.5625.

11.40 $df_{numerator} = 24, df_{denominator} - 24$.

11.42 Because $F_{STAT} = 1.2109 < 2.27$, do not reject H_0.

11.44 (a) Because $F_{STAT} = 1.2995 < 3.18$, do not reject H_0. **(b)** Because $F_{STAT} = 1.2995 < 2.62$, do not reject H_0.

11.46 (a) $H_0: \sigma_1^2 = \sigma_2^2. H_1: \sigma_1^2 \ne \sigma_2^2$.
Decision rule: If $F_{STAT} > 1.556$, reject H_0.

Test statistic: $F_{STAT} = \dfrac{S_1^2}{S_2^2} = \dfrac{(13.35)^2}{(9.42)^2} = 2.008$.

Decision: Because $F_{STAT} = 2.008 > 1.556$, reject H_0. There is enough evidence to conclude that the two population variances are different. **(b)** p-value $= 0.0022$. **(c)** The test assumes that each of the two populations is normally distributed. **(d)** Based on (a) and (b), a separate-variance t test should be used.

11.48 (a) Because $F_{STAT} = 1.0389 < 2.7324$ or p-value $= 0.9789 > 0.05$, do not reject H_0. There is not enough evidence of a difference in the variability of the battery life between the two types of digital cameras. **(b)** p-value $= 0.9789$. The probability of obtaining a sample that yields a test statistic more extreme than 1.0389 is 0.9789 if there is no difference in the two population variances. **(c)** The test assumes that the two populations are both normally distributed. **(d)** Based on (a) and (b), a pooled-variance t test should be used.

11.50 Because $F_{STAT} = 1.2303 < 6.39$, or p-value $= 0.8456 > 0.05$, do not reject H_0. There is not enough evidence of a difference in the variance of the yield between money market accounts and five-year CDs.

11.52 (a) $SSW = 150$. **(b)** $MSA = 15$. **(c)** $MSW = 5$. **(d)** $F_{STAT} = 3$.

11.54 (a) 2. **(b)** 18. **(c)** 20.

11.56 (a) Reject H_0 if $F_{STAT} > 2.95$; otherwise, do not reject H_0. **(b)** Because $F_{STAT} = 4 > 2.95$, reject H_0. **(c)** The table does not have 28 degrees of freedom in the denominator, so use the next larger critical value, $Q_\alpha = 3.90$. **(d)** Critical range $= 6.166$.

11.58 (a) $H_0: \mu_A = \mu_B = \mu_C = \mu_D$ and H_1: At least one mean in different.

$$MSA = \frac{SSA}{c - 1} = \frac{1986.475}{3} = 662.1583.$$

$$MSW = \frac{SSW}{n - c} = \frac{495.5}{36} = 13.76389.$$

$$F_{STAT} = \frac{MSA}{MSW} = \frac{662.1583}{13.76389} = 48.1084.$$

$$F_{0.05,3,36} = 2.8663.$$

Because the p-value is approximately zero and $F_{STAT} = 48.1084 > 2.8663$, reject H_0. There is sufficient evidence of a difference in the mean strength of the four brands of trash bags.

(b) Critical range $= Q_\alpha \sqrt{\dfrac{MSW}{2}\left(\dfrac{1}{n_j} + \dfrac{1}{n_{j'}}\right)} = 3.79 \sqrt{\dfrac{13.7639}{2}\left(\dfrac{1}{10} + \dfrac{1}{10}\right)}$

$$= 4.446.$$

From the Tukey-Kramer procedure, there is a difference in mean strength between Kroger and Tuffstuff, Glad and Tuffstuff, and Hefty and Tuffstuff. **(c)** ANOVA output for Levene's test for homogeneity of variance:

$$MSA = \frac{SSA}{c-1} = \frac{24.075}{3} = 8.025.$$

$$MSW = \frac{SSW}{n-c} = \frac{198.2}{36} = 5.5056.$$

$$F_{STAT} = \frac{MSA}{MSW} = \frac{8.025}{5.5056} = 1.4576.$$

$$F_{0.05,3,36} = 2.8663.$$

Because the p-value $= 0.2423 > 0.05$ and $F_{STAT} = 1.458 < 2.866$, do not reject H_0. There is insufficient evidence to conclude that the variances in strength among the four brands of trash bags are different. **(d)** From the results in (a) and (b), Tuffstuff has the lowest mean strength and should be avoided.

11.60 (a) Because $F_{STAT} = 12.56 > F_{0.05,4,25} = 2.76$, reject H_0. **(b)** Critical range $= 4.67$. Advertisements A and B are different from Advertisements C and D. Advertisement E is only different from Advertisement D. **(c)** Because $F_{STAT} = 1.927 < 2.76$, do not reject H_0. There is no evidence of a significant difference in the variation in the ratings among the five advertisements. **(d)** The advertisements underselling the pen's characteristics had the highest mean ratings, and the advertisements overselling the pen's characteristics had the lowest mean ratings. Therefore, use an advertisement that undersells the pen's characteristics and avoid advertisements that oversell the pen's characteristics.

11.62 (a) Because $F_{STAT} = 53.03 > F_{0.05,3,30} = 2.92$, reject H_0. **(b)** Critical range $= 5.27$ (using 30 degrees of freedom). Designs 3 and 4 are different from Designs 1 and 2. Designs 1 and 2 are different from each other. **(c)** The assumptions are that the samples are randomly and independently selected (or randomly assigned), the original populations of distances are approximately normally distributed, and the variances are equal. **(d)** Because $F_{STAT} = 2.093 < 2.92$, do not reject H_0. There is no evidence of a significant difference in the variation in the distance among the four designs. **(e)** The manager should choose Design 3 or 4.

11.72 (a) H_0: $\sigma_1^2 \geq \sigma_2^2$ and H_0: $\sigma_1^2 < \sigma_2^2$. **(b)** Type I error: Rejecting the null hypothesis that the price variance on the Internet is no lower than the price variance in the brick-and-mortar market when the price variance on the Internet is no lower than the price variance in the brick-and-mortar market. Type II error: Failing to reject the null hypothesis that price variance on the Internet is lower than the price variance in the brick-and-mortar market when the price variance on the Internet is lower than the price variance in the brick-and-mortar market. **(c)** An F test for differences in two variances can be used. **(d)** You need to assume that each of the two populations is normally distributed. **(e) (a)** H_0: $\mu_1 \geq \mu_2$ and H_1: $\mu_1 < \mu_2$. **(b)** Type I error: Rejecting the null hypothesis that the mean price in the electronic market is no lower than the mean price in the physical market when the mean price in the electronic market is no lower than the mean price in the physical market. Type II error: Failing to reject the null hypothesis that the mean price in the electronic market is no lower than the mean price in the physical market when the mean price in the electronic market is lower than the mean price in the physical market. **(c)** A pooled t test or a separate-variance t test for the difference in the means can be used. **(d)** You must assume that the distribution of the prices in the electronic market and in the physical market are approximately normally distributed.

11.74 (a) The researchers can ask the teenagers, after viewing each ad, to rate the dangers of smoking, using a scale from 0 to 10, with 10 representing the most dangerous. **(b)** H_0: $\mu_T \geq \mu_S$ and H_1: $\mu_T < \mu_S$. **(c)** Type I error is the error made by concluding that ads produced by the state are more effective than those produced by Philip Morris even though

it is not true. The risk of Type I error here is that teenagers can miss the opportunity from the better ads produced by Philip Morris to recognize the true dangers of smoking and the additional expenses the state will have to incur to produce and run the ads. Type II error is the error made by concluding that ads produced by Philip Morris are no less effective than those produced by the state even though ads produced by the state are more effective. The risk of Type II error here is that more teenagers will miss the opportunity to recognize the true dangers of smoking from the ads produced by the state. **(d)** Because both ads are shown to the same group of teenagers, a paired t test for the mean difference is most appropriate. **(e)** Statistically reliable here means the conclusions drawn from the test are reliable because all the assumptions needed for the test to be valid are fulfilled.

11.76 (a) Because $F_{STAT} = 22.7067 > F_\alpha = 1.6275$, reject H_0. There is enough evidence to conclude that there is a difference between the variances in age of students at the Western school and at the Eastern school. **(b)** Because there is a difference between the variances in the age of students at the Western school and at the Eastern school, schools should take that into account when designing their curriculum to accommodate the larger variance in age of students in the state university in the Western United States. **(c)** It is more appropriate to use a separate-variance t test. **(d)** Because $F_{STAT} = 1.3061 < 1.6275$, do not reject H_0. There is not enough evidence to conclude that there is a difference between the variances in years of spreadsheet usage of students at the Western school and at the Eastern school. **(e)** Using the pooled-variance t test, because $t_{STAT} = -4.6650 < -2.5978$, reject H_0. There is enough evidence of a difference in the mean years of spreadsheet usage of students at the Western school and at the Eastern school.

11.78 (a) Because $t_{STAT} = 3.3282 > 1.8595$, reject H_0. There is enough evidence to conclude that the introductory computer students required more than a mean of 10 minutes to write and run a program in Visual Basic. **(b)** Because $t_{STAT} = 1.3636 < 1.8595$, do not reject H_0. There is not enough evidence to conclude that the introductory computer students required more than a mean of 10 minutes to write and run a program in Visual Basic. **(c)** Although the mean time necessary to complete the assignment increased from 12 to 16 minutes as a result of the increase in one data value, the standard deviation went from 1.8 to 13.2, which reduced the t value. **(d)** Because $F_{STAT} = 1.2308 < 3.8549$, do not reject H_0. There is not enough evidence to conclude that the population variances are different for the Introduction to Computers students and computer majors. Hence, the pooled-variance t test is a valid test to determine whether computer majors can write a Visual Basic program in less time than introductory students, assuming that the distributions of the time needed to write a Visual Basic program for both the Introduction to Computers students and the computer majors are approximately normally distributed. Because $t_{STAT} = 4.0666 > 1.7341$, reject H_0. There is enough evidence that the mean time is higher for Introduction to Computers students than for computer majors. **(e)** p-value $= 0.000362$. If the true population mean amount of time needed for Introduction to Computer students to write a Visual Basic program is no more than 10 minutes, the probability of observing a sample mean greater than the 12 minutes in the current sample is 0.0362%. Hence, at a 5% level of significance, you can conclude that the population mean amount of time needed for Introduction to Computer students to write a Visual Basic program is more than 10 minutes. As illustrated in part (d), in which there is not enough evidence to conclude that the population variances are different for the Introduction to Computers students and computer majors, the pooled-variance t test performed is a valid test to determine whether computer majors can write a Visual Basic program in less time than introductory students, assuming that the distribution of the time needed to write a Visual Basic program for both the Introduction to Computers students and the computer majors are approximately normally distributed.

11.80 From the boxplot and the summary statistics, both distributions are approximately normally distributed. $F_{STAT} = 1.056 < 1.89$. There is insufficient evidence to conclude that the two population variances are significantly different at the 5% level of significance. $t_{STAT} = -5.084 < -1.99$. At the 5% level of significance, there is sufficient evidence to reject the null hypothesis of no difference in the mean life of the bulbs between the two manufacturers. You can conclude that there is a significant difference in the mean life of the bulbs between the two manufacturers.

11.82 Customer Product Rating Reviews: $-1.96 < Z_{STAT} = -1.6557 < 1.96$ and p-value $= 0.0978 > 0.05$, do not reject H_0. There is not enough evidence that there is a difference between adults and youths in the proportion who use customer product ratings/reviews. For sale listings with seller ratings: $-1.96 < Z_{STAT} = -1.2742 < 1.96$ and p-value $= 0.2026 > 0.05$, do not reject H_0. There is not enough evidence that there is a difference between adults and youths in the proportion who use for sale listings with seller ratings. For sale listings without seller ratings: $-1.96 < Z_{STAT} = -1.0172 < 1.96$ and p-value $= 0.3090 > 0.05$, do not reject H_0. There is not enough evidence that there is a difference between adults and youths in the proportion who use for sale listings without seller ratings. Online classified ads: $-1.96 < Z_{STAT} = -1.3079 < 1.96$ and p-value $= 0.1909 > 0.05$, do not reject H_0. There is not enough evidence that there is a difference between adults and youths in the proportion who use online classified ads. Message-board posts: $Z_{STAT} = -2.0624 < -1.96$ and p-value $= 0.0392 < 0.05$, reject H_0. There is enough evidence that there is a difference between adults and youths in the proportion who use message-board posts. Web blogs: $-1.96 < Z_{STAT} = -1.7397 < 1.96$ and p-value $= 0.0819 > 0.05$, do not reject H_0. There is not enough evidence that there is a difference between adults and youths in the proportion who use Web blogs. Dating site profile/personals: $= -1.96 < Z_{STAT} = -1.4188 < 1.96$ and p-value $= 0.1560 > 0.05$, do not reject H_0. There is not enough evidence that there is a difference between adults and youths in the proportion who use dating site profiles/personals. Peer-generated and peer-referenced information: $Z_{STAT} = -2.7267 < -1.96$ and p-value $= 0.0064 < 0.05$, reject H_0. There is enough evidence that there is a difference between adults and youths in the proportion who use peer-generated and peer-referenced information. Peer-posted event listings: $Z_{STAT} = -3.5878 < -1.96$ and p-value $= 0.0003 < 0.05$, reject H_0. There is enough evidence that there is a difference between adults and youths in the proportion who use peer-posted event listings.

11.84 The normal probability plots suggest that the two populations are not normally distributed. An F test is inappropriate for testing the difference in two variances. The sample variances for Boston and Vermont shingles are 0.0203 and 0.015, respectively. Because $t_{STAT} = 3.015 > 1.967$ or the p-value $= 0.0028 < \alpha = 0.05$, reject H_0. There is sufficient evidence to conclude that there is a difference in the mean granule loss of Boston and Vermont shingles.

11.86 (a) Because $F_{STAT} = 0.075 < F_{0.05,2,15} = 3.68$, do not reject H_0. **(b)** Because $F_{STAT} = 4.09 > F_{0.05,2,15} = 3.68$, reject H_0. **(c)** Critical range $= 1.489$. Breaking strength is significantly different between 30 and 50 psi.

CHAPTER 12

12.2 (a) For $df = 1$ and $\alpha = 0.05$, $\chi_\alpha^2 = 3.841$. **(b)** For $df = 1$ and $\alpha = 0.005$, $\chi^2 = 7.879$. **(c)** For $df = 1$ and $\alpha = 0.10$, $\chi_\alpha^2 = 2.706$.

12.4 (a) All $f_e = 25$. **(b)** Because $\chi_{STAT}^2 = 4.00 > 3.841$, reject H_0.

$$\chi_{STAT}^2 = 6.212 > 3.841 \qquad H_0$$

12.6 (a) Because $\chi_{STAT}^2 = 6.212 > 3.841$, reject H_0. There is enough evidence to conclude that there is significant difference between the proportion of people who think the expensive pill works to reduce pain and the proportion of people who think a cheap pill works to reduce pain. **(b)** p-value is 0.0127. The probability of obtaining a test statistic of 6.212 or larger when the null hypothesis is true is 0.0127. **(c)** You should not compare the results in (a) to those of Problem 10.30 (b) because that was a one-tail test.

12.8 (a) H_0: $\pi_1 = \pi_2$. H_1: $\pi_1 \neq \pi_2$.

Observed Frequencies

Row Variable	Column Variable		
	Less Than $50,000	More Than $50,000	Total
Fair	225	180	405
Unfair	280	320	600
Total	505	500	1,005

Expected Frequencies

Row Variable	Column Variable		
	Less Than $50,000	More Than $50,000	Total
Fair	203.5075	201.4925	405
Unfair	301.4925	298.5075	600
Total	505	500	1,005

Level of Significance 0.05 Number of Rows 2 Number of Columns 2 Degrees of Freedom 1 Critical Value 3.841459 Chi-Square Test Statistic $=$ $(225 - 203.5075)^2/203.5075 + (280 - 301.4925)^2/301.4925 + (180 - 201.4925)^2/201.4925 + (320 - 298.5075)^2/298.5075 = 7.64198$ p-Value 0.005703
Decision: Because $\chi_{STAT}^2 = 7.642 > 3.841$, reject H_0. There is enough evidence to conclude that there is a significant difference in the proportion of adults who think the U.S. tax code is unfair between the two income groups. **(b)** The probability of obtaining a test statistic of 7.642 or larger when the null hypothesis is true is 0.0057. **(c)** The results of (a) and (b) are exactly the same as those of Problem 10.32. The χ^2 in (a) and the Z in Problem 10.32 (a) satisfy the relationship that $\chi^2 = 7.642 = Z^2 = (-2.7644)^2$, and the p-value in Problem 10.32 (b) is exactly the same as the p-value obtained in (b).

12.10 (a) Because $\chi_{STAT}^2 = 2.3226 < 3.841$, do not reject H_0. There is not enough evidence to conclude that there is a significant difference between undergraduate and MBA students in the proportion who selected the highest-cost fund. **(b)** p-value $= 0.1275$. The probability of obtaining a test statistic of 2.3226 or larger when the null hypothesis is true is 0.1275. **(c)** The results of (a) and (b) are exactly the same as those of Problem 10.34. The χ^2 in (a) and the Z in Problem 10.34 (a) satisfy the relationship that $\chi_{STAT}^2 = 2.3226 = (Z_{STAT})^2 = (1.5240)^2$, and the p-value in Problem 10.34 (b) is exactly the same as the p-value obtained in (b).

12.12 (a) The expected frequencies for the first row are 20, 30, and 40. The expected frequencies for the second row are 30, 45, and 60. **(b)** Because $\chi_{STAT}^2 = 12.5 > 5.991$, reject H_0.

12.14 (a) Because the calculated test statistic $\chi_{STAT}^2 = 742.3961 > 9.4877$, reject H_0 and conclude that there is a difference in the proportion of people who eat out at least once a week in the various countries. **(b)** p-value is virtually zero. The probability of a test statistic greater than 742.3961 or more is approximately zero if there is no difference in the proportion of people who eat out at least once a week in the various countries.

12.16 (a) H_0: $\pi_1 = \pi_2 = \pi_3$. H_1: At least one proportion differs.

f_0	f_e	$(f_0 - f_e)$	$(f_0 - f_e)^2/f_e$
48	42.667	5.333	0.667
152	157.333	−5.333	0.181
56	42.667	13.333	4.166
144	157.333	−13.333	1.130
24	42.667	−18.667	8.167
176	157.333	18.667	2.215
			16.5253

Decision rule: $df = (c - 1) = (3 - 1) = 2$. If $\chi^2_{STAT} > 5.9915$, reject H_0.

Test statistic: $\chi^2_{STAT} = \sum_{\text{all cells}} \frac{(f_0 - f_e)^2}{f_e} = 16.5253$

Decision: Because $\chi^2_{STAT} = 16.5253 > 5.9915$, reject H_0. There is a significant difference in the age groups with respect to major grocery shopping day. **(b)** p-value $= 0.0003$. The probability that the test statistic is greater than or equal to 16.5253 is 0.03%, if the null hypothesis is true. **(c)** The stores can use this information to target their marketing on the specific groups of shoppers on Saturday and the days other than Saturday.

12.18 (a) Because $\chi^2_{STAT} = 20.3383 > 7.815$, reject H_0. There is evidence of a difference in the percentage working among the groups. **(b)** p-value $= 0.0001$.

12.20 $df = (r - 1)(c - 1) = (3 - 1)(4 - 1) = 6$.

12.22 (b) $\chi^2_{STAT} = 8.3536 < 9.2103$, do not reject H_0 and conclude that there is not enough evidence that men and women feel differently about executive pay. **(c)** $\chi^2_{STAT} = 16.7073 > 9.2103$, reject H_0 and conclude that there is enough evidence that men and women feel differently about executive pay. **(d)** As you can see from the results in (b) and (c), the same proportions will result in a different test statistic and, hence, potentially different decisions.

12.24 (a) H_0: There is no relationship between the commuting time of company employees and the level of stress-related problems observed on the job. H_1: There is a relationship between the commuting time of company employees and the level of stress-related problems observed on the job.

f_0	f_e	$(f_0 - f_e)$	$(f_0 - f_e)^2/f_e$
9	12.1379	−3.1379	0.8112
17	20.1034	−3.1034	0.4791
18	11.7586	6.2414	3.3129
5	5.2414	−0.2414	0.0111
8	8.6810	−0.6810	0.0534
6	5.0776	0.9224	0.1676
18	14.6207	3.3793	0.7811
28	24.2155	3.7845	0.5915
7	14.1638	−7.1638	3.6233
			9.8311

Decision rule: If $\chi^2_{STAT} > 13.277$, reject H_0.

Test statistic: $\chi^2_{STAT} = \sum_{\text{all cells}} \frac{(f_0 - f_e)^2}{f_e} = 9.8311$

Decision: Because the $\chi^2_{STAT} = 9.8311 < 13.277$, do not reject H_0. There is not enough evidence to conclude that there is a relationship between the commuting time of company employees and the level of stress-related problems observed on the job.

(b) Because $\chi^2_{STAT} = 9.831 > 9.488$, reject H_0. There is enough evidence at the 0.05 level to conclude that there is a relationship.

12.26 Because $\chi^2_{STAT} = 129.520 > 21.026$, reject H_0. There is a relationship between when the decision is made of what to have for dinner and the type of household.

12.30 (a) Because $\chi^2_{STAT} = 0.412 < 3.841$, do not reject H_0. There is not enough evidence to conclude that there is a relationship between a student's gender and pizzeria selection. **(b)** Because $\chi^2_{STAT} = 2.624 < 3.841$, do not reject H_0. There is not enough evidence to conclude that there is a relationship between a student's gender and pizzeria selection. **(c)** Because $\chi^2_{STAT} = 4.956 < 5.991$, do not reject H_0. There is not enough evidence to conclude that there is a relationship between price and pizzeria selection. **(d)** p-value $= 0.0839$. The probability of a sample that gives a test statistic equal to or greater than 4.956 is 8.39% if the null hypothesis of no relationship between price and pizzeria selection is true.

12.32 (a) Because $\chi^2_{STAT} = 11.895 < 12.592$, do not reject H_0. There is not enough evidence to conclude that there is a relationship between the attitudes of employees toward the use of self-managed work teams and employee job classification. **(b)** Because $\chi^2_{STAT} = 3.294 < 12.592$, do not reject H_0. There is not enough evidence to conclude that there is a relationship between the attitudes of employees toward vacation time without pay and employee job classification.

12.34 (a) Because $\chi^2_{STAT} = 11.635 > 7.815$, reject H_0. There is enough evidence to conclude that there is a relationship between the presence of environmental goals and the type of manufacturing process. **(b)** p-value $= 0.00874$. The probability of obtaining a data set that gives rise to a test statistic of 11.635 or more is 0.00874 if there is no relationship between the presence of environmental goals and the type of manufacturing process. **(c)** Because $\chi^2_{STAT} = 10.94 > 3.841$, reject H_0. There is enough evidence to conclude that there is a difference in improved environmental performance for teams with a specified goal of cutting costs. **(d)** p-value $= 0.000941$. The probability of obtaining a data set that gives rise to a test statistic of 10.94 or more is 0.000941 if there is no difference in improved environmental performance for teams with a specified goal of cutting costs. **(e)** Because $\chi^2_{STAT} = 0.612 < 3.841$, do not reject H_0. There is not enough evidence to conclude that there is a difference in improved profitability for teams with a specified goal of cutting costs. **(f)** p-value $= 0.4341$. The probability of obtaining a data set that gives rise to a test statistic of 0.612 or more is 0.4341 if there is no difference in improved profitability for teams with a specified goal of cutting costs. **(g)** $\chi^2_{STAT} = 3.454 < 3.841$, do not reject H_0. There is not enough evidence to conclude that there is a difference in improved morale for teams with a specified goal of cutting costs. **(h)** p-value $= 0.063$. The probability of obtaining a data set that gives rise to a test statistic of 3.454 or more is 0.063 if there is no difference in improved morale for teams with a specified goal of cutting costs.

CHAPTER 13

13.2 (a) Yes. **(b)** No. **(c)** No. **(d)** Yes.

13.4 (a) the scatter plot shows a positive linear relationship

(b) For each increase in shelf space of an additional foot, weekly sales are estimated to increase by $7.40. **(c)** $\hat{Y} = 145 + 7.4X = 145 + 7.4(8) = 204.2$, or $204.20.

13.6 (b) $b_0 = -2.37$, $b_1 = 0.0501$. **(c)** For every cubic foot increase in the amount moved, mean labor hours are estimated to increase by 0.0501. **(d)** 22.67 labor hours.

13.8 (b) $b_0 = -435.065$, $b_1 = 4.9555$. **(c)** For each additional million-dollar increase in revenue, the mean annual value will increase by an estimated \$4.9555 million. Literal interpretation of b_0 is not meaningful because an operating franchise cannot have zero revenue. **(d)** \$308,266 million.

13.10 (b) $b_0 = -140.1203$, $b_1 = 4.3331$ $\hat{Y} = b_0 + b_1X$. $\hat{Y} = -140.1203 + 4.3331X$ **(c)** For each increase of one additional million dollars of box office gross, the estimated mean DVDs sold will increase by 4.3331 thousands. **(d)** $\hat{Y} = b_0 + b_1X$. $\hat{Y} = -140.1203 + 4.3331(75) = 184.86285$ thousands.

13.12 $r^2 = 0.90$. 90% of the variation in the dependent variable can be explained by the variation in the independent variable.

13.14 $r^2 = 0.75$. 75% of the variation in the dependent variable can be explained by the variation in the independent variable.

13.16 (a) $r^2 = \dfrac{SSR}{SST} = \dfrac{20,535}{30,025} = 0.684$. 68.4% of the variation in sales can be explained by the variation in shelf space.

(b) $S_{YX} = \sqrt{\dfrac{SSE}{n-2}} = \sqrt{\dfrac{\sum_{i=1}^{n}(Y_i - \hat{Y}_i)^2}{n-2}} = \sqrt{\dfrac{9,490}{10}} = 30.8058$.

(c) Based on (a) and (b), the model should be very useful for predicting sales.

13.18 (a) $r^2 = 0.8892$. 88.92% of the variation in labor hours can be explained by the variation in cubic feet moved. **(b)** $S_{YX} = 5.0314$. **(c)** Based on (a) and (b), the model should be very useful for predicting the labor hours.

13.20 (a) $r^2 = 0.931$. 93.1% of the variation in the value of a baseball franchise can be explained by the variation in its annual revenue. **(b)** $S_{YX} = 56.4059$. **(c)** Based on (a) and (b), the model should be very useful for predicting the value of a baseball franchise.

13.22 (a) $r^2 = 0.7278$. 72.78% of the variation in DVDs sold can be explained by the variation in box office gross. **(b)** $S_{YX} = 47.8668$. The variation of DVDs sold around the prediction line is 47.8668 millions. The typical difference between actual DVDs sold and the predicted DVDs sold using the regression equation is approximately 47.8668 millions. **(c)** Based on (a) and (b), the model is useful for predicting DVDs sold. **(d)** Other variables that might explain the variation in DVDs sold could be the amount spent on advertising, the timing of the release of the DVDs, and the distribution channels of the DVDs.

13.24 A residual analysis of the data indicates a pattern, with sizable clusters of consecutive residuals that are either all positive or all negative. This pattern indicates a violation of the assumption of linearity. A curvilinear model should be investigated.

13.26 There does not appear to be a pattern in the residual plot. The assumptions of regression do not appear to be seriously violated.

13.28 Based on the residual plot, there does not appear to be a curvilinear pattern in the residuals. The assumptions of normality and equal variance do not appear to be seriously violated.

13.30 Based on the residual plot, there appears to be a nonlinear pattern in the residuals. A curvilinear model should be investigated. There is some right-skewness in the residuals and some violation of the equal-variance assumption.

13.32 (a) 3.00. **(b)** ± 2.1199. **(c)** Reject H_0. There is evidence that the fitted linear regression model is useful. **(d)** $1.32 \le \beta_1 \le 7.68$.

13.34 (a) $t_{STAT} = \dfrac{b_1 - \beta_1}{S_{b_1}} = \dfrac{7.4}{1.59} = 4.65 > 2.2281$. Reject H_0. There is

evidence that the fitted linear regression model is useful. **(b)** $b_1 \pm t_{\alpha/2}S_{b_1} = 7.4 \pm 2.2281(1.59)$ $3.86 \le \beta_1 \le 10.94$.

13.36 (a) $t_{STAT} = 16.52 > 2.0322$; reject H_0. **(b)** $0.0439 \le \beta_1 \le 0.0562$.

13.38 (a) $t_{STAT} = 19.50 > 2.0484$ or because the p-value is approximately zero, reject H_0 at the 5% level of significance. There is evidence of a linear relationship between annual revenue and franchise value. **(b)** $4.435 \le \beta_1 \le 5.476$.

13.40 (a) $t_{STAT} = 8.65 > 2.0484$ or because the p-value is virtually $0 < 0.05$; reject H_0. **(b)** $3.3072 \le \beta_1 \le 5.3590$.

13.42 (a) (% daily change in UOPIX) $= b_0 + 2.00$ (% daily change in S&P 500 index) **(b)** If the S&P gains 30% in a year, the UOPIX is expected to gain an estimated 60%. **(c)** If the S&P loses 35% in a year, the UOPIX is expected to lose an estimated 70%. **(d)** Risk takers will be attracted to leveraged funds, but risk averse investors will stay away.

13.44 (a) $r = 0.8935$. There appears to be a strong positive linear relationship between the mileage as calculated by owners and by current government standards. **(b)** $t_{STAT} = 5.2639 > 2.3646$, p-value $= 0.0012 < 0.05$. Reject H_0. At the 0.05 level of significance, there is a significant linear relationship between the mileage as calculated by owners and by current government standards.

13.46 (a) $r = 0.5497$. There appears to be a moderate positive linear relationship between the average Wonderlic score of football players trying out for the NFL and the graduation rate for football players at selected schools. **(b)** $t_{STAT} = 3.9485$, p-value $= 0.0004 < 0.05$. Reject H_0. At the 0.05 level of significance, there is a significant linear relationship between the average Wonderlic score of football players trying out for the NFL and the graduation rate for football players at selected schools. **(c)** There is a significant linear relationship between the average Wonderlic score of football players trying out for the NFL and the graduation rate for football players at selected schools, but the positive linear relationship is only moderate.

13.48 (a) $15.95 \le \mu_{Y|X=4} \le 18.05$. **(b)** $14.651 \le Y_{X=4} \le 19.349$.

13.50 (a) $\hat{Y} = 145 + 7.4(8) = 204.2$ $\hat{Y} \pm t_{\alpha/2} S_{YX} \sqrt{h_i}$

$$= 204.2 \pm 2.2281(30.81)\sqrt{0.1373}$$

$$178.76 \le \mu_{Y|X=8} \le 229.64$$

(b) $\hat{Y} \pm t_{\alpha/2} S_{YX} \sqrt{1 + h_i}$

$$= 204.2 \pm 2.2281(30.81)\sqrt{1 + 0.1373}$$

$$131.00 \le Y_{X=8} \le 277.40$$

(c) Part (b) provides a prediction interval for the individual response given a specific value of the independent variable, and part (a) provides an interval estimate for the mean value, given a specific value of the independent variable. Because there is much more variation in predicting an individual value than in estimating a mean value, a prediction interval is wider than a confidence interval estimate.

13.52 (a) $20.799 \le \mu_{Y|X=500} \le 24.542$. **(b)** $12.276 \le Y_{X=500} \le 33.065$. **(c)** You can estimate a mean more precisely than you can predict a single observation.

13.54 (a) $281.1 \le \mu_{Y|X=150} \le 335.5$. **(b)** $189.6 \le Y_{X=150} \le 427.0$. **(c)** Part (b) provides a prediction interval for an individual response given a specific value of X and part (a) provides a confidence interval estimate for the mean value given a specific value of X. Since there is much more variation in predicting an individual value than in estimating a mean, the prediction interval is wider than the confidence interval.

13.64 (a) $b_0 = 24.84$, $b_1 = 0.14$. **(b)** For each additional case, the predicted mean delivery time is estimated to increase by 0.14 minutes. **(c)** 45.84. **(d)** No, 500 is outside the relevant range of the data used to fit the regression equation. **(e)** $r^2 = 0.972$. **(f)** There is no obvious pattern in the residuals, so the assumptions of regression are met. The model appears to be adequate. **(g)** $t_{STAT} = 24.88 > 2.1009$; reject H_0. **(h)** $44.88 \leq \mu_{Y|X=150} \leq 46.80$. $41.56 \leq Y_{X=150} \leq 50.12$.

13.66 (a) $b_0 = -122.3439$, $b_1 = 1.7817$. **(b)** For each additional thousand dollars in assessed value, the estimated mean selling price of a house increases by $1.7817 thousand. The estimated mean selling price of a house with a 0 assessed value is -122.3439 thousand. However, this interpretation is not meaningful in the current setting because the assessed value cannot be below 0. **(c)** $\hat{Y} = -122.3439 + 1.78171X = -122.3439 + 1.78171(170) = 180.5475$ thousand dollars. **(d)** $r^2 = 0.9256$. So 92.56% of the variation in selling price can be explained by the variation in assessed value. **(e)** Neither the residual plot nor the normal probability plot reveal any potential violation of the linearity, equal variance, and normality assumptions. **(f)** $t_{STAT} = 18.6648 > 2.0484$, p-value is virtually zero. Because p-value < 0.05, reject H_0. There is evidence of a linear relationship between selling price and assessed value. **(g)** $1.5862 \leq \beta_1 \leq 1.9773$.

13.68 (a) $b_0 = 0.30$, $b_1 = 0.00487$. **(b)** For each additional point on the GMAT score, the predicted mean GPA is estimated to increase by 0.00487. Since a student receiving a 0 on the GMAT would not be admitted to graduate school, the Y-intercept does not have a practical interpretation. **(c)** 3.222. **(d)** $r^2 = 0.798$. **(e)** There is no obvious pattern in the residuals, so the assumptions of regression are met. The model appears to be adequate. **(f)** $t_{STAT} = 8.43 > 2.1009$; reject H_0. **(g)** $3.144 \leq \mu_{Y|X=600} \leq 3.301$. $2.886 \leq Y_{X=600} \leq 3.559$. **(h)** $.00366 \leq \beta_1 \leq .00608$.

13.70 (a) There is no clear relationship shown on the scatterplot. **(c)** Looking at all 23 flights, when the temperature is lower, there is likely to be some O-ring damage, particularly if the temperature is below 60 degrees. **(d)** 31 degrees is outside the relevant range, so a prediction should not be made. **(e)** Predicted $Y = 18.036 - 0.240X$, where X = temperature and Y = O-ring damage. **(g)** A nonlinear model would be more appropriate. **(h)** The appearance on the residual plot of a nonlinear pattern indicates a nonlinear model would be better. It also appears that the normality assumption is invalid.

13.72 (a) $b_0 = 14.6816$, $b_1 = 0.1135$. **(b)** For each additional percentage increase in graduation rate, the estimated mean average Wonderlic score increases by 0.1135. The estimated mean average Wonderlic score is 14.6816 for a school that has a 0% graduation rate. However, this interpretation is not meaningful in the current setting because graduation rate is very unlikely to be 0% for any school. **(c)** $\hat{Y} = 14.6816 + 0.11347X = 14.6816 + 0.11347(50) = 20.4$. **(d)** $r^2 = 0.3022$. So, 30.22% of the variation in average Wonderlic score can be explained by the variation in graduation rate. **(e)** Neither the residual plot nor the normal probability plot reveal any potential violation of the linearity, equal variance, and normality assumptions. **(f)** $t_{STAT} = 3.9485 > 2.0281$, p-value $= 0.0004$. Because p-value < 0.05, reject H_0. There is evidence of a linear relationship between the average Wonderlic score for football players trying out for the NFL from a school and the graduation rate. **(g)** $19.6 \leq \mu_{Y|X=50} \leq 21.1$. **(h)** $15.9 \leq Y_{X=50} \leq 24.8$.

13.74 (a) $b_0 = -2,629.222$, $b_1 = 82.472$. **(b)** For each additional centimeter in circumference, the mean weight is estimated to increase by 82.472 grams. **(c)** 2,319.08 grams. **(e)** $r^2 = 0.937$. **(f)** There appears to be a nonlinear relationship between circumference and weight. **(g)** p-value is virtually 0 < 0.05; reject H_0. **(h)** $72.7875 \leq \beta_1 \leq 92.156$.

13.76 (b) $\hat{Y} = 931,626.16 + 21,782.76X$. **(c)** $b_1 = 21,782.76$ means that as the median age of the customer base increases by one year, the latest one-month mean sales total is estimated to increase by $21,782.76. **(d)** $r^2 = 0.0017$. Only 0.17% of the total variation in the franchise's latest one-month sales total can be explained by using the median age of customer base. **(e)** The residuals are very evenly spread out across different range of median age. **(f)** Because $-2.4926 < t_{STAT} = 0.2482 < 2.4926$, do not reject H_0. There is not enough evidence to conclude that there is a linear relationship between the one-month sales total and the median age of the customer base. **(g)** $-156,181.50 \leq \beta_1 \leq 199,747.02$.

13.78 (a) There is a positive linear relationship between total sales and the percentage of customer base with a college diploma. **(b)** $\hat{Y} = 789,847.38 + 35,854.15X$. **(c)** $b_1 = 35,854.15$ means that for each increase of one percent of the customer base having received a college diploma, the latest one-month mean sales total is estimated to increase by $35,854.15. **(d)** $r^2 = 0.1036$. So 10.36% of the total variation in the franchise's latest one-month sales total can be explained by the percentage of the customer base with a college diploma. **(e)** The residuals are evenly spread out around zero. **(f)** Because $t_{STAT} = 2.0392 > 2.0281$, reject H_0. There is enough evidence to conclude that there is a linear relationship between one-month sales total and percentage of customer base with a college diploma. **(g)** $b_1 \pm t_{\alpha/2} S_{b_1} = 35,854.15 \pm 2.0281(17,582.269)$ $195.75 \leq \beta_1 \leq 71,512.60$.

13.80 (a) $b_0 = -39.0137$, $b_1 = 1.3878$. **(b)** For each additional unit increase in summated rating, the mean price per person is estimated to increase by $1.3878. Because no restaurant will receive a summated rating of 0, it is inappropriate to interpret the Y intercept. **(c)** $30.38. **(d)** $r^2 = 0.6586$. So, 65.86% of the variation in price per person can be explained by the variation in the summated rating. **(e)** There is no obvious pattern in the residuals so the assumptions of regression are met. The model appears to be adequate. **(f)** $t_{STAT} = 13.7484$, the p-value is virtually 0 < 0.05; reject H_0. There is enough evidence to conclude that there is a linear relationship between price per person and summated rating. **(g)** The linear regression model appears to have provided an adequate fit and shown a significant linear relationship between price per person and summated rating. Because 65.86% of the variation in price per person can be explained by the variation in summated rating, summated rating is moderately useful in predicting the price per person.

13.82 (a) The correlation of IBM and GE is -0.126, IBM and Apple is -0.011, and Apple and GE is -0.141. **(b)** There is a very weak negative linear relationship between the stock price of IBM and GE, almost no linear relationship between the stock price of IBM and Apple, and a very weak positive linear relationship between the stock price of GE and Apple. **(c)** It is not a good idea to have all the stocks in an individual's portfolio be strongly, positively correlated among each other because the portfolio risk can be reduced when a pair of stock prices is negatively related or nearly independent.

CHAPTER 14

14.2 (a) For each one-unit increase in X_1, you estimate that Y will decrease 2 units, holding X_2 constant. For each one-unit increase in X_2, you estimate that Y will increase 7 units, holding X_1 constant. **(b)** The Y-intercept equal to 50 estimates the mean value of Y when both X_1 and X_2 are zero.

14.4 (a) $\hat{Y} = -2.72825 + 0.047114X_1 + 0.011947X_2$. **(b)** For a given number of orders, for each increase of $1,000 in sales, mean distribution cost is estimated to increase by $47.114. For a given amount of sales, for each increase of one order, mean distribution cost is estimated to increase by $11.95. **(c)** The interpretation of b_0 has no practical meaning here because it would represent the estimated distribution cost when there were no sales and no orders. **(d)** $\hat{Y} = -2.72825 + 0.047114(400) +$

$0.011947(4500) = 69.878$ or \$69,878. **(e)** $\$66,419.93 \leq \mu_{Y|X} \leq$ \$73,337.01. **(f)** $\$59,380.61 \leq Y_X \leq \$80,376.33$. **(g)** The interval in (e) is narrower because it is estimating the mean value, not an individual value.

14.6 (a) $\hat{Y} = 156.4 + 13.081X_1 + 16.795X_2$. **(b)** For a given amount of newspaper advertising, each increase by \$1,000 in radio advertising is estimated to result in a mean increase in sales of \$13,081. For a given amount of radio advertising, each increase by \$1,000 in newspaper advertising is estimated to result in a mean increase in sales of \$16,795. **(c)** When there is no money spent on radio advertising and newspaper advertising, the estimated mean sales is \$156,430.44. **(d)** Holding the other independent variable constant, newspaper advertising seems to be more effective because its slope is greater.

14.8 (a) $\hat{Y} = 400.8057 + 456.4485X_1 - 2.4708X_2$, where $X_1 =$ land, $X_2 =$ age. **(b)** For a given age, each increase by one acre in land area is estimated to result in a mean increase in appraised value by \$456.45 thousands. For a given acreage, each increase of one year in age is estimated to result in the mean decrease in appraised value by \$2.47 thousands. **(c)** The interpretation of b_0 has no practical meaning here because it would represent the estimated appraised value of a new house that has no land area. **(d)** $\hat{Y} = 400.8057 + 456.4485(0.25) - 2.4708(45) = \$403.73$ thousands. **(e)** $372.7370 \leq \mu_{Y|X} \leq 434.7243$. **(f)** $235.1964 \leq Y_X \leq 572.2649$.

14.10 (a) $MSR = 15, MSE = 12$. **(b)** 1.25. **(c)** $F_{STAT} = 1.25 < 4.10$; do not reject H_0. **(d)** 0.20. **(e)** 0.04.

14.12 (a) $F_{STAT} = 97.69 > F_\alpha = 3.89$ with 2 and $15 - 2 - 1 = 12$ degrees of freedom. Reject H_0. There is evidence of a significant linear relationship with at least one of the independent variables. **(b)** The p-value is 0.0001. **(c)** $r^2 = 0.9421$. 94.21% of the variation in the long-term ability to absorb shock can be explained by variation in forefoot absorbing capability and variation in midsole impact. **(d)** $r^2_{adj} = 0.93245$.

14.14 (a) $F_{STAT} = 74.13 > 3.467$; reject H_0. **(b)** p-value $= 0$. **(c)** $r^2 = 0.8759$. 87.59% of the variation in distribution cost can be explained by variation in sales and variation in number of orders. **(d)** $r^2_{adj} = 0.8641$.

14.16 (a) $F_{STAT} = 40.16 > F_\alpha = 3.522$ with 2 and $22 - 2 - 1 = 19$ degrees of freedom. Reject H_0. There is evidence of a significant linear relationship. **(b)** The p-value is less than 0.001. **(c)** $r^2 = 0.8087$. 80.87% of the variation in sales can be explained by variation in radio advertising and variation in newspaper advertising. **(d)** $r^2_{adj} = 0.7886$.

14.18 (a)–(e) Based on a residual analysis, there is no evidence of a violation in the assumptions of regression.

14.20 (a) There appears to be a quadratic relationship in the plot of the residuals against both radio and newspaper advertising. **(b)** Curvilinear terms for both of these explanatory variables should be considered for inclusion in the model.

14.22 (a) The residual analysis reveals no patterns. **(b)** There are no apparent violations in the assumptions.

14.24 (a) Variable X_2 has a larger slope in terms of the t statistic of 3.75 than variable X_1, which has a smaller slope in terms of the t statistic of 3.33. **(b)** $1.46824 \leq \beta_1 \leq 6.53176$. **(c)** For X_1: $t_{STAT} = 4/1.2 = 3.33 > 2.1098$, with 17 degrees of freedom for $\alpha = 0.05$. Reject H_0. There is evidence that X_1 contributes to a model already containing X_2. For X_2: $t_{STAT} = 3/0.8 = 3.75 > 2.1098$, with 17 degrees of freedom for $\alpha = 0.05$. Reject H_0. There is evidence that X_2 contributes to a model already containing X_1. Both X_1 and X_2 should be included in the model.

14.26 (a) 95% confidence interval on β_1: $b_1 \pm S_{b_1}$, $0.0471 \pm 2.0796(0.0203)$, $0.00488 \leq \beta_1 \leq 0.08932$. **(b)** For X_1: $t_{STAT} = b_1/S_{b_1} =$

$0.0471/0.0203 = 2.32 > 2.0796$. Reject H_0. There is evidence that X_1 contributes to a model already containing X_2. For X_2: $t_{STAT} = b_1/S_{b_1} = 0.01195/0.00225 = 5.31 > 2.0796$. Reject H_0. There is evidence that X_2 contributes to a model already containing X_1. Both X_1 (sales) and X_2 (orders) should be included in the model.

14.28 (a) $9.398 \leq \beta_1 \leq 16.763$. **(b)** For X_1: $t_{STAT} = 7.43 > 2.093$. Reject H_0. There is evidence that X_1 contributes to a model already containing X_2. For X_2: $t_{STAT} = 5.67 > 2.093$. Reject H_0. There is evidence that X_2 contributes to a model already containing X_1. Both X_1 (radio advertising) and X_2 (newspaper advertising) should be included in the model.

14.30 (a) $227.5865 \leq \beta_1 \leq 685.3104$. **(b)** For X_1: $t_{STAT} = 4.0922$ and p-value $= 0.0003$. Because p-value < 0.05, reject H_0. There is evidence that X_1 contributes to a model already containing X_2. For X_2: $t_{STAT} = -3.6295$ and p-value $= 0.0012$. Because p-value < 0.05, reject H_0. There is evidence that X_2 contributes to a model already containing X_1. Both X_1 (land area) and X_2 (age) should be included in the model.

14.32 Because $t_{STAT} = 3.27 > 2.1098$, reject H_0. Variable X_2 makes a significant contribution to the model.

14.34 (a) $\hat{Y} = 243.7371 + 9.2189X_1 + 12.6967X_2$, where $X_1 =$ number of rooms and $X_2 =$ neighborhood (east $= 0$). **(b)** Holding constant the effect of neighborhood, for each additional room, the selling price is estimated to increase by a mean of 9.2189 thousands of dollars, or \$9218.9. For a given number of rooms, a west neighborhood is estimated to increase the mean selling price over an east neighborhood by 14.6967 thousands of dollars, or \$12,696.7. **(c)** $\hat{Y} = 243.7371 + 9.2189(9) + 12.6967(0) = 326.7076$, or \$326,707.6. $\$321,471.44 \leq \mu_{Y|X} \leq \$331,943.71$. $\$309,560.04 \leq Y_X \leq \$343,855.1$. **(d)** Based on a residual analysis, the model appears to be adequate. **(e)** $F_{STAT} = 55.39$, the p-value is virtually 0. Because p-value < 0.05, reject H_0. There is evidence of a significant relationship between selling price and the two independent variables (rooms and neighborhood). **(f)** For X_1: $t_{STAT} = 8.9537$, the p-value is virtually 0. Reject H_0. Number of rooms makes a significant contribution and should be included in the model. For X_2: $t_{STAT} = 3.5913$, p-value $= 0.0023 < 0.05$. Reject H_0. Neighborhood makes a significant contribution and should be included in the model. Based on these results, the regression model with the two independent variables should be used. **(g)** $7.0466 \leq \beta_1 \leq 11.3913$. **(h)** $5.2378 \leq \beta_2 \leq 20.1557$. **(i)** $r^2_{adj} = 0.851$ **(j)** The slope of selling price with number of rooms is the same, regardless of whether the house is located in an east or west neighborhood. **(k)** $\hat{Y} = 253.95 + 8.032X_1 - 5.90X_2 + 2.089X_1X_2$. For X_1X_2, p-value $= 0.330$. Do not reject H_0. There is no evidence that the interaction term makes a contribution to the model. **(l)** The model in (a) should be used.

14.36 (a) Predicted time $= 8.01 + 0.00523$ Depth -2.105 Dry. **(b)** Holding constant the effect of type of drilling, for each foot increase in depth of the hole, the mean drilling time is estimated to increase by 0.0052 minutes. For a given depth, a dry drilling hole is estimated to reduce the mean drilling time over wet drilling by 2.1052 minutes. **(c)** 6.428 minutes, $6.210 \leq \mu_{Y|X} \leq 6.646$, $4.923 \leq Y_X \leq 7.932$. **(d)** The model appears to be adequate. **(e)** $F_{STAT} = 111.11 > 3.09$; reject H_0. **(f)** $t_{STAT} = 5.03 > 1.9847$; reject H_0. $t_{STAT} = -14.03 < -1.9847$; reject H_0. Include both variables. **(g)** $0.0032 \leq \beta_1 \leq 0.0073$. **(h)** $-2.403 \leq \beta_2 \leq -1.808$ **(i)** 69.0%. **(j)** The slope of the additional drilling time with the depth of the hole is the same, regardless of the type of drilling method used. **(k)** The p-value of the interaction term $= 0.462 > 0.05$, so the term is not significant and should not be included in the model. **(l)** The model in part (a) should be used.

14.38 (a) $\hat{Y} = 31.5594 - 0.0296X_1 + 0.0041X_2 + 0.000017159X_1X_2$, where X_1 = sales, X_2 = orders, p-value = 0.3249 > 0.05. Do not reject H_0. There is not enough evidence that the interaction term makes a contribution to the model. **(b)** Because there is not enough evidence of any interaction effect between sales and orders, the model in Problem 14.4 should be used.

14.40 (a) The p-value of the interaction term = 0.002 < 0.5, so the term is significant and should be included in the model. **(b)** Use the model developed in this problem.

13.42 (a) For X_1X_2, p-value = 0.2353 > 0.05. Do not reject H_0. There is not enough evidence that the interaction term makes a contribution to the model. **(b)** Because there is not enough evidence of an interaction effect between total staff present and remote hours, the model in Problem 14.7 should be used.

14.50 (a) $\hat{Y} = -3.9152 + 0.0319X_1 + 4.2228X_2$, where X_1 = number of cubic feet moved and X_2 = number of pieces of large furniture. **(b)** Holding constant the number of pieces of large furniture, for each additional cubic foot moved, the mean labor hours are estimated to increase by 0.0319. Holding constant the amount of cubic feet moved, for each additional piece of large furniture, the mean labor hours are estimated to increase by 4.2228. **(c)** $\hat{Y} = -3.9152 + 0.0319(500) + 4.2228(2) = 20.4926$. **(d)** Based on a residual analysis, the errors appear to be normally distributed. The equal-variance assumption might be violated because the variances appear to be larger around the center region of both independent variables. There might also be violation of the linearity assumption. A model with quadratic terms for both independent variables might be fitted. **(e)** $F_{STAT} = 228.80$, p-value is virtually 0. Because p-value < 0.05, reject H_0. There is evidence of a significant relationship between labor hours and the two independent variables (the amount of cubic feet moved and the number of pieces of large furniture). **(f)** The p-value is virtually 0. The probability of obtaining a test statistic of 228.80 or greater is virtually 0 if there is no significant relationship between labor hours and the two independent variables (the amount of cubic feet moved and the number of pieces of large furniture). **(g)** $r^2 = 0.9327$. 93.27% of the variation in labor hours can be explained by variation in the amount of cubic feet moved and the number of pieces of large furniture. **(h)** $r_{adj}^2 = 0.9287$. **(i)** For X_1: $t_{STAT} = 6.9339$, the p-value is virtually 0. Reject H_0. The amount of cubic feet moved makes a significant contribution and should be included in the model. For X_2: $t_{STAT} = 4.6192$, the p-value is virtually 0. Reject H_0. The number of pieces of large furniture makes a significant contribution and should be included in the model. Based on these results, the regression model with the two independent variables should be used. **(j)** For X_1: $t_{STAT} = 6.9339$, the p-value is virtually 0. The probability of obtaining a sample that will yield a test statistic farther away than 6.9339 is virtually 0 if the number of cubic feet moved does not make a significant contribution holding the effect of the number of pieces of large furniture constant. For X_2: $t_{STAT} = 4.6192$, the p-value is virtually 0. The probability of obtaining a sample that will yield a test statistic farther away than 4.6192 is virtually 0 if the number of pieces of large furniture does not make a significant contribution holding the effect of the amount of cubic feet moved constant. **(k)** $0.0226 \le \beta_1 \le 0.0413$. You are 95% confident that the mean labor hours will increase by somewhere between 0.0226 and 0.0413 for each additional cubic foot moved, holding constant the number of pieces of large furniture. In Problem 12.36, you are 95% confident that the mean labor hours will increase by somewhere between 0.0439 and 0.0562 for each additional cubic foot moved regardless of the number of pieces of large furniture.

14.52 (a) $\hat{Y} = -120.0483 + 1.7506X_1 + 0.3680X_2$, where X_1 = assessed value and X_2 = time period. **(b)** Holding constant the time period, for each additional thousand dollars of assessed value, the mean selling price is estimated to increase by 1.7507 thousand dollars. Holding

constant the assessed value, for each additional month since assessment, the mean selling price is estimated to increase by 0.3680 thousand dollars. **(c)** $\hat{Y} = -120.0483 + 1.7506(170) + 0.3680(12) = 181.9692$ thousand dollars. **(d)** Based on a residual analysis, the model appears to be adequate. **(e)** $F_{STAT} = 223.46$, the p-value is virtually 0. Because p-value < 0.05, reject H_0. There is evidence of a significant relationship between selling price and the two independent variables (assessed value and time period). **(f)** The p-value is virtually 0. The probability of obtaining a test statistic of 223.46 or greater is virtually 0 if there is no significant relationship between selling price and the two independent variables (assessed value and time period). **(g)** $r^2 = 0.9430$. 94.30% of the variation in selling price can be explained by variation in assessed value and time period. **(h)** $r_{adj}^2 = 0.9388$. **(i)** For X_1: $t_{STAT} = 20.4137$, the p-value is virtually 0. Reject H_0. The assessed value makes a significant contribution and should be included in the model. For X_2: $t_{STAT} = 2.8734$, p-value = 0.0078 < 0.05. Reject H_0. The time period makes a significant contribution and should be included in the model. Based on these results, the regression model with the two independent variables should be used. **(j)** For X_1: $t_{STAT} = 20.4137$, the p-value is virtually 0. The probability of obtaining a sample that will yield a test statistic farther away than 20.4137 is virtually 0 if the assessed value does not make a significant contribution holding time period constant. For X_2: $t_{STAT} = 2.8734$, the p-value is virtually 0. The probability of obtaining a sample that will yield a test statistic farther away than 2.8734 is virtually 0 if the time period does not make a significant contribution holding the effect of the assessed value constant. **(k)** $1.5746 \le \beta_1 \le 1.9266$. You are 95% confident that the mean selling price will increase by an amount somewhere between $1.5746 thousand and $1.9266 thousand for each additional thousand-dollar increase in assessed value, holding constant the time period. In Problem 12.66, you are 95% confident that the mean selling price will increase by an amount somewhere between $1.5862 thousand and $1.9773 thousand for each additional thousand-dollar increase in assessed value regardless of the time period.

14.54 (a) $\hat{Y} = 163.7751 + 10.7252X_1 - 0.2843X_2$, where X_1 = size and X_2 = age. **(b)** Holding age constant, for each additional thousand square feet, the mean assessed value is estimated to increase by $10.7252 thousand. Holding size constant, for each additional year, the mean assessed value is estimated to decrease by $0.2843 thousand. **(c)** $\hat{Y} = 163.7751 + 10.7252(1.75) - 0.2843(10) = 179.7017$ thousand dollars. **(d)** Based on a residual analysis, the errors appear to be normally distributed. The equal-variance assumption appears to be valid. There might also be violation of the linearity assumption for age. You may want to include a quadratic term for age in the model. **(e)** $F_{STAT} = 28.58$, p-value = 0.0000272776. Because p-value = 0.0000 < 0.05, reject H_0. There is evidence of a significant relationship between assessed value and the two independent variables (size and age). **(f)** p-value = 0.0000272776. The probability of obtaining an F_{STAT} test statistic of 28.58 or greater is virtually 0 if there is no significant relationship between assessed value and the two independent variables (size and age). **(g)** $r^2 = 0.8265$. 82.65% of the variation in assessed value can be explained by variation in size and age. **(h)** $r_{adj}^2 = 0.7976$. **(i)** For X_1: $t_{STAT} = 3.5581$, p-value = 0.0039 < 0.05. Reject H_0. The size of a house makes a significant contribution and should be included in the model. For X_2: $t_{STAT} = -3.4002$, p-value = 0.0053 < 0.05. Reject H_0. The age of a house makes a significant contribution and should be included in the model. Based on these results, the regression model with the two independent variables should be used. **(j)** For X_1: p-value = 0.0039. The probability of obtaining a sample that will yield a test statistic farther away than 3.5581 is 0.0039 if the size of a house does not make a significant contribution holding age constant. For X_2: p-value = 0.0053. The probability of obtaining a sample that will yield a test statistic farther away than -3.4002 is 0.0053 if the age of a house does not make a significant contribution, holding the effect of the size constant. **(k)** $4.1572 \le \beta_1 \le 17.2928$. You are 95% confident that the mean assessed value will increase by an amount somewhere between $4.1575 thousand and $17.2928 thousand for each additional thousand-square-foot increase in the size of a house, holding constant the age. In Problem 12.67, you are 95% confident that the mean assessed value will increase by an amount somewhere between $9.4695 thousand and $23.7972 thousand for each additional thousand-square-foot increase in heating area regardless of the age. **(l)** Based on your answers to (a) through (k), the age of a house does have an effect on its assessed value.

14.56 (a) $\hat{Y} = 149.71 - 15.077X_1 - 2.698X_2$, where X_1 = ERA and X_2 = League (American = 0). **(b)** Holding constant the effect of the league, for each additional ERA, the number of wins is estimated to decrease by a mean of 15.077. For a given ERA, a team in the National League is estimated to have a mean of 2.698 fewer wins than a team in the American League. **(c)** 81.86 wins Confidence interval: 77.96 to 85.77 wins Prediction interval: 66.74 to 96.98 wins. **(d)** Based on a residual analysis, there appears to be a no relationship between the residuals and ERA or league. The equal-variance and linearity assumptions appear to be valid. **(e)** $F_{STAT} = 11.03 > 3.35$, p-value is virtually 0. Since p-value < 0.05, reject H_0. There is evidence of a significant relationship between wins and the two independent variables (ERA and league). **(f)** For X_1: $t_{STAT} = -4.66 > 2.0518$, p-value is virtually 0. Reject H_0. ERA makes a significant contribution and should be included in the model. For X_2: $t_{STAT} = -1.03 < 2.0518$, p-value $= 0.312 > 0.05$. Do not reject H_0. The league does not make a significant contribution and should not be included in the model. Based on these results, the regression model with only ERA should be used. **(g)** $r^2_{adj} = 0.6058$

(h) The slope of the number of wins with ERA is the same regardless of whether the team belongs to the American or the National League. **(i)** For X_1X_2: the p-value is 0.801. Do not reject H_0. There is no evidence that the interaction term makes a contribution to the model. **(j)** The regression model with only ERA should be used.

14.58 (a) Attendance $= -3,667 + 170.89$ Temperature $- 11.25$ team's winning percentage $+ 22.75$ opponent's winning percentage $+ 1,824$ if the game is a weekend game $+ 9,074$ if the game has a promotion being held. **(b)** $r^2 = 0.386$ 38.6% of the variation in attendance can be explained by variation in temperature, the Phillies winning percentage, the opponent's winning percentage, whether it was a weekend game, and whether a promotion was held. **(c)** Temperature $t_{STAT} = 2.52 > 1.993$ p-value $= 0.014 < 0.05$, reject H_0. Winning percentage: $-1.993 < t_{STAT} = -0.59 < 1.993$ p-value $= 0.559 > 0.05$, do not reject H_0. Opponent's winning percentage: $-1.993 < t_{STAT} = 1.84 < 1.993$ p-value $= 0.071 > 0.05$, do not reject H_0. Weekend $-1.993 < t_{STAT} = 1.04 < 1.993$, p-value $= 0.30 > 0.05$, do not reject H_0. Promotion: $t_{STAT} = 4.85 > 1.993$ p-value $= 0.000 < 0.05$, reject H_0. Temperature and whether a promotion was held have increased attendance. **(d)** Holding constant the temperature, the Phillies winning percentage, the opponent's winning percentage, and whether the game was played on a weekend, the mean predicted attendance was 9,074 higher when a promotion was held than when a promotion was not held.